CH00704274

PRELIMINARY PUBLICATION OF
PALEOANTHROPO
SECOND EDITION

MILFORD H. WOLPOFF
UNIVERSITY OF MICHIGAN

MCGRAW-HILL, INC.
COLLEGE CUSTOM SERIES

NEW YORK ST. LOUIS SAN FRANCISCO AUCKLAND BOGOTÁ
CARACAS LISBON LONDON MADRID MEXICO MILAN MONTREAL
NEW DELHI PARIS SAN JUAN SINGAPORE SYDNEY TOKYO TORONTO

Preliminary Publication of PALEOANTHROPOLOGY, Second Edition

ISBN 0-07-071679-X

Editor: Jan Scipio

Illustration: Karen Harvey

Cover Design: Jenny L. Friedman

Printer/Binder: Port City Press

Paleoanthropology: Outline of Text

INTRODUCTION

PALEOANTHROPOLOGY BIBLIOGRAPHY

GLOSSARY

INTRODUCTION

As we are increasing phenomenally our formulated knowledge of the particular part of space occupied by the earth, in its revolutions around its sun, through our astronauts' traveling to the moon and probing the planets of the solar and galactic systems to which this earth belongs, so too we are becoming cognizant that the biological persistence of our earthly human species is utterly dependent upon the thoroughness and speed with which the totality of that species come to comprehend their phylogenetic past and adapt themselves intelligently, in its light, to the planet that produced all the other forms of life upon it, as well as the form called sapient man.

Raymond A. Dart, 1973

Paleoanthropology is the study of our origins. I view it as more than a history or a simple narrative of past events. The subject is a science and not a history because there are reasons for what happened in the past, explanations for why a certain course of events occurred, and some of the theories offered in explanation of our origins can be proven wrong. Historically, the idea of human evolution has been a controversial one. For many, the controversy centers on whether there is any reality to the concept at all. Within the disciplines that study human evolution (anthropology and paleontology), the idea is universally accepted, but its specific applications are debated.

The proposal that humans might have descended from something that was other than human seemed to contradict certain aspects of the philosophical and religious thinking in the Western world. Yet most now find the general concept acceptable. This is no small accomplishment in a cultural framework with a biological folk knowledge that still refers to "mixed blood" in offspring of mixed parentage and retains the belief that there are things called "germs" that cause everything from mouth odors to diseases.

Controversy within the disciplines has a rather different basis. Three things contribute to what often appear to be fundamental differences in how the course of human evolution is best interpreted. These are basic differences in the philosophy of science, the scarcity of large samples of human fossil material, and the inability to fully prove any contention about what might have happened in the distant past.

Philosophical differences are often not recognized among the scientists themselves. Yet these contribute to the differences in approach that allow the same data to be viewed in very different ways. One might think of the main difference in approach as reflecting the difference between induction and deduction.

An inductive approach is practiced explicitly by many scientists. It is implicit in the so-called "scientific method" taught in most secondary schools. The approach involves gathering data, using these data to suggest hypotheses, and testing the hypotheses to determine whether they can be proven correct. Numerous authors propose that it is best to consider all possible explanations, or hypotheses, and choose the best one. The procedure is often formalized, as some use multivariate statistics to determine which is best, while others calculate conditional probabilities for competing hypotheses and compare these to decide which hypothesis is most likely.

The deductive approach differs from the inductive because of the contention that hypotheses can never be proven correct. As developed by Sir Karl Popper, it is argued that certainty lies only in the disproof, or refutation, of hypotheses. Consequently, scientists using this approach attempt to disprove the simplest explanatory hypothesis. If it cannot be disproved it is tentatively accepted.

As an example of how these approaches differ, let us consider an evolutionary event that occurred in East Africa some 2 million years ago. A new human species called *Homo sapiens* (née *erectus*) appeared for the first time in fossil-bearing deposits east of Lake Turkana in Kenya. The paleontological question is: Where did this new species come from? All workers recognize that no completely definitive answer can ever be given. A scientist using the inductive approach might list the most credible hypotheses and derive probabilities for them. These possibilities would include migration from another area, evolution from the smaller of the australopithecine species living in the Turkana area earlier in time (variously called *Homo habilis*, *Homo rudolphensis*, *Australopithecus habilis*, *Homo africanus*, or *Australopithecus africanus*, a story in and of itself), evolution from the more robust australopithecine form present earlier in time (variously called *Zinjanthropus boisei, Australopithecus boisei, Paranthropus boisei, Paranthropus robustus*, or *Australopithecus robustus*), or evolution from a different earlier form perhaps only poorly represented in this region. A scientist using the deductive approach would pick what appeared to be the simplest of these hypotheses and attempt to find evidence to disprove it. Because of the morphological similarities, the simplest hypothesis would probably be the second of those listed above (evolution from the smaller earlier australopithecine form). Disproof could be accomplished by finding an even more similar ancestral species, by showing that Homo erectus could be found earlier than the first appearance of the proposed ancestral species, or by demonstrating that the amount of evolutionary change that took place could not have happened over the time span allowed for it.

These approaches may not result in the same conclusion. Moreover, discourse between scientists using the different approaches may be misleading, since the same words and concepts can be used in very different ways.

Moreover, our science is limited in a way few others can match. Its data base will always be minimal because of the scarcity of fossils. Even if fossil remains were thousands of times more plentiful, they would represent only the smallest proportion of once living populations. Thus there are two aspects to this problem. First, events that took millions of years and involved billions of individuals must be reconstructed and interpreted from a handful of specimens. Second, these specimens may not represent the time or area where important changes were taking place, and they may not even accurately reflect the normal characteristics of the populations they come from. B. Wood once likened paleoanthropology to putting together a puzzle of thousands of pieces without either knowing what the final picture is to look like, or how many of the pieces are missing.

An expanding fossil record has seemed to fill in most of the gaps that once appeared in human evolutionary history. There is no longer a search for a "missing link" in human evolution. The contemporary problems result from the fact that there are many links (some would say too many) and involve the related questions of how these might best be put together and what underlies the pattern that results.

I have conceived of this book primarily to be used for a first course in human paleontology - a second course in biological anthropology that is prerequisited by an introduction to biological anthropology or a more general introduction to anthropology that presents the four-field approach. I have attempted to accomplish three things in preparing this basic introduction to human evolution. I have presented what I believe is a consistent framework for understanding the course of human evolution. My approach is deductive, and consequently the framework I propose is the simplest one that I believe cannot be disproved at the present time. I have tried to demonstrate the process of interpretation, relating the known data to this framework by showing how questions have been asked in a way that is testable rather than speculative. Finally, I have presented the fossil evidence for human evolution as I understand it to fit within the framework of evolutionary theory. It is my hope that this presentation will allow more than a memorization of dates and events, but rather will lead to an understanding of process and an appreciation of how much basic research and experimentation remains to be done in the field of human paleontology.

The book, of course, is written from my own viewpoint. It expresses the framework from which I view the human evolutionary process. I have tried to make this framework as explicit as possible, since I believe that a framework is not something that can be eliminated in order to provide "objectivity." In my view, "objectivity" does not exist in science. Even in the act of gathering data, decisions about what data to record and what to ignore reflect the framework of the scientist. The approach I follow provides for the existence of a framework, and suggests that progress best be made by attempting to disprove it.

However, lest the reader come to believe that the framework and interpretations I suggest are the only ones possible, I have provided a **Anatomy of a Controversy** in each chapter. The purpose of this is to focus in on one of the more controversial issues raised in the chapter and analyze other positions that have been taken regarding it. These sections act as both a further discussion and an indication of where some of the major points of disagreement lie in the field today.

I also furnish two bibliographies. At the end of the chapters are **References and Further Readings**: specific references to the materials discussed and more general interpretive references to follow up the topics raised. These are picked for relative simplicity, accessibility, and balanced current discussion of the topics, and would be appropriate for initiating term paper research. Whenever possible, they are discussions rather than descriptions. At the end of the book is a bibliography with three parts:

1. reference texts focusing on anatomies, osteologies, atlases, and catalogues
2. basic descriptions of human fossil specimens
3. edited volumes that are primary paleoanthrological

With rare exceptions these will not be repeated in the chapter bibliographies, even when material in the chapter comes from one of these sources. The reader is cautioned to look here for this information; generally speaking if a reference is not in the section behind the chapter, it is here.

Much of what appear here reflects what I teach in a junior/senior evolution course. However, while I cover the causes and outline the details of human evolution in this class, I would never expect to teach the entire contents of this book in a single semester. Rather, as I present the course, I emphasize different aspects and details of human evolution over a cycle of at least a half decade, depending on my interests and current research at the time and/or current publicized discoveries in particular years. There was no reason why a textbook should, or for than matter could, reflect this teaching strategy. Thus, I have used the "everything but the kitchen sink" approach to what is encompassed so this text could be used many different ways.

Another aspect of overwriting is found in the first 4 chapters, which I regard as introductory. It was my assumption in preparing the text that there is no more student preparation for the course using it than high school biology. This, of course, is often not the case, and in courses that have university level prerequisites it will be found that much of what is encompassed in these chapters can be assumed. Once again, I have tried to aim for maximum flexibility.

Finally, a substantial glossary is included, and boldfaced words are keyed to it. Words in the glossary are indicated when they are first used.

In most cases, I have based my observations and conclusions on studies of the original fossil materials. I am deeply indebted to a number of individuals, and their institutions, for permission to work on the fossil remains, as well as for the hospitality and encouragement I received all over the world. The community of human and primate paleontologists is small, and it has been gratifying to discover that the communication, interest, and cooperation within this community transcends geographic and political boundaries. I would like to acknowledge particularly my gratitude and indebtedness to the following individuals and institutions:

- K.D. ADAM Staatlisches Museum für Naturkunde, Ludwigsburg
- E. AGUIRRE Museo Nacional de Ciencias Naturales. Madrid
- P. ANDREWS Natural History Museum, London
- B. ARENSBURG University of Tel Aviv Medical School, Tel Aviv
- J.L. ARSUAGA Universidad Complutense de Madrid, Madrid
- M. AVERY and G. AVERY South African Museum, Cape Town
- H. BACH Schiller University, Jena
- O. BAR-YOSEF Harvard University, Cambridge
- J. M. BERMUDEZ DE CASTRO Museo Nacional de Ciencias Naturales, Madrid
- C.K. BRAIN Transvaal Museum, Pretoria
- P. BROWN University of New England, Armidale
- A. CHARNETZKI Universität Tubingen, Tubingen
- Y. COPPENS French Academy of Sciences, Paris
- V. CORRENTI Museum of Anthropology, University of Rome, Rome
- *I. CRNOLATAC Croatian Natural History Museum, Zagreb
- M.H. DAY Natural History Museum, London
- H. DELPORTE Musée des Antiquités Nationales de Saint Germain-en-Laye, Yvelines
- L. DeBONIS Université de Poitiers, Poitiers
- M-A. AND H. DeLUMLEY Institut de Paléontologie Humaine, Paris
- J. DEVOS Rijksmuseum van Natuurlijke Historie, Leiden
- M. DOBISÍKOVÁ Anthropologické Oddělení Nárdoni Museum, Prague
- DONG XINGREN Institute of Vertebrate Paleontology and Paleoanthropology, Beijing
- T.F. DREYER National Museum, Bloemfontein
- R. FEUSTEL Museum für Ur-und Fürhgeschichte Türringens, Weimar

- J. FRANZEN Natur-Museum und Forschungs-Institut Senckenberg, Frankfurt
- F. FULEP Magyar Nemzeti Muzeum, Budapest
- H.S. GREEN National Museum of Wales, Cardiff
- J-L. HEIM Musée de l'Homme, Paris
- A. HILL Yale University, New Haven
- F.C. HOWELL University of California at Berkeley
- W.W. HOWELLS Harvard University, Cambridge
- J-J. HUBLIN CNRS, French Academy of Sciences
- *A. HUGHES University of the Witwatersrand, Johannesburg
- T. JACOB Universitas Gadjah Mada, Jokjakarta
- J. JELÍNEK Morvaské Muzeum, Brno
- E. JOACHIM Rheinisches Landesmuseum, Bonn
- D.C. JOHANSON Institute for Human Origins, Berkeley
- C. JOLLY New York University
- W. KIMBEL Institute for Human Origins, Berkeley
- B. KLÍMA Academy of Sciences of the Czech Republic, Brno
- *G.H.R. VON KOENIGSWALD Natur-Museum und Forschungs-Institut Senckenberg, Frankfurt
- R. KRAATZ Universität Heidelberg, Heidelberg
- M. KRETZOI Magyar Allami Foldtani Intezet, Budapest
- M.D. and R.E. LEAKEY National Museums of Kenya, Nairobi
- B. LATIMER Cleveland Natural History Museum
- A. LEGUEBE Institut Royal des Sciences Naturelles de Belgique, Brussels
- C.O. LOVEJOY Kent State University, Kent
- LÜ ZUN'E Beijing University, Beijing
- R. MACCHIARELLI Museo Nazionale Preistorico ed Etnografico 'L'Pigorini', Rome
- *M. MALEZ Geološko-Paleontološki zbirka JAZU, Zagreb
- D. MANIA Landesmuseum für Vorgeschichte, Halle
- A. MANN University of Pennsylvania
- J. MELENTIS University of Thessalonika, Thessalonika
- A. MORRIS University of Cape Town, Rondebosch
- B.A. OGOT (formerly of) The International Louis Leakey Memorial Institute for African Prehistory, Nairobi
- D. PILBEAM Harvard University, Cambridge
- R. PROTSCH Goethe Universität, Frankfurt
- J. RADOVČIC´ Croatian Natural History Museum, Zagreb
- Y. RAK University of Tel Aviv Medical School, Tel Aviv
- B. SENUT Muséum d'Histoire Naturelle, Paris
- E. SERGI-NALDINI Italian Institute of Human Paleontology, Rome
- C. STRINGER The Natural History Museum, London
- J. SVOBODA Academy of Sciences of the Czech Republic, Brno
- J. SZILVASSÝ Naturhistorischte Museum, Vienna
- A.G. THORNE Australian National University, Canberra
- M. THURZO Slovenské Národné Múzeum, Bratislava
- A-M. TILLIER Université de Bordeaux, Bordeaux
- P.V. TOBIAS University of the Witwatersrand, Johannesburg
- *T. TOTH Térmészéttudományi Muzeum, Budapest
- E. TRINKAUS University of New Mexico
- J. VALOCH Moravian Museum, Brno
- B. VANDERMEERSCH Université de Bordeaux, Bordeaux
- E. VRBA Yale University, New Haven
- E. VOIGT McGregor Museum, Kimberly

- A. WALKER John Hopkins University, Baltimore
- WU RUKANG Institute of Vertebrate Paleontology and Paleoanthropology, Beijing
- WU XINZHI Institute of Vertebrate Paleontology and Paleoanthropology, Beijing
- *T. YAKIMOV Moscow State University
- ZHANG YINYUN Institute of Vertebrate Paleontology and Paleoanthropology, Beijing
- J. ZIAS Rockefeller Museum, Jerusalem

* deceased

I deeply appreciate the advice and encouragement provided by the Random House Personnel I interacted with during the preparation of the first edition, especially the Executive Editor, B. Fetterolf, and the Acquiring Editor, P. Metcalf. During the preparation of the second edition I worked very closely with my McGraw-Hill editors Sylvia Shepard, and later Jill Gordon. Working with these professionals was a real pleasure and they were of great help to me in manuscript preparation. I am deeply grateful.

It is simply impossible to relate the time and effort spent on the first and second editions by a number of my friends and colleagues, many of whom dropped what they were doing to try and answer my questions or make observations on specimens for me. They variously reviewed chapters, critically discussed ideas, provided access to unpublished manuscripts, sent casts, contributed analyses and estimates, helped me locate references or otherwise jarred my failing memory, and given generously of their time and extended great patience in helping me. I am grateful for help provided by P. Andrews, O. Bar-Yosef, D. Begun, B. Benefit, A. Brooks, B. Brown, R. Burling, R. Caspari, G. Conroy, T. Crummett, D. Evon, W. Farrand, L. Jellma, D. Frayer (for unending favors and help), L.O. Greenfield, R. Klein, A. Kramer, M. Lampl, B. Latimer, C.O. Lovejoy, A. Mann, M. Marzke, M. McCrossin, J. McKee, P. Miracle, J. Mitani, S. Molnar, J. Monge, J.C. Ohman, M. Ostendorf-Smith, Y. Rak, T. Rocheck, K. Rosenberg, C. Ruff, M. Russell, L. Schepartz, A. Sillen, E. Simons, F. Smith, J. Speth, C. Stanford, F. Thackery, E. Trinkaus, A.C. Walker, C. Ward, S. Ward, C. Weitz, and J. Yellen. Several of my friends have critically read much or all of the first or second edition text, and I am particularly grateful to the long-suffering D. Frayer, A. Kramer, P. Miracle, Maria Ostendorf-Smith, K. Rosenberg, and L. Schepartz. Various University of Michigan students have made substantial and very useful comments, often in writing, that have been particularly helpful in revising the first edition. Nobody who has read this agrees with anything like all of it, and I want to clearly state that responsibility for what is written here lies solely with me. In preparing this edition I had the opportunity and pleasure to review an enormous and impressive literature. But there is a downside to this information explosion - I apologize for what I forgot. I am absolutely sure that there are ideas and critical papers that I inadvertently left out. It comes with the territory of more age and less memory.

Generous support for my research on the human and primate fossils was provided through numerous grants from the National Academy of Sciences, the Faculty Assistance fund and the Rackham Graduate College at the University of Michigan, and the National Science Foundation. The department of anthropology at Michigan has provided interesting times. I am particularly appreciative of the secretarial staff and especially Debra Graddick, for many small favors.

REFERENCES AND FURTHER READINGS

DART, R. A. 1973 Recollections of a reluctant anthropologist. *Journal of Human Evolution* 2:417-428

KUHN, T. 5. 1970 *The Structure of Scientific Revolutions*, 3rd Edition. University of Chicago Press, Chicago.

MAYR, E. 1982 *The Growth of Biological Thought: Diversity, Evolution, and Inheritance.* Belknap/Harvard University Press, Cambridge.

POPPER, K. R. 1961 *The Logic of Scientific Discovery*. Science Editions, New York.

PART ONE

THE
BASIS FOR
HUMAN EVOLUTION

CHAPTER ONE

Background for Studying
the Past

Paleoanthropology is the study of human evolution. It is the science dedicated to the working out of our roots, based on our understanding of the evolutionary process and the **fossil** evidence for the past events that exemplify it. Paleoanthropology combines a narrative about what happened to our recent and remote ancestors, and a series of explanations that try to explain why it happened that way. These explanations, the hypotheses of any science, are its real content. Interest in human origins and the study of human evolution has a long history and both the development and the implications of this topic are deeply embedded in western thought (there are particularly readable presentations of various aspects of paleoanthropology's history in, among others, books by M. Brown, M. Leakey, R. Leakey, R. Lewin, E. Trinkaus and P. Shipman, and the volume edited by F. Spencer). Paleoanthropology could not have existed *as a science* before Darwin and Wallace, and the theory of evolution they developed.

The events that led to the emergence of living people began far in the past. In attempting to understand them paleoanthropology became a multidisciplinary field, drawing on many other sciences in developing hypotheses about the course, pattern, and causation of human evolution. Important information can be gleaned from today's survivors. They provide detailed information about relationships between the living - the relationships of today are based on the past, and can help reconstruct it. Living people are the testing grounds for hypotheses relating anatomical form to function, and helping to understand the details of how human populations adapt to their environments. Besides this information, there are records left to us from prehistory such as the preserved fossilized remains of once living organisms, humanly modified artifacts that reflect some aspects of human behavior, and evidence of the habitats in which they died. The fossilized remains of humans, their ancestors, and their relatives, are the most direct evidence for human evolution, but its study relies on many other sciences: archaeology, paleoecology, geology, and taphonomy, to name several.

Fossils are studied in a variety of contexts, with very different questions in mind. Comparisons are made of their **morphology** (form), to better understand **phylogeny** (the genealogy of species) and to try to reconstruct the relationship between form and function in the once living organisms. Scientists go beyond the individual fossil specimens as they attempt to understand behavioral and genetic characteristics of the extinct populations that the fossil remains sample, however inadequately. Since the evolutionary process involves changes in the average and distributional (i.e. range, variability) characteristics of these populations over time, determining their sequence through time is crucial as well.

This chapter begins with a discussion of what fossils are and how they are formed, followed by the more difficult problem of determining how long ago the organisms that they preserve actually lived. The fossils that exist in museums and other collections are such an extraordinarily small proportion of the creatures that once lived on our planet that the circumstances surrounding their preservation could easily result in a biased sample of the past. Moreover, problems in dating fossils are so great that even after decades, in some cases more than a century, of trying the age of many human fossil remains cannot be determined with any degree of precision. Thus a discussion of human evolution can profitably begin with the problems posed by the preservation and aging of fossils.

What Are Fossils?

The fossil evidence for human evolution has been likened to a puzzle in which many of the pieces have been thrown away. The difficulties of piecing it together are exacerbated by an uncertainty about the picture being reconstructed. This evidence is limited, fragmentary, and generally incomplete. Yet, fossils provide the only secure framework for charting prehistoric events.

Fossils are the remains or imprints of once living organisms. To become fossils there is chemical (or in the case of replacement, physical) alteration from the organic biological structure of a once-living organism into a longer lasting mineral structure. Fossilization is a ongoing process. Unfortunately only a very small number of organisms are preserved as fossils; it has been estimated that the total weight of all the organisms that have ever lived on earth would equal the weight of the planet itself! Fossils can form in several different ways. The most common is the preservation of certain harder portions of the organism, especially shells and teeth as these have the greatest amount of minerals in them, but also bones (and rarely even softer tissues). When an organism dies, a combination of physical, chemical, and biological processes usually leads quickly to its destruction. This can be prevented only if the corpse is surrounded by a biologically inert medium that protects it from these processes, and even then the body may have already been partially altered or destroyed before its burial (see figure 1.1). Natural burials could occur in streams or lakes; in caves; in peat, mud, amber or tar; or more rarely in ash falls resulting from volcanic eruptions. It is possible that rapid freezing (for instance, by falling into a crevice in a glacier) or mummification in a bog will preserve a human body. There are well-documented cases of both. Otherwise, preservation takes place because the chemistry of the corpse is altered, as minerals in the soil differentially replace some of the body tissues. Except for those rare individuals who were intentionally buried, most human remains from the past are preserved because they were buried by natural processes, in deposits resulting from water action (along streams or lakes) or in caves.

These facts place certain limitations on which organisms became fossils. The process is accidental, but it is not at all a matter of blind luck. It takes energy for natural burial, either the energy of the individual falling into some crevice or walking into a bog, or the energy of some other process burying the corpse. Wind-blown soil, or volcanic ash could accomplish this, but the most common process involves water as the energy source. Individuals who lived near water have a much better chance of having been buried and preserved. They may be buried by water-borne sediments in a flood, or fall or be swept into the water and buried on the bottom. Fortunately for the human fossil record, people have been dependent on drinking large quantities of water for some time, certainly for the last 2 **myr** (million years),and there is much evidence from the archaeological record of human activities that they often lived near water. Earlier in human evolution people did not live in caves, but caves often form where there is a flow of water so that human water dependence created additional opportunities for accidental burial. For instance, trees were relatively safe sleeping sites for early humans living in grasslands areas. Because trees grow around cave entrances when water flow continues, parts of the victims of predation at these sleeping sites can fall into the caves, to be preserved. C. Brain was able to demonstrate this process at the South African cave of Swartkrans, where the puncture holed in the back of a early human's head were an exact match for the lower canines of a leopard. Later in the course of human evolution, caves were regularly occupied by people, and more recent cave deposits often contain human fossils, sometimes in great number. Paleontologists dealing with even more ancient human ancestors, or relatives, have much less fossil evidence to work with. For instance, the fossil history of the African apes over the last 10 myr is very poorly known. Ape ancestors lived in forests, generally away from bodies of water. While a recent study of chimpanzee remains in the Kibale Forest in Uganda shows that their bones do not decay quickly and can accumulate on the forest floor, natural burial processes are rare.

Many body tissues are partially composed of inorganic (non-carbon) minerals. These are the so called "hard tissues," a significant part of the bones and teeth. Hard tissues are already on the way to becoming fossils because of their high mineral content, while the remaining "soft tissues" are only rarely preserved in the mammalian fossil record. Indeed, fossilization is not the simple preservation of the mineral-bearing portions of the body, but instead involves the impregnation, solution, or replacement of the organic material. Minerals in the soil such as calcium phosphate can replace the organic as well as the mineral content of bones and teeth. The fossil may also incorporate chemicals that might be locally common such as pyrite, fluorine or uranium salts, the less common metallic phosphates and silicates, and sulfates of calcium, barium, strontium, or lead. Usually, the more minerals in a tissue, the more readily it can be preserved. Teeth, over 90 percent mineral in content, are the most common fossils. Harder, denser bones such as the skull and mandible are preserved much more commonly than softer and more porous bones such as ribs - 10 times or more so according to one study of the natural survival of body parts of discarded food animals. Even on a single bone survivorship of parts is not uniform. For instance, the shaft of a human long bone endures natural processes much better than its ends. It is often the case that the end of a long bone closer to the body (proximal) survives more often than the end facing away from the body (distal), because the proximal ends are usually denser.

The condition of a fossil often depends on what happens to the organism before the bones are buried. **Taphonomy** is the study of this process, and taphonomic studies have revealed that deposits of fossilized bone are rarely a random sample of the once living organisms. For instance, if scavengers have eaten a carcass only certain parts will remain; predominantly those left over from the meal of the primary carnivore and not gnawed to destruction during the scavenger's meal. Human hunters, at least in the more recent prehistoric times of the Ice Ages, often choose young prime adults from their prey populations, smashing their long bones into small pieces to extract the marrow. If bones are disturbed by water before fossilization, lighter, less dense bones will separate from the heavier, denser ones. Bones may be trampled by animals or cracked and broken by the drying heat of a tropical sun.

Under certain chemical conditions, the mineral content of bones may dissolve while the softer organic content remains. The bones may then undergo "plastic distortion," bending and twisting into new shapes. Another possibility is the disintegration of the original bone, leaving an open space for a mold of its exact form. This mold may then fill with material, leaving a fossil cast. In some cases the bone itself forms the mold. When the inside of a cranium fills up with debris, a cast of the brain-form called an **endocast** is created .

Since the process of fossilization depends on local soil conditions, its speed and the details of its progress can vary greatly from place to place. At one time I was trying to reconstruct fragmentary Neandertal remains from the Krapina cave, in Croatia, more than 100 **kyr** (thousand years) old (see figure 1.1). I remember my astonishment in finding that a highly speckled piece of frontal bone fit exactly on an otherwise cream-colored Neandertal skull. The specimen must have been broken apart before it was buried in the cave, and these pieces fossilized in different parts of the cave, where the soils varied enough to cause different bone coloration. The problems in a single cave are vastly multiplied when different areas are compared. In one area fossilization may achieve significant results in only a few thousand years, while in another notable mineral replacement may take millions of years. Thus the age of a fossil cannot be determined from how mineralized it has become.

In sum, fossilization is rare, and the conditions surrounding death and burial are usually so traumatic that only parts of the original organism become fossilized. Yet the fossils themselves, interpreted in an evolutionary and ecological framework, provide the primary data for the study of human evolution.

Dating Past Events

The past is an immense span of time, really vast beyond comprehension. How long ago ancient humans and their ancestors lived can be in millions, even tens of millions of years. Numbers so large can be easily written down but it is difficult to fully grasp what they mean. Most people have trouble forming a mental image of six or seven distinct objects, let alone millions of years. Try to imagine a row of seven distinct apples (if that is no problem, try 11).

GEOLOGIC TIME

A time scale for the earth's history, likened to a 24 hour day can help comprehend the scale of the events. Beginning with the origin of the planet about 4.5 billion years ago, life appeared within a "mere" billion years, and the evolution of most of the diversified forms occurred within a small segment of the entire span. With the entire age of the earth likened to a 24 hour day, with the earth's origin at midnight, each second of the day would be equal to about 50,000 years, and each minute to 3 million years. By this scale:

Earth originates	midnight
earliest fossils	5:45 a.m.
earliest vertebrates	9:02 p.m.
earliest mammals	10:45 p.m.
earliest primates	11:43 p.m.
earliest higher primates	11:48 p.m.
earliest hominids (**australopithecines**)	11:58 p.m.
Homo sapiens	36 seconds before midnight

Recorded history could not be measured on this scale.

There are many ways to tell how long ago past forms lived, based on the assessment of the age of their fossil remains, or of the geological deposits the remains were found in or could be related to. These assessments are the basis for the times on the clock of the earth's history described above. The methods for determining age at death depend on what information is available. Generally, we can divide dating procedures into two types: those that give a numerical date estimate in years and those that give a relative age in comparison with something else. Relative ages can be very important when numerical ages are not possible, and each provides an important check on the other. Of all the knowledge from other disciplines that paleoanthropologists must rely on, date determinations have proved to be the most error-prone, and the interpretations of the past developed by paleoanthropologists have been extremely sensitive to these errors.

NUMERICAL DATING: RADIOMETRIC TECHNIQUES

At present, the most accurate techniques for numerical age determinations are "radiometric" - an age in years (metric) that is based on radioactivity. There are two forms of radiometric dating based on the fact that unstable nuclei **decay** (break apart into constituent nuclei with a sum total of less nuclear energy) at predictable rates. The first either involves counting the number of unstable nuclei decaying over a short time span, or estimating how many have decayed since a fixed point of time in the past. The second process counts the number of electron byproducts of the nuclear decay process that are trapped within certain molecular structures. These trapped electrons are potentially unstable and can be released by heat or light.

In the first process, the nuclei making up the unstable **isotope** (chemically identical but atomically different forms of an element) undergo radioactive decay, regularly breaking apart into several smaller nuclei of what are then different elements. An example of this would be the gradual decay of uranium into lead. When a nucleus breaks apart, energy in the form of small rapidly moving atomic particles is also released. The release of high energy particles is the radioactivity that is a decay by-product. The decay of uranium was one of the first sources of radioactivity to be discovered because the amount of radioactivity released is high. The number of nuclei decaying at any time (i.e., the number of atoms that break apart) can be measured as the amount of radioactivity. That number is characteristically different for each isotope.

The probability of any particular nucleus decaying at a given moment is constant for a given isotope. Therefore, the *number of* atoms decaying depends on the number of atoms present. For instance, if there are 10,000 atoms present, and if the probability of one decaying in a given second is .001, then the number that probably will decay in that second is

$$10,000 * .001 = 10$$

For any specific isotope the *number of* atoms that decay decreases over time. Using the above example, after the first second we cannot again expect that ten atoms will decay in the next second, because there are no longer *10,000* atoms present. The number has reduced to 9,990 atoms. Each second there will be fewer atoms decaying because there are fewer of the isotope's atoms that remain.

After a given length of time, only some of the original atoms will remain. The length of time it takes for half of the atoms to remain, called the **"half-life,"** is specific for each isotope. This is because the probability of decay is different for each isotope. After one half-life, the amount of radioactivity is also halved (although the probability of any specific atom of that isotope decaying will always be the same). After the span of another half-life, half of the remaining atoms will be present (or, 1/4 of the original number of atoms), and after yet another half-life only half of these will remain (1/8 of the original). This predictability for nuclear decay allows its use in dating past remains.

Nuclear decay may be used for date determination whenever a "starting point" can be identified. This is done in one of several ways: (1) by comparing the ratio of a particular isotope to its decay by-products, (2) by comparing the ratio of a radioactive isotope to the amount of the isotope that was present before the process began, or (3) by counting the number of tracks high energy by-products leave through certain crystals as they are released.

The second type of radiometric dating depends on the capture of the electrons that are radioactive decay byproducts. Certain molecules can trap and hold these, developing unstable electron configurations from which the electrons can subsequently be released and measured. Energetically excited electrons are captured in the defects, or "holes", created by impurities within certain crystalline materials. The radioactive source is usually naturally occurring uranium, thorium, or potassium. The number of trapped electrons is proportional to (a) the number of traps in the material (sensitivity), (b) the strength of the natural radioactivity (dose), and (c) the length of time of exposure to radiation (age). From the measurement of the number of trapped excited electrons, structural knowledge of the crystalline material (for "a"), and estimation of the radioactive dose the material has been exposed to, it is possible to ascertain how long it has been since the trapping began.

age = accumulated dose (measured)/dose rate (estimated)

Error

All forms of radiometric dating are subject to error. Some errors result from contamination of the object being dated, but others are the direct result of the fact that the dating technique is based on probabilities. It depends on the average behavior of atoms over a *long* period of time as measured in a laboratory over a *short* time span. The short-term result may not be the same as the long-term average. This is similar to what may happen if one flips a coin. Many tries will always result in heads an average of 50 percent of the time and tails 50 percent of the time. However, if the coin is flipped just three times, it is possible (and not especially rare) to have three heads in a row. Predicting the long-term average from such a short-term sample could be very misleading.

Consequently, all radiometric dates have an associated probability range and they are always reported with this range. The range may be as small as 1 or 2 percent, or as large as 50 percent, depending on the age of the material dated, how rapidly the decay process takes place and how accurately the decay products can be measured. The probable error surrounding the average date means that the date most likely falls within the reported range. The size of the range is a measure of how accurate the date is. Two fossils may each be dated 25,000 ± 200 BP (before present). This means the individuals most probably lived between 24,800 and 25,200 years ago. While they may possibly have lived at exactly the same time, there is also a good chance that they lived as much as 400 years apart. The most accurate statement about their age is that they both lived within the 400 year span; to admit that they lived within the same thousand year span is even more probable but not very accurate as far as the date is concerned, while to claim a narrower span gives a more precise age estimate but makes it less likely that it is correct for both specimens. Generally, this error factor increases when the age of the specimen or object is extremely ancient (because there has been so much radiometric decay that few atoms are left to change) or recent (because there has been so little radiometric decay that the decay products cannot be easily measured).

Dating Techniques Based on the Number of Nuclear Decays

The first radiometric dating technique to be used was based on the decay of radiocarbon (carbon 14). In the upper atmosphere, nitrogen, the most common gas in our atmosphere, is transformed into carbon 14 (an unstable form of carbon) as the result of bombardment by cosmic rays. The carbon 14 filters down into the lower atmosphere, where it mixes with normal carbon 12 and is absorbed by all living things by eating. As a result, the amount of carbon 14 (in proportion to carbon 12) in a living organism is more or less the same as that in the atmosphere. When the organism dies, however, no new carbon is introduced, and the proportion of carbon 14 becomes less and less as the result of its radioactive decay. Therefore, the amount of carbon 14 in proportion to carbon 12 in once-living material can be used to determine how long it has been since the organism died. The amount of carbon 14 is measured by counting the number of nuclear decays over a fixed, but a relatively short, period of time.

There are two limitations to this technique. One is that the half-life of carbon 14 is only 5,730 years. If a bone is 57,300 years old, ten half-lives have elapsed and only 1/1024th of the original carbon 14 would remain. This amount is so small that it is simply not possible to measure it accurately, and radiocarbon dating is not accurate for bones much older than 28,000 years (or less than 5 half-lives) after which 1/32 of the original carbon 14 would remain. Dates said to be older than this are not really numerical dates at all, but only mean "older than 28,000 years". The other disadvantage is that there is not that much carbon 14 in bone tissue to begin with. The dating method requires the destruction of bone to determine how much regular carbon (carbon 12) is present. This means that the older the bone, the more of it must be destroyed to determine its age, and there is a natural reluctance to destroy large portions of ancient human remains. A variant of this technique, accelerator dating, uses high energy bombardment of a fossil's carbon in a particle accelerator, rather than actual decays, to estimate the amount of carbon 14. The technique, called AMS (accelerator mass spectrometry) dating, has great promise because it requires less material to measure the remaining radioactivity and should date much more accurately (or date from poorer materials) within the radiocarbon range and provide the possibility for older dates. At present, as far as dates important to paleoanthropology are concerned, it has not fully lived up to this potential. AMS dating has clarified some of the older dates because of its greater accuracy, but it has not significantly extended the date range.

Numerous other radiometric techniques have been developed for numerical dating. These techniques do not determine a date for the object itself, but instead estimate an age for the deposit that the fossil is found in. All of these must depend on an event that relates the age of the object to the age of the deposit. One dating technique that has proved to be extremely useful is the potassium-argon (K-Ar) method. The isotope potassium 40 decays into the inert gas argon (and an isotope of calcium). In many types of rocks the argon gas is trapped and can accumulate as the potassium decays. If these rocks are carefully analyzed with regard to eliminating contamination, the ratio of potassium 40 to argon 40 will tell how long it has been since the argon began to accumulate. The hitch is that the "date" is not necessarily the age of the rock or the age of the deposit, but only the length of time since the argon began to accumulate. Therefore, for this method to be used in determining the age of a deposit, there must be some event that links the beginning of argon accumulation with the deposit. The most common datable event is a volcanic eruption. If potassium-bearing rocks or ash results from such an eruption, all of the argon accumulated earlier will have escaped if the rock was sufficiently heated. Argon will begin to accumulate again when the rock cools. If the rock was deposited when solidifying, the age of the rock will be the age of the deposit. The K-Ar technique is useful wherever there have been volcanic eruptions and has provided the first dates for many really ancient human fossils. Coincidentally, it has been useful for dating in many other circumstances (it was the technique used to determine the age of the moon craters). However, it is very sensitive to contamination from atmospheric argon.

A more recently developed and more accurate technique based on the same decay process is argon-argon dating. The ^{40}Ar/^{39}Ar technique depends on the same potassium to argon decay process, but differs in that the concentration of a different argon isotope (argon 39) is used to estimate the amount of potassium 40 in the sample. The Argon 39 is created from potassium 39, which has a known ratio to potassium 40, by exposure to high energy radiation. In single crystal ^{40}Ar/^{39}Ar dating, the rock sample is irradiated to convert the potassium isotope to argon, and then heated to near its melting point to release the argon gas from the interior of mineral grains or crystals, thereby allowing the ratio of ^{40}Ar to ^{39}Ar in the gas to be measured. The mechanics of the ^{40}Ar/^{39}Ar technique are much easier than K-Ar because both isotopes are collected from the same rock sample. It can be used on a wider range of materials because smaller samples of potassium 39 are required (heating is by laser so the source of the gas can be highly resolved and quite specific). In fact, it has become known as the 'single-crystal technique because only one crystal at a time can be irradiated. Contamination of these laser heated samples is more difficult, and more accurate dates are generally obtained. Since its applications are broader, old sites are being redated using ^{40}Ar/^{39}Ar. For instance, the ages of the earliest humans in Indonesia have been reassessed using a single crystal application, as small crystals of volcanic glass are dated.

The half-life of the potassium-argon decay process is very long, about 1250 myr, and therefore unlike carbon 14 it can be used to date rocks that were heated billions of years ago. The disadvantage of this long half-life is that it takes argon a considerable time to accumulate. When little time has elapsed since accumulation began, not enough argon is present to date the rock accurately. While carbon 14 dating cannot be used on specimens that are too old, the K-Ar and ^{40}Ar/^{39}Ar techniques cannot be used when the deposits are too young. Although many recent dates have been claimed for the K-Ar technique, it does not yet seem accurate enough to use, without unacceptably high ranges of error, on deposits younger than about 200,000 years unless they are unusually high in their potassium content.

Other radiometric technique using different elements include Uranium series dates, based on the natural decay of uranium and thorium isotopes into lead. The uranium and thorium isotopes most often used have very different half-lives (table 1.1)

Table 1.1
Isotopes and Half-Lives for Uranium Series Dates

Isotope			Half-Life
Uranium 238			45,000 million years
Uranium 234			245,000 years
Thorium 230			75,400 years

These decay processes involve a number of intermediate steps, and it is by measuring the ratios of these intermediate by-products that an age estimate can be made. The fact that uranium is easily soluble in water while its intermediate decay products tend to precipitate out of solution makes water-deposited structures such as the stalagmites and stalactites of caves, corals, or carbonates built up in water, potential sources for dates. The method has proved to be useful over the 50,000 - 400,000 year age range and thereby largely spans between the radiocarbon and K-Ar ranges. Its greatest disadvantages are the often tenuous link between cave travertines and the sedimentary deposits with human and/or cultural remains, and the large error range often associated with the dates. Uranium series dates have been attempted for bones and teeth, again based on the principle that soluble uranium atoms can be taken up from ground water in biological structures while insoluble thorium will not. The potential problems in biological materials are similar to those discussed below for the electron capture methods.

The decay of uranium 238 can be used in another technique, fission track dating. The procedure can be used to date many crystal structures with a uranium 238 content because of the tracks made in the crystal by heavy high energy particles, created whenever the decay splits the nucleus (instead of much more commonly emitting small particles). The technique dates the last time that the rock was heated, and the potential time range is very great. Since volcanic glass is a good candidate for the technique, it often acts as an independent check for K-Ar dates. Another important use of fission track dating is the dating of small, smooth, and often teardrop-shaped glassy rocks called tektites, which are probably of meteoric origin. In certain areas (such as Indonesia) tektites can be found in deposits that also contain human remains.

Dating Based on the Number of Trapped Electrons

There are two techniques for age determination based on the number of electrons from cosmic radiation and radioactive decay that have been captured in crystalline impurities. These differ in the way the trapped electrons are detected.

In Electron Spin Resonance (ESR) dating, the trapped electrons are caused to resonate in a magnetic field. The technique works best for electrons trapped in the crystal structure of tooth enamel. Teeth begin at ground level (no trapped energetic electrons) when their enamel is first formed. The dose is a function of both background radiation and the amount of radioactive material, usually uranium, the tooth has absorbed during the fossilization process. When ESR dates are attempted, two different models for their exposure to radioactivity are usually considered: in the "early uptake" model all of the internal radioactive material is considered to enter the fossil close to the time of burial, while in the "linear uptake" model the absorption of radioactive materials from the surrounding sediments is thought to be constant over time. It has been argued that there is an internal consistency check, and that the relation of dates from ESR and Uranium series can be used to ascertain which uptake model is more realistic. At present ESR has not been successful for aging other biological materials, such as bone.

In Thermoluminescence (TL) dating the trapped electrons are released in the form of visible light when the material trapping the electrons is exposed to heat. It is easier to use non-biological materials for this process. The crystalline structure of flint makes it particularly useful, and the material can be "set to ground level" for excited electrons (i.e., no trapped electrons because the previously excited electrons are released) when it is heated in a sufficiently hot fire (about 300-400 degrees centigrade, depending on the duration). Burnt flints are quite common throughout much of human prehistory because the material is so desirable in tool making. Thus TL dating can be used to estimate how long it has been since burnt flints were burnt.

In the past decade, probably no techniques for dating have been so promising, and have led to so many surprises, as these electron capture methods (figure 1.2). Dates became possible for human remains older than 30 kyr that successfully resisted all previous attempts, because they extended the potential for dating into more ancient time periods where carbon 14 is impossible. Even though these techniques are less accurate than radiocarbon (their resolution is lower), they have proven to be invaluable by giving previously unobtainable age estimates. Both the potentials and the problems are well illustrated in the new TL and ESR dates for the western Asian sites of the Skhul, Tabun, and Qafzeh caves, in Israel. These are places where the remains of archaic peoples were found, beginning in the 1930's. The remains were quite variable and some paleoanthropologists believe they include the earliest people of modern form - the reason why their age is so important. The caves are linked together by **archaeological** (stone tool and debris) and **faunal** (animal remains) **comparisons** and were once thought to be less than 40,000 years in age because of a radiocarbon date from Tabun, driving home the fact that old radiocarbon dates are not *actual dates* but *minimum date estimates*. Using electron capture methods, dates in excess of 90,000 years were subsequently published for layers where humans were buried in the caves of Qafzeh and Skhul, and even older dates for Tabun. Because no other dating techniques covering this age-range are possible at these sites, it was argued that their validity was reflected in the fact that the two sites with similar human remains, Qafzeh and Skhul, were dated with two different techniques to approximately the same age. But *both* of these techniques require a number of assumptions that often cannot be met (discussed by R. Grün and his colleagues). Moreover, as A. Jelinek points out they are not independent confirmations of each other because both are sensitive to the background radioactivity in soil elements that produce the electrons to be captured. In stable environments these are constant, but in environments where wet and dry periods alternate and the depth of ground water changes dramatically (definitely the case for Israel during the **Pleistocene** - the era of periodic ice ages beginning some 2 myr ago and extending to the present) this background is not constant and the measurement of today's soluble uranium may give a great underestimation of how much background dose the materials were exposed to earlier. An underestimated dose rate gives an overestimated age. Additional problems with TL stem from the burnt flints that are dated. The initial heating, hopefully "zeroing" of the flints, is done in campfires that may differ dramatically in the maximum temperature they attain and the duration of the maximum temperature. If the material is not really "zeroed" because the fire that burnt the flints was not hot enough (or hot enough for long enough), the date is wrong (it will appear too old because too many electrons were counted). A `second problem is that flints can be moved from one layer to another at many sites because of animal trampling (for instance in Europe the most common inhabitants of caves were cave bears) and geologic processes such as frost heave.

Table 1.2

Qafzeh Layers, Dates (in kyr)$^{\Psi}$, and Hominid Positions
courtesy of B. Vandermeersch and O. Bar-Yosef

Qafzeh Layer	Hominids	TL Dates	ESR dates Early Uptake	ESR dates Linear Uptake
XV			92.1-94.2 (93.1)*	112-114 (113)*
XVa	3,6,7,13 (fetus),18,32 4/21•,4a/22•,		94.7	116
XVII	8,9,10,11,12,14,15,16,17	87.8-107.2 (97.5)*	95.2	103
XVIII		87.9-93.4 (90.3)		
XIX[1]	5	82.4-98.8 (90.5)	82-119 (101.2)	101-145 (119)
XX				
XXI		89.2-109.9 (96.7)	73.7-118.0 (91.4)	89-143 (112)
XXII	11	85.4-91.2 (97.7)		
XXIII		95		
XXIV				
Site average		92±5	96±13	115±15

$^{\Psi}$ From Schwarcz et al and Valladas et al
* Dates in parentheses are the average for the layer
• In XVa or XVII
[1] Two Uranium series dates for this level are 88.6 and 106.4 kyr

These problems can combine, and create a serious amount of uncertainly that is reflected in contradictions encountered in the age estimates from some sites. At Qafzeh, for instance, the error ranges for the for the dates from the archaeological layers with human remains (XV-XXII, see table 1.2) overlap so much that there is no tendency for deeper dates being older. There is actually only one date for the part of the cave with human remains, not a series of consecutive dates from different layers that confirm each other by the deeper ones being older. Furthermore, the date estimate for each layer has a probable error range so great (usually close to ±10%) that each determination includes the dates estimated for all of the other layers, and a statistical attempt to find an average trend to the dates does not result in the deeper layers appearing older, as they should. This could mean that the layers are very close together in time, but amino acid epimerization of the ostrich egg shells (see below, pp.; xx) buried with the human remains suggests that the different layers were actually far apart in time, the work by A. Brooks and colleagues suggesting between 20 and 40 kyr for the span of the hominid bearing layers. One explanation for this discrepancy is that some of the flints that were dated may have moved between layers, scrambling the individual dates. The ostrich egg shells could not have moved this way or they would be so fragmented that they no longer were identifiable. This explanation is supported by the fact that the date ranges of the TL and amino acid determinations from the individual layers are actually very similar. However, other possible explanations are that contamination from non-constant exposure to natural radioactivity (for instance, from changing ground water levels), or similar inadequate initial heating temperatures, have similarly effected all of the flints. The fact remains that there is more uncertainty in the accuracy of these Qafzeh dates than one might assume when only one average age is reported, and not the age and error for each layer making up the average.

For the ESR technique additional problems come from a variety of sources. One of these is the choice of the uptake model used. While some of the researchers have asserted that the linear uptake model "better describes the uptake model in most cases (e.g. Schwarcz and Grün) there is no reason to believe that either early or linear uptake is necessarily a valid model for the history of electron exposure (consider the changing ground water situation again), and there may be no way to accurately model uptake. Yet, without an accurate model of radiation exposure for the teeth used in ESR, the dates are very inaccurate. Perhaps this is why while the *average* early uptake model ESR date from Qafzeh may seem to approximate the modal TL determination, the actual *range* of dates is much greater for each level. Moreover, another more serious problem plagues the technique. Work by M. Jonas and colleagues suggests that the ESR signal may integrate several distinct sources (this may account for why so many ESR dates approximate 100 kyr). H. Schwarcz believes the second source comes from organic matter in the teeth, as this gives a very similar resonance signal. The number of trapped electrons grows with age, while the organic material deteriorates, so the problems are most acute with young samples, or very old ones with a low radiation dose. The number of trapped electrons is only an accurate way to estimate age when a single source is counted.

TL and ESR dates are even more problematic for the nearby Skhul cave, said to contain similar human remains (but see Chapter 12). Here, the range of ESR dates for the human layer is over tens of thousands of years greater than the TL error range (119±21 kyr). The ESR ages for two animal teeth are 65.2 and 92.5 kyr assuming the early uptake model, and 91.8 and 108 kyr assuming linear uptake (bear in mind that each of these dates has a probable error range as well). In this case the linear uptake model (average of about 100 kyr) more closely approximates the TL determinations (although the "approximation" is not very good), possibly due to different circumstances in the caves, or perhaps a reflection of general inaccuracy). Because the deposits are very shallow, under 2 meters, it is unlikely that the teeth come from two different burial events to date, 30,000 or so years apart; in fact, the exact provenience of the teeth that were dated is unknown because their findspots were never recorded except generally and now all the cave deposits are gone. Instead, I would conclude that this range is much too great to reflect an accurate process of estimation and it is unlikely that the average across so wide a range of values for what is supposed to be a measurement of the same thing can possibly be accurate. Moreover, Uranium series dates for Skhul (79±4 kyr) published by H. Schwarcz better approximate the early uptake model (average of about 79 kyr). At the moment, it would appear that the resolution of ESR dates is considerably less than that of TL dates.

The situation is so unclear that paleoanthropologists, the consumers in this case, are uncertain about whether these techniques provide dates with a high enough resolution to be useful. Some who accept the accuracy of these early dates for western Asian humans often had already concluded the sites were much earlier than thought for other reasons, for instance from biostratigraphical or archaeological analysis (estimations that use the sequence of evolving animal faunas or of changing stone-tool industries to determine the date). Other paleoanthropologists who question the validity of the early dates are often those whose biostratigraphic, archaeological or evolutionary interpretations work better if there were later dates for the sites. Even recognizing the fact that some of the dates are much better established than others, this is clearly not the best way to do science, and we may look forward to improved resolution and independent verification as the electron capture dating techniques improve. Clearly, sites dated by a variety of techniques, with results in basic agreement, can be treated with reasonable confidence, but in other cases skepticism is healthy, and historically justified.

Under some conditions ESR can be applied to human teeth, just as carbon 14 may be applied to human bone. This is usually not desirable because both techniques are destructive. Otherwise, these radiometric procedures are indirect in that they provide dates that the skeletal material must be related to. The accuracy of indirect numerical dates is a step removed from the dating procedure itself and the inaccuracies inherent in them, since they also depend on how certainly the specimen can be associated with the dated deposit. Moreover, when dating depends on a correlation with other deposits, there is a further reduction in accuracy. In sum, while numerical dating procedures give an age in years, we must not forget that this is an estimate, and not a birthday.

Numerical Dating: Biological Methods

There are several numerical date determination techniques that are based on the assumption of regular predictable change in biological materials. Some of these are direct, involving changes that occur during fossilization. Others are based on the genetic material of living organisms and date to a time when one species divided into two that exist today (the age of the last common ancestor). These must assume a predictable regularity in genetic change during the evolutionary process, a problem that will be examined in Chapter 2.

The only widely used dating technique based on the fossilization process depends on certain natural changes (racemization) that take place in amino acids (part of the structural proteins in bone) after death. **Racemization** is a different process than simple organic decomposition. The racemization process involves a conversion of the amino acids in the bone from the original "left handed" form to a "right handed" form, and at equilibrium about half the amino acids will be of each form. A date can be estimated before the equilibrium value is reached, since at equilibrium as many "left handed" forms are changing to "right handed" as *visa versa*. Amino acid racemization is most likely to provide a valid basis for date determination when the fossil bone has a known history of constant temperature, usually on the ocean or lake floor or in a cave. It is also important to have a constant temperature history after excavation - in one instance a fossil was stored in a museum near a radiator, and after a short time the racemization technique could no longer be used to estimate when the individual died. Amino acid racemization has been used to estimate dates for some important specimens. However, the technique and the assumptions it requires about the pre- and post-excavation history of specimens provide many opportunities for error, and as far as human remains are concerned the racemization dates have not been notably reliable.

A similar process affects the naturally occurring protein amino acid isoleucine. This protein is concentrated in some egg shells, notably the crystalline structure of ostrich eggs. **Epimerization** is the process of changing this protein from a left to a mixture of left and right handed forms. It has proven useful because isoleucine has been found in specimens that are quite old (as much as 10 myr ago), and ostrich egg are used as grave goods, thereby associating them with burials and other archaeological artifacts.

A different approach to age determination is to try and estimate how long ago the last common ancestor of two existing species lived. One could determine the skeletal differences between two species, estimate how long it should have taken for these differences to accumulate over time, and from these facts determine how long ago the common ancestor lived (difference divided by rate is time). But skeletal anatomy does not change at a constant rate and estimating time of divergence this way could not be accurate. What about changes in the genetic material? Some of these appear to be more constant than skeletal changes and may proceed at a predictable rate over long time spans (this is discussed in more detail in Chapter 2). Beginning a quarter-century ago, genetic changes became the basis for a so-called **"molecular clock"** - a means of estimating how long ago the last common ancestor of two living species existed from the amount of genetic difference between the species.

The first "molecular clock" was based on an indirect estimate of genetic divergence, measured by the body's immunological system. Experiments were based on the fact that immunological responses are specific for particular proteins that don't belong in the body. Thus, the strength of an immune reaction is a measure of structural (and by implication genetic) similarity - the reaction will be strongest to the protein that the particular immune response was expecting, and weaker as the protein differs from the expected. Thus, the technique is based on the body's immunological system's ability to recognize differences in proteins that were due to simple genetic changes. As developed by V. Sarich, then in the laboratory of A. Wilson, the basis of the technique was the strength of the immune reaction in a "standard" species, for instance rabbits, to the blood of other species to determine how closely related they are. For instance, a small amount of human blood might be injected into a rabbit to promote the production of human-specific antibodies. The rabbit's antibodies would then be exposed to chimpanzee, gorilla, and orangutan blood and the strength of each reaction measured. The blood invoking the strongest reaction, in this case chimpanzee, is the closest to human blood. The *strength* of this reaction was said to be linear to the relationship of the species, twice as strong meaning twice as closely related. A further assumption, that the blood differences were due to random mutations, was used to propose that twice as strong also meant a last common ancestor half as distant in the past.

This immunological-based "molecular clock" didn't work. With regard to primate evolution, there seemed to be no way to achieve consistent calibration. A reasonable date for primate origins gave hominoid (monkey/ape/human) divergences that appeared much too early, while reasonable hominoid divergence dates gave an unacceptably late date for primate origins. One possible explanation for this was that the relation of divergence magnitude and divergence date was not proportional (double the amount of difference does not mean twice the time separating the species). The idea that this relationship may not be linear fits the data much better, but unfortunately there was no theoretical reason to expect it to be true. Other problems came from the fact that the protein changes reflected in the immunological analysis appeared to continue at different rates in different taxa. These rates were found to be slower in the apes, and even slower in humans, because of a combination of longer generation times and the fact that placentas are more likely to pass hemoglobin (red blood cell) molecules between mother and fetus in species with long gestation lengths and long life spans. This leakage of biological materials can create immune reactions, depending on tissue incompatibilities, and this puts the immune system under a different pattern of selection, one in which the rate of change is slowed down because some of the fetuses with changes may encounter a fatal immune reaction from their mother.

The greatest difficulties came with the use of this "molecular clock" to time the divergence of humans and their closest relatives; that is, human origins. Credibility for the technique was not enhanced with Sarich's publication of a 3.5 ± 1.5 million year date for the last time humans, chimpanzees, and gorillas shared a common ancestor (the chimpanzee/human divergence would presumably be even more recent), and his subsequent reference to the australopithecines found to be earlier than this date as only "dental humans". There were too many problems for this technique to be believable.

A more direct "molecular clock" uses biotechnology that was unknown when the immunological studies were initiated. It is based on the assessment of the actual genetic changes - on DNA differences between the species (DNA is the genetic molecule that carries one's hereditary information, found in the nuclei of all cells. Except for egg or sperm cells, there are 23 pairs of chromosomes, or DNA molecules, in human cells - one of every pair from each parent). For the method to work it must be assumed that these differences accumulated at constant rates since the species diverged. If the magnitude of the divergence rate, the speed at which the DNA continues to acquire increasing differences between the species, can be determined accurately, then the amount of genetic difference between two species estimates how long they have been diverging. This is similar to the way that the distance between two cars traveling from the same spot in opposite directions may be used to estimate how long ago they were at that spot *as long as their speeds are known.*

One "molecular clock" is based on the DNA-DNA hybridization method. The hybridization, in this case, is not directly between different species, but is between parts of their chromosomes that have been broken across the base pair links that hold the two strands of double stranded DNA molecules together - and hold the genetic code. Unpaired strands of DNA from the chromosomes of two different species are allowed to mix and join together in test tubes, with one of the species' DNA radioactively marked. This hybridization process results in paired DNA molecules, and a predictable number of these will be with one side of each DNA molecule from either species. The relationship between the species is estimated by how strongly these hybrid pairs are bonded together. The stronger the bonding, the more similar their information is and therefore the more closely related the species. The principle behind the method, then, is that a very large sample of nuclear genes in two living species will differ in proportion to how long ago the last common ancestor lived. The use of a large sample of genes is thought to eliminate the effects of non-random processes that can cause genetic differences, for instance natural selection, as discussed in Chapter 2.

Once the DNA's hybridize, high temperatures are used to break the bonds linking them. The actual measurement of strength (i.e. relationship) is in the temperature it takes to break apart half of the hybrid chromosomes - stronger bonds require more energy and therefore break at higher temperatures. This "clock" is calibrated by comparing species with divergence times "known" from the fossil record, since the relation of bond strength, as measured by temperature, is proportional to divergence time. DNA-DNA hybridization was used to resolve the question of how humans and the two African ape species, gorillas and chimpanzees, are related. When the relation of three species is considered, two of them must be more closely related and determining which two is the "resolution". The hybridization study seemed to show that humans and chimpanzees are more closely related than humans and gorillas, or chimpanzees and gorillas. The human-chimpanzee divergence date was estimated at 7 myr. The first hybridization study was criticized for resolving the trichotomy (the question of the relation of the three species) with more resolution than the temperature data actually allowed, although subsequent analyses in different laboratories provided the same results. While the divergence pattern therefore appears to be well-supported by the hybridization experiments, subsequent work has questioned the estimated divergence times. Overall rates of nuclear gene change, even when constant, can differ dramatically from group to group and there is evidence that this rate is particularly slow in the primates, and even slower in the human line, when compared with other mammals. Therefore, an average mammalian rate cannot be used to "calibrate" a higher primate "molecular clock". Additional evidence of variability in mutation rates (they are more episodic than constant), and a stronger influence of selection than had been thought, combine to additionally discredit this "clock". Hybridization may show the *order* of divergence without being able to *accurately date* when they took place.

In the nucleus are the paired maternal and paternal chromosomes that contain the body's hereditary information. In addition, there is a single DNA chromosome in each cell's **mitochondria** - the small self contained bodies within the cell's cytoplasm that control the cell's production of energy from food through the production of ATP (adenosine triphosphate). This mitochondrial DNA (mtDNA)contains the hereditary information for each mitochondrion, and provides the basis for a rather different "molecular clock", although one largely based on the same assumptions. There are two important differences between nuclear and mitochondrial DNA that are important for the molecular clock:

1. The mtDNA clones (exactly duplicates) itself when mitochondria reproduce, except for the occasional mutation.
2. The mtDNA is only passed on from mother to offspring since each of us gets our cytoplasm (and its contents) only from our mother's egg.

The amount of genetic information in mtDNA is very small, only about 16,500 base pairs, or about 0.0005% of the over 3 billion pairs in the nuclear DNA, and the molecule evolves at a much faster rate than nuclear DNA. The mtDNA "clock" assumes that differences in the mtDNA of two individuals are a consequence of mutations, and that the more different two mtDNA strands, the longer their separate histories of mtDNA evolution. The "clock" must be calibrated the same way as the hybridization "clock"; that is, based on known split times as determined from the fossil record. Applied to the relation of the three large African primates, chimpanzees, gorillas, and humans, the mtDNA "clock" provides the same splitting *sequence* as DNA-DNA hybridization but the attribution of dates to these splits is again more problematic. In one series of studies a "clock" for human-chimpanzee divergence is calibrated from an estimated orangutan divergence time, while in another the human-chimpanzee divergence is used to calibrate a mtDNA "clock" for the origin of *modern* humans. Thus, the mtDNA clock is also used to date evolutionary events that are much more recent than the human-chimpanzee divergence. These dates have engendered a certain amount of controversy, and will be discussed further as neutral evolution in Chapter 2, and in terms of the divergence times estimates in Chapter 3.

RELATIVE DATING TECHNIQUES

Relative dates relate the age of a fossil to the age of something else, such as other fossils, Paleolithic cultures, or geologic events. Relative dating is used when numerical dating is impossible. Also, it is an integral part of indirect numerical dating procedures. Because relative dating procedures are dependent on both associations of specimens to the deposits they are found in, and on the ability to properly identify and compare world wide phenomena, a different series of problems affects its accuracy.

Dating within Sites

Relative dating is primarily used in relating fossils to each other, or to the deposit in which they are found. Such dating may be based on chemical changes, structural changes due to the fossilization process, or the **stratigraphic** (the location where the fossil was buried, relative to other buried layers or features) position of the specimen. It is most accurate, and almost certainly least misleading, when it is applied to local specimens, preferably from the same site. The chemical approach depends on the fact that when bones are buried, they gradually absorb certain elements from the soil, while they loose others that were accumulated during life. The longer the bones are buried, the more they absorb. These chemicals can then be measured and their amounts in different bones compared. For example, if human fossils have been in the ground as long as the surrounding fossil fauna, the percentages of the various elements should be the same in the two. On the other hand, if the human bones were buried into a more ancient layer, or otherwise became mixed with older fauna, then they will have less of the various elements. Structural changes due to the fossilization process are used similarly. The extent of fossilization can be studied so that fossils from the same site can be compared to determine whether they have been in the ground for the same time, or one buried for a longer time than the other. Finally, a stratigraphic analysis is based on the circumstances of burial and depends on the fossil's position in a sequence of deposits holding other fossil or archaeological remains.

It is common to use several different elements for this dating procedure. The earliest analyses were based on fluorine. At the turn of the century, Gorjanović-Kramberger, a Croatian paleontologist, first used fluorine to show that the human fossils at the Neandertal site of Krapina were contemporary with the extinct fauna also found at the site. It is unfortunate that the same technique was not applied in western Europe until much later; an earlier use would have discredited the antiquity (and ultimately the reconstruction) of the most famous hoax in the history of paleoanthropology, fraudulent Piltdown cranium. In the second decade of this century fragments of a skull and mandible were discovered in southern England, mixed with Pliocene (the epoch before the Pleistocene, see table 1.3) animal remains. At the time a Pliocene human was the earliest one found anywhere. After it was reconstructed by experts at the British Museum of Natural History (now the Natural History Museum) from a number of small fragments, Piltdown was found to fit the expectations for an early human from one of the theories of human evolution that was then current. The reconstruction combined a high, rounded, large-vaulted cranium with an ape-like jaw, showing that brain size and modern cranial features evolved before the jaws changed to their human form. This combination, we now realize, was never part of a living organism but was created by mixing some smashed bones of a recent human skull and an Orangutan mandible with its canine tooth filed flat down to the level of the other teeth. All these were stained to look like fossils. A fluorine test on the Piltdown material was not done until over 35 years later (50 years after Gorjanovic´- Kramberger's use), when it showed that the primate remains had very little fluorine compared to the Pliocene animals. The hoax was discovered once the suspicious circumstances of the specimen's **provenience** (the exact circumstances of how a specimen is related to the deposit in which it is found) were revealed.

Other elements commonly used for chemical dating include nitrogen and uranium. Chemical dating depends completely on local soil conditions and cannot be extended to compare one site with another even if they are near each other. Depending on the local conditions, chemical dating may not work consistently, or may work so poorly that it is useless. Fortunately chemical dating is most important in one focused circumstance where is works best - testing the hypothesis that human remains are directly associated with the geological deposit surrounding them. This is an important question because of the practice of burial, which became common during the last 100,000 years.

The fossilization process creates physical changes that can be used in a similar manner. The changes of greatest interest have to do with the extent to which the crystals that comprise the bone structure change during the fossilization process, become larger and are more distinct when X-rays are passed through them. Crystals are important because their structure can be studied using methods that do not require destruction of the specimen. The comparisons require that bones of the same animal taxon are used. One of the most interesting applications of this approach is in the analysis of the first non-human fossil discovered. In 1891, men working for the Dutch paleontologist E. Dubois found the top of the skull of an ancient human at the Trinil site in Indonesia. A year later these workers discovered the femur of another individual nearby. Because this skull was quite unlike a modern human, small and primitive in appearance, he classified it in a new group, as "*Pithecanthropus*" (literally "ape-man"), but because the femur was like a modern one (although diseased) he later added the name "*erectus*" to reflect its posture. (As an aside, these names are italicized, as are all taxonomic names, because they are in Latin and in the English language it is necessary to italicize all foreign words}. Now, microscopic study of this first "*Pithecanthropus erectus*" suggests that the logic leading to the name may be inappropriate because the pieces are not associated - they are not the remains of the same individual. The Trinil femur is much less fossilized than the skull, indicating that it has been in the ground for a shorter period and therefore is younger in age. The name *"Pithecanthropus erectus"* is no longer considered valid, but this is for quite different reasons described in Chapter 10. Ironically, however mistaken the basis, Dubois was quite correct in his contention that fossil species from Trinil was indeed an erect one!

Regional Dating

A secondary use of relative dating determines the position of the fossil-bearing deposit in the local stratigraphic sequence, archaeological sequence, or sequence of animal evolution. Each of these represents a potential source of dating because they change in a regular (although not necessarily constant or continuous manner). This is done by determining the order of events that occurred locally and then relating the deposit to these events. In a **stratigraphic sequence** such a succession may depend on a local series of distinct volcanic lavas or **tuffs** (ash from eruptions) or a series of climatic fluctuations (wet/dry, or warm/cold) that are reflected in long sequences of fossil soils. For instance, in a **loess sequence** (a series of wind-deposited materials), the soils that are laid down under moist conditions concentrate magnetite and thereby have a high susceptibility to magnetism (the magnitude of the susceptibility is a measure of the available moisture), while loess laid down under arid conditions has less magnetite and therefore a poor susceptibility. The oscillating climate can be traced in thick loess deposits such as those in China for as long as 2.5 myr. In an **archaeological sequence** dating can depend on the appearance of new tool types or changes in tool-making technologies, or on changing frequencies of tools. A **biostratigraphy**, or sequence of animal evolution, is built from the changes in animal species or the appearance of new species. These sequences generally hinge on frequency differences or the appearance of new things and the disappearance of an old form (whether cultural or zoological) is not necessarily useful as the absence of evidence cannot always be taken as the evidence of absence.

There are many examples of relative dating. In the 2-million-year-old deposits of East Lake Turkana, in Kenya, the stratigraphic positions of humans many miles apart can be related to each other by tracing the volcanic tuffs through their exposures from one area to another. The relative positions of many European Neandertals can be determined only by the sequence of temperature oscillations local to western Europe. These can be determined from the fauna, as well as from the composition of ancient soils and other geologic features affected by temperature.

Dating by use of a cultural sequence is the most problematic of these techniques. The evolution of human technology has been characterized more by the addition of new tools than by the discarding of old ones. In order to butcher an animal so that it could be conveniently carried away, people living today have been seen to use the most primitive-looking pebble tools - artifacts comparable to the earliest tools that can be recognized. If we judged solely from the presence of *very* simple tools, we might be tempted to date an event that actually happened recently to millions of years ago. This has actually happened when trying to estimate the entrance of humans into the New World - "primitive technology" led some to believe this habitation was quite early, in one case even that humans evolved in the Americas. On the other hand, a steel ax head would clearly show that a site was very recent. Only the tools that appear most advanced can be used in defining the position of a site in a local cultural sequence. Moreover, the activities at the site must also be considered, since a site where an animal was butchered may have very different tools from an area where people lived. The same principle is used when analyzing the position of a site in a sequence of fauna evolution. Only the most modern appearing species are important in the comparisons as their earliest appearance within a region can be expected to be concurrent.

Table 1.3
Divisions of the Cenozoic Era[a]

Sub-Era	Period	Epoch	Sub-Epoch	Beginning Date (myr)
Quaternary	Pleistocene (Anthrogene)	Holocene		0.01
		Pleistocene	Late	0.13
			Middle	0.78
			Early	1.75
Tertiary	Neogene	Pliocene	Late	2.6
			Early	5.2
		Miocene	Late	11.2
			Middle	16.0
			Early	23.8
	Paleogene	Oligocene	Late	28.6
			Early	33.7
		Eocene	Late	37.0
			Middle	49.0
			Early	55.0
		Paleocene	Late	60.5
			Early	66.0

[a] Dates from Cande and Kent (1992)

The same techniques can be used to locate the position of a fossil-bearing site in a wider-scale sequence of geologic, cultural, or faunal changes. However, the wider the area considered, the greater the potential for error. For instance, almost every important human technological innovation appears everywhere today, throughout the inhabited world. This dissemination may be the consequence of diffusion from a single source, or parallel independent invention at different times by peoples who are not in contact. Consequently, similar technological changes in various areas need not have taken place at the same time.

Relative dating by fauna depends on evaluating and recording the evolution and spread of wide ranging species. The earliest appearance of certain species in an area can be used to date it, under some circumstances. The beginning of the Pleistocene epoch (the period of ice ages) itself was, until recently, defined by the appearance of modern genera of horses, elephants, and cattle. Other useful animal groups include hyenas and other carnivores, as well as pigs.

The more local the attempt, the more accurate faunal dating can be. One recent development has been the use of microfaunas (species of very small animals such as moles or mice) for comparisons. There are promising possibilities for relating small species of rodents over wide areas that are just beginning to be explored. Yet the inaccuracies of faunal dating and the problems that occur when different habitats are involved present difficulties in many comparisons that cannot always be overcome. One effect of this has been the attempt to use other sorts of widely occurring phenomena to establish relative dates.

A very different worldwide sequence of events has proved to be extremely useful in dating. This is the sequence of changes in the earth's magnetic field. A number of times in the past, the direction of the earth's magnetic field has changed, or "reversed." During such a **paleomagnetic reversal**, the end of a compass that points north today would point south. The reason for the magnetic changes is not known for certain, and the evidence suggests that the reversal process takes no longer than 5 kyr years, during which time the magnetic field does not disappear but rather drops to 20 to 40 percent of its normal value. Since the direction of the magnetic field is recorded in many different types of rocks that contain iron compounds and the magnetic field has reversed many times, it is possible to determine a sequence of paleomagnetic "reversed" and "normal" intervals (known as **chrons**, or epochs - a main subdivision of time in which the polarity is generally the same). This sequence has been very accurately dated by K-Ar techniques, and paleomagnetic dating is commonly used as an addition to potassium-argon numerical dating.

A detailed **paleomagnetic stratigraphy**, a sequence of past magnetic pole reversals and normals, has been determined for the virtually all of the earth's history (for instance, see Harland *et al*). The various chrons of normal and reversed paleomagnetism, as well as the specific magnetic events within them - the **subchrons** (shorter periods of 10 - 100 kyr when the polarity reverses within a chron) - are all are named and accurately dated. The method can be extremely valuable, since under some circumstances it can give dates more accurately than numerical methods. This occurs when there is a potassium-argon date combined with a paleomagnetic stratigraphy.

For instance, if two sites are dated to approximately 900 kyr ago with the K-Ar technique, and if there is an approximately 10 percent error to the dates, these sites could be as much as 180 kyr apart. However, if they both are paleomagnetically normal (i.e., the magnetic field is the same as today), they would have to be within 70 kyr years of each other (in this case) because a well-dated normal subchron was known to occur between 970 kyr and 900 kyr ago, interrupting a long period of reversed polarity (table 1.4). This is a considerable improvement in accuracy. On the other hand, without the numerical dates the sites would be much more difficult to relate. In the absence of any other information, there would be no way to correlate them at all. However, faunal comparisons might show that they were both in the vicinity of a million years old, in which case the paleomagnetic data would be useful. Paleomagnetism can be extremely helpful, allowing very high accuracy, but only when there is additional information about the dates.

One problem in interpreting the sequence of polarity reversals stems from the fact that there were more changes in the magnetic field than previously thought, and many of these were of very short duration. Thus, as table 1.4 shows within the Brunhes Normal polarity chron (780 kyr until today) eight distinct subchrons of polarity reversal have been recognized. Within the Matuyama Reversed polarity chron (2,600 kyr to 780 kyr ago) there are six normal sunchrons. When one of these can be clearly identified, it can lend accuracy to the technique just because their spans are so short. For instance, the Jaramillo is a very short (1.049-0.984 kyr) normal subchron within the Matuyama reversal and the discovery of some Javan fossil remains within it dates them with some accuracy. Others such as the "X event are even shorter, 0.02 kyr in this case. However, without unambiguous identification of *which event is sampled,* the combination of accuracy and uncertainty can create confusion in a paleomagnetic sequence. There are also magnetic excursions of limited geographic spread in which a local reversal is recorded because of a temporary tilting of the main magnetic field to the axis of the earth's rotation. If a short reversal period is recognized in one area but not another, it can throw comparison "out of phase." Furthermore, since the sequence involves only two types of events, a "normal" or "reversed" magnetic field, matching one paleomagnetic sequence to another is impossible without numerical dates to show how at least part of the sequences fit together. Thus the paleomagnetic sequence is *not* a form of numerical dating. Paleomagnetic reversals must be used with caution, and with as much corroborating evidence as possible.

Table 1.4
Paleomagnetic Sequence for the Late Pliocene and Pleistocene[1]

Beginning Date (kyr)	Polarity Chron	Subchron
42	-	Laschamp
128	-	Blake
182	-	Jamaica (= Biwa I)
290	-	Levantine (= Biwa II)
390	-	Biwa III
460	-	Emperor
580	-	Big Lost
635	-	Delta
780	Brunhes (+)	
850	+	Kamikatsura
1049	+	Jaramillo
1200	+	Cobb Mountain
1750	-	(end of Olduvai begins Pleistocene)
1983	+	Olduvai
2229	+	Réunion
2440	+	'X' event
2600	Matuyama (-)	

[1] dates as revised in Cande and Kent

The Pleistocene Glaciations

Most of the other attempts to use widespread phenomena for dating are based on the sequence of **Pleistocene glaciations**, the ice ages of the recent past, and the effects of these glaciations on temperature, moisture, and the level of bodies of water. The original work on glaciations was done in the European Alps in the mid-nineteenth century. Studies of local stratigraphic sequences led to the idea that four main glaciations had occurred during the Pleistocene, and there was evidence of a fifth earlier one. Beginning with the most recent, the names given to the Alpine glaciations are Würm, Riss, Mindel, Gunz, and Donau. The periods between these glaciations were called **interglacials**. In western Europe the names generally used correspond to the Alpine sequence.

Subsequent to the development of the 5 glacial concept, it was discovered that each of the glaciations was actually a sequence of distinctly colder periods (**stadials**) separated by warmer periods (**interstadials**). As they were recognized, the stadials and interstadials were also given specific names. Today we are living in an interglacial, in a world whose temperate and more northern regions are heavily influenced by the last 100 kyr cycle of stadials and interstadials which in turn was preceded by an interglacial of only 20 kyr length.

Evidence for alternating warm and cold periods is found all over the world. In some areas there is direct evidence of glaciations. In others, where glaciations did not occur, different events were used to determine the glacial sequence because of the *effects* of glaciations. For instance, during a glaciation the sea level becomes lower because much of the water from the oceans ends up as ice deposited on the land. During periods of low sea level, beaches were formed that are now under water. On the other hand, during the interglacials the sea level was somewhat higher than it is today, because the water now "locked" in the ice of existing glaciers and ice sheets was deposited in the oceans. Beaches formed during the interglacials are higher than the beaches of today. Detailed studies have attempted to determine the sequences of beach formation and relate them to the periods of glaciation.

River terraces are also used for this purpose. When the sea level is lowered, rivers flow faster because they have further to drop before they reach the sea. Since they flow faster, they tend to cut deeper. During the interglacials, when the sea level was higher, the rivers did not have as far to drop and thus flowed more slowly. Instead of downcutting, they formed broad terraces, which can presumably be related to the glacial sequence. Finally, a continent-wide series of wet and dry periods was thought to have been identified in Africa. These were respectively called **"pluvials"** and "interpluvials" and were theorized to result from a greater moisture content in the atmosphere during the glaciations.

Table 1.5
The Alpine Glacial Sequence

Alpine Glacial	Alpine Interglacial
	Holocene
Würm	
	Eemian
Riss	
	Hoxnian
Mindel	
	Cromerian
Gunz	
	Tiglian
Donau	

Definitions of the Pleistocene, and the divisions within it, were at one time based completely on the Alpine glacial sequence (table 1.5). The Pleistocene itself was defined as the period of ice ages and was broken into three portions (table 1.3): Early (or Lower), Middle, and Late (or Upper). The Recent, or Holocene, is the post-Würm interglacial period that begins slightly more than ten thousand years ago. Its beginning, the ending of the last glacial advance, is poorly defined however, since this could mean

- the point when the glaciers of the last and most severe advance first began to melt, 14,450 ± 200 years ago,
- the point when the last mini-glacial advance ended and a very rapid warming began, 11,550 ± 70 years ago
- the point when the modern distribution of glaciers was reached, about 8,000 years ago.

The Holocene is an interglacial, and an unusually stable one at that, dividing the Würm from the next period of glacial advances (if, after more decades of worldwide pollution, there is one).

From what appeared to be a distinguishable sequence of five worldwide events, it seemed possible to relate deposits in widely separated areas or on different continents by using a wide range of evidence including pluvials, (long periods of elevated rainfall), beach or river terrace sequences that reflect higher or lower water levels, or direct consequences of glaciations. With increased knowledge about the details of the ice ages, it has become evident, however, that defining a worldwide sequence of glaciations extending through the Pleistocene will probably be impossible - they have been very rapid and there simply were too many. Definitions and correlations of the glacials are best for the most recent glaciation, and increasingly unclear and inaccurate for earlier stages. Moreover, the relations of these glaciations to the subdivisions of the Pleistocene (table 1.3), once the basis for their definition, are now unclear and the beginnings of the Early and Middle Pleistocene are based on paleomagnetic events.

Some 50 cold and 50 warm periods have taken place over the past 2.5 myr, beginning when there was a major cooling of the Earth's climate. They were not all of equal magnitude or consequence - only 21 of the cold periods were major in their magnitude. Exceptional climate shifts, from particularly warm to especially cold periods, occurred some 0.48, 0.85, 1.2, 1.7, and 2.4 myr ago. The climatic cycles of the last million years correspond to some 8 really major continental glaciations, but it is not clear which are which when the sequence in one area is compared with the sequence in another. For instance, while the individual glacial advances, or stadials within the last (Würm) glaciation are very well defined and dated, the stadials of the previous glaciation (Riss) may each reflect a different advance and what is commonly defined as the first stadial of the Mindel encompasses from 4 to 5 different advances (table 1.6).

The "worldwide associated phenomena" were actually there. The atmospheric and ocean temperatures are clearly linked together, part of a widespread complex system that also includes sea levels, oceanic ice, and atmospheric dust, carbon dioxide, and methane. Thus, according to a review by S. Lehman the climate shifts now detailed for the North Atlantic and Greenland spanning the last 100 kyr had equivalents in Florida, Chile, and Antarctica. However, in many cases local conditions mask or amplify the more general climatic reorganizations associated with glacial advances or retreats. One scientist, W. Broecker, is reported to have quipped that what was once seen as a stately series of climatic oscillations now appears to have been more like drunken lurches. Moreover, sequential beaches or river terraces may be affected by differences in precipitation in one area, and by elevation changes in the land surface (perhaps the result of plate tectonics or of the changes in weight from advancing or retreating glaciers) in another. These cannot always easily be correlated, especially by the commonly used "counting back" from the top method to identify which glacial event is being observed. It is not even certain that the river terraces on the main rivers of Western Europe, the Rhine, Danube, Somme, and Thames, can be correlated at all. There does seem to be some evidence that shows continent-wide dry periods in Africa associated with the glaciations, but again, sequences cannot always be correlated as local conditions can overwhelm the effects of the continental drying. Another problem is that the separate advances (stadials) within glaciations increased in severity during each glaciation. The effects of the last one (for instance in low beaches, river terraces, or terminal moraines) could erase the evidence left of earlier ones as indeed the effects of one glaciation could cover up the evidence of earlier ones. The earth's geologic history is like a **palimpsest** - an ancient parchment on which older documents are erased so that new texts can be written.

Perhaps the issues can be best understood through a discussion of the causes of the glacial advances and retreats. Over the past two million years of continental glaciations, the earth's climate has oscillated between two different, stable, climatic modes. These oscillations, often as rapid in their onset as just a few decades, are defined by a combination of factors. In the glacial mode, ice sheets advance in the northern hemisphere and mountain glaciers expand everywhere. This mode persists, although oscillating in severity in 23 kyr and 41 kyr year cycles, for about 100 kyr as the continental glaciers achieve their maxima. Before the beginning of the Middle Pleistocene the 41 kyr cycle predominated, afterwards the 100 kyr cycle. The intervening warm periods, the interglacials, are much shorter and approximate 15 kyr in length. The regularity of the glacial cycles, and the cycles of moderation within them defining the stadials, show that three periodically varying characteristics of the earth play an important role: (1) the tilt of the earth's poles relative to the plane of its orbit, fluctuating between 24.5 degrees (the strongest seasonality) to 21.5 degrees in a 41 kyr cycle; (2) the shape of the earth's orbit, varying from more elliptical (greater seasonality) to more circular over a 100 kyr cycle; and (3) the earth's wobble, a 23 kyr cycle which can determine whether the northern hemisphere's winter occurs when the earth is closest to the sun in its elliptical orbit, or furthest from it. These astronomical conditions are necessary for ice ages, and help control their timing and duration, but they do not completely explain them.

Studies of glacial ice, and small air bubbles trapped in it, show that during glacial times the polar temperatures were considerably cooler than today (by as much as 12° centigrade), there was 30 times more dust in the air and the atmospheric carbon dioxide was at 2/3 the interglacial level (and the amount of methane even less). The difference in carbon dioxide levels, in particular, seems to reflect a major ecological shift in the oceans due to the disruption of the North Atlantic deep water circulation (this is part of a world wide oceanic circulation that also involves the return of warm salty water to the Atlantic around Africa and South America). It is this variation in deep water circulation that triggers the flips of the earth's climate from one stable mode to the other. The effect is greatest in the Northern Hemisphere, where masses of icebergs are released and cover the oceans at the times of the coldest periods; for instance seven times within the last ice age, some 7-12 kyr apart.

During the interglacial mode deep water flowing northward in the Atlantic Ocean rises to the surface at about the latitude of Iceland, releasing an enormous amount of heat (30% of the yearly solar radiation in the region) as it cools in the frigid air. It is this heat, and not the gulf stream, that warms the winters of Western Europe. When this saltier, chilled, water sinks back to the ocean bottom it is depleted of nutrients because of the increased biological activity at the surface and this slows the formation of calcium carbonate from carbon dioxide at the ocean bottom, leaving more in the atmosphere. The sinking is controlled by the water's density, so anything that decreases the salt content of surface water such as changes in precipitation, evaporation, or melting ice will dampen the process and reduce the flow of heat to the poleward oceans. In other words, all of the cyclic variations discussed above can affect it.

During the glacial mode this circulation is largely shut down because of the northern ice cap and the associated oceanic ice. The increased dust and decreased methane, which is mainly produced in swamps, suggest a drier glacial climate. Moreover dust, plus low proportions of the "greenhouse" (i.e. heat entrapping) gasses (carbon dioxide and methane) markedly contributed to global cooling. The glacial periods, as marked by the buildup of continental ice sheets, are long, relative to the warm periods between. These short interglacials are the other stable climatic mode. The continental ice sheets melt away in just a few thousand years, dramatically raising the sea level. The North Atlantic "conveyer belt" starts to work again, carrying warmer water up and water with decreased nutrients down. The increasing temperature in the North Atlantic, the proximity of warmer water to the ice, and increasing amounts of greenhouse gasses combine to warm the Northern Hemisphere and contribute to this rapid melt-off.

Further confusing this issue, both modes are marked by very rapid climatic flickers. These rapid changes, evidently between preferred states or stable climatic modes that might be as much as 7° C apart. They are set off by a variety of factors, some of which are cyclic, such as the amount of ice in icebergs from the collapsing ice sheets. The rapid climatic flickers have been detailed over the part 90 kyr with frequencies between 5 and 20 years. They lump into longer term bundles in which the warm oscillations become progressively cooler, culminating in massive discharges of icebergs into the Atlantic every 7-12 kyr that have dramatic effects on sea and air temperatures. During the period of emergence from the last ice age, the climate shifted from glacial to interglacial conditions twice, one shift taking no more than 3-5 years and a second whose onset was marked by a dramatic snowfall change in a single winter!. Yet, this Holocene climate now is seen as unusual in its stability. During the previous interglacial the temperatures over Greenland varied even more markedly than during the glaciation, as much as 12° C in decades, with stable periods as brief as 70 years (what was then almost 2 human lifespans). Sensitive climatic analysis can uncover these, but without a high-resolution stratigraphy of changes it may be difficult to determine whether a past temperature estimate indicates part of a cycle, or reflects a flicker within it.

The Alpine glaciations are gross reflections of these worldwide climate changes. The problems of correlation with them are not insurmountable, but they do increase considerably with antiquity. Correlations on the same continent with the Würm stages, and perhaps even with the later portions of the Riss, may be very accurate if a sufficiently detailed sequence is available in the areas correlated. Much earlier than this, however, the correlations often become close to useless. There were at least eight major glaciations since the beginning of the Middle Pleistocene. The Late Pleistocene is marked by four distinct stadials in some areas, fewer in others. The record of *major* cold stages extends to approximately 2.5 myr when cold periods first began to intensify - there have been some 21 in all. It is little wonder that many scientists have turned to the oxygen isotope stages as a framework to compare sites from different regions of the world. The glacial stages have grown to be too confusing and difficult to confidently equate from one region to another.

Oxygen Isotope Stages

Most of our understanding of the glacial history of the Pleistocene comes from the analysis of sea cores, although to an increasing extent ice cores have been successfully analyzed the same way. Studies of the changes reflected in these cores have a striking advantage over studies of other climatic records - they are continuous rather than disruptive. A hollow drill is used to take a long core from the ocean floor, containing a sequence of sediments that may be as long as several kilometers. The amount of ocean water deposited on the land in the form of continental glaciations, at the time of sedimentation, can be closely estimated by determining the ratio of the oxygen 18 isotope to "normal" oxygen 16. Oxygen 18 is chemically the same as oxygen 16, but it is slightly heavier. Therefore when ocean water evaporates the lighter isotope is favored and a disproportionately smaller number of oxygen 18 atoms are taken away. If that evaporated water becomes entrapped in glaciers and is not returned to the sea, the glaciers will have a lower $^{18}O/^{16}O$ ratio, and the ocean by default will have an elevated ratio. As a result, as the continental ice builds up during a glacial period the ratio of the isotope to regular oxygen is higher in inorganic compounds such as calcium carbonate as well as in the carbon-based compounds in the shells of marine animals. When the continental ice melts, less of the isotope is available and the ratio is lower. This fact means that sea cores taken from different areas reflect the same glacial sequences.

The isotope ratios in these cores have been used to build up a sequence of oxygen isotope stages that reflect past climate changes. Dating the stages has been complex, with dates from the very top based on the carbon 14 technique. Date estimates for the lower levels are less certain, and depend on (1) paleomagnetic links to terrestrial deposits dated with potassium-argon, (2) astronomical estimates based on the variations in the Earth's orbit and tilt described above (the estimated accuracy for these is about 5 kyr), or (3) estimations based on the assumption of a constant sedimentation rate. Estimates based on the latter two are shown below. The continued promise of Uranium series dates for this span is as yet unrealized. The mean resolution of the technique is estimated to be about 3000 years. Because the sequence is worldwide, dates can be verified by cross-checking between regions in which the same events can be recognized. A dated oxygen isotope sequence can link relative and numerical estimates and allow date comparisons between widely separated sites, even though these are often based on different techniques. Earlier than the last glacial cycle, whose terrestrial stages are extremely well worked out in many areas, It is becoming increasingly popular to drop the Alpine terminology entirely and to use the oxygen isotope stages to link sites to the same period.

In this sequence the astronomical "dates" are actually predictions, based on the mathematical modeling of perturbations in the earth's orbit and axis of rotation as discussed above. The sedimentation dates are based on a few absolute dates, recent ones and the end of the last major paleomagnetic reversal which dates the beginning of the Middle Pleistocene everywhere. Between these the dates are estimated by assuming a constant rate of sedimentation. These two sets of dates are close, but do not match exactly. There are several reasons for this. One is that the oxygen isotope ratio also reflects locally varying air temperatures when the land ice formed. A second is the position of the poles relative to the continents. The pole position moves, albeit slowly, and when the north polar region is located near or over land masses, summer temperatures can be cooler and more snow remains to build up and help initiate extensive glaciations. This creates a factor that is independent of the astronomical one.

⇒ **[note: this could be on an inner book-flap]**

Table 1.6 $^\lambda$
Middle and Late Pleistocene Oxygen Isotope Stages

Stage	Astronomical date	Sea Core Sedimentation date	Sequence of Alpine Glacial Subdivisions$^\chi$
1$^\alpha$			Holocene
	12,000$^\beta$		
2			**Würm III and IV**
	35,000	32,000	
3			
	65,000	64,000	
4			**Würm II**
	74,000	75,000	

Stage			
5a			
	84.000		
5b			**Würm I**
	93,000		
5c			slightly warmer period
	105,000		
5d			**Würm I**
	122,000		
5e			Riss-Würm (Eemian)
	129,000	**128,000**	
6			**Riss III**
	198,000	195,000	
7			
	252,000	**251,000**	
8			**Riss II**
	302,000	297,000	
9			
	339,000	**347,000**	
10			**Riss I**
	362,000	367,000	
11			
	423,000	**440,000**	
12			**Riss 0**
	478,000	472,000	
13			Mindel-Riss (Hoxnian)
	512,000	502,000	
14			**Mindel II**
	565,000	542,000	
15			
	620,000	592,000	
16			**Mindel I**
	659,000	627,000	
17			
	689,000	647,000	
18			**Mindel I**
	726,000	780,000	Beginning of Brunhes Normal[δ]
19			
		818,000	
20			**Mindel I**
		837,000	
21			Gunz-Mindel (Cromerian)
		883,000	
22			
		897,000	

[α] Odd numbered stages are relatively warmer.

[β] Boldfaced dates are **terminations**, approximate midpoints in deglaciations leading to interglacials. More details of these are given in table 1.7.

[χ] These associations are suggested by O. Bar-Yosef and are used with his permission.

[δ] Beginning of the Middle Pleistocene, dated to 780 kyr.

[λ] Modified from Aitken (1990), Harland *et al* (1989) as corrected with data from Cande and Kent (1992), Winograd *et al* (1992), and Wymer (1988)

Another relevant likelihood is that local factors disturb and modulate the regular effects of the earth's orbital and axis variation. Important local factors affecting the onset of glacial changes include only weakly linked changes in the magnitude and position of ocean currents and jet streams, ocean productivity, cloud cover, and concentrations of atmospheric dust, carbon dioxide, methane, and water vapor. The importance of this complexity can be seen in Winograd and his colleagues' analysis of the first continental core extending deep into the Pleistocene. They extracted a core of calcite from an open fissure extending well below the water table, covering a half-million years, from 560 kyr to 60 kyr. The calcite was impregnated with ground water allowing an oxygen isotope analysis. The advantage of this core is that direct Uranium series dates can be determined (21 were taken) for the times of the oxygen isotope changes. Given the difficulties in estimating how long it took water to reach the depth from which the core was taken, the main pattern of oxygen isotope oscillations seems to be very similar to sea core and ice sheet determinations. However, some of the temperature changes were initiated at different times, sometimes lagging behind but at other times preceding the astronomical predictions. How much of this difference responds to the local conditions discussed above, or to the fact that sea and land cores are monitoring different events (ocean cores reflect the magnitude of ice in the continental glaciers, land cores reflect the air temperature), remains unclear at the moment. Further confusing this comparison is the increasing evidence that the glaciations were comprised of short episodes, punctuated by sudden warmings (by up to 7° C) with a duration of only a few decades.

Table 1.7
Comparisons of Estimated Termination Dates
- the midpoints of deglaciations -

Termination	Astronomical Estimate (kyr)[α]	Land Core (kyr)[β]	Sea Core (kyr)[α]	Antarctic Ice Core (kyr)[β]
I	12		13	12
II	129	140	128	140
III	252	253	251	
IV	339	338	347	
V	423	417	440	

[α]   from Aitken (1990)
[β]   from Winograd et al (1992)

Apart from the land cores, there is no direct relation between these Oxygen Isotope stages and continental climate changes or date estimates. Of course independent age assessments (for instance, numerical dates) could be related to the stages, but the idea of using these is to embed dates from different sources in a single, consistent, and independently verifiable framework. There is no doubt that relating this framework to events on land is the weak link. Generally, the approach is to correlate isotope stages with cyclic or regular sequences of terrestrial events. Correlations with any sequence that responds to environmental changes are possible because of the widespread nature of the climatic changes reflected in the cores. The obvious sequence is the glacial one and the best estimate for this relation is in table 1.6; but other cyclic changes linked to climate, from alternating loess deposits to biostratgraphies based on stages in the evolution of animal species (these have been developed for animals as diverse as moles and elephants).

In the real word of site analysis, there is no direct indication of Oxygen Isotope stage, and attempts to provide accurate dates use as wide a range of techniques as possible. Conflicts between dates from different techniques must be convincingly resolved for the dates to be widely accepted, because there are too many assumptions and far too much room for error. Oxygen Isotope stages are a useful way to relate widely separated sites, but identifying the position of any one locality in the sequence depends on biostratigraphy, climatic reconstruction, numerical dating, and as much additional information as possible.

MORPHOLOGICAL DATING OF HUMANS

Morphological dating of human remains might be thought of as a special form of faunal dating. The fauna in this case is of only one type - the **hominids**, who are humans and their collateral relatives and ancestors back to the time of the divergence of chimpanzee and human lines. The process involves using the morphology of hominid specimens to determine how long ago they died. Because of the reality of evolutionary change we know that skeletal anatomy does vary overtime, and this might seem quite sufficient for arranging fossils in the order of their age. However, morphological dating is potentially circular for three reasons: (1) biological samples are variable and some of that variation involves features that might be used to ascertain age; (2) features that may indicate antiquity in one species, or in one race within a species, may reflect geographic variation in another; and (3) dates may be the very basis for determining the pattern of evolution and sorting out which variations suggest temporal factors and which suggest geographic factors, so that these cannot be turned around and used to determine the dates (of course a single person would never do this, but if studies are separated by many years, or in different languages, there is a real potential for circularities).

Generally in the morphological dating of faunal assemblages, the most modern of the species appearing is used to relate one assemblage to others in an ordered framework. Morphological dating of a single species, in this case hominids, involves using the anatomical features of a *sample* of hominids to suggest the approximate date of the sample. The fact is that morphological dating cannot be expected to work for individuals. The overlap in size and form between most features of past and present humans is so great that isolated portions of skeletons - jaws, teeth, leg bones, and so on - sometimes cannot even be identified taxonomically until their age is known. This is especially true for teeth - there is a report of australopithecine-sized molar teeth in U.S. Navy recruits!

Morphological dating has been greatly misused in the past, particularly in attempts to establish great antiquity for humans in the Americas by claiming that certain crania were very "primitive" looking. In reaction to the misuse, the idea of morphological dating has fallen into disrepute. The reaction is probably too extreme. Morphological evolution did occur, and on the average, samples from different times can be distinguished from one another. The better we come to understand the course of human evolution, the easier it should be to apply morphological dating to help date human fossil material. It is interesting for us to contemplate whether if there were no known dates at all, could a realistic human evolutionary sequence be built up on entirely morphological grounds that would not be significantly different from the sequence we recognize from other dating evidence.

Perhaps the main point to remember is that morphological dating can really be accurate only for *samples*. The larger the sample, the better the estimate. Dating *individuals* by their morphology is a more risky business because there is a great amount of variation in humans at any given time. There is no doubt that the technique should be used when appropriate; it is part of the total body of evidence for dating fossils.

Summary

Paleoanthropology is the field of inquiry that comes of the applications of evolutionary science to human prehistory. It is comprised of a number of hypotheses that, combined, are the explanation for the narrative that paleoanthropologists have uncovered over the past 150 years or so. Parts of the narrative can be surmised from the characteristics of living people, but most of the evidence for the patterns and details of human evolution come from the fossil record. However, the fossil record is not a random sample of past life, because so many taphonomic factors that are independent of an individual's life history can influence which dead animals become fossils, and since very few once-living organisms fossilize. The conditions surrounding fossilization must be kept in mind when fossils and their apparent environments are analyzed. Age determination of fossil remains is fundamental to both the narrative and to unraveling the evolutionary process. The age can be numerical, or a relative determination linking the time of the fossil's life to other fossils, or to other important events such as the continental glaciations of the ice ages. It depends on their associations and the conditions of their preservation. Numerical determinations can be based on nuclear decay or electron capture; each results in a numerical age in years (and an associated probable error range). The radioactive source may be in elements within the bone, elements in the surrounding deposit, or in some instances both because of the fossilization process. Numerical estimations can also me made from comparing living species for certain parts of the genetic code that seem to change at a constant rate. Other procedures for determining dates are relative, relating human fossil remains to the fossil fauna (or flora) surrounding them, or relating stratigraphic, faunal, or cultural elements among different sites. These techniques provide ages relative to one another and can be used to build up a sequence, although not an absolute time scale, for evolutionary events. While many worldwide phenomena - the continental glaciations, reversals of the magnetic field, widespread faunal or floral changes - have been used in dating, these have often been found less accurate or widespread than had been hoped. Of them, the oxygen isotope stages, as defined by the ratios of oxygen isotopes in cores taken from the ocean's bottom, provide the most useful basis for framing and comparing worldwide climatic events and have the potential of transformation into numerical dates. The absolute time scale that is now known shows that the appearance of humans and their earliest distinct ancestors is very recent when viewed in the context of the full history of life on earth.

ANATOMY OF A CONTROVERSY
The Controversies of Anthropology - The Anthropology of Controversies

Consider the following:

- The August 23, 1987 issue of *Image*, the Sunday Magazine of the San Francisco Examiner, featured a lead article called *Bone Wars* with the following headline: *"Two of the biggest egos in the study of human evolution are slugging it out over ..."*
- During his time writing the "News and Comment" editorials in *Science*, R. Lewin continually reviewed the acrimonious interactions and colorful activities of professional paleoanthropologists, finally writing a book about their controversies.
- On the event of closing *Mosaic,* the extraordinary science magazine published by the National Science Foundation, A. Fisher who is one of the business' best science writers ended the last issue with an essay about his experiences. He concluded "[the *Mosaic* editor tells me that] his most serious and persistent problem has not been with writers, but with infighting among scientists, many of whom nurse deep and festering resentments toward rivals". Choosing from all sciences, the example of this problem that Fisher used was about an anthropologist's review of one of his papers summarizing recent developments in paleoanthropology.
- Even *The New Yorker* got into the act with a parody about the discoverer of the "Black Skull" and the American Museum.

How did paleoanthropology come to have the reputation of the godfather for contentious sciences?
Paleoanthropology hardly holds a monopoly on controversy, or on scientists willing to engage in it. *The Double Helix* records the simmering cauldron of egos involved in the unraveling of the DNA molecule, and more recently the public debates over the validity of polywater and cold fusion come to mind. I don't believe that the professional academics drawn to paleoanthropology are particularly different than the academics in other sciences and perhaps one needs to understand the life of academics better - it is said that their battles are so nasty because the stakes are so small. A department chairperson-friend once marveled at how similar academic politics are to high school. Professionals in all disciplines try to promote their views and attempt to degrade the views of others by holding conferences in which only one side of a controversy is represented, writing unreviewed editorials that declare their side of a debate to be factual while the other side is rubbish, or publishing "year's best" anthologies, dictionaries, or

encyclopedias to which only friends and like-minded colleagues are asked to contribute. Any journal editor or grant program director will attest that anonymous peer review for papers and grants, the backbone of fairness in any academic profession, is also an occasional outlet for some to anonymously and therefore "safely" engage in the most demeaning and destructive personal criticisms. Yet however much these serve to raise the level of irritation while lowering the level of discourse, they are behaviors that all academic scientists will find familiar. What creates the perception of so much controversy in paleoanthropology? I have found that four things conspire to make my profession appear to be an unusually contentious field: the public interest in human evolution, an exceptionally broad precept of what constitutes expertise, the particularly restricted nature of the data set, and deep differences in the understanding of how to do science.

Public interest is an enviable problem for paleoanthropologists as it assures jobs and funding for research. The role of public interest, however, is not always positive. Putting scientists on the public stage, especially when fired up by the certainty of their convictions (at the moment) can bring out their worst, and then preserve it for the ages. The slower process of peer review may be a dam on the flow of news, but is also serves to divert water to douse a fire it is easy to be burnt by -- the white-hot heat of inspiration. Paleoanthropologists are no better or worse than other scientists when it comes to these public performances, but they seem to be in the spotlight much more often. Regrettable words are said, inconclusive positions set in stone, disputes or irritations of the moment blown out of proportion, and it is all there for the world to hear.

A second problem is the fact that human evolution is *our* evolution. A. Mann was once cited as saying: "everybody has a theory on man's origins. ...The mailman has a theory of man's origins". The mailman, of course. has no platform to espouse this theory from, but others do. The fact is that the popular magazine columns on human evolution are usually not written by paleoanthropologists espousing their views either, or for that matter by anthropologists of any specialty. In one case there is a monthly commentary authored by a physiologist who studies birds and another by a paleontologist whose dissertation was written on invertebrates. Their public judgments about discoveries and advances in Paleoanthropology, and their implications, are far more widely read than the words of the paleoanthropologists who make the advances, but these judgments are not particularly more insightful or objective because they come from outside the field. To the contrary, because these (and other) public reviewers of Paleoanthropology have no corpus of knowledge about the discipline to temper their opinions, they are as subjective and biased as any others, if not more so, and all too often ignorant as well. This situation is demoralizing for young graduates who have devoted years of graduate work to try and attain some understanding of the profession. Moreover, it puts much more noise into the system than most other sciences have to deal with. The public, as well as many other scientists, gains much of their knowledge about paleoanthropology this way and it creates problems, misconceptions, and misunderstandings that are beyond anybody's capability to correct. It is ironic that one of these columnists is often heard to complain about the controversial nature of paleoanthropology. Of course, it would be intolerable to have major interpretive columns about mollusk evolution written by paleoanthropologists.

A third problem is the nature of the data. Even in the event that writers wanted to study the subject matter before pronouncing opinions about it, the fact is that there is only a limited data set to study, and too often very limited access to fossil specimens or even replicas (casts) of them. Who owns the fossil evidence for human evolution? In most instances it seems to be the people who discover it. Most of these very hard working scientists act in a thoroughly professional manner, opening their material for all to see and allowing all scientists to study, usually with the proviso that the first description be written by the discoverer. For instance, immediately after its discovery, courtesy of R.E. Leakey a cast of WT 15000, the early *Homo sapiens* "stripling youth" from Kenya, was in A. Walker's Laboratory at John Hopkins University where anybody could examine it. As I write, just this week there is a conference on a newly discovered Miocene ape fossil from southern Africa that anybody could attend. But limited data can be controlled, and some paleoanthropologists choose to let only a favored few friends or professional allies examine new and potentially important specimens, developing power over others by exercising control. Those who are allowed to work on the new materials are seen as knowledgeable, are invited to conferences, get grants, and so on. Control is exercised in other ways as well. In some cases western excavators strike deals with third world scientists and officials where the excavations take place. Monetary support and paid trips to the US are traded for exclusive excavation permission and control over the materials discovered. People in third world countries can be justifiably desperate for these resources and this approach is successful. The point is that competition over limited data would be intense under the best of circumstances, and these are far from the best of circumstances. It is a natural arena to breed controversy and create the setting for future episodes of Bone Wars.

A fourth problem is in the nature of science. As D. Pilbeam once put it, we don't see things as *they* are, we see them as *we* are. Science, as I have learned it, is a process of deduction and testing that has best been described in the writings of K. Popper and his followers. Scientists build and try to refute testable hypotheses about the nature of things, in this case human evolution. Working hypotheses are explanatory constructs that are acceptable at the moment because they have not yet been disproved, and the "working" part is the attempt to disprove them. Data, the facts of science, do not exist by themselves. They exist within an interpretive framework that is so strong that it guides the very information we gain from the world around us - how else could geneticists have "seen" the 47th and 48th human chromosomes for so long, or could most paleoanthropologists have accepted Piltdown for almost a half-century? These frameworks are the goal of the scientific process. The fact that frameworks organize data prevents objectivity from ever being the reality, but their very subjectivity is the understanding that scientists aim their refutation attempts at.

Perhaps there is no more of an anathema to scientists with this approach than the idea that "the data speak for themselves". Yet, this precept is the centerpiece of the inductivist, or positivist, approach to science in which the world is examined, theories result, and they are tested against an objective reality to determine the probability (i.e., prove) that they are true. Sophisticated analytical techniques now exist to regularize this testing procedure, and these have come to fulfill A.C. Clarke's prediction that any sufficiently advanced technology will appear as magic. The less well these procedures for examining large data sets are understood, the more often their results become the reality that science is supposed to elucidate. There are cases when the very question asked is lost in the process of gaining an answer, and there are too many instances of techniques in search of questions.

All too often these diametrically opposite approaches to science create the most intractable controversies (this is discussed in an interesting essay on the reactions to a recent fossil discovery, by G. Clark). These provide the tools by which the same data can be examined by scientists who reach the opposite conclusion about their meaning. And worse, the differences in scientific approach render meaningful communication between the scientists impossible - they use the same words with different understandings of their meanings. One classic example of this is over the understanding of human bipedal (two legged) locomotion and its origins. The question was when humans became bipedal (i.e., when does skeletal evidence show bipedal behavior). The Popperian (deductivist) approach was to (bio)mechanically model bipedal behavior and determine from the analysis which skeletal differences reflected the differences in locomotion. Armed with this information, predictions were made about the expected skeletal anatomy of early humans based on the model, and the anatomy of the fossils from the early human time span was examined to see if the predictions could be refuted. Paleoanthropologists such as C.O. Lovejoy examined these fossil data, attempting to refute the bipedalism interpretation of their anatomy. When he showed that the predictions could not be refuted, he accepted the proposal that the earliest humans were bipedal as the best working hypothesis about their locomotor behavior.

The positivist approach is to objectively examine the data of early hominid skeletal remains to determine their locomotor system. In classic studies by M. Day, B. Wood and H. McHenry, multivariate analyses of the measurements of ape and human locomotor systems were used to create a matrix of related data points that reflected the skeletal differences. It was assumed the differences in measurements (as analyzed) reflected the differences in function. Locomotor systems that measured like those of apes meant that the primate measured used ape-like locomotion. When measurements of early humans were compared with this matrix, they were found to fall between the ape and human conditions. It was concluded that their locomotion was therefore between ape and human patterns, and unlike neither.

Two different conclusions from the same data, and each conclusion became the subconscious reality of locomotion to its authors. These problems reflect differences in the epistemology of science, and are usually below the level of realization of the scientists whose work they plague. Moreover, they are hardly unique to paleoanthropology. Nevertheless, differences in understanding how science is done combine with other sources to heighten the perception and the reality of controversy.

REFERENCES AND FURTHER READINGS

AGUIRRE, E., and G. PASINI 1985 The Pliocene-Pleistocene boundary. *Episodes* 8(2):116-120.

AITKEN, M.J. 1990 *Science-Based Dating in Archaeology.* Longman, London.

AITKEN, M.J., and H. VALLADAS 1992 Luminescence dating relevant to human origins. *Philosophical Transactions of the Royal Society,* Series B, 337:139-144.

BATESON, P.P.G. 1988 The active role of behavior in evolution. In M.W. Ho and S.W. Fox (eds): *Evolutionary Processes and Metaphors.* John Wiley and Sons, New York. pp. 119-207.

BEHRENSMEYER, A.K. 1984 Taphonomy and the fossil record. *American Scientist* 72(6):558-566.

BEHRENSMEYER, A.K., and A.P. HILL (editors) 1980 *Fossils in the Making. Vertebrate Taphonomy and Paleoecology.* University of Chicago Press, Chicago

BELL, R. 1992 *Impure Science: Compromise and Political Influence in Scientific Research. John* Wiley & Sons, New York.

BINFORD, L.R. 1981 *Bones. Ancient Men and Modern Myths.* Academic Press, New York.

BONNICHSEN, R., and M.H. SORG (editors) 1989 *Bone Modification.* Center for the Study of the First Americans, Oronto (Maine).

BOWLER, P.J. 1986 *Theories of Human Evolution: A Century of Debate, 1844-1944.* John Hopkins University Press, Baltimore.

BRAIN, C.K. 1981 *The Hunters or the Hunted? An Introduction to African Cave Taphonomy.* University of Chicago Press, Chicago.

BROECKER, W.S., and G.H. DENTON 1990 What drives the glacial cycles? *Scientific American* 262(1):49-55.

BROOKS, A.S., P.E. HARE, J.E. KOKIS, G.H. MILLER, R.D. ERNST, and F. WENDORF 1990 Dating Pleistocene archaeological sites by protein diagenesis in ostrich eggshell. *Science* 248:60-64.

BROWN, M.H. 1990 *The Search for Eve.* Harper and Row, New York.

BROWN, T.M., and M.J. KRAUS 1993 Soils, time, and primate paleoenvironments. *Evolutionary Anthropology* 2(1):11-21.

BUTZER, K.W. 1964 *Environment and Archaeology. An Introduction to Pleistocene Geography.* Methuen, London.

CANDE, S.C., and D.V. KENT 1992 A new geomagnetic polarity time scale for the Late Cretaceous and Cenozoic. *Journal of Geophysical Research* 97(B10):13.917-13.951.

CANN, R.L. 1988 DNA and human origins. *Annual Review of Anthropology*, B.J. Siegel, A.R. Beals, and S.A. Tyler eds. Annual Reviews, Palo Alto. Volume 17:127-143.

CARTMILL, M., D. PILBEAM, and G. Ll. ISAAC 1986 One hundred years of paleoanthropology. *American Scientist* 74(4):410-420.

CLARK, G.A. 1988 Some thoughts on the black skull: an archaeologist's assessment of WT-17000 (*A. boisei*) and systematics in human paleontology. *American Anthropologist* 90(2):357-371.

CLARK, J.D. 1993 Coming into focus. *American Anthropologist* 95(4):823-838.

CURTIS, G.H. 1993 Old fossils and the rocks that dated them, A personal history on the union of geochronology and paleoanthropology. In A.J. Almquist and A. Manyak (eds.): *Milestones in Human Evolution*. Waveland, Prospect Heights. pp. 101-113.

DAY, M.H., and B.A. WOOD 1968 Functional affinities of the Olduvai Hominid 8 talus. *Man* 3:440-445.

DONOVAN, S.K. (editor) 1991 *The Process of Fossilization*. Columbia University Press, New York.

DOWALL, M., and P. WELCH 1983 *Humans*. Simon and Schuster, New York.

DESMOND. A. 1989 *The Politics of Evolution*. University of Chicago Press, Chicago.

EVE, R.A., and F.B. HARROLD 1986 Creationism, cult archaeology, and other pseudoscientific beliefs. A study of college students. *Youth and Society* 17(4):396-421.

EISLEY, L. 1961 *Darwin's Century*. Doubleday, Garden City.

FERRELL, J.E. 1987 Bone wars. *Image* (August 23).

FISHER, A. 1992 An appreciation of *Mosaic* and the devoted people who made it all possible. *Mosaic* 23(3):52-53.

GOULD, S.J. 1981 *The Mismeasure of Man*. Norton, New York.

GRÜN, R. 1993 Electron spin resonance dating in paleoanthropology. *Evolutionary Anthropology* 2(5):172-181.

GRÜN, R., and C.B. STRINGER 1991 Electron spin resonance dating and the evolution of modern humans. *Archaeometry* 33(2):153-199.

HARLAND, W.B., R.L. ARMSTRONG, A.V. COX, L.E. CRAIG, A.G. SMITH, and D.G. SMITH 1989 *A Geologic Time Scale*. Cambridge University Press, Cambridge.

HENDERSON, J. 1987 Factors determining the state of preservation of human remains. In A. Boddington, A.N. Garland, and R.C. Janaway (eds): *Death, Decay, and Reconstruction*. Leeland, Manchester. pp. 43-54.

HENNEBERG, M. 1989 Morphological and geological dating of early hominid fossils compared. *Current Anthropology* 30(4):527-529.

HILL, A.H. 1986 Tools, teeth, and trampling. *Nature* 319:719-720.

HOLDEN, C. 1981 The politics of paleoanthropology. *Science* 213:737-740.

ISAAC, G.Ll. 1985 Ancestors for us all: towards broadening international participation in paleoanthropological research. In E. Delson (ed): *Ancestors: The Hard Evidence*. Alan R. Liss, New York. pp. 346-351.

JELINEK, A.J. 1992 Problems in the chronology of the Middle Paleolithic and the first appearance of early modern *Homo sapiens* in southwest Asia. In T Akazawa, K. Aoki, and T. Kimura (eds): *The Evolution and Dispersal of Modern Humans in Asia.* Hokusen-Sha, Tokyo.

JONAS, M., LI PING ZHOU, E. MARSEGLIA, and P. MELLARS 1994 New analysis of ESR spectra of fossil tooth enamel. *Cambridge Archaeological Journal* 4(1):139-146.

JUKES, T. 1993 Evolution. In A.J. Almquist and A. Manyak (eds.): *Milestones in Human Evolution.* Waveland, Prospect Heights. pp. 125-135.

KANOWSKI, M. 1987 *Old Bones. Unlocking Archaeological Secrets.* Longman Cheshire, Melbourne.

KAPPELMAN, J. 1993 The attraction of paleomagnetism. *Evolutionary Anthropology* 2(3):89-99.

KERR, R.A. 1993 How Ice Age climate got the shakes. *Science* 260:890-892.

KOTTLER, M.J. 1974 From 48 to 46: cytological technique, perception, and the counting of human chromosomes. *Bulletin of the History of Medicine* 48:465-502.

KOWALSKI, C.J. 1972 A commentary on the use of multivariate statistical methods in anthropometric research. *American Journal of Physical Anthropology* 36:119-132.

KUHN, T.S. 1962 *The Structure of Scientific Revolutions.* University of Chicago.

LANDAU, M. 1991 *Narratives of Human Evolution.* Yale University Press, New Haven.

LEAKEY, M.D. 1984 *Disclosing the Past. An Autobiography.* Doubleday, Garden City.

LEAKEY, R.E. 1984 *One Life: An Autobiography.* Michael Joseph Press, London.

LEHMAN, S. 1993a Flickers within cycles. *Nature* 361:404-405.

___. 1993b Ice sheets, wayward winds, and sea change. *Nature* 365:108-110.

LEWIN, R. 1981 The politics of paleoanthropology: personalities and publicity enliven efforts to decipher the story of human origins. *Science* 213:737-740.

___. 1987 *Bones of Contention. Controversies in the Search for Human Origins.* Simon and Schuster, New York.

___. 1988 Conflict over DNA clock results. *Science* 241:1598-1600 and 1756-1759.

LOVEJOY, C.O. 1974 The gait of australopithecines. *Yearbook of Physical Anthropology* 17:147-161.

___. 1979 Contemporary methodological approaches to individual primate fossil analysis. In M.E. Morbeck, H. Preuschoft, and N. Gomberg (eds): *Environment, Behavior, and Morphology.* Gustav Fischer, New York. pp. 229-243.

MARKS, J. 1991 What's old and new in molecular phylogenetics. *American Journal of Physical Anthropology* 85(2):207-219.

___. 1992 Review of "Piltdown, a Scientific Forgery", and "The Piltdown Papers" by F. Spencer. *American Journal of Physical Anthropology* 87(3):376-380.

MARSHALL, E. 1987 Gossip and peer review at NSF. *Science* 238:1502.

MAYR, E. 1982 Reflections on human paleontology. In F. Spencer (ed): *A History of American Physical Anthropology 1930-1980*. Academic Press, New York. pp. 231-237.

___. 1988 *Toward a New Philosophy of Biology: Observations of an Evolutionist*. Belknap Press of Harvard University Press., Cambridge.

McEACHRON, D.L. 1984 Hypothesis and explanation in human evolution. *Journal of Social and Biological Structures* 7:9-15.

McHENRY, H.M., and R.S. CORRUCCINI 1976 Fossil hominid femora and the evolution of walking. *Nature* 259:657-658.

___. 1978 Analysis of the hominoid *os coxae* by Cartesian coordinates. *American Journal of Physical Anthropology* 48:215-226.

MELNICK, D.J., and G.A. HOELZER 1993 What is mtDNA good for in the study of primate evolution? *Evolutionary Anthropology* 2(1):2-10.

PETERHANS, J.C.K., R.W. WRANGHAM, M.L. CARTER, and M.D. HAUSER 1993 A contribution to tropical rain forest taphonomy: retrieval and documentation of chimpanzee remains from Kibale Forest, Uganda. *Journal of Human Evolution* 25(6):485-514.

RADOVČIC´, J. 1988 *Dragutin Gorjanovic´-Kramberger and Krapina Early Man: The Foundation of Modern Paleoanthropology*. Školska knjiga and Hrvatski prirodoslovni muzej, Zagreb.

READER, J. 1988 *Missing Links: the Hunt for Earliest Man*. Second edition. London: Penguin Books.

ROUSSEAU, D.L. 1992 Case studies in pathological science. *American Scientist* 80(1):54-63.

SCHWARCZ, H.P. 1992a Uranium-series dating and the origin of modern man. *Philosophical Transactions of the Royal Society*, Series B, 337:131-137.

___. 1992b Uranium series dating in paleoanthropology. *Evolutionary Anthropology* 2(1):56-62.

SCHWARCZ, H.P., and R. GRÜN 1992 Electron spin resonance (ESR) dating of the origin of modern man. *Philosophical Transactions of the Royal Society*, Series B, 337:145-148.

SCHWARTZ, H.P., R. GRÜN, B. VANDERMEERSCH, O. BAR-YOSEF, H. VALLADAS, and E. TCHERNOV 1988 ESR dates for the hominid burial site of Qafzeh in Israel. *Journal of Human Evolution* 17(8):733-736.

SHIPMAN, P. 1981 *Life History of a Fossil: an Introduction to Vertebrate Taphonomy and Paleoecology*. Harvard University Press, Cambridge.

SMITH, F.H. 1977 On the application of morphological "dating" to the hominid fossil record. *Journal of Anthropological Research* 33:302-316.

SOLECKI, R.S. 1971 *Shanidar, the First Flower People*. Knopf, New York.

SPENCER, F. 1990 *Piltdown. A Scientific Forgery*. Oxford University Press, New York.

SPENCER, F. (ed) 1982 *A History of American Physical Anthropology 1930-1980*. Academic Press, New York.

STEVENSON, J. 1987 Fossil news. *The New Yorker* (May 11):36-37.

STEWART, T.D. 1949 The development of the concept of morphological dating in connection with early man in America. *Southwestern Journal of Anthropology* 5:1-16.

THEUNISSEN, B. 1988 *Eugène Dubois and the Ape-Man from Java*. Reidel, Dordrecht.

THOMSON, K.S. 1993 Northern exposures. *American Scientist* 81(6):522-525.

TOBIAS, P.V. 1984 *Dart, Taung, and the 'Missing Link'*. Special Publication of the Institute for the Study of Man in Africa. University of the Witwatersrand Press, Johannesburg.

___. 1992 Piltdown. An appraisal of the case against Sir Arthur Keith. *Current Anthropology* 33(3):243-293.

TRINKAUS, E., and P. SHIPMAN 1993 *The Neandertals*. Knopf, New York.

TUTTLE, R.H. 1981 Paleoanthropology without inhibitions. *Science* 212:798.

VALLADAS, H., J.L. REYSS, J.L. JORON, G. VALLADAS, O. BAR-YOSEF, and B. VANDERMEERSCH 1988 Thermoluminescence dating of Mousterian 'Proto-Cro-Magnon' remains from Israel and the origin of modern man. *Nature* 331:614-616.

VON KOENIGSWALD, G.H.R. 1956 *Meeting Prehistoric Man*. Thames and Hudson, London.

WATSON, J.D. 1968 *The Double Helix*. Athenum, New York.

WEAVER, K.F. 1985 The search for our ancestors. *National Geographic* 168(5): 560-623.

WINOGRAD, I.J., T.B. COPLEN, J.M. LANDWEHR, A.C. RIGGS, K.R. LUDWIG, B.J. SZABO. P.T. KOLESAR, and K.M. REVESZ 1992 Continuous 500,000-year climate record from vein calcite in Devils Hole, Nevada. *Science* 258:255-260.

WOLPOFF, M.H. 1976 Data and theory in paleoanthropological controversies. *American Anthropologist* 78:94-96.

___. 1994 Review of *The Origin of Modern Humans and the Impact of Chronometric Dating*, edited by M.J. Aitken, C.B. Stringer, and P.A. Mellars. *American Journal of Physical Anthropology* 93(1):131-137.

WOODCOCK, D.W. 1992 Climate reconstruction based on biological indicators. *Quarterly Review of Biology* 67(4):457-477.

WU RUKANG and LIN SHENGLONG 1985 Chinese paleoanthropology: retrospect and prospect. In Wu Rukang and J.W. Olsen (eds): *Palaeoanthropology and Paleolithic Archaeology in the People's Republic of China*. Academic Press, New York. pp. 1-27.

ZUCKERMAN, S. 1951 *An* ape or *the* ape? *Journal of the Royal Anthropological Institute* 81:57-65.

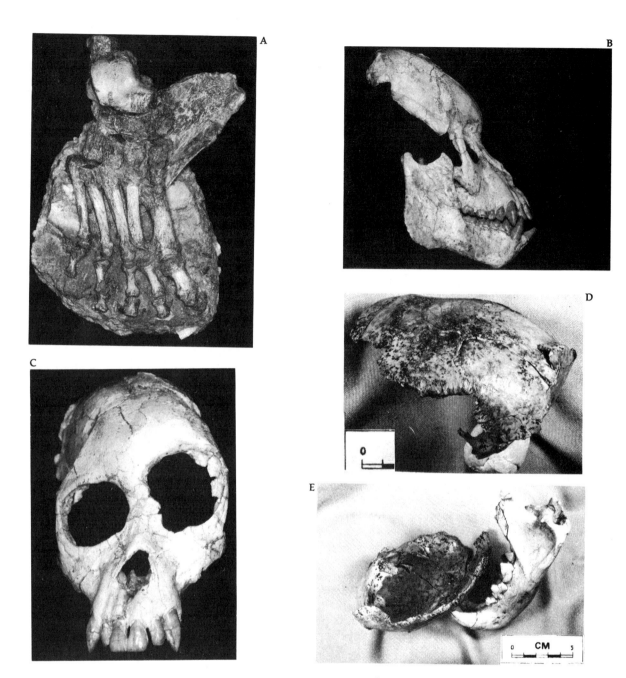

FIGURE 1.1 Different conditions of fossil preservation for human remains. Photo A is the best possibility, a perfectly preserved foot of a female Neandertal from the French site of La Ferrassie. This individual was buried about 50,000 years ago. Photos B and C are an 18-million-year-old fossil ape skull from Rusinga Island, Kenya, attributed to Proconsul africanus. The entire back of the skull is missing. Note the very irregular shape of the left eye socket, the result of crushing. Photos D and E are an even more distorted specimen, a 2-million-year-old skull of a juvenile from the South African australopithecine site of Swartkrans. The faceless skull shows both plastic distortion and direct breaks; the plastic deformation results in curves and angles that did not exist during life, while the visible breaks are augmented by the fact that the entire face is broken off. The lower jaw shown in Photo E is that of a leopard, also from Swartkrans. C.K. Brain, former director of the Transvaal Museum in Pretoria, has demonstrated that the projecting canines of this leopard's jaw fit exactly into two holes at the back of the skull. He hypothesizes that a leopard killed the Swartkrans youth and carried the body up into one of the trees that grew about the mouth of the cave (with its lower jaw grasping the skull as shown). As the leopard ate its kill, or perhaps later, part of the skull fell from the tree into the cave. While some of the breaks are due to the cat, others come from the weight of the accumulating soil on top of the skull.

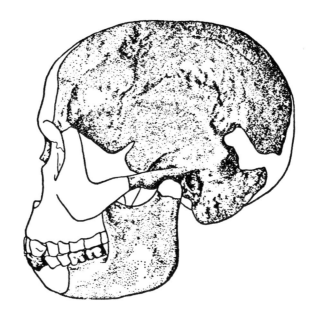

FIGURE 1.3 Reconstruction of the Piltdown "skull", from Hooton (1947). Scholars at the British Museum (Natural History) believed it was an early form of Pliocene human, and this was almost universally accepted, but it turned out to be a fraudulent combination of orangutan jaw and recent human cranial pieces.

FROM Hooton, E.A. 1947 Up From the Ape, revised edition. MacMillan, New York, figure 49.

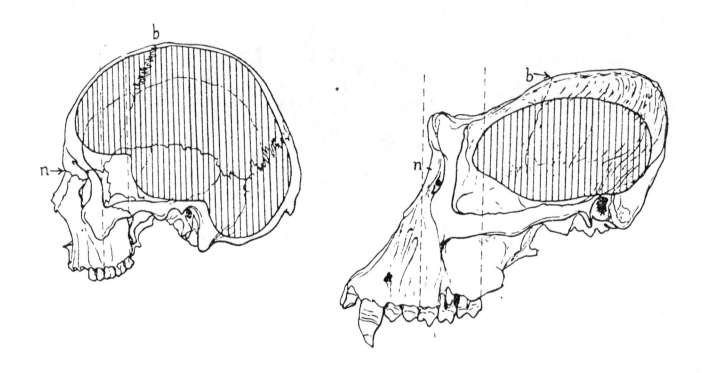

FIGURE 1.4 Brain size is one of the most important developments in human evolution. Shown here is a comparison of the brain cavity in a human and gorilla - one of our closest relatives and a primate with much larger body size. Adapted from Weidenreich (1943).

FROM Weidenreich, F. 1943 The skull of *Sinanthropus pekinensis*: A comparative study of a primitive hominid skull. Palaeontologia Sinica, n.s. D, No. 10 (whole series No. 127), figure 270.

CHAPTER TWO

The Process of Evolution

If fossils are the remains of evolutionary events, and dating is the means of determining their sequence, it is the process of evolution that provides the *explanation* of what happened. This chapter presents the basics of evolution, beginning with a definition of the term. The four causes of evolutionary change are discussed in some detail. This is followed by an examination of the concept of species and the mechanisms of species formation, the pattern of evolutionary changes and constraints acting on it, and finally an outline of how evolutionary relationships are determined.

Evolutionary theory provides the key to understanding both the history of organisms on our planet and their present diversity. Its discovery in the last century ranks with the great conceptualizations in the physical sciences, since evolution has become the paramount unifying framework for all biological studies. Yet, our understanding of evolution is anything but static. With increasing knowledge and a more sophisticated theoretical perspective, the realization of how evolution works has evolved, just as the organisms themselves have. This chapter is meant to serve as an introduction to evolution; it cannot explore all the detailed ramifications that have come to characterize the results of applying a profoundly simple insight to the incredible complexity of life.

The Meaning of Evolution

Evolution, arguably the most important biological concept ever discovered, is quite simple to define. Evolution is the genetic transformation of **populations** through time, created by alterations in the genetic makeup of populations from generation to generation. The consequences of this process are changes, in the adaptations and diversity of populations. This mechanism of descent with modification is responsible for the pattern and variety of life on earth - a tall order for so simple a concept.

The "theory" part of the "theory of evolution" is concerned with *how* these changes in genetic makeup occur, and *what effect* they have on populations. Evolutionists have critically examined the mechanisms that cause genetic change, the problem of whether these mechanisms need be viewed at the level of the gene, the individual, or the species, the issue of whether changes are gradual or episodic, and the extent to which evolution is directional. However, there is really no question about two facts:

1. The process of evolution is an actuality - a hypothesis more than one hundred years old that has not been disproved - *for there to be no evolution, every generation would have to be exactly the same genetically as the previous generation.*
2. *E*volution is the singular explanation for this history of life on our planet - it is not a hypothesis about how life came to be, but is an explanation and description of the processes that have governed its changes over time.

EVOLUTION AS GENETIC CHANGE

Evolution can be defined as the process of *genetic change in populations* from generation to generation. Evolution occurs whether that change is "good" or "bad," "advantageous" or "disadvantageous", because evolution is the *process* of change, regardless of its direction. The idea is analogous to speed: a moving car has a speed regardless of what direction it is moving in.

Hereditary information is stored on a very special molecule found in the nucleus of each living cell, known as **DNA**. This molecule has two critical features: the ability to carry information by means of the exact sequences of chemical units (bases) that attach to it, and the ability to accurately reproduce itself.

There are only four bases to carry the information of inheritance, just as there are only 26 letters in the English alphabet. Similar to English, these bases (letters) form words, which describe the actual information. Unlike English, the genetic words are always only three letters long. This is more than sufficient to handle a potentially infinite amount of information because of a second level of information transmission.

Each DNA "word" (a **codon** made of three base "letters") is the code for a specific amino acid. The proteins and enzymes that are formed of long amino acid sequences may be thought of as "sentences"; their production is the main activity of most cells. Like English sentences, the protein or enzyme sentences can be of any length. Consequently, the finite information at the DNA level is ultimately transformed into a potentially limitless number of biological messages, just as the finite number of letters in the alphabet can be used to produce a limitless number of English messages. The DNA is the genetic material in the nucleus of each cell, or its **genome**, carrying the hereditary information. A **gene** may be thought of as a structural unit of the DNA molecule, the codon. However, it is somewhat more complex, and confused by the fact that "gene" was defined long before the structure and function of DNA was understood. Genes, in fact, are regions that control the translation of genetic into protein information and may be few or many codons in length. The basic idea of the gene as a unit of genetic material carrying hereditary information is sufficient for an understanding of "genetic change."

The **population** in our definition of evolution is a group of organisms (human or otherwise) that regularly breed together. All the genes of the individuals in a population are referred to as its **gene pool**. Evolution, most accurately, is **change in a gene pool from generation to generation**. While the effect is on the gene pool, there are a number of causes of evolutionary change. The changes may respond to processes that directly affect the individual members of a population through their survival or reproduction. However, the effects may be more directly on the survival or reproduction of their genes; for instance, a change in a single gene (a **mutation**) may have an impact on the evolutionary process. At a different, higher, level the fact that related groups of individuals have a good chance of sharing the same gene may be important in how the evolutionary process proceeds, because when they help each other they may be promoting the survival of the shared gene or genes. Changes may also impact even larger biological units, which include populations among their constituents. For instance, when new species form from small isolated populations at the peripheries of older ones, random changes play a more important role than at other times. This is because random changes have a greater chance of spreading through a small population than they do through a large one, and a rare variation in the main body of the species can, just by chance, become common in a new species because it was accidentally common in its small founding population. Genes may greatly increase in number simply because they are common in a small but very successful population founding a new species and subsequently expanding in its number of individuals.

FREQUENCY CHANGES

The simplest and easiest to understand gene pool change is when there is an introduction of new genetic material, or a new gene, as the result of a mutation. However, the vast majority of gene pool changes are the result of changing frequencies of genes already present. The frequency of a gene is a simple measure of how often it occurs. It can be thought of as the proportion of individuals that carry the gene. If in a classroom of 50, five people have blond hair, the frequency of blond hair is:

$$\frac{\text{number with blond hair}}{\text{total number in the class}} \qquad \frac{5}{50} = \frac{1}{10} = 0.1$$

The proportion, or percentage, of people with blond hair is simply the frequency multiplied by 100, or:

$$0.1 \times 100\% = 10\%$$

Gene frequencies are calculated the same way, within a gene pool. If the frequency of a gene changes from one generation to another, no matter why that change happened and no matter how small it might be, evolution has occurred. Almost all evolutionary changes that can be observed in the present or past are the result of gene frequency changes. Therefore, *the actual course, or direction, that evolutionary change takes depends in part on the genes already in the gene pool.* It also depends on the cause of the gene pool change.

The Causes of Evolution

Anything that causes a gene pool to change from generation to generation is a cause of evolution. There are only four general categories for these causes: selection, mutation, genic exchange, and drift. These will be discussed separately, but they most often work in combination. We will first consider the effects of these mechanisms of change on individuals, but selection, in particular, also occurs at the level of the genes, and at the level of the species.

SELECTION

Selection at the individual level is the result of having differing numbers of offspring survive to parent the next generation. Any population has a mix of different individuals: smaller and larger, faster and slower, darker and lighter. If some individuals have more surviving offspring than others, their genes are represented at higher frequency in the next generation and there may be more individuals who are taller, or slower, or darker - whatever is favored through the contribution of more surviving offspring. This results in a gene frequency change, which by definition is evolution. Differing numbers of surviving offspring can result from both differences in fertility (how many offspring are born to individuals during their life span) and differences in survivorship (how many of those offspring survive to adulthood to have offspring of their own). These two processes are combined in the definition of selection as differential contribution to the gene pool of the next generation, or differential reproduction.

There are many reasons for differential reproduction. Presumably, if the reasons are natural, it is natural selection, while if they are artificial, it is artificial selection. "Natural" and "artificial" can be hard to distinguish, however, and it is better simply to use the word "selection" to refer to all cases when differences in contribution to the next generation within the population result in changes in the gene pool.

In the past, selection was closely tied to the idea of "survival of the fittest." With the gradual acceptance of Darwin's ideas in the nineteenth century, one widespread interpretation of his writings was that only the strongest and most able survived to have offspring. The idea occurred in sources varying from biology textbooks to political tracts such as Hitler's *Mein Kampf.* "Survival of the fittest" sounds right, since the most "fit" should be the ones with the most surviving offspring. Yet the idea reminds me of a story told by the eminent evolutionist G.G. Simpson. Two adult stags with enormous antlers were battling over who was to receive the attentions of a nearby doe. During this epic battle, a third stag, smaller and younger, found the doe and left with her. Who was the fittest? "Conventional wisdom" might tell us it was one of the large stags, but in terms of evolution it was the stag with the doe. The point is that "survival of the fittest" can only be an accurate definition of the selection process if "fittest" means those with the most surviving offspring. These may or may not be the strongest or the most powerful, but whatever features they have will be present in higher frequency in the next generation.

The real contrast to the "survival of the fittest" description of selection is the knowledge that it is usually not a dramatic process, a "life or death" or an "all or none" effect. Selection can be extremely effective without being either dramatic or pronounced. Most often it is a slight advantage in **differential reproduction** (through fertility or longevity differences) that results in gene pool changes, and not a "struggle for existence" in which the individuals better adjusted to their environment (i.e., better **adapted**) have all the offspring while the more poorly adapted have none. In fact, differential reproduction has become the cornerstone of the modern definition of **fitness**, a term that refers to characteristics and not individuals and is a measure of how much better (or worse) genes for a particular feature are represented in the next generation. The small amount of reproductive advantage that usually improves fitness is reflected in the fact that even the most rapid-appearing evolutionary changes turn out to be very slow when examined closely. This can be easily exemplified by the evolution of human brain size during the Pleistocene, the epoch in which most of the brain size changes in human evolution occurred.

Over the course of recent human evolution, one of the most pronounced changes occurred in the size of the brain. Within an evolutionary sequence over considerable time, brain size is related to intelligence. The cause of brain size increase in our ancestors is related to the fact that one of the most important human adaptations is to rely on intelligence for survival. With intelligence important for survival, it follows that increases in intelligence will be advantageous and should be favored by selection. That is, individuals with more intelligence would be expected to have a better chance of surviving to adulthood and of having more surviving offspring. This may not be true for every individual, but it should represent an average trend. To put the observed changes in context, one of the realizations of this century is that the human fossil record shows some features change rapidly, while others change slowly, and still others do not change at all. (The fact that features may change at different rates is called mosaic evolution.) During human evolution, brain size has been one of the most rapidly changing features, and compared with evolution in other organisms, it is one of the most rapid changes that can be found.

Yet how fast is this change? The simple answer is that while there is a potential for evolutionary changes to be very rapid, over long time spans changes can be very slow. To use round figures, some two million years ago, just before the beginning of the Pleistocene, the average human brain size (as measured by the volume inside the cranial vault, or the cranial capacity) was about 500 cc (close to a half quart). Today, again using round figures, average cranial capacity is tripled to about 1,500 cc. The rapid brain size increase, then, is 1,000 cc in two million years - a tripling of capacity. On the average the increase per year is 1,000/2,000,000, or only 1/2,000th of a cc. If the average length of a generation is 20 years, the "rapid" change is 1/100th of a cc per generation! 1/100th of a cc is about the volume of a fingernail clipping. The change per generation is so small that if it is still in progress today at the same rate, it could not be measured.

The point to all this is that even a very rapid change over long periods of time can result from a very small change accumulating each generation. When there are sudden kill-offs from particularly long droughts, cold winters, dramatic predation events (for instance, when a new or particularly effective predator is introduced - in historic times this has often been human hunters), and the like, the evolutionary process can be quite rapid and easily observable. P. Grant describes just this process, in his studies of the same finches that were important in Darwin's development of evolutionary theory. Yet, selection does not depend on dramatic events, or have to cause much change at any particular time, to have significant effects, because of the immense periods of time involved in the evolutionary process. Parenthetically, this is not the only pattern of change due to selection; as we will discuss below, evolution due to selection does not necessarily proceed with either a constant rate of change or a consistent direction (for instance, in actuality there have been no significant changes in brain size for the past 100,000 years, showing that the constant rate calculation above is, at best, an approximation).

One of the key points in understanding the action of selection is that it can act only on the variation already present. The prerequisite for selection is genetic difference. All individuals in a population differ from each another, and it is the *combinations* of different features that make some better adapted to their environment. If there was no genetic variation, differential reproduction could not cause genetic change. Differences, then, are a crucial aspect of the evolutionary process. Populations that maintain differences in many features have a good potential to continue to survive and adapt to a changing world, while populations that deplete their variation restrict future possible responses.

There are many genetic mechanisms that help maintain variation within populations, for instance independent assortment and **recombination** of the paired chromosomes during reproduction and the occasional new genes created by mutation. Selection itself is a source of continued genetic variation, when the selection acts against the extremes of a normal range of variation producing stable genetic configurations called **balanced polymorphisms**. This works because in complex genetic traits the extremes in the **phenotype** (the final physical form) are usually caused by **homozygotic** genetic combinations - combinations in which the contribution of each parent is the same. The middle or mean values are much more likely to be **heterozygotic** combinations - combinations in which the contribution of each patent is different. For instance in a very simple system one extreme might be caused by an "A" from each patent (AA), the other extreme caused by a "B" from each patent (BB), and the middle a combination (AB). Selection against the extremes, even if it is total, will not eliminate the three possible genetic combinations an individual could have for this simple system, their **genotypes** (AA, AB, and

BB). This is because in the next generation independent assortment will assure that all 3 possible genotypes can come from the heterozygotes if only they survive. This is called a **polymorphism** because it involves many (poly) forms (morphism). It becomes a **balanced polymorphism** when the relative numbers of each of the 3 genotypes do not change from generation to generation. This can be expected when the number of "A" lost because of selection is equal to the number of "Bs" lost.

If selection can only change frequencies of genes already present, how can new, or novel, features occur in the evolutionary process? The appearance of novelties usually results from new *combinations* of genes, rather than from the appearance of new genes. Consider the analogy of evolution and a poker game. In the analogy, the cards are the genes, the deck is the gene pool, and each hand is the player's genotype (all of an individual's genes). Shuffling the deck and re-dealing it represents the independent assortment of chromosomes during reproduction. Let us imagine that in this poker game all hands, winning and losing, are returned to the deck, but the winning hand is duplicated before it is returned (this would increase the size of the deck, which is irrelevant for this analogy). If the first winning hand was four aces and a deuce, then eight aces and two deuces would be returned. This would simulate the process of selection because the frequency of the cards (genes) in the winning hand (best adapted features) would increase in the deck (gene pool) each shuffle (generation).

What would such a game be like and what would be the effect on the card deck (gene pool)? One might expect the frequency of the higher valued cards to increase, but if by chance the first few games were won by three or four of a kind of a low valued card, the frequency of those low cards would increase. Then, as the game continued, the chances of getting multiples of those low cards would be greater, and more winning hands might increase their frequency even further. This is what is meant by the precept that evolutionary change depends in part on the features already present in a population. It also reflects the importance of chance in the evolutionary process,

What about new features? At the beginning of the game, there are a large number of different cards, although only four of each type. At first, no hand of five kings can occur. Later in the game, if the frequency of kings increases because of the history of winning hands, a hand of five kings becomes possible. This is a novel feature, the result of different frequencies of cards already present, and not of the appearance of a new type of card. The analogy suggests how most novel features appear in real populations. They result from new combinations made possible by differing frequencies of genes already present. Once a new feature occurs, selection may act to increase its frequency by further increasing the frequency of genes that, in combination, produce it. During human evolution many, perhaps most, of the important features that spread across the range of our widespread species fit this model. For instance, modernizing features that characterize all recent and living human populations, such as larger brains, reduced skeletal markers of strength, and more delicate facial structures, almost certainly did not spread across our species as the consequence of a single new "modernizing gene" dispersing. These features appeared in different populations because of changing frequencies of existing genes. This process depends on the species-wide distribution of most genetic variations and the precept that population differences respond to differing gene frequencies and not different genes. At least in part, the dissemination of modernizing features could respond to changes in the causes of selection promoting their advantages. Ideas that change the "rules" about what makes up a "winning hand", along with changing gene frequencies, were the vehicles for the worldwide expansion of the modernizing features.

The card game is a useful analogy because most features are like the winning card combinations in that they are made up of a number of genes (like a pair, or a 4-card straight). They are **polygenic** (poly - many, genic - genes) in that their development and final form are influenced by a combination of many genes (or cards). Polygenic features are usually polymorphic - their appearance in populations is varied, a reflection in part of their varied genetic makeup.

A polygenic background, however, is not the only cause of polymorphism in characteristics. The many possible gene combinations certainly underlie different forms of features, but genes are not the only determinant of final form. Virtually every characteristic is also influenced by the environment. In general, the following holds for most features:

$$Phenotype = genotype + environment$$

where the **phenotype** is the final physical form, the **genotype** is the particular combination of genes that an individual has, and the environment refers to any aspect of the surroundings, habitat, or behavior that affects the development of the phenotype. The relation holds for all physical features, from blood types to relative limb lengths to the growth and patterning of neuronal connections in the brain, and there is increasing evidence that it holds for certain aspects of behavior as well.

Consequently, selection does not act directly on the gene pool, although that is where the ultimate consequences of selection have their effect. The proximate object of selection is the living organism. The proximate focus is the relation of the phenotype to the environment, and selection only influences the gene pool insofar as the differences in the genotype are reflected by differences in the phenotype. The greater the component of inheritance, the more rapidly a response to selection can be established. However, if there is any inherited aspect to a feature at all, the usual case unless the feature in question is something like hair or fingernail length, there will be a genetic response to differential reproduction. The genotype influences the phenotype through growth and development, but the phenotype influences the genotype as well. This is a cross-generational influence and its instrument is selection.

Finally, selection does not affect all members of a population equally, or at the same time. Age plays an obvious, for instance infectious diseases have a far greater evolutionary influence in childhood. Especially in social species, sex differences are an important element in adaptation. **Sexual dimorphism** (sex differences in characteristics not directly related to reproduction and/or birth) reflect varying patterns of selection acting on each sex, perhaps for instance the consequence of sex differences in acquiring foods or in locomotion or range. These can also be the result of **sexual selection**, in which different phenotypes are favored in males and females because of different reproductive potentials (this does not work well in species where monogamy is the predominant mating pattern, as monogamy tends to equalize the reproductive rates of the two sexes). For instance, in most primates males are larger than females. One explanation (of several) for this dimorphism, proposed by R. Trivers, is found in sexual selection. Larger males may be able to out compete smaller ones and fertilize more females. The situation is not symmetric, however, and size does not have the same competitive edge for females. Larger females cannot be fertilized by more males, and all females are likely to bear children, regardless of size. Of course, if a gene prospers because of the reproductive success it confers on one sex, it will be more common in the genotypes of both sexes in the next generation. For this reason, the expressions of many secondary sex differences are keyed to hormone levels, as these reliably reflect sex.

In sum, selection results in changes in the gene pool by changing the frequencies of various genes. The genes of individuals with more surviving offspring are more common in the next generation, while the genes of those with fewer surviving offspring are rarer. Changing gene frequencies within a population results in changing proportions of anatomical variants, for polymorphic features. Since most characteristics are polygenic, and their final form is influenced by the action of many genes, new frequencies can result in novel characteristics through combinations that could not occur before the frequencies changed.

The action of selection is limited by two things. First, the speed with which it can cause change in a characteristic depends partly on the extent to which the characteristic is inherited. The strength of the genetic component is a compromise between the advantages of genetic adaptation and individual adaptability. On the one hand, characteristics with a high genetic component will reappear in high frequency, conferring their advantages with regularity for many individuals in a population. The inheritance of an beneficial genetic combination for this trait would not confer much of an advantage for individuals if the environment could drastically alter how the trait was expressed. In traits like these the environmental influence is minimized. However, for that very reason these characteristics cannot rapidly respond to short-term (within an individual's life span) changes in the environment through immediate modification. An example of such a trait might be an inherited immunity to certain diseases or particular limb proportions that balance the requirements of locomotion and climate. On the other hand, characteristics with a lower genetic component can respond rapidly to immediate environmental changes but cannot easily respond to permanent differences in selection; there may be important variants that are not developed when they are needed. Many of the structural features that play an important role in human evolution reflect this compromise; for instance bone, discussed in Chapter 4. Individual activity can stimulate extra bone growth during the body's development, but if the extra bone is only a consequence of an individual's activity there would be no mechanism that results in more genes for larger bones in the next generation.

The second limitation is in the genetic variation present in a population, since selection can only promote choices drawn from existing differences. The amount of variation present in populations is also a compromise, since great variation usually means that only some individuals will be extremely well adapted, while little variation is an evolutionary dead end because it limits the potential for further evolutionary change. The pattern of that variation, also a limiting factor for selection, often reflects past evolutionary success but adaptation to the conditions met by the forefathers may not be useful in the future. Moreover, the pattern of existing variation has a potentially strong historic component which introduces a random factor into the process. In the poker analogy, a winning hand of 4-of-a-kind may be just as effective whether it is 4 kings or 4 deuces, but the long-term consequences of which was doubled before it was returned to the deck could be immense, depending on whether kings or fours were important later in the game.

Selection is not the only cause of evolutionary change, but it is the most important and probably accounts for the majority of the changes that can be observed in living populations or in their fossil record.

MUTATION

Mutations are changes of genetic information on the chromosomes resulting from physical or chemical alteration. Radiation, chemicals, and temperature extremes can cause mutations. All of these **mutagens** (phenomena that cause mutations) are part of the normal environment, and mutations appear constantly in all species. When the changes are in the eggs or sperm, they may be inherited.

Mutations are random. One cannot predict exactly which mutations will occur, or what changes mutations might result in. The effects of mutations will differ, depending on whether the mutations occur in a part of the genome active during growth and development, or whether the mutations are in a repetitive or inactive section of a chromosome. However, this does not mean that one cannot predict their cumulative *effects* on organisms. Mutations in many parts of the genome have no effect on the phenotype at all. Some regions of the chromosomes are silent. When the codons (base triplets) are examined, the base pairs the DNA molecule uses for encoding information are mainly first two nucleotide pairs of each triplet - these code for the particular amino acid specified by the triplet while in most cases the third is free to vary. The mutations in the third nucleotide pair are neutral because they have no effect on the final protein and therefore no influence on differential reproduction, and on the average the third pair mutates at rates five or more times more rapid.

Other mutations may be expressed because they change one amino acid into another. These can also be neutral, if the amino acid change is irrelevant, but their neutrality may be for a particular environment or at a specific time. Neutral mutations are similar to style changes in new car models that have no influence on the auto's performance capabilities. Style changes might go on accumulating for year after year, like the ballooning tail-fins that adorned the cars of my teenage years, and could lead to differences that are predictable in their magnitude because they were caused by changes at a constant rate. Similarly, under certain conditions mutations may accumulate in a regular clock-like manner in many portions of the genome.

Mutations that are not neutral may still have predictable effects. For instance, deleterious mutations in characteristics that have become non-functional may interrupt the developmental process, leading to reduction or simplification of the feature. This is probably the best explanation for some vestigial structures such as the eyes of cave fish. A mutation may randomly alter part of what is usually a very complicated process - the interrelated steps that lie between the genetic code for a characteristic and the actual expression of that characteristic. The most likely effect of a random change in a complicated process is that the process will work imperfectly, or not work at all. Neutral mutations, however, are unlikely to account for structural reduction in functioning organs, as some have proposed. In these more common cases the resulting evolutionary changes comes from a shifting balance of selection and not from accumulating mutations. A very few mutations are advantageous. In the vast majority of these cases the advantage is small.

Mutations were once thought to be the most important source of novelties, or major evolutionary change, since it was believed that really new features could arise only as the result of mutation. This was called the "hopeful monster" theory: while most mutations are disadvantageous (monsters), the very occasional advantageous one (hopeful monster) could lead to significant evolutionary change. With the development of the modern synthetic theory of evolution, this idea became difficult to support. It was soon realized that most of the variation that could be observed from generation to generation was due to recombination of the genetic material, especially pronounced in its effect on polygenic traits, and was not due to mutations. The discovery that traits were polygenic itself created difficulties for the hopeful monster theory, because it became apparent that novelties were not likely to be caused by a single mutation. Finally, the problem of what organisms a hopeful monster would be able to interbreed with successfully, and what the offspring would look like, proved insurmountable. The hopeful monster explanation for major evolutionary change was replaced by other explanations for novelties, including gradual changes in polygenic characteristics leading to the appearance of new features by new combinations, and the consequences of genetic reorganizations in small populations during the process of species formation - a process that will be further discussed below.

Yes, major changes are not impossible. Something like this must have happened in human evolution, as our species has 46 chromosomes while out closest African ape relatives have 48. Either a chromosome pair was lost from the larger ancestral number, or two chromosomes combined (fused together) to form one at the time of hominid origins. Which process occurred, loss or fusion, is unknown, but this makes a big difference in terms of the genetic information that might have been lost at the time of hominid origins. At the moment the importance of major mutational or chromosomal changes is unclear.

Mutations are now thought to usually play a much more subtle role in the process of evolution. Mutations are ultimately the source of all new genetic material. Without mutations, the variation of all organisms would be limited by changes in frequency and new combinations of existing genetic material. While the *possible* recombination based variation is great, it is much less than the variation that actually occurs, especially over long periods of time, because to some extent selection will deplete genetic variation. Mutation introduces new genetic material into gene pools at a very slow rate. For instance, the maximum number of new mutations a person might pass on in each generation is estimated at about 5. The vast majority of these are lost by accident over subsequent generations, since in each generation there is a chance that the mutated gene will not be part of the genetic material passed on to the next generation (this is an example of drift, discussed below). Selection against harmful mutations accounts for the loss of even more. Only a very small number of mutations are added to the gene pool, and usually as neutral rather than as particularly advantageous genetic changes. These generally do not result in observable differences, in either the average or the variation of particular characteristics. Yet this new material ultimately provides the basis for future evolutionary change.

The accidental proliferation of mutations through a population is the basis of the neutral mutation theory of evolution, discussed below. This spread is a reflection of random change, but it is the "other side of the coin" from the much more common process of mutation loss. If the chances of a single mutation's loss in 10 generations is 999 out of 1000, the mutation will be distributed widely 1 out of 1000 times. Over long time periods these accumulations are not negligible.

GENIC EXCHANGE: GENE FLOW AND MIGRATION

Genic exchange is the third factor that can cause gene pool change. It includes two mechanisms. **Gene flow**, the movement of genes as entities, might occur when populations come in contact and mates are exchanged, when a member or members of one social unit join another, or when mate exchanges are formalized as in exogamy rules that forbid choosing a mate from one's own group. These can cause genic exchanges to extend over wide regions, just as a wave crest moves across a body of water without any particular water molecule moving very far. **Migration** involves the movements of genes caused by individuals moving, and includes new individuals entering (immigration) or leaving (emigration) a population, introducing or removing genetic material.

Migration usually acts in conjunction with selection or drift, which we will discuss in the next section. Selection and migration work together in two ways. First, the genetic changes introduced into a small population may be filtered out or promoted, depending on whether by themselves or in combination with existing genes they are advantageous or disadvantageous. However, if migration is the mechanism of genic exchange, and the number of migrants is very large or the immigration occurs over a long time, a change need not be advantageous to be retained. New genetic material that is not strongly disadvantageous, or perhaps is idiosyncratic, may be preserved in a population as the influx of genes reaches a balance with selection. Second, there are selectivity effects. For instance when individuals leave a population, the reasons for their leaving might result in selection for certain characteristics in the migrating group. Over the course of a migration, limiting environments might be encountered where there might be intense selection for a small number of characteristics, creating a kind of a genetic **bottleneck**, an environmental filter through which only certain adapted genes will pass. For instance, the ancestors of the Amerinds (Native Americans) entered North America over a land bridge between Siberia and Alaska. In this case, migration and selection worked together, since only groups that could adapt to Arctic conditions were able to cross the land bridge. The environmental conditions acted as a sieve, passing only populations with the requisite cultural and biological adaptations. However, as the Americas were populated, local adaptation continued, and today only the most northern populations remain Arctic adapted. Yet this "bottleneck effect" may account for certain features shared by all modern Amerinds.

The relative importance of genic exchange in human evolution cannot be overemphasized. We humans have evolved from the onset as a colonizing species, and in this we differ dramatically from our closest relatives, the other large apes. Over the course of the Pleistocene, human populations have dispersed from a limited number of African environments, and have come to effectively utilize every habitat on the planet. During this dispersal, two evolutionary mechanisms affected the dispersing populations the same way, limiting their genetic variability and thereby promoting an anatomical homogeneity. These are the small population effects of drift (see below) and the bottlenecking effect. After these initial dispersals the human populations differed considerably from region to region, especially at the peripheries of the human range. Many of these differences have persisted until today, even as the human species evolved in similar ways in all regions. Genic exchange, both as migrations and gene flow, has been critical in this process as advantageous gene combinations could spread widely and be promoted all across the human range. But more than this, the Pleistocene networks of genic exchange created an evolutionary pattern in which both internal diversification and common evolutionary direction played important roles in human evolution. The consequences of this mechanism for structuring internal diversification must be added to the fact that the spread of ideas also plays a critical role in the worldwide pattern of human evolution, as advantageous features appear because of differing frequencies of existing genes so that their spread can be advanced by changes in the causes of selection promoting their advantages. Human evolution happened everywhere because every area was always part of the whole.

DRIFT

The fourth cause of evolutionary change is genetic drift. **Drift** is a random change that is not due to selection, mutation, or migration. Genetic drift can best be described as **sampling "error"** - an error in the sense that the gene pool of a sample may not exactly replicate the gene pool of the population from which it was drawn. Differences between successive gene pools are, by definition, evolutionary. Think, for instance, of a population of 100 individuals with an average height of 5 1/2 feet. If a sample of three is drawn at random from the population, the chances are that the average height of this sample will *not* be *exactly* 5 1/2, feet. The difference between the population and the sample is a potential example of drift. If a larger sample, say ten, is drawn from the population, the average height of the sample has a better chance of being 5 1/2 feet, and if the sample is 50, the chances are extremely good that its average will be close to identical to that of the population. Drift, then, is a phenomenon of small samples. The sample may be the result of migration from a larger population (over space), or it may be the next generation of that population (over time). In either case, if the sample is small, the chances are that its gene pool will not be exactly the same as the gene pool of the parent population.

One might expect that evolutionary change due to drift would be completely random. However as in the case of mutational change, while the *process* is random, the *result* of the process may not be. The effect of drift is the fluctuation of gene frequencies. One result might be to eliminate genes that appear in low frequency. In a human population, half the people will not be active in reproduction (they are either too young or too old) and each generation is a small sample of the whole, differing to some extent from the previous generation because of drift. For instance in a population of 100, only some 50 will be of reproductive age and of these 25 couples only some will have offspring over time spans as long as a decade. A gene at low frequency may vary upwards and downwards in its frequency of appearance, but if it ever varies to nothing, it is eliminated from the population. For instance, a gene may be held by only two people. There is a chance that all of their offspring will carry it, and an even greater chance that at least some of their offspring will carry it. However, there is also a chance that none of their offspring will carry it. When this occurs, the gene is lost to the next generation. This is the way that most neutral mutations are lost, although a very few may become widespread through the same accidental process.

One potentially important effect of drift may occur during the process of species formation. If a new species is formed as the result of isolation of a small population, many of the common characteristics of the new species may be the result of random sampling from the parent species. Genes common in the parent species may be rare or absent in the small population, or conversely rare genes in the parent population may be more common or even ubiquitous throughout the new gene pool. Bearing in mind that the direction of subsequent evolution partially depends on the variation already present, the consequences of drift may allow the new species to evolve in a very different direction from its parent species. This small population effect may also link genic combinations responsible for species success to other variants that become common because of drift, and subsequently spread with the successful species. Thus the role of purely probabilistic change in evolution may be significant, as drift has the potential to play an important part in species formation, affecting the contents of the new gene pool and the organization of its variability. In the long-term evolution of a group of animals, such as the living primates, it is legitimate to question how many of the established features thought to be the result of selection may have resulted from random processes expressed as drift.

The influence of drift in human evolution is complex. One quite visible effect in the fossil record is seen in the recognition of what might be thought of as idiosyncratic similarities in populations. Small populations tend to develop many "look-alikes" because of the genetic variation lost by drift. This becomes especially apparent in the Late Pleistocene, where the remains of individuals from the same population can be compared, but it can be seen earlier as well. For instance, in the period after a million years ago when human populations were first well established outside of Africa, the few samples that remain of the most peripheral of these groups seem to show that they are especially homogeneous. A good example of peripheral homogeneity is found in the half million years old crania from the Chinese fossil site of Zhoukoudian, where the 6 most complete crania are recognizably similar to each other. Relative homogeneity at the peripheries seems to be a widespread phenomenon, and may be important in geographic differentiation as regionally varying features such as facial shape or specific tooth morphologies appear and achieve different frequencies from place to place much earlier at the peripheries of the human range then they do at the center.

Another effect of drift is to increase variability between populations. Because drift is a random process, different genes can be lost in various groups, increasing the differences between them. In a species that is wide-ranging this effect would be weakest at the center, where populations are largest and most closely packed with more genic exchange. In contrast, at the peripheries and marginal areas of the range the populations are smallest and most isolated. These peripheral populations have the best chances for drift, and they will differentiate most strongly because of the random process. For instance, it might be that in the central ancestral populations of our species there was variation in the shape of the eye sockets (I've picked an **osteological** (bone) feature because it can be found in fossils and thus we know about its past, and a non-adaptive variation in it so drift may have played a role in its dispersion). In the central populations the mix of shapes would continue, while in one smaller marginal population, perhaps western, more rounded sockets may become common accidentally. Fewer genes controlling other shapes may have been passed on (the shuffling of independent assortment - none of the hands dealt in a card game are the same), or a group of people with other forms may have met with accidental death (for instance, from a flooding river or a collapsing cave roof). For no adaptive reason (the other shapes were *not* lost because they were an impediment to survival or prevented people from having offspring), rounded eye sockets became common as the other genetic variants disappeared. It is possible that the more rounded variant became more common in other populations as well, but far more probable that in different populations affected by drift, different shapes became common when eye socket shape was affected at all (itself random). Thus in a different small peripheral population, perhaps eastern, squared sockets became common. The resulting pattern of variation, for the entire species, is to expect more within-population variation at the center, less at the peripheries, but more between population variation in the peripheries. Without any new genes, or the loss of any old ones, the total eye socket variation of the species is increased because of its internal subdivisions and the affects of drift. This center *versus* edge effect is important in understanding the origin of human races, a point discussed in Chapter XX. One final point about drift's action. Because drift has its greatest effect in species with small sized local breeding populations, it was a more important process when humans lived in small bands of hunter gatherers than it is today, with large villages, towns and cities linked internally with culturally defined interbreeding networks.

Drift plays a quite different role in evolutionary changes at the genic level, acting with mutation as described above. At the level of the genome, mutation accumulation may be at a fairly constant rate, as neutral mutations amass in species by chance (i.e., by drift). The close to constant accumulation of mutations in the genome is responsible for the success of certain kinds of molecular dating such as the DNA-DNA hybridization technique described in Chapter 1. The constant rates observed in molecular evolution seems to reflect the significant role of drift in establishing neutral mutations. Even though the mutation rate per nucleotide pair is very low, about one mutation per 100 million generations, the fact is that there are something like 3500 million nucleotides on our chromosoms, and evolutionary time is very long. There is so great an opportunity for mutations that their random accumulation due to drift becomes quite probable.

Thus, when studied broadly there is a good relationship between genetic difference and time of divergence - a relationship underlying the so-called "molecular clock". This relationship, however, is far from perfect and perhaps "molecular sundial" might be a better description than "molecular clock" (especially if the reader remembers that some days are very cloudy), but the relationship is good enough to show that different evolutionary processes are emphasized at the genic and phenotypic levels. Selection seems to play a much more significant role than drift and mutation in organizing variability and influencing the direction of change expressed in the phenotype, which is shaped by the combined activities of many genes. If we could study only those genes with significant influence on phenotypic variation, the description of neutral molecular evolution would not apply. However, these particular genes cannot be easily identified or isolated in the genome and the description of neutral change due to drift is a valid one. This suggests that significant variation in the phenotype is controlled by genetic variation in only a small part of the genome, a conclusion also implied by the 1% genetic difference established between chimpanzees and humans.

Species and Speciation

Species are the fundamental building blocks of evolution since their boundaries alone provide the limits to variation and change. New species can only form from older ones, in an evolutionary role that is significant because they can encapsulate and make permanent variations that were transient or only part of the range in the parent species, and because they repackage a gene pool in a way that creates new diversity.

SPECIES AND LINEAGES

Evolution is a process that describes changes in populations rather than in individuals. It is the population, and not the individual, that evolves. However, the population is not the only unit of evolution because genetic change can spread from population to population if they are in the same species. Different species are often thought of as different "types" of organisms. In any particular area this is quite accurate. One cannot confuse dogs with cats or with squirrels. At any particular place the species are usually represented by populations that are very distinct from one another. However, the "type" idea of species does not apply when broader geographic regions are considered. Instead, populations of a species, although similar, are seen to differ from each other. If populations are widespread, these differences can be quite great because of differences in environment and adaptation. This is readily apparent in humans when we look at populations from different parts of the world. Which, then, would be the "type" of the species?

The question is unanswerable, and species has a very different definition. A **biological species** is *a group of populations that can actually or potentially interbreed and produce fertile offspring, and which are reproductively isolated from populations in other species.* The species is the main unit of evolution because genetic change can spread anywhere within a species, but cannot spread from one species to another. Even further, many scientists recognize species as the only natural biological unit, because its definition is based on biological criteria and its limits define the limits to evolutionary change. Taxonomic units below the species level (**subspecies**, **races**) are much more arbitrary in their delineation, while above the species level the higher taxa (**genera**, **families**, **orders**) are consequences of species and their relationships.

Species, of course, existed in the past, and many past species can be related to present ones through ancestry. A **lineage** is *a group of ancestral-descendent species that is reproductively isolated from other lineages.* Looking at these definitions another way, a species is a lineage at a particular point in time.

Because the biological definition of species is reproductive rather than morphological, a species can include much more variation than the older "type" concept allowed - a more realistic description of the natural world. Animals once considered to be in separate species, such as dogs, coyotes and wolves, are now known to be in the same species since they regularly interbreed and produce fertile offspring when they are in contact. Species such as these that show marked differences between populations are called **polytypic** (poly = many, topic = types). Species without great differences between populations are **monotypic** (mono = single).

The biological species definition is based on reproductive behavior, which creates a problem in the identification of fossil species - they can never be determined with certainty. This is because reproductive behavior cannot be directly observed in fossils, and it can only be inferred from analogies with living species. Some of the useful criteria are fairly dramatic morphological differences, distinct ecological variation, or clear evidence that there are different criteria for mate recognition in distinct fossil population samples. There is an additional difficulty because fossil samples are virtually never from a single time and necessarily include a temporal element to their variation. This complicates the meaning of reproductive isolation, and makes it difficult to compare really equivalent things, such as a male and female from the same population or variation in a cohort.

Ultimately, it is the lineage rather than the species that takes on evolutionary significance: each lineage evolves separately from all others and has its own unique evolutionary tendencies. At any given time, the members of a lineage are a biological species, but the time element can be important in understanding their variation without invoking the problem of different species. That is, there may be considerable temporal as well as geographic variation within the time span of a single species. Thus, the lineage is a more realistic description of the evolutionary process. The problem comes from the fact that identifying lineages is much more difficult than dealing with biological species, where large samples of individuals may be observed for both their anatomy and behavior, and where direct testing of reproductive hypotheses is possible. Identifying lineages depends on interpretations. Does there appear to be common descent? Does there appear to be reproductive isolation?

Analogy can be used in two ways to help infer reproductive behavior. First, variation within a fossil sample (see figure 2.2) can be compared with variation known to occur within one closely related living species. Second, variation between two fossil samples can be compared with the known variation between two closely related living species. The variation within a living species suggests the maximum amount of morphological difference that can be expected within a single gene pool. When one source of variation is environmental, perhaps a consequence of whether or not the species is polytypic, a more exact expectation for variation may be sought by studying other polytypic species. Variation between closely related species suggests the morphological differences that can help distinguish separate gene pools. Morphological criteria are most useful in defining lineages when the distribution of morphology reflects the causes or consequences of reproductive isolation.

SPECIATION

All new species must originate from other species. In this process, called **cladogenesis,** one ancestral species becomes two (or more) descendent species, as new reproductively isolated entities are formed. The splitting may be rapid (geological instantaneous) or may take some time to occur, and can happen only when populations are geographically, or spatially, isolated from each other. When there is a geographic separation, it is possible for differences in selection or drift to result in true reproductive isolation. The reproductive isolation may be genetic (interbreeding no longer produces fertile offspring), morphological (interbreeding is no longer physically possible), or behavioral (interbreeding no longer occurs because of different mating seasons or different signals for recognizing sexually receptive mates). Whatever the case, **speciation** (species formation) has not occurred until reproductive isolation is established, and gene pools can become reproductively isolated from each other only when descendent populations are not in physical contact.

It is more difficult for cladogenesis to occur in species with populations that occupy wide **ranges** (the amount of territory they occupy over the course of a year), such as some of the terrestrial baboons, than in species with populations that occupy limited ranges, such as some of the narrowly adapted arboreal monkeys, or gorillas. There are two reasons for this. First, wide ranging populations are generally more often in contact with each other. There are fewer potential sources of geographic isolation. Second, wide ranging species are often more generally adapted and therefore can utilize many different resources, so that when physical isolation does occur, the adaptive responses to differing environments may already be within the species' range and because adaptive responses require little if any additional genetic divergence it takes a long time for reproductive isolation to result. Dogs, bears, and humans are good examples of broadly adapted wide ranging species. The human fossil record shows a much lower than average number of speciations.

One of the common misunderstandings about cladogenesis comes from the observation of living species. Since members of living species can be clearly distinguished by their morphology (anatomical form), it is often thought that the anatomical difference is the cause of the speciation. Actually, this is the reverse of what happens. Great morphological differences between populations can only evolve after speciation, and therefore after reproductive isolation. Apart from mate recognition, morphological differences are more a consequence than a cause of speciation.

If the members of a species share nothing else, they must share the ability to produce fertile offspring, and to do so, also the ability to recognize potential mates. **Mate recognition** often involves both morphological and behavioral aspects, and surely must be under intense selection. Isolation of a small peripheral population, of course, does not insure changes in the species wide system of mate recognition, just as it does not insure that changes in such a population will be adaptively successful. However, when a peripheral population comes under different selection than the parental one (perhaps because of a differing or changing peripheral environment), then the changes affect successful adaptations. If those adaptations can be subsequently preserved because of changes in the mate recognition system, a successful speciation will have occurred. This model of speciation suggests that of the many speciations, or partial speciations, that may have happened over time, only a very few have been successful.

The process of speciation involves no new mechanisms of change. However, the conditions during speciation are often unique and can differ from the normal process of adaptive change in ways that give much more importance to mechanisms other than selection. Evolutionists usually are concerned with changes in features that contribute to success or failure. Yet it is individuals who survive to have greater or fewer numbers of surviving offspring, and within species the genomes that evolve must compromise many pulls and pushes by the forces of evolution acting on different features, as they affect adaptations and adaptive strategies throughout an individual's entire life history. This idea of the genome incorporating these compromises expressed as sets of what might be thought of as **co-adapted genes,** proposed by geneticists such as S. Wright, R. Lande and A. Templeton, liken stable species configurations to a series of dips across a flat landscape that might be thought of as an adaptive plateau. Species, or geographic demes within them, have gene pools with frequencies that gravitate toward these stable dips, or **adaptive valleys**, which are effective genetic compromises for specific adaptive **niches**. Gene pools that are between them will quickly fall into one or another. Each dip represents a distinct adaptive configuration for the entire gene pool and for these to change, to get from one dip to another, gradual change of individual features may not be enough. What is required is a more drastic **genetic reorganization** - what E. Mayr has called a genetic revolution. The process of speciation may provide the opportunity for such reorganizations, especially when it involves the isolation of small populations at the species' edge, where selection is strong because the habitat is least desirable, and where the potential for drift is greatest. Drift plays a particularly important role in this process because of its potential to dislink stable compromises in small populations, a prerequisite for new adaptive configurations to appear. However, as Wright envisaged the process, adaptive evolution without speciation could also readily respond to ecological changes in species with a subdivided internal architecture.

The **Punctuated Equilibrium** model of evolutionary change is an extreme version of this speciation effect. According to this theory, most important evolutionary changes are not the result of gradual evolutionary processes in species at all - it is argued that most species undergo little or no change over long periods of time (i.e., they are in equilibrium). But occasionally, during peripheral speciation the combination of an increased intensity of selection and changes due to drift in the small, newly isolated, population, can combine to produce a new, better-adapted species through a genetic revolution. This is a period of very rapid genetic change, called a punctuation in this model. The new species may spread and rapidly replace the older species over its full range and then remain in relative equilibrium until the process happens again. The model therefore combines (1) the precept of rapid evolutionary change, often based on reorganization of the many balances and compromises in the genome, that creates the possibility of entering a new adaptive valley during speciation, and (2) the absence of change between speciations.

Moreover, there are two additional mechanisms that act to speed the rate of change during speciations, and thereby add to the precept that important evolutionary changes are associated with cladogenesis. One of these is competition between species (see below). New species would compete most strongly with their closest relatives as these have the most overlapping demands. Such competition could speed up the pace of evolution, as the species changes to avoid the intense competition. The other is part of a climate-change based hypothesis that leads to the suggestion that species extinctions during periods of changing climate opens up new opportunities and cladogenesis will be more rapid. The idea here is that if there are more new species, there is a better chance that some will be successful.

Because the fossil record is very incomplete for most species, there has been a great deal of debate over how important the punctuated equilibrium process may have been in evolutionary history. The less evidence we have, for instance the lack of a substantial fossil record in an intermediate period between two well represented fossil samples, the easier it is to support interpretations that suggest there was not any change over long periods of time, and then periods of rapid change. Two points can be connected any number of ways. Yet, the absence of evidence for gradual change is not evidence of absence of gradual change. In some cases where a fairly complete evolutionary sequence is known, many paleontologists have argued that gradual evolutionary changes within species take place - Pleistocene human evolution is an example of this. When there are periods of relative **stasis**, there are several explanations that still require a role for evolutionary processes. It is not inevitable, as S. Gould argues, that stasis means stoppage - a reflection of coadapted genes whose mutual relationships resist change. Others, like G. Williams, point out that most species evolution is in response to changing adaptive niches, but many environmental changes are cyclic or short-lived. What appears to be long term stasis may result from tracking populations that persisted in stable environments.

On the punctuated side of the punctuated equilibrium model, it is difficult to dismiss the evidence that speciations often, perhaps usually, involve an accelerated period of evolutionary change. Small isolated peripheral populations can respond most readily to the more intense selection that may be expected at an ecological margin, or with changing environmental conditions. Moreover, in small populations adaptive complexes involving the co-presence of numerous features can be disturbed by the random effects of drift and new adaptive complexes may emerge. Thus, during speciation there is an unusual opportunity for dramatic changes in adaptation that would be much more difficult to achieve during longer spans of gradual change. Finally, because speciation based on small isolated populations involves an unusual element of chance, that is drift, accident alone can play an important role in compiling the gene pool of the new species. The contents of this gene pool have long term consequences for the evolution of the lineage. Features that are linked to the species success because they are in the successful gene pool may be hypothesized to contribute to that success when they actually do not. None of this precludes the independent evidence that species are characterized by long periods of more gradual oscillating changes as well.

The realization of an unusual importance for punctuated evolutionary change comes from a comparison of rates of evolution observed over short periods in local populations (**microevolution**) and rates of evolution observed in species over long periods of time (**macroevolution**). In describing the slow rate of macroevolution above, we calculated an average rate of change in human cranial capacity of 1/100cc per generation. The question is whether this macroevolutionary rate can possibly be the consequence of microevolutionary change. The answer is uncertain, which is why the distinction between gradual evolutionary change and punctuated equilibrium is much more blurred than might seem to be the case when the ideas are stated at their extremes.

One could argue that microevolutionary change never results in the macroevolutionary rate because it is unclear what source of selection (i.e., advantage) could possibly lead to a rate of change *so slow*. The most widely accepted model is to relate brain size evolution to increasing intelligence, and it is reasonable to assume that the behavioral capacities of an early human ancestor with a brain size of 500 cc are very much less than the capacities of a person living today with an average brain size three times as great, 1,500 cc. But when measured in living populations, the correlation between brain size and any measure of intelligence is very low, so selection on intelligence is unlikely to cause an increase in brain size. Brain size is much more clearly related to body size within populations, or to climate when population means are compared (populations from colder environments have larger heads, even relative to body size). Besides, it is very difficult to envision what type of intellectual advantage would be reflected by changes in cranial capacity averaging about 1/100cc per generation, especially when the normal range of cranial capacity in living people is 1000 cc; that is, 100,000 times greater than this average generational change. Despite numerous attempts, differences in intelligence have not been clearly linked to brain size variation, even across the total range of living human brain sizes, let alone for distinctions as small as the minuscule average difference between generations. We would expect that selection on increased intelligence, if there is any, should have a much greater effect than this rate of change would suggest. Yet, we also might expect that the lack of correlation predicts that selection on intelligence would have no effect on brain size at all. This contradiction makes it an apparent mystery as to why brain size and intelligence increased so much during human evolution.

Punctuated equilibrium provides an alternative explanation, hypothesizing that long term macroevolutionary change is not an extension of the visible short term microevolutionary changes that can be observed today, but instead proposing that in the long run brain size and intelligence changed together in fits and starts, in a number of speciations hypothesized to occur during human evolution. The association of brain size with intelligence reflects the fact that while larger brains do not necessarily mean greater intelligence, significant intelligence increases do require larger brains. Thus, the low level of correlation in living populations need not be an impediment to understanding change if gradual change is not evoked as its cause. True, but not necessarily correct.

The actual rates of brain size increase throughout the Pleistocene need not be the same as the Pleistocene average, just as (using an analogy suggested by R. Dawkins) the Israelites' exodus across the 200 miles of Sinai, said to take 40 years, did not necessarily occur at the constant rate of 24 yards per day. Gradual evolution does not mean constant rate of evolution, fits and starts do not require punctuations during speciations. Indeed, studies of species in their natural habitats show that very rapid evolutionary episodes occurring every several generations, oscillating in direction, can underlie much slower general trends. Moreover, the absence of a clear correlation between brain size and intelligence could be the result of the inadequate measures of intelligence used, or of the lack of sufficient variation in brain size *or* intelligence for a correlation to appear. Correlations between features require variation in both features. The lack of variation in one will reduce the calculated strength of the relationship even if the underlying relationship is strong, just as the strength of the powerful correlation between height and weight is reduced when it is calculated for a basketball team, where the variation in height is small. Finally, population genetics models suggest that brain size is held in a balanced polymorphism because of selection against the extremes. In western societies, there the topic has been studied at length, individuals at either extreme of the intelligence range, however it is measured, seem to have fewer surviving offspring. It is the variation in this balance, rather than shifts in the mean, that probably underlies evolutionary change. However, small differences in a balance may be affected by large changes in the forces creating the balance, a precept that helps reconcile the different magnitudes of change seen in comparing microevolution and macroevolution.

One final point. The observation of rapid periods of change associated with speciations depends not only on the rapidity of change during the speciation process, but also on the subsequent events. If the daughter species is better adapted than the parental one (note: this is not at all an inevitable consequence, but it does happen from time to time), in many places across the species range the fossil record will show rapid change where the daughter species replaced the parental one.

In all, besides creating new species, the speciation process accelerates the rate of evolution, and stimulates the possibility of major adaptive changes by allowing a significant reorganization of the genome. This precept does not require a subsidiary assumption that speciation is the only way that evolution can work, a claim made by some of the scholars who developed the punctuated equilibrium model. Punctuated equilibrium is not an alternative to gradual change, which after all is *not constant* change, but rather is part of the same evolutionary package.

SPECIES DEFINITIONS: SPECIES AS GENEALOGICAL ENTITIES

The biological species, as defined above, is a protected gene pool (table 2.1). Within it, the morphological integrity of the members - the fact that they can usually be distinguished from members of other species - is a *consequence* of the breeding barriers defining it. By outlining limits to genetic variation, one or more coadapted genetic systems (depending on whether the species is monotypic or polytypic) might evolve, reflecting stable dips across an adaptive plateau. Thus, variation within a species is both limited, and in some sense discretely distributed.

The foundation of the species is found in its breeding behavior, and this creates several problems when species are considered in their true multidimensional character; that is, over time. Recognizing the preeminence of a distinct lineage in the species concept is quite different from diagnosing the existence of a distinct lineage. One problem is that an interbreeding diagnosis cannot be applied to populations far removed in time, especially geologic time as we might encounter if we were interested in whether 40,000 year old Neandertals and modern humans are in the same species. A second problem is that fossil remains usually provide no information about interbreeding. Although morphological differences between species are a result of gene exchange barriers, these differences can also occur within polytypic species, and conversely some closely related species can be very similar to each other.

The solution to these problems comes from a more genealogically oriented concept of species, one which considers species in their temporal dimension. **Genealogical species** are distinct individuals with definite beginnings and ends and each with a unique ancestry. The importance of genealogy in the species definition is the insistence that all members of the species share common descent. Another way to put this is that genealogical species are **monophyletic**. A monophyletic group, analogous to an American family, consists of a number of related individuals who are all the descendants of their last common ancestor. There are two definitions that fit this description (table 2.1).

Phylogenetic (Morpho) Species

Earlier this century, some paleontologists objected to the fact that biological species criteria cannot be directly applied to the fossil record. They developed the idea of a species definition based on morphological difference - the **morphospecies**. Adding the genealogical criteria discussed above resulted in the phylogenetic species concept. A **phylogenetic species** has been defined as a group of individuals meeting two criteria: (1) their identity can be diagnosed by at least one shared unique feature, and (2) the group must be monophyletic so that there is a parental pattern of ancestry within the group, but not beyond it. According to this definition the phylogenetic species is the minimum biological unit that can be diagnosed. Members of phylogenetic species are easy to recognize because each species is defined by the presence of one or more unique features. This makes the phylogenetic species concept particularly attractive to paleontologists. The problem is that biological variation in the past organized according to the phylogenetic species concept has no relationship to present biological variation organized according to the biological species concept that forms the cornerstone of the modern synthetic theory of evolution.

Evolutionary Species

It is desirable to use a species definition to organize our knowledge about the past that is directly comparable with the present. Without this, the detailed knowledge of life today can never be used in interpreting the past. The phylogenetic species is a flawed and undesirable solution to the problems involved in using the biological species to interpret samples of past populations. It is not, however, the only genealogical species concept. An **evolutionary species** has been defined as a single monophyletic lineage of ancestral-descendant populations which maintains its identity from other such lineages and which has its own evolutionary tendencies and historical fate. The evolutionary species concept thus retains the essence of the biological species - reproductive isolation (the reason why it can maintain its identity and have unique evolutionary tendencies - while avoiding many of its deficiencies: lack of time-depth, absence of morphological criteria for diagnosis, and perhaps most importantly emphasis on reproductive ties (genic exchanges) alone as a major cohesive force. It differs from the phylogenetic species in that the species is defined by reproductive isolation rather than one or more shared unique characters; in fact, morphological distinctiveness is not a necessary requisite. Nevertheless, an evolutionary species can be morphologically diagnosed (i.e. identified), using criteria developed below.

Fundamental to the evolutionary species concept is the observation that reproductive boundaries are the underlying basis for the main characteristic shared by the populations of a species - its unique evolutionary pattern. Within these boundaries there is an internal cohesiveness that helps maintain this pattern, resulting from three factors: (1) the limits to genic exchange, (2) natural selection in fundamental niches, establishing a limited number of stable dips across an adaptive plateau reflecting coadapted combinations of genes, and (3) ecological, developmental, and historical constraints (as discussed below).

Evolutionary species can be seen as a biological species extended over time, but they are more. This broader concept of an evolutionary species addresses the weakness of the biological species concept that is of greatest concern to paleontologists - the difficulty of translating the main criterion of actual or potential interbreeding into useful models of morphological variation. The evolutionary species has its unique evolutionary tendencies that can be readily interpreted as morphological criteria (for instance, see the discussion of *Australopithecus boisei* in Chapter 7). Another consequence of this definition is the focus on the evolutionary importance of behavioral mechanisms that promote species recognition during mate choice and mating.

Throughout this text, discussions of species assume the *evolutionary species* definition. Thus, when focus is on the dynamics of a species at a particular time, it is the biological species concept that applies.

Table 2.1
Species Definitions

Basis	These two species have a genetic basis ***		These two species have a genealogical basis ***
Species	**Biological Species**	**Evolutionary Species**	**Phylogenetic Species**
Definition	A group of populations able to interbreed and have fertile offspring, that are reproductively isolated from all other such groups	single monophyletic lineage of ancestral-descendant populations evolving separately and maintaining its identity from other such lineages, with its own evolutionary tendencies and historical fate	a group of individuals meeting two criteria: (1) their identity can be diagnosed by at least one shared unique feature, and (2) the group must be monophyletic so that there is a parental pattern of ancestry within the group, but not beyond it

Levels of Selection: The Organization of Populations

Now it is time to look once more at the mechanisms of evolution, because species play a role in how these mechanisms cause change. This role, or actually roles, are a function of two attributes of species - the processes of their creation, and their internal organization as it affects related individuals. Selection is the mechanism of change that must be considered. We have examined its consequences at the individual and local population levels, but now we must also consider it as a species level, and genic level, mechanism. For the species, selection is the process of differential species reproduction (speciation patterns) and survivorship (extinction patterns). For the gene, selection may not necessarily favor individual reproductive success and survivorship since the same gene can be distributed among different individuals (with a higher probability if they are related); selection is channeled by population structures that affect related individuals, as these will influence the success of any particular gene within a population.

SELECTION AT THE SPECIES LEVEL

In the genealogical approach to taxonomy, species are individuals and their evolutionary relationships are based on shared ancestry, just as the genealogical relationships of individuals. But to what extent can the analogy of species and individuals be extended to the evolutionary realm of differential reproduction? Is there a process of species selection, or more generally what G. Williams calls "clade selection"?

There certainly is a sort of differential reproduction for species themselves, because species have beginnings and ends - in that they are created and become extinct, they can be said to be born and die. Anything that systematically affects their survivorship or reproduction can orient the direction of evolutionary change. For instance, in most cases species formation through cladogenesis is dependent on the geographic isolation of peripheral populations. Species that are more likely to have geographically isolated populations at their peripheries, are more likely to speciate. These tend to be narrowly adapted species. The basis for the relation of speciation rate to adaptation may be linked to the importance of the mate recognition system each species develops in the process of speciation (see discussion above). Narrowly adapted species are more likely to have to rapidly respond to environmental changes at their peripheries. If their existing adaptation does not already include the genetic basis for successfully reacting to the changing requirements, they must respond with genetic change to persist. Of course if they do not respond, or if the response is unsuccessful, the population becomes extinct and there is no speciation. When this response is successful, and affects the mate recognition system (whether directly or as an indirect effect of other morphological or behavioral changes), reproductive isolation is the consequence. A slower speciation process would bypass the mate recognition system and result in change that made fertile offspring impossible - this is the ultimate consequence of changes in the mate recognition system in any event.

Conversely, while broadly adapted species could have isolated peripheral populations this is less probable. And, when the peripheral populations of broadly adapted species *are* isolated, response to environmental change is more likely to already be within their adaptive repertoire, so significant genetic changes (that might create differences in the species-wide mate recognition system) are less likely to result. Speciation, therefore is less probable. Because the length of an evolutionary species' existence is linked to the speciation rate, low speciation rates necessarily mean lengthened survivorship. More generally adapted species, in other words, last longer.

Differential reproduction of species is more than a statistical phenomenon. There are distinct evolutionary trends, particularly toward narrowed adaptation, within an evolving group of species. The proliferation of narrowly adapted species and the trends to further narrow subsequent adaptations are a consequence of the likelihood that those offspring of a species that are narrowly adapted will themselves have a higher probability of speciation. For example, many Holocene species have reduced markedly in size, and have narrower ranges, than their Pleistocene ancestors. While trends toward size decrease may be a consequence of individual selection in each of these species, it is also possible that the greater environmental richness of the post-Pleistocene created the opportunity for more distinct adaptive niches and smaller, more narrowly adapted species, could take advantage of these. They had an increased rate of speciation and therefore proliferated.

On the other hand species selection models predict that more broadly adapted species, for instance like our ancestors, are more likely to persist longer and not speciate. Terminal Pleistocene size reductions did not affect the human species. Selection at the species level is not a substitution for the selection process at the individual and population levels discussed above but rather adds another dimension to the evolutionary process.

BEHAVIOR AND EVOLUTION: SELECTION AT THE GENIC LEVEL

The ultimate cause of gene frequency change is the ability of individuals to survive and have surviving offspring. Yet frequency changes necessarily apply to a population, and numerous studies of human populations have shown that it is common for the best populational adaptation to be different from, even contradictory to, the best individual adaptation for many population members. Contradictions between the best adaptation for the individual and the best adaptation for the population are most evident in the evolutionary analysis of behaviors.

The question of which level selection acts upon becomes particularly significant in the analysis of behaviors. Behavior is the ultimate interface between morphology and environment. The evolutionary importance of behavior cannot be overstated; indeed, in most cases it is likely that morphological changes must follow changes in behavior. The idea that there is a genetic influence on behaviors is not new. Such an influence was shown clearly decades ago with experiments demonstrating that the frequencies, even the modalities, of certain animal behaviors could be changed by selection. If there is a genetic component to behavioral variability, the genetics of behaviors are subject to the forces of evolution. However, a great gulf separates the demonstration of a genetic component to behavior from simplistic models indicating a genetic basis for particular behaviors (i.e., a gene for a behavior) . Understanding the evolution of behaviors is, in principle, not harder than understanding morphological evolution - itself a monumental task! However, behavioral evolution presents some uniquely difficult problems. Many of these lie in the understanding of **altruisms** in which behavior beneficial to a group may be harmful to an individual, for instance a soldier going to war, or in unreciprocated altruisms as when a person sacrifices themselves to save the lives of others (**reciprocal altruism** is easier to understand as both interacting parties benefit). These behaviors are anything but rare - at times they seem to reflect the very fabric that holds societies together. They are complex, and it is not possible that only one or several genes controls their variation.

Yet, it is also unlikely that important behaviors are fully independent of the genome, and the question remains of how any genetic influence on their expression could persist when selection would seem to make them self-extinguishing.

An answer to this question was developed in the context of **sociobiology**, defined by E.0. Wilson as the "study of the biological basis of all social behavior." Some sociobiological analyses have been over simplistic, incorporating relatively simple explanations in which "genes cause behaviors" in attempting to explain the evolution of behavior from the simplest to the most complex social creatures. However, more interesting analyses have been developed and provide insight into the evolution of social behaviors in general, and human cultural behavior in specific.

Central to the evolutionary modeling of behavioral change is the view of evolution from the genic perspective, leading to the idea of **inclusive fitness**, a characterization of how well a feature's genetic material is represented in the next generation because of the survival of relatives (many of who will share the genes), in addition to one's own survival. Thus the differential reproduction of a gene, rather than of an individual (or species), is the focus of analysis. For instance, an offspring has about 1/2 of each parent's genetic material and shares about 1/2 the genome of each sib of the same parents. The number of genes shared with more distant relations is less: 1/4 with half-sibs, 1/8 with first cousins, and so on. Behavior that enhances the survival of one's biological relatives increases the probability of an additional genetic contribution (albeit indirect) to the next generation, and consequently adds to one's inclusive fitness because it includes other instances of survival for a particular gene beside one's own. This is called **kin selection**. The British biologist J. Haldane once quipped that he would lay down his life for two brothers or eight first cousins. Sociobiologists have attempted to demonstrate that the evolution of genetically based behaviors always acts to maximize inclusive fitness.

Understanding the evolution of societies seems to particularly benefit from the inclusive fitness approach, since altruism (whether reciprocal or not) underlies so many social relationships, and kin selection seems to account for many of the "social payoffs" that individuals find desirable. But when applied to the evolution of human behavior and human societies, sociobiology lies in a hotbed of controversy because "social payoffs" are culturally defined and so much of human culture lies outside the genome, existing independently of the individuals who participate in it. Nevertheless, the evolution of human behavior has come to be a major area of study, with a focus on the importance of the inclusive fitness concept in explaining human behavioral variation and evolution. Human behavioral evolution proved to be much more complex to understand than phenotypic change because of the importance of the behavioral interactions that form the basis of social behavior. Behavioral studies at the time that sociobiology was developing were largely physiological in their orientation and grappled with the issues of instinct and environment, emphasizing the great complexities of instinctual behaviors. Awareness of how behavioral evolution might be modeled in a more evolutionary context was provided by the inclusive fitness insight, as genes seemed to unite the very individuals whose interactions are the focus of behavioral studies. Behavioral genes can be expected to increase in frequency if the behaviors increase the survival of related groups, and early sociobiological studies assumed that specific genes could be found controlling particular human behaviors .

But it is now widely recognized that specific genes do not control specific behaviors. Most human behaviors of interest in an evolutionary framework are intelligible only in fundamentally cultural contexts and structural settings. It is possible that only the deep underlying structural bases for behavioral classes respond to some degree of genetic control (such as the common underlying deep structures for all human language grammars). This distinction implies the potential for models of behavioral evolution that are much more complex, and interesting, than the earlier genes-control-behaviors approaches. For instance, the structural model is an example of what E. Mayr calls an "open behavioral program," one which is modifiable during life. The unique aspect of human behavioral evolution, in this view, is the development of species-specific organizational elements in what became an increasingly complex array of behaviors. Such elements act both to limit the range of possible structures and to provide a common basis for the necessary logical ordering within structures. This ordering allows behaviors to be interpreted within and between human groups. Evolution could be expected to affect the deepest shared aspects of behaviors - the kinds of things we learn easily and the contexts we learn them in - and *not* specific behaviors. For example, a shared organizational element in our species might be the substitution of gender for sex as a criterion for role definition. Presumably past evolution acted at this deepest level, and not over the question of which roles and their interactions such a substitution affected.

In fact, focus has shifted away from the idea of behavioral genes and on to the evolutionary implications of open behavioral programs. Individuals have a wide variety of options in their interactions. Sociobiologists have come to focus on which options are actually exercised, theorizing that those chosen will have the highest social or ecological pay-off. Thus, individual behaviors have replaced individual genes as the objects of study, with the caveat that the behavioral variation has some relation to underlying genetic variation - a supposition much more in tune with assumptions that underlie studies of anatomical evolution. Maximization of inclusive fitness is still the expected object of the evolutionary process, but the relations of behaviors to fitness is very complex, as optimization is defined by culturally determined criteria. Some scientists have argued that adaptation is not really reflected at the behavioral level at all, but is manifested only at the psychological level of behavioral analysis. They contend that the goal of evolutionary theory might best be focused on understanding human psychology in a Darwinian context.

The various structures that govern the behaviors of individuals in groups have come under scrutiny - kinship, society, and ultimately culture - as there was a potential for studying them in an evolutionary context. Sociobiologists have ultimately broadened their interests in human behavioral evolution, with different groups examining the evolutionary contexts of behavioral correlates of reproductive success, the complex relationship and simultaneous inheritance of genes and culture, the environmental and physiological determinants of human fertility, and the interpretation of brain functions as adaptations to past environments.

The study of human social evolution has become entangled in the broader studies of primate societies, reflecting the more general trend to examine primate comparisons as the background for understanding human evolution (this is discussed further in Chapter 5). The comparative method is fundamental to all evolutionary studies, but the problems of homology plague behavioral studies as much as the studies of anatomy and it is far from clear that human and non-human primate social behaviors can be validly compared. This is because human social behaviors are expressed in a language-dependent cultural context that primate societies lack, and direct comparisons may be at a level too far below the least common denominator. While all primate societies have populations, biological males and females, and degrees of genetic relatedness, the fact is that only humans have a language-dependent culture, genders, and genealogical relationships based on culturally defined kinship. Comparisons outline where humans are unique, but do not necessarily show how and why those uniquenesses evolved. It is just this kind of assumption that had decades of linguists trying to explain how human language evolved from primate call systems (it now appears that these two communication systems are unrelated - see Chapter 4). Moreover, continued comparisons with the apes, especially with chimpanzees who are now widely regarded as the human **sister group**, almost invariably assume the modern chimpanzee behavior reflects the ancestral condition for both species, although the last common ancestor lived some 7 million years ago, in an ecological setting where no chimpanzees are found today (this problem is further discussed in Chapter 5).

The verdict on human behavioral evolution is not yet in. The promise of a Darwinian framework for human culture and society has not yet been realized, and may prove to be unobtainable. Yet, as studies of human behavioral evolution converge on more traditional paleoanthropological analyses (for instance, in the Lovejoy human origins hypothesis that is discussed in Chapter 5), the influence of inclusive fitness theory is undeniable.

Evolutionary Constraints

The magnitudes and directions of evolutionary changes respond to selection (at different levels), mutation, genic exchange, and drift, as described above. But these changes are not without their limitations, there are genetic and other structural constraints on the directions that such changes can take. These constraints are an important consequence of the developmental pathway from genes to organisms. This pathway is complex, and populations are far more than conglomerates of independent individuals whose similarities stem from the genes they share. Much of the pattern of variation within species, and the systematic differences between closely related ones, reflect these constraints. Before its source was understood, the similarities imposed led anatomists to conjecture the influence of an archetype or bauplan that was a part of the species-type. These ideas were replaced as the interbreeding species concept was developed, but the observations they were meant to explain still remain valid.

ALLOMETRY

Long term trends in the evolution of organisms that cross-cut species boundaries seem to require special explanation. It has been argued that such trends might reflect certain limitations on variation, apart from the constraint that evolutionary change can only proceed from the genetic material already on hand. One type of long term trend is found in **allometric scaling**, the consistent patterns of change associated with body size increases or decreases. When body size changes, body proportions must change disproportionately - a mouse that was elephant-size would break its much-too-slender legs from its own body weight. One reason for this disproportion is that the limb lengths are a linear measure of size, their cross sections (the aspect that resists weight and other forces) increase by the square of the linear increases, and the weight of the organism increases by the cube of the linear increase. The limb structures do not improve their weight resistant qualities as quickly as weight increases, if they maintain the same proportion.

More generally, the scaling of various body structures to body weight often fits a pattern of allometry when body size increases during the evolution of a lineage. This allometric pattern is expressed by the relation:

$$Y = AX^k$$

where **Y** is the varying size of the body structure (dependent variable), **X** is the varying body weight (independent variable), **A** is a constant, and **k** is the coefficient of allometry. The constant and coefficient are particular to the species, and to the variables compared, but the *form* of the relation is virtually universal. Such a species-wide regularity in scaling has proved hard to explain. Earlier in this century the relation was commonly observed, and the formula empirically found to express it was originally derived from a growth model in which the growth rate was assumed to be proportional to the body mass present. However, this model does not accurately describe the growth of most vertebrate structures.

R. Lande was able to demonstrate mathematically that the allometric relation was a consequence of **genetic correlation** between two structures, or **pleiotropy** - the sharing of some common genes between two structures. When there is selection on one of the structures promoting change over time, the correlated structure will also change because of the shared genes; this correlated change is allometric, and its pattern will fit the allometric formula. Thus, changes in body size (for instance) can be expected to change all body structures genetically linked to it - the effect of scaling should be allometric.

With allometry as the expected scaling relationship, we can examine whether scaling can account for related changes. For instance both body size and brain size increase dramatically, early in the evolution of our species *Homo sapiens*, some 1.8 million years ago. We would like to know if the increase in brain size is an allometric (expected scaling) consequence of the body size increase. Since they both expand at the same time it is probable that some of the brain size change is a consequence of larger body size. However, it is also possible that the enlargement in brain size was not as great as what one would expect from the body size increase, or that the brain size increase exceeds the requirements of larger body size. In either of these cases, departure from the allometric prediction would suggest a source of selection acting on brain size that is independent from the requirements of increasing body size. One way to examine which of these three possibilities is most likely to be correct is to determine what the general scaling coefficient for brain size is in primates closely related to these early humans, and consider the expected changes predicted by this more general pattern. In this case, there is a general primate allometric relation of brain to body size, with the coefficient (**k**) in a number of species ranging between 0.15 and 0.20. If this range of coefficients is used to predict how much brain size change would be expected from the body size increase in early *Homo sapiens*, the brain size increase is shown to be much larger than expected. We can assume that the expanded brain size is beyond the ability of scaling alone to explain. Some of the brain size increase responds to selection that is independent of body size, affecting genes that control brain size and structure on that part of the genome controlling brain size that is not shared with body size.

When there are separate evolutionary changes in pleiotropically related variables, the magnitude of their genetic correlation reduces. In these cases we would expect that subsequent allometric change (due to selection acting on only one of the variables) would be smaller because the coefficient of allometry (k) is less.

HETEROCHRONY

Another evolutionary constraint is a consequence of the growth process of organisms, that is their **ontogeny**, and the influence of this process on the relationships of species. **Heterochrony** refers to evolutionary changes caused by variation in the relative time of appearance and rate of development for features. It has two forms: **paedomorphic** changes cause the adult descendent to resemble the juvenile ancestor; and **peramorphic** changes cause the juvenile descendant to resemble the adult ancestor.

Paedomorphosis has been cited as a driving force in human evolution, as human adults resemble ape children in their relatively large heads, high foreheads, small faces, and general gracility. Such a comparison is misleading, as humans did not evolve from living apes - humans and chimpanzees have a common ancestor some 7 million years ago - and the pathway leading to the modern human condition was more complex than the simple reduction of muscularity and robustness that a paedomorphic model would require. However, if human adults have come to resemble young australopithecines, on the direct line of human descent, the process could be described as paedomorphic. But what would it take for the paedomorphic explanation to be valid? The two mechanisms underlying paedomorphosis are **neotony** (the slowdown of development) and progenesis, the earlier cessation of growth by shifting reproduction to a younger age. It is hard to believe that neotony applies in this case, as australopithecines already have a elongated maturation times (see Chapter 4)

Similar problems plague peramorphosis. Juvenile gorillas resemble adult chimpanzees, but even if gorillas evolved from a chimpanzee-like ancestor (gorillas, of course, could not have evolved directly from chimpanzees as they are both living species), allometry may be a better explanation for their morphological relationship than peramorphisis since gorillas are considerably larger than this hypothesized chimpanzee-like ancestor. The allometry explanation makes sense because many of the skeletal features of gorillas resemble the largest chimpanzees and have been interpreted as the consequences of a continued growth process. This example shows both the relationship of heterochrony and allometry, and the importance of correctly identifying the ancestral condition in evolutionary studies. We will return to this importance, and discuss some suggestions about how this may be accomplished.

The potential for heterochrony forces us to remember that individuals have life histories, and that evolutionary change must be seen in this individual time depth and not just in the greater time depth between generations or over eons. Small changes early in life history may have dramatic effects later, and this creates the possibility for significant morphological change without a large corresponding genetic one. A single mutation in a regulatory gene could attain disproportionate influence on adult morphology if the affected process is early in ontogeny; although, of course, the more influential the random mutation is, the more likely it will be deleterious. We view the evolutionary process from the vantage point of the present and from here these probabilities are different (they are, literally, *post hoc*) because only the advantageous changes will have persisted. Whatever their *ad hoc* (before the event) probabilities, we live with the consequences of what actually happened, however seemingly improbable. Thus, a small shift in developmental timing may have effected the anatomy of the cranial base and the throat below it, as their development is related. In humans this region is unique in that the low position of the vocal cords in the throat, a position required by the physics of human speech, creates the potential for food to be accidentally inhaled. This anatomy is quite different in newborns, which is why they can suckle milk and breath at the same time, a sure recipe for choking in adults. If the newborn anatomy is like the ancestral condition, which seems to be the case, it may be that the unique adult human anatomy may have a very small heterochronic cause.

With the potential for cause and effect being so disproportional, it is possible that heterochrony provides insight for the problem of how mutations and drift seem to create a neutral pattern of constant, even clock-like, evolution at the genic level, while selection creates directionality and inconsistent rates of change at the phenotypic level. As discussed above, part of the resolution for this apparent contradiction stems from the fact that only a very small part of the genome contributes to phenotypic change, while studies of genic change typically sample large numbers of indiscriminately picked genes. Some of the genes seem particularly important in regulating the activities of others. A small alteration of their timing, that is heterochrony, has the potential for very significant anatomical alterations. This small number of heterochronic genes have the potential to create fairly dramatic changes in the phenotype (these would be the object of favorable selection in those cases when they were advantageous) but contribute so little to the total number of genome changes that in aggregate they could still appear to wholly neutral.

Evolution as a Process

Evolution is a process, an ongoing phenomenon that continually changes the genetic makeup of populations and ultimately results in their continued success or eventual failure. While some of the causes of evolutionary change are random, *the results of evolution are not.* In viewing the diversity of life on earth, and in tracing its history, there are some generalizations regarding the process of evolution that seem to be as valid in understanding human prehistory as they are in understanding the evolution of other organisms. Some have thought of these generalizations as rules or laws of evolution but they are not. Any systematic process will produce limited and regular results, and these ones from the evolutionary realm are no exception. They are based on observations made in the present, but are especially important in providing a framework for interpreting the causes of what happened in the past.

OPPORTUNISM

One of the most important generalizations gained from paleontology is that evolution has been **opportunistic**. Individuals take advantage of all the resources available that they can use. Evolutionary change is always occurring either as new resources become available or because resources already present can be utilized for the first time. The process of evolution should not be thought of as a passive response to environmental change, because much evolutionary change occurs as populations develop the ability to use resources that are already present, or more efficiently take advantage of resources already in use.

For example, human adaptation to the regions near the glaciated areas of the Old World came as populations developed the technology and adaptive strategies necessary to deal with highly seasonal, cold, environments. As mammals, humans had the biological where-withal to adapt to the cold, but the periodic glaciations began much earlier in the Pleistocene than humans were able to adapt to them. People did not live in these areas before the glacial cycles began, and were forced to adapt to them by the changing environment. Of course, changes in the environment result in either successful evolutionary change or extinction, but the converse does not follow. All evolutionary change is not necessarily due to changes in the environment. Yet, over the life of species many, perhaps even most, evolutionary changes result from new potentials evolved by the species itself, which in turn result in change because of the opportunistic nature of evolution.

ROMER'S RULE, PREADAPTATION AND EXAPTATION

Preadaptation refers to an old invalid proposal that species are in some manner "predesigned" to meet the requirements of their habitat. Yet, like so many of the older evolutionary ideas, the concept holds some validity if viewed a different way. Romer's rule, named after the eminent vertebrate paleontologist, outlines the role of preadaptation in evolution, although the "rule" is really only a generalization of a sequence of events that often takes place.

Romer's rule states that new adaptations are often allowed by changes that initially better adapt a species to its old way of life. The changes appear to be "preadapted" to the new adaptation in retrospect, but to believe the changes took place *to allow* a new adaptation is to put effect before cause. Romer's rule is a special case of opportunism.

A good example can be drawn from one interpretation of early hominid evolution. At one point, hominids or perhaps prehominids shifted from a forest to a grasslands adaptation. On the African savanna, food resources are particularly hard to obtain during the dry season, when animal herds have dispersed and much of the plant life is dry and dormant. Adaptation to the grasslands was not possible until a predictable abundant dry season food resource could be obtained. Many of the dormant plants store substantial food resources underground during this season as roots and tubers, but roots and tubers are unavailable to most primates because they have nails rather than claws on their fingers and these are unsuitable for digging. Thus the development of a simple digging stick, similar to the tools that some living chimpanzees use, was probably one of the most important factors that allowed these early hominids to adapt to the grasslands.

One could say that the invention of the digging stick "preadapted" the early hominids to a grasslands habitat. However, they probably did *not* invent the digging stick *to* change their adaptation from forest to grasslands. Instead, this invention almost surely was used to improve the forest adaptation, similar to the way that sticks are used by chimpanzees today. Chimps fashion tools made of sticks with a certain length, diameter, and suppleness. Some populations use them for collecting termites while others use them for digging up ant nests. In both cases modified sticks are used as a regular part of the subsistence technology, improving the forest adaptation by providing access to desirable foods during certain times of the year. If this can be taken as a parallel to the early hominids, digging sticks became a useful part of the hominid forest adaptation *before* any dry season shift to a grasslands habitat was possible. According to this interpretation, some early hominid populations opportunistically moved into this new habitat, taking advantage of the newly-attainable resources.

"Preadaptation" is a word with many meanings. I understand it to refer to an adaptation that *allows* occupation of a new habitat, and not an adaptation that evolved *in order for* a new habitat to be occupied. As such, it becomes an important part of the view that evolutionary change is opportunistic and that the process of evolution is primarily active rather than a basically passive response to changing conditions.

The implication of preadaptation is that all adaptive features may not have originally evolved to fulfill their present functions. Natural selection, in other words, did not always develop features for the functions they now fulfill. Adaptation, the fit of an organism to its environment, may or may not be the consequence of a long term historical process in which this fit progressively developed through selection. **Exaptation** is the name given for a character that evolved to fulfill a different function than the one it currently serves. Adaptation might best be left to describe the cases when the historic genesis and current functions are the same. Recognizing the exaptation concept is important because it can provide insight into the evolutionary origins of features that transcend the functions that these features serve today. At the same time, however, exaptation inserts a note of caution to the wide use of the **uniformitarianism** principle, that the present can be used as the key to interpreting the past. (uniformitarianism, originally a concept in geology, is the precept that the processes observable in the present can be used to explain the past).

r AND K STRATEGY

Adaptive strategies are often species-specific, and are governed by a combination of historic accident, the current composition of the gene pool, and particular environmental circumstances. Yet there are certain repetitive strategies to improve fitness that appear and reappear regularly. Some problems have only a limited number of optimal solutions. One example of this is found in the so-called **r** and **K** strategies for optimizing the survival of offspring.

When a species enters a new habitat, or evolves new means for adapting to an old one, populations can respond to the new opportunities by increasing in number. One way to do this is to maximize the rate of reproduction (**r**) and have more babies more often. A second way is to make better use of the habitat's **carrying capacity (K)**, the number of individuals that can be optimally supported, by improving adaptation. These are quite different strategies, and species fall on a broad continuum between their extremes; turtles that lay as many as a quarter-million eggs have maximized their rate of reproduction, while complex social mammals who spend a significant part of their life history in learning how to use their environment to their best advantage have maximized the carrying capacity. These strategies are an important aspect of adaptation, whether a species enters a new niche or not, as the environment is never really a constant and evolutionary success is measured by the numbers of surviving offspring.

The **r** and **K** strategies have both a broader and a more limited domain. Species selection, discussed above, is really based on **r** strategy, as species proliferation is a direct consequence of the rate of speciation, while species longevity is its inverse. That narrowly adapted species have a higher rate of speciation can, in a general sense, be considered an example of **r** strategy.

On a much smaller scale we can view evolutionary changes within species in terms of **r** and **K** strategies, even though the species as a whole may be considered **r** or **K** adapted. For instance, the large bodied apes (gorillas, chimpanzees, orangutans) use a **K** adapted strategy. Through a very long period of learning (the longest of any mammal except humans), they maximize the behavioral flexibility and social complexity of a very small number of offspring who have high rates of survivorship. These apes pay a steep evolutionary price for the **K** strategy adaptation, as long periods of child dependency will increase the average time between births (birth spacing) and thereby decrease the rate of reproduction (**r**) for the species. It has been hypothesized that early in human evolution, male parenting provided an increased efficiency and predictability of provisioning for the young and their mothers, which allowed births to be spaced more closely together and therefore more children to be born during a female's life span (this model is discussed in more detail in Chapter 5). This could be described as a shift to **r** strategy, although it must be seen in the context of the fact that both ape and human species, with their single births, are considered **K** adapted when compared within the broad spectrum of mammalian variation in which species that give birth to litters with 10 or more every year are the **r** adapted species.

ADAPTIVE RADIATION

When a population enters a new habitat, opportunities for adapting to a new set of resources abound. This is especially true during the initial occupation, if there is minimal competition from similar species. Under these conditions, one common response is a rapid population growth, population splitting, and the development of different adaptive patterns. This can result in a multiplication of species through cladogenesis called an **adaptive radiation**. An adaptive radiation is an example of selection above the species level, since the consequence is an increase in the number of species. While the descendent species share many characteristics with the parental species which first occupied the new habitat, subsequent adaptations to more narrow portions of the habitat can cause the rapid appearance of a wide variety of differences among a group of closely related species.

Adaptive radiations seem to have been common in evolutionary history. For instance, **marsupial mammals** (mammals with pouches for their developing fetuses, including opossums and kangaroos) were in Australia long before the generally better-adapted **placental mammals** (mammals that keep their fetuses in the womb and have effective placentas to keep them nourished) who have been replacing them in recent times. Without competition from placental mammals, the marsupials evolved many species that parallel placental forms, such as the dog-like Tasmanian wolf, along with species that have no real parallel among the placentals, such as the kangaroo. Although the Tasmanian wolf looks and behaves much more like a dog than like a kangaroo, numerous anatomical details show its relations are with the latter instead of the former. Several different adaptive radiations have characterized primate evolution; for instance Oligocene monkeys in South America and Miocene apes in East Africa. The best known example is found in the prosimian primate fauna from Madagascar. These radiations and other details about primates and their evolution are discussed in Chapter 3.

ECOLOGY AND COMPETITIVE EXCLUSION

As was pointed out earlier, the species in a particular area (**sympatric species**) usually cannot be confused with one another. It was this observation that led to the idea that species were different "types" of organisms, an idea that proved to be of little use when the geographic variation of populations within a species was discovered. However, the underlying basis for the fact that populations of different species in a limited area are generally distinct, points to an important consequence of competition between populations, one which helps us identify lineages in the fossil record.

Populations occupy particular niches, limited portions of the environment in terms of space, resources used in survival, position in the ecosystem, and so on. Species populations within a given area each have their own unique niche. To some degree the niches overlap, causing the populations to compete for resources. In most cases, this competition has no important consequence because there are more than enough resources for both competing species. Several species of leaf eating monkeys, for example, can coexist in the same tree as long as there is enough food for all.

Some aspects of a niche, however, act to limit the number of individuals in a population. These are called **limiting resources**; they vary from population to population (and from season to season) but include such things as food supply, predators, physical space, and disease. When there is niche overlap between two species and competition over limiting factors, one of three things occurs:

1. One of the populations leaves the area to avoid competition.
2. One or both of the populations changes its adaptation to eliminate the competition (**character displacement**).
3. One of the populations is more successful and prevails while the other becomes extinct.

That these are the only three consequences possible when there is niche overlap in limiting factors is called the **competitive exclusion principle**.

Reflecting the consequences of this principle, the surviving species in a given area are usually quite distinct from one another and are not in competition for limiting factors. In an area where many similar species coexist, the selection allowing the similarities does not involve part of the niche that is a limiting factor. For instance, in the case of several species of leaf-eating monkeys occupying the same tree, food supply is not a limiting factor for them during the season when they are found together, although leaves may be a limiting food resource during other seasons, and their importance in the diet played a significant role in past selection for particular morphological adaptations.

The importance of species competition was recognized by Darwin, who suggested that limitations due to competition were as effective as limitations resulting from climatic adaptations, if not more so. The competition, however, need not be dramatic. Moreover, it may not be visible between living species since the present niche divergence could be the result of past competition. Thus, competitive exclusion can be helpful in interpreting past evolutionary history from the fossil record by providing an adaptive framework. If samples thought to represent closely related lineages are continually found together, they would be expected to become increasingly different over time. The exact differences that accumulate give important insight into the area of competition and can be used to help reconstruct the differences in adaptation.

SPECIALIZED AND GENERALIZED

The words **specialized** and **generalized** often lead to confusion because they are used in two different ways by authors describing the evolutionary process. The words may be used in the adaptive sense. A specialized species is one that is specifically adapted to a narrow set of resources, whereas a generalized species is adapted to a wide range of resources. Both types of adaptation have been successful, and both can be found in primates. Some of the African monkeys, for instance, are particularly specialized for leaf eating both in their dentition and in compartmentalization of their stomachs, providing for a very efficient digestion of leaves without a great amount of chewing. Other African monkeys are generalized, eating a wide range of foods over the course of a year. If the two types of monkeys are in the same area and compete over leaves, the specialized species may "win" the competition and members of the generalized species would be forced to eat foods that are more difficult to obtain, prepare, or digest. However, the evolutionary consequence of this competition could be the increased ability of the more generalized monkeys to live in leaf-poor areas where the specialized species cannot survive, while the specialized forms come to subsist on mature leaves that the more generalized monkeys cannot easily digest. These complex ecological relations would reflect present or past competition, with consequences structured by the competitive exclusion principle.

But these words are also used in a very different phylogenetic sense - specialized to mean **derived**, or **apomorphic** which is defined as different from the ancestral condition, and generalized to mean **primitive**, referring to a **plesiomorphic** feature that is similar to the ancestral condition (figure 2.3). This use is discussed in greater detail below. Because even the most ancient primates had five digits on their hands and feet, the appearance of five digits in humans is generalized in this phylogenetic sense, although the five digits allow adaptively specialized behavior. The same ancient primates, however, had very small brains, so the large brains of modern humans are specialized in the phylogenetic sense. Yet the behavior of our species is very wide ranging and adaptively generalized. The two sets of meanings have no relation to each other.

The problems of confusing these become particularly acute when the term **overspecialization** is used. The European Neandertals, for instance, are sometimes said to be "extinct because they were overspecialized." What does this mean? If specialization is used in the adaptive sense, it would have to mean that the Neandertals became specifically adapted to one environment and there were so many qualitative genetic changes that they could not re-adapt when that environment changed. For instance, perhaps lacking the complex, effective technological adaptations to cold that living people such as Eskimos enjoy, their physiological adaptations to cold (large noses, short limbs, rounded trunks, and large heads) involved so much genetic change that subsequent adaptations to other warmer climatic conditions were precluded. In the phylogenetic sense it would have to mean that several of their characteristics were unique, different from those of their ancestors. If the equivalent characteristics of living people are more similar to the Neandertals' ancestors (more generalized), the theory that the phylogenetically specialized Neandertals were the ancestors of modern Europeans would presumably become unacceptable because it is unlikely that "evolution reversed itself" a number of times. In this case, neither of the interpretations appears to be defensible. The first is wrong because the most important Neandertal specializations to glaciated Europe were cultural and therefore easy to change without any genetic evolution at all. The genetic specializations of the European Neandertals almost certainly were based on gene frequency differences and not the loss or gain of genes, and therefore could be easily changed. The second is also wrong for two reasons: living people are not clearly more similar to the ancestors of Neandertals than the Neandertals are themselves, and even if they were, it is not completely true that evolution cannot be reversed.

IRREVERSIBILITY OF EVOLUTION

The idea that evolution cannot be reversed is both true and not true. It is true on the level of the species. Once a species becomes extinct, it can never evolve again. Even if random factors did not play an important role in species formation, this would be true because the genetic basis for the species' evolution is gone; the ancestors themselves are extinct. However, the idea does not apply at the level of individual characteristics. These may disappear and reappear - if selectively advantageous - any number of times during the evolution of a lineage.

The late L.S.B. Leakey was responsible for the discovery of a species of small hominid species living in the latest Pliocene that he named *Homo habilis*. The *H. habilis* crania had high, rounded heads with only weakly developed superstructures such as brow ridges and other bone thickenings. They were followed in time by early humans with lower, flatter heads and much more robustly developed muscle attachments and cranial superstructures. Then these early humans were called "*Pithecanthrupus*" in Indonesia, "*Sinanthropus*" in China, and "*Homo leakei*" in Africa. Leakey argued that modern humans were much more similar to *H. habilis*, with higher, rounder heads and weakly developed muscle attachments and other cranial thickenings. He reasoned that therefore the earliest humans in Africa, *H. leakei* in his terminology, were not ancestral to modern humans but rather that his species, *H. habilis*, was the direct ancestor, because evolution would have to reverse itself. In fact, the early humans were not too specialized to be human ancestors. This is exactly the way irreversibility of evolution *does not apply*. Individual features like the browridge, the development of the cranial bone thickenings, and features related to muscle attachments, are known to change and "reverse" over the course of evolution of many lineages. These cannot be used to determine which fossils may or may not be human ancestors. Leakey was wrong for another reason. His characterization of modern humans was really only a characterization of modern Europeans. A more accurate worldwide assessment of normal human variation shows that within our own species today, the features he used vary far too much to have any phylogenetic significance; that is, they cannot be used as markers of evolutionary relationships because they vary within one of the species being related.

EVOLUTION IS MOSAIC

One of the things that becomes apparent from the previous discussion is that different characteristics may evolve at very different rates. G.G. Simpson called this **mosaic evolution**. To take the extreme, it is obvious that over the course of human evolution the size of the brain has changed dramatically, and humans are the only primate species obligated to walk on two legs - bipedally. The brain size change continued throughout human evolution, while the change to bipedalism took place at its very onset. Selection can act on individual characteristics with very different intensity and in very different ways. While this may all seem obvious, the implications of mosaic evolution are sometimes forgotten.

In the nineteenth and earlier twentieth centuries, much time was spent in the search for a "missing link" between humans and apes (even though humans did not descend from any of the living apes -- both apes and humans evolved from a common ancestor). This "missing link" was envisioned as being literally halfway between ape and human, and its features were conceptualized by taking the midpoint between human and ape features. Consequently, when a real "missing link" was discovered, it was not recognized. The first australopithecines were found to have a brain size very similar to that of apes, while their obligate bipedal locomotion (a mode of progression - or more exactly *our* mode of progression - that disallows any other form of locomotion such as brachiation or quadrupedal walking) was identical to that of today's humans. Neither is midway between. Moreover, the posterior teeth (molars and premolars) are unlike either humans or apes, and they are not anywhere between them. Relative to body size, these teeth are much larger than the posterior teeth of either humans or apes. But scientists were looking for a creature with teeth, brains, and a pattern of locomotion halfway between those of humans and apes. Since the australopithecines did not fit this description, most authors originally considered them aberrant apes. As it turns out, among the australopithecines are true human ancestors, and they may well be halfway between living people and the common ancestors of apes and humans in time. However, they are not halfway between apes and humans in morphology. The australopithecines were generally not recognized as the "missing links" when they were found because the mosaic nature of evolution was not considered. The morphology of the australopithecines cannot be fully explained as an ape-like creature evolving into a human. Their unique set of characteristics results from the successful adaptation of a species to its environment.

Phylogeny, Taxonomy, and Taxa

Perhaps the most obvious consequence of the evolutionary process, and certainly the most controversial one, is the hierarchy of related organisms. These relationships are fundamental to evolutionary studies, because the pattern of relationship is a direct consequence of the evolutionary process - it is the observation that evolution explains. Biological relationships are implicit in the diversity of living organisms, but their full explication requires knowledge of the past as well. However there are some important limitations to evolutionary studies based on the fossil record. A collection of fossils is usually not a sample of a single population. With few exceptions, each fossil specimen almost certainly represents a different biological population. The problem is that evolutionary relationships are not between individuals but between populations, and it is rarely possible to identify populations among fossils. Therefore, the species is the lowest *taxonomic* level that can be compared. Added to the fact that the species is widely considered the only "natural" taxonomic unit, and that evolutionary species can be considered individuals as they have distinct beginning, ends, and evolutionary tendencies, species are the cornerstone for evolutionary studies, and the basis for establishing evolutionary relationships.

One consequence of the evolutionary process is the understanding that species are related to each other. Indeed, while similarities and differences between species were recognized earlier, awareness of the fact that some species are more closely related than others, and that species formed a hierarchy of relationships in which higher categories (genera) are made up of sets species, even higher categories made up of the sets of genera, and so on, could not predate the development of evolutionary theory. Species relationships are hierarchical in that they are all based on branchings from common ancestors, and branches can never re-merge to for a single branch. Thus closeness of evolutionary relationship, like relationship as it is meant in genealogical studies, can depend on the recentness of common ancestry. The classification of organisms is thus quite unlike the classification of books in a library where groupings can be done by any number of criteria and books can appear in different categories. In a formal sense, evolutionary, or phylogenetic, relationships are the secondary data of human paleontology. A **phylogeny** is a hypothesis about how fossil and living species are related in a genealogical framework. Without an idea of the genealogy of species, no study of evolution is possible.

THE BASIS FOR COMPARISON: HOMOLOGY

Phylogeny is based on comparisons. The fundamental basis for any comparison is that it is likes that are compared, not apples to oranges! But comparable features are not necessarily similar - one of the fore-fins of an ancient fish ultimately evolved into a bird wing and a human forearm - and similar features are not necessarily alike - octopus and human eyes are very similar structures with quite different evolutionary ancestries.

When are alike things different, and when are they the same? In the biological world, similar features in different species must have one of three bases:

1) The features are the same because of descent - they evolved from a single identical feature in the last common ancestor of the species compared. This is **Homology**. An example would be the grasping hand of a human and a chimpanzee.

2) The features are the same because of descent and chance - they evolved from a single feature in the last common ancestor which differs from the features in the two descendants. During the separate evolution of the two species, the features *independently changed* to become the same. This is **Homoplasy**, or **Parallelism**. An example would be thin molar enamel in gorillas and chimpanzees. The last common ancestor had thick enamel.

(3) The features are the same because of chance alone - they evolved from two different features in the last common ancestor and independently came to resemble each other. This is **Convergence**. An example of this would be the eye of a horse (or any other vertebrate) and the eye of an octopus. The last common ancestor of these species lacked eyes.

Since homology assures that comparisons will be valid because they are between features that are alike due to descent, its identification is essential in relating species. Unfortunately, homologies can be difficult to identify. Similarities due to homology and homoplasy can be easily confused, particularly because in both cases the traits have the same (homology) or very similar (homoplasy) genetic bases. In many studies it is necessary to establish a hypothesis of the phylogeny itself to examine whether homology or homoplasy underlies some of the similarities, and since the phylogeny can be based only on homologies there is a real potential for circularity. As discussed below, this circularity is avoided with the assumption that generally similarities are due to descent from a common ancestor with the similar feature, and not its accidental or independent appearance. This is referred to as the assumption of **parsimony**, as there are fewer assumptions in the common descent explanation. Only similarities that are not the unique consequence of descent from a common ancestor are regarded as homoplasies. Other ways to identify homologies include the study of ontogeny (an individual's history of growth and development) to determine if supposed homologies have the same embryonic and developmental basis.

These homologies are often called **cladistic homologies**, because they are based on comparing different lineages, or **clades**. A second type of homology is **patristic homology**, and characterizes the comparison of features in an ancestral (i.e., paternal) and descendant species. An example of a patristic homology might be the wing of a bird and the forelimb of one of its ancestors. Because patristic homologies reflect evolutionary derivation but not necessarily structural identity, two different patristic homologies (i.e., homologies in two different descendent species with respect to their last common ancestor) are not necessarily also cladistic homologies. They may be homoplasies if they have independently evolved a similar form, or they may be just plain different.

THE RESULTS OF COMPARISON: PHYLOGENY

Systematics, the science concerned with the diversity of organisms and the relationships among them, provides the basis for determining phylogenetic relationships, while **taxonomy** is concerned with the theory and practice of classifying organisms once these relationships are known. These relationships, of course, are based on the anatomy that has been preserved. Features correlated with each other or features with a low genetic input to their variation are considered less important, and whenever possible the total functional (or morphological) patterns made up of many individual features are compared as a whole.

How taxonomy and phylogeny are, or should be, related has been a heated topic of discussion among evolutionists, as authors such as N. Eldredge discuss. One school of thought contends that no relationship should exist and that organisms should be classified solely on the basis of their morphological similarities. Most of those who classify, however, recognize the principle that a taxonomy is a genealogy of species, and therefore that the taxonomy should reflect genealogical relationships. **Phylogenetics** is the study of how genealogical relationships can be determined from morphological similarities that are homologous. According to this approach, relationships are defined by cladogenesis, the branch points occur when an ancestral species splits into two descendent sister species. The relationship between two taxa is measured by the number of derived homologous features they share, and must be considered a hypothesis of phylogeny that may be overturned, or refuted, with further data. Hominid taxonomy reflects our current understanding of hominid phylogeny. This understanding is fluid, changing with time as more fossil material is discovered and more information is gleaned from the specimens already at hand.

The characterization of features as plesiomorphic (primitive) or apomorphic (derived) is the cornerstone of the phylogenetic approach to systematics. Relationships between species are determined solely from shared derived features (**synapomorphies**), as only these accurately reflect common ancestry. The most closely related species, or species groups, are those that have the largest number of synapomorphies. Shared primitive features, **symplesiomorphies**, are identified by outgroup comparison. An outgroup is chosen that is taxonomically close, but equally related, to the species compared and features shared with that outgroup are assumed to be the result of descent from the last common ancestor, and therefore are plesiomorphic. Primitive features can also be identified by ontogenetic studies and embryological analysis, as it can be assumed that most recent evolutionary changes usually happen relatively late in ontogeny (but see the discussion of heterochrony). Ancestry, to the extent that it can be hypothesized, is suggested by the substitution of apomorphic for plesiomorphic characteristics in the descendant. A hypothesized ancestor is not expected to have a apomorphic form of characteristics if the descendent has the plesiomorphic form (reversal of evolution). All plesiomorphies were once apomorphies - it should be understood that these terms are relative.

To exemplify these concepts, figure 2.5 shows one possible phylogeny for hominid species. This is modeled after work by B. Wood and uses species names and relations he believes are valid (these are discussed in Chapters 8 and 9). A specimen and its cranial capacity in cubic centimeters is shown for each of the species. If we use chimpanzees as our outgroup, larger brain size is a synapomorphy for most of the hominid species - only *A. Africanus* and *H. habilis* preserve the plesiomorphic (ancestral=small) condition in this scheme. The extremely large brain size of *H. sapiens* is an autapomorphy. The interesting question is how brain size sorts out in this scheme. It links the 3 species on the right as a synapomorphy, but what about *H. rudolfensis* in the left cluster? There are 3 possibilities:

1. *H. rudolfensis* should have been put in the right cluster (this would use one feature, brain size, to create the taxonomy)
2. larger brain size is the ancestral condition (plesiomorphic) for the two *Homo* species on the left, but subsequently reduced for *H. habilis* (perhaps the species became much smaller)
3. smaller brain size is plesiomorphic for the two *Homo* species on the left, and it independently increased in *H. rudolfensis* - it would then be a homoplasy with the species in the right side group.

Note that none of these explanations make the taxonomy valid, because it does not reflect the phylogeny. For the taxonomy to reflect this phylogeny, the two *Homo* species in the left group would have to be put in the genus *Australopithecus*, or some other third genus.

Figure 2.5
A Phylogenetic Scheme for Some Hominid Species

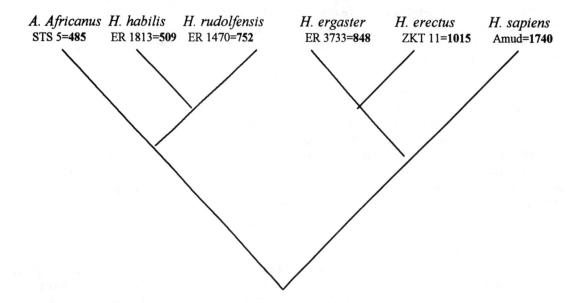

A. Africanus	H. habilis	H. rudolfensis	H. ergaster	H. erectus	H. sapiens
STS 5=485	ER 1813=509	ER 1470=752	ER 3733=848	ZKT 11=1015	Amud=1740

Realistically, phylogenetic relationships are hypothesized from many features and not just one like brain size, no matter how important it might be. These multifactoral analyses provide the best means of identifying homoplasies, as the branching pattern will reveal that some similar features attained their similarities separately. While studies show that as expected, homologies are much more common than homoplasies (the assumption of parsimony, when features are similar this is most probably due to common descent and not independent acquisition), the number of homoplasies is highest in closely related species. In phylogenetic studies of hominids, a large number of homoplasies have been identified. In fact, the numerous homoplasies are one of the main reasons why there are so many competing hominid phylogenies. It can be difficult to choose the best hypothesis when several alternative hypotheses are very similar.

GRADE AND CLADE

A final pair of concepts that are often confused contrast two different reasons for the sharing of features between populations. A **grade** is a grouping characterized by a general level of organization. Grades are composed of independent lineages that may or may not be monophyletic; that is, have common descent. The large bodied apes are an example of a grade. They share a number of anatomical similarities because they are closely related (symplesiomorphies) and other similarities because of commonalties in their adaptations to a forest habitat, a partially arboreal niche, and a combination of arboreal brachiation and quadrumanous (four-handed) climbing and terrestrial quadrupedalism (four legged locomotion). They are not monophyletic as humans are one descendent of their last common ancestor that are not in the group. Thus the large bodied apes, and in general any group of species defined by grade, are not a valid taxon. Some implications of this problem are discussed as part of the controversies of taxonomy in Chapter 3. **Clade** is synonymous with lineage (a lineage is a clade, though a clade may be one or many lineages). In broader perspective it is any monophyletic group. Its defining attribute is shared common descent. Common decent is important when considering the sources of intraspecies variation, but clade cannot strictly apply as genic exchange makes it unlikely that any group of populations will be monophyletic. Alternative words applying to a race or subspecies viewed over time include **deme** and **intraspecies clade**. No formal definition based on evolutionary criteria has been applied to the genealogical aspects of intraspecies variation.

The terms are often applied as contrasts when they describe variation within polytypic species. Grade features are shared because of a common level of organization, while clade features are shared because of common descent. In living humans, large brains are a grade feature shared by all populations. It is possible that this reflects a common ancestry for all living people in a population that had large brains - this would make brain size a clade feature as well. However, it is also possible that large brains are shared because of the common requirements of complex cultural behavior. Elements of cultural behavior may spread without populations spreading and replacing others. Gene flow can (but does not necessarily) help establish a world wide distribution of large brains without the ancestry of all living large brained populations lying in a single ancient large-brained population. In either case, brain size would be a valid grade character that may not reflect clade. It could characterize all living populations without characterizing their last common ancestor.

Looking at clade features, the human races spread around the world today characteristically differ enough for their skeletal features to be racially identified by forensic specialists - the basis of Quincy's success on television, and much more. Some of the skeletal features that are useful to forensic specialists can be found in past populations. For instance, faces that are transversely flat and vertically short with forward facing, anteriorly positioned cheeks are found throughout the fossil record of human evolution in China. This facial anatomy is an example of a clade characteristic that describes human evolution in east Asia. These features reflect common descent from an ancestor who already had them.

Grade and clade may be diagnosed from the same characteristics - this is the source of confusion. There is an Australasian clade of prehistoric and modern humans that can be diagnosed, in part, by the size and form of their supraorbital tori (brow ridges). In some other regions of the world, for instance sub-Saharan Africa, these tori reduce dramatically at the beginning the Late Pleistocene, and this is taken as evidence that modern humans first appeared there. Can the same feature both mark clade (common descent) in one region, and grade (modern human origins) in another? It is easy to answer this question negatively, but unlike species level variation the concept of grade is not easily invalidated. The brain size example demonstrates that a common feature defining the level of organization within a monophyletic group is not necessarily a consequence of common descent within species. Perhaps caution is the best defense, as far as the confusion of grade and clade is concerned.

TAXONOMIC NAMES

In discussing the pattern of evolution the technical language is very important. From the paleoanthropological perspective each fossil specimen could belong to a unique species, itself a member of a genus and part of a taxonomic hierarchy that reflects the genealogical relationships of life on earth. On the other hand many specimens could sample the same species and differ because of sexual dimorphism, racial or subspecies variation, or just idiosyncrasy. While the distinction between a specimen and the species it belongs to may be clear in theory, there is a continued confusion between the names of organisms represented by fossils and the names of the taxa to which they belong. This confusion is totally apart from the additional confusing questions of whether the taxa have been validly described, or whether the attribution of a specimen to a taxon is valid.

In a classic paper, G.G. Simpson proposed a five tier hierarchy for names (table 2.2). This ranges from the names of the specimens to the names of the classifications that order their relationships. Every fossil specimen has its own name, usually in the form of a museum number. For instance, the fifth hominid found at Laetoli is called LH (the catalogue abbreviation for Laetoli Hominid) 5. The 11th cranium from Zhoukoudian (ZKT 11) is also the LII skull because it is the second specimen found at the location in the cave designated "L". And, a fossil may also have another name. In the case of OH 5, the massive jaw and teeth of the Olduvai specimen led to the nickname "Nutcracker man," and the Hadar female AL 288-1 was named "Lucy" after the song playing in the camp when she was discovered.

Quite distinct from the name of the fossil specimen is the name of the group to which it belongs, and the place of this species in a general classification of animals. The group name may be informal (not part of a taxonomic scheme). Examples of this include European, San, and Neandertal. Even when these informal names are derived from a taxonomy (for instance Neandertal from *Homo neanderthalensis*) they are not part of a taxonomy and have no taxonomic implications. Thus we use the term australopithecine to refer to a large number of human relatives and ancestors in various genera and species that lived in the Late Miocene, Pliocene and the Early Pleistocene without necessarily believing that there is a subfamily for them called Australopithecinae. If we thought there was such a subfamily, we should use the subfamily name and not its anglicized version.

Table 2.2
Simpson's Hierarchy of Names

	N_1	Sample	specimens	La Chapelle, SK 847
	N_2	Population	groups	Neandertals, australopithecine
	N_3	Taxon	nomina	Homo sapiens, Dryopithecinae
	N_4	Category	hierarchic terms	species, subfamily
	N_5	Classification	system	phylogenetic, phenetic

A **taxon** is a group of organisms recognized as a formal unit, at any level of a hierarchic classification. The groups themselves are the N_3 terms while the names of the taxa are N_4 terms according to Simpson's scheme. Examples (from higher to lower levels) are phylum, class, order, family, tribe, genus, and species. Each taxon may be modified by super-, sub-, and infra-. The endings required by each category are shown in table 2.3. The hierarchical relationship between these taxonomic categories means that each taxon is made up of a set of lower taxa - genus is a group of species, family is a group of subfamilies, and so on.

Table 2.3
Word Endings Identifying Classificatory Terms

Category	Ending	Example from *Homo*	Anglicized name
Superfamily	-oidea	Hominoidea	hominoid
Family	-idae	Hominidae	hominid
Subfamily	-inae	Homininae	hominine
Tribe	-ini	Hominini	
Subtribe	-ina	Hominina	

The composition of taxa is determined by inference from samples. However, the taxon is not the same as the sample. OH 5, for example, was placed originally in the genus *Zinjanthropus* and the species *boisei*. A genus consists of a monophyletic group of species more closely related to one another than to any other species group. The term *Zinjanthropus* encompasses all specimens that ever lived that are thought to belong to that category; that is, all the members of the species *boisei,* and of all the other species of *Zinjanthropus*. The characteristics of the genus are the combined characteristics of all its member species. Since all of the individuals were not all fossilized, and since those that were fossilized will not all be found, these characteristics must be estimated from the known sample. The smaller the sample, the less accurate the determination, so this is quite a weighty baggage for OH 5 to carry because when it was named it was the only specimen in the single species of *Zinjanthropus*. Similarly, *Homo sapiens* refers to all members of the genus *Homo* in the species *sapiens* that ever lived. It is represented in the fossil record by a very small sample of this total from which the characteristics of the taxon must be inferred.

The classification system itself is part of this hierarchy. There are many bases for classification, for instance branching (a tree-like system in which the contents of each taxon is unique) versus categorization (a library-like system in which an individual could potentially appear in many different taxa). Moreover, there are different organizational bases. The most important of these is genealogical (based on common ancestry) versus phenetic (based on similarities in anatomy). Biological classification today is branching and its basis is genealogical.

It is probably a poor idea to use taxonomic names to reflect observed differences, unless those differences are thought to reflect phylogeny. There are lower levels of the naming hierarchy that can accomplish this much better. Many sources of difference, moreover, are not phylogenetic and individuals may vary because of sex, age, regional source, pathology, or just plain accident. There are many terms that reflect similarities and differences (ape, adult male, European, Sterkfontein ape-man, Cro Magnon) but carry no taxonomic implications. These, and not taxa, should be used when appropriate and taxonomy be reserved for those cases when it can be used to reflect a hypothesis of phylogeny.

Summary

The process of evolution is a universal phenomenon, affecting all life forms through genetic changes in populations. Four factors cause genetic change: selection, mutation, drift, and genic exchange. Of these, selection appears to be the most important, causing frequency changes in gene pools through relative differences in fertility and survivorship. Selection seems to proceed slowly over long periods of time, but studies of living populations show that the actual pattern of changes oscillates dramatically, even over the course of a few years. Long term changes are defined by the averages across these oscillations, and do not necessarily reflect the direction and especially not the magnitude of the short term changes. The main role of mutation seems to be the gradual introduction of new genetic material. For the phenotype these changes are only gradually and unevenly introduced into populations when they contribute to advantageous gene combinations, but at the level of the genotype neutral mutations appear to be the main driving force of genetic change. Drift acts mainly to introduce an element of randomness to the evolutionary process, eliminating most new mutations and other rare genetic variants. During species formation drift may play an important role in small populations, disrupting stable gene combinations and reorganizing the pattern of genetic variation. Migration and rapid replacement can be a major cause of large evolutionary changes when such a new species is successful. Migration and gene exchanges as evolutionary forces are particularly important in conjunction with selection or drift, and have played an important role in maintaining the genetic unity of our species, as it spread around the world.

The evolving entity is the biological species, or when considered over time the lineage, since the boundaries of the species (or lineage) are non-arbitrary - the permanent barriers to gene flow and the spread of genetic change. An evolutionary species is a genealogical unit whose protected gene pool has its own evolutionary tendencies, unique origin and historical fate. Speciation occurs when reproductive barriers appear; this almost always requires spatial isolation, and is often at the peripheries of the parent species' distribution.

Selection, the differential reproduction and survivorship of individuals, can operate at both higher and lower levels. For species as evolving entities, selection is defined as the rate of speciation (which is by necessity the converse of species survivorship) and some evolutionary trends are the consequence of the fact that narrowly adapted species can speciate more readily than broadly adapted ones. At the genic level, selection favors the survivorship of genes wherever they appear, and any particular gene will appear more commonly in clusters of relatives than in random samples taken from the population as a whole. This is the basis of the kin selection concept, and part of the body of theory underlying many studies of human behavioral evolution. Behavior is no less subject to evolutionary change than morphological features. The genetic models for behaviors are complex, and in many cases the genetic influence may be on the logical ordering and interrelationships of behavioral classes rather than on specific behaviors.

To the extent that one can generalize for many species, there is a pattern to the way that evolutionary changes proceed. At the microevolutionary scale species change rapidly, fluctuating in direction even over the course of a decade. These oscillations may or may not affect a longer term directionality to the changes. Thus, species undergo periods of relatively little change that are interspersed with more gradual fluctuating trends, shorter periods of rapid change, and discontinuities that reflect different stable adaptive valleys. Evolutionary change is not limitless, however. It cannot transcend the information existing is a population's gene pool, and thereby is constrained by history. Its direction is also constrained by allometry, a consequence of pleiotropy that patterns scaling, and by heterochrony, the constraints of development and life history.

Evolution is an active opportunistic process and not simply a passive response to environmental change. "Breakthroughs" often occur because of newly developed abilities of species to utilize resources already present in their environments. Such breakthroughs sometimes allow species to utilize previously unoccupied niches, resulting in a rapid multiplication of closely related forms called an adaptive radiation. When a feature's use in adaptation differs from the function it was originally evolved to serve, this co-opting of function is called exaptation. The exaptation process can lead to what appears to be a preadaptation, as a feature seems to have evolved for a function it cannot serve until the evolutionary process was completed. Opportunities presented to species, whether from changing environments or changing abilities to use environments, are realized by improving the rate of reproduction (r strategy) or improving the ability of the species to use the resources in the environment (K strategy).

A phylogeny is a hypothesis concerning how species are related. The taxonomic names given to species reflect this hypothesis. Phylogeny is difficult to determine for fossil samples because populations are almost never represented, and species (or lineage) determinations must depend on inferences about reproductive barriers. The competitive exclusion principle can be helpful in these inferences when samples of possibly closely related species are sympatric since competition over limiting factors will result in extinction, population movement, or character displacement when gene flow between competing populations is impossible. The genealogical relationships between species are determined from the comparisons of derived features. Since evolution is mosaic and characteristics in a lineage do not change at the same time or rate, unique homologous features shared by species must be the basis for ascertaining their degree of relationship.

Evolution applies to humans as surely as it applies to other organisms. The evolutionary history of our species has been unique. No earthly organism with the potential of humans has ever evolved before, and decades of examining the sky across the broad spectrum of electromagnetic radiation have failed to reveal evidence of a species with an intellect like our own elsewhere in the universe. The goal of this book is to try to understand how and why humans evolved.

ANATOMY OF A CONTROVERSY
Neutral Evolution and The Molecular Clock:
An Accurate Timepiece or a Stopped Watch Right Twice a Day?

Molecular clocks are a product of neutral mutation theory, and a truly innovative approach to determining divergence times for living species. The idea of a molecular clock is based on the regular ticking of neutral mutations that can accumulate at a constant rate in the genome, in regions where it is assumed that selection or drift play only negligible roles. Molecular clocks are somewhat dependent on the fossil record, since the rate of the regular genetic changes they depend on must first be calibrated from paleontologically determined divergence dates, but presumably once calibrated they can provide past divergence times from living species alone. The question is: do molecular clocks work - are they an alternative means, better than the fossil record, for asking how long ago the last common ancestor of two species lived? As R. Cann once quipped, it is unclear whether any fossils have descendants, but all living people have ancestors.

Perhaps the most innovative of the molecular clocks came from the laboratory of the late A. Wilson. It is based on the presumption of regular mutational changes in mitochondrial DNA . The mitochondrial clock has been used to estimate divergence times for many species, including a resolution of the chimpanzee/gorilla/human trichotomy, but its most controversial use has been to estimates the times of divergences *within a single species* - our own. Thus unlike the earlier immunological clock (see Chapter 1), this clock was not used for dating the origins of all humans, but was focused on a much more recent event - the origin of *modern* humans. Because the DNA-DNA hybridization technique was used to estimate DNA differences when the mtDNA studies began, the mtDNA clock had a great advantage over divergence estimates based on nuclear DNA changes - the rate of mtDNA evolution is much faster. This means that the hybridization technique should be able to date more recent events, and there should be higher resolution for the dates. There was some hope for resolving a great controversy that had developed over the question of whether the DNA-DNA hybridization technique that was used to analyze nuclear DNA had validly resolved the chimpanzee-gorilla-human trichotomy. The question was whether this technique has sufficient resolution to clearly determine which two species are more closely related. Because mtDNA changes much more rapidly, its analysis is much more accurate in this relatively recent time range.

The mtDNA is not subject to the card shuffling of recombination that the nuclear DNA endures during reproduction, and it is totally passed down along the female lines because mitochondria are inherited as part of the egg's cytoplasm, and reproduce in the cytoplasm by asexual cloning. Therefore, existing mtDNA variants evolved from and can in theory be traced to a single original mtDNA source. Subsequent variation appeared from one descendent to another because of mutational changes. According to the Wilson theory this source was a woman who was believed to have lived in Africa. The "mitochondrial clock", however, seemed to indicate that the people themselves, not just their mitochondria, all descended from this source, who A. Wilson dubbed "Eve". This is because the clock gave a date for "Eve" that showed her to have lived long after people had spread all around the world from their African homeland.

The basis for the requirement of complete replacement without mixture is that if "Eve's" descendants had mixed with other peoples as their population expanded, we would expect to find other mtDNA lines present today, especially outside Africa where "Eve's" descendants were invaders. This is because it is common for men of successful invading people to take wives from the people they invade, thereby perpetuating and even proliferating the mtDNA of the people being replaced. However, the mtDNA of "Eve's" contemporaries cannot be found among the people of today - only "Eve's" and those of her female descendants. The most credible explanation for this absence is that none of the other women who lived in the distant past mixed with these invaders - an explanation that means "Eve" founded a new species, since by definition members of different species do not have fertile offspring. "Eve" is therefore the sole progenitor of both mitochondrial and nuclear DNA, according to the theory that is based on this molecular clock. Because of the estimated time or origins, this theory requires that the history of mtDNA is also the history of human populations.

The time shown on the mtDNA "clock" therefore is critical to the "Eve" theory. The reading of a recent origin comes from the solution to a problem raised by the limited mtDNA variability reported for modern humans. This limited variability is used to infer a shallow time depth for the origin of all mtDNA, a recent divergence from a common mtDNA ancestor. If the assumption assumed that the mutation process is responsible for all the variability in mtDNA is valid, and if the mutation rate can be accurately determined, the time since the last common mtDNA ancestor lived can be ascertained. This time was found to be approximately 200,000 years ago by the Wilson group - a very approximate date since the estimates *ranged* from 50 to 500 thousand years ago according to one paper by M. Stoneking and R. Cann, two of Wilson's students.

There are several basic problem areas for the mtDNA clock. The validity of a "molecular clock" that accurately times splitting events in the mitochondrial chromosome must be based on information from many loci, and its reliability rests on the assumption that the consequences of a regular rate of "ticking" (i.e. mutations) in the past is preserved in the distribution of existing mtDNA variants. The second assumption is the neutrality assumption - a regular rate of ticking requires that mutations accumulate as they occur, randomly but constantly. However, there are difficulties with the mitochondrial analysis that come from the very source of other advantages - in reproduction the mtDNA clones instead of recombining. For this reason the whole molecule in inherited in one unbroken piece and all variation on it is equivalent to a single genetic locus. The mitochondria are critical in the cell's energy production, and mutations that disturb this function lead to very serious diseases. People with these mutations would have great disadvantage in reproduction and survival. However, any advantage or disadvantage for part of the mtDNA must affect all of it because there is no recombination, and this disturbs the regular rate of mutation accumulation. These advantages or disadvantages can be great. Wilson once suggested that perhaps the reason "Eve's" descendants were so successful was that they carried a gene for language on their mtDNA. If true (which seems very unlikely - for very good reasons the suggestion has never received support), this would confer great advantage to these individuals. In any case many mutations in the mtDNA are not neutral - a critical assumption one must make for the molecular clock to work, since to keep time it must tick at a regular rate.

The second difficulty is a consequence of female transmission without recombination. Every time a generation without daughters is encountered a unique mtDNA line is lost, and along with it all record of its mutations. The potential for random losses is very much greater than in nuclear DNA, 25% every generation for each family in a stable population and higher in an oscillating one. Therefore the surviving record of past mtDNA mutations in different populations varies and may not accurately reflect how many mutations there actually were. This record depends on the exact population size histories for each of them. Thus, the effect of the random losses alters the reconstruction of the tree of human mtDNA branching by pruning off the evidence of many past divergences. Each of these overlooked divergences is a mutation that cannot be counted when the number of mutations is used to determine how long ago "Eve" lived. The number of uncounted mutations depends on how active the pruning process was, and this in turn is a direct consequence of the exact history of population size fluctuations for each population, which can never be known. Therefore the observed number of mutations along each mtDNA lineage is not a simple consequence of how long the mutation process has been going on. It is also responsive to how many times the evidence of a past mutation has been lost - a process that varies from population to population as each has its own history This is why there are some vertebrate groups with rates of mtDNA evolution that are dramatically slower than Wilson and his colleagues have claimed for humans (these include cichlid fish, jackals, blackbirds, and eels). There really is no single universal rate, as required for a molecular clock.

A third difficulty comes from trying to estimate the effects of another source of lost mutations. In a series of widely cited studies, L. Vigilant and colleagues addressed the question of "back-mutation" (since there are only 4 DNA bases, a second mutation of one stands a 1/4 chance of becoming "hidden" by mutating "back" into the original base it mutated from). They estimate the hidden mutations by comparing the first and third position mutations in the base triplets, as the third position changes less often change the amino acid object of the code and are therefore more likely to be neutral. C.O. Lovejoy and colleagues show that their technique was flawed and that many more mutations in the human genome were hidden than they realized. Of greater potential is their demonstration of varying numbers of hidden mutations in different parts of the mitochondrial genome. With different "clocks" for the same individual, the use of genetic difference to time past evolutionary events would seem highly problematic

A final difficulty is revealed by the statistics that are used to estimate the normal range of variation for the clock's readings. A. Templeton reminds us that the estimated date for "Eve" is very inaccurate because mtDNA is a single locus - this is like having a sample size of 1! Even under the most favorable assumption, that the only source of error is in the estimate of the mutation rate, the dates have uncertainties in the hundred's of thousands of years.   For instance, estimates of this rate have ranged from 1.4% to 9.3% base pair substitutions per million years (1.8%-9.3% in one paper by Wilson and colleagues alone). Moreover there are other sources of uncertainty:

- The uncertainties in the time of divergence used for the calibration (both recent migration times such as the peopling of Australia and ancient divergences such as the chimpanzee-human one have been used)
- When recent migrations are use for the calibration additional sources of error come from the extent to which the required assumptions - that the migrations happened only once and that they were one-way - are invalid;
- The unknown effects of fluctuating population sizes in the past, especially when these have been very small from time to time and random loss were able to play a significant role in the amount of remaining genetic variation;
- The random nature of the mutational process itself (even if everything else was known exactly it would introduce considerable uncertainty because the rate being estimated is intraspecific)

When all of the sources of error are taken into account, the *probable date range* for "Eve" appears to be *a million years or more*.

Neutral evolution has proved to be much more complex than once thought. As J. Marks discusses, the genome cannot be validly divided into unique-sequence (subject to selection) and repetitive sequence (subject to neutral mutations) components. Neutral evolution is a reality, but not the simple one once thought, and there is no obvious way to separate neutral from adaptive change, even at the allelic level. With an unacceptable error range, unknown demographic histories, and continued violation of the neutrality assumptions, for all intents and purposes there is no "molecular clock" that can time events (last common ancestors) within recent human evolution.

REFERENCES AND FURTHER READINGS

ALBERCH, P., S.J. GOULD, G.F. OSTER, and D.B. WAKE 1979 Size and shape in ontogeny and phylogeny. *Paleobiology* 5(3):296-317.

BARIGOZZI, C. (editor) 1982 *Mechanisms of Speciation*. Alan R. Liss, New York.

BARINAGA, M. 1992 "African Eve" backers beat a retreat. *Science* 255:686-687.

BARTON, N.H., and B. CHARLESWORTH 1984 Genetic revolutions, founder effects, and speciation. *Annual Review of Ecology and Systematics* 15:133-164.

BIELICKI, T. 1985 On a certain generic peculiarity of man. *Journal of Human Evolution* 14:411-415.

BOCK, W.J. 1970 Microevolutionary sequences as a fundamental concept in macroevolutionary models. *Evolution* 24:704-722.

___. 1980 The definition and recognition of biological adaptation. *American Zoologist* 20:217-227.

BONDE, N. 1981 Problems of species concepts in paleontology. In J. Martinelli (ed): *Concept and Method in Paleontology*. University of Barcelona, Barcelona. pp. 19-34.

BROOKS, D.R. 1983 What's going on in evolution? a brief guide to some new ideas in evolutionary theory. *Canadian Journal of Zoology* 61:2637-2645.

BROOKS, D.R., and E.O. WILEY 1986 *Evolution as Entropy. Toward a Unified Theory of Biology*. University of Chicago Press, Chicago.

BROWN, W.L. 1958 Some zoological concepts applied to the problems of evolution in the hominid lineage. *American Scientist* 46:151-158.

BROWN, W.L., and E.O. WILSON 1956 Character displacement. *Systematic Zoology* 5:49-54.

CADIEN, J.D., E.F. HARRIS, W.P. JONES, and L.J. MANDARINO 1976 Biological lineages, skeletal populations, and microevolution. *Yearbook of Physical Anthropology* 18:194-201.

CASPARI, E.W. 1967 Behavioral consequences of genetic differences in man: a summary. In J.N. Spuhler (ed): *Genetic Diversity and Human Behavior*. Aldine, Chicago. pp. 269-278.

___. 1972 Sexual selection in human evolution. In B.G. Campbell (ed): *Sexual Selection and the Descent of Man*. Aldine, Chicago. pp. 332-356.

CHARLESWORTH, B., R. LANDE, and M. SLATKIN 1982 A Neo-Darwinian commentary on macroevolution. *Evolution* 36:474-498.

CRAYCRAFT, J., 1989 Speciation and its ontology: the empirical consequences of alternative species concepts for understanding patterns and processes of differentiation. In D. Otte and J.A. Endler (eds): *Speciation and its Consequences*. Sinauer Associates, Sunderland. pp. 28-59.

CRAYCRAFT, J. and N. ELDREDGE (editors) 1979 *Phylogenetic Analysis and Paleontology*. Columbia University, New York.

DAWKINS, R. 1976 *The Selfish Gene.* Oxford University Press, Oxford.

___. 1986 *The Blind Watchmaker.* W.W. Norton. New York.

DEAN, D. 1992 The interpretation of dialectic and hierarchy theory: a hominoid paleobehavioral example. In E. Tobach and G. Greenberg (eds): *Levels of Social Behavior: Evolutionary and Genetic Aspects.* T.C. Schneirla Research Fund, Wichita State University. pp. 33-49.

DOBZHANSKY, T. 1963 Genetic entities in hominid evolution. In S.L. Washburn (ed): *Classification and Human Evolution.* Aldine, Chicago. pp. 347-362.

___. 1970 *Genetics of the Evolutionary Process.* Columbia University Press, New York.

ECKHARDT, R.B. 1989 Evolutionary morphology of human skeletal characteristics. *Anthropologischer Anzeiger* 47(3):193-228.

ELDREDGE, N. 1979a Cladism and common sense. In J. Craycraft and N. Eldredge (eds): *Phylogenetic Analysis and Paleontology.* Columbia University, New York. pp. 165-198.

___. 1979b Alternative approaches to evolutionary theory. Bulletin of the *Carnegie Museum of Natural History* 13:7-19.

___. 1985 *Unfinished Synthesis. Biological Hierarchies and Modern Evolutionary Thought.* Oxford University Press, New York.

ELDREDGE, N., and I. TATTERSALL 1982 *The Myths of Human Evolution.* Columbia: New York.

ERESHEFSKY, M. (editor) 1992 *The Units of Evolution: Essays on the Nature of Species.* MIT Press, Cambridge.

FISHER, A. 1991 The new synthesis comes of age. *Mosaic* 22(1):3-17.

FRAYER, D.W., and M.H. WOLPOFF 1985 Sexual Dimorphism. In B.J. Siegel, A.R. Beals, and S.A. Tyler (eds): *Annual Review of Anthropology.* Annual Reviews, Palo Alto. Volume 14:429-473.

FUTUYMA, D.J. 1987 On the role of species in anagenesis. *American Naturalist* 130:465-473.

___. 1992 History and evolutionary process. In M.H. Nitecki and D.V. Nitecki (eds): *History and Evolution.* State University of New York, Albany. pp. 103-130.

GINGERICH, P.D. 1985 Species in the fossil record: concepts, trends, and transitions. *Paleobiology* 11(1):27-41.

GHISELIN, M.T. 1987 Species concepts, individuality, and objectivity. *Biological Philosophy* 2:127-143.

GODFREY, L., and J. MARKS 1991 The nature and origins of primate species. *Yearbook of Physical Anthropology* 34:39-68.

GOULD, S.J. 1978 Sociobiology: the art of storytelling. *New Scientist* 80:530-533.

___. 1977 *Ontogeny and Phylogeny.* Belknap Press, Cambridge Massachusetts.

___. 1980 G.G. Simpson, paleontology, and the modern synthesis. In E. Mayr and W. Provine (eds): *The Evolutionary Synthesis.* Harvard University Press, Cambridge. pp. 153-172.

___. 1982 The meaning of punctuated equilibrium and its role in validating a hierarchical approach to macroevolution. In: R. Milkman (ed): *Perspectives on Evolution*. Sinauer Associates, Sunderland. pp. 83-104.

___. 1989 Through a lens, darkly. *Natural History* (9/89):16-24.

___. 1992 We are all monkey's uncles. *Natural History* (6/92):14-21.

GOULD, S.J., AND N. ELDREDGE 1993 Punctuated Equilibrium comes of age. *Nature* 366:223-227.

GOULD, S.J., and R.C. LEWONTIN 1979 The spandrels of San Marco and the Panglossian paradigm: a critique of the adaptationalist programme. *Proceedings of the Royal Society, London*, series B, 205:581-598.

GOULD, S.J., and E. VRBA 1982 Exaptation - a missing term in the science of form. *Paleobiology* 8:4-15.

GRANT, P.R. 1991 Natural Selection and Darwin's Finches. *Scientific American* (October):82-87.

GROVES, C.P. 1989 *A Theory of Human and Primate Evolution*. Oxford University Press, New York.

HARPENDING, H.C., A. ROGERS, and P. DRAPER 1987 Human sociobiology. *Yearbook of Physical Anthropology* 30:127-150.

HENNEBERG, M. 1992 Continuing human evolution: bodies, brains, and the role of variability. *Transactions of the Royal Society of South Africa* 48(1):159-182.

HOFFMAN, A. 1989 *Arguments on Evolution. A Paleontologists' Perspective*. Oxford University Press, Oxford.

HULL, D.L. 1987 Genealogical actors in ecological roles. *Biological Philosophy* 2:168-184.

HUTCHINSON, G.E. 1965 *The Ecological Theater and the Evolutionary Play*. Yale University, New Haven.

___. 1978 *An Introduction to Population Ecology*. Yale University Press, New Haven.

KIMBEL, W.H., and Y. RAK 1992 The importance of species taxa in paleoanthropology and an argument for the phylogenetic concept of the species category. In W.H. Kimbel and L.B. Martin (eds): *Species Concepts and Primate Evolution*. Plenum, New York.

KIMURA, M. 1979 The neutral theory of molecular evolution. *Scientific American* 241(5):98-126.

KOEHN, R.K., and T.J. HILBISH 1987 The adaptive importance of genetic variation. *American Scientist* 75(2):134-141.

LANDE, R. 1979 Quantitative genetic analysis of multivariate evolution, applied to brain:body size allometry. *Evolution* 33:402-416.

___. 1980 Sexual dimorphism, sexual selection and adaptation in polygenic characters. *Evolution* 34:292-305.

___. 1986 The dynamics of peak shifts and the pattern of morphological evolution. *Paleobiology* 12(4):343-354.

LEVINTON, J.S. 1988 *Genetics, Paleontology, and Macroevolution.* Cambridge University Press, Cambridge.

LEWIN, R. 1990 Molecular clocks run out of time. *New Scientist* (2/10/90):38-41.

LONG, J.C. 1993 Human molecular phylogenetics. *Annual Review of Anthropology,* B.J. Siegel, A.R. Beals, and S.A. Tyler eds. Annual Reviews, Palo Alto. Volume 22:251-272.

LOVEJOY, C.O., S.A. PANGAS, K.C. ADAMS, C.S. ADAMS, R.S. MEINDL, and J.A.K. HUDSON 1994 The two faces of Eve: a review of current evidence for the age of the last common mitochondrial DNA ancestor, with special reference to the control region. *Yearbook of Physical Anthropology (in press).*

MacPHEE, D. 1993 Directed evolution reconsidered. *American Scientist* 81(6):554-561.

MARKS, J. 1992 Beads and string: the genome in evolutionary theory. In E.J. Dover (ed): *Molecular Applications in Biological Anthropology.* Cambridge University Press, New York. pp. 234-255.

MAYNARD SMITH, J., R. BURIAN, S. KAUGMAN, P. ALBERCH, J. CAMPBELL, B. GOODWIN, R. LANDE, D. RAUP, and L. WOLPERT 1985 Developmental constraints and evolution. *Quarterly Review of Biology* 60(3):265-287.

MAYR, E. 1960 The Emergence of Evolutionary Novelties. In S. Tax (ed): *The Evolution of Life.* University of Chicago Press, Chicago. pp. 349-380.

___. 1963 *Animal Species and Evolution.* Belknap, Cambridge.

___. 1982a Speciation and macroevolution. *Evolution* 36:1119-1132.

___. 1982b *The Growth of Biological Thought: Diversity, Evolution, and Inheritance.* Belknap/Harvard University Press, Cambridge.

___. 1983 How to carry out the adaptationist program? *American Naturalist* 121(3):324-334.

MAYR, E., and P.D. ASHLOCK 1991 *Principles of Systematic Zoology.* Second Edition. McGraw-Hill, New York.

MONOD, J. 1972 *Chance and Necessity.* Fontana, London.

OTTE, D., and J.A. ENDLER (eds) 1989 *Speciation and its Consequences.* Sinauer Associates, Sunderland.

RIDLEY, M. 1986 *Evolution and Classification: the Reformation of Cladism.* Longman, London.

___. 1993 *Evolution.* Blackwell, London.

RODSETH, L., R.W. WRANGHAM, A.M. HARRIGAN, and B.B. SMUTS 1991 The human community as a primate society. *Current Anthropology* 32(3):221-254; 32(4):429-433.

ROGERS, A.R., and H.C. HARPENDING 1986 Migration and genetic drift in human populations. *Evolution* 40:1312-1327.

SAPP, J. 1987 *Beyond the Gene: Cytoplasmic Inheritance and the Struggle for Authority in Genetics.* Oxford University Press, London.

SARICH, V.M. 1968 The origins of the hominids: an immunological approach. In S.L. Washburn and P.C. Jay (eds): *Perspectives on Human Evolution*. Holt, Rinehart, and Winston, New York. pp. 94-121.

SHEA, B.T. 1989 Heterochrony in human evolution: the case for neotony reconsidered. *Yearbook of Physical Anthropology* 32:69-101.

___. 1992 Developmental perspective on size change and allometry in evolution. *Evolutionary Anthropology* 1(4):125-134.

SIMPSON, G.G. 1953 *The Major Features of Evolution*. Columbia University Press, New York.

___. 1961 *Principles of Animal Taxonomy*. Columbia University Press, New York.

___. 1963 The meaning of taxonomic statements. In S.L. Washburn (ed): *Classification and Human Evolution*. Aldine, Chicago. pp. 1-31.

SMITH, R.J. 1984 Allometric scaling in comparative biology: problems of concept and method. *American Journal of Physiology* 246:152-160.

___. 1993 Categories of allometry: body size versus biomechanics. *Journal of Human Evolution* 24(3):173-182.

SPUHLER, J.N. 1988 Evolution of mitochondrial DNA in monkeys, apes, and humans. *Yearbook of Physical Anthropology* 31:15-48.

SYMONS, D. 1989 A critique of Darwinian Anthropology. *Ethology and Sociobiology* 10:131-144.

TEMPLETON, A. 1981 Mechanisms of speciation -- a population genetics approach. *Annual Review of Ecology* 12:23-48.

___. 1992 The "Eve" hypotheses: A genetic critique and reanalysis. *American Anthropologist* 95(1):51-72.

THORNE, A.G., and M.H. WOLPOFF 1992 The multiregional evolution of humans. *Scientific American* 266(4):76-83

TRIVERS, R.L. 1972 Parental investment and sexual selection. In B.G. Campbell (ed):L *Sexual Selection and the Descent of Man*. Aldine, Chicago. pp. 136-179.

VIGILANT, L., M. STONEKING, H. HARPENDING, K. HAWKES, and A.C. WILSON 1991 African populations and the evolution of human mitochondrial DNA. *Science* 233:1303-1307.

VRBA, E.S. 1980 Evolution, species, and fossils: how does life evolve? *South African Journal of Science* 76:61-84.

___. 1994 A hypothesis of hetrerochrony in response to climatic cooling and its relevance to early hominid evolution. In R.S. Corruccini and R.L. Ciochon (eds): *Integrative Paths to the Past. Paleoanthropological Advances in Honor of F. Clark Howell*. Prentice Hall, Englewood Cliffs. pp. 345-376.

VRBA, E.S., and N. ELDREDGE 1984 Individuals, hierarchies and process: towards a more complete evolutionary theory. *Paleobiology* 10(2):146-171.

WEISS, K.M. 1988 In search of times past: the roles of gene flow and invasion in the generation of human diversity. In C.G.N. Mascie-Taylor and G. Lasker (ed): *Biological Aspects of Human Migration.* Cambridge University Press, London.

___. 1993 A tooth, a toe, and a vertebra: the genetic dimensions of complex morphological traits. *Evolutionary Anthropology* 2(4):121-134.

WILEY, E.O. 1981 *Phylogenetics. The Theory and Practice of Phylogenetic Systematics.* John Wiley & Sons, New York.

WILEY, E.O., D. SIEGEL-CAUSEY, and D.R. BROOKS 1991 *The Compleat Cladist: a Primer of Phylogenetic Procedures.* University of Kansas Museum of Natural History, Lawrence.

WILLIAMS, B.J. 1981 A critical review of models in sociobiology. *Annual Review of Anthropology* 10:163-192.

WILLIAMS, B.J. 1987 Rates of evolution: is there a conflict between Neo-Darwinian evolution and the fossil record? *American Journal of Physical Anthropology* 73(1):99-109.

WILLIAMS, G.C. 1992 *Natural Selection: Domains, Levels, and Challenges.* Oxford University Press, New York.

WILSON, A.C., and R.L. CANN 1992 The mother of us all. *Scientific American* 266(4)::68-73.

WOLPOFF, M.H. 1985 Tooth size - body size scaling in a human population: theory and practice of an allometric analysis. In W.L. Jungers (ed): *Size and Scaling in Primate Biology.* Plenum, New York. pp. 273-318.

WRIGHT, S. 1943 Isolation by distance. *Genetics* 28:114-138.

___. 1967 "Surfaces" of selective value. *Proceedings of the National Academy of Sciences USA* 58:165-172.

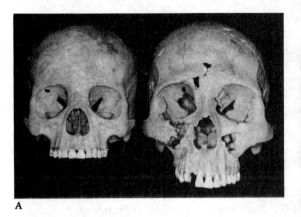

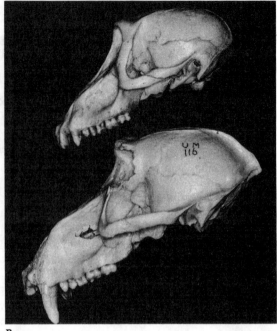

FIGURE 2.1 The critical factor of variation. Variation, providing the basis for evolutionary change, is present in all species. In many primates, one important cause of variability is found in the presence of consistent sex differences. Photo A is a male cranium (right) and a female cranium (left) from a recent American Indian site, and Photo B shows crania of a male baboon (bottom) and a female baboon (top) from a single population in Kenya.

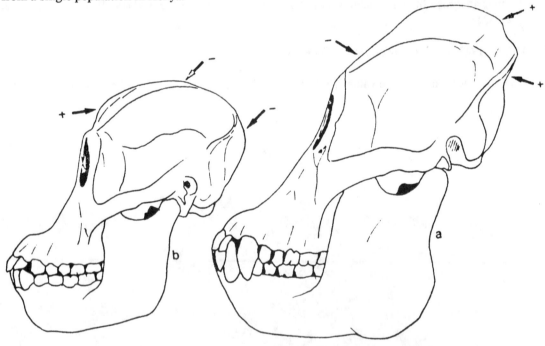

FIGURE 2.2 One important source of variation is allometric, particularly when size difference is a consequence of sexual dimorphism. Shown here are two orangutans. The male (a) is considerably larger in body size and has a larger face and masticatory structures, without a much larger braincase. Cresting is markedly greater in the male (+) and this has other influences on the braincase such as the flatter forehead (-). Some of these differences also characterize the comparison of robust and gracile australopithecines. This is because there are similar allometric influences reflecting dietary differences, but in this case *not* associated with substantial differences in body size as many (including this author) once believed, or because the more robust forms are males and the gracile ones females as authors such as C. Brace have proposed.

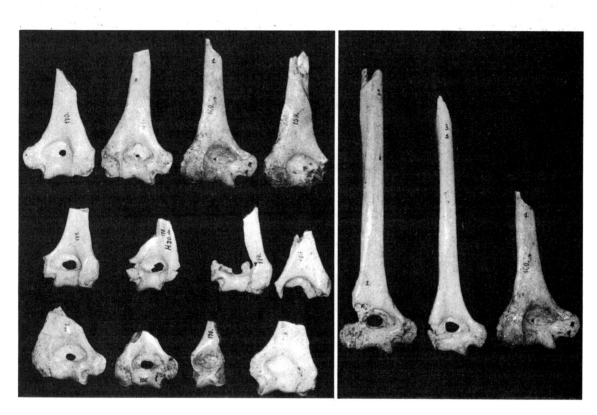

FIGURE 2.3 Variation within a large sample is normal in hominids (among others) whenever more than a few individuals are found. This figure shows all of the distal (furthest from the body) humerus (upper arm bone) ends from the Croatian Neandertal site of Krapina. Some of the features, such as the size of the bone and prominence of the large projection at the end of the bone, reflect genetic variation. Other characteristics, such as whether or not there is a hole through the bone in the position of the elbow joint, are purely a function of how old the individual was when death occurred.

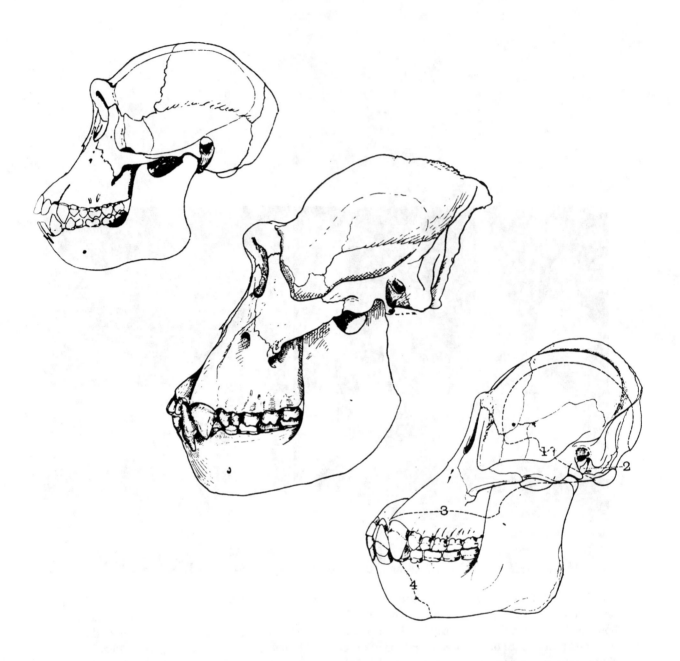

FIGURE 2.4 Shown here are the three "great apes": chimpanzee (l), gorilla (c), and orangutan (r). Their pattern of unique feature-sharing illustrates the problems of assigning polarities, which shared features are homologies and which homoplasies, which homologies are derived and which are primitive. Each pair of two share some unique features. Knowledge of the last common ancestor suggests that gorillas and chimpanzees uniquely share a projecting bar-like supraorbital because of descent from an ancestor with this feature (synapomorphy), but uniquely share thin molar enamel as a homoplasy. The relatively small incisors of orangutans and gorillas are a symplesiomorphy, the expanded chimpanzee incisors being an autapomorphy.

FROM Duckworth, W.L.H. 1915 Studies in Anthropology, Revised Edition, Volume 1. Cambridge
    University Press, Cambridge, figures 107, 109, and 149.

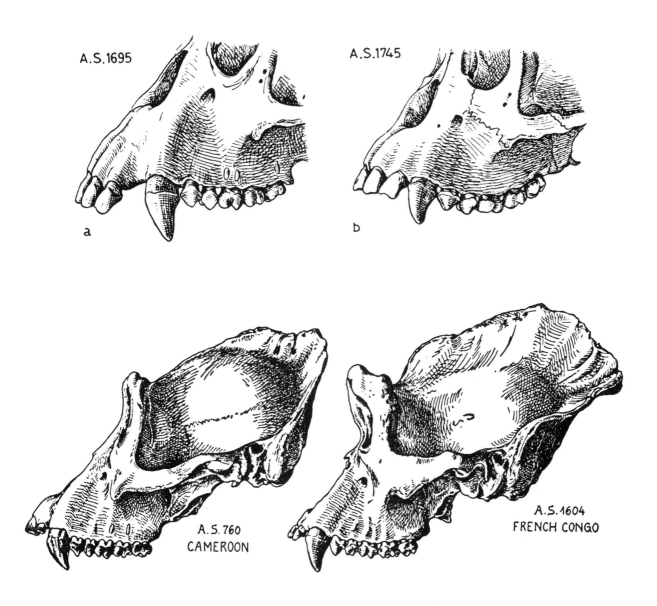

A.S.1695

A.S.1745

a

b

A.S.760
CAMEROON

A.S.1604
FRENCH CONGO

FIGURE 2.7 The individual element of variation. 2.7a shows two chimpanzee faces, one with and the other without a **canine fossa**. 2.7b shows differences in two gorilla crania, Both figures are after Schultz (1963 and 1969).

FROM. Schultz, A.H. 1963 Age changes, sex differences, and variability as factors in the classification of primates. In: Classification and Human Evolution, ed. S.L. Washburn. Aldine, Chicago. **pp.** 85-115, figure 1; and 1969 *The Life of Primates.* Universe, New York, figure 76.

FIGURE 2.8 Variation due to ontogeny. Shown here is a comparison of a juvenile and adult gorilla, after Duckworth (1915). Heterochrony has been used to explain the resemblance of the juvenile gorilla to human adults, although this is clearly incorrect as gorillas did not evolve into humans.

FROM Duckworth, W.L.H. 1915 Studies in Anthropology, Revised Edition, Volume 1. Cambridge University Press, Cambridge, figures 105 and 106.

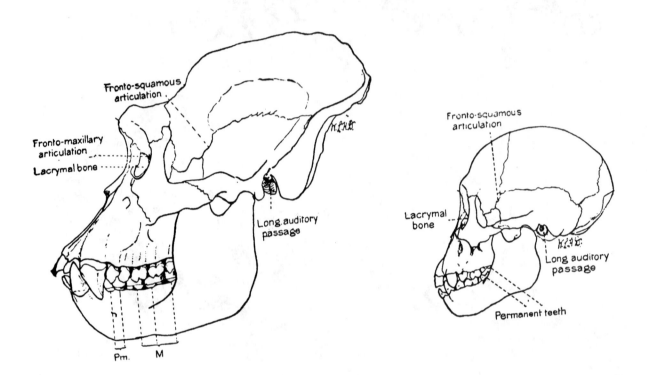

CHAPTER THREE

Primate Evolution

As our closest living relations, primates deserve more than glancing attention. Typically, primate studies have had one of three orientations. Primates are often studied for their own sake. They represent an interesting group whose behavior, morphology, and evolution present their own particular problems. A rather different orientation is the study of primates as surrogate humans. While this may have the least direct relevance to more evolutionarily directed research, its obvious application to medical science has resulted in funding more research in this area than any other dealing with primates. A third orientation is the study of primates to develop a context for a better understanding of human evolution.

Living primates have been used as models for how early humans and their ancestors may have adapted and behaved. Studies of primates have also helped distinguish what is unique in our heritage from what is shared with our nearest relatives. Finally, studies of fossil primates provide evidence concerning when, where, and why humans emerged as a distinct lineage.

The first section of this chapter provides some basic information about the distribution and variation of living primates. The next section discusses the three major trends that have been shared in the evolution of most primate lineages: arboreal adaptation, dietary plasticity, and parental investment. These trends are general, shared adaptive tendencies resulting from a combination of similar genetic material (common ancestry) and similarities in adaptation. The last section presents a brief review of primate origins and some of the basic changes that occurred in primate evolution before the appearance of humans and their unique ancestors. More detailed attention is paid to the origin of the anthropoid primates and to the emergence and evolution of the ape-like forms in the African Miocene that were specifically ancestral to or close collateral relatives of the earliest hominids.

Overview of the Primates

Primates are not just our closest relatives. Humans are one of the over 200 varied primate forms. The primates are one of the major divisions of the placental mammals - an order (other orders are carnivores, rodents, etc.). Therefore, living primates are part of a monophyletic group that are more closely related to each other than they are to mammals in other orders. Primates vary dramatically in size and anatomy, for instance ranging from the smallest lemurs (an example of an **Old World primate**, meaning any primate from Africa or Eurasia) and marmosets (an example of a **New World primate**, meaning any primate from North or South America) at less than 0.1 kg to gorillas (and the extinct ape *Gigantopithecus*) at over 200 kg. Most are arboreal (tree dwelling) but some are **terrestrial** (ground dwelling), with consequent anatomical differences. Some have very large brain size, while for other species brain size is smaller, not much different relative to body size than usual for many other similarly-sized mammals. Nevertheless, the fact that they are placed together in an order implies that they share a *unique combination* of features. The most important elements of skeletal anatomy common to most primate species include:

- nails instead of claws at the ends of the digits
- divergent thumb and big toe
- forward orientation of the **orbits** (eye sockets) and narrowing of the distance between them
- enclosure of the outside of the orbit by a ring of bone, the postorbital bar
- large to very large brain size relative to body size, as reflected in cranial vault size
- a generalized dentition with a small anterior snout and transversely arranged incisors

Each of these has exceptions, for instance the non-divergent big toe of humans and mountain gorillas, the claws of marmosets and the dental combs of lemurs. These are not exceptions from the general primate anatomy that failed to evolve (plesiomorphs), but are secondarily derived (autapomorphs), in that they evolved from the common primate condition in the ancestors of these species.

This particular combination of features is a reflection of three adaptive trends that have developed throughout primate evolution. While every primate does not adapt all three of these ways, their anatomy and behavior show the consequences of past adaptations. For instance, a number of human features such as the arm motions used in pitching a baseball are exaptations based on the first of the primate adaptations listed below.

1. Adaptation to living in trees (**arboreal**).
2. Maintenance of dietary plasticity (the ability to eat many different kinds of foods).
3. Investing large amounts of parental care in a very small number of offspring.

An understanding of features shared by primates, especially shared by species most closely related to humans, provides a necessary background for discussing human origins and evolution. A surprising number of features and abilities widely considered to be uniquely human are actually part of our primate heritage. The important questions in human evolution center about the origin of features specific to humans, and these can only be identified in the context of primate evolution.

THE LIVING PROSIMIAN PRIMATES (Table 3.1)

The order Primates is usually divided into two groups, or suborders: Prosimii and Anthropoidea. These are often referred to as the lower primates and the higher primates, but the concept of "lower" and "higher" is really a reflection of the anthropocentrism of the last century, envisioning that there was a great tree of life and that humans stood on its very top.

TABLE 3.1
Taxonomy of the Suborder Prosimii
Modified After Fleagle (1988) and Goodman and colleagues (1994)

Infraorder Lemuriformes
      Superfamily Adapoidea
         Family Adapidae*
      Superfamily Lemuroidea
         Family Cheirogaleidae
         Family Daubentoniidae
         Family Indriidae
         Family Lemuridae
         Family Lepilemuridae
      Superfamily Lorisoidea
         Family Galagidae
         Family Lorisidae
Infraorder Tarsiformes
         Family Omomyidae*
         Family Tarsiidae

---

* Extinct Taxon

Most living and recent prosimians are generally not as strongly characterized by the third primate trend (a high degree of parental investment in a few offspring), although there some exceptions. Moreover, many of the arboreal features are not as well developed in some prosimian species and a number of primitive (early mammal-like) features are retained. The two infraorders of prosimians are limited to the Old World in their distribution. One of these, the Lemuriformes, includes a superfamily (Lemuroidea) found only on the island of Madagascar, off the east coast of Africa. The species are widely variable, a consequence of an adaptive radiation in their ancestors and the fact that no Anthropoidea reached the island until human colonization in the Holocene. The prosimian species not found on Madagascar show the consequences of competition with Anthropoidea species and have largely adapted to avoid competition during the daytime. Most of the Lemuriformes share the dental comb and clawed second foot digit described below. In all of the species, the first digit (thumb, big toe) is **divergent** (offset in its direction from the remaining digits), allowing some grasping ability.

The Lemuriformes include two Superfamily groups, the lemurs and lemur-like prosimians of Madagascar, and the Loris and Loris-like primates of Africa and the tropics of Southeast Asia. Lemurs and lemur-like forms were once much more widespread but are now restricted to the island of Madagascar, where they lived without competition from anthropoid primates until humans arrived within the last 10,000 years. Over this last brief period of their evolution, many of the Malagasy prosimians became extinct. In the earlier absence of competition with Anthropoidea species, the Lemuriformes underwent an adaptive radiation leading to the evolution of living species that inhabit a much wider range of habitat than all the other prosimians combined. In many ways these Malagasy prosimians have come to parallel the anthropoid primate adaptations, although some forms are unique. The Lemuridae (and extinct Lepilemuridae) are mainly omnivorous and arboreal, although some of the larger extinct species may have lived on the ground. Only a few share the nocturnal adaptations of the other prosimians. In the trees they are generally quadrupedal, and they parallel the African and South American monkeys in much of their locomotor and some of their social behaviors. On the other hand, their behavioral repertoire is much less complex, their sense of smell is more strongly emphasized (living species have a moist **rhinarium** - an external wet nose), and they retain sensitive facial hairs (**vibrissae**). Like the Lorisoidea species (see below), all of the digits have nails, except the second toe with a large claw that is often used for cutting through rotten wood or vegetation and for grooming. Also resembling many Lorisidae, lemurs have an unusual dental adaptation known as a **dental comb**. In this feature the incisors and canines of the lower jaw are of similar size and form, short peg-like teeth that are set horizontally across the front of the mouth. The apparatus resembles a drug store hair comb and like it, is used for grooming.

Indriidae are a family of larger Lemuroidea with relatively longer hind limbs, generally living in the higher forest canopy. Resembling tarsiers in their locomotion (see below), they cling vertically to upright trunks and branches. Leaping from branch to branch is an important part of their locomotion. They are mainly leaf-eaters. The third Malagasy family (Daubentoniidae) has only one surviving species, the aye-aye, adapted to a rodent-like niche on the island. Its dental anatomy is strikingly rodent-like. This primate has two expanded anterior teeth (the central incisors) in the upper jaw that grow constantly during life, wearing to a chisel-like edge. The incisors are used for gnawing and opening hard-shelled fruits.

The other branch of the infraorder Lemuriformes, the superfamily Lorisoidea, is composed of small primate species that inhabit forested areas in both Africa and Southeast Asia. They reflect a much more limited range of variation than their Malagasy relatives. The Lorisidae are larger, slow moving African and Asian primates whose main activities take place at early dawn and late dusk (crepuscular) or at night (nocturnal). Their adaptation to this **niche** (the part of an environment that a population of organisms uses) may be a reflection of the competitive exclusion principle, the consequence of an ancient competition with anthropoid primates when they evolved. Because they are active when light is dim, their eyes are large. The orbits face more forward than most Malagasy primates and there is a greater degree of **visual overlap**, fundamental to three-dimensional vision. The snout is short, and as with most other prosimians there is a moist rhinarium. All the digits have nails except for the second toe, which has an elongated claw. Diet includes lower forest canopy insects as well as higher level fruits and leaves. Insects are seized with the hands or tongue. Galagidae (bush babies) are small, quick moving crepuscular

African species restricted to forest and brush. They are largely insectivorous, stalking their prey and seizing it with their hands.

The second prosimian infraorder is Tarsiiformes, represented today only by the tarsiers. Most researchers consider these the most anthropoid-like of the living prosimians, based on similar anatomical details of their eyes and eye sockets, features of the cranium and face described below, and their **heterodontic** (different sizes and forms) anterior upper teeth (incisors and canines). At the same time they share a number of features with the other prosimians. These include the large digit and claw for grooming, the lack of fusion or joining between the sides of the mandible where they meet at the midline in an unfused mandibular **symphysis** and multiple rather than single births. Because the tarsier's similarities with the anthropoids are derived, unlike the ancestral condition, while their resemblances with other prosimians presumably reflect the ancestral condition, some authors have classified the tarsiers in a group with the anthropoid primates. The problem is complex, however, and this classification remains controversial.

Tarsiers are small and are restricted to islands in Southeast Asia (Indonesia, Borneo, and the Philippines). Their very large orbits face forward, the snout is short, and the external rhinarium is dry and small in the living members of *Tarsus* (see figure 3.1). The dentition is fairly specialized, especially in its loss of one of the lower **incisors**, but an anthropoid condition is seen in the large size of the postcanine (behind the **canine**, meaning **premolars** and **molars**) dentition relative to body size. When in the trees, the tarsier clings vertically to upright branches. The skull is consequently better balanced on the neck vertebrae in this vertical position. Like the Lorisidae species, the tarsier's activity is mainly nocturnal and the eyes are extraordinarily large. The hind limbs are modified to allow jumps of up to six feet - a remarkable distance for a creature the size of a small kitten. Tarsiers are carnivorous, eating mainly insects, frogs, snakes, and other small amphibians and reptiles.

ANTHROPOIDEA (Table 3.4)

The suborder Anthropoidea is comprised of monkeys, apes, and humans. An infraorder taxonomic division reflects the basic geographic diversity of the suborder - there are New World and Old World species. These are the New World Platyrrhini (Superfamily Ceboidea), so named because their nostrils face to the side, and the Old World Catarrhini (Superfamilies Cercopithecoidea and Hominoidea) with downward-facing nostrils. There are a number of general comparisons that can be made with prosimians. Variation in the dentition is conservative within the suborder. For instance considering the incisor teeth, in almost all species there are two incisors in each quadrant (on both sides of each jaw), and there are no unusual incisor specializations such as the dental comb. The midline join of the two mandibular halves, its symphysis, is always fused (this is probably related to the different strain (deformation) pattern in the jaw that results from chewing forces on more vertically implanted incisors). The orbits face more forwards and are entirely enclosed by a cup of bone. The eyes have both rods and cones so that these primates can see in color. A consistent dental difference is the loss of a premolar (four in all, one in each quadrant) in the living catarrhines, while other distinctions range from the anatomy of the external edge surrounding the bony ear opening to the use of the **prehensile** (grasping) tail during locomotion in some New World forms. Most catarrhines show expanded complex social behavior in their more intricate role relations and more elaborate parental investment in offspring.

New World Monkeys (Platyrrhini: Ceboidea)

The New World monkeys (Superfamily Ceboidea) are divided into the true monkeys (Family Cebidae), the ape-like atelines (Family Atelidae) and the marmosets (Family Callithricidae). They reflect an adaptive radiation that is some 30 myr. In size they range from the smallest marmoset at 0.1 kg to the largest ateline (muriqui at about 10 kg, other spider monkeys up to 12 kg) - small range compared with the Malagasy radiation. Most species are diurnal but none are terrestrial. In many respects, the Callithrichidae are American parallels to the prosimians, for instance paralleling the aye-ayes with claw-like nails, in this case on all of their digits except the first toe. The Cebidae are represented by a wide range of living species, variants of leaf, fruit, and insect-eating forms that are like the monkeys of the Old

World (see below) in many respects. Cebidae are larger than the marmosets, and only one species is nocturnal. They share numerous features with the other anthropoid primates, including forward-facing orbits, the complete loss of claws, absence of the external wet nose, and the appearance of certain features of the brain associated with complex behavior. Atelidae include fruit-eating spider monkeys, the closest New World parallel to the apes. The spider monkey species are gibbon-like in many respects, including their globular brain case, small jaws, and long slender limbs with elongated fingers and toes (paralleling some of the Cercopithecoidea species, the external thumb is often reduced or even absent). They suspend themselves using two to four grasping limbs during feeding, and are well-adapted brachiators (**brachiation** is an arm-over-arm **suspensory** locomotion). Atelidae are the largest of the New World monkey families, ranging up to the 10 kg woolly howler monkey, a leaf-eater with the powerful jaws and large teeth necessary for grinding down this difficult-to-chew food source.

Old World Monkeys (Catarrhini: Cercopithecoidea)

Old World monkeys (Superfamily Cercopithecoidea) are probably the most diverse, and taken as a group the most successful, of the primate families. They are represented by a leaf-eating subfamily (Colobinae) and a more generalized omnivorous form (Cercopithecinae). Their adaptive range is somewhat different from the platyrrhines: unlike the South American species they have a long evolutionary history of sharing their niches with Hominoidea and many prosimian species. Some of the cercopithecoid species have evolved terrestrial adaptations; in fact, terrestriality goes a long way back in the old world monkeys. Cercopithecoids share a unique combination of anatomical features that includes:

- very **dimorphic canines** (different in males and females) with the male form large and dagger-like (this morphology is also characteristic of living ape species, but not humans)
- **bilophodont** lower molar teeth, the two front and two back **cusps** (raised bumps on the surface of molar and premolar teeth) are each connected by a ridge, or **loph**,
- narrow faces (especially the nose and the toothrow, but the **cercopithecine** incisors are narrow as well),
- sitting pads at the lower rear of the buttocks (**ischial callosities**),
- long trunk often with a long (but never prehensile) tail.

The distribution of the living animals suggests that the Colobinae might have evolved in Southeast Asia (only one living **colobine** genus (*Colobus*) is African) and the Cercopithecinae in Africa (only one living genus (*Macaca*) is outside of Africa). However, the fossil record is unclear on this issue.

The Colobinae have evolved large **sacculated** (subdivided)stomachs, analogous to cattle, that hold protozoa and special cellulose-digesting bacteria allowing them to digest leaves and seeds without prolonged chewing. Compared with their sister subfamily, they have broader faces with short snouts, but narrower incisors, molars with high cusps (for shear action during chewing), deeper jaws (more masticatory force through the molars), hind limb dominance (longer, stronger hind limbs for climbing), and reduced or absent thumbs. They are virtually all arboreal.

The Cercopithecinae are much more adaptively generalized, and can be distinguished skeletally by narrower faces with broader incisors, shallower jaws, and molars with lower cusps. Most living forms have cheek pouches for storing food, and equal length limbs used in a basically quadrupedal form of locomotion with their palms facing down. Many of the species are adapted for living on the ground. The family includes the only primate species besides humans (and some gorilla groups) that are fully terrestrial as well as the only other living primate species with successful adaptations to temperate habitats. They are adapted to a much broader range of habitats and are more behaviorally complex than their leaf-eating relatives. Were it not for humans, the ecological diversity and large populations found in this subfamily would qualify them for the description of the most evolutionarily successful of the living primates.

The smaller-sized species include the mainly arboreal mangabeys and guenons and fully terrestrial patas. The latter is among the few primate species adapted to dry, open country. A group of larger species is formed of a closely related set. These include the baboons and the baboon-like forms (geladas, mandrills, and macaques). Mandrills are adapted to the forest floor, while baboons and geladas range from open woodlands to drier, treeless areas. The behavior of baboons is one of the best studied of all primate species; many anthropologists have felt that the open country adaptations of the baboons and the closely related geladas parallel adaptations in earlier humans (Chapter 5). Their social behavior is extraordinarily complex and acts as a critical part of their adaptation to habitats sparse in trees. The macaques, by far the most flourishing of the cercopithecoids living outside of Africa, have been extremely successful in adapting to humans and the conditions they create. Their populations are found across the entire Old World, from Gibraltar to Japan, and in the recent past this range was even larger. Their numbers may be larger now than even in the recent past.

Apes and Humans (Catarrhini: Hominoidea)

The Superfamily Hominoidea includes apes and humans. We are more closely related to the chimpanzees and gorillas of Africa than to the Southeast Asian large ape (orangutan) or to the Asian lesser apes (gibbon, siamang). In fact, humans and the African apes are more closely related than the African apes are to their Asiatic relatives, and as discussed in Chapter 1 there is considerable support for the hypothesis that humans and chimpanzees are more closely related than gorillas and chimpanzees; that is, chimpanzees are the closest relatives of humans. These relationships are reflected in the taxonomy of the Hominoidea. The living hominoid species can be divided into two families, Hylobatidae and Pongidae. Hominoid species are distinguished by

- relatively large brains
- broad faces, including noses, palates, and central incisors
- low crowned and low cusped premolars and molars, molars with the main molar cusps separated by grooves
- a reduced number of **lumbar** (lower back, see below) vertebrae
- more erect positioning of the trunk during locomotion and feeding
- a broadened trunk that is flattened in the anterior-posterior direction
- use of the forelimb in climbing, involving adaptations for raising the arm over the head, straightening the elbow, and rotating the hand and the entire limb:
    - a shoulder joint (**glenoid**) orientation to the side
    - a rounded **humerus** head (the articulation with the shoulder at the glenoid)
    - greater flexibility at the wrist and for the increasingly opposable thumb
- greater mobility at the hip and ankle
- a large big toe
- the absence of a tail

The Hylobatidae (gibbons and siamangs) are the smallest and most arboreally adapted of the apes. The two species are placed in the same genus *Hylobates,* and one of them had distinct geographic subspecies. Hylobatidae species are about as genetically different as humans and gorillas. The hylobatid form of arm-over-arm locomotion, or brachiation, is developed to a fine art. Some of the anatomical consequences include relatively long arms and shortened lower trunks. These apes are largely ripe fruit- and insect-eaters. Studies of *Hylobates lar* reveal that intolerance of adults to other adults of the same sex results in the formation of stable small "family" groups. Their social structure, along with the delicate form of their crania and the fact that when these animals are on larger tree branches or terrestrial they walk bipedally, led some earlier workers to believe they held a special relation to humans. This idea did not *Pan* out.

Living Pongidae are divided into two taxonomic groupings (Ponginae and Anthropithecinae), reflecting the consequences of Asian and African adaptive radiations during the Middle Miocene, 16-11.2 myr ago.   The group is also divided in a non-evolutionary way, into humans and the great apes (chimpanzee, gorilla, orangutan). The Asian orangutan *(Pongo)* is the single surviving genus of the Ponginae, the Asian adaptive radiation of the Pongidae. *Pongo* is a small remnant from what was a diverse Eurasian Miocene large ape clade. A close relative, *Gigantopithecus* (Pongidae, Ponginae), persisted in China to as recently as the Middle Pleistocene but it is probably now extinct. The orangutan is a large ape restricted today to the forests of Borneo and Sumatra. The subspecies differences are recent since these islands (and many others) are part of the Asian mainland during the glaciations, when the sea levels are lower.   *Pongo is* a rapidly diminishing genus; fossil evidence shows that orangutans once ranged widely across Southeast Asia and China, and dental remains reveal extinct species both smaller than *Pongo pygmaeus*, and very much larger.

Skeletally, compared to the southern branch of the **pongids**, orangutans are distinguished by shorter, higher crania with weakly developed **supraorbital tori** (a thickening of the bone above the eye sockets, or brow ridges) closely following the superior orbital contour. The orbits are relatively small, vertically tall and rounded, and close together. The snout below the nose is very **prognathic** (projecting). Their postcanine teeth are low cusped and highly wrinkled with thick enamel; the upper central incisors are very large but the **lateral** incisors (the incisors that are away from the midline of the body) are much smaller and peg-shaped. The postcranial skeleton shows numerous adaptations for suspensory behavior in a large primate, including very long arms, long curved fingers with a very reduced thumb, and short, mobile legs. When the females and **subadults** (a category of the young including infants, children, and juveniles) are arboreal, these large apes use all four limbs in a form of slow locomotion that allows them to reach the outermost branches for the fruits that they favor. Orangutan terrestrial locomotion involves using the first (closest to the body) of the three finger bones on their hands for weight support; they literally walk on their fists. Field studies of orangutans have dispelled many of the earlier conceptions regarding their behavior. It has been discovered that males spend a large amount of time on the forest floor. While most often solitary, males control fairly large territories that include the territories of several females. The females and accompanying young are almost always arboreal. There is an interesting contrast between orangutans and gibbons in the expression of sexual dimorphism. Apart from features directly concerned with reproduction, male and female gibbons barely differ in size or form, while orangutan sexual dimorphism is extreme, involving range, habitat, and even diet. Orangutan males are much larger than females (120 kg compared with 60 kg) and also differ in a number of characteristics, including large projecting canines and the development of strength-related features such as special bony **crests** for the attachment of larger muscles, and skeletal buttresses to resist the effects of greater muscle forces.

The African apes are included in Anthropithecinae, the African branch of the Pongidae. Humans are the other living **anthropithecine**. These living species comprise what H. Weinert, who recognized the divergent nature of the orangutan and the chimpanzee/human sister grouping, named the "summo-primates". The surviving anthropithecines form a monophyletic group that is strongly indicated by skeletal morphology and nuclear and mitochondrial DNA analysis. Some unique cranial resemblances (see figure 3.3) within this group include:

- an expanded supraorbital torus that is continuous across the base of the forehead, at the upper border of the orbits,
- a prominent center to the supraorbitals (**projecting glabella**),
- a deep groove separating the top of the supraorbitals from the front of the forehead,
- a sinus (an open space within the bone) extending from the inner walls of the orbits up into the frontal bone (**frontoethmoidal sinus**),
- a true **incisive canal,** a vertically oriented tube-like passageway from the nasal floor to the top of the palate that separates the palate's anterior (**premaxilla**) from the rest of the palate roof
- a tendency for a broader distance between the inner walls of the orbits

- outward angle to the inner orbital walls so that the bones of the inner orbit can be seen in front view and the tear-duct extends onto the face at the lower inner orbital corner
- a relatively elongated cranial vault

There are three living anthropithecine species. Logically, two of them must be the more closely related, or sister groups. While many features seem to link chimpanzees and gorillas, most of these are a consequence of their unique, shared patterns of arboreal and terrestrial locomotion and positional behaviors and should not be unduly weighed in our attempts to understand the relationships of the three species. Within these species, some features link chimpanzees and humans more closely; for instance, relatively great expansion of brain size after birth. In orangutans and gorillas the ratio of adult to newborn brain weight is about 2.3, while the chimpanzee and human mean values are 2.8 and 3.3 respectively (see table 3.2). Dental synapomorphies include occlusal details of the molars, broadening of the lower incisors, and the reduction in upper incisor **heteromorphy** (different forms) - the lateral incisors resemble the centrals in being shovel-like and symmetric rather than peg-like and asymmetric. Similarities in the face and cranium include a vertical **ascending ramus** for the mandible, a short anterior **palate (premaxilla)**, and **orbital pillars** (the lateral or outside margins of the orbits) that are flat and narrow rather than concave and broad.

Few paleoanthropologists, however, have promoted the idea that humans and chimpanzees are sister species, and discussed the consequences of the fact that our closest relatives are chimpanzees. Preëminent among them was the German paleoanthropologist H. Weinert, who first published on this question during the 1940's but whose works have been most easily accessible to English speakers because of his essay in A.L. Kroeber's famous 1953 compilation *Anthropology Today*. This must have been the basis for the German language examinations of many of my colleagues, but the essay's content had little influence. Perhaps this is because some of Weinert's pre-war work was less than competent; for instance, the Eyassi hominid reconstruction discussed in Chapter 12. More likely, however, it stems from Weinert's statements on the inequality of races and his activities as a member of the Nazi party, including his collaboration with the Office of Racial Policy and his postwar vocal dissension from the 1951 UNESCO statement on race (reviewed in the R. Proctor essay).

Arguably the best evidence for the chimpanzee/human sister group is biochemical. M. Goodman and his colleagues examined the actual DNA sequences for some very long pieces of nuclear DNA, over 10,000 base pairs in length. Focusing on a portion of the DNA that does not effect the phenotype, they found a 2.1% difference between chimpanzees and gorillas, but only a 1.6% difference between chimpanzees and humans. R. Britten and J. Powell separately reached similar conclusions from a DNA-DNA hybridization studies and two independent mtDNA analyses support the chimpanzee/human sister grouping as well. A group of researchers led by M. Ruvolo found a 13.3% difference between chimpanzees and gorillas in a 700 base pair segment that they sequenced, but only a 9.6% difference between chimpanzees and humans. An independent group led by S. Horai examined a much larger set, of over 4700 base pairs encompassing genes for 11 transfer RNA's and 6 proteins, and found an even more dramatic difference supporting a chimpanzee/human sister grouping. To quantify the difference they assumed a 13 myr divergence date for the orangutans (the date may be a correct estimate, but as discussed later in the chapter this is unclear) and calculated the most likely divergence dates for the three African anthropithecines: 7.7 myr for the separation of gorillas from the chimpanzee-human line, and 4.7 myr for the chimpanzee-human divergence.

The gorilla is the largest of the living primates. Today populations are found in two regions of West Africa about 700 miles apart. To the west are lowland gorillas, while in central Africa gorillas live in mountainous areas. Both are primarily terrestrial (few trees can safely hold an adult). Gorillas have extreme sexual dimorphism in body size, with the females averaging about half the weight of males. They have short wide trunks (the number of lumbar vertebrae is reduced to 3-4 from the larger ancestral condition of at least 6), very long forearms and broad hands with large thumbs. The hind limbs are short and the big toe more closely parallels the other digits in its orientation than is the case for other non-human primates. Gorilla groups consist of a few adults and offspring, usually a single adult male and several unrelated females. Gorillas spend large portions of the day eating stems and leaves of secondary growth plants, which are relatively low in nutritional value. The normal locomotion is quadrupedalism of a special form called "knuckle-walking"; the arms are used in support, with the weight resting on the backs of the middle digits of the fingers. In terms of behavior, nothing could be more misleading than the "King Kong" image for gorillas. As their large size provides protection from most carnivores (except humans), aggressive behaviors are only rarely observed in the wild.

Chimpanzees are less than half the size of gorillas and differ from them in the low level of size differences between males and females. They also differ from gorillas in their expanded incisors, simpler molar morphology, smaller faces and less robust cranial morphology. Several authors have argued that the main differences between these ape species are due to allometric scaling (differences in proportion that are a consequence of differences in size, see Chapter 2 pp. XX). The cause of the scaling may be heterochronic, as gorillas grow about twice as rapidly as chimpanzees, although along the same trajectory. Chimpanzee females attain sexual maturity later than gorilla females; they grow longer, and therefore there is less sexual dimorphism in the adults. With gorillas, chimps share the enlarged brain size, prolonged maturation of the young, flexibility in thumb motions, and a number of other anatomical features normally associated with their arboreal adaptations. Also like gorillas their locomotion is not primarily or even usually arboreal, They spend most of their waking hours on the ground as knuckle walking quadrupeds (84% of their locomotor activities are terrestrial, according to D. Doran, who also notes that females spend more time in trees). In the afternoon and again at night chimpanzees may build nests and sleep in trees. Although bipedal locomotion is common, chimps are rarely bipedal for more than a few steps.

Most primatologists recognize two chimpanzee species, common chimpanzees (*Pan troglodytes*) and bonobos (*Pan paniscus*). Bonobos were originally distinguished in the Frankfurt Zoo on the basis of copulatory position, and naturalistic studies have confirmed significant differences in reproduction, both physiological and behavioral. They appear to be geographically distinct as well; the bonobos live in a more forested region than common chimpanzees, lying south of the Zaire River. Body size overlaps between the two species but some elements of morphology and social behavior differ. The reproductive and other behavioral differences, and the distinct ranges, certainly seem to fit the evolutionary species definition - especially since some of the differences may impinge on mate recognition. Yet, their genetic potential for hybridization with common chimpanzees is unknown and it is unclear whether their behavioral and physiological differences would withstand a period of population contact. Moreover, the subspecies of common chimpanzee differ as much, if not more, from each other anatomically than either differs from the bonobos (in part discussed in the *Pygmy Chimpanzee* volume edited by R. Susman). In my view, the jury is not yet in over the issue of whether bonobos are a distinct species, or a subspecies within a single polytypic chimpanzee species *Pan troglodytes*.

Chimpanzees occupy a wide range of habitats, from savanna-woodlands to dense rain forests. Social behavior appears to be very complex and structured. Moreover, comparisons of groups living in open woodlands of East Africa (the species ranges as far east as Tanzania) with forest-adapted groups indicates an ecological component to behavioral differences within the species, and different groups pass on different traditions of behavior. For instance, in some areas the males form cooperative hunting groups, at times including females, while in others the hunting is solitary and the prey is not shared. Mothers form feeding clusters at one Ugandan study area where cooperative male coalitions are rare but in the famous Gombe area in Tanzania the mothers do not cluster while male coalitions are common. Similarly, the patterns and details of tool use differ dramatically across the species' range. Explanations for these variations include the classic explanations for behavioral variation:

- differences in ecological adaptation, for instance food density and dispersion
- genetic differences, addressing the fact that there is greater genetic variation among chimpanzees than human populations normally show, and assuming that the behaviors have a genetic basis
- different traditions, emphasizing the role of learned behavior and the affects that accidental discoveries may have

Studies of chimpanzee behavioral variation are in their infancy and these conflicting models are far from resolution.

While chimpanzees adults of both types can at various times be fairly solitary primates, there is significant long term community structure. Mothers seem to maintain fairly close social relations with their offspring (especially female offspring) and traditions are passed along female lines. Yet it is primarily the young females that migrate between groups. Thus, the males in a community are more closely related and community structure seems to be oriented around their often cooperative and gregarious interactions. The closer male relationships have also been used to explain why intergroup aggression, often lethal, is almost always between males.

The composition of chimpanzee groups combines some elements of social organization that are fairly stable, and others that are fluid. This social structure has been described as a fission-fusion system in which fluid, ephemeral alliances create temporary subgroups, often of a single sex, within the chimpanzee community whose stability rests on intense mother-daughter relationships and the interactions within groups of related males. The temporary social groupings involved in hunting, grooming, gathering, patrolling, and mating can be quite different. Bonobos form more stable affiliations and social groups are more often of mixed sex. In a number of instances females have been observed to dominate males. It has been suggested that the greater cohesiveness between the sexes in bonobo groups may reflect their emphasis on more herbaceous vegetation and consequent use of larger food patches that support more individuals feeding together.

Chimpanzee diet is omnivorous and varies seasonally, including fruits, leaves, insects, bark and meat. Organized hunting has been observed, with cooperation among several adults in trapping and capturing the prey (which is often a red colobus monkey). Meat is shared among both adults and children. At one hunting site in the Ivory Coast, the dominant males were observed sharing the choicest parts of the (red colobus) prey with the female who had killed the monkey. Various elements of chimpanzee behavior impinge on what was once considered to be uniquely human. Chimpanzees make tools and use them for a variety of tasks, including gathering water and various foods. Captive chimps have been taught to communicate in American Sign Language and seem to be able to transmit fairly complex information, although without true language skills. Other experiments seem to confirm their ability to understand and use symbols.

Apart from the fascination and interest most people have in this most human-like of the primates, the chimpanzee offers an entirely different perspective to our own evolution. Why did humans carry these abilities to their present levels of complexity and importance? Why are chimpanzees, in contrast to the humans with whom they share so much, amongst the *least* successful of the anthropoid primates?

Primate Arboreal Adaptations

The primate adaptation to trees is not the only arboreal pattern that leads to success. Animals as diverse as squirrels and birds share only a few features with primates and yet are equally well adapted to life off the ground. How, and why, does the adaptive pattern common to primates differ?

NAILS INSTEAD OF CLAWS

One of the most important limitations which has guided the specific pattern of primate arboreal adaptation is the replacement of claws by nails on the digits (always on the first toes and usually on the other digits). Claws are semicircular in cross-section, tapering to a thin, pointed, and structurally strong tip. The primate nail is broad and flat and has little strength. Nails cannot be used to adhere to trees while climbing . Instead, the advantage conferred by nails seems tied to the presence of large, flat, sensitive tactile pads on the underside of the digits. It is the touch sensitivity of these tactile surfaces that seems to have been the object of selection - the broad underside of the digits required a flat broad nail on the opposite side. Moreover, dermal ridges (fingerprints) provide increased friction between these soft pads and the surface that is gripped; in climbing, this can help maintain a firm grasp. In the context of primate evolutionary history, it is possible that selection for these tactile pads came before arboreal adaptation, and that the subsequent adaptation to the trees was accomplished with characteristics that were already present in the earliest primates. Whatever the case, the lack of gripping claws limited the nature and direction of arboreal adaptation in the primates.

FREE MOBILITY OF THE DIGITS

It is quite possible that the loss of sharp claws and their replacement by nails in the early primates were initially a response to selection for grasping as part of a developing hand-to-eye coordination adaptation that included tactile pads and a number of visual changes discussed below. The adaptation is for visually focused predation, on the insects and small mammals that are found in the lower forest canopy. As an explanation for primate origins, this has become known as the visual predation hypothesis. This explanation for primate origins is widely accepted, and if correct the implication is that primate digital mobility and the ability to grasp have become a central exaptation in their arboreal adaptation. In most cases, primate digits are relatively long and prehensile. Their mobility results from the segmentation of digits into two or three terminal bones (**phalanges**), and the form of the joints between these digits. Moreover, in the course of primate evolution, there is a trend to further refine grasping ability through the enhancement of thumb and big toe **opposability**. When the axis of motion of the thumb and big toe are offset from the axis of motion of the other digits, opposability is possible. By itself, this offset position allows significantly greater grasping and manipulatory ability. In living prosimians and New World monkeys, the thumb morphology allows very limited rotation as well as opposability, making possible an even greater range of grasps and grips. The combination of full rotation and opposability in hominoid thumbs allows use of the so-called **precision grip** (the grip you apply when you turn a screwdriver with your thumb and forefinger), although this grip is difficult for the great apes because of elongation of their other digits. If the rotatable thumb evolved in the common ancestor of the apes and humans, which is the most likely hypothesis, it might have appeared before extensive adaptation to **brachiation** (under branch, the arm-over-arm locomotion of the living apes) reduced the value of this morphological change in the apes, whose short thumbs relative to finger length limit the grasping advantages of this complex.

A similar development occurred in the big toe of many primates. In some species, this digit is also opposable, but never truly rotatable. The loss of toe opposability in humans and mountain gorillas is a relatively recent evolutionary change. This change is linked to several other evolutionary developments limiting foot mobility, shared by the two African apes, and humans. These species have generally limited foot mobility. Unlike most other larger primates who hold their heel in a semi-elevated position when walking (this helps maximize foot flexibility -- an arboreal adaptation), these African primates walk with their heel striking the ground and subsequently use the heel as part of the foot's weight support. The limited mobility is a compromise adaptation for walking on both branch tops and on the ground.

GENERALIZED LIMB STRUCTURE

As part of their arboreal adaptation, primates have evolved elongated limbs relative to their body sizes, particularly enhanced mobility at many joints, and retained most of the separate limb bones characteristic of the early placental mammals (see figure 4.1, labeled gorilla). For instance, all primates preserve the **clavicle** (collar bone), although this has been lost in many other mammal species. The clavicle allows unusually great mobility of the forelimb. In most quadrupeds we are familiar with (horses, cats) the main limb motion at the shoulder is front-to-back (**anterior-posterior**), and the shoulder (**glenoid**) joint allows almost no motion to the side. Primate shoulders allow motion to the side and when the forearm is in this position and there are forces on it, whether from climbing or clubbing, these forces would dislocate the shoulder, were it not for the clavicle which acts as a strut, stabilizing it. Thus, the clavicle usually makes the shoulder stable when there are forces acting on the arm that bring it to the side - a direction of motion that is outside the range of normal limb movement in terrestrial quadrupeds. The importance of this stabilizing function is seen, perversely, in its occasionally dramatic failure - the clavicle is one of the most common bones to be broken in falls, when the hand is thrust outward to catch the body's motion. Its participation in movements of the upper limb can be felt when the hand is placed behind the head - a motion impossible in most non-primates. Mobility of the forelimb is furthered in the hominoids by having the **scapula** (shoulder blade) in a lateral position, with the flat part of the bone oriented parallel to the back rather than vertical to it.   On the scapula, the shoulder (glenoid) joint, where the humerus (upper arm bone) articulates with the scapula, is thereby angled more outward than downward. The clavicle also acts as a strut, preventing **medial** motion (motion toward the midline of the body) of the laterally positioned shoulder. In addition, primates have retained two separate bones in the lower part of the forelimb, the **radius** and **ulna**. This allows a much greater flexibility in turning the hand - **pronation** (palms down) and **supination** (palms up). This flexibility is especially well developed in the living Hominoidea, where the hand bones at the wrist articulate only with the radius, rather than with both radius and ulna (the normal, more stable, articulation in most other primates). At the other end of the lower forelimb, the ulna has a fixed-joint articulation with the humerus, only allowing bending at the elbow joint. The rotation of the radius about the fixed ulna, and the freeing of the writs articulation from the fixed ulna, combine to allow an maximum amount of hand rotation. All these features are the consequence of selection for locomotion in the three-dimensional world of tree branches. The especially free mobility for rotation at the wrist in the Hominoidea is most likely an adaptation to suspensory activities such as brachiation and arm hanging. Its presence in people suggests that some suspensory activities were important earlier in human evolution.

Primates have maintained functionally distinct **vertebrae**: **cervical** (neck), **thoracic** (rib-bearing), **lumbar** (lower back), **sacral** (fused into a **sacrum,** the back part of the **pelvis**), and **caudal** (tail) vertebrae. The most important adaptive variations occur in the lumbar region. For instance, lumbar shortening to a modal value of 3-4 vertebrae has occurred in the large brachiators, whereas the greatest number of lumbar vertebrae, 7, are in primates that spring or leap from branch to branch. Living Old World brachiators have also lost all functional caudal vertebrae. The reduction of the lumbar segment in brachiators acts to increase the stability of the lower spine, to shorten the trunk, and to raise the center of gravity. These are useful adaptations for brachiation, since a brachiator in many ways approximates a pendulum. A short trunk allows use of the legs to control the pendulurn motion: extended legs slow the down-swing but make the best use of gravity by maximizing momentum, while bent legs accelerate motion during the up-swing. This effect is less important in small-bodied brachiators such as gibbons because the change in limb position has much less of an effect on their momentum. This is an example of allometry; because body mass increases in proportion to the cube of limb lengths, momentum changes that result from bending or straightening limbs are less dramatic in smaller-bodied animals. These brachiating primates have a longer lumbar segment, of 5 vertebrae. The reduced number of lumbar vertebrae in modern humans (5), contrasting with 3-4 in the living large bodies apes, plus the fact that the three earliest complete hominid lumbar spines known (two of *Australopithecus* and the third of early *Homo sapiens*) each has 6 lumbar vertebrae, combine to suggest that we did not pass through an ape-like brachiating stage in our ancestry (this point is developed further in Chapter 5, pp. xx-xx). As far as our ancestry is concerned, it remains true that our flattened trunk, shoulder joint, and wrist morphology, reflect a history of arboreal adaptation, but there are other arboreal activities that require this morphology, such as vertical climbing and arm-hanging. The lengthened lumbar column in the early hominids indicates only that the specialized arm-over-arm locomotion is unlikely to have been important. This interpretation is supported by the evidence of limited foot mobility in the living African hominoids discussed above, also suggesting the absence of specialized arboreal behavior over the recent course of human evolution.

VISUAL ADAPTATIONS

Perhaps the most fundamental aspect of primate arboreal adaptation is its basis in sensory developments; vision is improved and the information it provides much more detailed, while the other senses become less important. In the primate adaptation to trees, sight is the most important sense. The emphasis on sight may be an exaptation for arboreal life, since improvements in vision may be part of the hand-to-eye adaptation that preceded the primate arboreal adaptation. M. Cartmill proposes that primate visual evolution first appeared as part of a predation adaptation that relied on visually tracking small prey (this theory explains the appearance of hand-to-eye coordination in primates by subsequently grabbing the prey). Whether an adaptation or an exaptation, the advantage brought by the primate visual adaptation to the arboreal adaptation is that it allows the greatest amount of sensory discrimination in a three-dimensional world.

Two major developments have occurred in primate visual evolution: the elaboration and refinement of the mammalian cone-type retina and the progressive overlap of the visual fields. The cone-type retina, with its central fovea, allows both fine discrimination and color vision. This greatly increases the amount of information obtained through vision. The overlapping of visual fields results in **binocular** (or stereoscopic) **vision** - the ability to see in three dimensions (to gauge depth). This ability is only possible when there is sighting of a single object with both eyes, and is of obvious adaptive importance to arboreal creatures over a broad range of behaviors, from predator avoidance to food location. The sense of hearing, however acute, cannot play the same role as vision in gaining information from the environment. Determining direction from sound is limited to the horizontal plane (or specifically to the plane between the ears since this can be changed by tilting the head). While this is adequate for creatures that live on the ground, it cannot serve as well when up and down become additional important dimensions of existence.

In primate evolution, the orbits have come to face increasingly forward, widening the range of the visual field that can be seen through both eyes. This makes stereoscopic vision possible because the brain requires information from both eyes to calculate depth (the same information a trigonometry student would need, the angle of each eye in sighting the object and the distance between the eyes). This trend has gone further in the living anthropoids than it has in the living prosimians. Because forward orientation of the orbits exposes the lateral (outside) edge of the orbit, there is a concomitant development of an **orbital bar** on the outside of the orbit for all primates, and complete enclosure of the back of the orbit in anthropoids (see Figure 3.1). There are concomitant expansions in the visual portions of the brain, discussed below.

REDUCTION OF THE SENSES: SMELL AND HEARING

As the sense of vision became more important in primate evolution, the sense of smell became less so. Many of the morphological and physiological features providing for high discrimination in detecting different smells that appear in most mammals have been progressively lost in the primates. To some extent reliance on the sense of smell became less important with the development of complex grasping and manipulative ability. Primates can examine by touch rather than smell. In all, the combination of stereoscopic vision and manipulation seems a more advantageous way of exploring the environment for primates. Decrease in the importance of smell has not developed equally among living primates. For example, while lemur and loris species still retain an external wet nose (moist **rhinarium**), this is lost in anthropoid primates.

There is also a reduction in the size of the external nose. Primitive anthropoids such as the Oligocene genus *Aegyptopithecus* have a projecting external nose along with a long snout (the middle and lower face comprising the muzzle), projecting dramatically in some specimens but not as much in others. In the living apes, the snout is much shorter and the nose does not protrude beyond it, indicating significant reduction in the internal surface area of the air passageway where the chemical reactions of the sense of smell take place. With a few exceptions, in the earliest hominids the nose does not project beyond the large snout. In our species, *Homo sapiens,* with further snout reduction there is an projecting external nose. The nose is apparently maintained at this minimal size (while the snout reduced around it) to retain its effectiveness in smell, and in some cases also in temperature and moisture regulation.

The general reduction of the size of the snout in primate evolution is associated with the decreasing importance of the nose and the reduction of structures involved in the sense of smell. On the other hand, long snouts are not necessarily associated with an increased importance of smell. In the cercopithecoids, especially baboons, mandrills, and geladas, snout expansion has secondarily evolved in response to the development of very large canines and to a lesser degree expanded incisors. To some extent this has also occurred in the pongid lineage. Modern pongids have undergone front tooth expansion compared with the ancestral condition, while in hominids continued snout reduction seems related to decreasing use of the front teeth.

All primate ears function in a similar manner. There are, however, differences in the sensitivity to higher or lower frequencies, and a good deal of anatomical variation in the way that the bony housing surrounding the internal ear is constructed. The reduction of hearing sensitivity in Anthropoidea is reflected in some of these anatomical differences, but it is unclear whether this is an evolutionary trend within the primates or a consequence of the fact that many prosimian species are nocturnal and therefore have a heightened hearing sense.

TRUNK UPRIGHTNESS

Development of the ability to function with the trunk in an upright position is the final aspect of arboreal adaptation to be discussed. Tree-dwelling provides grasping species with numerous opportunities to hold the trunk in this position: vertical climbing and clinging, sitting, suspensory activities, and so on. With the evolution of arm-hanging and brachiation as common postures in the apes, the requisites for maintaining the trunk in this position gained importance. Although equivalent opportunities for prolonged vertical trunk orientation are less common for a terrestrial primate quadruped, even these primates can hold the trunk in an upright position for more than a few moments. This position is important in feeding from trees and bushes, allows an increased visual range and limited carrying, and plays a role in certain socially defined gestures. Consequently, a number of morphological correlates to trunk uprightness have evolved in the primates. These provide an important exaptation for the bipedalism of apes and hominids.

The most important change is a rearrangement of the viscera and diaphragm to allow support when the trunk is in a vertical position in a quadrupedal position the viscera are largely supported by the rib cage). In addition, the articulation of the neck and head changes its position from the very back of the head in early terrestrial mammals to a position more forward and underneath the head in the later appearing primates. In humans, with trunks always held in the upright position, this articulation is completely underneath the skull, at its approximate center. Finally, trunk uprightness requires a larger heart (relative to body size) as gravity plays a stronger role in resisting the movement of blood, especially to the brain which, for other reasons, expands during primate evolution and thereby requires a greater blood supply.

Dietary Plasticity

Primate adaptations to diet are found in body size, in the digestive tract, and in the dentition. Body size is particularly important because smaller mammals have higher **metabolisms** (the metabolic rate is the speed at which the body's chemical reactions produce energy). At the small end of the primate size range, the requirements of higher metabolism are translated into higher energy food sources. Broadly adapted omnivores must be larger for two reasons: (1) larger size lowers the relative caloric intake required for metabolism so lower energy food resources become viable dietary items, and (2) feedings can be separated for enough time to allow for the efficient digestion of certain structural carbohydrates such as leaf cellulose. There are three principal dietary classes represented in the diets of larger primates:

1. **faunivore**: animal parts (including insects)
2. **frugivore**: the reproductive parts of plants (fruits, flowers, buds, seeds, etc.)
3. **folivore**: he structural parts of plants (leaves, stems, bark)

These are dietary foci within a broad omnivorous range that characterizes most species, because primates rarely specialize completely - they are renown for their plasticity. Thus, primate species regularly are in two and can be in all three of these dietary classes, with sources of dietary variation both geographic and seasonal.

The single most important factor in the primate ability to utilize widely different foods has been the retention of another primitive feature: different types of teeth. Early mammals have four functionally distinct types of teeth: incisors, canines, premolars, and molars. These are shown in figure 3.2. The teeth are used for different purposes, and the presence of different tooth types allows a wide range of possible dental functions in both diet and environmental manipulation.

There are two dental arches, an upper (**maxillary**) and lower (**mandibular**). If a line is drawn down the middle of either, one side is the same as the other. That is, there is **bilateral** (two sided) **symmetry**. Usually, although not always, each jaw gives the same dental pattern, or the number of teeth of each type (four tooth types are recognized, based on anatomy and function). This pattern is conveniently written as a formula, giving the number of teeth of each type in one quadrant: incisors/canines/premolars/molars. In the earliest mammals, the dental formula was probably 3/1/4/3, although recent discoveries suggest that early mammals may have had five rather than four premolars. For the four-premolar interpretation, the total number of teeth would be 44 (3 + 1 + 4 + 3 = 11 x 4). The course of primate evolution is characterized by a reduction in the total number of teeth, but with only a few exceptions, no tooth *type* has been lost.

The maintenance of four different types of teeth is a reflection of the adaptability primates have in both diet and manipulation. Few primates have a highly specialized diet compared with much more dramatic specializations in other mammals (for instance, horses). While primate species may intensively utilize one food resource seasonally, naturalistic studies have almost always shown that a wide range of foods is eaten over the year. To put this another way, no primate dietary specialization has resulted in dental specializations that preclude using a wide range of food resources. Moreover, most primates use their teeth to some degree as an extension of their grasping ability, to manipulate (explore and modify) their environment. The major changes in primate dental evolution must be interpreted within this general context.

There are two types of dental change which have occurred in primate evolution: reduction of the number of teeth, and morphological changes.

CHANGE IN TOOTH NUMBER

Prosimian dental formulas show some differences from the primitive mammalian pattern. With a few exceptions, most prosimians have a 2/1/3/3 dental formula, as do most New World monkeys (Ceboidea). In the anthropoid primates of the Old World, a further reduction has occurred and the usual dental formula is 2/1/2/3. In modern humans this is sometimes 2/1/2/2 since a number of people never develop their third molars (wisdom teeth).

Tooth numbering can be confusing and should be explained. Each type of tooth is numbered, starting with the tooth that is closest to the midline (the point between the central incisors), on a path taken along the jaw. Generally, this number is written as a subscript if the tooth is in the lower jaw (mandibular) and a superscript if the tooth is in the upper jaw (maxillary). The tooth abbreviations are I (incisor), C (canine—usually written without number since there is only one), P (premolar), and M (molar). Thus, M^3 refers to the upper third molar (wisdom tooth). There are two M^3s, right and left. The incisor lost in primate evolution is the third one, so the remaining incisors are numbered one and two. The problem comes in the premolars. It is thought that the premolar lost in prosimians and New World monkeys is the most forward one, so the premolars of these forms are numbered two, three, and four. The premolar lost in the Old World anthropoid primates is thought to be the next forward one, so the remaining premolars are numbered three and four (one and two are missing). Thus, it is a paleontological convention to number living people's premolars P3 and P4.

The orthodontic and dental literature usually numbers these teeth one and two, and refers to them as **bicuspids**. This dental convention is not used by paleontologists for two reasons. First, it does not reflect evolutionary history. If we were to name the most forward premolar P1, this tooth would not be homologous for a New World and an Old World primate. With the paleontological system, the P3 of a baboon and the P3 of a spider monkey are homologous, although they are functionally and anatomically quite different. Second, while the premolars of humans have two cusps (are bicuspid), this is not true of the premolars for many other primates, including some early hominids.

CHANGE IN TOOTH FORM

Relatively little morphological change has occurred in the evolution of the incisors. The upper incisors tend to be broad and spade-like (**spatulate**) in most anthropoid primates. In the prosimians, excepting the rodent-like specialization of the aye-aye it is normal for the incisors to be smaller and more peg-like than in other primates. In many prosimians, the lower incisors, along with the canines, form a large **procumbant** (protruding) dental comb, which as discussed before is used in grooming and feeding. Primates that feed with their hands tend to have reduced incisors, unless these teeth are used extensively in food preparation. Hominid incisors are generally thought to be reduced from a more pongid-like (e.g., chimpanzee) condition. However, fossil apes also have moderate to small incisors; the modern chimpanzee condition may be the result of incisor size increase from the ancestral size.

Canine size varies remarkably in primate evolution. However, only three significant morphological variants occur. The usual primate canine form is that of a conical, pointed tooth with a sharp back edge. This sharpened back (**distal**) edge occludes with the front (**mesial**) surface of the adjacent tooth in the opposite jaw to form a shearing complex (see figure 3.4). Thus the distal edge of the lower canine shears against the mesial edge of the upper canine. The most important action is the closing of the sharp distal edge of the upper canine against the sharp mesial edge of the lower premolar (the first in sequence). This action has the affect of closing the edges of a scissors against each other - anything caught between is cut (see Figure 3.4). The **canine cutting complex** is an important part of both dietary adaptations and other behaviors. Cutting can play a part in obtaining foods as well as in preparing them for grinding between the molars and premolars. In other aspects of primate adaptation, the canines can be used for threats and for defense against other species, while in some of the anthropoid primates, the canines (and gestures using them) have become important in dominance behavior and other aspects of role definition.

A second canine variant is the participation of the lower canines in the prosimian dental comb (figures 3.1 and 3.2). Finally, the third variant is the incisor-like canine form. Hominid canines function as incisors and have become particularly **incisiform** (shaped like incisors), but L. Greenfield points out that to a lesser degree this incisor-like form characterizes most female apes. Incisiform canines usually do not project beyond the toothrow; wear most often takes place only at the occlusal surface and not along the distal edge. Although hominid canines are incisor-like, they are somewhat thicker and their larger roots suggest that in the past the crowns were also larger and subject to forces which no longer occur such as food preparation and aggressive or defensive biting.

Canines in many anthropoid primate species have extreme sexual dimorphism, expressed as both size and form differences between males and females. In dimorphic species, female canines are incisiform, often quite small and barely projecting beyond the toothrow, while the males have much larger dagger-like canines. Even in modern humans, the canine shows the most sexual dimorphism of any tooth. Sexual dimorphism in canines is probably the result of other functions for the tooth than food gathering, preparation, and mastication. For instance in terrestrial cercopithecoids, such as baboons, the male canines play a role in maintaining male dominance both in fights and in displays that expose the front teeth such as the snarl. They are also used in group defense by males. Female canines are not used this way. They are free to be used as incisors, but to be effective for this they must be much smaller.

The general evolutionary trend in primate premolar evolution is to increase the number of cusps. These raised surfaces on top of molars and premolars help keep the posterior dentition in alignment during the slow process of permanent tooth eruption, when there are gaps between the erupting permanent teeth because of lost deciduous teeth. In many mammals the cusps also function in shearing by meeting cusps on the corresponding tooth on the opposite jaw with alternating sharp edges, similar to the way the upper canine and the most anterior lower premolar shear against each other. This is a common configuration in many cercopithecoids. In most pongids, the cusps do not function this way, although the ridges between the cusps in some gorilla molars approximate this function. Generally, the cusps seem more important in spacing and aligning the teeth during chewing, especially before the dentition is fully erupted. They help guide the teeth of the opposing jaw into their proper position. This is particularly important in the pongids, given the trend for a prolonged period of maturation, since part of this trend includes a long period during which the dentition is not complete (see below). Excepting the anterior lower premolar, the other premolars of the anthropoid primates are molarized (become more like molars) and are bicuspid. They evolve as part of a functional complex with the other **postcanine** or **cheek teeth** (the posterior grinding teeth, sided by the cheek, P3-M3)

In most nonhuman anthropoid primates, the anterior lower premolar has maintained the primitive single-cusped form. This cusp is large and canine-like; the front edge is sharp, occluding with the upper canine for shearing and cutting. Since the cross-section of the crown is more or less oval and the tooth is used for cutting, this premolar form is called **sectorial**. Dentitions with two different premolar forms are **heterodontic** (teeth of the same type with different forms). In recent hominids, the canines function like an incisor. Consequently, the anterior lower premolar, which no longer shears against the canine, has also changed its form. This tooth is bicuspid, like the other premolar, and the dentition is therefore called **homodontic** (teeth of the same type with similar forms).

Molar evolution is probably better understood and more often studied than the evolution of any other body part. This is largely because teeth are more often preserved as fossils than bones, the molars are found more often than other teeth, and there are many details on their occlusal surface to study. Molar cusps all have specific names, and variation in the pattern that the cusps and fissures between them form is distinctive between certain groups of primates. For instance, the molar cusp pattern on the lower jaw distinguishes some primates with the same dental formula, such as Old World monkeys and apes. Most of the monkey species have bilophodont lower molars, four cusps on each tooth with the front two and back two connected by ridges. Humans and apes have a cusp pattern in which the usual 5 cusps are separated by grooves. The most common groove pattern is called **Y-5**, but there is variation in both the groove pattern and in the number of cusps. In other cases, such as when comparing chimpanzees and humans, the molar cusp pattern is the same but certain elements of molar structure such as the thickness of the enamel have been found to differ.

In primate evolution there has been surprisingly little change in molar cusp pattern, especially when compared with the dramatic changes in some other orders, although phylogenetic variation in specific primate molar features can be observed. Generally, primate molar evolution involves only slight modifications of pattern from the primitive mammalian form; mainly, the addition of a single cusp in the upper molars, the addition of two or three cusps in the lower molars, and the subsequent loss of one of the original cusps on these lower teeth. The relative stability of molars and premolar morphology reflects their continued importance in grinding and crushing foods. In fact, differing diets play one of the important roles in controlling variation in the occlusal details of the molars, as they are superimposed over the more basic cusp patterns. Diet also plays a role in determining variation in other teeth, and in the relative sizes of the teeth. Returning to the three common primate dietary categories, we can examine the dental modifications common in each.

Faunivores, especially insect specialists such as New World marmosets or Old World tarsiers, have sharp, pointed incisors and **postcanine** teeth (literally behind the canines, premolars and molars) that have high sharp shearing cusps (especially the insectivores among them).

Frugivores are best represented by species emphasizing fruits in their diet, but there are nut and seed specialists as well. These species tend to have large, procumbant (protruding) anterior teeth (to open nuts, seeds, or fruits) and low flattened postcanine teeth, adapted in various ways for grinding and crushing. The posterior premolars often add extra cusps, becoming **molariform**. Various primate species have adapted to diets that emphasize nuts and seeds, and require an especially great amount of force during chewing, by evolving relatively large postcanine teeth with thick enamel. While this might be considered a specialization in the adaptive sense, it actually makes the species more generalized since larger teeth do not prevent the species from eating foods that only require small teeth.

Folivores have smaller anterior teeth. Their postcanine teeth are enlarged and often have sharp crests **(lophs)** between the cusps that shear across teeth in opposite jaws. In combined leaf and fruit eaters the shearing of the molar crests is predominant. The greatest modification in form can be found in those primates which eat grasses, a food that requires a particularly great amount of molar shearing during chewing. In these species, all cercopithecines, two transverse shearing crests connect the cusps in the lower molars, creating two-crested or **bilophodont** teeth (figure 3.5).

Parental Investment

The Anthropoidea are characterized by a third trend, a K strategy adaptation (Chapter 2, pp. XX) that can best be described in terms of parental investment. Parents spend more time in raising fewer children. The primate offspring learn more, and the chances for individual survival are greater. Improved learning is important for two reasons, more efficient or wide-ranging utilization of habitat resources, and more complex and intellectually demanding social relationships. Some of the anatomical consequences of this trend can be seen in the reduction of litter size to normally single births, the reduction of female teats to two, the increase in relative brain size, and so on. There is also a significant prolongation of the growth process. Living primates reflecting the consequences of this trend almost always live in social groups, and it is reasonable to link this adaptive strategy to requirements developed during the evolution of primate societies. Social learning involves the most complex understandings primates are likely to require: role expectations, role relationships, kin recognition, social communication, long-term reciprocal altruism, to name a few. The trend is probably best summarized as the evolution of intelligence. While living humans represent the extreme expression of this trend, to varying degrees it appears in all of the anthropoid primates. It consists of two interconnected elements and their consequences, increased brain complexity and prolongation of all life periods.

ELABORATION OF THE BRAIN

Mammalian brains consist of two more-or-less symmetric halves (hemispheres) that surround a central core extending down to the spinal chord. The highly wrinkled cerebral hemispheres are covered by a very thin (2 mm or so) layer rich in neurons, the brain cells (some 100 billion in humans). This **cerebral cortex** is subdivided into numerous areas that specialize in sensory input and output, motor control, regions of association, and other mental processes. Many of these regions have structural characteristics that can be identified anatomically on the outer surface of the brain. The main changes in the brain during primate evolution, its expansion and elaboration, are related to three evolving behavioral complexes:

1. increasing complexity, accuracy, and speed of learning, and the associated aspects of behavioral adaptability;
2. the evolution of complex social behavior and communication, and the appearance of substantial role differences between members of primate societies;
3. the development of superior forms of vision, including binocular and color, and improved hand-to-eye coordination.

The specific changes in primate brains related to these behavioral complexes involve both size and form. Turning first to size, there is a general relationship of brain size to body size, an allometry that encompasses all mammalian groups and is very predictive in terms of the brain size that can be expected to be associated with any particular body size across a wide body size range. Deviations from this prediction take on importance, as these represent differences from the brain size differences that can be expected as a consequence of body size differences. Most prosimians have brain sizes that could be expected from the general pattern of brain-body size scaling in most mammals, but for some prosimian species and all the species in Anthropoidea the brain sizes tend to be much larger than expected. For instance, average chimpanzee brain size is about 2 and a half times greater than expected for as mammal of average chimpanzee body size. This relative expansion of size is an important aspect of brain evolution. Brain sizes that deviate above the allometric line have more information processing capacity, and we can expect that the increase is connected to the increasing complexity of behaviors in anthropoid primates. For instance, relative brain size in primates can be related to certain ecological variables such as diet (frugivores have higher brain weights than folivores), foraging strategies (particularly the difficulty of extracting the edible components of foods), range, and even more strongly to life span. Determining cause and effect is difficult and the relationship between the ecological and brain size variables may be interactive rather than causal. A good case can be made for the relation of brain size and the complexities of social relationships.

The second aspect of brain evolution is the change in form (see figure 3.6). Brain anatomy is not independent of brain size variation. For instance, in allometrically larger brains (brains that are larger because the body size is larger) the regions receiving messages from, or controlling the activities of, particular body parts may not be required to expand the same way. Moreover, the brain surface decreases in its proportion to brain volume as brain size expands because of the square-cube law - the surface area of a regular shaped object expands in proportion to the square of its linear dimensions while the volume expands faster, in proportion to the cube of its linear dimensions. Neurological activity at the brain surface is important. Within about 2 mm of the brain surface are layers of interconnected neurons that, according to many scientists, comprise the main information processing capacity of the brain. To maintain the same proportional surface area in the face of size expansions, larger brains have more closely packed, deeper and more elongated convolutions (**sulci**), and deeper fissures (**gyri**) that break up its surface and expand its total area.

Apart from the greater number of convolutions in larger brains, two different types of anatomical changes can be observed throughout the course of primate evolution. First, primate brain evolution is **mosaic**, in that different parts of the brain evolve in different patterns and at different rates. For instance, the **neocortex** (the gray outer part of the brain) appears to be particularly important in the evolution of complex social behavior. The size of the neocortex expands throughout primate evolution. In the living primates, neocortex size relative to total brain size (without the neocortex) is some 2.5 times greater in the very social baboons than it is in most prosimian species, and humans have a 50% further expansion. R. Dunbar suggests that the size of the neocortex is related to group size, and specifically to the number of social units (as defined by cliques of mutually grooming animals) within a group, across a broad range of primates. Dunbar posits that the underlying cause is found in the information-processing capacity of the neocortex as it relates to the number of social relationships an individual can simultaneously maintain. Neocortex expansion, in fact, has such a wide variety of affects in information processing ability that its explanation is probably somewhat more complex.

Varying mosaic changes characterize other structural parts of the brain. While the increasing importance of vision results in size expansion for posterior portions of the brain that are responsible for the input and recognition of visual signals, other brain areas that process inputs from hearing and smell contracted. Changes associated with vision are the most prominent of any in nonhuman primate evolution. In some anthropoid primate species, new areas of the brain developed and expanded during the course of evolution. An "association area," where inputs from the various senses can be integrated, appeared and expanded in the hominoids.

A second aspect of change in brain morphology is more difficult to observe. This change involves the ways in which brain cells are connected. The only direct indication is the increase in surface complexity. Brain size expansion alone requires more complex connections between the cells, but the trend goes beyond this. The integration of information required by three-dimensional and color vision led to the development of new neural connections. In virtually all mammalian species sensory input from each size of the body goes to the opposite side hemisphere of the brain (and motor control originates from the opposite side hemisphere). However for three-dimensional information to be extracted from binocular vision, input from both eyes must be well integrated for the brain to interpret overlapping visual images as three-dimensional. In primate species with binocular vision, the visual information crosses over so that information from each eye goes to the visual areas on both sides of the brain - the left parts of both visual fields to the right hemisphere, and the right parts of each visual field to the left. Another example is found in the progressive tendencies for primate brains to have architectural asymmetries. In humans these asymmetries reflect hemispheric dominance and are keyed to the areas active in speech and language, fine motor control of the hands and particularly handedness, and discrimination of certain spatial relationships. The asymmetries in nonhuman primates are more difficult to interpret, even through their expression is a demonstrable evolutionary trend within the order. Generally, architectural asymmetries are probably linked to hemispheric dominance, but which functions are effected remains unclear. It has been suggested that some of the asymmetric architecture is related to information processing, while consideration of handedness has been discounted since nonhuman primates do not show systematic hand preference.

Finally, related to the asymmetries discussed above there is the tendency for anthropoid primates to inherit behaviors, or more accurately the ability to logically associate certain classes of behaviors subsequently learnt. Although this series of changes is related to brain evolution, it has proven particularly difficult to key them to anatomical variations. This is because the key changes are not so much in anatomical structures as in neural circuitry. In these behaviorally complex primate species it is not the particular behaviors but rather their organization, in the logical structures that relate behaviors to each other, that are inherited. In a manner of speaking, the operating system is inherited so that the programs can be written and executed. This makes a number of behaviors much easier to learn, and more importantly allows them to be learned quickly and accurately. Moreover, it promotes the ability of members of different populations of the same species to correctly interpret each other's complex behaviors. A good example of inherited behavioral structure, or **prestructuring**, is found in language ability, discussed in more detail in Chapter 4. As E.H. Lenneberg shows, language is not learned through a Skinnerian "trial and error" process. Instead, some of the deep logic underlying grammar, the meaningful relationships between words, seems to be present even as the words themselves are learned. Similar prestructuring may underlie all complex human social interactions involving numerous role differences. To what extent this is also characteristic of learning in the other pongids is obscured by the almost exclusive focus on ecological and inclusive fitness causality now characteristic of primate studies, but similar questions have been asked by primatologists in the past and we can expect that they will be addressed again in the future.

GESTATION AND THE PLACENTA

Primate evolution is marked by a progressive increase in the efficiency of the placenta. Increasing the efficiency of providing nutrition for the fetus allows for lengthening the period of gestation, another primate trend. These developments are advantageous in an order reducing the frequency of multiple births and relying more on learned behavior. There is clearly a trend in primate evolution to develop K strategy adaptations by investing increasing amounts of time and energy, both prenatal and postnatal, in a smaller number of offspring. Anthropoid primate species are generally characterized by single births. The survival potential of the offspring is enhanced through parental molding and modification of behavior. The evolution of this strategy is fully dependent on a more complex brain, as outlined above, and increased brain complexity requires a prolonged period of fetal development. This can be clearly seen in the generation length comparisons in table 3.2, especially when body size is held constant

It is possible that the increasing placental efficiency and prolonged gestation periods have had another effect on primate evolution, particularly in Anthropoidea. There is some evidence that the more intimate mingling of blood systems of the mother and fetus, over a long period of time, affects the survival of mutant proteins by increasing the effectiveness of maternal antibodies. This would result in a higher rate if incompatibility-related miscarriages, and subsequently fewer surviving mutant proteins. It might therefore act to slow down the rate of evolutionary change in a species, all other factors being equal, because the rate of change depends in part on genetic variability. One possible result is to decrease the rate of genetic differentiation under conditions of geographic isolation, and consequently to prolong the time necessary to establish reproductive isolation in geographically isolated populations. In other words, the effect could be to slow down the rate of speciation.

PROLONGED LIFE PERIODS

Besides the progressive increases in generation lengths, another aspect of this trend is the lengthening of postnatal life periods. This trend, as most of the others discussed, is more pronounced in the anthropoid primates and has its greatest expression in the hominids. An increasing length of time for maturation is a trend that extends through the hominoids. For instance, while humans populations vary considerably in the time when women have their first birth, even the minimum *average* age is considerably later than the chimpanzee mean of 13-14 years for wild populations, according to C. Tutin, and the gorilla mean is even less, under 11 years. The !Kung average is about 18 years and the minimum population mean for first births is approximately 17 years, according to J. Wood. Table 3.2 breaks the total life span into three periods. They are necessarily interrelated as changes in each affect the others.

Lengthening in the period of child dependency on the mother, the infantile phase, extends the time of the most effective learning. A great deal of primate learning is between mother and child, and takes place during the period of intense relationship before weaning. A close relationship continues beyond that point, however, until additional offspring are born. The evolutionary trend is to increase the amount of learned behavior - a primate survival strategy already discussed. Growth is not simply slowed down to lengthen the period of child dependence, however, as the pattern is complex. Human (and to a slightly lesser extent chimpanzee) newborns have a large adult brain size compared with newborn size. In the chimpanzee the newborn brain weight is not particularly great, for instance resembling large cercopithecoids in relation to mother's body weight. In living humans newborn brain size is about twice as great relative to mother's body weight. Moreover, human brain growth continues at the very accelerated fetal rate through the first year of life, the most intense period of learning This combination reflects the extreme expression of a trend to vastly expand the amount of social learning in all anthropoid primates. The tendency is to have offspring with the contrasting combination of physical **atriciality** (late in development, physical helplessness) and behavioral (i.e., social) **precociality** (early in development, rapid social maturity). These helpless offspring are protected and cared for over an extended infantile period by one or both parents while they quickly learn to function in, and all too soon manipulate, their social milieu.

TABLE 3.2
Comparison of primate life periods
Modified after Campbell and Wood (1988),
Gladikas and Wood (1990), Harvey and Clutton-Brock (1985),
and Napier and Napier (1985)

	Fetal Phase (days)	Wean-ing age (days)	Infantile Phase (years)	Juvenile Phase (years)	Adult Phase (years)	Total Life span (years)	Birth Interval[α] (years)	Adult Brain expansion[δ]
Lemur	135	135	0.8	1.8	24	27	1.4	2.9
Baboon	175	420	1.6	4.4	23	29	1.7	2.3
Gibbon	205	730	2.0	6.5	23	30	2.7	2.1
Chimpanzee	228	1460	3.0	7.0	34	44	5.6	2.8[ε]
Modern Human[β]	267	720	6.0	12.0	50+	68	3.0	3.3

[α]The interval between births for which the offspring whose birth begins the interval does not die within it.

[β]The human values for weaning age, the juvenile phase, total life span, and birth interval are all quite variable.

[δ]Ratio of adult to neonatal brain weight

[ε]Unlike the Clutton-Brock determination, this is based on two published newborn brain weights: 162g and 128 g.

The lengthened juvenile phase corresponds to the period marked by the time between full parental dependency and the expectation of adult behavior. For primates, this is a period of play, which functions as a way of practicing adult behavior. Lengthening of this period results from an increased amount of learned behavior and the progressive elaboration of social behavior and role differentiation that characterizes primate evolution. For instance, in baboon society, many different adult behaviors can be appropriate, depending both on the circumstances and the social status of the individual. Both of these factors change considerably during a normal baboon's life span.

Finally, there is an increase in the length of the adult phase of the life span. It is reasonable to believe that this increase is the result of the adaptive advantages of learned behavior, and to some extent this must be true. However, the increase is also likely a result of the trend for decreasing the frequency of multiple births. Giving birth to fewer offspring at a time requires a longer reproductive span to maintain the total number of offspring born, unless there dramatic improvements in survivorship (of the sort characterizing survivorship in some human populations with the appearance of modern medicine). Moreover, the increased adult life span extends into senescence, at least for living people. During this post-reproductive period the body finally loses its ability to respond to stresses and life will terminate from natural causes. P. Turke argues that senescence may be a consequence of antagonistic pleiotropy. Important physiological responses earlier in life, for instance immune reactions to disease or bone reactions to injuries and breaks, may later have undesirable consequences such as the breakdown of the immune system or the development of arthritis. These pleiotropic relations make senescence a necessity, but its onset is put off by selection that results from a longer reproductive span (as long as mid-life reproduction continues) or from middle age activities that promote the survivorship of offspring. The later selection requires a social context, underscoring the importance of social evolution in these primate trends.

One result of these changes is the lengthening of the average period between births. Excepting humans, primate females generally do not mate while they still have a dependent infant. In humans, lactation strongly reduces fertility as well. This prolongs the period between births and adds to the selection for a longer reproductive period discussed above. Prosimian births are multiple and may be spaced between a half year and 2.5 years apart, Baboon births are singular, and close to two years apart, and chimpanzee births five to six years apart (a median of 5.6 years for Gombe chimpanzees has been published). My work suggests that early hominid births were spaced only about three to four years apart. In modern humans, birth spacing is a much more variable consequences of social behavior (in part as expressed through the diet available to reproductive aged women), changing roles, and different expectations during the period of infant dependency. Human births can be spaced as little as two years apart or less, although most traditional groups average three years and some non-traditional societies have much wider birth spacing. In combination with the long human life span, the ability to alter birth spacing and thereby have large numbers of offspring in spite of single births has led to many human population expansions and has contributed to our past evolutionary success. Some scientists believe that the potential for shortened birth spacing may be intimately connected with hominid origins.

A Brief Review of Primate Evolution

The fossil history of primates is complete enough to be confusing. This may seem to be a contradiction, but it is really an inevitable consequence of the problems involved in interpreting the fossil record. It follows the "Washburn Law" (originated by the Berkeley paleoanthropologist S.L. Washburn) - the less we know about the fossil record, the more confidently we can speak about it. When only a few fossil primates were known, it was easy to relate these to one another and provide a relatively simple picture of primate phylogeny. With more fossil material, and renewed interest in comparative studies ranging from morphology and biomechanics to biochemistry, a number of important questions can be asked of the fossil record for the first time, and in spite of our increased knowledge, the lack of many clear answers increases the level of uncertainty.

Developments in the understanding of primate evolution have been dramatic. Even as the fossil record has ballooned because of the explosion of fieldwork during the last decade, the number of recognized primates has diminished as major groups have been excluded from the order, including the living tree shrews and the plesiadapiformes of the Paleocene and Eocene. Perhaps again following Washburn's Law, this has made primates and their origins easier to delineate. However, the resulting understanding of primates, and their evolution, is probably easier to understand and interpret because it is a more accurate understanding. It might be best to conclude that as we know more, we ask more.

PRIMATE ORIGINS

The time, place, and reasons underlying the origin of the primates provide a good example of the state of primate paleontology. Many earlier constructions were constrained by attempts to explain (or, alternatively, the inability to explain) the morphology of numerous Paleocene and Eocene species that are no longer considered primates (E.L. Simons provides an excellent review of these, written when they were considered to be early primates). The classic explanation of primate origins comes from comparative anatomy. Since elements of the arboreal adaptation are shared by virtually all living primates, it was argued that arboreal adaptation represents the ancestral condition and therefore the cause of primate origins. According to this once widely accepted explanation, the unique primate characteristics evolved as a response to the arboreal adaptation. This adaptation evolved gradually, and according to the late W.E. LeGros Clark the living primate species represent the virtually unmodified descendants of different stages of the evolving adaptation. His classic definition of primates on the basis of evolutionary trends (rather than a set of unique features) reflects this perspective. More recently, two different accounts for the origin of this adaptation have received attention. F. Szalay proposed that the first primates represent the consequences of a herbivorous adaptation in arboreal insectivorous ancestors. In an alternative arboreal theory, R.W. Sussman suggested that the primate complex evolved to take advantage of an adaptive radiation and dramatic diversification in fruit-bearing plant (angiosperm) evolution. He argued that the grasping pattern appeared to allow the small primates to cling to branches in a stable position while they ate (this is a much better adaptation than positioning the body over the branches as many fruits grow at the branch ends). The visual adaptations were useful in locating objects in a 3-dimensional world.

Yet, other mammals share many of the primate characteristics, especially the visual ones. For instance, optic convergence and color vision are characteristics of cats. Moreover, there are numerous arboreal adaptations that are based on very different sets of features. Tree squirrels use nails rather than claws and lack the primate visual adaptations and brain expansions. An alternative explanation called Visual Predation, developed by M. Cartmill, credits the development of certain critical primate features to an adaptive stage preceding the classic primate arboreal adaptation described above. His idea is that primates originated as nocturnal or **crepuscular** (dim light, dawn or dusk) visual predators in a lower forest canopy habitat, emphasizing the opportunities for catching small prey at the branch terminals. Their adaptations to visual predation limited the directions that the subsequent arboreal adaptation could take. This explanation envisions primates as initially small, shrub-layer predators, developing hand-to-eye coordination, grasping based on tactile pads (and nails) and thumb opposition, color binocular vision, and so on. This is a way of life very similar to that of today's loris species. The subsequent arboreal radiation presumably made use of this earlier adaptive complex in an example of exaptation.

While these competing theories are not fully resolved, the dismissal of the "archaic primates" (Plesiadapiformes) from the primates gives much support to the visual predation explanation. One of the orders was shown to be uniquely related to the colugos (the so-called "flying lemurs", which are not primates). It now seems more probable that the main primate adaptive characteristics appeared together, not as gradually as once thought, and reflect an adaptive shift. Both the angiosperm and the visual predation theories account for many (but not always the same) elements of this adaptive complex, and one suggestion (made by D.T. Rasmussen) is that the early primates may have climbed onto the branch ends as they searched for fruit, and developed visual adaptations and a high metabolism to catch insects they encountered there.

ANCIENT AND MODERN PROSIMIANS

The Eocene epoch sees the appearance of the first prosimian primates, perhaps as early as some 53 myr ago. When they first appeared, North America and Europe were part of the same continent. The earth's landmasses are part of the seven sections or plates that comprise the outer crust. These plates float above the hot mantle, with movements caused by the slow radiation driven convention currents beneath as one edge of a plate is accreted with material forced to the surface while another edge sinks toward the mantle. Movement is only a few centimeters each year, but over the eons there seems to be a 500 myr cycle building up a single "supercontinent" and then dispersing it into separate continents such as those of today. The last such supercontinent was Pangea, and its breakup began about 180 myr. As part of the most recent dispersal process, North America and Europe separated just after the first prosimians appeared, and the newly evolved primate forms on these continents became increasingly divergent. South and North America were unconnected, and South America and Africa were somewhat nearer each other making rafting between them easier, but the earliest primates do not appear in South America until the Oligocene. The Eocene prosimians almost surely reached Africa from Europe when these continents connected later in the Eocene. These primates underwent several adaptive radiations and became common in many faunas from North America, Europe, and eventually Asia. They all share a number of primitive primate features that quite credibly reflect an ancestry of visual predation and may denote a common arboreal adaptation:

1. the orbits are forward and surrounded by bone (orbital bar).
2. dentitions with canines and 2-4 premolars in each quadrant.
3. the digits have nails and are relatively elongated and mobile.
4. there is an opposable, grasping big toe.

There are two Eocene prosimian families, now extinct, the lemur-like Adapidae (figure 3.7) and the tarsier-like Omomyidae. They are often classified in the respective infraorders Lemuriformes and Tarsiiformes. However, both are extremely plesiomorphic in comparison with the living taxa and according to J.G. Fleagle the earliest representatives of each are very similar to each other. Their positions at the bases of the two prosimian infraorders must be considered tentative, at best.

TABLE 3.3
Comparison of Eocene Prosimii and Oligocene Anthropoidea crania, modified from Conroy (1990)

	Eocene Omomyidae	Eocene Adapidae	Oligocene Parapithecidae
Characteristic			
Average body size	>500g	<500g	300-3000g
Mandibular symphysis	unfused	unfused or fused	fused
Lower dental formula (species range)	1/1/3/3 to 1/1/3/3	2/1/4/3/ to 2/1/3/3	2/1/3/3, 1/1/3/3, 0/1/3/3
Incisor form	pointed	spade-like	spade-like
Canine cutting	absent	present	present
Canine dimorphism	absent	present	present
Encephalization[*]	0.42-0.97	0.39-0.50	0.36-1.53[**]
Orbital bar	present	present	present
Enclosed back of orbit	none	none	partial to complete

[*]The index of encephalization is a measure of relative brain size, expressed as a ratio to the brain-body size allometric expectation. An index of 1 means the expected brain size for a mammal of the same body size, 0.5 means half the brain size as expected, and 2.0 means double the expected brain size. Living prosimians range from 0.67 to 1.89, with a mean of 1.09.
[**]This range reflects the different estimates for body and brain sizes for incomplete specimens

Adapid and omomyid cranial features are contrasted in table 3.3. The best represented of the adapids are the lemur-like *Adapis* and *Notharctus*. Evidence suggests that these are arboreally adapted genera, broadly ancestral to the living Lemuriformes now restricted to Madagascar. They appear to have been diurnal and the larger species show adaptations for leaf eating. The omomyids include well-represented genera such as *Rooneyia* and *Tetonius*. They are the smaller of the two families and appear adapted for a nocturnal, insect eating niche. In all of the prosimian taxa known from the northern latitudes, there is a decline in number toward the end of the Eocene (the Eocene terminates 33.7 myr ago). They virtually absent from the fossil record in the Oligocene. Primates do not seem to appear in the north in large number again until the dryopithecines of the Middle Miocene.

ANTHROPOIDEA (?? map of fossil primate sites)

Origin

One of the more vexing problems we deal with is concerned with the origin of the "higher" primates - Anthropoidea, which includes monkeys, apes, and humans. Historically, studies based on living species have created two competing hypotheses about anthropoid ancestry - a lemur-like (Adapid) ancestor and a tarsier-like (Omomyid) ancestor. Living tarsiiforms seem more similar to anthropoid primates than living lemuriforms. However, the fossil record shows a number of striking morphological similarities between Eocene adapids (especially some south Asian taxa such as *Amphipithecus*) and the Eocene and Oligocene Anthropoidea. It is fair to say that a good deal (but by no means all) of anatomical evidence supports the tarsier-like ancestry hypothesis, and because of their shared characters some authors place the Tasriers with the anthropoid primates, defining a new suborder (replacing Anthropoidea and modifying Prosimii) that they would name the "Haplorhini".

African sites with Eocene (and, for that matter Oligocene) fossils are uncommon, and primates are extremely rare. The earliest of the higher primates known was discovered by M. Godinot and colleagues in the Early to Middle Eocene deposits of North Africa - three fossil teeth from the Algerian Sahara that are dated to 50-46 myr. Named *Algeripithecus minutus,* it is not a direct ancestor for the Fayum Oligocene species but rather appears to have been their closest relative. The specimen is tiny, with an estimated body weight between 5 and 11 ounces. Its importance stems from the fact that it appears uniquely related to the catarrhines, and in particular to the much larger *Aegyptopithecus*. This would suggest that the catarrhine adaptive radiation had begun by this early time, and that the line leading to old world monkeys and apes had already diverged from the other higher primates. One implication of this early date is that because the earliest New World primates are 25 myr old, an early platyrrhine origin (i.e. before *Algeripithecus*) would provide ample time for their accidental dispersal to South America across the Atlantic ocean.

Catarrhine primates from later in the Eocene were virtually unknown, until excavations by E. Simons and colleagues during the decade of the 1980's. They worked in the Fayum deposits, left from a tropical, swampy, forested Eocene/Oligocene Egypt. Before these discoveries, only a few fragmentary and undiagnostic remains had been recovered from the African late Eocene such as the small molar attributed to the parapithecine-like taxon *Biretia piveteaui*. The Fayum work revealed the presence two hominoid genera classified in the Oligopithecinae, *Catopithecus* and *Proteopithecus*, and later at the very end of the Eocene remains of the genus *Oligopithecus*. The author appreciates the potential for confusion that comes from the realization that the *oligo*pithecines are all found in Eocene deposits.

According to D. Rasmussen and E. Simons, who provided the Subfamily's name, these oligopithecines ranged in size from an estimated 0.5 to 1 kg. Their size and the detailed structure of their molars suggests a mixed insectivore/frugivore adaptation, and like the later Oligocene Fayum hominoids their orbit size suggests a diurnal adaptation. Also resembling these later species, relative brain size is small and unlike modern hominoids.

Perhaps most importantly, with unique catarrhine ancestors this early and hominoids present by the end of the Eocene, we can assume that Anthropoidea had already appeared, probably in the early Eocene if not even before. By implication, then, the age of the two main primate suborders, Prosimii and Anthropoidea, are most likely the same. As Simons suggests, the longstanding issue of whether lemur-like or tarsier-like prosimians include the ancestors of Anthropoidea may be resolved with the surprising answer, "neither".

The more basic problem of *why* Anthropoidea arose remains unclear. D. Gebo speculates that this origin involved an adaptive change from relying primarily on vertical supports to a more generalized locomotive repertoire using horizontal supports. The dental differences, so well known because teeth preserve best of all body parts, suggest that the accumulation of anthropoid features was gradual, according to Rasmussen and Simons. They point out that anthropoid dental features and relatively enlarged brain size appear later than most of the cranial ones. The *Algeripithecus* teeth suggest a diet with more hard foods than similarly sized omomyids and adapiforms, and it may be significant that this adaptation also distinguishes the Oligocene Fayum hominoids from their late Eocene oligopithecine predecessors. A study of the endocast of a later Oligocene taxon, *Aegyptopithecus,* suggests an almost pongid level of basic neural organization in spite of its relatively small cranial capacity. This strongly indicates a behavioral distinction for the suborder, at least by the time of the Oligocene, but what this may have been remains unknown, as does the answer to whether anthropoid behaviors are as old as Anthropoidea and possibly connected with its beginnings. The origin of the anthropoid primates remains an open topic from the theoretical perspective, the perspective of data analysis, and the perspective of data collection

TABLE 3.4

Taxonomy of the Suborder Anthropoidea$^\alpha$

Infraorder Platyrrhini
  Superfamily Ceboidea
    Family Callithrichidae
      Subfamily Callitrichinae
    Family Cebidae
      Subfamily Cebinae
      Subfamily Aotinae
    Family Atelidae
      Subfamily Pithecinae
      Subfamily Atelinae
Infraorder Parapithiformes
  Superfamily Parapithecoidea
    Family Parapithecidae
Infraorder Catarrhini
  Superfamily Cercopithecoidea
    Family Cercopithecidae
      Subfamily Cercopithecinae
      Subfamily Colobinae
  Superfamily Hominoidea
    Family Propliopithecidae
      Subfamily Oligopithecinae
      Subfamily Propliopithecinae
    Family Pliopithecidae
    Family Proconsulidae
      Subfamily Proconsulinae
      Subfamily Oreopithecinae
    Family Hylobatidae
    Family Pongidae
      Subfamily Afropithecinae
      Subfamily Dryopithecinae
      Subfamily Ponginae
      Subfamily Anthropithecinae

α Oligocene through present taxa

Oligocene Species from Egypt

The Old World Oligocene Anthropoidea virtually all come from the Fayum, and are dated by the paleomagnetic reversal stratigraphy and the potassium-argon technique to between 35 and 33 myr ago. During the Oligocene the Fayum was little changed from the Eocene, a tropical lowland coastal plain, a warm, swampy region with tall trees and meandering streams with their flood plains This was fortunate because it provided rare circumstances for the preservation of arboreal species (it is unlikely that the primates lived on the swamp floor), but unfortunate in that it reflects the accidents of preservation in only one of the many possible habitats that Oligocene anthropoid primates may have lived in: they only sample a local group of swamp forest adapted species on a continent that has the most dramatic diversity of primates known today. Without more detailed knowledge of the early Oligocene Anthropoidea from other habitats, it will be difficult to accurately reconstruct their place in primate evolution.

There are four different groups of Oligocene primates now known from the Fayum: two prosimians and two anthropoid Superfamilies (the Parapithecoidea and the Hominoidea). The closest ecological (and to some extent morphological) analogs to the Fayum anthropoids are the New World anthropoids, the platyrrhine monkeys. The parapithecoids retain three premolars, while there are only two premolars in the propliopithecoids. Parapithecoids are the smaller of these anthropoids, the Oligocene species ranging from an estimated 1.2 to 3 kg (an Eocene parapithecoid is even smaller). With only a few exceptions their dentitions suggest adaptations to frugivory (larger species also show adaptations for leaf eating). Small orbits in the one known cranium, of *Apidium*, reflects a diurnal adaptation.

The hominoid Family Propliopithecidae include the Eocene oligopithecines (discussed above) and the Oligocene propliopithecines. The later are often regarded to be broadly ancestral to proconsuls, apes, and humans. Propliopithecine genera are markedly sexually dimorphic in body size; the four *Propliopithecus* species ranging from 4-6 kg and *Aegyptopithecus* estimated at about 6 kg, the size of a cat. Remains of the *Propliopithecus* species are mostly jaws and teeth, revealing a small hominoid primate with ape-like molars - low crowns (in most species) with five cusps on the lower teeth separated by grooves (the so-called Y-5 pattern, see figure 3.5). In concert with the broad **spatulate** incisors, a frugivorous diet is suggested. A few postcranial remains suggest arboreal quadrupedalism. The foot was capable of powerful grasping and it is possible that *Propliopithecus* could suspend itself by its hind limbs. One would suppose this was a feeding posture.

Aegyptopithecus is known from numerous crania, jaws and teeth, and some postcranial remains. Once described as a "monkey with an ape's teeth", *Aegyptopithecus* is represented by markedly variable crania exhibiting a much more complex mosaic of features (figure 3.8). Brain size is relatively small (about 32 cc) and the olfactory areas of the brain appear to have been unreduced. Yet, the endocast suggests a brain with modern ape-like organization, emphasizing a large visual area and an expanded area just in front of it called the parietal association region. Other advanced features include the complete enclosure of the relatively small orbits, their forward orientation, and the great distance between them, as well as the fused mandibular symphysis with buttressing on its internal surface and the general proportions of the face and forehead. However, the combination of moderate to long snouts, small brain with a fairly large olfactory area, and vertical orientation of the neck muscle attachments at the back of the cranium, all resemble the few other Eocene primate crania.

Aegyptopithecus incisors are moderately broad, and spatulate in morphology, while the postcanine teeth are large and retain a **cingulum**, an extra shelf of enamel on the side of the tooth near the occlusal surface (on the **lingual**, or tongue, side of the upper teeth and the **buccal**, or cheek, side of the lowers). The molars increase in size from **anterior** (front) to **posterior** (back) and their enamel is not especially thick. However, they are part of a powerful masticatory apparatus, as evidenced by the deep, thick mandibles and the prominent **temporal lines** marking the attachment limits of the **temporalis** muscle. In the older adults, these lines meet each other at the middle of the skull and form a crest for its entire length, beginning just behind the orbits. This anatomy shows that the temporalis muscle, a major contributor to powerful bite force (see Chapter 4), was very well developed. The canines are sexually dimorphic, with the male teeth especially large and projecting. The posterior surface of the upper canine forms a cutting edge against the anterior surface of the lower premolar. These dental and associated muscular details suggest a largely frugivorous diet but with more folivory than *Propliopithecus*. It is reasonable to propose that *Aegyptopithecus* diet required more grinding and crushing than the diet of similarly sized *Propliopithecus* species.

Postcranial remains indicate a robust (powerful, muscular) arboreal quadruped that lacks many of the specializations for suspensory postures. Unlike any other known hominoid primate, *Aegyptopithecus* had a tail - contributing to the ability to balance during above-branch quadrupedalism.

LARGE BODIED APES OF THE AFRICAN MIOCENE

Towards the end of the Oligocene and during the Miocene epoch, approximately 24 to 5 myr ago, descendants of *Aegyptopithecus* initially inhabited forests in Africa, and later a wider variety of habitats all over the tropical regions of the Old World. It would appear that Miocene catarrhines underwent three adaptive radiations. They involved groups that began to diverge as early as the end of the Eocene and had different periods of maximum success, but for the most part they were proven unsuccessful by the end of the Miocene. From one adaptive radiation evolved the superfamily Cercopithecoidea - the Old World monkeys who as a whole comprise the most successful of these radiations. The other radiations were within the hominoids. A second led to the proconsuls (family Proconsulidae) - extinct hominoid forms that, although ape-like, parallel the monkeys in their adaptive strategies, and many consequent locomotor and **dentognathic** (teeth and jaws) adaptations. The third radiation is also within the superfamily Hominoidea, giving rise to the apes and ultimately hominids, the latest major hominoid line to appear. Hominids are the only really successful branch of the Pongidae, the adaptive radiation of apes. In this context the non-taxonomic term "ape" refers to all of the Hominoidea, living or extinct, except for the hominids. "Ape" is not a taxonomic group for just that reason - it is not monophyletic. "Hominid" refers to all the species on the clade that includes humans, after the division with chimpanzees. It is also non-taxonomic, as there is no family Hominidae for it to refer to in the taxonomy (table 3.4) used here.

African Miocene faunas define three broad periods, each characterized by different patterns of primate evolution in East Africa where the earliest hominoid fossils are found. The East Africa of today, with its open grasslands and strong seasonality, is largely an artifact of human habitation. Seasonality came with the Pleistocene and earlier widespread woodland and brush were destroyed in the Holocene by cutting and fire, especially in slash-and-burn agriculture, and grazing by domestic cattle and goats. The Early Miocene (23.8 to 16 myr) regional faunas remained relatively stable in East Africa and most areas with primates were forested with tropical forest in the lower regions and deciduous woodlands at higher altitudes. Primate sites sample areas where fossilization was likely (see Chapter 1), largely on the flood plains of rivers or lakes, or in several cases sandwiched between layers of volcanic ash that turned to soil. Hominoids, proconsuls, and cercopithecoids, the three Catarrhine superfamilies that evolved from the Oligocene propliopithecoids, appeared either during this period or in the case of the proconsuls just before it. Middle Miocene faunas (16 to 11.2 myr) reflect the consequences of the central highlands uplift; more open-country habitats appear, with open woodland and bush environments. The habitat of East Africa became more diversified during this time. This period saw several adaptive radiations of pongids and the establishment of apes outside of Africa. The Late Miocene (11.2 to 5.2 myr) is a period of increased drying and cooling in East Africa, and the continued environmental diversification into mixed habitats with grasslands, brushlands, and heavier forests in lower or wetter areas. Primate faunas became considerably rarer in the fossil record over the span of this period and the proconsuls became extinct at its beginning. Cercopithecoids predominated as many of the earlier African hominoid species disappeared. Anthropithecines became distinct in this period, and at its end the first hominids appeared.

The Proconsuls

The earliest group of ape-like Miocene fossils to appear are the proconsuls - a wide ranging extinct group of taxa whose exact relation to the Pongidae remains unclear. They may be a catarrhine superfamily (Proconsuloidea) separate from the Hominoidea - or a separate family within the Hominoidea - the solution I apply here). Whatever the case, the proconsuls are clearly not ancestral to any of the living hominoids. Their remains are common, over 1500 specimens (mostly jaws and teeth) have been recovered. They are known in eastern Africa from over a 12 myr span, approximately 22-10 myr ago. While the East African region is characterized by dry open grasslands today, this ecology is a consequence of Holocene burning, agriculture, and grazing. Earlier these areas were brush or open woodland with forest in the wetter areas. During the Early Miocene and part of the Middle Miocene it was a heavily forested region that gradually became a high area, as the land surface rose to form central highlands at the present position of the Rift Valley. Most evidence suggests that the proconsuls were rainforest adapted.

Species in the five genera of the proconsuls range from only several kilograms to the largest, *Proconsul major*, exceeding 50 kg. Confusing taxonomy within the proconsul group is the fact that the East African fossil remains only sample the eastern-most fringes of a total distribution that may well have extended through West Africa (where fossil discoveries are extremely rare). Sexual dimorphism was large within many of the species, providing additional complications.

While *Proconsul* jaws, teeth, and isolated postcranial remains of the are very common, cranial bones are rare. Crania, and the one of the best preserved partial postcranial skeletons, are known for females of the smallest species. One of these crania, associated with a much of a postcranial skeleton, is subadult. A second more complete adult female skull, reconstructed by A. Walker and colleagues, has a cranial capacity of 167 cc. and an estimated index of encephalization (see table 3.3) of 1.50, larger than monkeys of similar body size. Her skull is short and tall with a long vertical **nuchal plane** (the lower portion of the occipital bone where the neck muscles attach) and a rounded forehead, and has a moderately projecting snout (moderate **prognathism**). The facial skeleton is lightly built, lacking the **browridges** (a thickening of the bone at the base of the forehead) that appear over the eyes of all living apes and many hominids of both sexes. Both of these features are feminine for small apes; it is unclear to what extent the males might have had better developed browridges and larger snouts. Orbit shape is unusual in that it is squared off, and the distance between the orbits (**interorbital breadth**) is small. The anterior teeth (incisors and canines) of these females are small but their crowns are tall and the canines project well beyond the level of the other teeth. The premolars are moderate in size, with thin enamel, and the molars generally increase in size posteriorly. The enamel and molar cusp details suggest a primarily frugivorous diet. R. Kay, as well as P. Andrews and L. Martin, suggest it was primarily comprised of soft fruits, in particular, because of the thin molar enamel and small incisor size (large incisors probably evolved in the hominoid primates to strip the outer layers off of harder fruits), but it should be emphasized that the adaptive radiation exhibits the size and morphological diversity of the living monkeys, and there was undoubtedly a wide range of dietary diversity as well.

The postcranial skeleton is of great importance. There are many isolated limb fragments, including the partial *Proconsul* female from Rusinga and 9 other partial Rusinga skeletons. These remains demonstrate that *Proconsul* was an arboreal quadruped and not a **quadrumanous** (four-handed grasping) climber or dedicated brachiator. While individuals may have hung by their arms during feeding, the main form of arboreal locomotion seems to have been climbing and quadrupedal walking on branches. According to C. Ward, arboreal primate quadrupeds such as monkeys emphasize flexibility and movement in the lower back, while apes emphasize stability and shortening in the lower spine region, requirements for climbing and arm hanging. The *Proconsul* skeletons have long flexible lower backs and other monkey-like adaptations. The forearm and wrist were not as mobile as in living apes and humans, and the wrist anatomy and short, straight digits reflect **palmigrade** (palms placed flat on the ground) walking. While *Proconsul* skeletons lack a number of locomotor adaptations related to arboreality that are held in common by living apes and humans, like some of the other hominoids, according to M. Rose, the thumb was relatively long and could be fully rotated and opposed. Moreover *Proconsul,* unlike its Oligocene ancestor, did not have a tail.

African Pongidae of the Early Miocene: Afropithecinae

The Pongidae is the family of the Hominoidea we will focus on. The origin of the Pongidae (the family including apes and humans) is in Africa, and the links of this family to *Aegyptopithecus* of the Oligocene are quite clear, as will be discussed below. Prior to the divisions into the *Pongo* and African ape - human clades, pongids are known from three sites in the latest part of the Early Miocene: Kalodirr (17-18 myr) and Buluk (older than 17 myr), from Northern Kenya respectively west and east of Lake Turkana; and Ad Dabtiyah, a 17 myr site in Saudi Arabia. The location of the Saudi specimen may seem surprising but Saudi Arabia is part of the African plate and during the Early Miocene it was geographically and faunally a part of Africa. The larger remains from these sites are *Afropithecus turkanensis* (there is a smaller hominoid from Kalodirr, of unclear taxonomic affinities). Thus, the oldest pongids known so far are much younger than the oldest proconsuls; or put another way, the pongid-proconsul split is much earlier. It can be assumed that the pongid-hylobatid split is earlier as well. Even though the ancestry of the hylobatids is unclear (the living species are remnants of a once geographically broad adaptive radiation), there is sufficient evidence to show that *Afropithecus* is more closely related to apes and humans than gibbons are - it shares a number of synapomorphies with humans and apes that gibbons lack.

Afropithecus was a large primate, compared with its ancestors and contemporaries, with a robustly build cranial vault and large jaws and teeth with very thick enamel. The Kenyan remains of *Afropithecus turkanensis* are abundant; 46 specimens (19 with cranial parts) from Kalodirr and 11 mostly dentognathic fragments from Buluk. The Kalodirr cranium (WK 16999) is an interesting and very diagnostic specimen, about the size of a large dog. There are a surprising number of features that closely resemble *Aegyptopithecus* remains, although these are much smaller in size and twice as old. Some of these comprise what B. Benefit and M. McCrossin describe as the ancestral catarrhine morphotype - the plesiomorphic condition for fossil and living monkeys and apes. They surmise that *Aegyptopithecus* or something much like it is a common ancestor for this clade. These plesiomorphic features are italicized in the list of *Aegyptopithecus-Afropithecus* resemblances (table 3.5)

Table 3.5
Resemblances of *Aegyptopithecus* and *Afropithecus*[1]

- *Along the midline, the frontal bone and facial skeleton down to the teeth is set in a straight line from the top of the vault to the incisors.*
- The *steep frontal* is bordered by a very large **temporal fossa** (the opening enclosed by the outer cheek bones, or **zygomatics**). This fossa is a passage way for the temporalis muscle, as it extends from the mandible to its attachment on the side of the cranium.
- The **temporal lines**, created by the edge of the temporalis muscle, form crests. *They converge strongly toward the midline, producing a shallow concave triangular area between them and the supraorbital rim called the **frontal trigone**.* Where they meet at the middle of the skull they produce a **sagittal crest** on the short frontal bone. The sagittal crest begins at the front of the bone, just behind the orbits (in contrast the crest in apes and early hominids begins much further back, at the very rear of the frontal).
- *The supraorbital tori are weakly developed. They resemble those of orangutans, small evenly rounded and cylindrically shaped, closely following the contours of the upper orbital rim.*
- Below them the *orbits* are small, but relatively tall, and *are separated by a wide distance.*
- The **lacrimal duct** (tear duct), near the medial (inside) edge of the orbits in all primates, is on the face side of the orbital rim. This anatomy is also found in the African apes, in humans, and in certain of the Late Miocene European thick enameled apes. (In orangutans and their relatives the duct is also along the orbital edge, but instead is situated on the inner orbital wall, "around the corner" as it were.)
- The *cheeks are vertically tall*, their base extends almost all the way down to the toothrow and they are very broad (this breadth extends out to the orbital pillar, the outer rim of bone enclosing the orbit in anthropoids, which are also unusually broad).
- *The nose is teardrop shaped, its lower border dipping in the middle, and the nasal bones are tall.*
- The **incisive foramen**, the lower (palatal) opening of the **incisive canal** that connects the top of the palate with the bottom of the nasal chamber, is relatively large and the opening is doubled.

- The **corpus** of the mandible (the horizontal part holding the teeth and their roots) is vertically tall from front to back, but tallest at the front, at the base of the long sloping symphysis.
- On the inside of the symphysis the transverse **internal buttresses** are weakly developed (these buttresses strengthen the front of the jaw during chewing - remember that the earlier anthropoids already have fusion of the two halves at the symphysis because of the **masticatory forces** - forces created during chewing - that pass through it).

[1] Italicized features are plesiomorphic, part of the ancestral catarrhine morphotype

The *Aegyptopithecus-Afropithecus* resemblances show that there is a clear link between *Aegyptopithecus* and the Miocene pongids. This link may be both adaptive and phylogenetic. Many of the similarities reflect a common adaptation, to dietary items requiring grinding and crushing. Differences in body size and molar enamel thickness (see below), however, indicate that they are not the *same* items. Moreover it is reasonable to assume that these numerous shared features reflect an ancestral-descendent relationship. If *Afropithecus* is the earliest of the African Pongidae, as the evidence now suggests, it is on (or is close to) the line of human ancestry and this phyletic position establishes *Aegyptopithecus* as a remote human ancestor as well (in fact, as an ancestor of all living anthropoids). The features that *Aegyptopithecus* and *Afropithecus* share define what is plesiomorphic for subsequent pongids.

Table 3.6
Relative Molar Enamel Thickness*

Taxon	Relative Thickness	Category
Small *Proconsul*	8.5	thin
Gorilla gorilla	10.0	thin
Pan troglodytes	10.1	thin
Large *Proconsul*	12.8	intermediate
Pongo pygmaeus	15.9	intermediate
Afropithecus (Ad Dabtiyah)	17.4	thick
Sivapithecus	19.7	thick
Australopithecus africanus	22.2	thick
Homo sapiens	22.4	thick
Afropithecus turkanensis	28.5	hyper-thick
Swartkrans *australopithecine*	29.6	hyper thick
Australopithecus boisei	34.9	hyper thick

* Adapted from Andrews and Martin (1991). Direct thickness measurements are problematic because the enamel thickness differs at different parts of the tooth crown. Relative thickness relates enamel volume to the volume of the underlying dentin (figure 4.11, internal tooth anatomy), presumably scaling it to body size (although this has never been demonstrated).

A number of other *Afropithecus* features differ from the earlier Oligocene anthropoids. These are important because they show the direction of evolutionary change, and outline the basis for relating *Afropithecus* to all later pongids. The most dramatic of these is size - the smallest of the adult *Aegyptopithecus* **frontofacial** pieces (part of a cranium just preserving the palate and face and the frontal bone above and behind it) is barely taller than the *Afropithecus* orbit! Many of the other differences can be related to a much longer and broader nose, taking up more room between the orbits (at their expense, they are narrower) and lengthening the middle of the face (the nose is far in front of and below the bottom of the orbits while in *Aegyptopithecus* these are relatively closer together and about the same height from the toothrow). The snout is prognathic and the large incisors are particularly procumbant, emerging from the upper jaw at an almost horizontal orientation. Other dental distinctions include the large but low canines with marked sex differences, premolars expanded buccolingually, and very thick **enamel** caps on the molars.

Sexual dimorphism, at least in postcanine tooth sizes and the dimensions of the mandibles, is somewhat greater than average values for living apes. In this regard *Afropithecus* is similar to the proconsuls described above. The other striking similarity with the proconsuls lies in the detailed anatomy of the postcranial skeleton. *Afropithecus* is the approximate size of the medium to large *Proconsul* species, and it shows most of the same adaptations to above-branch quadrupedal walking. If we surmise that these similarities reflect archaic morphology, from before the clades diverged, they must be plesiomorphies as well. In fact, according to C. Ward virtually all of the large bodied Early and Middle Miocene African apes share the same suite of postcranial adaptations, regardless of body size, suggesting very similar locomotor adaptations. However, in cranial and dental comparisons the proconsuls are quite different. They have shorter snouts, larger broader orbits, and quite different morphologies of the short middle face and long forehead. Proconsuls have mandibular symphyses with a different pattern of internal buttress development; the upper torus is very strong while the lower torus is usually absent (in *Afropithecus* it is well developed, extending far backwards). Comparing similar sized dentitions, proconsuls have taller, more slender canines, and smaller, narrower premolars with more vertical sides. The molars increase in size from front to back, have much thinner enamel covering their cusps and often have much stronger cingulum development on the lower teeth.

The Ad Dabtiyah specimen is a partial maxilla with postcanine teeth. The broad expanded premolars with sub-equal cusps (of the two cusps on each of these teeth, the outer or buccal cusp is larger) and the lingual cingula on the molars indicate affinity with the Kalodirr remains. Other resemblances include the similar sizes of the first and second molars. However, relative thickness of the molar enamel is not as great

The *Afropithecus* specimens seem to make use of similar, although slightly drier and more open woodland environments in different ways than some of their proconsul cousins, and the differences are important for understanding the distinctions of the earliest pongids. For instance, they share their habitat with a much wider taxonomic diversity of primates than the proconsuls usually do. The consequences of distinct patterns of masticatory differences are seen in the

- mandibular buttressing,
- relatively expanded incisors,
- closer-to-equal molar sizes,
- expanded upper premolars,
- postcanine teeth that wear rapidly to a flat grinding surface,
- very much thicker molar enamel.

These suggest frugivory based on harder-to-peal fruits and other hard reproductive parts such as seeds, as well as a more folivorous element than the proconsuls, including fibrous dietary items with more structural integrity that required more muscle forces to chew. For instance, there is a clear link between molar enamel thickness and bite force. Greater bite force is why humans have thicker enamel on their last molars in spite of the fact that they are in occlusion for a much shorter time than the more anterior molars. In any event, both associated habitats ands structural anatomy show that the proconsuls adapted quite differently. They were hardly evolutionary failures - they persisted and proliferated for some 10 million years or more. Yet, it is the pongid and cercopithecid radiations that left descendants and not the proconsuls.

Middle Miocene African Pongids: Dryopithecinae

At the beginning of the Middle Miocene a connection of the continents and suitable conditions where they meet provided the opportunity for African fauna to migrate to Eurasia, and Eurasian fauna to Africa. These faunal exchanges spread anthropoid primates throughout the Old World tropics, and monkeys and apes are found across Eurasia after this time. Dryopithecinae originated in Africa during this period and subsequently underwent a very successful Eurasian adaptive radiation with a broad distribution of varying Miocene forms. These range from species with

- gracile (relatively thin) to robust mandibular bodies,
- intermediate (orangutan-like) to thicker molar enamel,
- relatively small but sometimes very procumberant incisors ,
- and postcranially species with mixed terrestrial and arboreal (primarily above-branch) adaptations.

D. Begun suggests that there may have been broadly different adaptive locomotor grades in the Eurasian **dryopithecine** species. These are said to show varying degrees of cranial and dental similarities to the anthropithecines, particularly to gorillas. But according to other scientists such as B. Benefit and M. McCrossin, no Miocene ape has the shoulder and upper arm morphology of modern apes. More evidence will be needed to resolve the issue.

Focusing on Africa, where hominid ancestors are most likely to be found, the African branch of the Dryopithecinae have been discovered at a number of Middle Miocene sites. Except for a Namibian ape, *Otavipithecus*, all of these are from a fairly restricted region of Western Kenya and Uganda. The continued evolution of mixed terrestrial and arboreal above branch adaptations can be observed in the early dryopithecine sample from Maboko Island and later at Fort Ternan, discussed below. Most African dryopithecine specimens show evidence of a powerful masticatory apparatus that is shared with subsequent African and Eurasian apes from the later Miocene. This is plesiomorphic, already present in common ancestors for these apes such as *Afropithecus*. However while *Afropithecus* was ancestral to all of the subsequent pongids, it was not necessarily the *last common ancestor* for the Asian and African apes. Moreover, several of the Middle Miocene African specimens show specific gorilloid features. These may denote an early date for the split with the gorilla lineage, or alternatively may mean that these gorilloid features are plesiomorphic in the anthropithecines. Finally, it should be remembered that the Middle and Late Miocene African pongid sample is orders of magnitude smaller than the Eurasian one, and a real clarification of its systematics will almost certainly require a lot more specimens.

Ultimately, by the end of the Middle Miocene, the dryopithecines gave rise to the two subsequent geographically distinct radiations of Miocene pongids, the anthropithecines of Africa and pongines of Eurasia. This second Eurasian adaptive radiation (Ponginae) is more ape-like than the dryopithecines in cranial, dental, and some elements of postcranial anatomy (but none showing a below-branch adaptation similar to any living ape). The **pongine** radiation includes *Sivapithecus, Gigantopithecus,* and the several species of *Pongo* and their immediate ancestors. The known postcranial adaptations suggest that a mixed terrestrial and arboreal over-the-branch locomotion was common to the pongine species and the African anthropithecines, but a last common ancestor for them with clearly associated postcranial remains is yet to be identified. Several of the pongines survived to the Pleistocene - the *Pongo* species and *Gigantopithecus* (table 3.7).

It is likely that many of the below branch postcranial adaptations that subsequently appeared in the African and Asian apes are homoplasies found in closely related species that developed similar adaptations These shared features of the Asian *and* African great apes that humans lack, such as the reduction of lumbar vertebrae to four or less, thumb reduction or loss, and the appearance of certain shoulder specializations for arm hanging, show that some great ape similarities *must be* homoplasies because they appeared independently *after* the Middle Miocene. Within the African clade, the anthropithecines, additional similarities (many discussed earlier in this chapter) may also be homologies. Their interpretation depends on whether or not the last common ancestor for the living pongids was a knuckle-walker (as workers such as S.L. Washburn have long proposed, but in the total absence of evidence). Knuckle-walking in this common ancestor would imply that many characteristics of human postcranial anatomy are apomorphic, even those not associated with obligate bipedalism, as they evolved from a more ape-like condition. If, however, the common ancestor was not specialized for this unique combination of arboreal below branch and terrestrial knuckle-walking, human postcranial features apart from those associated with bipedalism may reflect the primitive condition. Should this be so, the branching order implies that African ape similarities must have evolved independently. The question of homoplasies in the living apes, in other words, is not whether there are any, but rather of how many there are.

Otavipithecus (13 myr)

After the plethora of East African discoveries, a fossil ape from Namibia was quite unexpected. This specimen (Berg Aukas 1), a juvenile right mandible with most of the **cheek teeth**, P_4-M_3 (there is a P_3 root). The incisor region shows that these were small anterior teeth, but the canine and anterior premolar sockets show these teeth were quite large and suggest the specimen is male. The molars are similar to some of the other dryopithecines, with a simple Y-5 cup pattern, absence of cingula, increasing size towards the back (but M_3<M_2), and like some of the European dryopithecine species it has thin molar enamel. This later feature distinguishes it from the similar-sized *Kenyapithecus* remains (see below), as does the thin symphysis cross-section and generally thin mandibular body, vertical canine roots, enlarged anterior premolar roots, and bulging molar cusps. While it is not exactly like any other dryopithecine species, the similarities to this group are greatest. The dentition reveals adaptation to a diet that requires minimal incisal preparation and minimal grinding and crushing, perhaps focusing on leaves and the reproductive parts of plants such as berries, buds, and flowers.

Moroto

The face and palate of a large ape, UMP 62-11, were discovered at the Middle Miocene site of Moroto, Uganda. First attributed to *Proconsul major,* this is now generally considered to be incorrect and L.S.B. Leakey's assessment, that it is a pongid that is possibly a direct ancestor of gorilla, has received renewed attention. Certainly the African pongid classification can be supported, for instance the tear ducts are in the anthropithecine position that characterizes the entire clade, as described above, and unlike the tear duct morphology of the Asian apes. Yet, the question of a unique relationship to gorilla is more problematic. It is true that the face, more similar to the anthropithecines than to any proconsul, in some respects specifically resembles gorilla. The midface is shallowly concave in profile and long, with the upper border of the nose well below the lower border of the orbits. The nasal opening is narrow (all the facial breadths are narrow, at least compared with gorillas - even female gorillas). The height of the nose is extraordinary tall, reflecting the long midface, but the **alveolar height** (the distance from the base of the nose to the front teeth) is small. The anterior teeth, especially incisors, are large, but are not particularly procumbant - the gorilla differs in having an even larger central incisor size, all other things being equal. Premolars are buccolingually expanded and strongly heterodontic, but again the gorilla differs, in this case by also having **mesiodistally** (front-to-back direction, or length) expanded premolars. The gorilla morphology is more similar to M 16649, the Maboko *Kenyapithecus* maxilla described below, but has much thinner enamel than both. Thus, the case for a specific, or unique, relationship to gorillas is weak, although there clearly are many resemblances. The large, low crowned canines, broad premolars, and equal sized thick enameled molars specifically resemble *Afropithecus* and R.E. Leakey and his colleagues have suggested including Moroto as a separate species of *Afropithecus.* However, the Moroto nose and surrounding face is broader, the front of the palate is particularly shallower and wider, the sides of the postcanine teeth are steeper and their cingula are better developed, These details argue against an especially close relationship.

Postcranially, the similarities to *Afropithecus* are even less. There is a **lumbar** (lower back) vertebra associated with the Moroto face. Using it to estimate body size gives about 38 kg, according to W. Sanders and B. Bodenbender, about that of a female chimpanzee (table 5.2). Its morphology is unlike either proconsuls or monkeys, and according to C. Ward unlike the Kalodirr *Afropithecus* as well (all of the *Afropithecus* postcranial elements are very proconsul-like). The Moroto vertebra uniquely resembles living anthropithecines, in having features that reflect a broad torso and stiff lower spine. According to Ward the morphology reflects an adaptation to holding the trunk upright and stable in the **dorsoventral** (back to front) direction for long periods of time above a fixed pelvis - important elements in **quadrumanous climbing** as well as a common feeding position for the African apes. At the same time, it lacks some of the more specialized features found in living ape vertebrae that reflect their unique quadrupedal behavior. This raises the possibility that the knuckle-walking adaptations of chimpanzees and gorillas may be secondary to their other locomotor adaptations, and more recent. Moreover, it also lacks the specialized adaptations to obligate bipedalism that are found in human lumbar vertebrae. It is better not to read too much into a solitary piece of back, but if these interpretations are sustained with further discoveries, they would suggest that the knuckle-walking adaptation of the African apes was not present. If Moroto is directly ancestral to the living anthropithecines, this reading of the fossil evidence suggests that the behavior is a homoplasy in chimpanzees and gorillas because it must have developed independently. This is because humans and their immediate ancestry lack any remnants of an adaptation to knuckle-walking, and the chimpanzee-human divergence was last.

Kenyapithecus: an African dryopithecine?

A handful of remains attributed to the genus *Kenyapithecus* were first described for the Fort Ternan site by L.S.B. Leakey, who classified them as *Kenyapithecus wickeri*. Leakey later postulated that there was an earlier ancestral species, *"Kenyapithecus africanus"*, and although the composition of this species is now quite different than Leakey envisioned, it is much better represented in the fossil record. *"Kenyapithecus africanus"* is clearly earlier than the division of clades leading to the living Asian and African pongids, and *Kenyapithecus wickeri* may be so as well (although this is much less clear). The earlier species lacks most of the postcranial and some of the dental synapomorphies of the living apes, and in fact is the most afropithecine-like of the dryopithecines. *Kenyapithecus africanus* is not particularly distinct from the *Kenyapithecus wickeri* remains, but if this later species proves to postdate the divergence between Asian and African clades (Ponginae and Anthropithecinae), *Kenyapithecus* would no longer be the appropriate genus name for both samples. We will discuss the African *Kenyapithecus* species here in order of age.

Nachola (or Emuruilien) Remains (16-15 myr)

More than 150 *"Kenyapithecus africanus"* fragments have been recovered thus far from Nachola, in the Samburu Hills of the Eastern Rift Valley, Kenya. They are characterized by molars with thick enamel and cingula, a well developed backward projecting lower mandibular torus (as in the Fort Ternan and Kaloma mandibles, see below), canines that are rotated out of alignment with the postcanine teeth (in living apes the shear facet of the canine is oriented along the axis of the postcanine teeth), and broad deep cheeks. These features associate them with the other *Kenyapithecus* remains. One maxilla preserves the anterior palate, a region whose morphology clearly distinguishes the living African and the East Asian pongids according to S. Ward and B. Brown. The African condition is plesiomorphic because it is shown in the dryopithecine remains of both Africa and Europe. The Nachola maxilla, like the African apes and humans, has its anterior palate separated from the rest of the palate roof by a tube-like passageway between the nasal chamber and the top of the mouth called the **incisive canal**. In the Asian pongids the canal is much more horizontal in its orientation because of the upward rotation of the front of the palate (the alveolar portion of the face under the nose) called **airorhynchy**.

The Nachola sample resembles the other Miocene pongids in being sexually dimorphic. Two otherwise very similar maxillae have very different sized canines. These are the oldest of the *Kenyapithecus* remains, old enough to be ancestral to the most ancient of the thick-enameled apes outside of Africa - from (what was then) a subtropical, seasonal forest at Pasalar, Turkey, 15-14 myr.

Maboko Formation: Maboko Island, Majiwa, and Kaloma (from older than 14.7 to 13.8 myr)

In Western Kenya, on Maboko island at the north end of Lake Victoria and at two adjacent sites on the Kenyan shore less than 2 km to the north, there are a number of small dryopithecine fossils that appear to represent one or two *Kenyapithecus* species ranging from the same size to somewhat smaller than *Kenyapithecus wickeri*(see below). These specimens differ somewhat from the Nachola remains, especially in details of the occlusal morphology of the molar teeth. P. Andrews suggests that the somewhat contradictory environmental evidence indicates a dry, deciduous forest with marked seasonality.

The first Maboko *Kenyapithecus* found was the so-called "*Sivapithecus africanus*" maxilla. M 16649 is a facial fragment of uncertain provenience. It was once thought to come from Rusinga but its preservation (if not its morphology) is quite unlike the other Rusinga fossils. Maboko Island is the most likely source for this specimen. The specimen is a small piece of upper jaw with P^3-M^2. The premolars are very enlarged, buccolingually like those of *Afropithecus* although much more steep-sided, and also **mesiodistally** (front to back) expanded unlike the earlier pongid. They appear to also have thick enamel caps. The specimen is unlike many of the other Miocene pongids in that the base of the cheek, where it meets the outer wall of the palate, is lower and more forward than is usual - a configuration found later in the Pliocene hominids.

Other isolated teeth from the Maboko formation are of the same approximate size. These include a juvenile mandible and over 100 isolated teeth. The mandible, MB 20573, preserved some deciduous molars, a permanent molar, and a newly erupted very procumberant incisor. This tooth is *Proconsul*-like in relative crown diameters and shows none of the crown expansion characteristic of the living apes. Also like *Proconsul* and unlike apes the crown is vertically tall. The symphysis is markedly sloping, with its thick base extending far to the rear. This anatomy is associated with the incisor orientation. Because of this symphseal anatomy and incisor orientation McCrossin and Benefit suggest that the anterior teeth were important in feeding and may have been used to open large thick rinded fruits and nuts (the potential importance of the later is also suggested by the large molar size and thick enamel, according to R. Kay). The teeth emerge in the eruption-order of living apes, and if their eruption times are the same MB 20573 was 6-7 years of age.

A smaller species or subspecies might be represented by specimens such as the Kaloma mandible MJ 5. It is the size of the *Proconsul* from Rusinga, but the body of the jaw is much thicker and the molars are larger with thick enamel both on the cusp tips and the basins between them. There is a small lower transverse torus across the inside of the sloping symphysis and it is likely the incisal preparation of foods was not as important in this taxon..

There are a number of large but fragmentary postcranial elements. The postcrania are not found directly with the dentognathic remains. Their attribution is unclear because there are proconsul jaws and teeth found on the island as well and the anatomy of the postcranial remains resemble proconsul postcrania (but then, as C. Ward likes to point out, the postcranial of virtually all African Miocene hominoids resemble the proconsuls). The Maboko postcrania are thought to be associated with *Kenyapithecus* and not a proconsul species on the argument that all of the large dentognathic specimens can be attributed to *Kenyapithecus,* so the large postcranial remains should be as well. Body size suggested by the more complete elements is 23-30 kg, according to B. Benefit. What is certain is that these Maboko postcranials, including a large portion of a humerus, share none of the unique below-branch adaptations of living apes. Particular details of the humerus are most like baboons, and even lack ape specializations for climbing (although, of course, baboons can climb with great speed and agility without these specializations and it is unclear to what extent the ape features are a consequence of their larger body size). Forelimb and hindlimb fragments indicate forelimb dominance, with the humerus as long as or longer than the **femur**. They suggest a mixed arboreal and terrestrial adaptation.

The resemblances of the dentognathic remains from this site to the original sample named *Kenyapithecus wickeri* (from Fort Ternan, see below) are so great that the same species may be represented within the Maboko sample. It is almost certainly present at the upper layers of the site, which are of Fort Ternan age. B. Brown and S. Ward have argued that Maboko is part of an early sample uniquely ancestral to the African hominoid clade, and by extension this would have to be true for Fort Ternan as well. However, my assessment is that the Maboko remains are early and plesiomorphic enough to also be ancestral to the Asian apes.

Fort Ternan (14 myr): The First of the Anthropithecines?

The Fort Ternan site is the base of what was a forested volcano toward the end of the Middle Miocene. The activity of the volcano provided volcanic deposits that could be radiometrically dated. The volcano was one of those formed during the East African rifting process, as the motion of the earth's tectonic plates separated parts of the African continent, opening a gap or valley that extends from the

Levant to south-central Africa (the volcanic activity surrounding this rift valley has been most fortunate in preserving and dating human and ape fossils from the Miocene and more recently). Almost completely surrounding this volcano was a drainage river; the fossil deposits are in what were then shallow gullies just on the other side of the river, where carbon isotope studies show that the soils formed in and near these gullies were formed under woodland conditions (in the tropics, trees and most shrubs differentially accumulate the carbon 13 isotope {C_3 plants}, while grasses have a much smaller proportion {C_4 plants}). In the deposits are fauna from denser woodlands, including snails, rodents, *Proconsul nyanzae*, and a small related hominoid. Beyond this area the country became open woodlands, brush, and grasslands, and Fort Ternan has elements of one of the earliest distinct savanna-type faunas (from the Miocene) in East Africa. For instance the grassland and open woodland fauna found there, such as giraffe, antelope and ostrich-like forms, marks one of their earliest appearances in East Africa (none of this faunal assemblage, which probably co-evolved with grasses, is found in East Africa before 15 myr). The reconstruction of the prehistoric ecology and the forms present in the deposits are important because they bear on the question of whether the pongid discovered there was open country adapted, brushland adapted, or woodland fringe adapted. Analysis of the animal remains show that most (70%) of the individuals that could be identified by species were adapted to wet savanna conditions, or open grasslands with bushes, and the preservation of their remains suggests they were not transported before they were buried. The summary of such disparate evidence is uncertain. It is not possible to determine which of the nearby ecosystems that *Kenyapithecus wickeri* lived in, although the preservation of an associated mandible and maxilla for the best-preserved specimen suggests that it also was not transported far. The potential role of East African open or wooded grasslands in Middle Miocene pongid evolution is provocative, but remains unclear.

Kenyapithecus wickeri is the name that was given by L.S.B. Leakey to the pongid he found at Fort Ternan. The associated upper (FT 46) and lower (FT 45) jaws (an association first recognized by P. Andrews, long after the two pieces of the specimens were discovered) give just enough information to reconstruct the midline and the general shape of the lower face, and a few isolated additional teeth help complete this reconstruction (figure 3.9). However, nothing remains of this primate above the nose or below the jaw.

The reconstructed specimen provides evidence of the incisors, canines, and posterior teeth that gives insight into its canine functions and chewing adaptations. The teeth form a straight line backward from the canine, and the two toothrows diverge from each other posteriorly. At the front, the canines are not far apart; there is little room left for the incisors, which, by inference, were probably quite small as in *Kenyapithecus africanus*. The set of the incisor roots, slope of the mandibular symphysis, and development of its lower torus suggest that the incisors were procumberant, also as in the Maboko juvenile. This pattern is quite unlike the expanded anterior teeth of living apes. The toothrow shape appears to be the ancestral condition in hominoids.

The Fort Ternan *Kenyapithecus* differs from similar-sized proconsuls in the size of its canine, which is relatively small compared to the molars. The small size along with details of canine form suggest that this specimen was a female. Relative canine size best matches the proportion found in female gorillas. It is probable that males had larger and more projecting canines. Canine function, like all of the Miocene pongids, produced a cutting surface between the back of the upper tooth and the front of the lower anterior premolar, and both of these surfaces are sharp. This premolar is sectorial, with the single dominant cusp common in ape and proconsul teeth, but also with a small cusplet on the lingual (tongue) side, along the transverse shear ridge; later, when bicuspid (two cusped) lower P_3's evolved in the hominids, the second cusp might have its origin in this seemingly minor detail. In all, the Fort Ternan primate shows no significant modification from the Miocene pongid condition in which the back of the projecting upper canine cuts against the front of the most anterior lower premolar (see Chapter 4).

Compared to the size of the palate, the postcanine teeth are expanded in size, and their enamel is quite thick. The body of the mandible is not tall, but it is thickened and appears capable of withstanding powerful masticatory forces. At the front of the mandible, the symphysis is long and sloping as in *Afropithecus*, but differs from this earlier species in its pronounced lower buttress across the back surface of the symphysis that extends far to the rear along the mandible's base. This internal surface anatomy of the symphysis is similar to the Kaloma mandible, but the shelf is more pronounced as in the Maboko juvenile. This morphology is common in the African apes, where it is called a **simian shelf** (figure 3.10). This internal buttress also gives evidence of powerful chewing. When there is food between the molars, the *Kenyapithecus* mandible tends to be twisted, as one twists a wishbone by pushing one end up and the other down. In the mandible, twisting is caused by a combination of the force of the food and the forces of the muscles. In addition, other muscular forces pull the sides of the mandible together. Similar to the wishbone, the mandible is weakest at its front; natural selection leads to the appearance of extra bone to strengthen this area when powerful chewing is an important adaptation. With the thick mandibular body and thick molar enamel, the morphological combination of the mandibular features suggests that powerful forces between their molars were regularly produced when chewing.

Powerful chewing is also suggested by the morphology of the cheeks. The **zygomatic process** of the maxilla (the base of the cheek) swings widely to the sides of the face. Since the temporalis muscle passes to the inside of this process, occupying the temporal fossa between the zygomatic and the side of the cranial vault, the wide outward swing suggests that a large space was enclosed. This, in turn, indicates that the temporalis muscle was large. An additional effect of this cheek form produces a more horizontal orientation for the masseter muscle (Figure 4. jaw muscles), since the masseter must have a more horizontal angle in order to reach from the base of the jaw to the widely positioned zygomatics. The combination of a shallow lower jaw and widely separated **zygomatic arches** (the sides of the cheeks that enclose the temporal fossae) create more transverse force during the jaw motions of chewing. This provides for a more rotary chewing motion that is effective when forceful mastication is required by the diet. This suggestion is supported by a study of the direction of the scratches on the FT 46 molars. These were made by food particles as they passed across the teeth, and are almost always in the side-to-side direction. Jaw motions in this direction would be impossible if there were large interlocking canines. This adaptation is reflected, to a lesser extent, in the earlier African pongids but it is most impressively developed in this Fort Ternan female.

There are some other isolated hominoid teeth from the site. If the larger isolated canines are in the same species as FT 45/46, as I believe, this *Kenyapithecus* was strongly sexually dimorphic. Marked dimorphism is the normal plesiomorphic condition for the pongids. However, confusing the issue are a number of additional isolated teeth than were attributed to *Proconsul nyanzae* on morphological criteria, and this is not the most recent appearance for proconsul remains in East Africa. Moreover, there is an isolated lower portion of a humerus (FT 2751) of *Proconsul nyanzae* size, with morphological details that are very similar to this species. The bone has been attributed to *Proconsul,* but the fact that virtually all of the Miocene postcranials closely resemble this genus confuses the issue. No completely overlapping part of a humerus is known from Maboko (none have preserved the entire lower end of the bone), but according to McCrossin the comparable anatomy of Maboko *"Kenyapithecus africanus"* specimens is quite similar.

The Fort Ternan dryopithecine is too incomplete for any certain conclusions about its phyletic affinities. It resembles subsequent ape and human ancestors in many features and preserves no morphology that would exclude it from the ancestry of any living pongid (including both orangutans and humans). In fact, it is a very credible last common ancestor for both the Anthropithecinae and the Ponginae. However, it may be too late to fill this phylogenetic role (it is about the same age as Pasalar, widely regarded as the earliest of the Asian radiation), and in fact could be an early anthropithecine - no anatomical detail excludes this either. No feature unique to the Miocene ponginae of Asia can be found in this sample and the resemblances to the anthropithecines may all be plesiomorphic. The fact is that the Fort Ternan material will not clearly resolve the question of when the orangutan clade originated.

In my opinion the dental, mandibular, and postcranial similarities with the Maboko specimens suggest two uncertain hypotheses.

- The *Kenyapithecus* species at these sites may be the same
- *Kenyapithecus wickeri* may be the last common ancestor of the African and Asian apes

Only time can tell whether these become widely accepted interpretations.

European Dryopithecines

Of the many dryopithecine sites from the Miocene of Europe, two have yielded dryopithecine specimens that are particularly important clues for resolving several questions about anthropithecine evolution. These are Rudabánya in Hungary and Ravin de la Pluie in Greek Macedonia (specimens from both are discussed in the first edition of this book). The earlier of these, Rudabánya, includes jaws and teeth that are similar to those of "*Kenyapithecus africanus*", and two large craniofacial pieces. Unlike the jaws and teeth, and to some extent the postcrania, the craniofacial pieces do not closely resemble any of the earlier African hominoid crania. While there are some similarities with orangutans (and their Sivapithecini ancestors from the Miocene), the craniofacial pieces uniquely resemble the anthropithecines in a number of other features according to D. Begun. This could mean that these features evolved before the divergence of the orangutan clade, or suggest that the Rudabánya species branched off the African line after the orangutan divergence. Most interestingly, the anthropithecine-like features are particularly similar to living gorillas and unlike the corresponding characteristics shared by Pliocene humans (australopithecines) and chimpanzees.

An even more gorilla-like face was discovered at Ravin, the slightly more recent find spot of a large number of dental and mandibular specimens. The Ravin face has a gorilla-like supraorbital torus, quite different from the Rudabánya face, continuously developed and emerging in a shelf-like manner from the base of the (relatively expanded) frontal bone. The orbital shape, lateral margins of the forehead, details of the lower face and anterior teeth, and the projection of the nasal bones also resemble gorillas uniquely of the anthropithecines. Unlike gorillas, however, the molar enamel is hyper thick, matching the robust australopithecines of the Pliocene and early Pleistocene.

The problem is how to interpret these resemblances. It could be that one or both of the European species are part of the gorilla clade, certainly a possibility given their date. However, as D. Begun argues it is also possible that characteristics are shared with gorillas because gorillas are the most plesiomorphic of the anthropithecines. The gorilla-like features of certain Miocene African specimens discussed above would support this later interpretation. The fact that phylogenetic relations are not built out of plesiomorphic resemblances would exclude these European apes from the gorilla clade (a clade must be defined by derived features), and at the same time would buttress the importance of the characteristics uniquely shared between chimpanzees and australopithecines as supporting a close relation between them.

Late Miocene Anthropithecines

Fossil remains

After Fort Ternan, Middle Miocene pongid remains are scarce until the hominids appear at the end of the period. Considering the scrappy nature of the primate remains at Fort Ternan, one interpretation of the contrasts between this period and the abundant primate remains from the earlier part of the Miocene is that the pongids were unable to adapt to the rapidly spreading grasslands in East Africa (after ca 15 myr). After the divergence of the Ponginae, these African pongids comprise the anthropithecine clade (subfamily Anthropithecnae). The sequence of divergences within this clade seems clear, but the fossil remains are sparse and fragmentary, and provide very ambiguous information about the dates and details of the divergences.

Ngorora (13-10 myr)

Five isolated teeth come from sites in the Ngorora formation, just west of Lake Baringo, Kenya. These are:

BN 1378: a virtually unworn upper molar
BN 1469: I^1
BN 10489: P_4
BN 10556: poorly preserved canine
BN 23144: lower canine

The premolar may be *Proconsul* according to A. Hill and S. Ward, and if so it is the latest appearing of this diminishing primate group in the African fossil record. Hill attributes the incisor to *Proconsul* as well, but believes that BN 23144 from the same site is probably not of that genus. The molar is thick enameled but otherwise much like a chimpanzee M^2. It can probably be attributed to *Kenyapithecus wickeri*. The paleoecology at this site suggests that forested conditions prevailed.

Samburu Hills (or Baragoi) Maxilla (10-6 myr)

A large maxilla showing some similarities to the much earlier maxilla from Moroto was discovered in the Namurungule formation of the Samburu Hills, on the east side of the Rift Valley in Kenya. According to H. Ishida and colleagues, SH 8531 preserves the full postcanine toothrow, and the canine and partial incisor sockets. There are a number of gorilla-like features, including the inflated bone ad the base of the cheek, the form of the nasal opening, and the arched roof of the palate. The canine root is small and elliptical in cross section with its long axis aligned in an anterior posterior position, rather than rotated as would be expected in a hominid canine. Contrasting with the Moroto dentition the molars are sub-equal in size (increasing markedly towards the rear) and have even thicker enamel and more pronounced lingual cingula, although with the gorilla-like condition of poorly defined occlusal ridges and deep wrinkles between the cusps. The postcanine teeth have been specifically likened to gorilla in their general elongated shape. Elongated maxillary premolars characterize all living anthropithecines, but these are particularly gorilla-like as is the detailed anatomy of the P^3. The postcanine teeth are the size of a male gorilla (but with much thicker enamel) but the P^3 and canine root suggest the specimen is female.

Lukeino (between 6.3 and 5.6 myr)

An unerupted lower first molar has been found at Lukeino, in the Tugen Hills west of Lake Baringo, Kenya. LU 335 is intermediate in size between the mean values for the *Kenyapithecus* and the larger Pliocene hominid first molars, but within the hominid range. In its size and proportions Lukeino could be an early hominid, and this possibility is not precluded by its date - although at the moment there are no other certain hominid remains dated older than 5.8 myr. An early, detailed, analysis of its crown components suggested that it is more similar to chimpanzees than to Pliocene hominids. Moreover, Lukeino lacks the diagnostic early hominid "waisting" produced by the buccal side indentation at the middle of the tooth. However, the crown component analysis was done before some of the earlier Pliocene hominids were found. S. Ward and co-workers argue that the cusp and crown proportions of Lukeino and teeth from the 5 myr Tabarin hominid mandible (see Chapter 6) are very comparable. It is extraordinarily similar to one of the 4 myr Allia Bay first molars (20422), and a three-dimensional crown components analysis by P. Ungar and colleagues shows significant differences from chimpanzees and a unique resemblance to early hominids in the constriction of the cusp tips relative to the bulging base of the tooth. Thus, its taxonomy remains unclear. It certainly could represent a last common ancestor for the chimpanzee and hominid clades (if so, Ungar and colleagues argue, this common ancestor is not at all like chimpanzees), but it is also possible that Lukeino is the earliest hominid known at the moment and that the ancestral condition for molar morphology is unknown.

Lothagam and Tabarin (between 5.8 and 5.0 myr)

These two jaw fragments, discussed more thoroughly in Chapter 6, are generally regarded to be hominids because of their detailed dentognathic resemblances to *Australopithecus afarensis*. If so they are the earliest and should provide a minimum human-chimpanzee divergence date. One can question whether the earliest hominids and their immediate pre-divergence thick-enameled ancestors would necessarily be different in any aspects of the posterior tooth row and supporting jaw, all that is preserved of these specimens. While their variation could be incorporated within the later Miocene anthropithecine pattern, if these are hominids, they suggest an enhancement of the powerful masticatory complex.

A Mosaic of Features

The African pongids of the Middle and Late Miocene share a number of synapomorphies. Many of these are plesiomorphic for the subsequent hominids, and indeed in many respects the hominids retain these and are more plesiomorphic than their anthropithecine cousins - a source of continued nagging taxonomic problems. The African pongids had two adaptive radiations. In the Middle Miocene the larger and smaller dryopithecine forms, for instance as represented respectively at Moroto and Maboko, have different combinations of features found in surviving African apes and humans. Neither has features that make it a more probable ancestor for any particular living species and it is unlikely that African apes and humans have unique ancestries in the Middle Miocene. L.O. Greenfield persuasively argued this case in his Late Divergence Hypothesis, where he maintained that the human-chimpanzee divergence was too late for *Ramapithecus* to have been a hominid. The time of the divergence of the orangutan clade cannot be recognized unambiguously, but there are hints. The Asian orangutan ancestors, the Sivapithecini branch of the Ponginae, is not known to be older than 12.5 myr according to Andrews. Begun, on different evidence, argues that the clade was district by the time of Rudabánya, which gives the same minimum divergence estimate. The 14 myr Fort Ternan primate could be a last common ancestor for all of the living apes, supporting the more recent divergence estimate for the Asian ape. However, Fort Ternan is near the beginning of the spread of East African mosaic environments, poor habitats for living apes, and the scanty remains from this site are too incomplete to resolve this issue. At the moment no Middle Miocene specimens provide a convincing maximum estimate for the Asian ape divergence time.

Within the African remains, continual resemblances are found with gorillas. The best explanation for these similarities, and for the gorilla-like morphology of some European dryopithecines, is that gorilla morphology is plesiomorphic for the living anthropithecines; "archaic", in this clade, seems to mean gorilla-like. This would support the large body of genetic evidence also indicating that *Gorilla* diverged first of the living anthropithecine genera.

The second adaptive radiation, within the Late Miocene anthropithecines, is a critically important topic for us since it directly addresses our origins. It is represented only by the gorilloid Baragoi maxilla and the Lukeino molar. These specimens, if correctly dated and interpreted, could suggest an earlier gorilla divergence and a last common chimpanzee-hominid ancestor as late as the very end of the Miocene. On the other hand, there are just a few fossil specimens and the Baragoi maxilla is only dated to a broad range. Apart from the anthropithecine fossils there are few independent ways of examining the branching sequence. The three that have been attempted agree in showing a chimpanzee-hominid sister grouping.

- Ontogenetic data, discussed above, links chimpanzees and humans most closely, as they share the greatest delay in the time of first births, large head-size at birth, and a great amount of brain expansion to adult size after it.
- Synapomorphies link the earliest hominid crania with chimpanzees, as discussed in Chapter 6 (but this is not true for the dentitions or postcrania skeletons).
- The largest mtDNA data set analyzed to date, published by S. Horai and his colleagues, indicates clearly that humans and chimpanzees diverged last, and by a considerable extent.

The Horai data are particularly interesting, as they can be interpreted to largely reconcile differences between mtDNA and fossil divergence estimates. His anthropithecine divergences (7.7 myr for gorilla, 4.7 myr for chimpanzee) depend on a 13 myr estimate for the orangutan divergence. An earlier appraisal of the orangutan divergence time, for instance 15 myr if the Fort Ternan *Kenyapithecus* is an anthropithecine, would give divergence estimates of about 9 myr for gorillas and 5.5 myr for chimpanzees. Estimates between 7.7 and 9 myr for gorilla divergence, and 4.7-5.5 myr for chimpanzee divergence, come close to fitting the fossil record, but remain problematic as the earlier dates seem more likely (the oldest known hominid is 5.6-5.8 myr) but orangutan clade divergence is probably after Fort Ternan, suggesting the younger divergence ages. Perhaps the primate mtDNA evolutionary rate is slow, a suggestion several geneticists have advanced, but the fact is that uncertainties in the accuracy of the mtDNA "clock" remain (although there is much more accuracy in interspecies than intraspecies divergence determinations).

Most of the issues surrounding hominid origins cannot yet be fully resolved from these data. In particular, the outstanding question of locomotor evolution remains unanswered so that the importance of the shared knuckle-walking adaptation of chimpanzees and gorillas is unknown (knuckle-walking has great phylogenetic significance if earlier afropithecines lack it, perhaps importance enough to overturn the hypothesis of the chimpanzee/human sister group, but becomes another shared plesiomorphy if the later Miocene afropithecines are found to be knuckle-walkers). What seems clearest is the Miocene anthropithecine ancestry of hominids, the late Miocene appearance of hominids, and the nature of hominid plesiomorphies. For these reasons hominid origins remain a very controversial topic in evolutionary studies. Too little is known of the origin of the African apes for there to be controversy, but clearly in the case of chimpanzees these origin issues focus on the same event since hominid origins are chimpanzee origins as well. Before becoming immersed in the controversy, it is first necessary to identify those characteristics that are unique to hominids, in the hope that these will help in identifying the earliest hominids and provide insight into why they diverged and evolved in a different direction.

Summary

The living primates are an order of (largely) arboreal mammals, characterized by their nails, grasping hands (and often feet), emphasis on vision (and the development of color and depth perception that improve the quality of visual information), and a large brain size relative to body size. Characteristics of the habitats inhabited by primate species, their ranges and adaptations, result from the common expression of three distinct evolutionary trends within the order: an arboreal adaptation; dietary plasticity; and expanded parental investment,. The results of these trends have generally limited the evolutionary potential of primate taxa. In terms of numbers and diversity, most of them have not been extraordinarily successful. A few, however, have met with marked success. These have almost always been anthropoid primates, and some amount of terrestrial adaptation characterizes their habitat usage.

Primates, as an order, may have been more successful in the past. Earlier forms in the Eocene were widespread and are common in fossil assemblages. Prosimians are found in the fossil records of North America, Eurasia, and Africa. Anthropoid primates originated at about the same time as prosimians, during the earlier Eocene, but while earliest New World primates are 25 myr old no Old World forms are known from outside of Africa until the Middle Miocene. Primates proliferated during the Paleogene and early Neogene. For instance, in the restricted Eocene/Oligocene Fayum swamp forest deposits there are 10 primate genera, a much higher number than found n even more varied and mosaic environments today. Ape-like primates were more successful earlier in primate evolution. The cercopithecoid radiation replaced most of them in the later Miocene, leaving only a few surviving species of which humans are the uniquely successful ones.

The Middle Miocene hominoids that are ancestral to living humans and apes, are known earliest from East Africa, with subsequent species appearing in Europe and Asia These Miocene apes are not like the living pongids in anatomy, diet, or habitat. Most of the species eventually became extinct, perhaps during the major faunal changes in the late Miocene. In any event, Miocene pongid diversity is very much greater than modern pongid diversity. The African forms were semiterrestrial quadrupeds with an arboreal adaptation limited to above branch activities, well adapted to the emerging East African environmental mosaics. Their procumberant incisors, and large jaws with thick enameled molar teeth, adapted them to a diet including fibrous or hard shelled fruits and nuts that required fairly powerful chewing forces. Their locomotion included quadrumanous climbing and the trunk was often held in an upright position, possibly a common feeding posture. These species had a high degree of sexual dimorphism. Later in the Miocene more under-branch adaptations appeared. One of the very Late Miocene anthropithecines is the last common ancestor of hominids and chimpanzees.

ANATOMY OF A CONTROVERSY
The Contradictions of Human Classification - Just What Does an Ape by Any Other Name Smell Like?

The taxonomy of humans and apes is, to say the least, in considerable flux. So dramatic are the changes being suggested that some of the most recent surveys of primate evolution and relationships (for instance surveys by R. Martin and G. Conroy) have proposed that the taxonomy should no longer reflect the current hypotheses of phylogeny because these keep on changing, because the resulting taxonomies no longer reflect common word use, and because as a consequence the newer taxonomies are creating confusion in a system meant to promote clarification.

Since the beginning of the last century, even before the first publications about evolution, taxonomists recognized a clear division between apes and humans at the family level, both divisions of the superfamily Hominoidea The apes were classified in the family **Pithecidae**, named by J. Gray in 1821 (and virtually simultaneously named the **Simiidae** by J. Flemming in 1822) and renamed as the **Pongidae** by D. Elliot in 1913. Humans were put in the family **Hominidae** by J. Gray in 1825. From Pongidae and Hominidae come the terms **pongid** and **hominid** that have been in common use since. The advantage of these terms is that pongid substitutes for **ape**, a word with much broader application (it includes gibbons, siamangs, and is incorrectly used for some monkeys such as the Celebes black ape). Hominid substitutes for **human**, a word that carries a great load of behavioral baggage that was never meant to apply to the human ancestors of the late Miocene and Pliocene. Everybody seems comfortable with the idea that Lucy is a hominid while few would describe her as human.

This division was established on phenetic grounds (a phenetic taxonomy is one based on overall similarity rather than genealogy). It clearly mirrors the precept that the living great apes (chimpanzee, gorilla, orangutan) appear to be more similar to each other, morphologically and behaviorally, than any of them are to humans. Given the atmosphere of evolution-denial, perhaps not even as common then as it is now, this taxonomy was reasonably acceptable because it distinguished humanity at a major taxonomic level and thereby emphasized the separation of humans from the zoological world. Three developments now question this basic division:

1. General acceptance of the phylogenetic approach to classification, which is genealogical and not phenetic

2. The understanding that orangutans, and not humans, are the first of the large bodies hominoids to diverge

3. And most controversial of all, the resolution of the chimpanzee/gorilla/human trichotomy, which seems to be that chimpanzees and humans, *not* chimpanzees and gorillas, are the more closely related species.

If taxonomy is to continue to reflect phylogeny, the division of Hominoidea into hominids and pongids is no longer valid. This is because of the insistence that taxonomic groups be monophyletic. No monophyletic group can include the three great ape species without including humans as well, even if the resolution of the African hominoid trichotomy is incorrect and gorillas and chimpanzees are the true sister groups.

In 1978 J. Schwartz, with I. Tattersall and N. Eldredge, reviewed primate classification and proposed a division into Asian and African hominoids, reflecting the first and second points above. Both were placed in the Hominidae and the division was below the subfamily level. The same division was proposed at the family level by M. Goodman, and later M. Weiss and A. Mann who thereby were able to retain Pongidae and Hominidae, albeit with quite different meanings - pongid would refer only to orangutans, while humans would be joined by chimpanzees and gorillas as hominids. Many authors were uncomfortable when using the traditional word "hominid" to also refer to the African apes. This problem was solved at the subfamily level in the Weiss and Mann scheme with a division between Paninae (chimpanzees and gorillas) and Homininae, which gave us the hominines to replace the hominids. The same scheme, with divisions of the Hominidae at a lower taxonomic level, was proposed by L. Martin. To keep "hominids" meaning only humans, R. Ciochon suggests 3 families: Panidae, Pongidae,

Hominidae. G. Conroy points out that "this proposal would retain the classical usage of the term *hominid* while not distorting the true cladistic relationships of the great apes"... but ... "this newer terminology creates havoc with such familiar terms as *pongid, hominid,* and *ape* ..." Others such as R. Foley recognize the African clade but seek to avoid the terminological controversy by refusing to give it any name at all. Finally, no scheme yet proposed acknowledges the chimpanzee/human sister grouping. To the contrary, all the new taxonomies assume that chimpanzees and gorillas are the sister groups, and therefore are vulnerable to the increasing acceptance of the hypothesis of the chimpanzee/human grouping. This vulnerability could require more taxonomic schemes.

Taxonomy is more than an accurate reflection of the organization we perceive in the biological world. It must also serve as a way of communicating clearly. As such, there is much to be said for the view that it should be conservative, not changing with every new hypothesis. In his extraordinary compilation on primate systematics, R. Martin argues for stable classifications and against linking classifications with changing phylogenetic hypotheses. He is quite willing to retain the phenetic classification of Hominoidea that predominated in the last century and most of this one. Martin argues that if African apes were to be classified as hominids we would have to "cope with such statements as 'bipedal locomotion is a fundamental feature of hominids, excluding chimpanzees and gorillas' ".

At the moment, then, we have two extreme reactions to the new developments: (1) accepting one of many of the new schemes of hominoid taxonomy that reflects the new understandings of phylogenetics and hominoid relationships but "creates havoc" with widely understood categories such as hominid, pongid, and ape; or, (2) retaining the older, widely understood phenetic classification, which however would decouple hominoid taxonomy from our understanding of hominoid evolutionary relationships. Can a single taxonomic scheme provide accuracy and stability? Is there a taxonomy that will retain the meaning of hominid, allow pongid to refer to the three great apes, and make no assumptions about the final resolution of the African hominoid trichotomy? I have a modest proposal.

Within the superfamily **Hominoidea** I recognize two families for the living primates: **Hylobatidae** for the lesser apes (gibbon and saimang), and the family including all of the great apes and humans that I would call **Pongidae**. Other schemes have named this clade Hominidae, but neither family name has the same meaning as in the older phenetic classifications. There is no compelling historical reason to favor one over the other. Pithecidae and Simiidae both have priority over Hominidae (their first use is older). Moreover, as early as 1866, Darwin's apostle E. Haeckel proposed a genealogical scheme in which humans were classified "in a higher ape group". Pongidae, the nomenclatural descendant of Pithecidae and Simiidae, makes more sense as the name for this group. Using Pongidae would retain the traditional uses of the widely used terms pongid and hominid. **Pongid** continues as a referent to all the great apes. Pongidae, however, would also include humans and their ancestors, by this definition, but there is no reason why we cannot continue to use the (now) non-taxonomic term **hominid** to refer to only those taxa on or branching from the unique clade leading to living humans; in other words, its current and historical meaning. Hominid becomes, in this taxonomy, a non-taxonomic term or N_2 term (see Chapter 2 p. XX) because there is no family Hominidae for it to refer to. There is an equivalent non-taxonomic term to reference the other pongids that are not hominids - **ape**, which also would retain its current and historical meaning.

Four subfamilies describe the most fundamental (deepest) division of the Pongidae: **Afropithecinae** (afropithecines) is the earliest and most primitive of the groups; **Dryopithecinae** (dryopithecines) include the last common ancestors of the living hominoid primates and were the first to establish a distribution across the Old World; the African ape and human clade, **Anthropithecinae** (anthropithecines), and the Eurasian clade **Ponginae**. In phyletic terms, Afropithecinae is ancestral to Dryopithecinae, and Dryopithecinae is ancestral to Ponginae and Anthropithecinae. The Afropithecinae genera are newly discovered and the naming of the subfamily is straightforward. Dryopithecinae is the most appropriate name for their archaic descendants for several historic reasons, including the early use of the subfamily name, but most importantly because of the traditional application reflected in the widely accepted use of Dryopithecinae in the extremely influential 1965 Simons and Pilbeam taxonomic revision. Genera in it include some or all of the African *Kenyapithecus* remains as well as European (and possibly Asian) groups such as *Rudapithecus*. As far as Quaternary (i.e., Pleistocene and later) species are concerned, the Eurasian Ponginae are represented by two genera, *Pongo* and *Gigantopithecus,* while there are four genera in the African Anthropithecinae: *Gorilla, Pan, Australopithecus,* and *Homo.* Anthropithecinae is an appropriate name for the African clade because tradition will not allow *Homo* to be used to derive the name for a subfamily including humans and the African apes [see discussions in Martin (1990) and Fleagle (1988)]. The final division within the living anthropithecines is at the tribe level, Gorillinini and Hominini. Should the hypothesis of a chimpanzee/human sister group hold, as I expect, the Hominini would include these two genera. If the chimpanzee/gorilla hypothesis gains acceptance instead, *Pan* can switch clades without the names changing. This stability fits Martin's precept that a taxonomy should not have to change with any and every change in phylogenetic hypothesis.

Thus, in the sense of being insulated from the most likely changes in phylogenetic hypotheses, this taxonomy is stable. It is also conservative, retaining most or all of the traditional colloquial meanings of **pongid, hominid,** and **ape**. Yet it fits our current understanding of the phylogeny of the living species of Hominoidea. Finally, although it is not a valid ground for rejecting or accepting it, in today's atmosphere of evolution-denial this taxonomy serves one additional purpose. It makes explicit what we evolutionists have long known - that humans are an African ape. We are a very special species of ape, but what makes us special is the evolutionary pathway we have traveled since our origins. Our origins did not make us what we are, and it is not our genealogy that makes us unique. Our beginnings started us on a path that has led to an extraordinary degree of success. It is now time for us to focus on the steps taken along the way.

TABLE 3.7
Homo in the Hominoids
Classification of the *Quaternary* Genera
in the Superfamily Hominoidea[*]

    Family Hylobatidae
        Hylobates(2)
    Family Pongidae
        Subfamily Ponginae
            Tribe Sivapithecini
                Gigantopithecus(1)
            Tribe Pongini
                Pongo(3+)
        Subfamily Anthropithecinae
            Tribe Gorillinini
                Gorilla(1)
            Tribe Hominini
                Pan(1 or 2)
                Homo(2 or 3)
                Australopithecus(3 or 4)

---

[*] In parentheses following each genus is the number of Quaternary species, this being the time span of *Homo*'s existence

REFERENCES AND FURTHER READINGS

ALEXANDER, R.D. 1974 The Evolution of Social Behavior. *Annual Review of Ecology and Systematics* 5:325-383.

ANDREWS, P, 1992a Evolution and environment in the Hominoidea. *Nature* 360:641-646.

___. 1992b Reconstructing past environments. In S. Jones, R. Martin, and D. Pilbeam (eds): *The Cambridge Encyclopaedia of Human Evolution.* Cambridge University Press, New York.

ANDREWS, P., and L. MARTIN 1991 Hominoid dietary evolution. *Philosophical Transactions of the Royal Society of London*, Series B, 334:199-209.

ANDREWS, P., and A. C. WALKER 1976 The primate and other fauna from Fort Ternan, Kenya. In G. L. Isaac and E. R. McCown (eds): *Human Origins: Louis Leakey and the East African Evidence.* Benjamin, Menlo Park.

ANKEL-SIMONS, F. 1983 *A Survey of Living Primates and their Anatomy.* MacMillan, New York.

ARMSTRONG, E., and D. FALK (eds) 1982 *Primate Brain Evolution.* Plenum, New York.

BAILEY, W.J. 1993 Hominoid tricotomy: a molecular view. *Evolutionary Anthropology* 2(3):100-108.

BEGUN, D.R. 1992 Miocene fossil hominids and the chimp-human clade. *Science* 257:1929-1933.

BENEFIT, B.B., and M.L. McCROSSIN 1991 Ancestral facial morphology of Old World higher primates. *Proceedings of the National Academy of Sciences USA* 88:5267-5271.

___. 1993 Facial anatomy of *Victoriapithecus* and its relevance to the ancestral cranial morphology of Old World monkeys and apes. *American Journal of Physical Anthropology* 92(3):329-370.

BOESCH, C., and H. BOESCH 1990 Tool use and making in wild chimpanzees. *Folia Primatologica* 54:86-99.

BROWN, B., and S.C. WARD 1988 Facial and basicranial relationships in *Sivapithecus* and *Pongo.* In J.H. Schwartz (ed.): *Biology of the Orang-Utan.* Oxford University Press, Oxford.

CAMPBELL, K.L., and J.W. WOOD 1988 Fertility in traditional societies. In P. Diggory, M. Potts, and S. Teper (eds): *Natural Human Fertility.* MacMillan, London. pp. 39-69.

CARTMILL, M. 1992 New views on primate origins. *Evolutionary Anthropology* 1(3):105-111.

CHENEY, D.L., and R.M. SEYFARTH 1990 *How Monkeys see the World.* University of Chicago, Chicago.

CIOCHON, R.L. 1983 Hominoid cladistics and the ancestry of modern apes and humans. In R.L. Ciochon and R.S. Corruccini (eds): *New Interpretations of Ape and Human Ancestry*, eds. Plenum, New York. pp. 783-843.

CIOCHON, R.L., and D.A. ETLER 1994 Reinterpreting past primate diversity. In R.S. Corruccini and R.L. Ciochon (eds): *Integrative Paths to the Past. Paleoanthropological Advances in Honor of F. Clark Howell.* Prentice Hall, Englewood Cliffs, pp. 37-67.

CIOCHON, R.L., J. OLSEN, and J. JAMES 1990 *Other Origins: The Search for the Giant Ape in Human Prehistory*. Bantam, New York.

CONROY, G.C. 1990 *Primate Evolution*. W.W. Norton, New York.

CORRUCCINI, R.S., and H. M. MCHENRY 1980 Cladometric analysis of Pliocene hominids. *Journal of Human Evolution* 9(3):209-221.

CULOTTA, E. 1992 A new take on Anthropoid origins. *Science* 256:1516-1517.

DEACON, T.D. 1989 The neural circuitry underlying primate calls and human language. *Human Evolution* 4(5):367-401.

DE BONIS, L., and G. KOUFOS 1993 The face and mandible of *Ouranopithecus macedoniensis*: description of new specimens and comparisons. *Journal of Human Evolution* 24(6):469-491.

DORAN, D.M. 1993 Sex differences in adult chimpanzee positional behavior: the influence of body size on locomotion and posture. *American Journal of Physical Anthropology* 91(1):99-115.

DUNBAR, R.I.M. 1992 Neocortex size as a constraint on group size in primates. *Journal of Human Evolution* 22(6):469-493.

ELLIOT, D.G. 1913 *A Review of the Primates*. Volumes 1, 2, and 3. American Museum of Natural History, New York.

ESSOCK-VITALE, S., and R.M. SEYFARTH 1987 Intelligence and social cognition. In B.B. Smuts, D.L. Cheney, R.M. Seyfarth, R.W. Wrangham, and T. Struhsacker (eds): *Primate Societies*. University of Chicago Press, Chicago. pp. 452-461.

FALK, D. 1987 Brain lateralization in primates and its evolution in hominids. *Yearbook of Physical Anthropology* 30:107-125.

FLEAGLE, J.G. 1988 *Primate Adaptation and Evolution*. Academic Press, New York.

___. 1994 Anthropoid origins. In R.S. Corruccini and R.L. Ciochon (eds): *Integrative Paths to the Past. Paleoanthropological Advances in Honor of F. Clark Howell*. Prentice Hall, Englewood Cliffs, pp. 17-35.

FLEAGLE, J.G., and W.L. JUNGERS 1982 Fifty years of higher primate phylogeny. In F. Spencer (ed): *History of American Physical Anthropology (1930-1980)*. Academic, New York. pp. 187-230.

FLEAGLE, J.G., and R. KAY (editors) 1995 *Anthropoid Origins*. Plenum, New York.

FLEMMING, J. 1822 *The Philosophy of Zoology: or a General View of the Structure, Functions, and Classifications of Animals*. Constable, Edinburgh.

FOLEY, R. 1987 *Another Unique Species. Patterns in Human Evolutionary Ecology*. Wiley, New York.

GALDIKAS, B.M.F., and J.W. WOOD 1990 Birth spacing patterns in humans and apes. *American Journal of Physical Anthropology* 83(2):185-191.

GEBO, D.L. 1986 Anthropoid origins - the foot evidence. Journal of Human Evolution 15:421-430.

___. 1992 Plantigrady and foot adaptation in the African apes: implications for hominid origins. *American Journal of Physical Anthropology* 89(1):29-58.

GIBBONS, A. 1990 Our chimp cousins get that much closer. *Science* 250:376.

___. 1992a Chimps: more diverse than a barrel of monkeys. *Science* 255:287-288.

___. 1992b Hungarian fossils stir debate on ape and human origins. *Science* 257:1864-1865.

GOODMAN, M. 1986 Rates of molecular evolution: the hominoid slowdown. *Bioessays* 3:9-14.

GOODMAN, M., W.J. BAILEY, K. HAYASAKA, M.J. STANHOPE, J. SLIGHTOM, and J. CZELUSNIAK 1994 Molecular evidence on primate phylogeny from DNA sequences. *American Journal of Physical Anthropology* 94(1):3-24.

GOODMAN, M., J. CZELUSNIAK, and J.E. BEEBER 1985 Phylogeny of primates and other eutherian orders: a cladistic analysis using amino acid and nucleotide sequence data. *Cladistics* 1:171-185.

GOULD, S.J. 1983 Chimp on the chain. *Natural History* 12/83:18-27.

GRAY, J.E. 1821 On the natural arrangement of vertebrose animals. *London Medical Repository Record* 15:296-310.

___. 1825 Outline of an attempt at the disposition of the Mammalia into tribes and families, with a list of the genera apparently pertaining to each tribe. *Annals of Philosophy* (new series) 10:337-344.

GREENFIELD, L.O. 1972 Sexual dimorphism in *Dryopithecus africanus*. *Primates* 13:395-410.

___. 1980 A late divergence hypothesis. *American Journal of Physical Anthropology* 52:351-366.

GREGORY, W.K. 1927 How near is the relationship of man to the chimpanzee-gorilla stock? *Quarterly Review of Biology* 2(4):549-560.

HAECKEL, E. 1866 *Generelle Morphologie der Organismen*. Reimer, Berlin.

HARRISON, T. 1993 Cladistic concepts and the species problem in hominoid evolution. In W.H. Kimbel and L.B. Martin (eds): *Species, Species Concepts, and Primate Evolution*. Plenum, New York. pp. 345-371.

HARVEY, P.H., and T. CLUTTON-BROCK 1985 Life history variation in primates. *Evolution* 39:559-581.

HASEGAWA, M., H. KISHINO, and T. YANO 1989 Estimation of branching dates among primates by molecular clocks of nuclear DNA which slowed down in Hominoidea. *Journal of Human Evolution* 18(5):461-476.

HILL, A. 1994 Late Miocene and Early Pliocene hominoids from Africa. In R.S. Corruccini and R.L. Ciochon (eds): *Integrative Paths to the Past. Paleoanthropological Advances in Honor of F. Clark Howell*. Prentice Hall, Englewood Cliffs, pp. 123-145.

HILL, A.H., and S. WARD 1988 Origin of the hominidae: the record of African large hominoid evolution between 14 my and 4 my. *Yearbook of Physical Anthropology* 31:49-83.

HOLLOWAY, R.L. 1968 The evolution of the primate brain: some aspects of quantitative relations. *Brain Research* 7:121-172.

HORAI, S., Y. SATTA, K. HAYASAKA, R. KONDO, T. INOUE, T. ISHIDA, S. HAYASHI, and N. TAKAHATA 1992 Man's place in Hominoidea revealed by Mitochondrial DNA genealogy. *Journal of Molecular Evolution* 35:32-43.

HORN, A.D. 1979 The taxonomic status of the bonobo chimpanzee. *American Journal of Physical Anthropology* 51:273-282.

KAY, R.F. 1981 The nut-crackers - a new theory of adaptation of the Ramapithecinae. *American Journal of Physical Anthropology* 55:141-151.

___. 1984 On the use of anatomical features to infer foraging behavior in extinct primates. In P.S. Rodman, and J.G.H. Cant (eds): *Adaptations for foraging in nonhuman primates.* Columbia University Press, New York. pp. 21-53.

KELLEY, J. 1992 Evolution of apes. In S. Jones, R. Martin, and D. Pilbeam (eds): *The Cambridge Encyclopaedia of Human Evolution.* Cambridge University Press, New York. pp. 223-230.

KELLEY, J., and D. PILBEAM 1986 The dryopithecines: taxonomy, anatomy, and phylogeny of Miocene large hominoids. In D.R. Swindler (ed): *Comparative Primate Biology.* Volume 1: *Systematics, Evolution, and Anatomy.* Alan R. Liss, New York. pp. 361-411.

KORTLANDT, A. 1972 *New Perspectives on Ape and Human Evolution.* Department of Animal Psychology and Ethology, University of Amsterdam, Amsterdam.

___. 1983 Marginal habitats of Chimpanzees. *Journal of Human Evolution* 12:231-278.

LAVILLE, C.L.B., R.P. SHELLIS, and D.F.G. POOLE 1977 *Evolutionary Changes in the Primate Skull and Dentition.* C.C. Thomas, Springfield.

LEAKEY, L.S.B. 1962 A new Lower Pliocene fossil primate from Kenya. *Annals and Magazine of Natural History*, Series 13, 4:689-696.

___. 1967 An Early Miocene member of Hominidae. *Nature* 213:155-163.

___. 1968 Lower dentition of *Kenyapithecus africanus. Nature* 217:827-830.

LEAKEY, R.E., M.G. LEAKEY, and A.C. WALKER 1988 Morphology of *Afropithecus turkanensis* from Kenya. *American Journal of Physical Anthropology* 76(3):289-307.

LE GROS CLARK, W.E. 1959 *The Antecedents of Man.* University of Edinburgh Press, Edinburgh.

LENNEBERG, E.H. 1967 *Biological Foundations of Language.* Wiley, New York.

LITTLE, B.B. 1989 Gestation length, metabolic rate, and brain and body weights in primates: epigenetic effects. *American Journal of Physical Anthropology* 80(2):213-218.

LUCAS, P.W., R.T. CORLETT, and D.A. LUKE 1986 Postcanine tooth size and diet in anthropoid primates. *Zeitschrift für Morphologie und Anthropologie* 76(3):253-276.

MACHO, G.A., and M.E. BERNER 1993 Enamel thickness of human maxillary molars reconsidered. *American Journal of Physical Anthropology* 92(2):189-200.

MARTIN, L. 1986 Relationships among extant and extinct great apes and humans. In B. Wood, L. Martin, and P. Andrews (eds): *Major Trends in Primate and Human Evolution*. Cambridge University Press, Cambridge. pp. 151-187.

MARTIN, R.D. 1986 Primates: a definition. In B. Wood, L. Martin, and P. Andrews (eds): *Major Trends in Primate and Human Evolution*. Cambridge University Press, Cambridge. pp. 1-31.

___. 1990 *Primate Origins and Evolution: A Phylogenetic Reconstruction*. Princeton University Press, Princeton.

___. 1993 Primate origins: plugging the gaps. *Nature* 363:223-234.

MAIER, W. 1984 Tooth morphology and dietary specialization. In D.J. Chivers, B.A. Wood, and A. Bilsborough (eds.): *Food Acquisition and Processing in Primates*. Plenum, New York.

MARKS, J. 1994 Blood will tell (won't it?): a century of molecular discourse in anthropological systematics. *American Journal of Physical Anthropology* 94(1):59-79.

McCROSSIN, M.L., and B.R. BENEFIT 1993 Recently recovered *Kenyapithecus* mandible and its implications for great ape and human origins. *Proceedings of the National Academy of Sciences, USA*. 90:1962-1966.

___. 1994 Maboko Island and the evolutionary history of Old World monkeys and apes. In R.S. Corruccini and R.L. Ciochon (eds): *Integrative Paths to the Past: Paleoanthropological Advances in Honor of F.C. Howell*. Prentice-Hall, New York. pp. 95-122.

MCGREW, W.C. 1992 *Chimpanzee Material Culture: Implications for Human Evolution*. Cambridge University Press, New York.

NAPIER, J. R., and P. H. NAPIER. 1985 *Natural History of the Primates*. M.I.T. Press, Cambridge.

OSBORN, J.W. 1987 Relationship between the mandibular condyle and the occlusal plane during hominid evolution: some of its effects on jaw mechanics. *American Journal of Physical Anthropology* 73(2):193-207.

___. 1993 Orientation of the masseter muscle and the curve of Spee in relation to crushing forces on the molar teeth of primates. *American Journal of Physical Anthropology* 92(1):99-106.

PICKFORD, M.H.L. 1982 New higher primate fossils from the Middle Miocene deposits at Majiwa and Kaloma. Western Kenya. *American Journal of Physical Anthropology* 58:1-19.

PROCTOR, R. 1988 From *Anthropologie* to *Rassenkunde* in the German anthropological tradition. In G.W. Stocking Jr. (ed): *Bones, Bodies, Behavior. Essays on Biological Anthropology*. University of Wisconsin Press, Madison. pp. 138-179.

POVINELLI, D.J. 1987 Monkeys, apes, mirrors, and minds: the evolution of self-awareness in primates. *Human Evolution* 2(6):493-509.

RADINSKY, L. B. 1975 Primate Brain Evolution. *American Scientist* 63:656-663.

RASMUSSEN, D.T. E.L. SIMONS 1992 Paleobiology of the oligopithecines, the earliest known anthropoid primates. *International Journal of Primatology* 13(5):477-508.

ROGERS, J. 1994 Levels of the genealogical hierarchy and the problem of hominoid phylogeny. *American Journal of Physical Anthropology* 94(1):81-88.

ROSE, M.D. 1992 Kinematics of the trapezium-1st metacarpal joint in extant anthropoids and Miocene hominoids. *Journal of Human Evolution* 22(4/5):255-266.

RUFF, C.B., and J.A. RUNESTAD 1992 Primate limb bone structural adaptations. In B.J. Siegel, A.R. Beals, and S.A. Tyler (eds): *Annual Review of Anthropology*. Annual Reviews, Palo Alto. Volume 21:407-433.

RUFF C.B., A.C. WALKER, and M.F. TEAFORD 1989 Body mass, sexual dimorphism, and femoral proportions of *Proconsul* from Rusinga and Mfangano Islands, Kenya. *Journal of Human Evolution* 18(6):515-536.

SAITOU, N. 1991 Reconstruction of molecular phylogeny of extant hominoids from DNA sequence data. *American Journal of Physical Anthropology* 84:75-85.

SANDERS, W.J., and B.E. BODENBENDER 1994 Morphometric analysis of lumbar vertebra UMP 67-28: implications for spinal function and phylogeny of the Miocene Moroto hominoid. *Journal of Human Evolution* 26(3):206-237.

SCHULTZ, A. H. 1963 Age changes, sex differences, and variability as factors in the classification of primates. In: Classification and Human Evolution, ed. S.L. Washburn. Aldine, Chicago. pp. 85-115.

____. 1969 *The Life of Primates*. Universe, New York.

SCHWARTZ, J.H., I. TATTERSALL, and N. EDLREDGE. 1978 Phylogeny and classification of the primates revisited. *Yearbook of Physical Anthropology* 21:95-133.

SHEA, B.T. 1985 On aspects of skull form in African apes and orangutans, with implications for hominoid evolution. *American Journal of Physical Anthropology* 68(3):329-342.

SHIPMAN, P. 1986 Paleoecology of Fort Ternan reconsidered. *Journal of Human Evolution* 15(3):193-204.

____. 1990 Primate origins up in the air again. *New Scientist* (23 June):57-60.

SIMONS, E.L 1972 *Primate Evolution*. MacMillan, New York.

____. 1992 Diversity in the early Tertiary anthropoidean radiation in Africa. *Proceedings of the National Academy of Sciences, USA* 89:10743-10747.

SIMONS, E.L., and D. PILBEAM 1965 Preliminary revision of the Dryopithecinae (Pongidae, Anthropoidea). *Folia Primatologia* 3:81-152.

SIMONS, E.L., and D.T. RASMUSSEN 1989 Cranial morphology of *Aegyptopithecus* and *Tarsus*` and the question of the Tarsier-Anthropoidean clade. *American Journal of Physical Anthropology* 79(1):1-23.

____. 1991 The generic classification of Fayum Anthropoidea. *International Journal of Primatology* 12(2):163-178.

SMITH, B.H. 1989 Dental development as a measure of life history in primates. *Evolution* 43(3):683-688

STRAUS, W.L. Jr. 1967 The riddle of man's ancestry. In W.W. Howells (ed): *Ideas on Human Evolution*. Atheneum, New York. pp. 69-104.

SUSMAN, R.L. (ed) 1984 *The Pygmy Chimpanzee. Evolutionary Biology and Behavior.* Plenum, New York.

SUSSMAN, R.W. 1991 Primate origins and the evolution of the angiosperms. *American Journal of Primatology* 23:209-223.

SWINDLER, D.R., and J.E. IRWIN (eds) 1986 *Comparative Primate Biology. Systematics, Evolution, and Anatomy.* Alan R. Liss, New York.

SZALAY, F.S., and DELSON, E. 1979 *Evolutionary History of the Primates.* Academic Press, New York.

TELEKI, G., E.E. HUNT JR., and J.H. PFIFFERING 1976 Demographic observations (1963-1973) on the chimpanzees of Gombe National Park, Tanzania. *Journal of Human Evolution* 5:559-598.

THOMAS, H., S. SEN, J. ROGER, and Z. AL-SULAIMANI 1991 The discovery of *Moeripithecus markgrafi* Schlosser (Propliopithecidae, Anthropoidea, Primates) in the Ashawq Formation (early Oligocene of Dhofar province, Sultanate of Oman). *Journal of Human Evolution* 20:33-49.

TURKE, P.W. 1993 Evolution of the 100 Year Lifespan -- and Beyond: Implications from the Evolutionary Theory of Senescence. *In Press.*

TUTIN, C.E.G. 1980 Reproductive behaviour of wild chimpanzees in the Gombe National park, Tanzania. *Journal of Reproduction and Fertility,* Supplement 28:43-57.

UNGAR, P.S., A. WALKER, and K. COFFING 1994 Reanalysis of the Lukeino molar (KNM-LU-335). . *American Journal of Physical Anthropology* 94(2):165-173.

WALKER, A.C. 1992 Louis Leakey, John Napier, and the history of *Proconsul. Journal of Human Evolution* 22(4/5):245-254.

WALKER, A.C., D. FALK, R. SMITH, and M. PICKFORD 1983 The skull of *Proconsul africanus*: reconstruction and cranial capacity. *Nature* 305:525-527.

WALKER, A.C. and M. TEAFORD 1989 The hunt for *Proconsul. Scientific American* 260(1):76-82.

WARD, C.V. 1993 Torso morphology and locomotion in *Proconsul nyanzae. American Journal of Physical Anthropology* 92(3):291-328.

WARD, C.V., A. WALKER, M.F. TEAFORD, and I. ODHIAMBO 1993 Partial skeleton of *Proconsul nyanzae* from Mfangano Island, Kenya. *American Journal of Physical Anthropology* 90(1):77-111.

WARD, S.C., and B. BROWN 1986 The facial skeleton of *Sivapithecus indicus.* In D.R. Swindler (ed.): *Comparative Primate Biology. Volume 1: Systematics, Evolution, and Anatomy.* Alan R. Liss, New York. pp. 413-452.

WARD, S.C., and D.R. PILBEAM 1983 Maxillofacial morphology of Miocene hominoids from Africa and Indopakistan. In R.L. Ciochon and R.S. Corruccini (eds.): *New Interpretations of Ape and Human Ancestry.* Plenum, New York. pp. 211-238.

WEINERT, H. 1944 *Ursprung der Menschenheit. Über den Engeren Anschluss des Menschengeschlechts an die Menschenaffen.* 2nd Edition. Enke, Stuttgart.

___. 1953 Der Fossile Mensch. In A.L. Kroeber (ed): *Anthropology Today.* University of Chicago, Chicago. pp. 101-119.

WEISS, M.L., and A.E. MANN 1990 *Human Biology and Behavior*, 5th Edition. Scott, Foresman and Company, Glenview.

WOLPOFF, M.H. 1983 *Ramapithecus* and human origins: an anthropologist's perspective of changing interpretations. In R. Ciochon and R. Corruccini (eds): *New Interpretations of Ape and Human Ancestry.* Plenum, New York.

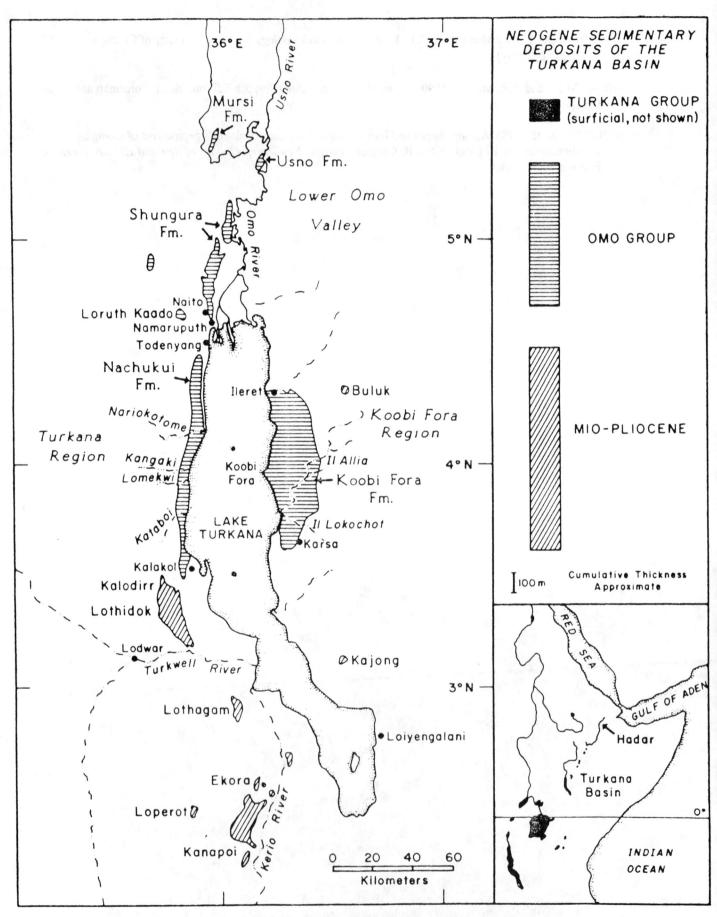

Map 3.1 Miocene and Pliocene hominoid sites in East Africa.

From: Feibel, C.S., F.H. Brown, and I. McDougall 1989 Stratigraphic context of the fossil hominids from the Omo group deposits: northern Turkana basin, Kenya and Ethiopia. American Journal of Physical Anthropology 78(4):595-622.

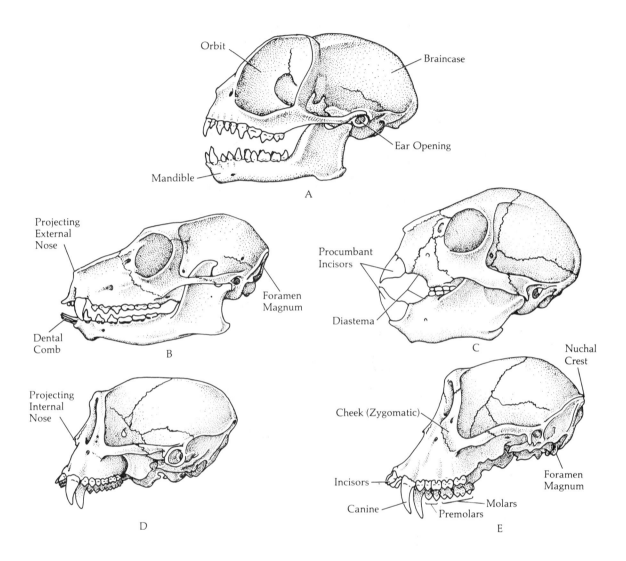

FIGURE 3.1 Cranial forms in some living primates, from Schultz (1969). The crania compared include three prosimians and representatives of the Anthropoidea from the New and Old Worlds. These are (A) a tarsier, (B) a lemur, (C) an aye-aye, (D) a New World cebus monkey, and (E) an Old World macaque. The skulls are drawn to the same approximate size and are not to scale.
FROM: First edition, figure 3.2.

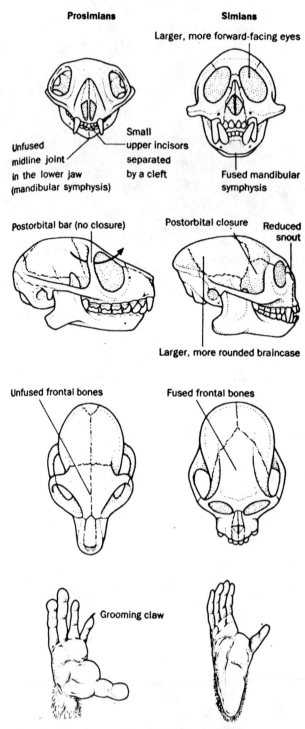

Prosimians

Simians

Larger, more forward-facing eyes

Unfused midline joint in the lower jaw (mandibular symphysis)

Small upper incisors separated by a cleft

Fused mandibular symphysis

Postorbital bar (no closure)

Postorbital closure

Reduced snout

Larger, more rounded braincase

Unfused frontal bones

Fused frontal bones

Grooming claw

The main distinctions between prosimians and simians (anthropoids).

FIGURE 3.2 The main distinctions between prosimians and anthropoids, after Gingerich (1992).
FROM Gingerich, P. 1992 Evolution of prosimians. In S. Jones, R. Martin, and D. Pilbeam (eds): *The Cambridge Encyclopedia of Human Evolution.* Cambridge University Press, Cambridge. p. 201.

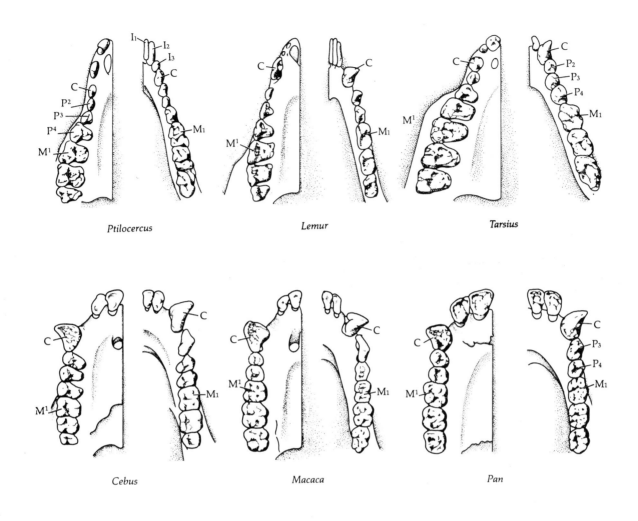

FIGURE 3.3 Upper and lower dentitions of prosimians (above) and higher primates (below), after Schultz (1969, figure 44). In all cases, the lower dentition is to the right. Note the retention of three incisors in the tupaiiform (upper left), the lower dental comb in the lemur, and the reduction to two premolars in the Old World higher primates (macaque, chimpanzee).

FROM: First edition, figure 3.3.

FIGURE 3.4 Locomotor categories in the anthropoid primates, after Fleagle (1992).
FROM Fleagle, J. 1992 Primate locomotion and posture. In S. Jones, R. Martin, and D. Pilbeam (eds): *The Cambridge Encyclopedia of Human Evolution.* Cambridge University Press, Cambridge. pp. 75-79.

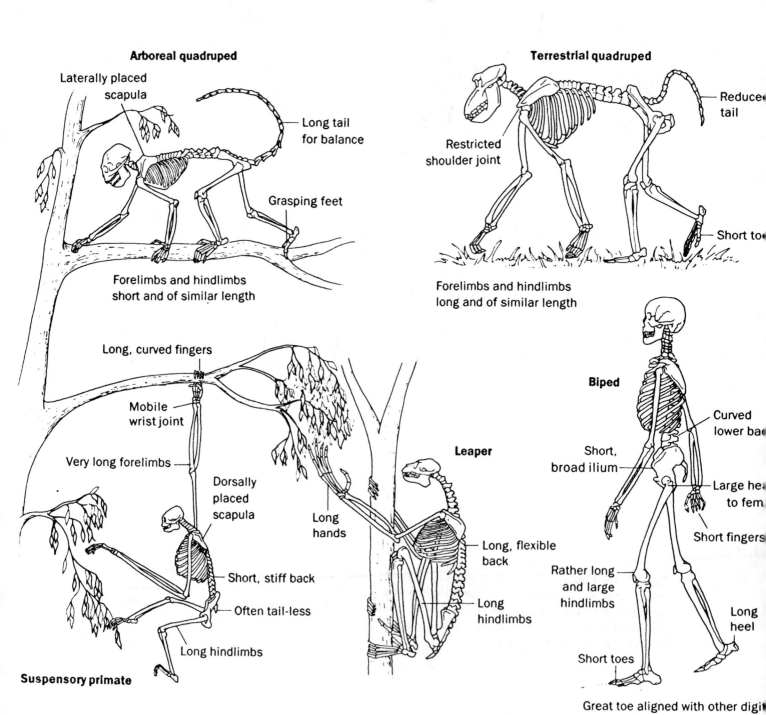

Arboreal quadruped

Laterally placed scapula

Long tail for balance

Grasping feet

Forelimbs and hindlimbs short and of similar length

Terrestrial quadruped

Reduced tail

Restricted shoulder joint

Short toe

Forelimbs and hindlimbs long and of similar length

Long, curved fingers

Mobile wrist joint

Very long forelimbs

Dorsally placed scapula

Long hands

Short, stiff back

Often tail-less

Long hindlimbs

Suspensory primate

Leaper

Long, flexible back

Long hindlimbs

Biped

Curved lower back

Short, broad ilium

Large head to femur

Short fingers

Rather long and large hindlimbs

Long heel

Short toes

Great toe aligned with other digit

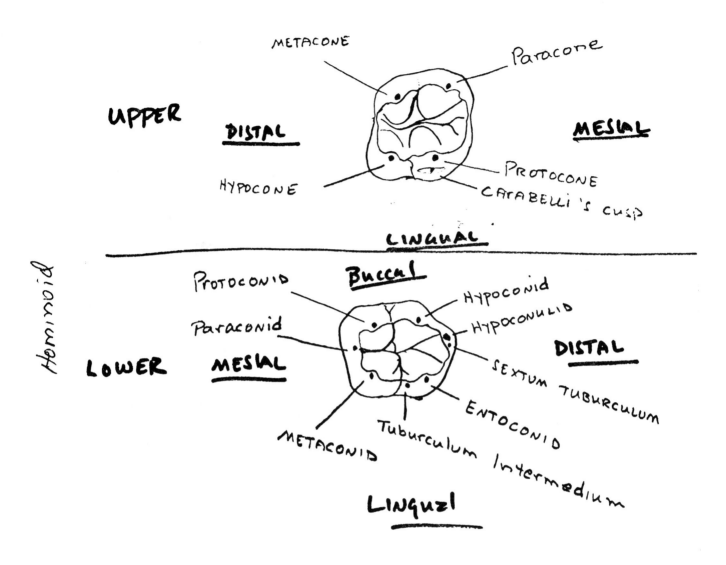

FIGURE 3.6 Molar cusp anatomy. The cusp pattern is shown and the cusps are names for upper and lower hominoid molars, and the lower molar of a bilophodont cercopithecoid is compared.

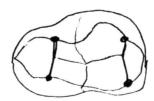

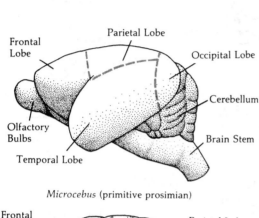

Microcebus (primitive prosimian)

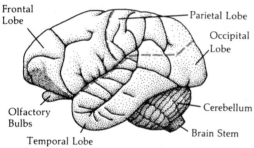

Cebus (platyrrhine monkey)

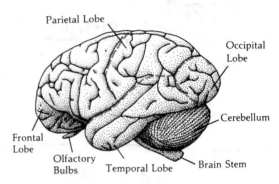

Pan troglodytes (chimpanzee)

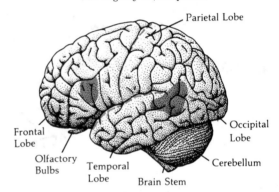

Homo sapiens

FIGURE 3.7 Comparison of the brain (in side view) in four living primate species, after Jolly and Plog (1976). In a general way, this represents an evolutionary sequence: Microcebus, Cebus, Pan troglodytes, and Homo sapiens. Cerebellum Note the relative expansion of the temporal, parietal, and frontal lobes and the increased complexity of the surface. The olfactory bulbs decrease in size. The four brains are drawn to the same size. Some of the areas believed important for the production of speech and language in humans are situated on the left cerebral hemisphere and are shown in Homo sapiens.
FROM: First edition, figure 3.5

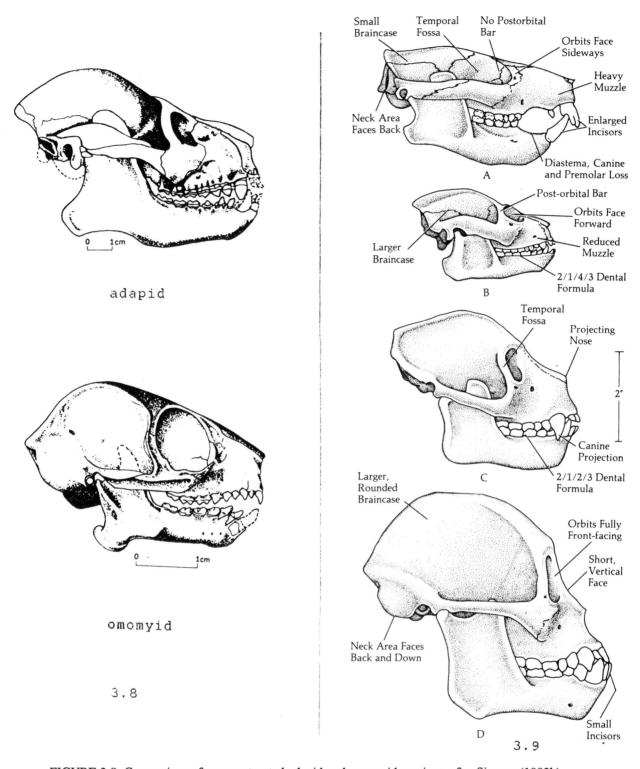

adapid

omomyid

3.8

A

- Small Braincase
- Temporal Fossa
- No Postorbital Bar
- Orbits Face Sideways
- Heavy Muzzle
- Enlarged Incisors
- Neck Area Faces Back
- Diastema, Canine and Premolar Loss

B

- Post-orbital Bar
- Orbits Face Forward
- Reduced Muzzle
- Larger Braincase
- 2/1/4/3 Dental Formula

C

- Temporal Fossa
- Projecting Nose
- 2"
- Canine Projection
- Larger, Rounded Braincase
- 2/1/2/3 Dental Formula

D

- Orbits Fully Front-facing
- Short, Vertical Face
- Neck Area Faces Back and Down
- Small Incisors

3.9

FIGURE 3.8 Comparison of a reconstructed adapid and omomyid cranium, after Simons (1992b).
FROM Simons, E.L. 1992 The fossil history of primates. In S. Jones, R. Martin, and D. Pilbeam (eds): *The Cambridge Encyclopedia of Human Evolution.* Cambridge University Press, Cambridge. pp. 199-208.

FIGURE 3 9 Crania of primates representing the Paleocene, later Eocene, Oligocene, and Miocene forms: (A) **Plesiadapis; (B) Adapis parisiensis,** Eocene lemuriform primate; (C) **Aegyptopithecus zeuxis,** Fayum catarrhine drawn from a cast of partly reconstructed skull), (D) female **Proconsul africanus,** early Miocene pongid (after a reconstruction by Davis and Napier).
FROM: First edition, figure 3.7

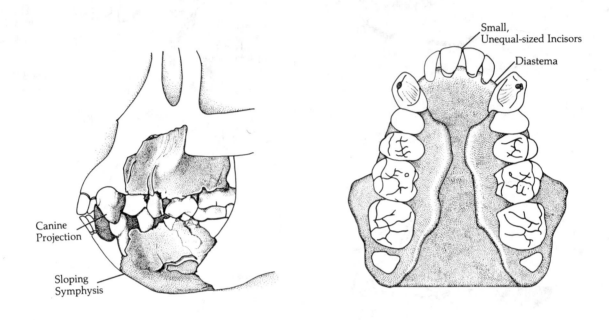

FIGURE 3.11 Lateral view of the Fort Ternan specimen, as reconstructed by A. Walker (after Andrews and Walker 1976).
FROM: First edition, figure 6.1.

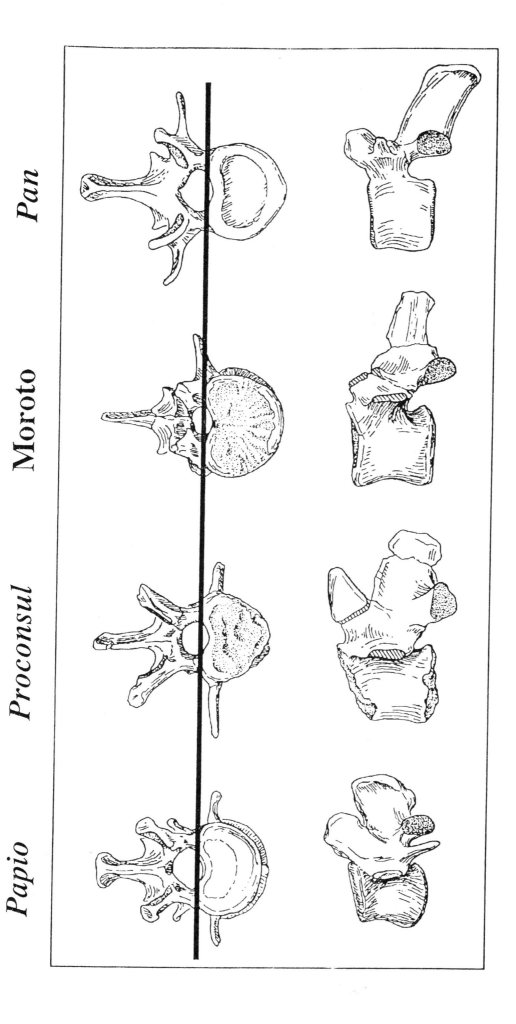

FIGURE 3.13 The Moroto vertebrae, compared as seen from above with a baboon, proconsul, and chimpanzee, courtesy of C. Ward.

PART TWO

THE APPEARANCE OF THE HOMINID LINE

CHAPTER FOUR

Hominid Features

In the context of the primate background discussed in Chapter 3, only a relatively few morphological and behavioral complexes are distinctly different in humans and their ancestors. Following a general discussion of how morphology and behavior can be related in fossil samples, this Chapter outlines the three morphological complexes that distinguish our lineage. These unique morphological complexes involve aspects of the hip and hindlimb, brain, and jaws and teeth. They are associated with behavioral changes, and the nature and details of these behavioral changes are discussed. It is in this intricate relation of behavior and morphology that the process of evolution can be seen most clearly, translating the activities of once living populations into permanent inherited gene pool changes.

A discussion of hominid origins presupposes an understanding of exactly what it was that originated. From the preceding chapter, it should be clear that hominid origins did not involve the appearance of grasping hands or binocular vision; these are features common to all living higher primates, and specifically were attributes of the immediate prehuman anthropithecine precursors. There are three morphological complexes that have come to uniquely characterize the hominid line. None of these is truly unique by itself, as each represents an extension or elaboration of developments that appear in at least some other higher primate species. Moreover, each represents a complex interplay between form and behavior. The three unique hominid complexes are :

1. the development of obligate bipedal locomotion, including pelvic changes that altered birthing to require midwifery for its normal success;
2. the development of language and culture, learned behavioral systems whose complex structure is strongly influenced by genetic variation, and the evolution of associated changes in the brain (encephalization) as the pathways for learning them and their organizational constraints increasingly came under genetic control;
3. developments in the masticatory system that combine dental and craniofacial adaptations for very powerful grinding, molars that erupt over a long time span, and changes in the functions of the anterior teeth, especially the canines.

The attempt to explain these uniquenesses is, in reality, the development of testable hypotheses about them. In a thoughtful essay, M. Cartmill argues that real uniquenesses cannot be explained because "they do not conform to overarching laws that apply to similar cases". I do not agree with this contention, as it is the explanations that link real novelties with the regularities created by the evolutionary process, not the novelties being explained. Paleoanthropology in my view is a valid science insofar as it generates and tests hypotheses about the course of human evolution. These hypotheses, as much as the facts they explain, are the real corpus of the discipline.

The details of these three unique complexes will be expanded below, following a discussion of how form can be related to function in the study of fossilized skeletal remains and their living counterparts - bone. Hypotheses about their appearance are presented in Chapter 5. Many of these details are anatomical. There are a number of sources that can provide background and additional information about them. The author's experience is that *Human Evolutionary Anatomy* by L. Aiello and C. Dean will be particularly useful.

The Living and the Dead

There are many valid approaches for dealing with the behavioral and biological aspects of prehistory. Yet, the most direct link between the living and the dead is the fossil record; as D. Frayer once said, the real evidence for human evolution. This record is comprised of teeth and bones, in various conditions, degrees of completeness, and states of preservation. Their interpretation is the key to the past.

FORM AND FUNCTION

Understanding the evolution of these morphological complexes requires an analysis of how form relates to function in fossil remains. This relation can sometimes be determined by analogy with living populations. When form and function can be related in living primates, there is a logical basis for inferring function *from* form in fossils. One good example involves the large orbits of some fossil primates. In this case, the large orbits indicate large eyes. In living primates, this morphology is inevitably an adaptation to activity in dim light, and it is logical to assume that the same interpretation applies to the fossils in question.

A second way to relate form and function is based on the **biomechanical analysis** (the interpretation of the skeletal mechanics) of functional systems. This is a particularly effective technique when there are skeletal changes that influence the mechanical aspects of bone structure or the spatial relations of bones to each other. Usually, a functional model of the bone or bones is developed in either a static or dynamic framework, and the observations most relevant to the model are isolated so that they can be analyzed for fossil specimens. The advantages of this approach are twofold: it avoids the potential confusion of false correlations that might come from simple comparisons drawn from living species, and it allows for the understanding of functioning systems that have no analogs among the living primates, or other species. An example of biomechanical analysis will be found in the analysis of early hominid locomotion.

GENETICS AND THE ENVIRONMENT

Relating form and function in fossil bones raises the immediate question of what factors are responsible for the final bone form. To what extent is this form the result of inheritance, and to what extent is it the result of how the bone was used during growth and development? Bone is a living tissue, a complex composite of organic proteins (collagen) and minerals that can repair itself and alter its shape through a growth process to meet the demands of its environment. Bone can be significantly altered during growth, and long after most growth has ceased, by the forces that regularly act on it. These forces come from the muscles attaching to bones, from the body weight, and in the case of the jaws also from the load between the teeth during chewing.

The external form and the internal trabecular structure of the bone are related to its function. Bones are adapted to provide strength and resist the action of the forces that act on them, using the least amount of material. For every part of the skeleton, there is enough properly placed and oriented bone tissue to withstand, without damage, the forces that are normally encountered. In particular, the motor system and skeletal architecture are oriented to maintain the bending stress (the force causing bone to bend) as small as possible. Changes in bone function during life are followed by changes in internal architecture and alterations in external confirmation that accomplish the above. The cause of these changes is related to the changing pattern of force on the bone.

How does bone end up being so well adapted to the functioning of an organism during its life? Experimental evidence shows that changes in diet, activity levels, or the removal of muscles can strongly influence the final size and form of bone. During life bone is strained (deformed) by the normal activities of an organism. This deformation stimulates the remodeling process in the affected area as some bone tissue is added and other tissue removed. Functionally induced remodeling is part of a feedback system. Changes in internal and external geometry alter the bone so as to minimize its bending and twisting, and continue until as much of the stress as possible is compressive and the maximum strength is attained through the minimum material. This leaves the bone well adapted to effectively resist similar forces in the future.

The particular pattern of strain in human bones has been analyzed experimentally under varying conditions, and the form of the bone seems to be responsive to the everyday forces acting on it as predicted. Both the magnitude of these forces, and their regularity, can be very influential in this process. The converse is of greatest interest to paleoanthropologists, because it implies that from the particular form of human fossil bones, it is possible to determine the direction and strength of the forces that once acted on them. Demonstrations that these forces differed from time to time (such as provided by P. Bridges in studying the skeletal responses to the appearance of agriculture), or differ in the past from the forces known to occur today (as C.O. Lovejoy and E. Trinkaus were able to show in comparing Neandertal and modern tibiae), give insight into behavioral and adaptive differences between living people and their ancestors. A particularly convincing study by Trinkaus and colleagues examines the reaction of internal bone mass distribution in Neandertals with injured arms. The asymmetries that developed are nothing short of astounding, and the authors conclude that we should expect the shape and internal structure of long bones to reflect the life-long history of arm use.

Yet it is clear that there is a genetic basis to bone form that must also be taken into account. The problem is that selection between generations would be expected to cause the same changes in a bone as would differences in function during life. Bone will always develop to adapt itself to meet the demands it normally encounters, which is just what one would expect genetic change due to selection to result in. This is a question of overlapping predictions in the analysis of the factors that underlie bone form that cannot always be directly resolved. Clearly the details of a minimum bone form and structure must be genetically coded, but normal bone structure and the ability to withstand the normal forces acting on bone can only be achieved through responses to those forces during life. Normal, in other words, is defined for bone through an individual's activities.

In an evolutionary context where time-depth can be considered, the *speed* of change may be a key to separating evolutionary from developmental changes. A developmental change due to change in function can occur within a generation of the functional change. Something like this seems to have happened in recent human evolution. The common practice of boiling foods and the introduction of the knife and fork in Europe rapidly changed the forces acting on the mandible during chewing. With the additional food preparation, less chewing was required and the immediate result was a reduction in mandible size; with less muscle and dental force acting on the mandible, it did not grow as large. The teeth have a higher inheritance factor and added to the fact that virtually all of them attain their permanent size long before the mandible is finished growing, their size could not be directly influenced by this change in chewing. Unlike the mandible, the new behaviors did not cause them to reduce in size. The result is familiar to many of us: there is often not enough room in the reduced mandible for the last molar (wisdom tooth) to erupt. Without modern dentistry, this would result in genetic change as the result of selection acting on the teeth. Individuals with the greatest imbalance between adult jaw and tooth size might, on the average, have fewer surviving offspring because of infection (and its effects) due to impacted or partially erupted third molars. Individuals with smaller teeth, on the other hand, would be unaffected and the net result would be a reduction of tooth size over time. This process was appreciated by Charles Darwin, who wrote in the *Descent of Man*:

This shortening of the molar row, and particularly the third molar may, I presume, be attributed to civilized man habitually feeding on soft, cooked food, and thus using their jaws less. I am informed by Mr. Brace that it is becoming a quite common practice in the United States to remove some of the molar teeth of children, as the jaw does not grow large enough for the perfect development of the normal number.

This example serves to demonstrate two different things: the interplay between behavior (boiling and the use of the knife and fork) and morphology, and the interplay between developmental (mandibular) and genetic (dental) changes.

RECONSTRUCTING BEHAVIOR

Reconstructing behavior from fossil remains is another level of abstraction and requires information about more than one portion of the organism as well as about its environment. For instance, the arm bones in australopithecines, the earliest fossil hominids (Chapter 6) are unusually long and thick in comparison to living people, and the bone itself is structured to resist forces of bending and compression. A simple analogy could be made with the African apes. When these primates are quadrupedal, their arms support part of their body weight and bring the front of the trunk into a position higher than the rear of the trunk. Because of the additional forces acting on them, the arm bones are thick and structured to resist bending and compression. Thus one might suppose that the evidence of the arms shows that the australopithecines were quadrupedal at least some of the time.

However, this is not borne out by other evidence. Several things are particularly relevant here. Australopithecines are found in quite different habitats than living apes. Moreover, body weight provides only a portion of the force acting on bone—much more force is provided by muscle activities and these may be independent of weight support. Furthermore, the pelvic remains of these early hominids show that they were bipedal during locomotion and because of the consequent anatomical adaptations they could no more easily walk on all four limbs than you or I. This additional information makes it seem likely that forelimb length and thickness was a response to different behaviors than living apes exhibit, but perhaps roughly equivalent magnitudes of active muscle use, showing that these early hominids were far more powerful and active than any people today.

Finally, to go a step further, we may wonder what particular activities required these long, powerful arms in the early bipeds. This question is much more difficult to answer because it addresses the adaptive behaviors of a unique extinct species. There is no simple or single answer to this because a wide range of behaviors could benefit from greater length and muscular power than is common today. One behavior which might have been of particular importance is climbing. A number of detailed biomechanical analyses conducted by C.O. Lovejoy and his colleagues show that australopithecine hands, feet, and limbs lack any specific adaptations for either below-branch activities or above-branch quadrupedal or bipedal stance. As discussed below, the commitment to bipedal locomotion had already created an impediment to the **quadrumanous** (four-handed - using both hands and feet) climbing of apes by eliminating the grasping feet. However, an adaptation in the diminutive early hominids to vertical climbing in a human-like fashion, but considerably more often and/or more rapidly than any living population, is not precluded by these analyses. Even without other more specific arboreal adaptations, climbing provides access to additional food sources (fruits, nuts, and new leaves) and sleeping places. Further, an earlier climbing adaptation in the pre-hominid anthropithecines may have provided some important preadaptations to obligate bipedalism (an idea suggested by R. Tuttle, J.G. Fleagle and his colleagues, and others, and discussed further in chapter 5). If so, the behavioral pattern may have been an ancient one, even for the earliest hominids. After the changes in the foot required by obligate bipedalism, discussed below, grasping was no longer possible and climbing became more difficult. Yet, in considerably modified form it may well have continued to play an important role in subsequent human populations until selection, resulting from yet other behavioral changes, disrupted the adaptive complex even further. Climbing, then, is an ancestral behavior whose retention would help explain the unusual characteristics of forelimb strength and the long forelimb/short hindlimb proportions of the australopithecines. It is unlikely, however, to be a full explanation because the mechanics and efficiency of climbing are so far modified from the ancestral primate condition. To fully test this hypothesis is difficult as we cannot expect to find an early hominid fossilized in the process of climbing, but new paleoecological reconstructons showing that the earliest hominids lived in a more forested environment than previously thought provides new evidence supporting it.

HOMINID VERSUS MODERN HUMAN

The discussion above leads to one final comment concerning hominid features. What is typically hominid is not necessarily the same as what is typically human today. Some features that have characterized most of hominid evolution do not appear in living people, as in the case of long, powerful arms associated with bipedalism. During most of human evolution, the jaws and postcanine teeth were much larger relative to body size that those of either the living African apes or of living humans. Because postcanine tooth size is virtually identical in living humans and chimpanzees of similar body size, one might suppose from studying living species that there is no unique hominid adaptation in relative postcanine tooth size. Study of the earlier members of our lineage shows otherwise, as these hominids have extremely large postcanine teeth compared with apes of similar body size. Taking another example, sexual dimorphism expressed as dramatic difference in body size between males and females seems to have been common in humans until quite recently.

Where this distinction becomes especially important is in the interpretation of hominid origins and recognition of the earliest hominids. The first members of our lineage may be more *hominid-like* than their contemporaries in other anthropithecine lineages without necessarily being *more like living humans*.

Human Locomotion

Humans have been called the "featherless bipeds," and although they are not the only creatures without feathers that use their hindlimbs alone for moving about, there are certain aspects of human locomotion that are unique. Human bipedalism is obligate, in that no other form of locomotion is possible - because of leg lengthening our attempts at quadrupedal locomotion are called crawling. There is considerable evidence that bipedalism is the first of the unique hominid adaptations to appear. It certainly is the earliest there is definitive evidence for, and anatomical reflections of obligate bipedalism have become the single undisputed identifying factor for the earliest hominids.

TABLE 4.1
Energy Efficiency of Bipedalism and Knuckle-walking,
from Rodman and McHenry (1980)

Walking Speed km/hr	Species	Energy Cost oxygen ml/g/km**	Energy Cost percentage of normal quadruped
2.9	human	.193	86
2.9	chimpanzee*	.522	149
4.5	human*	.170	94
4.5	chimpanzee	.426	148

*   Normal walking speed (stride speed, for humans)

** Energy cost is indicated by the amount of metabolic energy it takes to move a body of a given weight for a fixed distance. This is measured by the milliliters of oxygen consumed per gram of body weight each kilometer traveled

The human form of bipedalism is not an adaptation to speed; most quadrupedal mammals of similar body size can outrun a human—even a chimpanzee running bipedally is a faster sprinter. The real advantages of human bipedalism are twofold. First, the consistent use of the hindlimbs alone for locomotion frees the hands for carrying and for manipulating the environment. Second, humans have evolved particularly low-energy forms of locomotion. Striding allows them to cover long distances without expending a great amount of energy and thus without developing a great deal of metabolic heat. Long distance running is also particularly efficient, primarily because of physiological mechanisms for effective heat loss and energy use. Why bipedalism evolved in our lineage is surely tied to these advantages. *What* bipedalism evolved *from* is more of a problem. We can use the African apes as a model for the ancestral condition, but it is probable that this model is not correct in all details. Some ways we know the model to be incorrect include the lower back shortening (the reduced number of lumbar vertebrae) and forearm and hand adaptations to below branch posturing and locomotion. While some aspects of human anatomy suggest that hominid ancestors had below branch adaptations at some point (see Chapter 5), it is unclear how many of the unique brachiation-related adaptations of living apes also characterized human ancestors. As discussed in Chapter 3, the fossil evidence is insufficient to determine whether prehominids were similar to the African apes in being knuckle-walkers, although this is the simplest explanation of the distribution of knuckle-walking in the three living species. There are many reasons why an accurate reconstruction of the ancestral behavior would be important. For the purposes of this discussion, one of them is the contrast of energy efficiency in the obligate biped, and particular inefficiency in the knuckle-walker.

The accurate analysis of human locomotion is more recent than one might think, the functions of the muscles during stride have really been well-understood for only the last quarter-century. This clearly influences the identification of the unique aspects of human bipedalism, and their origin. Two other factors have hampered this understanding. Both are discussed to some extent in the 'controversies' section of Chapter 1: the methodology, model testing based on the biomechanics of locomotion *versus* the use of multivariate statistics to search for associations between morphologies and behaviors, and the singeing effect of the heat of publicity over anything dealing with hominid origins, a point reported on several occasions by R. Lewin.

APE LOCOMOTION

While the African apes are typically considered "brachiating apes," field studies have shown that gorillas and chimpanzees spend most of their waking hours on the ground. When on the ground, they are generally quadrupeds, although they can be bipedal (discussed below). African ape quadrupedalism is characterized by a unique form of forelimb support called "knuckle-walking," in which weight rests on the backs of the middle digits of the fingers, and the wrist is maintained in a fairly straight position. This is, as mentioned above, a fairly inefficient form of locomotion (table 4.1). It is a compromise between the morphological demands of below branch feeding and locomotion and the requirements of terrestriality. Whether knuckle-walking preceded bipedal locomotion in hominids is a problem that simply cannot be answered at present. For this reason, the use of living apes as a model of what bipedalism may have evolved from will concentrate on the hindlimb, where the changes are straightforward.

In a simplified sense, a quadruped moves because of the forward force provided by the hindlimbs. Because the center of gravity lies in front of the hindlimbs, their motion produces a powerful forward force, and since these limbs begin their backward motion in a **flexed** (bent forward, or toward the body, at the joint) position, there is great power and distance as they **extend** (straighten out, or bend away from the body, at the joint). The forelimbs act more as struts to support the body weight and the forces resulting from forward motion; they also act to guide the direction of motion. Two main groups of muscles act on the hindlimb to produce motion. Their actions can be determined by their position relative to the joints between the limb bones since these joints are the only places where motion can take place. Muscles that act in front of the hindlimb joints can only produce a forward bending motion. At the hip this motion brings the femur (see figure 4.1) upward and forward, closing the angle at the joint *(flexion)*. At the knee this also brings the tibia forward, but in doing so it opens the angle between the femur and tibia (**extension**). At the ankle, muscles that act in front of the joint act to flex it. Muscles acting behind the joints cause the opposite motion. At the hip and ankle this is extension, while at the knee it is flexion.

In a quadrupedal ape (see figure 4.2), the *quadriceps* group (especially *rectus femoris)* and *sartorius* are powerful muscles that swing the leg forward when it is off the ground. Their leverage is obtained by the angle of the pelvis; because the pelvis is tilted forward and its top part, the **ilium** (figure 4.2), is very long, the pelvic attachment of these muscles lies far in front of the hip joint (the **acetabulum**, or hip socket, of the pelvis). After this limb touches the ground, and the forward motion of the trunk brings it into the approximate position shown in figure 4.3, the hip extensors begin to contract. In apes, these extensors are mainly in the hamstrings muscle group. The same forward tilt of the pelvis and long bottom portion, the **ischium**, positions the hamstrings well behind the acetabulum, providing for their leverage. The hamstrings also have an attachment at the back of the femur, and their fibers merge with the *tensor fasciae latae* muscle, passing to the side and front of the knee. Thus while they extend the hip, they also extend the knee, adding to the forward acting force on the trunk.

This pelvic morphology provides a normal (for a quadruped) pelvic inlet shape - the shape of the middle circumference at the inside of the pelvis that a baby first encounters during birth as it enters the bony part of the birth canal. This inlet is long and narrow (see figure 4.4), and the head of the baby (also long relative to its breadth) is oriented to take advantage of this, with the head facing toward the **pubis** (the front part of the pelvis). Since it is desirable for the pelvis to be long in the front-to-back direction, as described above, as M.M. Abitbol argues there are no evolutionary constraints from head size that limit the size of the birth canal. In fact, the pelvic inlets are unusual in the apes, in that they are much larger than the baby's head size at birth. In monkeys these sizes are almost the same, and as discussed below the human condition is to have head size larger than the pelvic inlet. W. Trevathan suggests that the discordance results from the very broad shoulders of apes, part of their arboreal locomotor adaptation but even newborn shoulders are so broad that broken clavicles are reported during ape births. It is shoulder breadth and not head size that is the limiting factor on these ape pelves.

Adaptations to the ape pattern of terrestrial locomotion involve far more than the hip and thigh, extending throughout the whole lower portion of the body. For instance, the angle at the knee, between the femur and tibia, is close to straight (180°) as seen from the front. This is because it is important to keep the leg supports apart for stability and apes have narrow hips (the distance between the acetabula is small). The knee and ankle are both highly flexible joints and have no position of particularly great stability. The foot, as reviewed by D.L. Gebo, shows a number of compromises between arboreal agility and grasping, and terrestrial stability and weight support (the compromises lean more toward the terrestrial in the much larger gorilla). Thus the back of the foot shows adaptations for **plantigrady** (placement of the heel on the ground, or other support surface, as the leg comes to the end of its forward swing). At the same time apes have long toe bones with joint surface orientations that emphasize transmitting force during **plantarflexion** (bending toward the bottom of the foot, for instance curling the toes when the foot is used for grasping). These joint orientations significantly limit **dorsiflexion** (upward bending at the joints between the toes and the main body of the foot), which is an important element of toe-off during bipedal walking, as is discussed below. With the divergent big toe, the emphasis on plantar flexion is a clear reflection of the foot's ability to grasp.

BIPEDAL APES

Apes can walk bipedally, but not for long periods of time. To maintain an upright stance, they must use the extensors and flexors in the same manner as in quadrupedal locomotion. Maintaining the required leverage for both these muscle groups is accomplished by continuing the same tilted relation of pelvis to femur in the bipedal position (see figure 4.2). This is done by flexing the knee. which sustains the hip in a flexed position. Therefore, for the locomotor muscles to retain their leverage, the hindlimb is not in a stable position; additional muscles must be used to maintain stability. Another area in which ape bipedalism is less than efficient is in trunk balance. During bipedal locomotion there is only one supporting leg. If the center of gravity of the body is not directly over this leg, the trunk would tend to fall toward the unsupported side. The **abductor** muscles acting to the side of the hip, the anterior gluteals (minimus and medius), are in a position to prevent this motion. Ape abductors do not have a good lever arm because their attachment on the pelvis is not far to the outside of the acetabulum position (figure 4.5). However, the long ilium puts the center of gravity in a high position, so *its* lever arm is long. When a ape walks bipedally, it can shift its trunk from side to side to keep the center of gravity over the supporting limb. Another advantage of the long ilium is found in the maximized length of the anterior gluteals. This gives them a long contraction distance, a useful leg motion during vertical climbing.

Ape feet lack two important adaptations that also create problems during their attempts at bipedal locomotion. Their big toe is neither positioned properly nor expanded enough in size compared with the other toes to be effective in toe-off (discussed below, but for the moment consider that walking on ice is walking without toe-off) and this problem is exacerbated by their very long toes with a limited range of dorsiflexion. A second difficulty is that there is no double-arch to the foot bottom. In all, African apes can regularly walk bipedally, but it is a muscularly inefficient form of locomotion for them.

DEVELOPING HOMINID BIPEDALISM

The evolution of hominid bipedalism can be understood from the preceding discussion of the problems facing a bipedal ape. Selection for human bipedalism began as the importance of bipedalism in the early, or perhaps earliest hominids increased. The anatomical changes involved making the locomotion consistent and efficient in terms of muscular expenditure through changes in the morphology of the pelvis, leg (especially femur as this is where most pelvic muscles attach), spine, and foot. H. Ishida estimates a 50% improvement in energy expenditure during bipedal walking with the change from the flexed-joint posture of chimpanzees described above to the fully upright posture of australopithecines and more recent humans. Most of our understanding of these changes is based on the work of C.O. Lovejoy and his colleagues. They are summarized below.

1. development of anterior inferior and anterior superior iliac spines for the flexors' leverage
2. backward projection of the ilium, giving the *gluteus maximus* leverage for extension
   3. vertically shortened ilium and angled **sacrum**:
   - orienting the upper body over the hip joint (the **sacroiliac** and **acetabular** joints are vertically aligned and closer together)
   - lowering the torso's center of gravity
   - but with the disadvantage of decreasing pelvic inlet **dorsoventral** (front to back) length
4. consequent increase in the pelvic inlet breadth and change in the birth position of the head
5. corresponding broadening at the pelvic rim, also providing
   - increased leverage for the balancing (abductor) muscles
   - a broader bowl-like upper ilium surface to support the viscera (the ribs do this in a quadruped)
6. shortening of the ischium
7. oblique orientation of the sacrum so that its base does not block the pelvic inlet and its top is correctly tilted to support **lumbar lordosis** (the concavity in the small of the back that brings the center of gravity over the sacroiliac joint and with its opposite curvature, the **thoracic kyphosis**, creates the trunk's vertical orientation)

Beginning with the muscular leverage problem, hominids maintain leverage for their hip flexors and extensors while at the same time maintaining lower limb stability. Instead of flexing at the hip and knee to tilt the pelvis back into its quadrupedal position, the lower limb can be straight in hominids because of changes in the form of the pelvis that provide leverage for the flexors and extensors in an untilted position. Considering the flexors, the vertically oriented pelvis positioned over straightened limbs, in the hominid upright position minimizes the length of their lever arm. In compensation, hominids evolved two projections on the front face of the pelvis to attain an advantageous position, providing leverage by placing these muscles in front of the hip joint. These are the **anterior** (front) spines: the anterior **superior** (upper) for *sartorius* and the anterior **inferior** (lower) for the pelvic attachment of *rectus femoris* (see figure 4.1).

Leverage for the extensors involved a different solution. A bipedal chimpanzee with limbs in a hominid-like configuration has no leverage for the hamstrings to bring the limb backward. A solution similar to the anterior spines, involving a projection at the rear of the pelvis, is awkward for a variety of reasons, and instead hominids attained a solution which solved both this problem and another as well. In hominids, the hamstrings do not provide forward force during stride. Instead, in the most dramatic change that accompanies obligate bipedalism the posterior gluteal muscle, *gluteus maximus,* provides this force, the few times it is necessary (see below) in stride and much more often in running or climbing. This muscle attaches broadly across the outside and back of the pelvis, extending to the back and side of the upper part of the femur shaft. The new position for *gluteus maximus* was attained by bringing the top rear portion of the pelvis backward and downward (figure 4.2); placing *gluteus maximus* behind the hip instead of off to its side. The backward extension of the ilium's rear edge creates a notch at the back of the bone called the **greater sciatic notch**, between the *gluteus maximus* attachment area and the more vertically oriented lower portion of the pelvis. In its new position, the muscle also acts to stabilize the trunk, preventing it from pitching forward when the flexors are used to swing one of the legs forward. The importance of *gluteus maximus* in trunk stabilization, as well as running and climbing, is reflected in the fact that it is the largest muscle in the human body.

Two associated changes involve the sacrum, the back part of the pelvis that is directly under the spine. The sacrum holds the entire weight of the upper part of the body. To keep this weight centered above a line passing through the acetabula, the joints with the lower part of the body, the sacrum must be tilted forward relative to the ilium. Actually, this re-creates the angle of the sacrum in the pelvis of a quadruped. If upper body weight is much in front of or behind a line between these hip-joints, there is twisting at the hip that creates the needs for muscle action to maintain stability at the joint - an ineffective solution for a problem better avoided. In a second change, the application point of the upper body weight is brought closer to the acetabulum by shortening the height of the ilium. The need to minimize twisting within the frame of the pelvis by keeping the sacral-vertebral joint and acetabular joints in a straight line constrains how far posterior the sacrum can be. Consequently this creates a restraint on the anterior-posterior dimension of the pelvis. In quadrupeds this anterior-posterior dimension is important because of their broad shoulders, but there was nothing to prevent the transverse axis of the inlet from becoming the elongated one. In bipedal hominids, the anterior-posterior dimension was shorted, the breadth between the hip joints increased, and the birth orientation of the head changed as a consequence. This is discussed further below.

The changes in the orientation of the sacrum also affect the base of the sinusoidal curves in the backs of hominid bipeds that are unique to them. The lumbar lordosis, thoracic kyphosis, and cervical lordosis of the vertebral column are a consequence of verticality and bring the center of gravity of the thorax over the acerabular axis (a line drawn between the acetabula).

With the decreasing importance and changed orientation of the hamstrings, the lower rear portion of the pelvis where they attach, the ischium, becomes shorter. Finally, the leverage for the abductor muscles, the anterior gluteals, that bring the trunk or the legs from side to side, already less than efficient in bipedal apes, is worsened by these changes. Moreover, with the decreased ilium height, the center of gravity is lower, lessening the contribution of shifting the trunk to lateral balance. However, the importance of lateral balance is much greater, as bipedalism requires that the body is usually supported by only one leg during locomotion. Together, the changes move the hip joints farther apart and *decrease* the leverage for the abductors in lateral balance. The compensation evolved in hominids is to increase the distance of these muscles outward from the acetabulum. On the pelvis this involves swinging the top of the pelvis dramatically outward (figure 4.3), lengthening the lever arm - the distance between the abductor attachment and the hip joint. On the femur this involves lengthening the neck (the bone between the head and the shaft (where the anterior gluteal muscles attach). Together, these changes place the anterior gluteals in a very advantageous position for the balancing function. This additional pelvic broadening is also required by the need to support the lower viscera during the upright stance. The outward or lateral flare of the hips is more prominent in men today (who, actually, have a more early hominid-like pelvis) than it is in the broader-hipped women because women's pelvic inlets must be broader as well in order to give birth to very large-brained babies. Besides this broadening, the top rim of the ilium is curved, almost circular as seen from above, and the front of the pelvis extends more anteriorly, which places the acetabulum slightly anterior to the exact side of the pelvis and puts the center of the iliac blade directly above it..

These are not the only pelvic changes involved in the evolution of hominid bipedalism. For instance, with the widened distance between the tops of the legs, special features had to evolve which provided for the ability to swing the leg toward the midline of the body during locomotion (the supporting foot should be as much under the center of gravity of the body as possible). However, the major changes discussed above are the most dramatic, and the most easily interpreted from fossil remains of the pelvis.

Associated changes in the femur, while less marked, are still clearly observable. The most important change, also affecting the lower leg (tibia and fibula) is a dramatic increase in bone length. Long legs are an important component of stride (see below), as they slow the frequency of the gait, increase the distance between footfalls, and increase forward momentum in the free-swinging leg (when there is rotation, momentum is mass times the distance from the center of rotation, the hip joint in this case, and a longer leg increases both). The *gluteus maximus* attachment shifts from the side of the bone to its rear. The distance between the head of the femur (the rounded top portion that fits into the acetabulum) and its vertical shaft increases in hominids as the result of the greater lateral flare of the ilium. There is a flattening of the femur's bottom, corresponding to its stable vertical position. And, because the top of the femur is brought far away from the midline of the body by lengthening the anterior gluteal lever arm, while its bottom must be close to the midline because the supporting foot must be under the center of gravity, human femur shafts have a significant angle relative to the vertically oriented lower leg. In contrast, an apes standing erect has a straight alignment between the lower and upper legs. At the top, the pelvis is narrower across the hips, while at the bottom the legs are further apart in erect stance.

The most important remaining changes are in the foot. These have been analyzed in a series of studies by B. Latimer and C.O. Lovejoy. The double arch of human feet, made up of a transverse arch and a very well expressed longitudinal (toe-to-heel) arch, is an adaptation to balance and weight support during bipedalism. However, the longitudinal arch serves an additional critical function by providing leverage for the muscles that are important in toe-off, plantar flexing of the foot as it leaves the ground. In humans the big toe is **adducted** (brought toward the midline of the foot and oriented like the other toes) and unusually **robust**, in the sense of large and thick compared to the other digits. All of the foot digits are relatively short and capable of unusual **dorsiflexion** (upward bending at the metatarsophalangeal joints, between the toe bones (**phalanges**) and the main body of the foot). Dorsiflexion is enhanced by a change in the orientation of the joint surface at the base of each toe bone (see figure 4.6). However this limits the range of plantar flexion, and being combined with the shortening of the toes and the adduction of the big toe *the ability of the human foot to grasp is lost.* The heel (posterior calcaneous) is large, in order to dissipate energy as the foot comes to the ground and the heel strikes it first.

Table 4.2
Average toe flexion for the second digit metatarsophalangeal joint
data from Latimer and Lovejoy (1990)*

	Dorsiflexion mean	Plantar flexion mean
Chimpanzee (n=24)	57°	81°
Australopithecus afarensis	75°	45°
Human (n=20)	74°	44°

*   Figure 4.6 shows this angle

THE HOMINID PATTERN OF LOCOMOTION

Human walking, a behavior reflected in the complex of changes discussed above, is a unique gait in the primates. Its special features are best reflected in stride, a particularly efficient translation of gravitational energy into forward momentum, as a large leg freely swings forward with minimal muscular energy when people walk at a maximally efficient pace. (At faster or slower paces there is muscular control of the swinging leg, slowing or speeding it). M. Abitbol has shown that human walking is more energy-efficient than quadrupedal locomotion in well-adapted quadrupeds such as dogs. For instance, respiratory rate is 1.7 times faster in quadrupedal dogs. As table 4.1 shows, human bipedal stride is *very much* more efficient than knuckle-walking. It is in this efficiency that at least part of the adaptive advantage to the human form of locomotion must be found. According to Lovejoy there are three primary components to stride. Each of these are linked to the anatomical changes discussed above.

      1.   Trunk progression, maintaining momentum
      2.   Trunk support, the lateral balance mechanism
      3.   Limb progression, the pendulum gait

Stride begins with toe-off as the non-supporting foot leaves the ground (just as the heel of the other foot strikes it). Toe-off relies on an adducted orientation for an expanded big toe, and a longitudinal arch along the foot, as powerful plantar flexion of this digit propels the foot off the ground while the muscles in front of the hip, *sartorius* and q*uadriceps femoris,* contract to bring the leg forward as the hip is flexed and the knee extended. They soon stop contracting; the leg continues to swing forward as a free pendulum for most of its arc. With a forward tilt to the trunk, the swinging pendulum action of the leg translates the brief flurry of muscle action and the force of gravity into forward momentum in the leg. This is the source of the body's forward motion, and it clearly accounts for the reason why human legs carry about 2/5 of the body's total weight. Toward the end of the swing, *gluteus maximus* and the hamstrings begin to contract (the hamstrings can effectively act as extensors because the upper leg is flexed), bringing the leg down to the ground under control. As the heel strikes the ground there is a continued short period of *gluteus maximus* activity, stabilizing the trunk against the action of *sartorius* and q*uadriceps femoris* as they begin the swing phase of the other leg by flexing at the hip. As the forward moving trunk passes over the now-supporting leg, the pendulum action begins again on the opposite side. Notice that in the striding gait the main hip extensor, *gluteus maximus,* does not act to thrust the body forward, as hip extensors must do in quadrupeds. The major muscle of the hip barely functions at all, and when it does it is a stabilizer and not a propulsive muscle! This is what makes human stride energy-efficient - really a matter of the silence of the hams.

It is the momentum of the forward swinging leg and the displacement of the center of gravity in front of the supporting leg that brings the body forward. The speed at which stride is most efficient differs from individual to individual because of differences in leg proportions and weight. Each one of us can find that speed by walking at our most comfortable rate. Stride can also differ in reaction to the weight of shoes. The biomechanical difference between stride in an individual who is bare foot *versus* wearing a pair of K-Mart steel-toe boots is probably greater than all of the changes in leg length and mass that effected this mechanism throughout the course of human evolution!

Walking involves more than an anterior-posterior leg motion. Lateral balance is accomplished by a combination of slight trunk shifts to bring the center of gravity closer to being over the supporting leg, and the use of the anterior gluteal abductors on the side of the supporting leg. These muscles fire for virtually the entire swing phase. Another problem requiring solution occurs during the swing-phase of gait, when the leg must be internally rotated to help bring the foot under the center of gravity at the point when it reaches the ground and begins to support the body. The best positioning for the supporting leg is accomplished, in part, by the inward cant of the femur (the acetabulum is positioned slightly forward of the exact side of the pelvis), but there must also be some internal rotation of the leg. Most of this is accomplished by the rotation of the pelvis at the hip joint of the supporting leg. No particular muscle is required for this, as it is a consequence of the mostly forward but somewhat inward direction the leg begins to move at toe-off. Y. Rak argues that to some extent, rotation about the supporting leg adds the breadth of the pelvis to the length of the leg in controlling stride length, but since the normal amount of internal rotation is about 10° this addition is very small.

Other gaits, of course, require the activity of *gluteus maximus* and other propulsive muscles. Running and climbing would be impossible without the extensive use of this major muscle, and the hamstrings play an important role as well. In the crouched position at the beginning of a race, a sprinter recreates many of the advantages of quadrupedalism. The hips and knees are flexed (the hamstrings regain their leverage) and the center of gravity is well in front of the hips. While accelerating during running, the hamstrings are also used as extensors; leverage is provided for them by leaning the trunk forward. Because these gaits require the activity of more muscles, they are more tiring. Many people utilize both the speed and distance advantages of running and the low energy advantages of striding by alternating between these gaits.

There is, however, more to the human adaptation for running. As D.R. Carrier has detailed, this form of locomotion required some additional adaptations to become energy-effective. While human slow and fast walking is energy efficient in terms of oxygen consumption (see table 4.1), the energetic cost of human running is relatively high in comparison with other mammals. Carrier reports that a running mammal of human size would be *expected* to consume about 0.10 milliliters of oxygen per gram of body mass per kilometer traveled, but they actually use more than twice as much. Yet, humans are particularly good long distance runners and there are numerous reports of hunters running down animals until they are slowed from overheating or exhaustion and can be killed. Six things combined to make humans energy-effective long distance runners:

1. Breathing independent of locomotion. Bipedalism releases the lungs from the dictations of the expanding and contracting chest cavity during quadrupedal running, so that breathing can be faster or slower than the rate of forelimb motion.
2. Long legs. These provide more than long stride length as they maximize the amount of distance that energy is translated into, at the expense of speed (or acceleration).
3. Arched foot. The elastic tendons that maintain the arch in the human foot also store energy: strain energy created at foot fall is briefly stored and returned as elastic recoil during toe off, likening the foot during running to bouncing a rubber ball.
4. Sweating. Sweat evaporation is the most efficient mechanism for dissipating metabolic heat, as many calories are used in changing the physical state of sweat from liquid to vapor (sweating is also discussed in Chapter 7, where the consequences of water dependence are considered).
5. Large thyroid and adrenal glands. These produce some of the hormones that mobilize and control the rate of muscular utilization of carbohydrates and fatty acids. Large body stores of these, used over the period of running, extend the time before the depletion of muscle glycogen leads to fatigue.
6. Larger lung size, reflected in a large chest cavity. In fact, the expansion by broadening of the upper part of the thoracic cage creates the "barrel-shape" characteristic of *Homo sapiens* but not earlier hominid species or any other hominoid.

Finally, while this discussion has concentrated on evolutionary changes in pelvis and hindlimb, the locomotor shift to hominid bipedalism may also have resulted in forelimb changes. These changes are somewhat more difficult to model because they came from the termination a function (use of forelimbs in locomotion), not from a change in function and certainly not from any particular requirements of bipedalism. Our forelimbs are certainly shorter and less muscular than those of similarly sized apes; yet, chimpanzee tool-making experiments show that their forearms and hands are surprisingly weak in these activities. Moreover, the specifics of what these involved is also obscure for two reasons. First, the locomotor pattern that characterized *prebipedal* hominids is still a subject of speculation (see Chapters 3 and 5). As a consequence, the immediate ancestral condition of the forelimb is unknown - in particular whether there were adaptations to knuckle-walking. In fact, it remains unclear whether any significant changes at all characterize the earliest hominid forelimbs. Because human forelimb length does not differ significantly from many other large primates, it is quite possible (see Chapter 6) that there was no reduction of forelimb length in the earliest hominids (the apes, by this interpretation, increased forelimb lengths during their separate evolutionary trajectories). The implication of this interpretation is that selection on early hominid forelimbs underwent no significant changes and their morphology reflects the ancestral condition, Second, with the exception of some changes in the hand there has been little subsequent variation in the forelimb during the course of hominid evolution, providing virtually no useful guidance for "backward reconstructons" of what this complex may have been like earlier. Three things are clear:

1. All early hominids (loosely, australopithecines) have forelimb lengths that are similar to living people, relative to trunk length or body mass (estimates) and much shorter than ape forelimbs.
2. A powerful human-like grip is not developed, digit lengths are short, but the thumb is longer than in any living ape.
3. The earliest identifiably hominid forelimbs show dramatic strength adaptations (especially in flexion of the radius and ulna).

These features could be reflections of an evolutionary pathway from virtually any earlier form of quadrupedalism, but it is most likely that they correspond to unique aspects of early hominid adaptation. It is has been popular to relate them to the special requirements of arboreal activities or vertical climbing in an adaptation that somehow compromised bipedal abilities, a theory suggested by R.L. Susman, J.T. Stern, and W.L. Jungers (in various combinations of authorship). However, for reasons discussed above and in the next chapter, the early hominid capacity for these arboreal behaviors was expressed in an anatomical framework that so strongly reflected the necessary adaptations to obligate bipedalism that all locomotor compromises were with the arboreal aspects of the early hominid repertoire.

THE HOMINID PATTERN OF BIRTHING

Apes, as discussed above, give birth like many other quadrupeds, with the baby's head oriented top-to-bottom, facing the pubis. The dramatic modifications of the pelvis that evolved with obligate hominid bipedalism so changed its internal shape that the birth process was altered in response. Based on the work of R.G. Tague, it would appear that evolutionary constraints on the back-to-front dimension of the bony birth canal resulted in a transverse expansion, increasing the distance between the acetabula (and exacerbating the problem of lateral balance, as discussed above). Babies of the earliest hominids rotated during the birth process to enter the pelvic aperture that surrounds the birth canal with heads oriented transversely (hip-to-hip). They continue through the canal in this orientation and subsequently emerge from the broad pelvic outlet in the same position, with the face pointing toward one hip (figure 4.7). A. Mann suggests the combination of broad inlet *and* outlet may have responded to the problems of birthing a large-shouldered hominoid baby - the head was too small to create an evolutionary constraint. Modern human birthing, as reviewed by K. Rosenberg, has become even more complex as the much larger fetal head size cannot exit through the pelvic outlet in the transverse orientation. This is because even with the head deformations that occur during birth, its breadth does not fit through the constrained anterior-posterior dimension. The head enters the inlet transversely oriented, but the baby rotates a second time as it descends through the pelvic aperture so that the birth position is, once more, front-to-back. This second change, according to Mann, occurred when head size became so large that it, rather than the shoulders, came to constrain the size and shape of the pelvic aperture. A rounder aperture was necessary and the proportions of the pelvic outlet required the second rotation for successful birthing (a difficult enough problem in recent and living humans as the average baby's head size has come to exceed the average dimensions of the pelvic aperture).

Unlike the orientation in quadrupeds, however, the front of the human baby's head normally faces the sacrum. The mother cannot see the head while birthing (she cannot clear the nose and mouth mucous or help in many other ways) and the process is so long and laborious that W. Trevathan characterizes it as requiring obligate midwifery. Human births are unlikely to be successful without help, and differing from every other hominoid primate they are social rather than solitary.

THE EARLIEST ADAPTATION?

Of all the unique hominid features, human bipedalism may be the first to have appeared. The stride adaptations, in particular, result in a complex of skeletal changes that can be seen in virtually every part of the pelvis and hindlimb. Functional interpretation of the locomotor patters of the earliest hominids has followed a rocky road, a full gamut from S. Washburn's "they could run but not walk" to F. Spoor's "they could walk but not run". But in a triumph of biomechanical analysis these diminutive hominids were clearly revealed to be obligate bipeds without compromises in their anatomy for any other form of locomotion, and the implication that this unique adaptation was their primary one is unavoidable. The birthing constraints that followed created a second set of limitations affecting pelvic anatomy. Clearly, the behavioral changes advantaged by this complex adaptation must be important in the process of hominid origins. This topic will be expanded in Chapter 5.

Features Associated with Intelligence

Intelligence, and the features associated with it, would seem to be the most evident if not the most important hominid characteristic. This hominid behavioral complex is an elaboration of a trend in all of the higher primates, and the initial developments in the hominid line must have been based on features and capabilities already present. There are novelties, however, the most important of which is human language. Other aspects of regular structure in human behaviors appeared as well, and culture ultimately came to rival the brain as a source of adaptive organization and information.

The evolution of intelligence in our lineage is marked anatomically by changes in relative brain size, as well as in the structure or organization of the brain. Analysis of these changes can be approached in three ways, all utilized in the discussions below:

- **comparative neuroanatomy:** comparisons of brain structure in living species
- **paleoneurology:** studies of **endocasts**, the impressions that the brain leaves on the inside of the cranium, created naturally during fossilization or made artificially if a fossil cranium is partially intact.
- **archaeology:** technological or organizational evidence of past behavior.

BRAIN SIZE AND INTELLIGENCE

The size and organization of human brains, and many aspects of their functioning, provide the bases for those most unusual of human capacities - the intellectual ones. One obvious characteristic of human brains is their size. In terms of absolute size, the approximately 100 billion neurons of the human brain make it the largest of all primates and one of the largest of all living animals. At some 2% of body weight, our brains consume 20% or more of our metabolic energy, according to R.L. Holloway. Within a related group of taxa, such as the Catarrhini, brain size and intelligence seem to be related between species. For instance, holding body size constant at perhaps 50 kg, a chimpanzee has a much larger brain than a large baboon and a human has a much larger brain than the chimpanzee. Virtually any measure of intelligence ranks these three in the same order.

Yet human intelligence cannot be completely attributed to the absolute size of the brain alone, since other less intelligent mammals may have equally or larger sized brains, for instance elephants or sperm whales. But if one turns to the allometric explanation, that their large brains are simply a consequence of the requirements of running their massive bodies, thereby implying that a large brain in a smaller mammal is intelligence-related, the fact is that other very large animals have *not* required large brains to run their massive bodies. Certain of the extinct dinosaurs, for instance the 5,000-pound stegosaur, survived many times longer than elephants or whales have to date with very much smaller brains than these giant mammals, the size of a grapefruit. The issue is confused as this does suggest there is more to the large brain sizes of massive mammals than simply running a gigantic body. Absolute brain size alone may be an indicator of intelligence, but it is an ambiguous one.

Perhaps the size of the brain relative to body size provides a better indication. In this measure, humans contrast dramatically with other large-brained mammals. For instance, while the human brain is about 2% the weight of the body, this proportion is more than two orders of magnitude less for the sperm whale, less than 0.02%. However, at the other end of the size scale, some of the smaller prosimians have an even higher ratio of brain-to-body weight than humans. One might explain the lack of human-like intelligence in prosimians by the argument that their absolute brain size is too small to sustain the necessary level of complexity. Yet porpoises have brains which are relatively equal in size to those of humans, and although their intelligence has yet to be clearly determined or validly compared with ours, one suspects that if a human level of complex intellectual activity was present, it would have been discovered.

One systematic approach to the relation of brain size to body size is taken by H. Jerison and others (for instance R. Dunbar, whose analysis of relative neocortex size is discussed in Chapter 3). Jerison has tried to estimate how much brain volume it takes to operate basic body functions and survival activities for taxa of various sizes, and from this to estimate the amount of "left over" volume (excess neurons) presumably associated with higher-level activities. Jerison's procedure is to determine the general allometric relation of brain size to body size for large taxonomic groups over a wide size range. Once this is accomplished, taxonomic groups with an exceptionally large relation stand out by deviating above the allometric curve that expresses the group-wide relationship. He noted a number of similarities that link the species falling above this curve (i.e. with excess neurons). Perhaps the most important of these for the purposes of this discussion is that they tend to be social mammals. The procedure works well within the primates: based on the allometric relationship general to placental mammals, Anthropoidea have more excess neurons than Prosimii. Carrying this further, humans have considerably more excess neurons than any of the apes, and the number of excess neurons have increased throughout human evolution.

It is difficult to deny the importance of the increasing relative brain size occurring through the latter third of through human evolution, and of the relation between the expansion of brain size and the evident increase in behavioral complexity and intelligence in our lineage. Yet, the picture is more complex than a simple direct relation of excess neurons and intelligence would indicate. For instance, chimpanzees fall well above the allometric curve and have numerous excess neurons, but gorillas fall below this curve. This difference would imply behavioral variation far beyond that observed. There are clearly some structural differences between hominid brains and the brains of our closest relatives which account for some aspects of the dramatic differences in behavioral complexity. As R.L. Holloway points out the human **cerebral cortex** and **cerebellum** are just the size predicted on the basis of primate allometry, but the **visual cortex** is 21% smaller than predicted, while the **parietal association cortex** just anterior to it is much larger (see figure 4.8).

For these and other reasons, Holloway disagrees with the excess neurons analysis as an explanation for human evolution, arguing in effect that counting neurons in brains with different neuroanatomical features (differing circuitry) compares apples and oranges. Holloway and others suggest that the organization of the brain is of primary importance. Within similar magnitudes of size, the organization has far more to do with behavioral complexity than the amount of "extra" volume. Neural organization in animal species, however, is understood in only the most general way. Actual neural circuits are extraordinarily difficult to trace; it can take a decade to determine and compare the left-to-right visual tracking systems of experimental animals such as frogs and turtles. Similar experiments cannot be performed on humans. Thus the prospects of tracing the neural circuitry for complex human behaviors in the near future are dim, at best.

This explains why most studies of human brain organization are of the "black box" type. In such studies, models of how the brain *should* function to account for its capabilities are constructed from the analyses of behavioral changes associated with brain damage from accidents, strokes, or tumor removal. "Black box" analysis can be extremely valuable. After all, the structure of the DNA molecule was determined this way. Without having viewed the structure of the molecule, Watson and Crick were able to determine how it had to be formed to account for its capabilities. However, brain function in humans is much more complex than DNA function. As yet, there is no way to test any of the "black box" models that have been proposed.

In all, while it seems clear that there must be some relation between brain size and intelligence, what this relation is and how it might be expressed in terms of the mechanics of brain operation remain unclear. The relation seems to account for systematic variation between some groups of closely related species, but it may not work between others and it certainly is a weak enough link to be very poorly expressed by the limited variation within species. The contention that brain size expansion in human evolution is associated with increasing intelligence is unquestionably valid, but neuroanatomists are a long way from being able to state explicitly what mechanisms link them.

CONSCIOUSNESS

Both paralleling and supplementing the approaches to brain size and intelligence are a range of considerations about how consciousness, or self-awareness, evolved. Assuming that consciousness is biologically rooted in the structure and function of brains, at the extremes are approaches that most comfortably fit the excess neuron relationship, and others that emphasize the uniqueness of human consciousness and could link its evolution to structural changes in the brain. D. Griffin argues the point that thinking and consciousness are not limited to humans, making the case that this topic is poorly understood mainly because of animal behaviorists' avoidance of the issues surrounding it. It was the unverifiable speculations about animal thought earlier this century that led to the widespread acceptance of B. Skinner's approach to animal behavior, treating the mental activities of organisms as irrelevant to understanding their behavior. In this approach it was assumed that because only the inputs and outputs to the mind could be observed and scientifically measured, they could be related to each other without concern for the internal mental processes that provide the actual relationship between them. Questions about mind and thought are questions about an area of behavior that cannot be addressed in the Skinnerian approach. Griffin, in contrast, does focus on these questions, and presents three lines of evidence to suggest that animals are conscious and can think:

1. There are similarities in neural function (areas of the brain, and neural connections and the way they are formed) linking humans and other birds and mammals that have been studied.
2. Animals are complex and versatile in their behaviors, consistently able to modify their behaviors in adaptive ways, even in new circumstances.
3. The complexities of animal communication reflect the complexities of the mental states they express.

According to Griffin's model, humans evolved their characteristic mental abilities by expanding on their general mammalian and specifically primate mental abilities. He distinguishes perceptual consciousness (mental awareness of perceptions) and reflective consciousness (self awareness, thinking about thoughts). The latter is an integral part of human thought, and while data suggesting the presence of reflective consciousness can only occasionally be found in other species, chimpanzees provide particularly good behavioral evidence of self awareness. As an example of 'more of the above', Griffin's model of human consciousness and thought would clearly fit an excess neurons model, since it assumes continuity with and links to other animal species, with the greater complexity and sophistication of humans a consequence of the fact that no other species has as many excess neurons.

A number of primatologists have proposed models for the evolution of human mental abilities based on these precepts, approaching the human problem as an extension or special case of the forces shaping the primate mind. One of the most influential of these is K. Milton's hypothesis that complex mental abilities have important functions in foraging for unpredictable resources. Cheney and Seyfarth have revealed much more complex mental abilities in non-human primates than previous workers had realized existed. The understanding of process and recognition of overlapping abilities serves to promote the recognition of non-human and human continuity.

At the other extreme is the contention that mind and thought, at least as they are expressed in humans, are a unique phenomenon that can be linked to human biology, evolutionary history, and socioecology. Articulately expressed by R. Alexander, human intellect is viewed as the consequence of a 'runaway social evolution'. He argues that intellect arose to deal with the specific contradictions between the aggressiveness required by intergroup competition and the social cooperation required within evolving human societies. For Alexander, consciousness consists of three cognitive elements with independent origins:

1. reflective consciousness (self awareness)
2. mental scenario (imagined possible alternatives) building
3. the ability to interpret the mental states of others

He argues that these combine to bring benefits for those who can mentally model alternative behaviors and accurately anticipate the responses of others - abilities that fit well with A. Wallace's cognitive equivalence structure analysis of social interactions, discussed below.

Fundamentally, Alexander envisages the brain as a social tool that evolved to its present elaborate form to deal with the uncertainties of complex social life. It is a maxim of information theory that as the amount of information in a system increases, the uncertainty within the system must increase as well. This is why the internal states of complex systems are much more difficult to establish accurately than the internal states of simple systems. Maximizing an automobile's performance is complex, there are many alternative pathways and it is virtually impossible to predict which is the most successful, while maximizing the performance of a bicycle is much easier because there is less to alter. What makes the human case different from other social mammals is encapsulated in what Alexander describes as 'runaway social evolution': the very capabilities that let people maximize their reproduction in a social context are, by necessity, shared within the society so that the consequence of social competition is even more intense social competition.

But there is more to human mental abilities than the direct consequences of social competition. A very different and far more aggressive series of competitive strategies characterize the intergroup relations that developed, according to Alexander, first between hominids and closely related primate species, and later directly between human groups, as hominids progressively achieved the ecological dominance they enjoy today. Evolving to meet these contradictory, socially defined demands in the context of the uncertainties implied by complex social structure is a reflexive consciousness that allows the creation of mental scenarios, or imagined possible alternatives, and adjusts the scenarios to best fit different imagined circumstances by predicting the responses of others. These abilities rely on the displacement of the immediate for securing advantages in the future, and almost certainly require the evolution of the ability for self-deception -- an important aspect of the ability to deceive others. Alexander argues that self-deception plays a critical role in group cohesion because it fosters the ability to achieve common goals and accept shared understandings or explanations of the world (dogmas, myths) that underlie social unity. In a parallel argument, Wallace (see below) contends that role differences in the shared cognitive maps of human interactions would be impossible without deception - the absence of a shared understanding of some social interactions.

Clearly this model is congruent with Holloway's concept of a neural reorganization during human brain evolution, discussed below. From an evolutionary standpoint, perhaps the most interesting question is the extent to which these evolutionary aspects of mind and thought can be linked to structural differences in human brains.

A MODEL OF HUMAN BRAIN FUNCTION

The neurons of the cerebral cortex are the site of mental activities. These cells receive signals through highly branched dendrites and send information along unbranched axons. Neurons differ from the gross to the molecular level, but cells with similar functions group together in modules that extend through the cortex. However, within these modules there is cellular specialization for different tasks. For instance in the part of the cerebral cortex at the back of the head that processes visual inputs, the visual cortex, one area responds to directional motion, another to color, and another to form. Information processing from the senses occurs hierarchically in these modules; as the distance from the input source grows, the neurons increasingly respond to the more abstract aspects of the input. This information flow is not along a single pathway. Sensory information is divided into multiple signals at the sense organs themselves, and their processing proceeds in parallel. The integration of this information, both from multiple inputs and from discrete functional areas, is quite complex and almost certainly multistage - it is not simply a matter of all the information converging to one place where it is interpreted. Instead, multistage integration allows for simultaneous perception and comprehension, a hallmark of mental process from those that are as simple as swatting a fly to the complexities of understanding language. An immense number of neural connections must underlie these processes.

Brains, of course, do much more than react to sensory stimuli. Acquiring new knowledge and retaining it are fundamental to the successful adaptations of individuals and of populations that share organized information, and are prerequisites of consciousness. There appear to be two types of learning. Explicit learning is fast, often only requiring a single experience, and when retained as memory it usually involves only a single event and the simultaneous stimuli of its specific circumstances. Implicit learning is a much slower process. It involves sequential inputs from repetitive instances, and when retained as memory there is information about the association of the inputs and the structure of causally related elements.

Obviously everything experienced in the environment is not remembered - what information is stored represents only part of sensory inputs. This is because recognizing the patterns of implicit memory requires the selective destruction of information. It is these patterns that represent the mind's interpretation, or "picture," of the physical world. The brain functions to recognize patterns by disregarding less relevant information. Such patterns can then either be reconciled with similar patterns already stored in the brain, or be stored themselves for future reference. The process of reconciliation involves a comparison between the newly perceived patterns and the stored patterns. The outcome of these comparisons determines how sensory input is processed, and whether the preexisting neural models of "reality" will be modified.

The storage of patterns depends on the actual configuration of connections between brain cells, called neural networks. Some of these connections are established by the genotype, initially or during the later growth of the cells. Others, however, are established and subsequently modified by the experiences of the living organism. Even these connections, however, are not independent of the genes. The mechanism of genetic influence can be seen in the differing neurological processes of short and long term memory. Short term memories rely on changes in the strength of existing connections between neurons while the long term changes require the activation of specific genes that cause the growth of new connections. Song birds, for instance, have been found to significantly increase brain volume when they learn their species-specific songs. Thus, in a real and direct sense, neural structures are both under genetic control (and therefore subject to the evolutionary process) and subject to modification through perception *and* behavior. It is the genetically determined preexisting connections that are of special interest to us. These are actually neural models of yet-to-be-experienced sensory relationships. The more neural models that exist, and the more complex they are, the easier it is for the individual to "learn" the relationships involved. This brings us to one of the primary distinguishing characteristics of human brains, *the inheritance of numerous complex neural models.* These models delimit the nature of "reality" as perceived by the mind, while at the same time they provide the basis for rapidly learning and dealing with an incredibly complex amount of related information. They clearly take up a large amount of room in the brain, and because they are inherited, these models are subject to evolutionary change. It is their evolution that largely accounts for the brain size expansion that characterizes the human lineage.

What are these neural models about? In humans, prestructured relationships (neurological circuitry whose form is, at least in part, under genetic control and therefore whose development requires only some environmental stimulus) appear to underlie a wide range of behaviors that are characterized by rapid learning, marked complexity, and variation within all human cultures but at the same time broad similarity between them. Examples range from skilled hand-to-eye coordination to abstract mathematical ability. More complex and specifically cultural examples include the structural aspects of language grammars, the "grammars" of kinship and other socially defined relationships, and unique cultural capacities such as belief systems.

STRUCTURAL ASPECTS OF HUMAN BRAIN FUNCTION

The initial recognition of organization as information enters the brain depends on connections between areas of the brain which process sensory input. The complexity that the recognition can attain would seem to depend on how complex and extensive these connections are. Moreover, the process of comparing altered or new patterns of organization with pre-existing neural models multiplies in difficulty as the patterns increase in complexity, and ultimately these comparisons come to require a large processing unit in the brain. Many of these structures, whose variation reflects different functions, can be recognized in the brain; fewer, however, can be identified on endocasts. The use of endocasts allows studies of brain evolution to use more than comparisons of living humans with closely related primates.

To begin with, there are primary areas on the cerebral cortex which directly process information from the environment gathered by each sense. There are also primary areas governing muscle functions that create the motor outputs. In the higher primates, there is a tendency for each of these to be surrounded by association areas, in which the functions of the primary areas are modulated. This is because, as mentioned above, neurons further away from the primary sensory area increasingly respond to the more abstract aspects of the input. Destruction of an association area usually results in loss of the ability to recognize objects, although they are still sensed.

In most mammals, the connections between the sensory (input) and motor (output) areas pass through the limbic system of the brain. This is the portion of the brain, located above the stem (see Figure 3.5), which is responsible for emotional control. As a consequence, when patterns are learned relating certain sensory inputs to certain motor outputs, there is a corresponding emotional association which can serve to discourage or reward the learning sequence. Only some of the primates are known to have neural circuitry that bypasses the limbic system with direct connections between the various sensory association areas. These direct connections carry a number of advantages; for instance, arbitrary object naming would be impossible without them since this requires a link between visual and auditory input. However direct connections also bear a disadvantage. Decoupling from the limbic system can make some learning situations more difficult because it makes it harder to associate successful stimulus-response loops with the "rewards" of pleasurable feelings.

Many human and other higher primate behaviors utilize sensory integration, and are far removed from limbic related simple conditioned learning sequences. This is because of the evolution of the parietal association area, at the rear of parietal lobe. In this area, sensory inputs can connect directly with one another without passing through the limbic system. Moreover, motor output can be controlled without limbic involvement. This allows the formation of complex patterns without any emotional association, directly merging information from different senses (cross-modal transfer). In addition, cross-modal association gives the ability to develop neural models of reality which associate relationships beyond those immediately perceivable in the sensory fields. Many scientists believe that this ability provides the basis for conceptualization, and underlies the appearance of symbolic behavior in humans and the great apes.

Recognition and comparison of these complex patterns requires the evolution of a processing unit, located in the frontal lobes. It would appear that several functions of these lobes are unique to humans and chimpanzees. One of these is the ability to treat elements in a sequential order and to separate the relevant from the irrelevant. This ability is applied to processing sensory inputs through the elaboration of connections between the frontal lobes and the various association areas. Thus the frontal lobes act in integrating, sorting, and ordering during the recognition of neural patterns from sensory input, and later they act in the comparisons of these patterns with pre-existing neural models, and the decisions as to how the input will be treated.

A series of related neurological developments are of dramatic importance in human evolution. These involve different parts of the brain and include the appearance of a verbal-auditory association area, a motor-speech area, and a tract of neural fibers connecting them - neuroanatomical features that have yet to be found in living nonhuman primates (although their rudimentary appearance in chimpanzees is suggested by both behavioral and anatomical studies). There is a tract of fibers connecting the parietal association area with the processing unit of the frontal lobes described above. Another function of the frontal processing unit is in relation to the speech areas, since it provides the connection between sensory input and the areas that process the information and control the motor production of speech. Finally, the hippocampus, a component of the limbic system, comes to functionally specialize by expanding its ability to store maps of the spatial environment (including representations of other human beings) on the right side and verbal semantic mapping on the left (the hippocampus is found in both hemispheres of most mammal brains).

LANGUAGE AND LATERALIZATION

The two hemispheres of the human brain are almost symmetrical halves. Each half is concerned with the sensory input from, and the motor control of, the opposite side of the body (except for the eyes - the right visual field of both eyes is connected to the left hemisphere, and visa versa). This pattern, crossing the sensory and motor pathways inside the brain, occurs in all mammals. The hemispheres are connected with each other through a thick series of nerve fibers called the **corpus callosum**. Thus information from one hemisphere is transmitted to the other, and the two hemispheres are functionally integrated. However, they can also operate independently. It is through experiments with brains that have been split (i.e., the corpus callosum surgically cut) that the separate functioning of the hemispheres can be determined. Input can be given to only one hemisphere in a split brain and the characteristics of that hemisphere can be studied.

TABLE 4.3
Some hemispheric differences in human brain function
adapted from Laughlin and d'Aquili (1974), Kolb and Whishaw (1985), and Wallace (1992)

Left (dominant) Hemisphere	Right (non-dominant) Hemisphere
Auditory	**Auditory**
Speech sounds	Melody recognition
Processing of consonant syllables	Vocal non-speech sounds (coughing, laughing, crying)
Symbol translation and analysis	Steady-state vowels
Language production centers	
Recall of auditory images of visual objects	
Visual	**Visual**
Perceptual recognition of conceptual similarity	Drawing, building models from a picture
Naming items perceived	Two- and three-dimensional space relations
	Perceptual recognition of identity
Tactile and Motor	**Tactile and Motor**
Localization and naming of body parts	Contralateral motor control
Contralateral motor control	Tactile pattern recognition
Fine-hand motor skills	Awareness of illness
Hand gestures during speech	
Conceptual	**Conceptual**
Short term memory	"Gestalt-synthetic" operations on perceptual material
Right-left differentiation	Spatial mapping
"Logical-analytical" operations on perceptual material	
Semantic mapping	
Temporal sequential ordering	

Experiments have shown that in most mammals the two hemispheres are similar, often close to being mirror-images of each other. Each has the capabilities and potentials of the other, and memory storage is duplicated in both. They differ quite significantly only in that they deal with the sensory and motor functions of opposite sides of the body. This is a redundant system which may use more storage space than is necessary, but it also allows normal functions to continue if there is damage to one side of the brain. In the course of human evolution there has been a good deal of hemispheric specialization. This seems to involve mainly the language and motor speech production areas, which appear on the left side of the brain, and corresponding areas which are concerned with manipulative ability and geometric perception on the right side. An extraordinary amount of *secondary* information (compiled input such as a 3-dimensional image) is passed through the corpus callosum, since hemispheric specialization requires much more communication between the hemispheres when functions are integrated and associated during normal behavior. The result of hemispheric specialization in hominids was a great increase in both the memory capacity of the brain and its ability to integrate different inputs without significant increase in size. Of course, the aspect of double storage and redundancy was lost, but for humans *culture has largely taken the place of redundant information storage*.

The evolution of language seems tied to the lateralization of language functions through hemispheric specializations (see table 4.12). In experiments with humans whose hemispheres have been surgically disconnected, it has been shown that the larger, dominant, hemisphere alone (the left, in right handed people) is capable of producing relatively normal language behavior. Both the motor and sensory regions involved in language production are found on this side. There are specific regions that have been isolated that mediate the use of vocabulary (nouns and verbs separately) and grammar. Different areas control their implementation. Other neural structures represent particular concepts. These are spread more evenly across both left (dominant) and right hemispheres. Brain functions associated with language, then, do not all occur uniquely in the dominant hemisphere. The right (non-dominant) hemisphere is responsible for the analysis of spatial relationships and the recognition and reproduction of complex visual patterns as in gestalt recognition. While by itself the right hemisphere shows little or no response to spoken language or information in the left visual field, it is capable of written response. In one interesting experiment with an individual with disconnected hemispheres, the subject could not verbally name an object presented to the right visual field, but could write its name with the left hand. In sum, the full range of language-related behaviors involves specializations of both hemispheres.

Thus the functioning of the human brain in language production is dependent on cross-modal transfer and the lateralization of specific functions. The evolution of cross-modal transfer is a prerequisite for combining language and manipulative functions. It may not be necessary to have cerebral dominance in order to have a human-like vocalized language, but these developments are tied together in the hominid line. It may be that the association is a necessary one; perhaps complex linguistic behavior required a degree of connectivity (circuitry between the neurons) that even in a hominid-sized brain could occur only if the cerebral hemispheres had specialized rather than redundant functions. Evidence supporting this possibility is found in another aspect of lateralization. With lateralization comes the appearance of a connecting tract between the motor-speech area and the frontal lobe in the left hemisphere, described above. This tract provides a pathway for information to reach the motor-speech area. The integration of these features suggests that they evolved together. It would appear that the evolution of the structural basis for human language is closely tied to lateralization and hemispheric dominance.

One of the consequences of hemispheric specialization is found in the structural asymmetries of the two hemispheres. According to Holloway, size asymmetry is highly correlated with both behavioral reflections of hemispheric dominance, and handedness. While other primates show some cerebral asymmetry, it is much more strongly expressed and shows more distinct anatomical consistencies, called petalias, in humans (petalias describe extensions of parts of one side of the brain beyond their corresponding parts on the other side). For instance, brains of right handed people typically have a longer left occipital and a broader left parietal region, but a broader right frontal.

HANDEDNESS

A phenomenon tied to the appearance of hemispheric dominance and ascertainable from the fossil record is handedness. 90% or more humans are right handed, involving functions controlled by the left frontal lobe of the brain. While other primates often show hand preferences, there is no evidence of skill differences and other aspects of true handedness in these species, according to a review by D. Falk. Moreover, unlike humans, the side preferred is about equally right and left in other primate species. Handedness and speech seem to appear at the same time in the developing human child, and the close association of these with the dominant hemisphere, suggest that they are controlled by overlapping neurological models. The demonstration of hand preference through asymmetric arm development provides indirect evidence of hemispheric dominance, a condition suggested for early hominids on the basis of their (weakly developed) endocast asymmetries, and by the fact that those few early human specimens with parts of the forelimb preserved from both sides are almost invariably asymmetrically larger on the right.

A more direct source of evidence for hand preference comes from analyses of the stone tools made by early hominids. N. Toth provided a striking confirmation for the endocast studies in his analysis of hand preference in tool manufacture. When successive flakes removed from the core of a stone tool during its manufacture can be identified, handedness is evident in the way the tool is turned as flakes are struck off. Right handed flakers hold the core in their left hand and turn it in a clockwise motion (as they view it), striking flakes off as the tool is turned. Left handed flakers hold the tool in their right hand and turn it in the opposite direction. Each direction produces a different pattern of overlapping flake scars on adjacent flakes. Not all flakes produced by right handed flakers have this orientation, but Toth was able to show that the majority do. The disproportion of tools made by right to left handed people he found is about the same as in a modern tool assemblage, and in experimental tool-making experiments by Harvard students (although an analysis of sidedness for flakes at the Middle Stone Age site of Klasies River Cave, South Africa, failed to reveal hand preference). The implication is that human tool makers from the earliest Pleistocene may usually have been right handed.

NEURAL REORGANIZATION

Studies by R. L. Holloway have focused on the endocasts of early hominid brain cases. These endocasts, depending on their condition, can reflect some or much of the gross external morphology of the brain. Endocast observations allow us to determine *when* some of the important structural chances occurred in human brain evolution. Holloway has been able to show four important ways in which the endocasts reveal that the earliest hominid brains differ from pongid brains. These are:

1. Expansion of the posterior parietal association areas at the expense of the visual area (primary visual cortex) located behind it
2. Greater complexity of the frontal lobes, especially in some of the speech areas
3. Expansion of the temporal lobes, again especially in some of the speech related areas
4. Some hemispheric asymmetry with human-like anatomical details (petalias), although the magnitude of asymmetry is much better expressed in later hominids

These characteristics (see figure 4.8) correspond to some of the unique aspects of the human neuroanatomy discussed above. The regions showing evidence of dramatic expansion in the early hominid endocasts are just those frontal and posterior parietal portions which seem to underlie some of the complex neural models whose behavioral manifestations are regarded as culture. Holloway believes that the earliest hominids had already undergone what he regards as the **neural reorganization** of the hominid line - the structural brain changes that underlie significant new behaviors that form the basis for human language and culture.

Specifically, the expansion of the frontal and the posterior parietal areas provides evidence for cognition, categorization, symbolization, cross-modal transfer, ordering, discrimination of relevant from irrelevant elements in numerous contexts, and a connected verbal-auditory association area and motor-speech area. Moreover, there are indications that motor areas for speech production were fairly well developed.

Thus Holloway's inference from the endocasts is that the earliest hominids were capable of a wide range of human-like behaviors, and that the underlying neural models governing some of these had already become encephalized (genetically encoded so that given the appropriate stimuli, at the right developmental time, the brain will develop significant elements of the neural nets underlying how the behaviors are learned and related). In particular, some of the evidence, especially in the temporal lobes of the early hominids, hints at the presence of both the neurological and motor requirements for a human form of language. Neural reorganization made certain kinds of complex behaviors much easier to learn for these ancient ancestors (just as individuals with an aptitude for mathematics, or foreign language learning, can become proficient at these much easier than others). Of equal importance, and much greater evolutionary potential, by developing a complex genetic basis the encephalization of certain abilities set the groundwork for their subsequent evolution. Our brains appear to differ from the early hominids in size more than in organization, but the behavioral implications of size alone, if this is the main source of difference, are indeed dramatic.

Table 4.4
Major Cortical Regions Involved in Early Hominid Evolution[1]

Cortical Region	Function
Posterior parietal and anterior occipital cortex	secondary and tertiary visual integration with the posterior occipital striate cortex (visual input)
Superior lobule of the posterior parietal	secondary somatosensory
Inferior lobule of the posterior parietal: angular gyrus	right: perception of spatial relations among objects left: symbolic-analytical processing
supramarginal gyrus	right: spatial mapping
Posterior superior temporal cortex Wernicke's area: posterior superior temporal gyrus	comprehension of language
Posterior inferior temporal	polymodal integration, visual and auditory. Perception, and memory of objects' qualities
Anterior prefrontal cortex: **Broca's area** (cap)	motor control of vocalizations, hand movements

[1]   Courtesy of R.L. Holloway

A GENETIC BASIS FOR LANGUAGE: BEHAVIORAL EVIDENCE

The study of linguistic abilities in a deaf child who learned ASL (American Sign Language) from his deaf parents provides independent behavioral evidence that a strong genetic basis for linguistic abilities *was* acquired, and consequently underlies the development and variability of human language. One of the key pieces of data used to show that linguistic abilities have a strong genetic component is based on the fact that there is a critical age for language acquisition. Evidence has traditionally come from studies of linguistic abilities in those rare children who were not exposed to language by that critical time in their development, usually because they were raised by animals or by extraordinarily abusive parents who kept them so isolated that they were not exposed to speech. These studies therefore rely on the pattern of linguistic development in children who are abnormal in many ways, and therefore may not accurately reflect what the human brain can provide by way of linguistic structuring in the absence of normal stimuli.

The new study is important because it involves an otherwise normal child, raised by loving parents who, however, were also deaf and very deficient in their use of sign language. This is because his parents were not taught ASL as children, but rather were sent to a school where they were taught to lip-read. They learned ASL much later in life, and never were able to fully master it. In contrast to his parents, who are the only sign language users he was exposed to, his grammar was correct and he was able to form complex sentences using grammatical rules that were beyond the abilities of his parents - evidence that he was relying on innate ability rather than learning in developing a grammatical knowledge of the language he used. It is one thing to correctly isolate the correct grammatical rules of a language while surrounded by both correct and incorrect and incomplete examples, a success that most of us attain, but quite another to learn these rules when the only examples are incorrect.

LANGUAGE EVOLUTION

Human language, as R. Burling has argued, is a part of a complex communication system made up of quite distinct elements that have different ontogenetic and evolutionary origins, and different functions. These include gestures and calls, "body" language, and structured verbal communication. The verbal communication part is truly unique to humans. It involves the use of a large **lexicon** (the collection of words in a language) in mutually understandable discourse that is based on sentences whose information content is defined by their structure, or grammar. The words are based on **phonemes** (individual sound units) that combine to produce **morphemes** (meaningful combinations of sound units). Two important differences from primate communication systems lie in the fact that phonemes can be combined in an infinite number of arbitrary morphemes, and the shared hierarchical nature of the syntactic (grammatical) rules used to generate sentences from thoughts. These shared hierarchical rules allow meaning to be conveyed as listeners regenerate, in their minds, each sentence they hear. As C. Laughlin and E. d'Aquili review in their discussion of the biogenetic basis for human behavior, language utilizes three kinds of structure:

1. **Surface structure**: the phenomenal arrangement of parts, or the expression.
2. **Underlying structure**: the unconscious cognitive elements and the rules that govern their production of surface structure (in language these comprise the generative grammar).
3. **Neural structure**: the neural networks used in cognition and the subsequent generation of surface structure from deep structure.

In fact, these authors, to whom I owe much for the ideas about language and culture presented here, believe that these structural categories describe more than human language. It is their contention that other aspects of human cognition and social behavior are generated and understood the same ways. Language is both the basis for human cognition, culture, and social behavior, and a model for understanding how they work in an evolutionary context.

In R. Alexander's scheme of the evolution of consciousness, human language plays a critical role as well. He believes that only through one of its unique attributes, displacement (the ability to communicate about things separate in time or space), are social scenarios of any real complexity possible (and see the discussion of equivalence structures, below). A critical role for language, in fact, is a masterful understatement of its importance in human evolution, for as we come to better understand how other aspects of culture function and evolve, it becomes clear that language, culture, and human thought are inseparable parts of the same unique behavioral system.

Has language evolved? It is unlikely to have sprung full-formed from the brow of some ancient ancestor (this would push "hopeful monster" well beyond its most liberally defined limits), but some authors have argued for a saltation explanation, positing a mutation that created human language ability. Of course, in an evolutionary context it is not language itself that has evolved but rather the genetic basis for learning it. Yet, when we discuss the evolution of **osteological** (bone related) or dental anatomy, we focus on the feature and not its developmental pathway. One implication of accepting a premise of sociobiology, that behaviors have a genetic background and are subject to the forces of evolutionary change, is that we can center our interests on the evolution of a behavioral system just as we focus on the evolution of a morphological one. It is proper to address the evolution of language (but not of *a* language, whose changes are within the context of existing genetic structure, just as continued exercise can cause muscles and bones to change form during life without genetic changes).

There is a curious interpretation of language evolution, coming from as widely different sources as N. Chomsky (a linguist) and S.J. Gould (an evolutionist). These scientists, and others, have suggested that while language did evolve, it was not for the purpose of communication. They envisage language as an exaptation, an accidental consequence of humanly large brains (an argument best developed in print by M. Piattelli-Palmarini). In a similar thesis, P. Lieberman holds that the hierarchical rules governing how language is produced from thought, the syntactic structures (sometimes referred to as a universal grammar as it is shared by all people) could not have evolved as an adaptation. He reasons that by promoting mutual intelligibility they *are* universal, and therefore have no genetic variation. Moreover, since syntactic structures are extraordinarily complex, no intermediate form would be advantageous. What these different theories have in common is the denial that human language could have evolved because of the advantages it brings to individuals in a social context. Never the less, this idea is widely accepted.

A number of scientists contend that language confers powerful adaptive advantages to both individuals and their societies, when both ends of the communication link are taken into account. There is considerable evidence for significant individual variations in language skills, according to S. Pinker and P. Bloom. They believe these involve syntactic differences that to some degree reflect variation in underlying structure and the ability to generate meaningful communication from it. As J. Tooby and L. Cosmides suggest, these variations are probably not qualitative and are unlikely to involve basic design features. R. Burling proposes that superior linguistic skills can improve differential reproduction because individuals with them attain higher social status and have more offspring. Genetic changes that improve mutual comprehension by promoting more complex communication are likely to be most often shared within groups of related individuals and can become more frequent because of genic level selection. Other individual advantages include the possibility of a link between grammatical complexity and technology during the course of human evolution (this is discussed by R. Holloway, G. Isaac, and S. Parker). Moreover, the social advantages that accrue from language use almost certainly frame a significant selective importance for language (and other cultural behaviors) in human evolution. One set of such advantages is that language provides a means of scenario building through displacement, and allows for scenarios to be shared, but with differing interpretations by the participants. This form of deception is fundamental to the appearance of role differences that are socially (rather than biologically) defined.

Other theories for explaining increasing language competence, however, rely on the advantages that populations with language have over populations that cannot speak. One currently popular theory ties human biological evolution to the appearance of language. The "Eve" theory of modern human origins is based on the hypothesized replacement of inarticulate populations around the world by an adaptively superior population of language-using modern humans. This theory assumes that the appearance of language was sudden and dramatic. Whether nor not a replacement explanation of modern human origins is tenable can be difficult to test, as the depth of the ongoing "Eve" debate has shown. However, as far as language evolution is concerned, very relevant data come from the timing of evolutionary changes reflecting language ability. The question examined is whether language seems to evolve gradually (not supporting the "Eve" theory), or in several great leaps. Such evidence can be generated by a combination of theory, about language origins and evolution, and fact, about the anatomy of the earliest humans bearing on this problem. The former will be discussed below, and the latter in Chapter 6.

The full scope of hypotheses about the origin and evolution of human language are well beyond the physical constraints and intellectual focus of this book. One particularly convincing scenario presented by D. Bickerton forms the basis of the hypothesis I believe to be most likely. Bickerton (with R. Burling, T. Deacon and many others) argues that human language probably did not evolve from a primate call system - primates calls are the evolutionary precursor of human *non*-verbal communication. Rather, he proposes that language has its roots in the evolving human mind and the abilities of the brains that support it. Mind is linked to language through representational systems, maps that the brain makes of experiences. Consciousness, in his view, is a way that we can represent ourselves and our world *to* ourselves. It is Bickerton's insight that language did not evolve as a system of communication, but rather as a system of representations, abstracting the real or the imagined. Communication, he points out, is not what language *is* but part of what it *does*. Before language can be used to communicate, there must be shared precepts to talk about. This is the function of representational systems.

Representations, as any kind of maps, cannot possibly reflect every detail of what they represent (just as it is said that knowledge is the selective destruction of information). At the same time, representations can have properties that never belonged to the original; for instance, abstractions of envisioned relationships and assumptions about them, and connections to other representations. R. Wallace suggests that the representations that underlay language have their origins in the spatial mappings of all animals. These neurological models of space, he proposes, become increasingly complex in species with seasonally varying adaptive strategies. In hominid evolution, additional complexity in the neurological models comes with the association of social as well as physical environments, as foraging strategies and subsequent food sharing increasingly come under social control. Perhaps of greatest importance, cognitive maps of social space must by necessity place the self in the social context - a requisite of consciousness as Alexander views it (also see O'Keefe, who argues similarly but from a stronger neuroanatomical basis).

Other mammalian species, of course, have well developed abilities for the cognitive mapping of spatial relations, but human cognitive mapping is unique in that it is also directly associated with communication. For instance, excepting humans, in all mammals that have been studied there are cognitive mapping structures found on both sides of the hippocampus - a bilateral component of the brain's limbic system. In humans only the right hippocampus is neurologically specialized for mapping - the left is involved in the production of verbal material. Other relations between cognitive mapping and human language include analogies between the syntactic transformations described below for language production and the topological transformations required by spatial mapping. The relation of cognitive mapping to communication, then, is based on the expansion of spatial mapping to spatial and social mapping and finally to social mapping alone.

Bickerton recognizes two hierarchical levels of these cognitive maps, or representational systems:

- **Primary representational system**: a construct of the mind that represents a map of the external world (it cannot be an exact replica, our senses don't give us that and in any event only some of the world is important for our existence)
- **Secondary representational system**: a second level of abstraction, a representation of our primary representational system provided by language, whose structural characteristics allow us not only to abstract and generalize from reality but to conceive of what could have been or never was, and to model ourselves as part of the social and physical world

All of the information from our senses is processed to attain meaning, and therefore primary representational systems may be species specific, or at least specific to groups of closely related species, because species differ in sensory inputs and how *they* are processed in the brain. Consciousness could be thought of as the ability to evaluate conflicting representations, and Bickerton clearly supports Griffin's contention that it is widely present across vertebrates. Consciousness creates a distance between creatures and the world by allowing them to react to representations, and not directly to stimuli. Representations lead to categories, which must be hierarchical. Categories combine cause-and-effect relationships, are exhaustive in that any level can encompass all of reality (grass and non-grass, for instance), and clearly rely on generalizations. Primary representational systems are, in Bickerton's view, the immediate precursors of language and these categories are protoconcepts for nouns, verbs, and so on. The question is what turns this into language.

Protolanguage is more than a hypothetical reconstructed stage in language evolution. In Bickerton's theory it is the biological underlayment for certain communication systems, for instance characterizing ape communication based on sign language, language used by children under 2, and pidgin languages (languages that develop when two human societies with mutually incomprehensible languages come into contact). Language and protolanguage are different communication systems - protolanguage is not simply "ungrammatical language". He suggests that it differs from human language in the following ways:

- It can be taught to other species
- The mechanisms for learning it are simple and can be triggered throughout life
- The significance of word ordering is different (grammatically dictated in language, habitual and dependent on the thought process in protolanguage)
- Meaning is independent of syntax (structure).

Bickerton argues that protolanguage evolved to incorporate nouns and verbs, names for important things or events, negation, questions, words for quantity, and past and future adverbs (although not true tenses). From this background came, uniquely in the human line, language. This secondary representational system can be thought of as a representation of primary representational systems. If the primary representational system provides a useful model of the world, a secondary representational system provides a model of the model, complete with an individual's actions and their expected or potential consequences. This model became the basis for the underlying structure that developed for language. Without a secondary representational system it is not possible to either scheme or dream about the future. This is an important consideration for examining the consequences of language, as it relates to planning strategies and other aspects of subsistence and land use organization. The advantages to a social primate are great enough for a secondary representational system to have evolved for these reasons alone, independent of communication. Yet, modeling really complex propositions about the world and one's potential activities in it probably does require words.

I view language as an inseparable part of human culture. For instance, in his discussion of the evolution of human capacity for beliefs, W. Goodenough makes the point that belief systems rely on the ability to implement alternative strategies based on recognizing different consequences of social interactions (see the discussion of equivalence structures in cultural interactions below), and argues that this forms the basis for imagination, belief, and ultimately culturally defined systems of belief. It might be more accurate to widen the narrow focus on language as a shared secondary representational system and consider it part of a shared cultural milieu (the same idea of an underlying structure, with a broader application). But sharing need not be limited to the secondary representational system. Protolanguage is communication, and consequently can incorporate shared elements as well. What is interesting is that protolanguage must be based on the same understandings of the shared elements whereas language, as part of the *cultural* milieu, must allow for different understandings of shared elements.

In Bickerton's view, protolanguage did not become true language without saltation, a major mutation incorporating syntax. He believes that this mutation was late in human evolution - a contention which I and others (for instance, see the review of this issue by Burling) find to be the weakest point in his scenario, if not simply indefensible. Language is a secondary representational system that has come to be used for communication because it is shared. Syntax, the hierarchy of rules that are used to generate grammatical vocalizations from thought, is the single most important (if not the only important) element separating protolanguage from language in his view, and by necessity must be the primary shared element (the universal grammar mentioned above). Parenthetically, I would add that there is every indication that some syntax is one of the important language elements that is encephalized. This would account for its pan-specific sharing, the timing of its development in ontogeny, and a number of its other aspects including the localization of several of its features on the brain. In any event, the complexity of syntax, which Bickerton hypothesizes to have originated as a single functioning system all at once, actually makes it improbable for it to have come as the consequence of a single, fortuitous mutation. There is no reason to suppose that the steps of cultural evolution, from the simple to the complex, were actually gigantic leaps. To the contrary, the concept of equivalence structures developed by A. Wallace (see below) explains a mechanism for sharing complex hierarchical constructs that could easily have evolved gradually in their complexity.

Bickerton's evidence for a single late mutational origin of language is primarily based on the sudden way that language replaces protolanguage in the two living analogies, children and pidgin speakers. In the former, he argues that language is much too complex to have been learned, and yet is regularly mastered in a period as short as 6 months. In the latter, creole languages (true mixed languages) rapidly replace pidgins. Even if these arguments are found to be linguistically compelling, there is a serious question of whether they are relevant to understanding the evolutionary process.

There are four sources of evidence that make the single-mutation-late-in-human-evolution idea unlikely.

1. Perhaps most primary, the complexity of language as a system is extraordinary. As linguists such as Burling argue, a single mutation to bring so complex and interdependent a working system from nothing would strain the laws of chance well beyond breaking.
2. R. Holloway contends that the major elements of neural reorganization are already present in the earliest hominid endocasts. He believes that the changes in neural structure thereafter were mainly volumetric, which implies that this major mutation either occurred very early in human evolution or had no effects on the brain's surface

anatomy. If the main requirement of continued encephalization was volumetric, the evidence for brain size evolution suggests that encephalization was gradual and not a single dramatic event.

3. The neurological structures associated uniquely with language production are far too complex for a mutational origin of all or part of this anatomical variation. Studies by T. Deacon, R. Wallace, and others document a neurological system whose complexity, however, could have evolved gradually.

4. Human language depends on the vocal-auditory channel, and the anatomy of this channel was required to change in the process of language evolution in order to create an air chamber that could produce enough phonemes, with characteristics that allowed them to easily combine as morphemes, to take advantage of the open and recursive characteristics of language and the potentially infinite number of messages that can be sent. In fact, one could argue that no other communication channel could take as effective an advantage of this evolving communication system. The evolution of the vocal-auditory channel involves certain anatomical changes in the throat, discussed in Chapter 6. The changes in skeletal anatomy that reflect these do not appear in the earliest hominids, but may well respond to their developing linguistic abilities. The anatomical changes are first found at the beginning of the Pleistocene, in at least two lineages. Skeletal modifications that reflect changes in the vocal-auditory channel characterize, at least, the last third of hominid evolution.

The fact is that syntax is not a monolithic "thing". Bickerton discusses five central features which he believes form an interdependent whole, and there may be more as many linguists are considerably more reductionist in their analysis of this most complex of all human behaviors. Whether this critical structural element of language appeared in fits and starts, or more gradually as selection acted on individuals with differing syntactic abilities, it is very *un*likely to have appeared all at once from nothing. Perhaps the most important point is that accepting Bickerton's quite valid distinction between primary and secondary representational systems (language) implies that there probably was no single, clearly definable point of "origin" for language.

THE EVOLUTION OF CULTURE

Culture is the single concept that is shared by all anthropologists (it is the secondary representational system of our discipline), but nevertheless it may be one of the most poorly defined - A.L. Kroeber and C. Kluckholm once reviewed over 100 definitions of culture and agreed that they were all inadequate. Paleoanthropologists are among the anthropologists concerned with this concept, as virtually all discussions of human uniqueness begin with it. The issue of whether some manifestation of human culture played a fundamental role in hominid origins is still among the most hotly debated (see Chapter 5). The question of whether culture is an important aspect of early hominid adaptation has received the widest range of answers. Over the past decades these have reflected the changing precepts of early hominid behavior, beginning with the mid-century's view of early hominids as somewhat slightly disadvantaged hunter/gatherers of the modern type. Today the pendulum of interpretation has swung to the opposite end of its arc, as early hominids are often regarded as differing from living apes in their ecology but not especially in their behavioral capacities. In fact, as we will discuss later (Chapter 13), some prehistorians have proposed that human culture evolved very recently, perhaps with the appearance of (what some call) "modern" *Homo sapiens* (say 200 kyr or so), or perhaps even as recently as 30-40 kyr. Questions about the role of culture in human evolution, then, have spanned virtually the entire period of hominid existence. Their resolution, if there is one, must begin with an understanding of what human culture is.

The temptation to characterize culture as "what humans do" has been impossible to resist. For instance, culture is often defined as the meanings, values, and standards that people learn and pass on as members of their societies, and its "extragenetic" or "extrabiological" nature is commonly emphasized. This has the effect of rendering cultural evolution impossible to model as it makes culture a monolithic "thing" that exists apart from people and could hardly have appeared incomplete, or in pieces. Another approach to the "what humans do" precept is to consider culture as a composite of many different attributes and abilities, each with its own separate origin. This makes culture an artifact of giving a single name to a broad umbrella covering many different things, and denies the possibility that culture, like language, is a functioning entity with a underlying structure and a shared behavioral "grammar" governing cognition, and shared representational systems - models of reality that provides for mutual expectations and interpretations. Culture-as-an-entity seems to place culture apart from biology and, in doing so, denies the possibility of its evolution. Culture-as-a-composite demands the conclusion that culture-as-an-entity has no real meaning, and that its constituent parts can, and must, be studied independently. Yet however problematic, the fact is that human culture *is* a unique mode of information transmission. Through its organization of behaviors, structural integrity, and complexity, it has come to rival the brain as a source of adaptive organization and information.

Culture is unique not just because it is human, but because it incorporates and links together the two common but independent ways that information is disseminated in animal societies, and passed from generation to generation, transmission by genes and by learned traditions. The specifically human capacity for culture, as the capacity for language, has a genetic basis and has evolved over the course of human prehistory. It is heritable, in the sense that variation in the expressions realized by individuals are a consequence of genetic and environmental variations, including variations in the social environment which is defined by culture. It is probable that the complexity of human culture could only have been attained because of the structural regularities and the rapid but accurate mode of individual learning this genetic basis allows. The idea that human biological and cultural evolution are two interrelated aspects of a unique evolutionary process (c.f. T. Dobzhansky) is based on this linkage of social and biological information transmission systems in the realization that all biological systems are systems of knowledge acquisition. As H. Plotkin perceives the evolutionary process, culture adds additional layers to the information gathering system encoded at the genetic level.

The socially shared and individually learned traditions of other anthropoids are themselves quite different from comparable behaviors in many other animals. Anthropoid traditions involve the social transmission of behaviors such as food processing, tool use, and gestural communication (a primary representational system used for communication) from generation to generation. Yet, it is not the behaviors themselves that are unique to the anthropoids. According to T. Nishada the uniqueness of traditions in the anthropoids is not in the specifics of what is transmitted, but rather in the combination of:

- the widespread nature of primate traditions
- the use of imitation in learning traditions
- the specific teaching of traditions (especially teaching avoidance by discouragement, but also encouragement for certain behaviors)
- the aspects of primate social organization, in particular the differentiation of social roles by age, sex, and rank, that allow traditions to be transmitted through many different channels in addition to the mother-infant link

Human culture must have developed from such a base, so we need consider how and why it evolved to differ.

The evolution of culture, like language evolution, is most effectively viewed as the evolution of both the expressed behavior and its genetic basis. Unlike many aspects of morphology, it is widely assumed that the genetic basis for culture (or, as often phrased, the genetic basis for the capacity for culture) has become equivalent, if not the same, from population to population. This implies that all of the existing variation between human cultures, and the processes of their change that have become the focus of contemporary social anthropology, are independent of genetic variation. The argument supporting this contention (for instance, as detailed by D. Rindos), runs as follows:

- over the course of human evolution, culturally transmitted behaviors were the focus of selection
- selection for culturally transmitted behaviors drove genetic changes improving the capacity for culture

- eventually this cultural selection created a "genetic revolution", fixing (removing the genetic variation from) the capacity for culture
- Cultural behaviors continue to change as they promote adaptation
- Therefore, variation in human cultures has no genetic basis.

In sum, according to this interpretation, which relies on a major mutation or a speciation, culture is so important to adaptation that its genetic basis has become homogeneous. In turn, if homogeneity in the genetic basis for culture could be demonstrated, it would be a powerful argument in support of a major mutation or speciation in human evolution establishing culture.

If true, this would imply that there is no biological sense in which one culture could evolve into another. The change from hunting/gathering to agriculture is not evolution in the biological meaning, although the change was a significant cause of biological evolution.

Yet, the evolutionist's interest in culture is a focus on what *can* evolve. In the evolutionary context the changes in the capacity for culture must have had important effects on the process of cultural evolution. *Something* has evolved over the course of human evolution, and a number of biobehavioral adaptations have evolved *with* it, as well as *to* it. These include:

- prolonged periods of individual maturation
- predisposal to learn certain highly structured behavioral patterns with a fair degree of intrapopulational uniformity in their structural aspects (language and kinship come to mind as prime examples)
- the expressions of these behaviors triggered at set times during ontogeny
- unique coding for cultural information and its transmission, including symbols and patterned technology (automatic responses such as grabbing a tool have become encoded)
- the appearance of culturally defined role expectations with clear biological origins, based on age, sex, and kinship

What is it, then, that has evolved? Several different answers to this question have developed in the anthropological literature. One is based on a reductionist view of culture, considering it the sum of the behaviors that cultural participants engage in. In this view, selection acting on these behaviors causes changes in culture because of the relation of these behaviors to fitness. This approach grows directly out of the Darwinian precept of an individual level for selection, although inclusive fitness theory (i.e. genic level selection) elaborates the approach and eliminates many contradictions in the older ideas.

An alternative answer to the question of what evolves is provided by the more holistic view of culture, the extrasomatic or extragenetic concept that suggests although culture has its basis and its origin in human biology, once in existence it becomes an autonomous tradition and effectively is an alternative to biology in its functions and effects. In this perspective, culture is totally independent of biology, except in the sense that one must have an adequate biological make up to participate in it. Culture, in this view, evolves quite independently of biology although the converse is not true and many biological changes may correspond to new adaptive environments created by changes in culture. The extrasomatic concept of culture has a long history in anthropology, and has become current once again as a response to the various proposals of a genetic basis for cultural variations.

Several coevolutionary models have appeared in the past decade in which (following the logic detailed above) genes are seen as evolving through natural selection while culture evolves in parallel by different mechanisms. These models avoid the assumption that variation in culturally defined behaviors corresponds to genetic variation, even if the correspondence is weak, Culture, in other words, is adaptive in ways that are different from biological adaptation. Cultural and biological adaptations parallel each other, but one is not an aspect of the other because cultural variation is independent of biological variation. The idea of **culturgens** appears in many of these coevolutionary theories. Culturgens are units of culture items - artifacts, behaviors, or "mentifacts" (mental constructs, or primary representations). These range in complexity from as simple as a handaxe or a particular taste preference to much greater complexities, for instance a kinship custom such as whether cousins on the father's side are named and treated differently than mother's side cousins. The link between genetic and behavioral changes, in coevolutionary models, is indirect because culture provides the fundamental framework for organizing behaviors. Thus, behavioral changes (whether or not they are adaptive) cannot directly cause changes in the genome because there are no genetic variations corresponding to the cultural variations. However, the basis of coevolutionary theories is that cultural changes could impact more general aspects of the genome, for instance configuration of behaviors that are easily learned, or the pattern of learning (generational instead of from peers, or visa versa), or the communication system that facilitates teaching. For example, an individual might have to choose between two culturgens such as whether a particular interaction will be honest or involve a deception. This choice is influenced by two factors:

1. genetically determined **epigenetic rules** (regularities occurring during the interaction of genes and environment that channel development) that guide information processing and the perception of interactions;
2. tradition, as expressed in the proportion of individuals in the population who have in the past made one choice over the other.

According to Flinn and Alexander, the coevolutionary process links culture and genetics through social learning - it is here that genetic variation is expressed as behavioral variability.

It is reasonable to assume that the link between culture and biology must be coevolutionary in some sense, if for no other reason than because of the alternatives: is possible that there is no such link, or that there is such a link and it is absolute - each cultural variation an exact expression of a genetic variation?. There must be a more complex and interactive relationship built on basic precepts such as those proposed by W.H. Durham:

1. Cultural mediation: selective pressures created by culture are part of the environment
2. Genetic mediation: genetically inherited features (learning biases) affect the ease or reinforcement with which cultural traits are transmitted

But have these models become too elaborate? I believe that one problem with existing coevolutionary models is exactly that - their daunting complexity and mathematical sophistication (in an unusual move, G. Richards presents a mathematics-free explanation of one such model, developed by C. Lumsden and E. Wilson). Yet, as complicated as they are mathematically, they still have not developed or detailed the complexities of what the culture-biology link must be. In my view this is because coevolutionary models have not regarded culture as a highly structured, internally fluid behavioral system and their assessment of culture is far too simplified to be useful. The mathematical sophistication itself may be the undoing of coevolutionary models, as it requires simplifications that are unrealistic and a mathematical background beyond the training of most anthropologists.

Epigenetic rules governing culture are "grammatically correct" interpretations of the social world that have been and keep on being continuously modified. They are shared in a way that creates the potential for meaningful interactions that can be interpreted within the social context (although not necessarily the same way). When these rules are modified there is a potential for genetic change. What exactly is inherited is expressed in how sensory data are abstracted and related to each other by incorporation into a secondary representational system. There are genetic predispositions for developing certain classes of similar secondary representational systems. Thus, genetic changes must reflect cultural changes, but do not directly cause them. By inheriting critical aspects of culture's "underlying structure", in effect "prestructuring" the way information will be processed, rapid learning that is keyed to specific circumstance or a particular time frame becomes possible, and high accuracy is guaranteed without any specification of content - hallmarks of the human cultural system. The information content can be as complex as the inherited structural models allow. Cultural evolution, then, involves the development of increasingly complex inherited models (secondary representational underlying structures) that order reality as it is encountered and provide the framework for interpreting social expectations and interactions as they are learned.

As reviewed by C.D. Laughlin and E.G. d'Aquili, there is significant evidence for the inheritance of models of reality (the "deep structure" of culture) - the genetically influenced neural models and the structures that relate them. This evidence comes from linguistics (as discussed above), psychology, structural anthropology, and learning theory. Much of it comes from behavioral universals, such as continuously observed dispositions toward identical reactions. Another source can be found in the works of the structural anthropologists such as C. Levi-Strauss, who suggested that numerous dissimilar institutions in different cultures (surface structures) are actually quite similar in underlying structure. Thus kinship systems and their relation to social organization can differ dramatically, while the principles of dual organization and marriage alliance are universal reflections of deep structure. Finally, from learning theory, the widespread dismissal of B.F. Skinner's stimulus-response theory lead to the realization that much learning and thinking takes place without any form of reinforcement. Combined with the studies showing significant individual differences in innate learning abilities that differ from subject to subject, many diverse scientists have come to agree with A.F.C. Wallace that "there may be certain cognitive capacities for forming kinds of schemata that are neurologically 'wired into' all human beings, are genetically determined, and are presumably a product of evolution".

Ultimately, the relation between biological and cultural evolution must involve a genetic background for culture, and not just for the capacity for culture. The coevolutionary nature of cultural evolution is visible in the dual evolution of its traditional and structural aspects, but these are linked by the requirements that each of these demands of the other, and by social learning. They are anything but parallel and independent. At the human level of complexity, culture is only made possible by an elaborate set of inherited syntactic structures organizing the culturally defined modeling of the social environment. *Language and consciousness are inseparable parts of culture*, in this view, which emphasizes that the definition of culture is based on its form and function, and not on a list of discriminatory criteria which are continually forced to change as we learn more about human and other primate behaviors.

A STRUCTURAL MODEL OF CULTURAL BEHAVIOR

Reflexive consciousness depends on the ability to predict the outcomes of interactions, and as discussed above the framework within which these predictions are imagined is the secondary representational system. For humans this is the secondary representational system of *culture*. One consequence of the complex relationships that are implicit in human culture comes back to a fundamental requisite of language. As part of the *cultural* milieu, language must allow for the possibility of different understandings of shared elements. Reconciliation of different, even opposed, individual strategies would be impossible without this ability, it is an important requisite of deception, and perhaps most fundamentally it underlies the ability to develop status differences. Understanding how this is accomplished brings us to a discussion of one part of the underlying structure of culture - shared cognitive maps.

A.F.C. Wallace suggests a simple model for understanding the combination of structural and individual elements in cultural behavior. His model provides insight into how the structural aspects of cultural behavior may reflect the neural models discussed above. Wallace introduces the concept of equivalence structure for describing the underlying structure of the simplest possible cultural interactions. An equivalence structure would be an example of a secondary representational system in a cultural context. It ties together the importance of consciousness and its expression through language in social scenario building. An example of a primary equivalence structure is shown in figure 4.9, part 1. In this representation, "a" represents the act(s) of individual A, and "b" the acts of individual B. The arrow means "is followed by." Thus, in the simplest possible relationship, whenever A does a_1 sooner or later B will do b_1 and vice versa.

The next most simple relationship is shown in figure 4.9, part 2. This is a secondary equivalence structure and demonstrates how more complex interactions might be structured. An action of A (a_1) is followed by an action of B (b_1), which in turn is followed by a second action of A (a_2). Conversely, the sequence might be initiated by B; or in another variant, a_1 may be followed by b_1 which in turn is followed by a repeat of a_1 and then finally by b_2. All of these possible interactions are described by the secondary structure.

The equivalence structures describe the interaction. Clearly, the individuals involved enter into the interaction with the expectation that their acts will lead to the interaction described. What Wallace demonstrates is that A's and B's understanding of the interaction need not be the same for the expectation to be valid.

He refers to the individual's understanding of the interactions as their "cognitive map." Several possible cognitive maps of the secondary equivalence structure are shown for A and B in figure 4.9, part 3. The important point is that every possible combination of these maps results in the same equivalence structure. This demonstrates that cognitive sharing (individuals sharing the same understanding of an interaction, or having the same cognitive map) is not necessary for stable social interaction. In fact, Wallace goes a step further, arguing that human societies *require* that at least some interactions be based on cognitive maps that are not shared. And indeed it is possible that the non-sharing of maps underlies the successful functioning of any human or human-like society in which there are role differences. The main requirement is that the maps be complementary.

The interpretations of these shared cognitive structures are the secondary representational systems of culture. These interpretations guide interactions that involve expectations that the participants do not share. These require communication beyond just information about emotional states and the immediate environment. R. Dunbar believes that just this combination of increasingly complex expectations and the need to communicate about them is important in human brain evolution. In particular, he argues that gossip, that is exchanges of information about individuals who are not present, allows the gossips to learn how to relate to them, often under circumstances not yet encountered. Moreover, he points out that language leads to categorization - a central requisite of primary representational systems. "Classifications and social conventions [neural models of social interactions] allow us to broaden the network of social relations ". This is a requisite for forming kinship systems, which I believe were a fundamental response to early hominid life history strategy. The necessity for more complex, displaced, and symbol based communication is probably just where the evolution of shared "cultural syntax" began.

Relating these concepts to the neural models discussed above leads to a more explicit idea of how cultural behaviors may be inherited and subjected to the forces of evolution. Particular cognitive maps are not inherited; they are practiced and learned by individuals. Yet in a functioning society these maps must be complementary and it is here that we may look for the influence of inheritance. This influence is expressed in:

- limitations created by the need for cognitive maps to be complimentary
- rules that are applied when equivalence structures are developed to govern a specific interaction.

Interactions are structured by congruent sets of equivalence structures that are shared within the species because they are inherited. This inherited aspect is the part of culture that evolves. It incorporates the underlying logical structure reflected in whole sets of maps that are mutually complementary, even as the individual maps are learned. This format provides a context for learning certain patterns of information about mutually interpretable social interactions, whether they are experienced or potential, over a contextually limited but very broad range. This is an ability that is complimentary to the use of language in imagining the consequences of ones participation in interactions that never happened. Unlike language, however, the critical aspect of the mutual interpretability in a cultural context is that it need not be the same for both participants. In fact, it is likely that both important differences in social roles, and underlying systems of social stratification based on criteria more complex than sex and age, necessarily rely on the ability to develop structurally correct cultural misinformation.

Selection could work on these sets of complementary maps by changing the logical characteristics of a set and thus defining a new complementary set. Alternatively selection could lead to additional complexity in each intermeshing map. In this was it would expand congruent sets to allow more combinations that would result in the same equivalence structure. This is probably just how hominid syntactic abilities, as framed in their shared secondary representational systems, evolved gradually from the simple to the complex. Selection would favor the complex as these systems changed in primary function from representational to communicative, and as the social environment came to require increasingly complex communication. Selection could not be expected to change the cognitive maps themselves, or to increase the likelihood that individuals would learn some maps within a set more readily than others. Ironically, this returns us to a consideration of the individual. The equivalence structure model for cultural interactions, and ultimately for cultural evolution, relies heavily on variation at the individual level. There must have been variation in the ability to form appropriate and complex equivalence structures while interacting with others, or selection could not have resulted in complimentary modeling of interactions or have provided the basis for the evolution of cultural complexity. Differences in human abilities point to a strong component of interpopulational variation today and there are good reasons to believe that these most complex of human behaviors, language and social interactions, develop and are expressed in patterns that are influenced by genetic variation.

CULTURE AS HUMAN BIOLOGY

R. Foley suggests that the concept of culture is not a useful one in early hominid studies. He bases this conclusions on what he perceives as the "three basic flaws" of culture as a concept in paleoanthropology

1. It is too high a level of abstraction to be of much empirical value.
2. It assumes a permanent relationship of the components that constitute this high level of abstraction
3. As the basic intention is to define something that is uniquely human, it is constantly redefined in the context of nonhuman primates that show continuities between humans and nonhumans

As I view culture here, this argument is wrong on all three counts. By incorporating the equivalence structure model of interactions, and the secondary representational system precept of language, the theory of culture presented here is of fundamental empirical value. The emergence of culture, whether it was gradual or more sudden, was necessarily related to a host of anatomical and ecological adaptations that ranged from a throat that can produce efficient vocalizations for streams of diverse but interpretable morphemes, to demographic and ecological reflections of slowed down maturation and complex patterns of division of labor. This view surely does not consider the relationships of its components permanent; to the contrary, it is at the level of these relationships that biological evolution can take place. Finally, culture as I have described it remains a unique human attribute and there is no indication it is shared by other primates, no matter how complex their traditions, because they lack the all of the human biological adaptations. Traditions are not part of the biology of nonhuman primates, in the sense that human culture is. As the framework for interpreting *human* behavior, there is no reason to expect culture to be redefined as we come to understand more about non humans. I conclude that culture is a fundamental concept in paleoanthropology

- it is the only valid framework for comparing human and nonhuman behavior,
- its evolution has a significant genetic component,
- it sets the behavioral expectations for biological functions based on age, sex, and kinship
- its functions in transmitting information and organizing behaviors are closely tied to anatomical evolution; when the pattern of evolution is gradual, changes in behavior will always precede changes in anatomy,
- the organizational and information transmission aspects of culture result in predictions from the hypothesis of early hominid culture that are potentially observable in early hominid anatomy, demography, and ecology (even given that, as J. Robinson once quipped, culture did not spring from the brow of *Australopithecus* in its modern form)

The early ethnologists were probably right in considering culture a "superorganic" phenomenon, but quite wrong in concluding this divorced culture from biology. Superorganic was always defined in terms of its surface manifestations, as a list of traits (this is why Foley is concerned with the effects of changing the list), with the proviso that as the traits combine to form human culture, the whole becomes greater than the sum of the parts. In fact, the whole *is* greater, but there is now a realization that this is because the relation between the whole and its parts is hierarchical, and much more complex than envisaged. Our understanding of underlying structure and its complex hierarchical relation to surface structure in language, and I believe more generally in culture as well, shows how underlying structure and the rules that relate it to surface structure can be inherited while the surface manifestations are not. It is the underlying structure, and the syntactic rules that are applied to it, that show variation and have been the object of evolutionary change. To consider culture as a functioning entity is not to assume it incapable of evolution (or that it must have evolved all at once), perhaps the greatest fallacy in the long arguments about the evolution of the cultural capacity. Cultural and cerebral evolution have gone hand-in-hand in the hominids, yet we do not take the presence of a functioning, well integrated brain today to mean the human brain evolved from a simplified precursor all at once. Culture has come to perform a number of biological functions, and not just in Malinowsky's sense of satisfying physical needs. Through aspects of its underlying structure, as expressed in the concepts of the secondary representational system and equivalence structures, the biological functions of human culture go deeply beneath the surface structure of human expressions and activities and include:

- delimiting behaviors by defining the contexts in which they will be interpreted,
- defining all aspects of biological interactions, including gender and kinship relationships
- providing the framework for social scenario-building and ordering the conscious version of reality,
- organizing, storing, and accurately transmitting information,
- providing a secure communication link that can serve to both communicate with others and with one's self

The fact is that culture is a complex integrated entity and must be defined by its organization and function, and not by the list of traits that characterize its surface structure. For humans, culture is biology.

Jaws and Teeth

The third important hominid distinction is found in the teeth and related portions of the upper and lower jaws. Unlike the previous two distinctions discussed, not all of these masticatory differences are visible in comparisons of present-day people and apes (see figure 4.10), and the proviso that hominid does not mean human is especially important here. Moreover, where hominids are distinct they are not necessarily unique. Especially in the posterior dentition, hominids differ because African apes evolved away from the ancestral condition. Hominids mainly contrast in a combination of three partially related adaptive systems:

1. anterior teeth (canines and incisors) - their size and morphology, and the morphology at the front of the jaws
2. chewing adaptations, probably best summarized as powerful grinding (hominids) *versus* slicing (apes)
3. tooth and root development, and tooth eruption times that reflect the slower maturation of hominid children

Taking a historic view there are rather different evolutionary patterns in the anterior and posterior parts of the dentition. These are reflected in both the morphology and function of the teeth, and the times of their eruption.

Teeth are a highly mineralized but quite positively living part of our bodies. Like all mammals, humans have two sets of teeth, the **milk** or **deciduous** teeth and the permanent dentition. Twenty of the permanent teeth develop under their deciduous counterparts (incisors under deciduous incisors, canines under deciduous canines, and premolars under deciduous molars) - their loss (or exfoliation) to some extent controls when the permanent teeth will erupt. Six other permanent teeth, the molars, are behind the deciduous dentition and cannot erupt until the jaws are large enough to contain them. This fact ties the time the first permanent molar will erupt and the time spans between the successive molar eruptions to the rate of facial growth, and therefore more generally to the rate of maturation. Between the eruption of the first permanent tooth (usually a lower molar) and the loss of the last deciduous one (usually a deciduous second molar, making way for the permanent fourth premolar), the dentition is **mixed**, with both deciduous and permanent teeth.

There are internal structural similarities that characterize all the teeth (figure 4.11). Each tooth has a hard outer layer capping its top, the **enamel**, covering softer and more resilient **dentin** which, in turn, encloses the **pulp cavity** that holds the tooth's arterial supply and innervation (these enter through the canals enclosed by the roots). The dentin is the main portion of each tooth, extending for its entire length. Dentin is covered by enamel over the exposed crown of the tooth, and by a softer, bone-like material called **cementum** over the length of the root. The cementum anchors the tooth to the ligament covering the alveolar bone (the details of the anchoring can be used to determine whether or not the tooth was used vigorously just before death because more force applied to the tooth will push it further into the socket during chewing and change the orientation of the connective fibers that develop. Dentin has about 1/5 the hardness of enamel, although it is harder than bone. Its elastic properties (the ability to deform when force is applied to it) support the much more brittle enamel and make it more difficult for teeth to break because of its cushioning effect. Since this tissue is softer than enamel, in parts of the crown where enamel is worn away and the underlying dentin exposed to wear, its rate of wear will be more rapid. Sharp edges can be maintained on an enamel surface if part of the enamel is thin, quickly exposing the dentin as the tooth wears. The more rapidly wearing dentin will undercut the enamel, causing it to break and maintain its sharpness. The distal surface of many primate canines maintain their sharpness this way (see figure 3.4, canine cutting).

Enamel is about 95% mineral in makeup, most of which is crystalline in nature. It is composed of millions of closely packed calcified prisms, each extending from the dentin surface to the outer surface (figure 4.11). Each prism is segmented by cross-striations, undulations along its length. Some workers regard these as marking a daily growth cycle as the enamel is formed, reflecting the regular metabolic changes over the course of each day, but the evidence for this is not strong. If daily growth is actually marked, the distances between different striations shows that the amount of enamel produced within a single tooth can vary each day from one anatomical region to another. The "daily growth" interpretation is also problematic when it is used to predict the length of time for crown formation (discussed further below). There may be alternative structural reasons for this regular segmentation, as discussed by S. Molnar and his colleagues.

Also dividing the enamel prisms into segments, although at a quite different angle, are the striae of Retzius. These are dark bands extending around the entire tooth as seen from above, much like growth rings of trees (they are interpreted similarly). These striae also begin at the dentin surface, but do not always extend to the enamel surface as the striae near the cusp tips curve completely around and reach the dentin surface on its opposite side. Where the striae of Retzius reach the enamel surface, they terminate as a series of alternating grooves, circling the entire crown, called lines of Pickerill. The elevations between the grooves, called **perikymata**, have attained great importance in attempts to determine how long it took enamel crowns to form in fossil hominids - a critical element in determining their age at death. The striae of Retzius are separated by 6-10 cross-striations, with an average of 7 or 8. If the cross-striae mark daily enamel growth, the perikymata would seem to reflect near-weekly growth increments. They can be counted on the crown's surface, an advantage over counting the striae of Retzius directly which would require sectioning the tooth in half. Newly erupted incisors have proven to be particularly useful for this. However, since not all striae of Retzius reach the enamel surface, the "missing" perikymata must be estimated. Other potential sources of error in estimating the number of striae of Retzius include the casting medium (they are counted on a cast of the enamel surface using a microscope). Perikymata counts are quite variable (table 4.5).

Table 4.5

Range of Perikymata Numbers and Estimated Incisor Crown Formation Times[α]
for Hominid Groups, from Mann et al (1991)

Hominid Group	Perikymata Number Observed	Estimated Crown Formation Time (years)
Australopithecus afarensis	116-180	2.7-4.0
Australopithecus africanus	135	3.1
Australopithecus robustus	57-86	1.6-2.1
Australopithecus boisei	82-101	2.1-2.4
early *Homo sapiens*	95-123	2.3-2.9
Neandertals	119-205	2.8-4.4
living *Homo sapiens*	75-202	1.9-4.4[β]

[α] assuming weekly formation of the perikymata

[β] the radiographically documented range of incisor crown formation times in humans is 2.5-7.2 years, according to Mann et al (radiography underestimates the beginning of calcification by several months).

THE ANTERIOR TEETH

The living apes are characterized by the canine/premolar cutting and slashing complex discussed in Chapter 3. Hominid canines and lower anterior premolars differ from their ape counterparts in both size and form. Hominid canines are much smaller, and their crowns are lower and more blunted even when unworn. They have come to approximate the incisors in their size and form, although the canines are generally thicker, have longer and more robust roots, and may be taller when they first erupt. The main point is that in hominids, the canines clearly function (and wear) like incisors and are mainly used to grip, hold, and tear. L.O. Greenfield has suggested a dual selection hypothesis to account for the transformation into hominid canine morphology. He envisions ape canines as under both forms of selection outlined above, one related to their adaptive value as weapons and in threat displays, and the other related to their use as incisors. Both functions are important in the apes, although Greenfield provides evidence that shows female and deciduous canines are better designed to be used as incisors, and are more likely to function this way. In some taxa the lower canines of males also function as incisors, occluding directly against the upper lateral incisors. With the incisor function already promoted by selection, human canines evolved when the value of male canines as weapons and in threat displays decreased.

The hominid lower front mandibular premolar (P_3) has also changed considerably. It no longer functions as part of a canine cutting complex as a tooth that cuts against the upper canine. Instead, it has been incorporated into the grinding and crushing portion of the posterior dentition. The one large projecting cusp of ape sectorial premolars became two similarly sized cusps on a more symmetrically shaped premolar crown in hominids. The contrast is even greater if apes and fossil hominids are compared (see Figure 4.15) because of the greater emphasis on powerful mastication, and the subsequently large posterior tooth sizes, in the early hominids.

With a change in the canine cutting complex comes a loss of gaps (**diastemata**) between certain teeth. In apes there is a diastema between the upper canine and incisor, in which the projecting crown of the lower canine fits. There is also a diastema between the lower canine and premolar for the projecting upper canine to fit into. These diastemata occasionally appear in living and fossil humans, but they are rare except in the earliest human fossils.

A contrast also occurs in the incisors. Today these teeth are much larger in chimpanzees than in humans. Since the larger teeth take up more space in the front of the jaw, spreading the distance between the canines, this tends to make the posterior tooth rows, behind the incisors, parallel to each other. The form of the dental arch resembles a "U". In hominids (figures 4.10 and 4.12), the smaller incisors and canines are set in a more gentling curving parabolic dental arch. The African Miocene hominoids show that as far as the incisors are concerned, it is the chimpanzees who have come to differ more in their evolution. These Miocene hominoids do not have chimpanzee-sized incisors, and it seems likely that hominids never passed through a large-incisor stage. In the chimpanzees, expanded incisors are important in food preparation. They use their anterior teeth for breaking open and peeling fruits with extremely tough husks. Gorillas use their large incisors for stripping and pulling leaves off stems. The use of large front teeth for gathering and preparing foods is also reflected in the size and orientation of the apes' jaw muscles (see below).

Table 4.6
Occlusal Eruption Times*

	Chimpanzee	Human Population Means		
		Minimum	Average	Maximum
I1	6.0	5.5	6.5	7.0
I2	6.5	6.5	7.5	8.0
C	8.5	9.5	10.0	11.0
P3	8.5	10.0	10.5	12.0
P4	7.0	10.5	11.5	12.5
M1	4.0	5.5	6.0	7.0
M2	7.5	10.5	11.5	12.5
M3	11.0	16.5	18.5	25.5

*Occlusal eruption times presented to the nearest half-year, the best resolution the data will allow. The most accurate set of chimpanzee data, published by Kuykendall, Mahoney, and Conroy (1992) and Nissen and Reisen for the third molar (1964), are for **gingival** (through the gums) **emergence**. These have been modified to reflect the slightly later times of **occlusal eruption**, when the tooth reaches the plane of the other teeth (the **occlusal plane**) and begins to wear against the teeth in the opposing jaw. Details of the difference between gingival and occlusal data are in Wolpoff (1979). The human data are for the range and mean of population occlusal eruption averages, from Brown et al (1978) and papers reviewed in Wolpoff (1979).

Eruption of the permanent incisors provides a physiological limit for the maximum length of child dependency by marking the latest time the weaning process can begin (mothers will not tolerate a suckling child with these large teeth). Incisor eruption, moreover, is also the beginning of independence for orally preparing (and to some extent gathering) foods. These life history changes meet quite similar demands in the maturation pattern of chimpanzee and human children (and by inference in the children of early hominids). They occur at the same time; as table 4.6 shows, average chimpanzee incisor eruption times fall within the range of human population means.

Chimpanzee canines erupt more closely in time to the incisors. The delay in human canine eruption (even the most rapidly erupting canine emerges on the average a year later and the human mean is 1.5 years later) is often attributed to the "humanization" process. Although the chimpanzee canines begin to function earlier than human canines in absolute time, because all of the chimpanzee teeth behind the incisors erupt earlier - a part of their more rapid maturation process - the canine eruption is actually later relative to the (shorter) maturation time. Chimpanzee canines erupt after a considerable amount of body growth, always after the second molar eruption. It has been suggested that since chimpanzees and other anthropoids use their canines to help define their social roles, their eruption is delayed in the maturation process so that they can have time to practice the important adult behaviors that use these teeth such as threats. Hominid canines, erupting later in absolute time, come to function relatively earlier in the maturation process, presumably because the canines have reduced importance in social roles.

There is much to be said for this argument, but it is unclear whether relatively late canine eruption reflects a social adaptation, or an exaptation. There are two different processes governing canine eruption time. Maturing more rapidly and holding large incisors, the front part of chimpanzee (and other ape) jaws grow much faster than in hominids. This provides room for the large permanent canine earlier in ontogeny, and the canines and P_3 erupt into this growing space at the same time. It may be that the human canine erupts later because the front of the jaw is smaller and grows more slowly, a point suggested by S.W. Simpson and his colleagues. The second process is the delayed maturation of hominid children, their slowed down growth process. While the maturation delay affects all of the teeth, it most strongly delays the eruption of the molars, starting with the first (table 4.6). As J. Monge and colleagues point out, this can be most dramatically seen when comparing the eruption of I2 (not strikingly different in humans and chimpanzees) with the markedly delayed human M2 eruption. These later molar eruptions place the canine eruption earlier in ontogeny, even though it is later in absolute time.

In sum, the main differences between hominid anterior teeth and those of the living apes lie in the loss of the anterior cutting complex involving the linked morphology and eruptions of the canines and P_3 and the subsequent functional (and partially morphological) incorporation of the canines into the incisor complex and of the P_3 into the posterior grinding complex. A second difference is the later eruption of human canines.

THE HOMINID GRINDING COMPLEX

All primates crush, grind, or chop their food between their posterior teeth into a digestible consistency, combining motions which move the teeth together (crushing) and motions which slide the teeth over each other (shearing). The crushing functions are more important for hard foods such as peanuts, while tough but more deformable foods like meat require shear forces between the teeth - every food requires its own ratio of crushing to shearing during mastication. Hominids differ from many other anthropoids, including the African apes, in their use of a grinding complex which can apply an unusual amount of pressure between the postcanine teeth while chewing, and stand up to the forces thus produced. In this complex the hominids closely resemble Miocene anthropithecines as well as their sister group, the Asian apes (including living orangutans and extinct *Gigantopithecus*). It is the African apes who have come to differ; the distinction, in other words, is theirs.

Chewing is a complex action of the lower jaw, involving motions in three directions. The basic chewing cycle common to all higher primates can be summarized as follows:

1. The lower jaw swings open and at the same time moves slightly forward.
2. The jaw begins to move back to a closed position. However, this is not the first motion in reverse. Instead, the motion is backward and toward the side with food between the teeth as the jaw closes on this food. On the other side there is a pivot at the contact of the mandibular condyle (Figure 4.1) with the cranium.
3. The food between the teeth is broken down through a combination of shearing and crushing until the food-bearing side is back in its original closed-mouth position.
4. The cycle may then be repeated on the same side or on the opposite side.

Hominids can produce more effective force during this cycle because of the size and orientation of the muscles that control the jaw (see Figure 4.14). The main muscles that produce vertical force are the anterior (front) portion of the **temporalis**, the **masseter** on the outside of the jaw, and the medial **pterygoid** internally. Transverse motion, occurring at the same time, is produced by the latter two muscles and the posterior portion of the temporalis. The combination of these two actions brings the surfaces of the postcanine teeth across each other while strong pressure is applied between them, a motion described as grinding. The closer these forces are applied to the food between the teeth, the more effective they are in grinding and crushing the food particles. As Figure 4.14 illustrates, the anterior portion of the temporalis is located directly over the molars in humans, whereas in chimpanzees it is behind most of the molars. Similarly the human masseter is closer to the postcanine teeth than the chimpanzee masseter. The effect of these architectural differences is to make human grinding and crushing more efficient, and the stronger development of the muscles that produce crushing force in the early hominids is part of their masticatory adaptation to particularly powerful crushing. The chimpanzee architecture emphasizes the posterior portion of the temporalis more strongly, and reflects a greater importance for shear forces during chewing. This muscle has a horizontal orientation, and it is also important in resisting forces applied to the canines and incisors when they are used for cutting, stripping, husking, and so on - significant functions in their adaptation that creates selection for large canine and incisor size.

Table 4.7
Reduction of Postcanine Tooth Size in Human Evolution
Using the distribution of lower second molar breadth to measure the process of postcanine reduction

1	4	8	45	90	95 **2.35**	36	3	2									Living Population (South Chinese)
		1	1	10	18	22 **2.4**	15	8	1								Late Pleistocene *Homo sapiens*
		1	1	2	4	5	3	3 **2.5**	6	3							Middle Pleistocene *Homo sapiens*
					1	3	2	7	7 **2.55**	2	2		1				Pliocene and Early Pleistocene *Homo sapiens*
							2	2	4	3	2 **2.65**	1	1				habilines
								1	2	3	4	7 **2.7**		2	1		*Australopithecus africanus*
						2	3	3	3	4 **2.6**	4	2		1			*Australopithecus afarensis*
1	10	17	43	66	80	39	9	3/2	16	33	62	10 3	66	30	6	2	Chimpanzee/ Gorilla
					2.35							**2.7**					
C	C	C	C	C	C	C	C	C/G	G	G	G	G	G	G	G	G	
2.1		2.2		2.3		2.4		2.5		2.6		2.7		2.8		2.9	Log M$_2$ breadth

While humans appear to be more efficient in grinding and crushing than the living apes, they are less well adapted in this direction than early hominids. Fossil hominids show evidence of much larger jaw muscles and a more anterior position for the masseter (figure 4.14). On the average, Pliocene hominids have larger posterior teeth than living humans; some specimens (figure 4.12), with smaller than modern body size, attaining premolars and molars as large as those of 400-pound gorillas, much larger than the posterior teeth of chimpanzees with body sizes similar to the fossil humans. *Australopithecus africanus*, one of the best known Pliocene hominid species, has postcanine sizes fully within the range of variation of gorillas (see table 4.7). It is seems bizarre to note that this species is often referred to as a "gracile australopithecine", but there are even larger toothed early hominids. The earliest hominid species, *Australopithecus afarensis,* is largely within this range; remembering the diminutive body size of these hominids, all evidence suggests that to have exceptionally large postcanine teeth is the ancestral condition for hominids

The importance of large postcanine teeth can be viewed in two different contexts.

1. They can apply more force to food without the enamel breaking or wearing unduly, because the force is distributed over a broader area.
2. They have a longer effective life - a particular advantage if some of the foods eaten wear the teeth quickly. This can happen if some of the foods are particularly abrasive, or if they are of low quality so that a great deal must be eaten every day.

Because the teeth were large, their roots were expanded and the portions of the upper and lower jaws holding the roots were also large. To hold these roots, the early hominids have very large faces and mandibles.

Hominids (especially Pliocene ones) and the African apes are not alone in contrasting these postcanine adaptations. Another pair of closely related primate species with a similar contrast are found among the baboons. C. Jolly has shown that the gelada baboons (*Theropithecus*) are analogous to the early hominids while the more widely distributed baboons of the genus *Papio* are analogous to the African apes. The parallel similarities (*Theropithecus* to hominids, *Papio* to African apes) are attributed to the same cause - dietary difference. *Papio* eats a broad range of foods, none of which require any particular masticatory specializations. In contrast, *Theropithecus* has a particular adaptive and dietary specialization to semi-arid open country involving collecting and eating seeds. While grasses form a large component of the gelada's diet, Jolly draws attention to those morphological characteristics that are part of the seed-eating adaptation. The gelada cranium differs from *Papio* (see Figure 4.16) in many of the same ways that early hominid and ape crania differ (Figure 4.15). In Figure 4.16, note that the gelada's jaws and teeth lie more directly below the cranium, while the mandible is taller and more perpendicular. The vertical part of the mandible (the ramus) begins at the position of the third molar in the gelada, while in the *Papio* the ramus begins well behind the third molar. Another contrast is in the position of the cheek. In the gelada the cheek begins over the second molar, while in the *Papio* specimen it begins over the third.

These variations reflect differences in the muscles of mastication. In *Theropithecus* the masseter attachment is in a more forward position relative to the teeth. The forward position is attained by more anterior cheeks (one of the attachments for the muscle) and a shift of the tooth row backwards to a more posterior position, placing a large portion of it directly beneath the anterior temporalis. The anterior temporalis is a relatively larger muscle in *Theropithecus*. These features combine to increase the force passing through the molars and premolars. In the teeth, *Theropithecus* has relatively thicker molar enamel than *Papio*. Larger and more robust fossil forms of *Theropithecus*, showing a more extreme version of the same adaptation, have molars and premolars that are relatively large compared with body size, while the incisors (and sometimes the canines) may be small.

Only some of the Pliocene hominid adaptations remain in humans today and in fact the molars of living people and chimpanzees molars are not much different in size. One part of this adaptation that has persisted much more clearly involves tooth enamel, much thicker in human teeth than in chimpanzee (or gorilla) teeth (figure 4.13) according to research by S. Molnar and D. Gantt. This has phylogenetic as well as adaptive implications. At one time it was argued that human and African ape enamel formed at different rates. If, as L. Martin's work suggested, the two African apes have rapidly developing thin enamel while humans have slowly developing enamel, it would link the African apes to the exclusion of humans. However, A. Beynon and his colleagues reviewed the evidence for different rates of enamel formation in the anthropithecines and found it lacking. The structural and developmental characteristics of anthropithecine enamel are very similar.

MATURATION AND TOOTH ERUPTION

A third difference between hominid and ape dentitions concerns the eruption of the permanent teeth. In both the sequence of erupting teeth and the time of their eruptions modern humans differ from the living apes and almost certainly also from the ancestral condition.

As discussed above, the eruption times for the anterior teeth of humans and apes are very similar, with chimpanzee incisors erupting at the same time as those at the fast end of the range of human population means, and the canines about a year earlier than the human minimum average. The canine development is quite different, however, as the much larger chimpanzee crown takes longer to develop.

Chimpanzee canines begin their development earlier, and erupt at an earlier time in the root formation process (eruption at an earlier time during root formation also characterizes the postcanine teeth, especially the molars). Chimpanzee premolars erupt earlier than their human counterparts, and the three molars much earlier. The three molars erupt into the space behind the milk teeth and therefore their eruptions are controlled by the growth of the jaw as room must be provided for them. The slower pace of human molar eruptions reflects their slower pace of ontogenetic development - delayed maturation. The long period of growth distinguishes humans from all of the apes, although least so from chimpanzees who, as discussed in Chapter 3, themselves have a maturational delay that is second only to humans among the primates.

One way to look at the eruption process is in terms of the flurry of eruptions that characterizes apes and humans. Four teeth - P3, P4, M2, and the canine, half the permanent set - erupt within a very short time of each other. This is about 7 to 8.5 years in chimpanzees, and 10 to 11.5 years at the human mean (9 to 10.5 in the fastest maturing populations), coming just before puberty in both species. The chimpanzee canine erupts at the end of this flurry (earlier in females, later in males) and therefore is the second latest tooth to appear, while second molar is the first of the four to erupt. The opposite occurs in humans, where the average human canine eruption is at the beginning of the flurry and the second molar is the last tooth. The biggest difference is in the eruption priorities of the canine and M2 - the difference is more extreme in women as men erupt their canines later (this is the greatest dimorphism in eruption times, averaging 9 months or more).

Another way to look a these differences is in terms of sequence polymorphisms, differences in the relative order of eruptions for the permanent teeth. There are two that are of particular importance.

- early canine eruption in hominids *vs* late canine eruption in apes, especially males
- marked M2 delay after I2 eruption in hominids *vs* close-to synchronic eruption in apes

The canine difference is a direct reflection of the large size of the tooth in apes. It takes longer to develop and its root requires a large jaw. The smaller hominid canine shifts to an earlier eruption time relative to the other teeth. The M2:I2 polymorphism, noted by J. Monge and colleagues, is a consequence of the delayed molar eruptions in the hominids. In apes these teeth erupt close to the same time, either could precede the other. In the hominids, including the earliest known, the longer period of maturation, and therefore of molar eruptions, places the eruption time of the M2 long after the I2. These two sequence polymorphisms encapsulate two of the most important early hominid distinctions.

Overall, the driving factor in these differences is mainly the maturation slow down in humans. Our permanent teeth, especially molars, erupt much later. The three chimpanzee postcanine teeth appear 3.5-4.5 years after the first molar, while in humans this is 5-5.5 year later even though the first molar itself is a much later erupting tooth. This has a feedback influence on tooth size and enamel thickness, as it means a longer period with an incomplete dentition, with more wear on the fewer teeth. The slow down in permanent tooth eruptions is important in interpreting early hominid remains. The ability to determine eruption times from the relative development of the teeth in immature fossil hominids makes it possible to infer the speed of their maturation.

Table 4.8
Eruptions Times after M_1

Years Until Eruption of:	Chimpanzee	Human
P3	4.5	4.5
P4	3.4	5.1
M2	3.6	5.3
M3	7.4	11.0
C	4.7	3.9

Figure 4.17
Range and Mean for Population Averages of Human Occlusal Eruption Times for Mandibular
Teeth, Compared with a Chimpanzee Sample
Chimpanzee data from Kuykendall, Mahoney, and Conroy (1992) and Nissen and Reisen (1964),
Human data from Brown et al (1979) and sources reviewed in Wolpoff (1979)

**Mandibular Occlusal Eruption Times:
Human Range and Chimpanzee Mean**

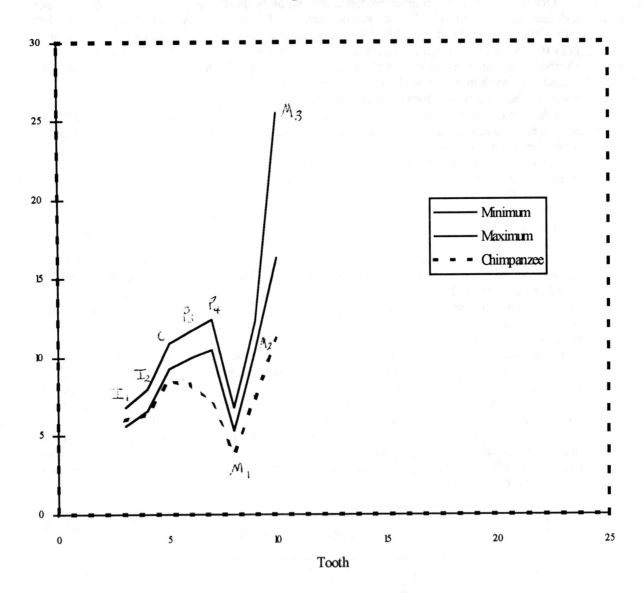

Tooth

Summary

The relation of form to function is complex, whether in living or fossil organisms, especially since most morphological features are multifunctional and behavioral systems are interrelated. In dealing with fossils, function can best be inferred from particular morphological features when there are clear analogs in living organisms and when the mechanics or physiology of the relationship are worked out in detail. Elaborate, unique behavioral systems are least likely to be well understood - the major problem in hominid origins.

Three behavioral complexes have come to distinguish the hominid line:

1. Obligate bipedalism
2. Language and culture
3. Elongated maturation period

Each of these complexes is associated with a series of anatomical changes. It is widely believed that the evolution of these are interrelated, but the details of the interrelationship are controversial and a critical aspect of competing hypotheses of hominid origins - the topic of the next chapter. Exacerbating the origins problem is the fact that we have only two models to examine these complexes in, living humans where they are best expressed and chimpanzees (or other apes) where they are not expressed at all. Unless we assume that they appeared in the earliest hominids exactly as they are today, interpreting the form and function relationship for these complexes in the now extinct australopithecines will always be difficult.

ANATOMY OF A CONTROVERSY
The Tooth, the Whole Tooth, and Nothing but the Tooth

In 1975 A. Mann published a seminal monograph in which he argued that early hominids had evolved the very human characteristic of a long maturation period. He based this conclusion on a study of early hominid jaws with milk or mixed dentitions, as he was able to show differences between the patterns of developing teeth in chimpanzees and more slowly maturing humans. Comparing the eruption times of human and chimpanzee teeth (figure 4.17), the longer period of human maturation is reflected in molar eruptions. Chimpanzee molars erupt closer together in time, while humans are further apart. Mann found that this difference could be observed in the relative development of unerupted molars, and presented evidence that suggested at the time the first molar has just erupted, chimpanzees and humans differ in the following ways:

Table 4.9
Mann's (1975) Analysis of Molar Formation at First Molar Eruption

	Second Molar	Third Molar
Chimpanzee	crown formed, some root	crown formation started
Human	incomplete crown	no presence

Mann tested the null hypothesis, of no significant or patterned difference between the early hominids and modern humans, using these and other relative development criteria (see table 4.9) to ascertain how different is different enough to disprove the hypothesis. He could not disprove it, and therefore suggested that the earliest hominids then known followed the human pattern of molar eruptions and therefore matured slowly. This proposal had far reaching implications for the evolution of complex behavior, and in particular meshed tightly with Holloway's observations of neural reorganization in these early hominids. Yet while the fact that longer periods between tooth eruptions reflect the longer time it takes human children to grow up is unassailably correct, a number of workers no longer regard maturation delay to characterize early hominids, and quite different approaches have been used to reconstruct their patterns of maturation. The debate over this and related problems has been fast and furious - bringing out some of the worst and some of the best in the politics of paleoanthropology. Are there data to support the rejection of Mann's proposals, and is it possible to address at all the question of how long it took the children of extinct hominids to grow up?

Mann's early work was plagued by two problems, the consequence of unknowns in the framework of the comparisons he was making (I owe much of this discussion of Mann's work to a review he published in 1990 with M. Lampl and J. Monge). One of these was the reliance on human tooth development and eruption times based almost solely on American children of European descent. While it was realized that dental eruptions normally vary widely between individuals within populations, it was not yet appreciated how greatly the population means can vary (I reviewed this range in 1979). Besides eruption times, **eruption priorities** (which tooth erupts first of a pair that emerge close together in time) can also differ between populations. For instance, in chimpanzees the first lower incisor average eruption time is about two years later than the first molar average. Modern human populations differ as the first permanent mandibular molar and central incisor often erupt at about the same time, but in Pima Indian and South Chinese children the incisor is often considerably later. In fact, the range of population means for this priority extends from incisor-first, to a lag of 2 years. While ranges of populational means for eruption times and priorities are important, it is unclear why there is so much variation. Climate, race (meaning genetic background), and masticatory habits of children all seem to play a role but none predominates. Moreover, confusing the comparisons of different populations are two problems of methodology. One of these is the definition of eruption. There are three different definitions, and sometimes it is not specified which is used:

- **Alveolar eruption**: emergence out of the crypt in the jaw bone that holds the tooth while it is developing
- **Gingival eruption**: emergence through the gum (this is the definition most often used by dentists and orthodontists as it can be easily observed in living children)
- **Occlusal eruption**: eruption to the **occlusal plane** (the level of the other teeth) where a tooth can wear against the opposing teeth (this is the definition I use. Because it is defined by wear it can be applied to isolated teeth and therefore is of most value to paleontologists)

These can differ appreciably, in a single individual by 1.5 years or more depending on the tooth. The second methodological problem is over the comparison of longitudinal and cross sectional studies. **Longitudinal studies** are much more difficult, but more accurate, as they trace eruptions in single individuals over the time that teeth erupt. **Cross sectional studies** estimate eruption times by observing the eruption status of teeth for individuals of known age. This is necessarily the way all eruption studies of dead individuals must proceed, but when compared with longitudinal studies the estimated ages are always older.

Further exacerbating the older studies, accurate times for stages of crown and root development, and eruption, were simply unknown for chimpanzees. It was not until 1981 that a large sample was examined. Dean and Wood scored relative development and eruption status for a cross sectional sample of chimpanzee skeletons. The resulting standards have been widely used, because prior to the developmental analyses of R. Anemone and his colleagues and the eruption study of a large mixed-longitudinal sample by K. Kuykendall and his colleagues, both about a decade later, the Dean and Wood standards were "the only game in town". Dean and Wood used eruption time estimates from a small number of captive chimpanzee children published much earlier to determine the ages of individuals in their skeletal sample, **seriating** the sample (putting it in order of the developmental status of the teeth) and interpolating between specimens for which the ages could be estimated. However, they used a mean age for each tooth because they did not have the actual ages for the chimpanzee skeletons they studied (remember that individuals eruption times vary widely, even within populations). They assumed that the lengths of time for crown formation and the completion of root growth were the same for each molar (they made the same assumption in the human sample they used for comparison). Moreover, they assumed that the developmental stages they observed were linear (for instance, this means they had to assume that the time it took for a crown to develop from 1/4 to 1/2 its size is the same as the time it took to develop from 1/2 to 3/4, or from 3/4 to full size). The accuracy of the innovative study was severely hampered by these assumptions, although it was presumed to be correct in every analysis discussed here.

Three arguments combined to discredit the precept that delayed maturation (and all that it implied) characterized early hominids. Each has cited the others in verification of its conclusions, but they must be considered individually as they are quite different (and to some extent contradictory).

The first of these is based on the study of perikymata on unerupted or newly erupted early hominid teeth. Beginning in 1985, T. Bromage, C. Dean, and their colleagues (in various combinations) put forth and defended the proposition that the enamel crowns in the teeth of early hominids formed faster than the crowns of living people, and therefore that maturational delay was recent in human prehistory. Their work was based on the way that enamel grows in developing crowns (see figure 4.11), as marked by the striae of Retzius internally, or externally by perikymata. The perikymata data were used for age determinations of various early hominid teeth, under the assumption that they form every 7 days. All of the perikymata counts reported were below the modern human range, said to be 165-202 based on a sample of 10. Summary data are replicated in table 4.5 (but in this table, taken from a more recent publication, a much wider human range is reported, as discussed below). The main conclusion of the early studies was that all of the perikymata counts appeared to be below the human range, implying that the teeth developed more rapidly than modern human teeth. The authors contended that specimens from all the australopithecine species, as well as early *Homo*, had been considerably overaged by using human dental development standards, while in reality their actual ages at death as determined by perikymata counts were much younger. This indicated the absence of delayed maturation in these Pliocene and Early Pleistocene hominids. The 1988 review by A. Beynon and C. Dean concluded that growth periods for the early hominids were similar to the modern great apes. They proposed that the last molar eruption was at 9.5 years, even earlier than chimpanzees. It was further suggested that the South African robust australopithecines formed tooth crowns even faster, more rapid than the other early hominids, but appeared to have a more human-like eruption pattern because of accelerated development of the incisors. This was thought to bring incisor and molar eruptions closer together, mimicking the human condition where these teeth also erupt closer together, but later in time - an example of convergence.

This was a surprising series of assertions given

- the lack of an independent test to verify that perikymata counts can be accurately replicated
- the absence of direct evidence that their number measures the length of time for crown development
- the very small size (n=10) of the human sample used to ascertain the range, below which specimens were claimed to develop their tooth crowns more rapidly than humans
- the use of a mean value to predict crown formation times when the range of days estimated to separate adjacent perikymata (6-10 days, and that assuming that cross striations each represent a day) suggests that all of the fossil hominid teeth *could* have developed within the range of human crown formation times,
- the absence of data for the development of ape teeth (it was assumed that "unlike humans" means "like apes").

In fact, analysis of only a slightly larger sample (n=12) reduced the minimum modern human incisor perikymata count to 75, as shown in table 4.5. This range encompasses all but one of the 18 early hominid fossil teeth reported thus far. Moreover, Mann and his colleagues have discovered that human perikymata appear to show strong average geographic differences. Again comparing counts for the incisors, the mean number for Europeans is 190, but for a mixed African/Near Eastern sample 103! This is a far greater difference than any claimed to separate early hominid species from each other, or from living humans. It is an unexpected difference, because no corresponding difference in actual crown formation times between Europeans other populations has ever been suggested. If the perikymata counts do not predict crown formation times, the hypothesis of a constant rate for perikymata is undermined.

Ape data, now available, further confuse the issues as they were found to have high perikymata counts instead of the low ones that were expected, according to D. Beynon and his colleagues. Moreover Dean, more recently than the earlier studies discussed above, reports formation times of 8-9 years for ape incisor crowns and Anemone and colleagues show that chimpanzee molar crown formation times are long, and not short as assumed. Table 4.10 shows that the chimpanzee second and third molar crown development times fit within the range of human means. The first molar crown development time, of course, must be shorter as this tooth erupts so much earlier.

Table 4.10
Molar Crown Formation Times (in years)*

	Chimpanzee (Anemone et al)	European (Moorrees et al)	European (Gleiser and Hunt)	Indian (Trodden)	Inuit (Trodden)
First	2.0	2.1	3.4	3.1	3.2
Second	2.5	2.8		3.9	2.5
Third	3.5	2.8		4.9	5.1

*The range of estimated crown completion times determined for 9 broken molars of *Australopithecus boisei* is 2.1-2.6 years according to C. Dean and colleagues, but 2.7-3.4 years based on the more recent studies of F. Ramirez-Rozzi which corrected the methodological difficulties in the earlier works.

Finally, C.B. Stringer and colleagues attempted to test the perikymata technique on a collection of human children from graves with headstones showing their ages at death. They found that Benin and Dean's assumptions provided ages that averaged only 75% the known age at death and conclude that "no one choice of periodicity is likely to accurately reflect those of a whole population of individuals". In sum, it is unreasonable to continue to accept conclusions about crown formation and implied tooth eruption times in individual fossil hominids based on perikymata counts.

The second argument against early hominid delayed maturation is based on an innovative attempt to ascertain whether early hominids best fit human or chimpanzee **eruption standards** (the pattern of average eruptions in a population, see figure 4.18). This determination, the work of B.H. Smith, was claimed to be independent of whether maturation was short or long. However, it was clearly assumed that if the early hominids best fit human eruption standards, their teeth erupted at human times, while if they better fit ape standards their teeth erupted more rapidly, reflecting the shorter maturation period of apes. The eruption standards she used were for children of European descent, published by Moorrees and his colleagues (this maximized the apparent differences between humans and apes as Europeans erupt their teeth late compared with many other populations.

Smith plotted the spans of tooth crown development and root development as a function of time for the European and ape children, marking the times of eruption (although never specified, this was probably gingival eruption) as a point on each continuum. While eruption times are known for a broad range of populations, the crown and root development data are known for only a very few, and they are all of European descent). A similar chart is shown in figure 4.19, but the much more accurate longitudinal chimpanzee data from Anemone et al are substituted for the Dean and Wood estimates (see table 4.11 for a comparison of how different these are). In this figure the developmental status for the permanent teeth of an idealized chimpanzee child at the age of 3.5 years is shown. If all the teeth develop and erupt at the average times, a vertical straight line will connect them, as indicated in the figure When these idealized developmental and eruption data for the chimp are plotted on the European standard, the connecting lines deviate dramatically from a single vertical one. Also shown in this figure is the development and eruption stages of an actual chimpanzee child known to be 3.5 years old. On the chimpanzee standard the data do not form a straight vertical line, because like all individuals this chimpanzee does not develop and erupt its teeth exactly at the average times. The chimpanzee of known age is also plotted on the European standard, where the deviations are much greater. This fact underlies the technique Smith used. She argues that the developmental and eruption status of the teeth of early hominid individuals can be plotted on human (meaning in this case European) and chimpanzee standards even though their actual ages are unknown. The plot that deviates less from a straight vertical line is the better "fit". The real chimpanzee fits the chimpanzee standards far better than the human standards.

The jaws of australopithecine children were examined and Smith made X-rays showing their unerupted teeth. When australopithecine children were plotted on these standards (see figure 4.20) it was found that gracile australopithecines, for instance those from the South African site of Sterkfontein or *Homo habilis* remains from East Africa, fit ape standards far better than European standards. Smith concluded that their ape-like pattern of tooth development and eruptions meant an ape-like speed of maturation. The robust australopithecines from southern and eastern Africa seemed to fit the human standards better, but she inexplicably concluded that this resemblance is "probably superficial", and not the reflection of a long maturation period.

Smith asserts that the perikymata data support her conclusions. However, we have seen that crown formation estimates from perikymata are too inaccurate to be used, and that the earlier reports of rapid crown formations and quick eruptions in the early hominid dentitions are without basis. It is probably better for Smith's arguments that this is the case, because if it could be shown that the early hominids formed their tooth crowns more rapidly than modern humans, comparing them to modern human standards would be invalid. Moreover, the fact that ape crown formation times seem to be as long as modern humans or even longer would make that comparison invalid as well. Indeed, the implication of an ape-like eruption pattern *and* more rapid crown formation times in the early hominids would be a rate of maturation *faster than living apes!*

There remains a question of whether Smith's method is valid. In one attempt to replicate the technique, Mann and his colleagues report that 25 out of 48 modern human children from two populations on two different continents best "fit" the ape standards (Smith has since questioned these results). How could this be? Two points must be considered here. First, in the Smith method *individuals* are compared to *averages for populations they are not members of,* and their deviation is used to judge which model of tooth development they best fit. But it is quite clear that the standards are population-specific. Moreover all parents know that children usually deviate markedly from the norm, as far as tooth eruptions are concerned. Before variation under two different models of expected eruption patterns can be compared, it is fundamental to first determine the normal range of variation around the mean for each standard; while this range is known for individual teeth in particular populations, it is yet to be estimated for fits to the standards - a critical determination as the point to using standards is that they allow comparisons of the whole dentition, which addresses the question of a difference in *eruption pattern* and not just individual eruptions. In any event, it is not clear that the *extent* of this deviation is the best criterion for choosing which model best applies; for instance, the *pattern* of deviation may be of greater importance. Moreover, the continued failure of this procedure to correctly identify human children probably reflects the fact that the developmental standards themselves are inappropriate or inaccurate. Publication of a longitudinal study of chimpanzee dental development clearly shows the cross sectional analysis used by everybody to be incorrect. To date, all of the complete developmental standards combining crown and root growth and eruption have been determined for children of European descent. Smith only accepts one of these as valid, that of Moorrees et al, and Mann and his colleagues criticize this study as suggesting an unusually early canine eruption. There are other problems as well as some studies are based on teeth extracted because of orthodontic problems and others come from school samples where the ranges are artificially truncated because of graduations. Criticisms of all these European studies may be justified, and a further related problem is that the European standards Smith uses mixes crown eruption times from one population with crown and root development data from another. The Trodden study of tooth development in Indian and Inuit populations is not complete enough to be used to develop alternative standards - data are missing for initiation in the anterior teeth and crown completion and root growth data for the third molars have very small sample sizes. None the less, this study suggests that the development standards for non-European populations will very likely be quite different from the Europeans.

Finally, there are problems in how the teeth have been scored for development, and Mann and his colleagues have shown that some specimens such as the isolated dentition of the *Homo habilis* ER 1590, regarded by Smith as better fitting ape standards, actually better fit the human ones. With G. Conroy and M. Vannier's groundbreaking computerized tomography (CT) of the South African australopithecines (discussed further below), more accurate data for unerupted teeth show most of the australopithecines to better fit European development and eruption standards. Comparisons to standards based on CT-derived data are shown for a gracile and robust australopithecine in figure 4.20. The difference between the data that can be ascertained from X-rays and from CT scans is evident from comparing analyses of the same specimen. McKee and McKee compared ratings of tooth formation from CT scans and radiographs. They found the inter-examiner error to be large, as the comparisons of STS 24 suggest. The maximum differences were in the incisors, canine and first molar - the most critical teeth for distinguishing chimpanzee and human eruption patterns according to table 4.12.

Following on her interpretation of early hominid dental eruptions as ape-like and rapid, Smith subsequently developed a series of primate-wide correlations relating first molar eruption times to brain weight and a number of life-history phenomena. These "confirmed" the ape-like life history features for the australopithecines that her earlier studies suggested, including early fertility, early maturation, and a short life span. Intriguing as these correlations may be, as the basis for predicting the timing of life history events, they cannot show australopithecines to have ape-like life histories if the initial research leaading to the conclusions that australopithecines develop and erupt their teeth rapidly does not hold up.

The third argument against delayed maturation is based on the relation of eruption times to the *pattern* of eruption, particularly as expressed by two priorities:

- The relation of lower molar and incisor development and eruption: whether the lower incisors and first molars erupt at about the same time or whether the incisor lags behind the molar by several years (ape pattern).
- The relative developmental status of erupting and unerupted molars: whether adjacent molars overlap (ape pattern) or are separate in the times of their development.

T. Bromage was the first to argue that Mann's criteria for separating the developing dentitions of chimpanzees and humans were incorrect and did not clearly separate children of these two taxa. He argued that perikymata counts and not relative tooth development could be used to ascertain the maturation rates of early hominids, an approach already discussed. Bromage used the Dean and Wood cross sectional data for this determination.

However two longitudinal studies of growing chimpanzees have now invalidated this data source, the Kuykendall et al eruption time determination and the Anemone et al study of crown and root development. The new eruption data are the first really accurate set (these are compared with the range of human occlusal eruption times in figure 4.17). The developmental data are quite different than the Dean and Wood cross sectional estimates, as shown in table 4.11 which compares the expected developmental stages of the other teeth at the time that the first permanent molar has erupted and shows slight occlusal wear. This particular time was chosen as it is the age of one of the chimpanzees in the original Mann study. He noted that at this developmental stage an M3 early in development was present in the chimpanzee and not the human - this became one of his main criteria for using eruption pattern in modeling the difference between the patterns of human and chimpanzee molar eruptions, and thereby to estimate eruption times for the early hominids that fit the human pattern of third molar delay. Bromage (in the study discussed above) and Conroy and Vannier have both shown illustrations of chimpanzees at this developmental stage without third molars. Now, the Amenone data show that third molar formation is initiated just at this time, explaining why some chimpanzees have this tooth present while others do not. Only slight differences in the eruption status of two specimens, or normal variation in the development or eruption times of either tooth, could account for this variation when the expected timing of the events is this close.

In fact, the initiations and durations for chimpanzee crown development differ considerably from the Dean and Wood estimates (Bromage's perikymata-based estimates did not fare well either - see below). Several other important conclusions were drawn from the Amenone study:

- There is considerable overlap in the duration of crown development for adjacent molars; in humans overlap is rare because the onsets of calcifications are delayed

- The close juxtaposition of incisor and first molar eruptions in humans come from later first molar eruption, not earlier incisor eruption
- Adjacent molar crowns do not develop at the same rate, there is an increase in duration of development from the front to back of the molar row
- There are major differences between apes and humans in the developmental rates of the roots, which are dramatically faster in the apes
- Chimpanzee incisor crowns develop more rapidly than human ones, but their canines are dramatically slower

Table 4.11

Various Contentions about Mandibular Tooth Development when the First Molar is Erupted and Shows Slight Occlusal Wear

	Mann's (1975) Single Chimpanzee	Cross Sectional Chimpanzee sample [Dean and Wood (1981)]	Longitudinal Chimpanzee sample [Anemone et al (1991)]	Modern European sample [all authors]
M2	crown complete, slight root	crown half formed	crown complete, no root	Crown almost or fully complete
M3	crown begun	crown absent	crown begun	crown absent
P3 and P4	crown complete, significant root	partly complete crown	partly complete crown	crown complete (P3)/ crown almost complete (P4)
C	partly complete crown	partly complete crown	partly complete crown	crown complete, varying root
I1	crown complete, slight root	crown complete, no root	crown complete, slight root	crown complete, partial root

Perhaps the most important conclusions are that chimpanzees can be distinguished from virtually all humans developmentally by their overlapping periods of development for adjacent molars. The work clearly shows that delayed maturation in humans has nothing to do with the period of crown development (the perikymata argument, incorrect in any event) but rather is the consequence of delay in the onsets of crown development and a much longer span of root development.

The seminal work on australopithecine dental development and eruption is by Conroy and Vannier, who used CT scans to examine the unerupted teeth in all of the immature South African australopithecines. Unfortunately, they uncritically accepted the perikymata-based arguments that australopithecine crown development was much faster than humans (in fact, using the Beynon and Dean eruption "standards" for gracile and robust australopithecines), adding an unexpected twist to the interpretations from an exemplary study, as they tried to explain how the human-like developmental patterns their data clearly showed could be interpreted to reflect the ape-like rapid eruptions required by the perikymata studies. The remarkable data they published for South African australopithecine dental development clearly show these early hominids to be human-like in their developmental pattern (figure 4.20 is based on their data). This can be exemplified by picking a particular time in the eruption sequence and comparing the developmental stages in australopithecines to the equivalent stages for chimpanzees and the normal range for Europeans. Table 4.12 does this for first molar occlusal eruption. All the taxa are similar in that there is considerable overlap with the normal European range. In most cases where chimpanzees are clearly distinguished from Europeans, the South African australopithecines resemble the

Europeans. Only in the developmental status of the unerupted canines do these australopithecines fit between the two, showing more canine development than chimpanzees at the time of M1 eruption, but less than Europeans.

Table 4.12

Comparisons of Taxa for Mandibular Tooth Development when the First Molar is Erupted and Shows Slight Occlusal Wear

Development Stage For:	Gracile Australopithecine STS 24 (from Conroy and Vannier)	Robust Australopithecine SK 63 (from Conroy and Vannier)	Chimpanzee (from Anemone et al)	Normal European Range (from Moorrees et al)
Incisors	4-5	5-6	3-4	5-7
Canine	4	4	2-3	5-6
P3	3-4	4	3	3-5
P4	3	3	3	3-5
M2	3	3	3	3-4
M3	absent	absent	1	absent

Calcification begins in stage 1
Isolated cusps unite to form an occlusal surface in stage 2
Enamel formation is complete at the occlusal surface at the beginning of stage 3
Crown is complete at the beginning of stage 4, root formation begins at its end
The root develops to about a quarter of its full length in stage 5

The CT scans of australopithecines have yielded a bonanza of new, critical data and the publication of eruption standards and developmental stages for chimpanzees based on longitudinal studies provides a very different basis for their comparison. We can summarize from all of this discussion that chimpanzees differ from humans in the following ways:

- First molar eruption is much earlier, both in absolute time and relative to anterior tooth development.
- Chimpanzee incisors develop earlier than some (but not all) human populations, there is overlap in their eruption times.
- Canines develop over a longer period, but erupt earlier.
- Adjacent molars overlap in their periods of development - a point only evident from the Anemone et al longitudinal study.
- The third molar can be expected to begin calcification at or close to the time of first molar eruption
- There is a shorter period of root development, and eruption is at a more incomplete stage of root growth

Chimpanzee tooth crowns do not differ significantly in development times except for canines, a point that has been demonstrated both longitudinally and perhaps less persuasively through the complete overlap of perikymata counts.

In the comparison made with two australopithecine specimens at the same stage of molar development and eruption, STS 24 and SK 63 (table 4.12, figure 4.20), the developmental stages of both australopithecines were within the expected European range for all unerupted teeth, and neither had a third molar crypt or crown. Developmental stages were unlike chimpanzees for the anterior teeth - all were more advanced in development than would be expected for chimpanzees with similar first molar development. For instance, the canine crowns were nearing or at completion at the time of first molar eruption whereas in chimpanzees the canine crown completion approximates second molar eruption. These two specimens are like humans and unlike chimpanzees in relative development, where relative development differs between the two living primates. More generally, the South African australopithecines are unlike chimpanzees and like humans in the following ways that reflect the length of time it took for them to mature:

- The anterior teeth develop closer in time to the first molar. Given the known eruption times for the living species, this almost certainly means that the australopithecine first molar erupts later than the chimpanzee first molar.
- Canine crown development ends much earlier, close to the time of first molar eruption rather than close to the time of second molar eruption as in chimpanzees (if the australopithecine first molar eruption was really early, this would be a remarkably early cessation of canine development).
- Adjacent molars do not overlap in their periods of development. For instance, to choose specimens well-illustrated in Conroy and Vannier, while the SK 64 M1 is developing there is no M2, SK 62 has a developing M2 but the enamel crown on the M1 is already complete and there is some 6 mm of root, STW 327 has a developing M3 crown but M2 is well past crown completion, erupting and with a good deal of its root.
- There is no trace of M3 development until well after the first molar has erupted

No longer constrained by the invalid theory that perikymata counts show australopithecine teeth to develop more rapidly (and with the detachment of eruption times from crown development times in any event), the new data, methods, and approaches show that the null hypothesis cannot be rejected as far as early hominid dental eruption patterns and maturation rates are concerned. This does not mean that every detail of australopithecine dental development and eruption is identical to modern humans. For instance, many australopithecine canines clearly erupt somewhat later in sequence than is common today, and eruptions of many teeth are somewhat earlier in the root development sequence than is the case for Europeans (J. Monge suggests that eruption late in the root development sequence is a response to the space limitations created by slowed jaw growth in populations that prepare their foods). Yet, the diagnostic similarities of the australopithecines are with the modern human condition. There are developmental markers that reflect delayed maturation, and these point unambiguously to the conclusion that australopithecine children took a long time to grow up.

And what of the worst and the best as they appear in this debate? The controversy, as reviewed by both Bower and Lewin, has been acrimonious, although with a few exceptions not particularly confrontational. One potential for clashes of views is in the review process for papers, since many of the papers supporting each position are reviewed by partisans of the others. It is here, behind the scenes, that a second, hidden battle is being fought. One paper, for instance, took four years to be accepted (comparing submission and acceptance dates - a process that regularly takes a half year or less). Responses were published to some of the criticisms raised in it, according to a footnote in the paper, before the paper saw print. On the positive side, the debate has led to a real flurry of research activity by all of the groups involved and we have infinitely better information about the patterns of ape-human differences and the extent of structural variation in teeth, and therefore more firmly established conclusions about the early hominids' maturational characteristics at our disposal now then would have been possible had there been no confrontation of ideas. This is the way science is supposed to work

REFERENCES AND FURTHER READINGS

ABITBOL, M.M. 1987a Evolution of the lumbosacral angle. *American Journal of Physical Anthropology* 72:361-372.

___. 1987b Evolution of the sacrum in hominoids. *American Journal of Physical Anthropology* 74:65-81.

___. 1987c Obstetrics and posture in pelvic anatomy. *Journal of Human Evolution* 16(3):243-255.

___. 1988 Effect of posture and locomotion on energy expenditure. *American Journal of Physical Anthropology* 77:191-199.

AIELLO, L., and C. DEAN 1990 *An Introduction to Human Evolutionary Anatomy.* Academic Press, New York.

AIELLO, L.C., and R.I.M. DUNBAR 1993 Neocortex size, group size, and the evolution of language. *Current Anthropology* 34:184-193.

ALEXANDER, R. McNEILL 1992 *The Human Machine.* Columbia University Press, New York.

ALEXANDER, M.P., D.F. BENSON, and D.T. STUSS 1991 Frontal lobes and language. *Brain and Language* 37:656-691.

ALEXANDER, R.D. 1979 Evolution and culture. In N.A. Chagnon and W. Irons (eds): *Evolutionary Biology and Human Social Behavior: An Anthropological Perspective.* Duxbury, North Scituate. pp. 59-78.

___. 1989 Evolution of the human psyche. In P. Mellars and C.B. Stringer (eds) *The Human Revolution: Behavioural and Biological Perspectives on the Origins of Modern Humans.* Edinburgh University Press, Edinburgh. pp. 455-513.

ALLMAN, J. 1987 Maps in context: some analogies between visual, cortical, and genetic maps. In L.M. Vaina ed: *Matters of Intelligence.* Riedel, New York. pp. 369-393.

ANDERSON, J.A. 1987 Concept formation in neural networks: implications for evolution of cognitive functions. *Human Evolution* 3(1):81-97.

ANEMONE, R.L., and E.S. WATTS 1992 Dental development in apes and humans: a comment on Simpson, Lovejoy, and Meindl (1990). *Journal of Human Evolution* 22(2):149-153.

ANEMONE, R.L., E.S. WATTS, and D.R. SWINDLER 1991 Dental development of known-age Chimpanzees, *Pan troglodytes* (Primates, Pongidae). *American Journal of Physical Anthropology* 86(2):229-241.

ARMELAGOS, G.J., D.S. CARLSON, and D.P. VAN GERVEN 1982 The theoretical foundations and development of skeletal biology. In F. Spencer (ed): *A History of American Physical Anthropology: 1930-1980.* Academic Press, New York. pp. 305-328.

BALDIA, M.O. 1982 Archaeology, evolution, culture and communication: a biologically based explanation of cultural evolution. In J. Jelínek (ed): *Man and his origins.* Anthropos 21:5-21.

BENYON, A.D., and M.C. DEAN 1988 Distinct dental development patterns in early fossil hominids. *Nature* 335:509-514.

BENYON, A.D., M.C. DEAN, and D.J. REID 1991 Histological study on the chronology of the developing dentition in Gorilla and Orangutan. *American Journal of Physical Anthropology* 86(2):189-203.

___. 1991 On thick and thin enamel in hominoids. *American Journal of Physical Anthropology* 86(2):295-309.

BICKERTON, D. 1990 *Language and Species.* University of Chicago Press, Chicago.

BISIACH, E. 1988 Language without thought. In L. Weiskrantz (ed): *Thought without Language.* Clarendon Press, Oxford. pp. 464-484.

BLOCH, M. 1991 Language, anthropology, and cognitive science. *Man* 26:183-198.

BOESCH, C., P. MARCHESI, N. MARCHESI, B. FRUTH, and F. JOULIAN 1994 Is nut cracking in wild chimpanzees a cultural behaviour? *Journal of Human Evolution* 26(4):325-338.

BOWER, B. 1987 Hominid headway. *Science News* 132:408-409.

BOYD, R., and P.J. RICHERSON 1993 Culture and human evolution. In D.T. Rasmussen (ed): *The Origin and Evolution of Humans and Humanness.* Jones and Bartless, Boston. pp. 119-134.

BRADSHAW, J. and L. ROGERS 1992 *The evolution of Lateral Asymmetries, Language, Tool Use, and Intellect.* Academic, San Diego.

BRIDGES, P.S. 1989 Changes in activities with the shift to agriculture in the Southeastern United States. *Current Anthropology* 30(3):385-394.

BROMAGE, T.G. 1987 The biological and chronological maturation of early hominids. *Journal of Human Evolution* 16(3):257-272.

BROMAGE, T.G., and M.C. DEAN 1985 Re-evaluation of the age at death of immature fossil hominids. *Nature* 317:525-527.

BROWN, T., J.D. JENNER, M.J. BARRETT, and G.H. LEES 1978 Exfoliation of deciduous teeth and gingival emergence of permanent teeth in Australian Aborigines. *Occasional Papers in Human Biology* 1:47-70.

BURLING, R. 1986 The selective advantage of complex language. *Ethnology and Sociobiology* 7:1-16.

___. 1992 The crucial mutation for language. *Journal of Linguistic Anthropology* 2(1):81-91,

___. 1993 Primate calls, human language, and nonverbal communication. *Current Anthropology* 34(1):25-53.

CAMPBELL, B. 1966 *Human Evolution. An Introduction to Man's Adaptations.* Aldine, Chicago.

CALVIN, W.H. 1983 A stone's throw and its launch window: timing, precision, and its implications for language and hominid brains. *Journal of Theoretical Biology* 104:121-135.

CARRIER, D.R. 1984 The energetic paradox of human running and hominid evolution. *Current Anthropology* 25(4):483-495.

CARTMILL M. 1992 Human uniqueness and theoretical content in paleoanthropology. *International Journal of Primatology* 11:173-192.

CARRITHERS, M. 1990 Why humans have cultures. *Man* 25:189-206.

CAVAGNA, G.A., and M. KANEKO 1977 Mechanical work and efficiency in level walking and running. *Journal of Physiology* 268:467-481.

CHOMSKY, N. 1986 *Knowledge of Language: Its Nature, Origin, and Use.* Greenwood Press, New York.

CONROY, G.C., and M.W. VANNIER 1991 Dental development in South African australopithecines. Part I: Problems of pattern and chronology. *American Journal of Physical Anthropology* 86(2):121-136.

___. 1991 Dental development in South African australopithecines. Part II: dental stage assessment. *American Journal of Physical Anthropology* 86(2):137-156.

COWEY, A. 1993 Seeing the tree for the woods. *Nature* 363:298

CURREY, J.D. 1984 *The Mechanical Adaptations of Bones.* Princeton University Press, Princeton.

DAMASIO, A.R., and H. DAMASIO 1992 Brain and language. *Scientific American* 267(3):89-95.

DEACON, T.D. 1989 The neural circuitry underlying primate calls and human language. *Human Evolution* 4(5):367-401.

___. 1992 Brain-language co-evolution. In J.A. Hawkins and M. Gell-Mann (eds): *The Evolution of Human Languages.* Addison-Wesley, Redwood City.

DEAN, M.C. 1987a Growth layers and incremental markings in hard tissues: a review of the literature and some preliminary observations about enamel structure in *Paranthropus boisei. Journal of Human Evolution* 16(2):157-172.

___. 1987b The dental developmental status of six East African juvenile fossil hominids. *Journal of Human Evolution* 16(2):197-213.

___. 1989 The developing dentition and tooth structure in hominoids. *Folia Primatologia* 53:160-176.

DEAN, M.C., A.D. BEYNON, J.F. THACKERAY, and G.A. MACHO 1993 Histological reconstruction of dental development and age at death of a juvenile *Paranthropus robustus* specimen, SK 63, from Swartkrans, South Africa. *American Journal of Physical Anthropology* 91(4):401-419.

DEAN, M.C. and B.A. WOOD 1981 Developing pongid dentition and its use for aging individual crania in comparative cross-sectional growth studies. *Folia Primatologia* 36:111-127.

DEMES, B., S.G. LARSON, J.T. STERN, W.L. JUNGERS, A.R. BIKNEVICIUS, and D. SCHMITT 1994 The kinetics of primate quadrupedalism: "hindlimb drive" reconsidered. *Journal of Human Evolution* 26(5/6):353-374.

DESMOND, A.J. 1979 *The Ape's Reflection.* Dial Press/James Wade, New York.

DEVINE, J. 1985 The versatility of human locomotion. *American Anthropologist* 87(3):550-570.

DOBZHANSKY, Th., and E. BOESIGER 1983 *Human Culture. A Moment in Evolution.* Columbia University Press, New York.

DUCHIN, L.E. 1990 The evolution of articulate speech: comparative anatomy of the oral cavity in *Pan* and *Homo. Journal of Human Evolution* 19(6-7)687-697.

DUNBAR, R. 1992 Why is gossip good for you? *New Scientist* (21 November):28-31.

DURHAM, W.H. 1992 *Coevolution: Genes, Culture, and Human Diversity.* Stanford University Press, Stanford.

FALK, D. 1987 Brain lateralization in primates and its evolution in hominids. *Yearbook of Physical Anthropology* 30:107-125.

FISHBACH, G.D. 1992 Mind and Brain. *Scientific American* 267(3):48-57.

FLEAGLE, J.G., STERN, J.T., JUNGERS, W.L., SUSMAN, R.L., VANGOR, A.K., and WELLS, J.P. 1981 Climbing: A biomechanical link with brachiation and with bipedalism. In M.H. Day (ed): *Vertebrate Locomotion. Symposium of the Zoological Society London* 48:359-375. Academic Press, London.

FLINN, M.V., and R.D. ALEXANDER 1982 Culture theory: the developing synthesis from biology. *Human Ecology* 10(3):383-400.

FOLEY, R.A. 1991 How useful is the culture concept in early hominid studies? In R. Foley (ed): *The Origins of Human Behavior.* Unwin Hyman, London. pp. 25-38.

FRANKEL, V.H., and M. NORDIN 1980 *Basic Biomechanics of the Skeletal System.* Lea and Febiger, Philadelphia.

FROST, G.T. 1980 Tool behavior and the origins of laterality. *Journal of Human Evolution* 9:447-459.

GARDNER, H. 1985 *The Mind's New Science: A History of the Cognitive Revolution.* Basic Books, New York.

GANTT, D.G. 1986 Enamel thickness and ultrastructure in hominoids: with reference to form, function, and phylogeny. In D.R. Swindler and J. Erwin (eds): *Comparative Primate Biology: Systematics, Evolution, and Anatomy.* Alan R. Liss, New York. 1:453-475.

GARN, S.M. 1963 Culture and the direction of human evolution. *Human Biology* 35:221-235.

GESCHWIND, N. 1979. Specializations of the Human Brain. *Scientific American* 241(3):180-199.

GIBSON, K.R. 1990 New perspectives on instincts and intelligence: brain size and the emergence of hierarchical mental construction skills. In S. Parker and K. Gibson (eds): *"Language" and Intelligence in Monkeys and Apes.* Cambridge University Press, New York. pp. 97-128.

___. 1991 Tools, language, and intelligence: evolutionary implications. *Man* 26:255-264.

GLEISER, I., and E.E. HUNT, Jr. 1955 The permanent mandibular molar: its calcification, eruption, and decay. *American Journal of Physical Anthropology* 13:253-283.

GOLDMAN-RAKIC, P.S. 1992 Working memory and the mind. *Scientific American* 267(3):111-117.

GOODENOUGH, W.H. 1990 Evolution of the human capacity for beliefs. *American Anthropologist* 92(3):597-612.

GORDON. K.D. 1987 Evolutionary perspectives on the human diet. In F.E. Johnston (ed): *Nutritional Anthropology*. Alan R. Liss, New York. pp. 3-39.

GREENFIELD, L.O. 1992 Origin of the human canine: a new solution to an old enigma. *Yearbook of Physical Anthropology* 35:153-185.

GRIFFIN, D.R. 1992 *Animal Minds*. University of Chicago, Chicago.

HOCKETT, C.F., and R. ASCHER 1964 The human revolution. *Current Anthropology* 5:135-168.

HOLLOWAY, R. L. 1966 Cranial capacity, neural reorganization, and hominid evolution: a search for more suitable parameters. *American Anthropologist* 68:103-121.

—. 1974 The casts of fossil hominid brains. *Scientific American* 231(1):106-116.

—. 1979 Brain size, allometry, and reorganization: toward a synthesis. In M.E. Hahn, C. Jensen, and B.C. Dudek (eds): *Development and Evolution of Brain Size: Behavioral Implications*. Academic Press, New York. Pp. 59-88.

—. 1983 Human paleontological evidence relevant to language behavior. *Human Neurobiology* (2):105-114.

—. 1988 Brain. In I. Tattersall, E. Delson, and J. Van Couvering (eds): *Encyclopedia of Human Evolution and Prehistory*. Garland, New York. pp. 98-105.

HOLLOWAY, R.L., P.L ANDERSON, R. DEFENDINI, and C. HARPER 1993 Sexual dimorphism of the human corpus callosum from three independent samples: relative size of the corpus callosum. *American Journal of Physical Anthropology* 92(4):481-498.

HOPKINS, W.D., K.A. BARD, A. JONES, and S.L. BALES 1993 Chimpanzee hand preference in throwing and infant cradling: implications for the origin of human handedness. *Current Anthropology* 34(5):786-790.

HYLANDER, W.L. 1985 Mandibular function and biomechanical stress and scaling. *American Zoologist* 25:315-330.

IRONS, W. 1979 Natural selection, adaptation, and human social behavior. In N.A. Chagnon and W. Irons (eds): *Evolutionary Biology and Human Social Behavior: An Anthropological Perspective*. Duxbury Press, North Scituate. pp. 4-39.

ISAAC, G.Ll. 1976 Stages of cultural elaboration in the Pleistocene: possible archaeological indicators of the development of language capabilities. In: *Origins and Evolution of Language and Speech. Annals of the New York Academy of Sciences* 280:275-288.

ISHIDA, H. 1991 A strategy for long distance walking in the earliest hominids: effect of posture on energy expenditure during bipedal walking. In Y. Coppens and B. Senut (eds): *Origine(s) de la Bipédie des Hominidés*. Cahiers de Paléoanthropologie, Centre National de la Recherche Scientifique, Paris. pp. 9-15.

ITZKOFF, S.W. 1983 *The Form of Man. The Evolutionary Origins of Human Intelligence*. Paideia, New York.

JOLLY, C.J. 1970 The seed eaters: a new model of hominid differentiation based on a baboon analogy. *Man* 5:5-26.

JERISON, H.J. 1991 *Brain Size and the Evolution of Mind.* American Museum of Natural History, New York.

KANDEL, E.R. and R.D. HAWKINS 1992 The biological basis of learning and individuality. *Scientific American* 267(3):79-86.

KENDON, A. 1991 Some considerations for a theory of language origins. *Man* 26:199-221.

KENNEDY, K.A.R. 1983 Morphological variations in ulnar supinator crests and fossae as identifying markers of occupational stress. *Journal of Forensic Sciences* 28(4):871-876.

KER, R.F., M.B. BENNETT, S.R. BIBBY, R.C. KESTER, and R. McN. ALEXANDER 1987 The spring in the arch of the human foot. *Nature* 325:147-149.

KIEN, J. 1991 The need for data reduction may have paved the way for the evolution of language ability in hominids. *Journal of Human Evolution* 20:157-165.

KIMURA, D. 1992 Sex differences in the brain. *Scientific American* 267(3):119-125.

KOLB, B. and I.Q. WHISHAW 1985 *Fundamentals of Human Neurophysiology,* Second Edition. W.H. Freeman, New York.

KOCHETKOVA, V.I. 1978 *Paleoneurology.* Winston and Sons, Washington D.C.

KROEBER, A.L 1917 The superorganic. *American Anthropologist* 19:163-213.

KROEBER, A.L., and C. KLUCKHOLM 1952 Culture: a critical review of its concepts and definitions. *Papers of the Peabody Museum of American Archaeology and Ethnology* 47.

KUMMER, B.K.F. 1965 Das mechanische Problem der Aufrichtung auf die Hinterextremität im Hinblick auf die Evolution der Bipedie des Menschen. In G. Heberer (ed): *Menschliche Abstammungslehre.* Fischer, Stuttgart. pp. 227-248.

KUYKENDALL, K.L., C.J. MAHONEY, and G.C. CONROY 1992 Probit and survival analysis of tooth emergence ages in a mixed-longitudinal sample of chimpanzees (*Pan troglodytes*). *American Journal of Physical Anthropology* 89:379-399.

LAITMAN, J.T., and J.S. REIDENBERG 1987 Advances in understanding the relationship between the skull base and larynx with comments of the origin of speech. *Human Evolution* 3(1):99-109.

LAMPL, M., J.M. MONGE, and A.E. MANN 1993 Further observations on a method for estimating hominoid dental development. *American Journal of Physical Anthropology* 90(1):113-127.

LANCASTER, J.B., and C.S. LANCASTER 1983 Parental investment: the hominid adaptation. In D.J. Ortner (ed): *How Humans Adapt.* Smithsonian International Symposia Series, Smithsonian Institution, Washington D.C. pp. 33-65.

LANYON, L.E. 1987 Functional strain in bone tissue as an objective and controlling stimulus for adaptive bone remodeling. *Journal of Biomechanics* 20:1083-1093.

LARSEN, C.S. 1987 Bioarchaeological interpretations of subsistence economy and behavior from human skeletal remains. *Advances in Archaeological Method and Theory* 10:339-445.

LASZLO, E., and I. MASULLI (editors) 1993 *The Evolution of Cognitive Maps: New Paradigms for the Twenty-First Century.* The World Futures General Evolution Studies Series, Volume 5. Gordon and Breach Science Publishers, Yverdon (Switzerland).

LATIMER, B.M., and C.O. LOVEJOY 1989 The calcaneus of *Australopithecus afarensis* and its implications for the evolution of bipedality. *American Journal of Physical Anthropology* 78(3):369-386.

—. 1990a Hallucal tarsometatarsal joint in *Australopithecus afarensis. American Journal of Physical Anthropology* 82(2):125-133.

—. 1990b Metatarsophalangeal joints of *Australopithecus afarensis. American Journal of Physical Anthropology* 83(1):13-23.

LAUGHLIN, C. D., and E. G. D AQUILI. 1974. *Biogenetic Structuralism.* Columbia University Press, New York.

___. 1992 *Brain, Symbol, and Experience.* Columbia University Press, New York.

LENNEBERG, E.H. 1971 Of language knowledge, apes, and brains. *Journal of Psycholinguistic Research* 1:1-29.

LEONARD, W.R, and M.L. ROBERTSON 1992 Nutritional requirements and human evolution: a bioenergetics model. *American Journal of Human Biology* 4:179-195.

LEVI-STRAUSS, C. 1967 *Structural Anthropology.* Doubleday, Garden City.

LEWIN, R. 1981 Cultural diversity tied to genetic differences. *Science* 212:908-910.

—. 1983 Were Lucy's feet made for walking? *Science* 220:700-702.

__. 1987 Debate over emergence of human tooth pattern. *Science* 235:748-750.

LEWIS, O.J. 1989 *Functional Morphology of the Evolving Hand and Foot.* Oxford University Press, New York.

LIEBERMAN, D., and R.H. MEADOW 1992 The biology of cementum increments (with an archaeological application). *Mammal Review* 2:55-77.

LIEBERMAN, P. 1991 *Uniquely Human: The Evolution of Speech, Thought, and Selfless Behavior.* Harvard University Press, Cambridge.

LIVINGSTONE, F.B. 1982 Cultural causes of genetic change. In G.W. Barlow and J. Silverberg (eds): *Sociobiology: Beyond Nature/Nurture.* AAAS Selected Symposium 35. Westview Press, Boulder. pp. 307-329.

LOVEJOY, C. O. 1974 The gait of australopithecines. *Yearbook of Physical Anthropology* 17:147-161.

—. 1979 Contemporary methodological approaches to individual primate fossil analysis. In M.E. Morbeck, H. Preuschoft, and N. Gomberg (eds): *Environment, Behavior, and Morphology.* Gustav Fischer, New York. pp. 229-243.

—. 1988 Evolution of human walking. *Scientific American* 259(5):118-125.

LOVEJOY, C.O. and E. TRINKAUS 1980 Strength and robusticity of the Neandertal tibia. *American Journal of Physical Anthropology* 53, 465 - 470.

LUMSDEN, C.J., and E.O. WILSON. 1981 *Genes, Mind, and Culture.* Harvard University Press, Cambridge.

MANN, A.E. 1975 *Some Paleodemographic Aspects of the South African Australopithecines.* University of Pennsylvania Publications in Anthropology Number 1, Philadelphia.

MANN, A.E., M. LAMPL, and J. MONGE 1987 Maturational patterns in early hominids. Nature 328:673-674.

___. 1990 Patterns of ontogeny in human evolution: evidence from dental development. *Yearbook of Physical Anthropology* 33:111-150.

MANN, A.E., J. MONGE, and M. LAMPL 1991 Investigation into the relationship between perikymata counts and crown formation times. *American Journal of Physical Anthropology* 86(2):175-188.

MARSHACK, A. 1992 The origin of language: an anthropological approach. In J. Wind, B. Chiarelli, B. Bichakjian, and A. Nocentini (eds): *Language Origin: A Multidisciplinary Approach.* Kluwer Academic Publishers, Dordrecht. pp. 421-448.

MARTIN, R.B., and D.B. BURR 1989 *Structure, Function, and Adaptation of Compact Bone.* Raven Press. New York.

MASCIA-LEES, F.E., J.H. RELENTHFORD, and T. SORGER 1986 Evolutionary perspectives on permanent breast enlargement in human females. *American Anthropologist* 88(2):423-429.

McCRONE, J. 1991 *The Ape that Spoke: Language and the Evolution of the Human Mind.* William Morrow, New York.

McHENRY, H.M. 1991 First steps? Analysis of the postcranium of early hominids. In Y. Coppens and B. Senut (eds): *Origine(s) de la Bipédie chez les Hominidés.* Cahiers de Paléontologie, Editions du Centre National de la Recherche Scientifique, Paris. pp. 133-141.

McKEE, J.E., and J.K. MCKEE 1991 Inherent errors in rating tooth formation in CT scans. *The Leech* 60(2):12-15.

MILTON, K. 1981 Distribution patterns of tropical plant foods as an evolutionary stimulus to primate mental development. *American Anthropologist* 83:535-98.

MOLNAR, S. and D.G. GANTT 1977 Functional implications of primate enamel thickness. *American Journal of Physical Anthropology* 46(3):447-454.

MOLNAR, S., T.R. PRZYBECK, D.R. GANTT, R.S. ELIZONDO, and J.E. WILKERSON 1981 Dentin apposition rates as markers of primate growth. *American Journal of Physical Anthropology* 55:443-453.

MOLNAR, S., and S. C. WARD. 1977. On the Hominid Masticatory Complex: Biomechanical and Evolutionary Perspectives. *Journal of Human Evolution* 6:557-568.

MOORREES, C.F.A., E.A. FANNING, and E.E. HUNT, Jr. 1963 Age variation of formation stages for ten permanent teeth. *Journal of Dental Research* 42:1490-1502.

NAPIER, J.R. 1967 The Antiquity of Human Walking. *Scientific American* 216(4):56-66.

NISHIDA, T. 1987 Local traditions and cultural transmission. In B.B. Smuts, D.L. Cheney, R.M. Seyfarth, R.W. Wrangham, and T. Struhsacker (eds): *Primate Societies.* University of Chicago Press, Chicago. pp. 462-474.

NISHIDA, T., H. TAKASAKI, and Y. TAKAHATA 1990 Demography and reproductive profiles. In N. Nishida (ed): *The Chimpanzees of the Mahale Mountains.* University of Tokyo, Tokyo. pp. 63-97.

NISSEN, H.W., and REISEN, A.H. 1964 The eruption of the permanent dentition of chimpanzee. *American Journal of Physical Anthropology* 22:285-294.

OHMAN, J.C. 1986 The first rib of hominoids. *American Journal of Physical Anthropology* 70(2):209-230.

O'KEEFE, J. 1985 Is consciousness the gateway to the hippocampal cognitive map? A speculative essay on the neural basis of mind. In D.A. Oakley (ed): *Brain and Mind.* Methuen, London. pp. 59-98.

OSBORN, J.W. 1987 Relationship between the mandibular condyle and the occlusal plane during hominid evolution: some of its effects on jaw mechanics. *American Journal of Physical Anthropology* 73:193-207.

PARKER, S.T. 1985 A social-technological model for the evolution of language. *Current Anthropology* 26(5):617-639.

PARKER, S.T., and K.R. GIBSON 1982 The importance of theory in reconstructing the evolution of language and intelligence in hominids. In A.B. Chiarelli and R.S. Corruccini (eds): *Advanced Views in Primate Biology.* Springer, New York. pp. 42-64.

PASSINGHAM, R.E. 1989 The origins of human intelligence. In J.R. Durant (ed) *Human Origins.* Clarendon Press, Oxford. pp. 123-136.

PIATTELLI-PALMERINI, M. 1989 Evolution, selection, and cognition: from "learning" to parameter setting in biology and the study of language. *Cognition* 31:1-44.

PINKER, S., and P. BLOOM 1990 Natural language and natural selection. *Behavioral and Brain Science* 13:707-784.

PLOTKIN, H.C. (ed) 1982 *Learning, Development, and Culture. Essays in Evolutionary Epistemology.* John Wiley, Chichester.

POTTS, R. 1991 Untying the knot. Evolution of early human behavior. In M.H. Robinson and L. Tiger (eds): *Man & Beast Revisited.* Smithsonian Press, Washington. pp. 41-59.

PULLEYBLANK, E.G. 1989 The meaning of duality patterning and its importance in language evolution. In J. Wind, E.G. Pulleyblank, E. DeGrolier, and B.H. Bichakjian (ed): *Studies in Language Origins* 1:53-65. John Benjamin, Amsterdam.

RAGIR, S. 1985 Retarded development: the evolutionary mechanism underlying the emergence of the human capacity for language. *Mind and Behavior* 6(4):451-468.

RAK, Y. 1991 Lucy's pelvic anatomy: its role in bipedal gait. *Journal of Human Evolution* 20(4):283-290.

RAMIREZ-ROZZI, F.V. 1993 Tooth development in East African *Paranthropus*. *Journal of Human Evolution* 24(6):429-454.

RICHARDS, G. 1988 *Human Evolution*. Routledge Press, London.

RILEY, T.J., R. EDGING, and J. ROSSEN 1990 Cultigens in prehistoric eastern North America. *Current Anthropology* 31(5):525-542.

RINDOS, D. 1985 Darwinian selection, symbolic variation, and the evolution of culture. *Current Anthropology* 26(1):65-88.

ROBINSON, J.T. 1963 Australopithecines, culture, and phylogeny. *American Journal of Physical Anthropology* 21:595-605.

RODGERS, A.R. 1988 Does biology constrain culture? *American Anthropologist* 90(4):819-831.

RODMAN, P.S., and H.M. McHENRY 1980 Bioenergetics and the origin of hominid bipedalism. *American Journal of Physical Anthropology* 52:103-106.

ROSENBERG, K.R. 1992 The evolution of modern human childbirth. *Yearbook of Physical Anthropology* 35:89-124.

RUFF, C. 1992 Biomechanical analysis of archaeological human skeletal samples. In S.R. Saunders and M.A. Katzenberg (eds): *Skeletal Biology of Past Peoples: Research Methods*. Wiley-Liss, New York. pp. 37-58.

RUFF. C.B., A.C. WALKER, and E. TRINKAUS 1994 Postcranial robusticity in *Homo*. III: Ontogeny. *American Journal of Physical Anthropology* 93(1):35-54.

SARMIENTO, E.E. 1988 Anatomy of the hominoid wrist joint: its evolutionary and functional implications. *International Journal of Primatology* 9:281-345.

SAUNDERS, S., C. DeVITO, A. HERRING, R. SOUTHERN, and R. HOPPA 1993 Accuracy tests in tooth formation age estimations for human skeletal remains, *American Journal of Physical Anthropology* 92(2):173-188.

SCHULTZ, A.H. 1950 The physical distinctions of man. *Proceedings of the American Philosophical Society* 94:428-449.

SCOTT, G.R., and C.G. TURNER II 1988 Dental anthropology. In B.J. Siegel, A.R. Beals, and S.A. Tyler (eds): *Annual Review of Anthropology*. Annual Reviews, Palo Alto. Volume 17:99-126.

SENUT, B. 1988 Climbing as a crucial preadaptation for human bipedalism. *International Journal of Skeletal Research* 14:35-44.

SHENNAN, S. 1989 Cultural transmission and cultural change. In S.E. van der Leeuw and R. Torrence (eds): *What's New? A Closer Look at the Process of Innovation*. Unwin Hyman, London. pp. 330-346.

SIMPSON, S.W., C.O. LOVEJOY, and R.S. MEINDL 1990 Hominoid dental maturation. *Journal of Human Evolution* 19(3):285-297

SMITH, B.H. 1986 Dental development in *Australopithecus* and early *Homo*. *Nature* 323:327-330.

___. 1987 Maturational patterns in early hominids. *Nature* 328:674-675.

___. 1992 Life history and the evolution of human maturation. *Evolutionary Anthropology* 1(4):134-142.

___. 1994a Sequence of emergence of the permanent teeth of *Macaca, Pan, Homo*, and *Australopithecus*: its evolutionary significance. *American Journal of Human Biology* 6(1):61-76.

___. 1994b Patterns of dental development in *Homo, Australopithecus, Pan*, and *Gorilla. American Journal of Physical Anthropology* 94(3):307-325.

SMITH, E.A., and B. WINTERHALTER 1992 *Evolutionary Ecology and Human Behavior*. Aldine de Gruyter, New York.

SMITH, R.J. 1978 Mandibular biomechanics and temporomandibular joint function in primates. *American Journal of Physical Anthropology* 49:341-351.

SPOOR, F., B. WOOD, and F. ZONNEVELD 1994 Implications of early hominid labyrinthine morphology for the evolution of human bipedal locomotion. *Nature* 369:645-648.

SPUHLER, J.N. 1959 Somatic paths to culture. In J.N. Spuhler (ed): *The Evolution of Man's Capacity for Culture*. Wayne State University, Detroit. pp. 1-13.

STEELE, J. 1989 Hominid evolution and social cognition. *Journal of Human Evolution* 18:421-432.

STRINGER, C.B., M.C. DEAN, and R.D. MARTIN 1990 A comparative study of cranial and dental development within a recent British sample and among neanderthals. In J. DeRousseau (ed): *Primate Life History and Evolution*. Wiley-Liss, New York. pp. 115-152.

SUSMAN, R.L., J.T. STERN Jr., and W.L. JUNGERS 1984 Arboreality and bipedality in the Hadar hominids. *Folia Primatologia* 43:113-156.

SWINDLER, D.R., and C.D. WOOD 1973 *An Atlas of Primate Gross Anatomy: Baboon, Chimpanzee, and Man*. University of Washington, Seattle.

TAGUE, R.G., and C.O. LOVEJOY 1986 The obstetric pelvis of A.L. 288-1 (Lucy). *Journal of Human Evolution* 15(4):237-255.

THACKERAY, A.I., and A.J. KELLY 1988 A technological and typological analysis of Middle Stone Age assemblages antecedent to the Howiesons Poort at Klasies River Main Site. *South African Archaeological Bulletin* 43(1):15-26.

TOOBY, J., and L. COSMIDES 1992 The psychological foundations of culture. In J.H. Barkow, L. Cosmides, and J. Tooby (eds): *The Adapted Mind: Evolution Psychology and the Generation of Culture*. Oxford University Press, New York. pp. 19-136.

TOTH, N. 1985 Archaeological evidence for preferential right-handedness in the lower and middle Pleistocene, and its possible implications. *Journal of Human Evolution* 14:607-614.

TOTH, N., and K.D. SCHICK 1992 Early stone industries and inferences regarding language and cognition. In K. Gibson and T. Ingold (eds): *Tools, Language, and Cognition*. Cambridge University Press, Cambridge. pp. 346-362.

TREVATHIAN, W.R. 1988 Fetal emergence patterns in evolutionary perspective. *American Anthropologist* 90:674-681.

TRINKAUS, E., S.E. CHURCHILL, and C.B. RUFF 1994 Postcranial robusticity in *Homo*. II: Humeral bilateral asymmetry and bone plasticity. *American Journal of Physical Anthropology* 93(1):1-34.

TRODDEN, B.J. 1982 *A Radiographic Study of the Calcification and Eruption of the Permanent Teeth in Inuit and Indian Children*. Archaeological Survey of Canada Paper 112, National Museums of Man, Ottawa.

TUTTLE, R. H. 1975 Parallelism, brachiation, and hominid phylogeny. In W. P. Luckett and F. S. Szalay (eds): *Phylogeny of the Primates*. Plenum, New York. pp. 447-480.

___. 1994 Up from electromyography. Primate energetics and the evolution of human bipealism. In R.S. Corruccini and R.L. Ciochon (eds): *Integrative Paths to the Past. Paleoanthropological Advances in Honor of F. Clark Howell*. Prentice Hall, Englewood Cliffs. pp. 269-284.

UETAKE, T. 1992 Can we really walk straight? *American Journal of Physical Anthropology* 89(1):19-27.

VAN VALEN, L.M. 1984 How persuasive is coevolution? In M.H. Nitecki (ed): *Coevolution*. University of Chicago, Chicago.

WALKER, A.C. 1976 Functional anatomy of the oral tissues. In J.H. Shaw, E.A. Sweeney , C.C. Capuccino, and S.M. Meller, and (eds.): *Textbook of Oral Biology*. Saunders, Philadelphia. pp. 277-295.

WALLACE, A. F. C. 1961. *Culture and Personality*. Random House, New York.

WALLACE, R. 1992 Spacial mapping and the origin of language: a paleoneurological model. In A. Jonker (ed): *Studies in Language Origins*, Volume 4. John Benjamins, Philadelphia.

WALLMAN, J. 1992 *Aping Language*. Cambridge University Press, New York.

WASHBURN, S.L. 1963 Behavior and human evolution. In S.L. Washburn (ed): *Classification and Human Evolution*. Aldine, Chicago. pp. 190-203.

WEIJS, W.A., and B. HILLEN 1986 Correlations between the cross-sectional area of the jaw muscles and craniofacial size and shape. *American Journal of Physical Anthropology* 70(4):423-431.

WOLPOFF, M.H. 1979 The Krapina dental remains. *American Journal of Physical Anthropology* 50:67-114.

Special Volumes

1976 The Origin and Evolution of Language and Speech. *Annals of the New York Academy of Sciences* 280 (S. Harnad, H. Steklis, and J.B. Lancaster editors)

1982 *Primate Brain Evolution. Methods and Concepts*. Plenum, New York (E. Armstrong and D. Falk editors)

1985 *Brain and Mind*. (D.A. Oakley editor). Methuen, London.

1990 The Brain. *Cold Spring Harbor Symposia on Quantitative Biology* 55.

1991 Primate Tooth Formation: A Symposium. *American Journal of Physical Anthropology* 86(2) (L.A. Winkler and D.R. Swindler editors).

1992 *Studies in Language Origins*. (A. Jonkers editor). John Benjamins, Philadelphia.

1992 Mind and Brain. *Scientific American* 267(3).

1993 *Tools, Language, and Cognition in Human Evolution*. Cambridge University Press, New York (K.R. Gibson and T. Ingold editors).

1993 *The Evolution of Lateral Asymmetries, Language, Tool Use, and Intellect.* (J. Bradshaw and L. Rogers editors). Academic Press, New York.

1993 *The Evolution of Cognitive Maps.* (E. Laszlo and I. Masulli editors). Gordon and Breach, Langhorne (Pennsylvania).

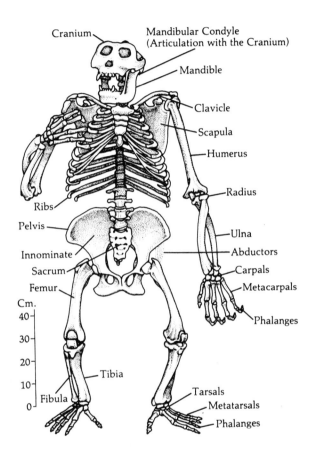

FIGURE 4.1 A bipedal gorilla in frontal view, showing the names of the bones. The condyle of the mandible and the position of the abductor muscles are also shown. Drawing is after Schultz (1969).
FROM: First edition, figure 4.2.

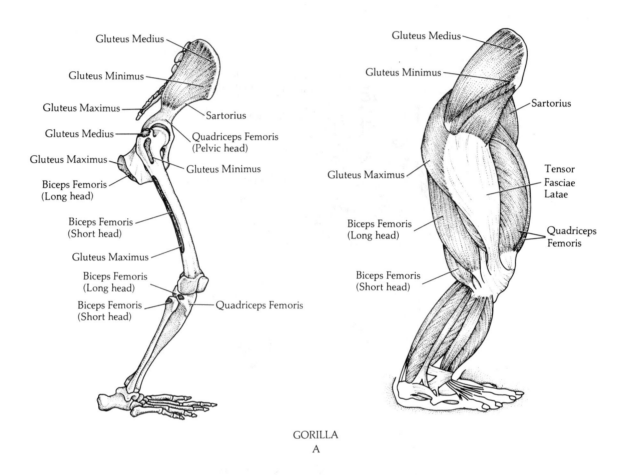

GORILLA
A

FIGURE 4.2 Bones and muscles of the hindlimb in (A) a gorilla and (B) a human, adapted from Napier (1967). The gorilla limb is shown in its quadrupedal position, while the human limb is in its bipedal position. In both primates, the main muscles that cause flexion at the hip are in the **quadriceps femoris** group and the **sartorius**. Since the **quadriceps** also passes in front of the knee, attaching by way of the patella to the front of the tibia, it causes extension at the knee as well as hip flexion. The hip extensors differ between these primates. In the gorilla, it is the **hamstrings** muscle group (**biceps femoris** is shown in the figure but the group also includes the **semimembranosus** and **semitendinosus** muscles) that causes extensions when the limb is in the position shown. The position of the limb is important because when in a more flexed position the **hamstrings** can also cause extension in the human limb. Only when the limbs are in the positions illustrated will extension cause forward motion of the ape. The human **hamstrings** do not bring the femur backward in the position shown; instead, the **gluteus maximus** is the main extensor. The third important motion at the hip is abduction (motion of the leg outward to the side and upward). In both primates, **gluteus minimus** and **gluteus medius** act to produce this motion, and in the gorilla this is the main function of **gluteus maximus.** **FROM:** First edition, figure 4.3.

FIGURE 4.3 Quadrupedalism and bipedalism in a chimpanzee compared with a bipedal human, based on a drawing from Kummer (1965). The spine, pelvis, and lower limb are shown, as is the position of the hip flexors: Q = quadriceps, H = hamstrings, and G = gluteus maximus. The figure shows (A) the chimpanzee in the quadrupedal position, (B) the chimpanzee in its normal bipedal position, (C) the chimpanzee in a human-like bipedal position, and (D) the bipedal human. Note that in its normal bipedal position (B) the chimpanzee maintains leverage for its hamstrings by flexing at the knee and hip. When the ape attains the human posture, extending at these joints (C), the hamstrings have lost their leverage to bring the leg backward.
FROM: First edition, figure 4.4.

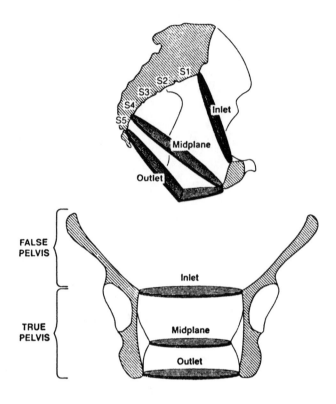

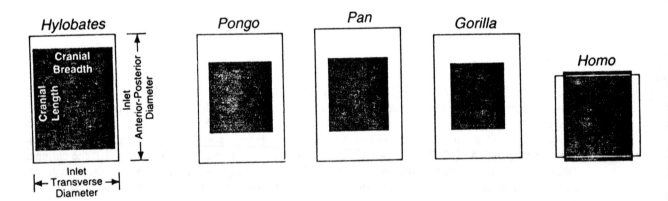

FIGURE 4.4 The pelvic aperture. Above are the sagittal and transverse views of the inlet, midplane, and outlet. Below is a diagrammatic representation of the relation between head size and pelvic inlet size at birth for apes, and humans. The three great apes are tighter-fitting than this diagram shows, as their large clavicles rather than head size are the limiting factor. Both are after Rosenberg (1992).

FROM Rosenberg, K.R. 1992 The evolution of modern human childbirth. *Yearbook of Physical Anthropology* 35:89-124, figures 2, 4.

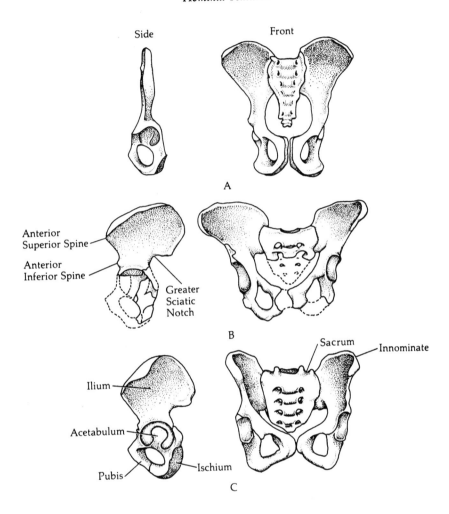

FIGURE 4.5 Front and side views of the pelvis in a chimpanzee (A), an early hominid (B), and a modern human (C) (adapted from Campbell, 1966) The early hominid side view is based on the reconstructed juvenile from Makapansgat; the front view is based on the Sterkfontein female pelvis. On the human pelvis, the three bones making up the hip bone (innominate) are named, and the position of the sacrum is shown. The sacrum and the innominates make up the pelvis. Note that there is more lateral flare in the hips of the early hominid pelvis than in the modern human one. This is because the birth canal in humans is broader and the acetabula are consequently farther apart.

FROM: First edition, figure 4.5.

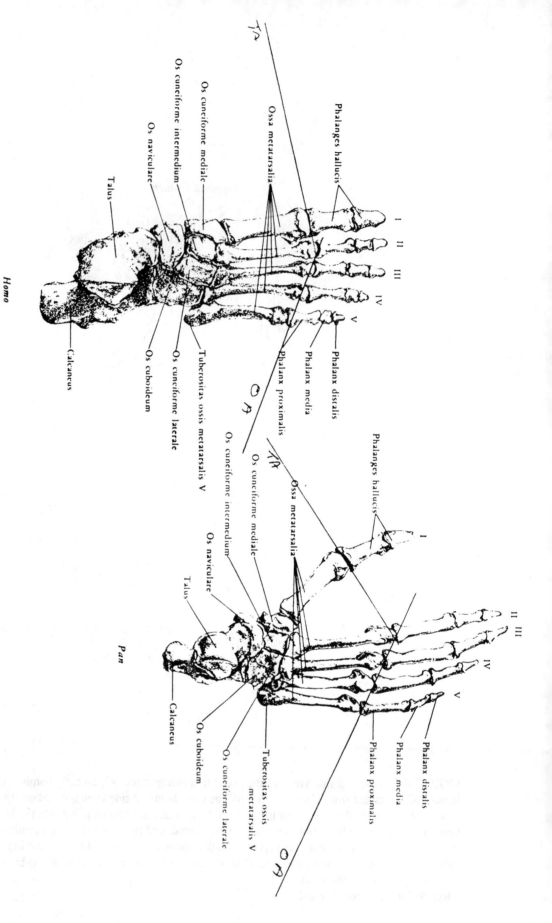

Phalanges hallucis

Phalanx distalis
Phalanx media
Phalanx proximalis

Os cuneiforme mediale
Os cuneiforme intermedium

Ossa metatarsalia

Os cuneiforme mediale
Os cuneiforme intermedium

Os naviculare

Talus

Tuberositas ossis metatarsalis V

Os cuneiforme laterale

Os cuboideum

Os naviculare

Calcaneus

Homo

Phalanges hallucis

Ossa metatarsalia

Talus

Calcaneus

Os cuboideum

Os cuneiforme laterale

Tuberositas ossis metatarsalis V

Phalanx proximalis
Phalanx media
Phalanx distalis

Pan

FIGURE 4.6 Comparison of a chimpanzee and human right foot in dorsal view, showing the contrast in the oblique axis (OA) at the 2-5 metatarsal heads and the transverse axis between the big toe and 2nd metatarsalphalangeal joints. During the early phase of push-off in hominid bipedalism, force is exerted first along the oblique axis and transferred to the transverse axis as is toe-off. In the apes there is no toe off.

FROM: Swindler, D.R., and C.D. Wood 1973 *An Atlas of Primate Gross Anatomy: Baboon, Chimpanzee, and Man.* University of Washington, Seattle, plate 26.

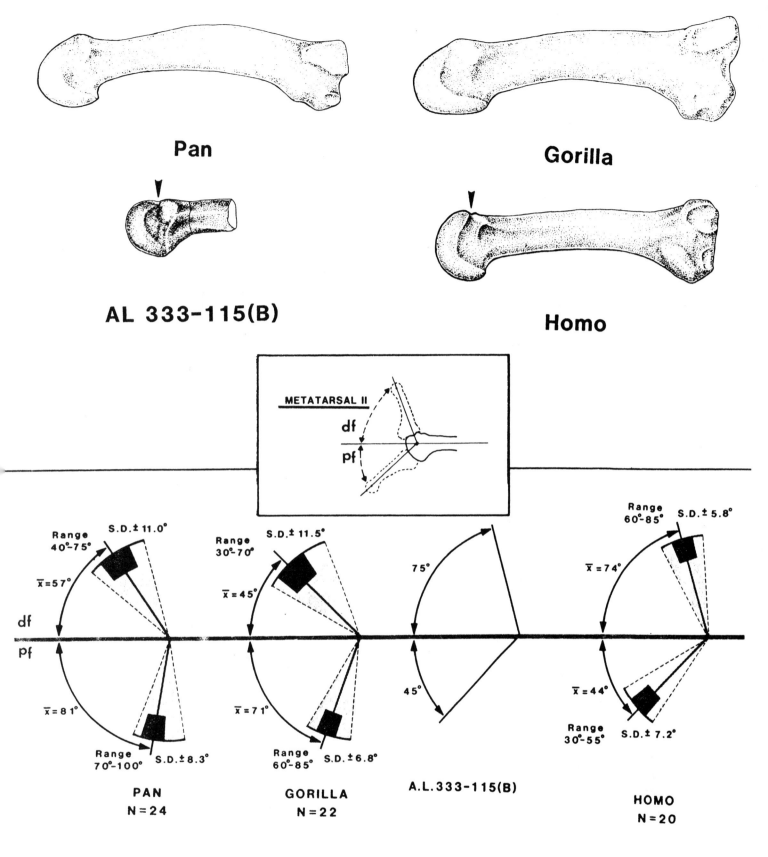

FIGURE 4.7 Second metatarsals for some ape and hominid species, and their angular ranges of dorsiflexion (df) and plantarflexion (pf). In the hominids the expanded metatarsal head creates a shallow sulcus between it and the shaft (arrow), and the axis of the head is more vertically oriented to the shaft. This helps provide a wider range of dorsiflexion activities while plantarflexion is more limited.

FROM Latimer, B.M., and C.O. Lovejoy 1990 Metatarsophalangeal joints of *Australopithecus afarensis*. *American Journal of Physical Anthropology* 83(1):13-23, figures 3, 4.

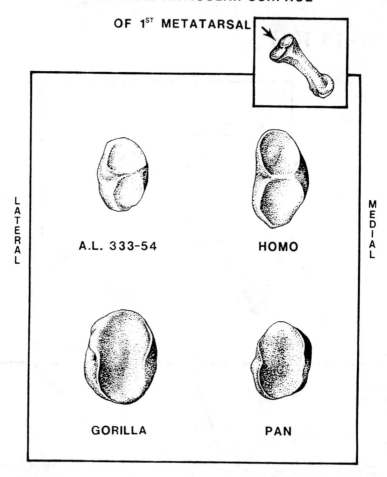

PROXIMAL ARTICULAR SURFACE OF 1ST METATARSAL

LATERAL

MEDIAL

A.L. 333-54

HOMO

GORILLA

PAN

FIGURE 4.8 The proximal articular surface of the first left metatarsal. The single articular surface in the two apes is a result of the axial rotation of the big toe.

FROM Latimer, B.M., and C.O. Lovejoy 1990 Hallucal tarsometatarsal joint in *Australopithecus afarensis*. *American Journal of Physical Anthropology* 82(2):125-133, figure 5.

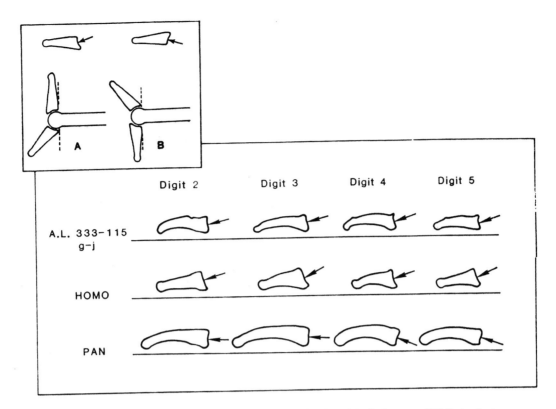

FIGURE 4.9 Articular orientations and excursions of proximal pedal phalanges. While both the australopithecine and chimpanzee have curved shafts, only the proximal articular surface of the chimpanzee is oriented vertically to the shaft. This orientation emphasizes more plantarflexion in the ape and is important in weight support on a curved support surface such as a branch.

FROM Latimer, B.M., and C.O. Lovejoy 1990 Metatarsophalangeal joints of *Australopithecus afarensis*. *American Journal of Physical Anthropology* 83(1):13-23, figure 5

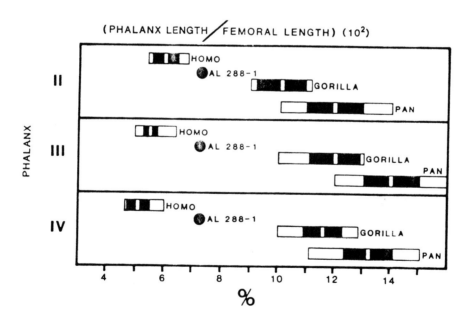

FIGURE 4.10 Relative phalangeal length. No matter which digit the single AL 288-1 phalanx represents, it is very short compared with the femur lengths of the two African apes, and it should be remembered that these apes have short femora!

FROM Latimer, B.M., and C.O. Lovejoy 1990 Metatarsophalangeal joints of *Australopithecus afarensis*. *American Journal of Physical Anthropology* 83(1):13-23, figures 6, 7.

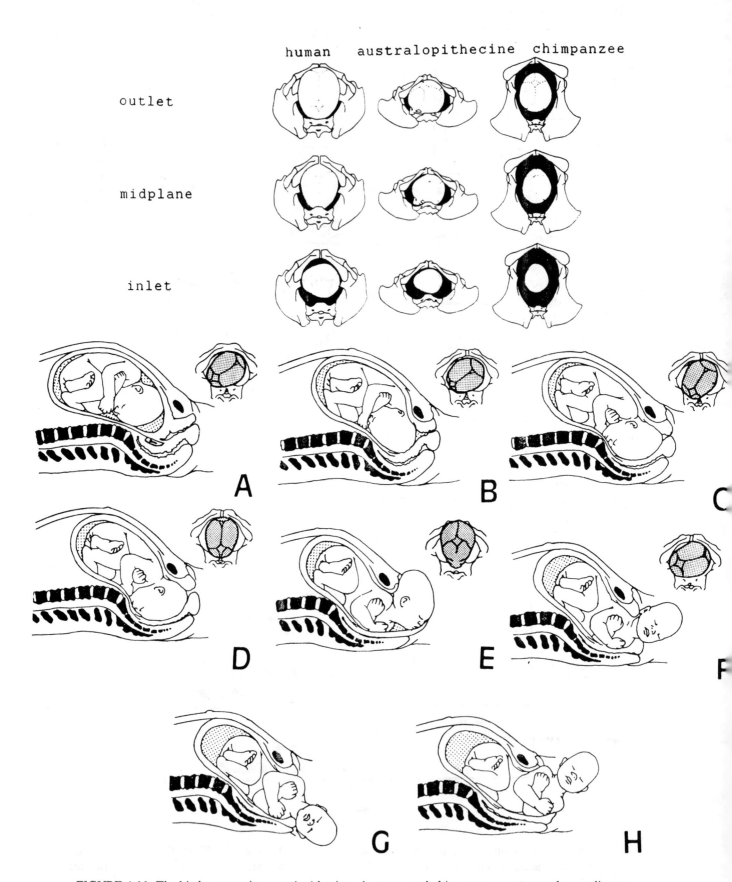

FIGURE 4.11 The birth process in australopithecines, humans, and chimpanzees, compared according to Tague (the three planes of the aperture are shown in figure 4.4). The actual positions of a baby during birth are shown below, after Rosenberg (1992).

FROM Tague, R.G., and C.O. Lovejoy 1986 The obstetric pelvis of A.L. 288-1 (Lucy). *Journal of Human Evolution* 15(4):237-255; Rosenberg, K.R. 1992 The evolution of modern human childbirth. *Yearbook of Physical Anthropology* 35:89-124, figures 2, 4.

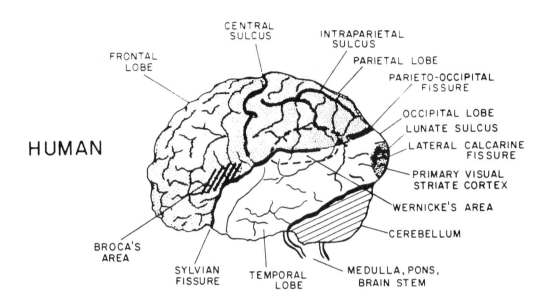

HUMAN

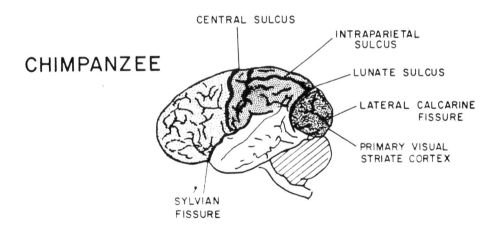

CHIMPANZEE

FIGURE 4.12 Main areas of the external brain surface, after Holloway (1988)
FROM Holloway, R.L. 1988 Brain. In I. Tattersall, E. Delson, and J. Van Couvering (eds): *Encyclopedia of Human Evolution and Prehistory.* Garland, New York. pp. 98-105.

;

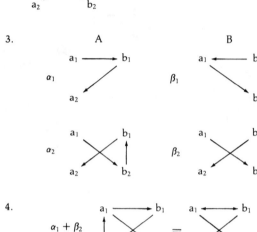

FIGURE 4.13 Equivalence structures and cognitive maps for simplified cultural interactions, after Wallace (1961). Parts] and 2 show the primary and secondary equivalence structures described in the text; part 3 shows some of the cognitive maps for A and B which can combine to form the secondary equivalence structure. These maps can be defined as follows:

α_1 A knows that whenever a1 is performed, B will respond with b1 and then A will perform a2.

α_2 A knows that whenever a1 is performed, B will respond with b2 and then bl, and A will then perform a2

β_1 B knows that whenever b1 is performed, A will respond with a1 and then B will perform b2.

β_2 B knows that whenever bl is performed, A will respond with a2 and then al, and B will then perform b2

Finally, part 4 gives an example of how these maps combine to form the secondary equivalence structure. All four possible combinations result in the same interaction.
FROM: First edition, figure 4.1.

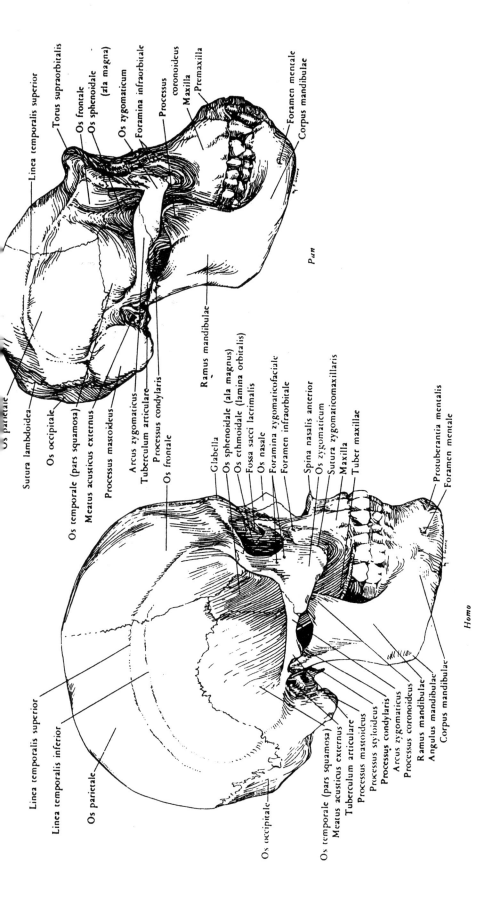

FIGURE 4.14 Three views of a human (above or left) and a chimpanzee skull, adapted from Swindler and Wood (1973). Elements of all three hominid distinctions are apparent. The difference in brain size is seen in the larger human brain case. Locomotor differences are reflected in the balance of the head on top of the spinal cord. The view from below (middle) shows that the large opening (foramen magnum), which indicates the place where the spinal cord enters the brain case, is in a more forward position in the human cranium because the head is balanced on top of the vertebral column. The side view shows that the ridge at the back of the cranium (nuchal ridge), marking the farthest extent of neck muscle attachment, is lower in the human skull because of the more forward foramen magnum. The third distinction is in the jaws and teeth. The chimpanzee face projects forward, holding large angled incisors and projecting canines. The human face is much more vertical, leaving the nose projecting forward, and lacks the incisor angulation. In the view from below, the contrast in the size of the canines and incisors, and in the form of the canines, is clearly visible. The chimpanzee tooth row has a u shape because of the large incisors and the marked angle at the canines. The human tooth row shape is more parabolic, with a gentle curve at the front and divergent posterior teeth. Note the diastema between the chimpanzee canine and incisor. The posterior teeth of these primates are virtually identical. Small posterior teeth, however, are a recent hominid characteristic.

FROM: Swindler, D.R., and C.D. Wood 1973 *An Atlas of Primate Gross Anatomy: Baboon, Chimpanzee, and Man.* University of Washington, Seattle, plates 1-3.

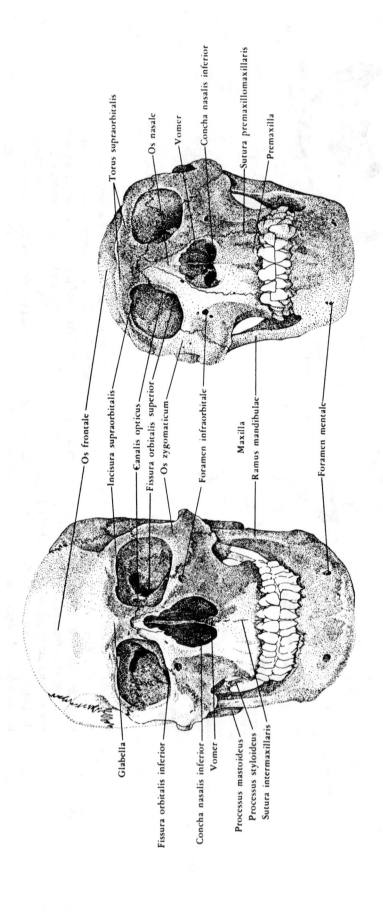

Torus supraorbitalis

Os nasale

Vomer

Concha nasalis inferior

Sutura premaxillomaxillaris

Premaxilla

Os frontale

Incisura supraorbitalis

Canalis opticus

Fissura orbitalis superior

Os zygomaticum

Foramen infraorbitale

Maxilla

Ramus mandibulae

Foramen mentale

Pan

Homo

Glabella

Fissura orbitalis inferior

Concha nasalis inferior

Vomer

Processus mastoideus

Processus styloideus

Sutura intermaxillaris

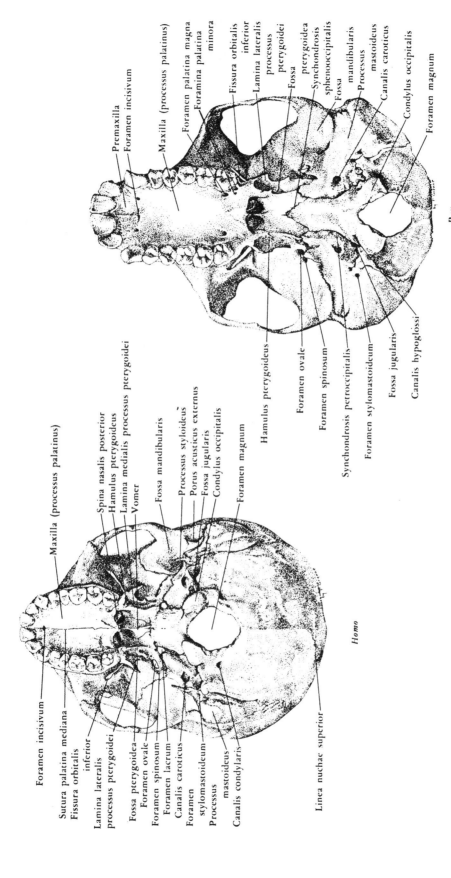

Homo

Foramen incisivum

Sutura palatina mediana
Fissura orbitalis
inferior
Lamina lateralis
processus pterygoidei

Fossa pterygoidea
Foramen ovale
Foramen spinosum
Canalis caroticus
Foramen
stylomastoideum
Processus
mastoideus
Canalis condylaris

Linea nuchae superior

Maxilla (processus palatinus)

Spina nasalis posterior
Hamulus pterygoideus
Lamina medialis processus pterygoidei
Vomer

Fossa mandibularis
Processus styloideus
Porus acusticus externus
Fossa jugularis
Condylus occipitalis
Foramen magnum

Pan

Premaxilla
Foramen incisivum

Maxilla (processus palatinus)

Foramen palatina magna
Foramina palatina
minora

Fissura orbitalis
inferior
Lamina lateralis
processus
pterygoidei
Fossa
pterygoidea
Synchondrosis
sphenooccipitalis
Fossa
mandibularis
Processus
mastoideus
Canalis caroticus
Condylus occipitalis
Foramen magnum

Hamulus pterygoideus
Foramen ovale
Foramen spinosum
Synchondrosis petroccipitalis
Foramen stylomastoideum
Fossa jugularis
Canalis hypoglossi

FIGURE 4.15 Longitudinal cross section of an incisor.

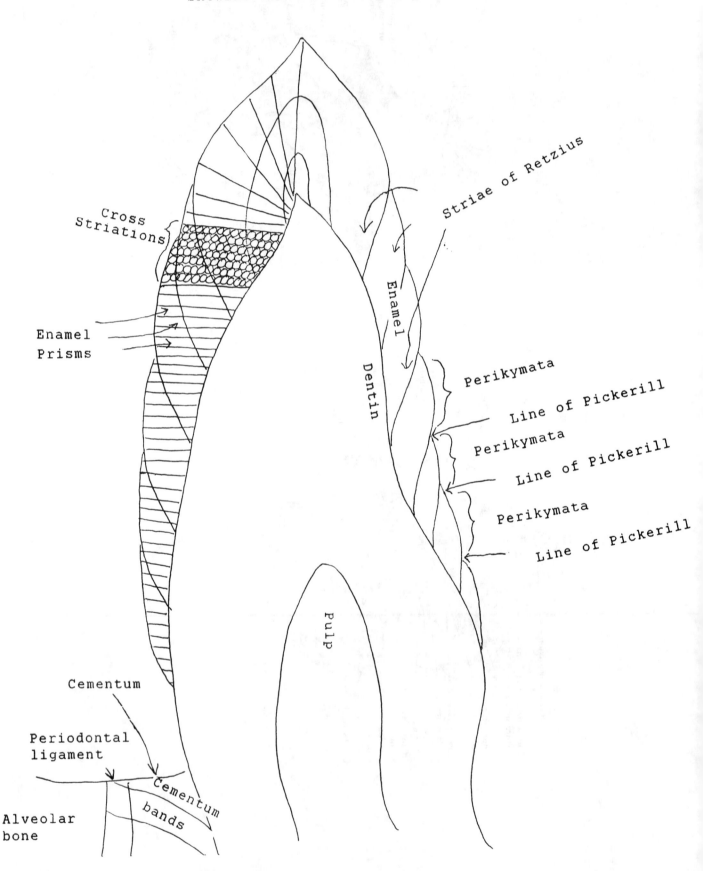

LOGITUDINAL CROSS SECTION
of an INCISOR
SHOWING ENAMEL STRUCTURE

Cross Striations

Enamel Prisms

Striae of Retzius

Enamel

Dentin

Perikymata

Line of Pickerill

Perikymata

Line of Pickerill

Perikymata

Line of Pickerill

Pulp

Cementum

Periodontal ligament

Cementum bands

Alveolar bone

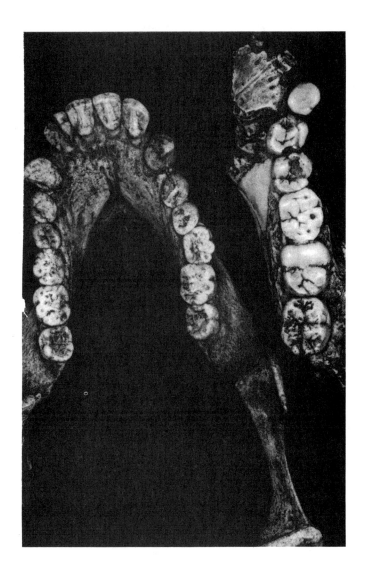

FIGURE 4.16 Mandibles of a chimpanzee (left) and one of the early hominids (right) from Kromdraai, in South Africa. Both specimens are casts. Note the larger anterior teeth in the chimpanzee and the larger posterior teeth in the Kromdraai (TM 1517) specimen. The photo also shows the difference in canine form (incisor-like in the hominid) and in the most forward of the premolars. This tooth is pointed with a single cusp in the ape, while in the hominid it is a large, flat grinding tooth.

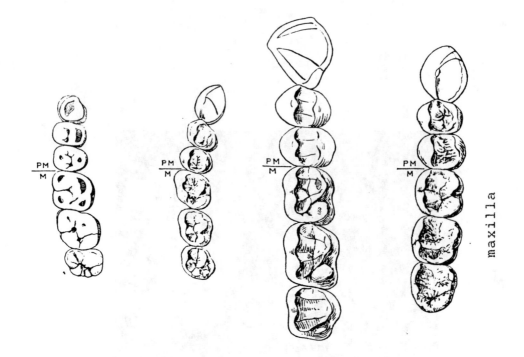

maxilla

FIGURE 4.17 Comparison of living pongid dentitions, after Duckworth (1915).
FROM Duckworth, W.L.H. 1915 Studies in Anthropology, Revised Edition, Volume 1. Cambridge
University Press, Cambridge, figures 172-179.

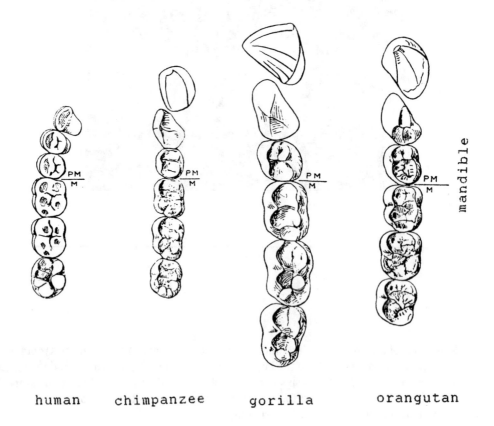

mandible

human   chimpanzee   gorilla   orangutan

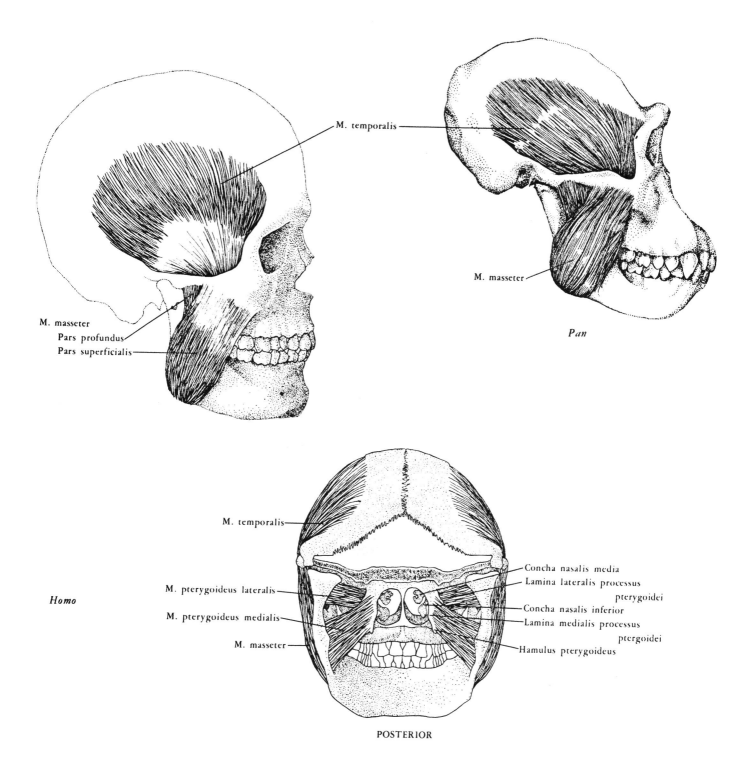

FIGURE 4.18 Position of the main muscles used in chewing, comparing a chimpanzee and a human, from Swindler and Wood (1973). In the human, the masseter overlaps more of the molar teeth, and the anterior and posterior parts of the temporalis muscle are close to equal in size. In the chimpanzee, the more projecting face places the masseter behind most of the teeth, and the posterior part of the temporalis muscle is larger and more horizontally oriented. The human complex is better adapted for bringing force through the back teeth, while the chimpanzee complex is better adapted for using the canines and incisors in cutting, gripping, and holding. Shown are a lateral and inferior view.

FROM: Swindler, D.R., and C.D. Wood 1973 *An Atlas of Primate Gross Anatomy: Baboon, Chimpanzee, and Man.* University of Washington, Seattle, plate 33 OR first edition figure 4.8.

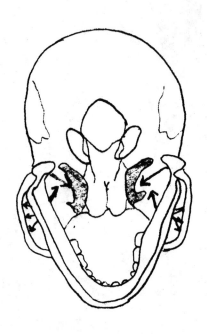

↑   Temporals

↑   Pterygoid

↑   Masseter

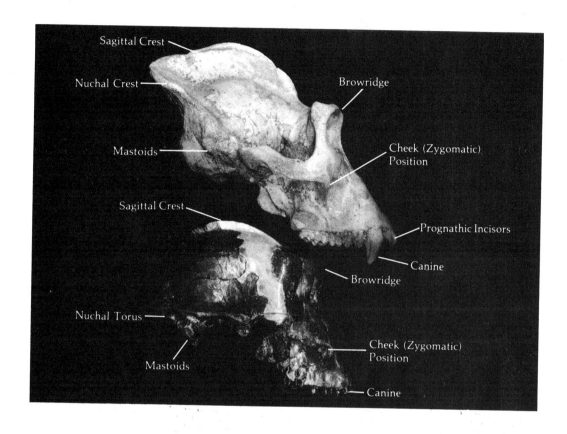

FIGURE 4.19 The crania of a male gorilla (above) and the most robust of the male australopithecines (below, Olduvai hominid 5). Both specimens are casts. The contrasts between these parallel the Theropithecus/Papio contrasts shown in Figure 4.20, except for the canine reduction and low nuchal ridge position in the hominid. Some of the relevant features are labeled.

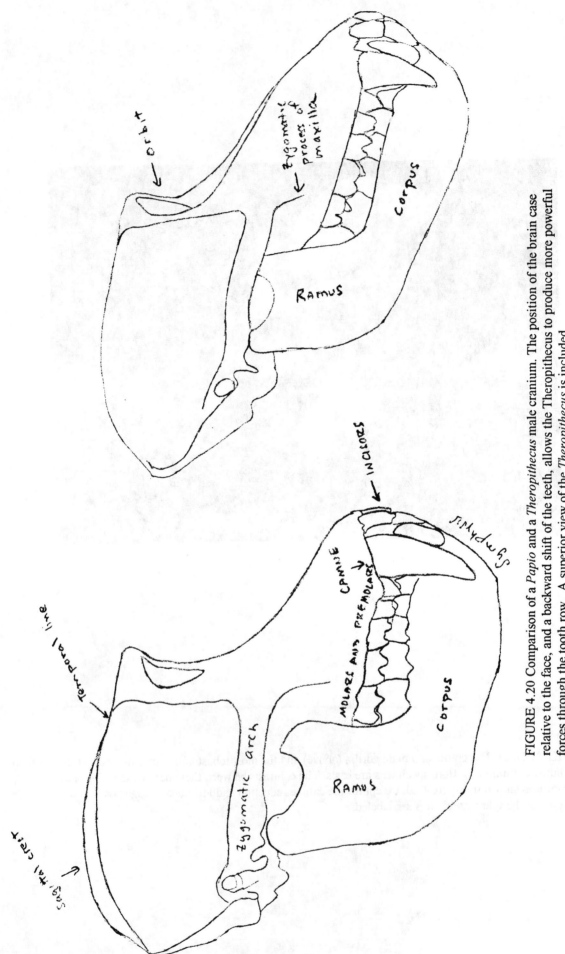

FIGURE 4.20 Comparison of a *Papio* and a *Theropithecus* male cranium. The position of the brain case relative to the face, and a backward shift of the teeth, allows the Theropithecus to produce more powerful forces through the tooth row. A superior view of the *Theropithecus* is included.

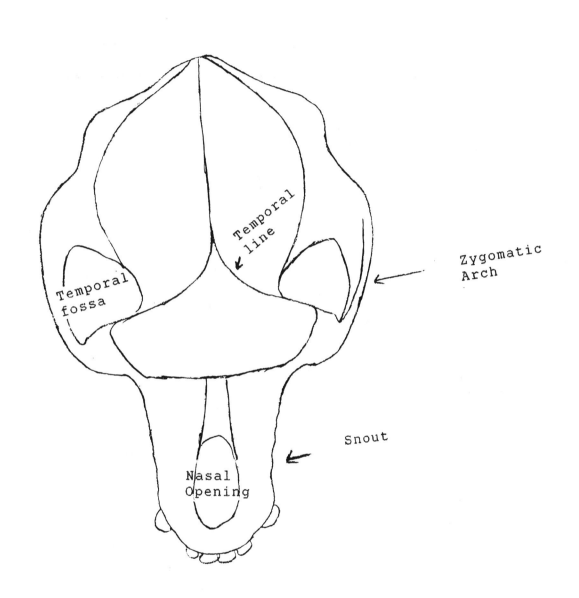

Temporal
line

Zygomatic
Arch

Temporal
fossa

Snout

Nasal
Opening

FIGURE 4.21 Eruption times, chimp and human
In text

FIGURE 4.22 The Smith eruption standards chart, showing an idealized and actual 3½ year old chimpanzee plotted onto human and chimpanzee standards. The idealized chimpanzee makes a straight line on the chimpanzee standard but deviates from the human expectations. The actual chimpanzee deviates from both expectations but better fits the chimpanzee ones (Smith has quantified this in a 1994 paper).

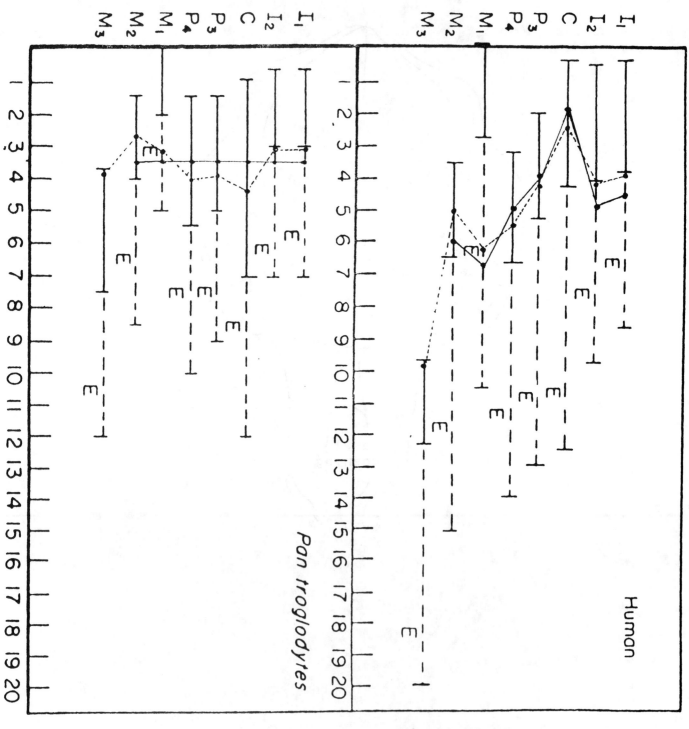

Dentition

Dentition

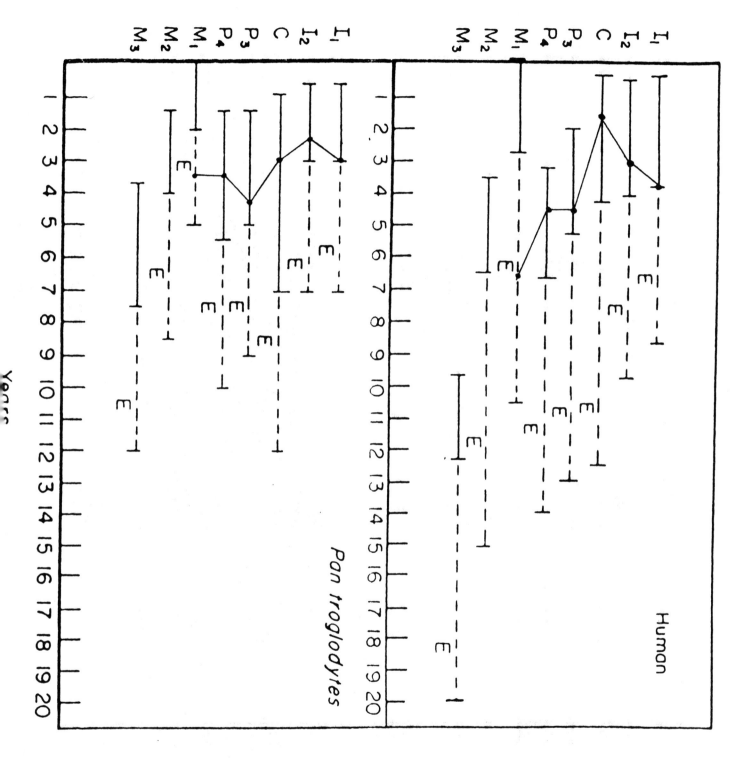

STS 24
coded by Smith

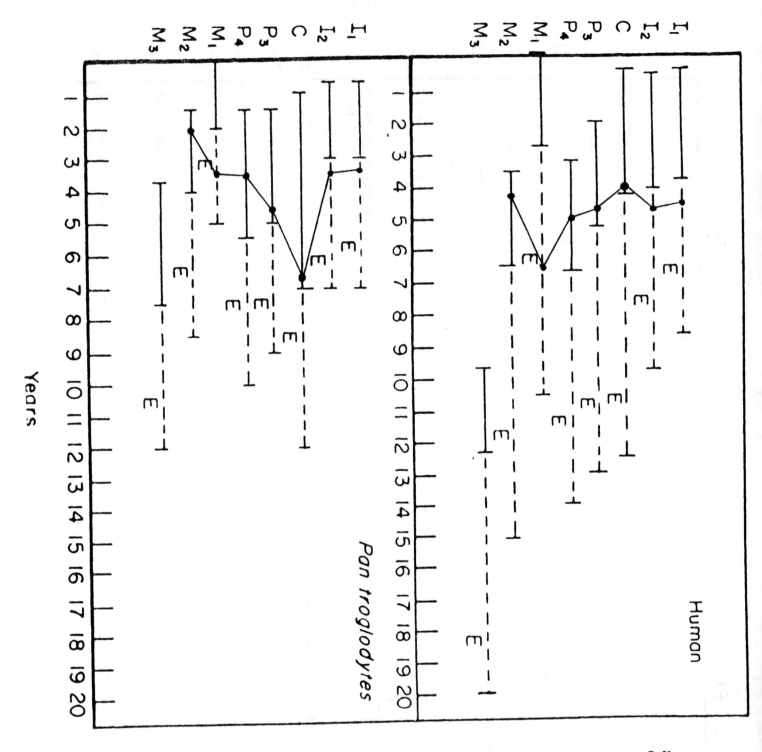

Dentition

Years

Human

Pan troglodytes

STS 24
CT DATA

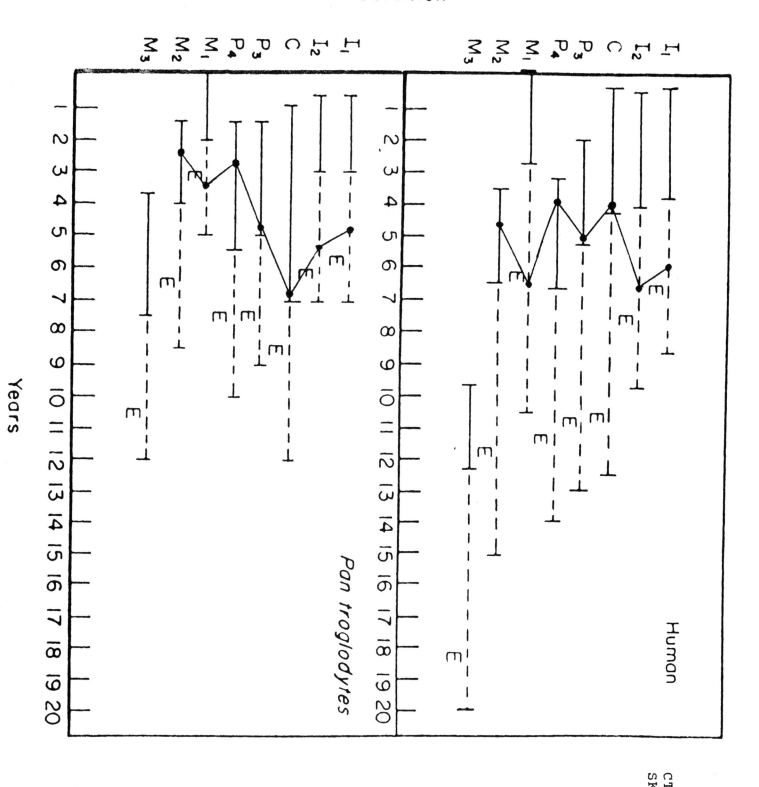

Dentition

FIGURE 4.23 Eruption standards applied to an australopithecine. The figure compares Smith's coding for the dental development of STS 24, appearing to deviate less from chimpanzees than from humans, with the coding made possible by Conroy and colleagues CT analysis of the specimen, showing less deviation from the human standards than from the chimpanzee ones. The latter analysis conforms with the relative I2-M2 eruptions in australopithecines, which are unambiguously human-like. Also shown is the CT data for a Swartkrans australopithecine mandible, SK 63, likewise best matching the human pattern.

CHAPTER FIVE

Why Are There Hominids?

The question of why hominids arose as a distinct lineage and the problem of how to recognize the earliest members of the lineage are connected. Without preconceived notions of what early hominids were like, we could never recognize a line distinct from their contemporary relatives in the fossil record. On the other hand, preconception could play the role of prejudgment. Theories about why hominids originated must ultimately be tested against the facts, in this case the fossils themselves. Thus the answers to the two questions could become circular. To some degree, it is this potential circularity that has helped keep the whole topic a hotly debated issue for at least a hundred years, and will probably always prevent fully definitive answers, but the heat and intensity of the debate has other origins as well. These include the misemphasis on the "*man*" in "fossil man" ("evolution of man", "descent of man", etc.), the specialization of theories (scientists argue from the knowledge they know best, but all have specialized differently), and of course that most constant of problems, the fact that it is *human* and not equine origins that we are discussing.

Having examined the complex of features that are unique in the hominids, one may reasonably ask "Why?" Why was there this particular lineage split in the anthropithecines? What factors led to the different evolutionary directions taken by the chimpanzee and hominid clades? Actually, it is convenient to break the question apart this way because it is possible that two different answers are involved.

Assuming for the moment that there is an adaptive difference between early prehumans (earlier hominids on the human clade) and prechimpanzees (earlier apes on the chimpanzee clade) that can be determined and that accounts for the difference in evolutionary directions, is it necessarily true that the adaptive differentiation occurred at the same time as the lineage division? For instance, suppose the adaptive difference lies in **savanna** (African open grasslands) versus forest adaptation. Did the lineage split take place *because* some populations became savanna adapted (or rain forest adapted) resulting in their genetic isolation and speciation? This punctuation model is only one possibility; the lineage split may have occurred *before* adaptive differentiation, and for entirely different reasons. Human and chimpanzee ancestors may have been separate species long before recognizable adaptive differences accumulated between them. If the second possibility describes what actually took place, it will be very difficult either to recognize early hominids or to understand why they originated (unless we are extraordinarily lucky). They would become recognizable and distinctive only after adaptive differences evolved.

What we can hope to learn from the fossil record is the nature of the adaptive difference, and gain some insight about when it may have occurred. If we can never be sure why hominids and pongids *diverged,* there is at least some hope of discovering why they became *divergent.* In this chapter, we will discuss and compare various theories concerning both the initial divergence and the adaptive differences. Although it might seem sensible to focus this review on the most current theories, it is useful to begin with Charles Darwin. In one form or another his ideas about human origins have influenced the thinking of scholars up to the present time.

Darwin's Model

While Darwin only devoted a single line to human origins in the *Origin of Species,* he returned to the topic 12 years later. Based on the very convincing arguments raised by T.H. Huxley, Darwin maintained that humans are most closely related to the African apes, less so to gibbons and orangutans, with the corollary that humans originated in Africa. Given how little was then known of these pongids, this idea was insightful; a much better case could be made today.

In addition, he suggested an adaptive model to account for hominid origins. He was struck by the dramatic differences between humans and apes in four areas:

1. bipedal locomotion,
2. canine reduction
3. tool use
4. large brains

Darwin hypothesized that these formed a functional complex and could be related to a shift from tree life to life on the ground. He argued that terrestrial adaptations in primates evolved from an arboreal ancestry as species changed their habitat "owing to a change in [their] manner of procuring subsistence, or to some change in the surrounding conditions". The quadrupedal terrestrial adaptation was attained by some primates such as baboons, while the hominids became bipeds. This difference, he supposed, reflected the hominid adaptation to hunting. A ground-dwelling ape, he argued, would benefit from bipedal locomotion since this would free the hands for carrying the weapons useful in hunting. With weapons such as clubs and thrown rocks as an aid to adaptation, and with increasing intelligence guiding their use, large projecting canines would come to be of little importance as their function in combat was taken over by the tools. Therefore, he proposed, the canines reduced in size. Intelligence expanded for other reasons as well. In particular, Darwin stressed the importance of cooperative behavior in the hunting adaptation, and attributed much of the expansion of the brain to the evolution of language.

E. Haeckel, one of Darwin's apostles introduced in Chapter 3 because of his notion that humans were to be classified with the apes, also saw bipedalism as the fundamental adaptation at the base of the hominid line. He regarded it as causal in the evolution of the manipulative hand and modifications of the skull that eventually came to include language and (in today's terms) culture. Haeckel hypothesized that hominids arose in the tropics, perhaps as early as the Late Miocene, and envisioned an australopithecine-like creature (more than a half-century before the first australopithecine was discovered) which he named "*Pithecanthropus*" - the ape-man (many of the South African paleoanthropologists still refer to the australopithecines as the "ape-men"). Finally, Haeckel was probably the first to originate an "Eve" theory for modern human origins. He proposed that "true *Homo*" appeared at the beginning of the Pleistocene somewhere in the Old World tropics, possibly originating in Africa, or Asia, or the lost continent of Lemuria - Paradise! Haeckel's ideas were very influential in his time, but by in large did not come down to us as part of any intellectual tradition. This is because his intellectual heirs developed and used them in ways that had much more unfortunate consequences than the views and approaches of Darwin, Huxley, and the other English-speaking evolutionists. In an excellent review of evolutionary thought in the German-speaking world of the last century, G.J. Stein points out that Haeckel's Darwinian notions about society ("civilization and the life of nations are governed by the same laws as prevail throughout organic life"), phylogenetics ("the morphological differences between two generally recognized species - for instance sheep and goats - are much less important than those ... between a Hottentot and a man of the Teutonic race"), and the progress of evolution ("the Germans ... deviated furthest from the common form of ape-like men") became the clear intellectual predecessors of Nazism.

THE CASE FOR AN ANTHROPITHECINE ANCESTRY

While various authors have advanced primates as diverse as gibbons and tarsiers for the position of our closest relatives (many of these phylogenetic schemes are reviewed by C. Jolly), the case for the African apes is overwhelming. Our detailed anatomical and behavioral similarities with these pongids, discussed in Chapter 3, allow no other interpretation in an evolutionary context. While specific features of some other primates also closely resemble our own, no other living creatures so closely approximate ourselves in the complex of details ranging from obvious anatomy to behavior and biochemistry. Modern comparative studies of chimpanzees, gorillas, and humans show that they form a closely related group. In this regard, Darwin was clearly correct. The genetic evidence supporting the hypothesis of a specific chimpanzee-human sister group, also discussed in Chapter 3, is quite convincing as well.

THE CASE FOR AN ARBOREAL ANCESTRY

The closeness of our relation to the African apes should not obscure the fact that we are *not* descended *from* them. We expect the last common ancestor of chimpanzees and humans, even if it was recent, to be dramatically different from living people. However, the same logic dictates that this common ancestor would be expected to markedly differ from the living chimpanzees. Where these differences might lie is of critical importance in reconstructing the hominid divergence .

The first question is one of an arboreal heritage. Did humans and chimpanzees share an adaptation to living in trees before the lineages diverged? On one level, the answer to this question is certainly yes. Most primate characteristics are the result of arboreal adaptation. Moreover, if Oligocene genera such as *Aegyptopithecus* from the Fayum are ancestral to the living hominids, the circumstantial evidence in both argues for an arboreal ancestral adaptation. The very unlikely alternative would be a pre-Oligocene origin for the hominids in an unknown terrestrial primate ancestor.

Comparative anatomy presents evidence for much the same conclusion, if one assumes that the many detailed resemblances of humans and apes are not the result of parallel evolution. These resemblances are intertwined with a complex of features bearing on more specific questions: was the common ancestor of humans and apes an arboreal climber, an arm-hanger, or even more specifically a brachiator?

Earlier in this century these questions were answered with a resounding "yes". The "brachiationism" model for human ancestry has been promoted by a number of scientists throughout this century, beginning with A. Keith, W. Gregory, D. Morton, and E. Hooton, his student S. Washburn, and his student in turn R. Tuttle. The idea persisted that the first hominids were "Darwin's 3rd Ape", a diminutive African form with the brachiating behaviors of the larger living apes that preadapted its hindlimb to terrestrial bipedalism (R. Tuttle discusses these ideas at some length). The brachiation model was undermined when field studies began to show that this locomotion is part of a wide range of behaviors in some of the ape species, and in the larger ones it can be quite rare during their adult life. Moreover, it was discovered that the anatomical features thought to reflect brachiation could be found in other primates that were not brachiators at all.

Brachiation as a means of arboreal locomotion is restricted to the large and especially small apes of Africa and Asia and a few genera of New World monkeys. Brachiation is a form of under branch, hand-over-hand locomotion which uses the forearms for support and power and the pendulum-like characteristics of the swinging body for forward momentum. The center of gravity of the body and most of its mass are below the support points on the hands. In considering whether hominids passed through a brachiating stage, we need to separate brachiation-associated characteristics from the more generalized shared features resulting from the common primate arboreal adaptations. This is not as easy as it may seem; one cannot simply assume that the derived features of gorillas and chimpanzees are associated with brachiation, since as adults these apes rarely brachiate. Moreover, brachiation is only one of many behaviors that require forearm support or specialized forearm activity in these apes. Many, if not all, of the morphological features associated with brachiation must be considered in the context of related activities ranging from hanging and reaching to climbing and the peculiar forms of quadrupedal locomotion that the morphology of arm-hanging and brachiating requires. Arm-hanging during feeding is more widespread in the primates. This feeding posture is associated with brachiation, although the opposite is not necessarily the case. Climbing is even more common, and requires the very motions once thought to preadapt (i.e.exapt) Miocene anthropithecines for the evolution of obligate bipedalism.

THE REQUIREMENTS OF A VERTICALLY CLIMBING ANCESTRY

The climbing hypothesis has been suggested by a number of authors over the years, but was perhaps most effectively expressed in a seminal paper by J. Fleagle and his colleagues. They argued that the motions and mechanical requirements of the skeleton in climbing more closely account for ape forelimb morphology than does brachiation. Moreover, work by J. Prost suggests that climbing requires hindlimb motions more like those needed in bipedalism than any other locomotion practiced by apes, including their own interpretation of bipedalism discussed in Chapter 4. He argued that obligate bipedalism, walking and running, was an exaptation expressed when the hominids became terrestrial, based on the anatomy that had evolved for efficient vertical climbing. For climbing trunks, large primates use long and powerful forearms (especially powerful in bending at the elbow), short legs, and grasping feet with offset big toes. M.W. Marzke and colleagues describe a **diagonal grip** used in climbing, in which the support is held diagonally across the fingers, without use of the palm - or minimal palm use for large supports - and little force applied by the short thumb. Chimpanzees grasp small sticks for throwing or clubbing the same way. N. Toth's tool making experiments with captive chimpanzees clearly show that this is not the **power grip** of humans (grasping with the fingers perpendicular to the object but the palm diagonal, and using the thumb for applying significant force, according to Marzke and colleagues), nor is it a particularly forceful hold.

Chest flattening may also be a requirement of climbing, especially climbing among branches (hoisting) in contrast to climbing trunks or other vertical supports, although the evidence here is not as clear. The behaviors promoted by this morphology are useful in climbing, but the morphology itself may not be necessary to climb. It is not shared by all vertical climbers. Chest flatness serves several functions. A long collar bone (**clavicle**) and widened chest combine to position the shoulder joint far to the outside of the body, and the flat back orients the scapula transversely (Figure 5.1). Combined, these result in an outward-facing shoulder joint, contrasting with the more downward-facing (i.e. groundward-facing) joint in quadrupeds. The joint itself is shallow (allowing wider motions), and the muscles that move the arm have improved leverage because of the flat trunk. This anatomy makes possible a series of powerful arm motions to the side and above the body that are impossible in quadrupedal primates. These motions are helpful when climbing a vertical support, but they would be more helpful in slowly executed hoisting behavior

THE REQUIREMENTS OF A BRACHIATING AND ARM-HANGING ANCESTRY

Brachiation and its associated **positional** (i.e. stationary) **behavior**, arm-hanging, require anatomical changes that go beyond the adaptations that are useful in climbing; in particular, a more powerful grip and longer arms. Fingers are much longer, to surround the support, and one common hand posture is to use a diagonal grip in which the four fingers are used as hooks, grasping diagonally without involvement of either the thumb or most of the palm. If the support is small enough relative to the hand, primates using this grip typically have long, curved finger bones with joints between the bones of each finger oriented so show that significant force is applied along each finger when they are wrapped around an object, or support.

Brachiators are characterized by particularly long arms relative to their trunks, specifically by long forearms and hands. The wrist characteristically is capable of extreme rotation (about 180 degrees), and the muscles are arranged so that powerful bending at the elbow can take place in almost any wrist position. In brachiators, the trunk tends to be flattened front-to-back, and short - the average number of lower back (**lumbar**) vertebrae is 3 whereas in living humans it is 5 and most quadrupeds average 7. The shortness of the trunk (and legs) quickens the speed of the free swinging (pendulum-like) portion of brachiation; brachiators emphasize the fact that a shorter pendulum swings more quickly, by tucking up their legs during the later part of the swing. Extended legs maximizes the forward momentum gained from gravity in the down-swing, while flexed legs maximize the forward speed during the up-swing. This morphological complex is restricted in its distribution to the pongids and hylobatids. This suggests that its importance in brachiation is in combination with other movements also facilitated by the features. For instance the morphological requirements of arm-hanging, at the shoulder and chest, are also requirements for a brachiator, but the brachiator will generate much stronger forces in the joints of the forelimb because of its motion.

O.J. Lewis views the knuckle-walking of African apes as a consequence of the limitations of their brachiating adaptations. R. Tuttle argues that these anatomical adaptations evolved to together, and has shown that some of the anatomical features in African ape wrists are specifically a reflection of the mechanical requirements of knuckle-walking. The evidence suggests that brachiation and arm hanging preclude a true palmigrade form of locomotion, and that as a consequence energetically inefficient knuckle-walking evolved as the form of quadrupedal locomotion for the African apes.

LOOKING BACKWARD

Characteristics reflecting these past adaptations that might be expected to appear in modern humans are in the arms and trunk. The pelvis, lower limb, and foot has been completely modified as part of the adaptation to obligate bipedalism. A long-legged adaptation with a double-arched foot holding an enlarged non-abducted big toe for toe-off is associated with the earliest expressions of striding bipedalism in hominids. The evolution of the dexterous human hand with its power grip, or squeeze, is a response to the requirements of tool and weapon use (for instance wielding clubs and maintaining their stability as they are used). *Many of the arm and trunk adaptations for climbing discussed above are shared by hominids and the African apes, and separate them from the quadrupedal cercopithecoids.* This argues most strongly that an adaptation to vertical climbing and hoisting had developed before the separation of hominid and chimpanzee lineages.

The question is whether specific adaptations for forelimb suspension and at least some aspects of the brachiation adaptation had evolved as well. Some features of chimpanzees and gorillas are not shared by living humans or any known hominid fossils, and these have been used to argue that this was the case. The shared features are mainly found in certain peculiarities of the wrist and fingers that appear to be the result of the knuckle-walking quadrupedal adaptation in the African apes. They have been used to support the notion of a chimpanzee-gorilla sister grouping, but the hypothesis of a chimpanzee-hominid sister grouping would seem to require that hominids passed through a knuckle-walking stage - a point recognized and promoted by S.L. Washburn throughout his career. The argument that they are homoplasies, however, is an equally compelling alternative. The shoulder, arm, wrist, and finger adaptations required by arm-hanging and brachiation make it difficult to attain any other form of quadrupedalism, as R. Tuttle has long maintained, and knuckle-walking would seem to be the nadir of terrestrial quadrupedalism. If it is unique in any way, it would be in its energetic inefficiency! That both African apes are knuckle-walkers, in other words, may not be a consequence of phylogeny but instead may reflect a parallel terrestrial adaptation superimposed on a common arboreal one by its anatomical requirements. That common arboreal adaptation would be climbing, arm-hanging, and brachiation in large bodied anthropithecines.

The issue, for human origins, is what aspects of the arboreal adaptations are shared by hominids, the sister group of chimpanzees. It is quite possible that none of the terrestrial adaptations (i.e. knuckle-walking related) are shared since humans and apes may have been quite different in their terrestrial locomotion after hominid divergence, and even before if late Miocene anthropithecines were arboreal bipeds as J. Stern and his colleagues suggest. The earliest known australopithecine wrist and hand remains show no remnants of knuckle-walking adaptations, according to O.J. Lewis. In fact, they show no remnants of any suspensory adaptations either, according to analyses by B. Latimer. He argues that arboreal, especially suspensory-related adaptations in the apes are under significant selection, as indicated by the morbidity J. Goodall found to be associated with falls in chimpanzees, and more generally with the large number of healed fractures found in ape skeletal collections. The morphology of the earliest known hominid hands and forearms is quite different from the ape morphology, *and the question is why* since there are no forearm or hand requirements of obligate bipedalism. Indeed, the requirements of obligate bipedalism fatally compromised the hindlimb and foot's use in climbing, bridging between branches, and suspensory adaptations and one would expect the reflections of these adaptations to be *even better expressed* in early hominid forelimbs and hands. If the ancestral adaptation was for vertical climbing and suspensory behaviors, Latimer argues, there was no reason or requirement of bipedalism to alter the morphology of the forearm and shoulder in the earliest hominids as these changes would make clearly dangerous activities even more dangerous.

One possibility is that the hand has been transformed by selection for the long dexterous thumb and its use in a power grip, as described in Chapter 4. Yet, while the early hominid finger bones are indeed very shortened compared with apes, the evidence for a true power grip is equivocal because the earliest hominid thumb is short compared with later hominids (although not as short as in apes), the finger tips are not broadened in a typically human fashion, and the bones of the palm do not seem to reflect the consequences of the powerful stresses that would be a consequence of the power grip (all of these power grip correlates come into play when one uses a hammer to drive in a large nail). The power grip transformations happen later, after tools appear and very likely as a consequence of their use. Therefore the non ape-like aspects of the earliest hominid hand remains are not the consequences of changes in selection due to tool use. If there is no selection from bipedalism or tool use to change an earlier brachiating adaptation in the hand, wrist, and forearm into the australopithecine morphology, why did it change from an anatomy useful in climbing and suspensory activities into one that makes these difficult or prohibits them entirely? The intriguing possibility exists that there was no such change because *there was no earlier brachiating adaptation*.

The fact remains that we cannot settle this issue convincingly yet because we know virtually nothing about anthropithecine postcranial adaptations before hominid origins. In the absence of direct evidence, indirect indications at present suggest two broad conclusions:

1. Shared unique morphology of human and African ape trunks and forearms suggests that the last common ancestor was a climber (both vertically climbing and branch-to-branch climbing).
2. Morphology of the earliest hominid postcranial materials strongly suggests that the last common ancestor was not a dedicated brachiator, certainly not as well adapted for brachiation as chimpanzees even though these primates only brachiate as a small percentage of their locomotor activities. The relevant australopithecine features are
   - the morphology of the hand and wrist, as discussed above, was under no selection to change from the ancestral condition and may lack adaptations to under branch suspensory posturing and locomotion because there weren't any
   - there is no lower trunk shortening; in fact, several specimens show six lumbar vertebrae and none have less

REASSESSMENT: THE ORIGINS OF HOMINID ORIGINS MODELS

Darwin originated the first and the most long lasting model of hominid origins. His assumptions, and the conclusions he drew from them, are now known to be incomplete and only partially correct. He was correct in his contention that humans are most closely related to the African apes and his supposition that humans evolved from an arboreal ape-like creature in Africa. However, it appears increasingly likely that this ancestor was not a modern ape anatomically, ecologically, and (by implication) behaviorally. Looking backwards suggests that the arboreal adaptation of this last common ancestor did not involve any special adaptations to arm-hanging and brachiation, beyond those already established by their vertical climbing and hoisting abilities. Some of the Miocene anthropithecines lived in much more open environments than today's African apes utilize, and if ecology has any significant influence on social organization in the primates, a widely accepted precept, we might expect Miocene anthropithecine species to reflect this. Moreover, some of the human uniquenesses that Darwin assumed, have been discovered in other primates, as the consequence of a century of laboratory and field research.. For instance, apes have shown surprising abilities to recognize self, to make and use tools, and to manipulate symbols (at least under experimental conditions). These shared behaviors support the contention of close relationship and make the evolutionary hypotheses of a gradual appearance for some of the characteristically human features more understandable, but at the same time their beginnings no longer need to be explained as part of an "origins" hypothesis. Yet we might ask what was the role of these abilities in hominid origins and why did they evolve a new magnitude of importance and complexity in humans?

In any event, it is quite clear that the wealth of data now available requires a reassessment of our understandings of human origins. How do we begin this? The anatomical data presented from comparisons of humans and the living apes, the limited morphological knowledge we have of the pre-divergence anthropithecines, and some of the relevant information that can be gained from the earliest hominids have been reviewed. These provide limits to the understanding of hominids origins we can gain but by themselves they are neither theories of hominid origins nor reconstructions of their unique adaptive behaviors. Such theories and reconstructions can only come from our modeling of hominid origins.

In an important essay, J. Tooby and I DeVore discuss how such models can be developed. They distinguish two kinds of models.

- **Referential models**: one real phenomenon is used as a model for its referent, a different phenomenon that cannot be directly observed. For instance, diets emphasized by living primates with particularly thick molar enamel might be used to infer the diets eaten by fossil hominids with particularly thick molar enamel.
- **Conceptual models**: sets of concepts and variables whose interrelationships are specified by potentially falsifiable theories. For instance, to use a limited example diets eaten by fossil hominids with particularly thick molar enamel might be inferred from the characteristics of the enamel itself, its structural hardness, brittleness, and wear resistance. This would assume that these characteristics had evolved to meet dietary demands. These inferences could be tested by examining the microwear on the enamel caused by scratches made during mastication, and an examination of the available food sources to ascertain whether any of these required mastication by teeth with these particular structural characteristics.

They argue that a valid reconstruction of hominid origins and evolution requires conceptual modeling. Referential models are limited in several ways. There is no certain means of ascertaining the valid referent. For instance, in examining the problem of interpreting australopithecine variation I once grappled with the question of whether the closest related species or the most ecologically similar ones would make the best referent. It is difficult to be objective in such a decision as one is always cognizant of whether the resulting comparisons fit or refute theoretical expectations. In the volume (edited by C.J. Jolly) where these ruminations appeared, it can easily be seen that **lumpers** who tended to regard variation at a lower taxonomic level (racial, populational, dimorphic, or individual) turned to living humans for their referential model, while **splitters** who tended to treat variation at higher levels (species, genera, etc.) turned to morphologically similar but genetically distinct monkey species for their referent.

Referential models seek critical similarities between hominids and referent species, attempting to explain the origin of hominid social behavior (if not hominid origins in general) on the basis of their importance. By focusing on the similarities, referential models such as these provide no means for examining the effects of differences on the evolution of hominid social behavior. The paper by Rodseth and his colleagues discussed in Chapter 2, comparing primate and human societies, is a good example of this. As a result, referential models tend to emphasize the similarities that can be found, often at the expense of differences. This is how we can explain the otherwise incongruous claims that human language may have evolved as an exaptation for something else, discussed in the last Chapter. Assertions like this come from referential models that cannot provide explanations for uniquenesses because they emphasize what is shared.

Conceptual models should avoid these problems, the authors argue, by providing a refutable framework for interpretations. Darwin's model of hominid origins would be a good example of this. Although based on comparisons, it provided an ecological theory of causation, attempting to explain how the unique aspects of hominids could be explained on the basis of changing adaptation. Several authors, in discussing this distinction of models, have misunderstood one important aspect of conceptual modeling. Like any theory, it doesn't matter where conceptual models come from, and the fact of the matter is that most conceptual models that have been developed for human evolution are based on referential models, and address the problems that these contain. Hominid origins only happened once, but this does not mean that models attempting to account for it are in principle irrefutable. The Darwinian model surely disproves that contention since, in its original form, it has been refuted. Yet, Darwin's model gave rise to a suite of theories about human origins, beginning with the discovery of the first australopithecines and extending to the present. It is with these that we will begin.

Dart and the Killer-Ape Hypotheses

Raymond Dart used Darwin's hypothesis as the basis for his interpretations when, in 1924, he correctly interpreted the hominid affinities of the Taung child from South Africa. He called the young child *Australopithecus africanus*, the man-ape of Africa. At that time, no truly early hominids were known, although the Piltdown remains from England, now recognized to be a faked fossil, were thought to be of the same Pliocene age, and suggested that human ancestors were characterized by large brains and ape-like canines. (Ironically Piltdown was "created" to fit the Darwinian model as well, but emphasizing a different combination of features; mainly, a large brain and ape-like teeth that were filed down to appear to function in a human-like way). The Taung fossil child was the opposite of Piltdown; the canines and other teeth were remarkably human-like, while the brain was small. Most scholars at the time interpreted the Taung fossil as an early ape, pointing out that it shared many similarities with chimpanzees and gorillas and only a few with hominids. Dart, however, understood the importance of the few features shared with hominids. The most outstanding of these were the small, flat-wearing canine; the position of the foramen magnum underneath the cranium which indicated a vertical spine and therefore erect posture; and certain elements of the natural endocast which suggested that the brain was slightly larger and structurally different from an ape's. These were the three anatomical elements predicted by Darwin—reduced canines, bipedalism, and changes in the brain.

And what of the remaining elements in the hypothesis? With the Taung child as an unexpected verification, Dart simply assumed the rest were there, claiming from the outset that Taung represented a form of tool-using, hunting hominid that employed a combination of intelligence, brute strength, and weapons to become what others have called "the most vicious carnivore on the savanna." Dart made these claims on the basis of a single 4-5-year-old specimen and in the absence of postcranial skeleton, tools, or any evidence of hunting behavior. The amazing thing is that although he may have overemphasized the importance of hunting, he was eventually proven correct in every one of his claims.

Later excavations at a South African cave called Makapansgat revealed more australopithecine specimens and a large quantity of broken and crushed animal bone. Dart believed that the animal bones were brought into the cave by the australopithecines living there, who broke up the bones and used them as tools and weapons. He argued that the use of animal parts preceded the use of stone tools, and created a name for an **Osteodontokeratic Culture** based on bones, teeth, and horns. Many scientists have since disputed the claim that these bones were broken up and used by the australopithecines. In fact, it is primarily this problem and the search for valid approaches to solve it that lead to the modern science of taphonomy. C.K. Brain's discovery of digging sticks made of animal horns, at the South African australopithecine site of Swartkrans, has at least settled the issue of whether or not these early hominids were tool makers.

S.L. Washburn was Dart's intellectual successor. With his students and colleagues he was very influential in creating a foundation for Darwin's theory in the behaviors of living primates, and in doing so effectively founded an important branch of primatology within biological anthropology, as it has until recently been conceived in the United States. Washburn's work emphasized meat eating, male dominance, and cooperative male hunting as the cause of early hominid differentiation and success, which he argued was a unique complex in the hominids because of their new-found ability to carry weapons. Much of his focus was on the foundation of male-male bonds, and the social mechanisms balancing aggression and cooperation.

He clearly influenced A. Mann, who linked canine size reduction to tool use through the change in eruption time. Mann argued that late canine eruption (i.e. late in the eruption sequence) for male apes had the effect of reducing the competition, or perhaps the seriousness of the competition, between juveniles so that they could practice adult behavior and form bonds. When tool use replaced the teeth in threat displays and fights, suggested Mann in this interpretation of Darwin's model, social control of aggressive behaviors became important as the physiological control of late canine eruption became irrelevant. As a result male canines erupted earlier and, with less room in the jaws of younger individuals, came under selection to reduce in size. [The discussion of eruption times in Chapter 4 suggests that "earlier" and "later' in this context is relative to the whole growth process. This is important to remember, since some of the chimpanzees with relatively later erupting canines actually erupt these teeth earlier in time, but their whole process of maturation is faster.] Mann, in fact, regarded the evolution of culture in an emerging context of socially defined roles and expectations as the central organizing force of hominid evolution. This fit well with the implications of maturational delay that he established for the early hominids (see Chapter 4). Mann concluded that the early appearance of maturation delay corresponded to the necessity for learning complex behaviors. It is unlikely that it required delayed maturation to learn how to make simple stone and bone tools properly Instead, a long learning period would seem to reflect a behavioral aspect of australopithecine adaptation that otherwise could not be directly observed. Moreover, he reasoned that the social learning that required this maturation delay must have resulted in important adaptive advantages because of certain related disadvantages. One of these is the increased susceptibility of the young to disease, starvation, and injury, especially in the context of fluctuating access to resources. Several sibs close together in age increase the potential role of infectious diseases. These consequences would place a special strain on australopithecine societies, a strain presumably countered by the advantages of the emerging behavioral system.

Another intellectual thread developed in a quite different direction. Also following Washburn, simplified, popularized, and even more sex-biased, renditions of human evolution based on Dart's writings were presented by R. Ardrey, D. Morris, and L. Tiger and R. Fox. Using selected naturalistic studies of living primates, these authors even further emphasized the importance of hunting among the early hominids. They claim, in effect, that humans originated when a group of apes became savanna-dwelling carnivores (i.e., "killer-apes"). Their contention was that access to animal protein was extremely advantageous in the developing hominid savanna adaptation. They envisaged this access as being facilitated by the evolution of bipedalism to carry weapons, and intelligence as the basis for cunning and foresight, and for communication and cooperation, particularly among the male hunters. To varying degrees, they hold this unique hominid heritage to be responsible for what they see as the "aggressive instincts" in modern humans. Their writings have led to the idea that many undesirable elements of human behavior, ranging from mob behavior to crime and ultimately warfare, are the result of this heritage and are somehow coded in our genes. A similar claim is made by some sociobiologists, although for different reasons.

Tooby and DeVore present the most recent version of this model. After insisting that conceptual rather than referential models are necessary for developing a valid understanding of hominid origins, they fall back on the chimpanzee as a referent and the hunting hypothesis of Darwin for the basis of their conceptual modeling of hominid origins. Tooby and DeVore dismiss the focus on the adaptive importance of three elements of this model emphasized by those concerned with gender-bias:

- **gathering** (food acquisition with postponed consumption),
- an "extreme" sex-based **division of labor** (separate food acquisition strategies for men and women)
- **mutual cooperation** between the sexes apart from food sharing

They reject the notion that these are important elements in modeling hominid origins because, in their view, they are only posited as "healthy correctives" that are "congruent with the social and intellectual climate engendered by feminism and its vigorous advocacy of the importance of women in all areas" (see Stanford and Allen for further discussion). Their emphasis on a predominant role for hunting proceeds from the reasoning that if gathering were more important than hunting, males would have given up hunting in favor of it. This male-oriented hunting hypothesis traces a clear thread of intellectual influence from Darwin to Washburn to his student DeVore.

Taking what is perhaps the most extreme approach, and using a data set that is primarily not paleoanthropological, K. Hill developed a more social-relationship oriented rendition of the Darwinian hunting hypothesis. He argued that the key hominid adaptation was male hunting and the subsequent provisioning of meat. Brain size increased as the hominids became carnivores (in Jerison's 'extra-neurons' analyses carnivores generally have larger brain sizes and herbivores smaller ones, compared with the general allometric trend). The subsidiary role for females in early hominid society was dictated by the burden of childbearing (and with increasing longevity, grandmothering) in Hill's model. Hominid society became structured by the female dependence on males for subsistence. To facilitate the trade of "sexual favors" for protein, visible estrus was lost ("concealed", in some discussions) and the females became sexually available at all times. **Estrus,** what many pet owners and animal breeders call "heat", is associated with menstruation in the anthropoid primates. It is a time when females show sexual interest and signal males what they are willing and available for breeding, but according to B. Sigmon, not necessarily a time when there is **ovulation**.

A very similar model was proposed by H. Fisher, whose reconstruction of hominid origins is also based on a female dependency, forced by the reproductive requirements of bearing numerous prematurely born children (to allow larger heads to fit through the birth canal - an idea first proposed by S. Washburn) with overlapping periods of dependency. She does, in contrast, much more greatly emphasize the importance of female food gathering and of sexual selection through female mate choice, and her precept of early hominids is much less data-free than Hill's. Yet, the similarities are striking; the dependence of females on males for provisioning and defense, and the social bonding created by "continuous female receptivity" following the loss of estrus. A. Zihlman, in a review of Fisher's first book which was accurately titled *The Sex Contract*, describes Fisher's conception of early hominid women as "sexual athletes", able to have multiple organisms every day of their adult life.

The killer-ape theories are male-focused variations on a single conceptual model - Darwin's. Moreover, killer-ape theories have come to be more than hypotheses about hunting and hominid origins. Their implications extend to claims about the basis of behaviors in living humans. The model of how cultural behaviors may have inherited aspects (see Chapter 4) suggests it is unlikely that any *specific* behaviors (aggressiveness, war making, etc.) could be inherited. However, the question remains of how important carnivorous behavior was in hominid origins, whether its socially cooperative aspects (c.f. Washburn and others) or its aggressive aspects (c.f. Ardrey and Morris) were more important in shaping the human psyche, and what if any effects this adaptive background might still have on human behaviors. Killer-ape models raise an additional issue, that of sex-bias in the conceptualizations of hominid origins. They are not the sole source of sex bias; for instance, sociobiologists such as M. Sheets-Johnstone's suggest that sexual selection for displaying (what she calls) "the large human penis" was "the prime and critical factor in the move to bipedality". However, the virtually exclusive male focus in killer-ape models has been the most influential source of this problem, and has evoked some of the strongest reactions.

A Savanna Chimpanzee

A series of more broadly based theories of hominid origins developed out of the killer-ape model. Generally, these posit that hominids arose when an anthropithecine with the behavioral capacities of modern chimpanzees adapted to the open savanna. Most of these theories do not so much replace the focus on hunting as an important part of human origins, as much as they flesh it out with a more complex view of early hominid adaptation. As a group the theories rely on three assumptions

1. the last common ancestor was much like a modern chimpanzee
2. the characteristic behaviors of early hominids are part of an adaptation to savanna that a creature with a chimpanzee's capacities might be expected to develop
3. behavioral variation in higher primates has a significant element of ecological causation

The one common thread of reasoning behind the related group of 'Savanna Chimpanzee' models is that hominids originated as a savanna adaptation. Chimpanzees were used to understand their behavioral capacities and dispositions, and baboons their actual behavioral patterns. This is mainly because the savanna adaptation of baboons had been described and treated as an early hominid analog by S.L. Washburn and I. DeVore in the middle 1960's, and despite the fact that baboons range widely and also include forest adapted populations, the third assumption of ecological causation is particularly important in these models and their savanna adaptations were emphasized.

THE BABOON MODEL

Even before the male sex bias of the "killer-ape" models became an object of focus and grounds for their rejection, they were modified into a more general "savanna chimpanzee" model by recognizing a gathering role for women and thereby positing sexual division of labor and reciprocal sharing as important elements of human origins and the initial hominid adaptation. Once again, the current version of these ideas can be traced to work by S. L. Washburn and his students (see Haraway's essay on Washburn's role in hominid origins theories). In a publication with C.S. Lancaster, he corrected some of the sex-bias of his earlier emphasis on cooperative male hunting and included gathering as part of his hypothesized early hominid adaptation. Even still, the predominant organizing principle of human social evolution was seen as hunting - not just a subsistence technique but a way of life responsible for no less than

- bipedalism
- elaborate tool kits
- development of language
- appreciation of beauty
- male aggressiveness and pleasure in killing
- bonding between males
- the monogamous family
- loss of female estrus
- the incest taboo

Washburn and Lancaster recognized, however, that a sexual division of labor and in particular an important role for gathering also set humans apart from the other primates, and they were the first to assert "receptacles for carrying vegetable products may have been one of the most fundamental advances in human evolution". This influential hypotheses, and those that developed from it, are the consequences of the belief that hominids originated when some of these primates adapted to the savanna in a manner analogous to that of living baboons, but with important differences because the anatomical and behavioral potentials of chimpanzees differ from those of baboons. Simply stated, the savanna chimpanzee model asks, "What would happen if a chimpanzee-like hominoid began to adapt to grasslands?" The answer, "*hominids*!" In particular, hominids much like living hunter/gatherers, although presumably with much more simple capacities and behaviors. One proponent of this model, A. Kortlandt, believes that chimpanzees were much more like hominids in the past, and that their presently restricted distribution and behaviors are a result of competition with more successful humans.

In the earlier versions of the model there was what L. Fedigan calls a "baboonization" of early hominid life. The emphasis was on what chimpanzee capabilities would bring to a baboon way of life, as opposed to the later emphasis on what a chimpanzee would be expected to do differently if faced with an adaptation to environments today only supporting baboons. The baboon adaptation (or more properly adaptations, since these vary by population and by season) to open grasslands is based on a complex of socially defined behaviors that are oriented around the need for organization in the defense of the troop (this, and a number of other aspects of the baboon adaptation as a basis for understanding human origins, is discussed by Strum and Mitchell). Troop defense based on social behavior requires the organization of troop members into a semi-rigid hierarchy and the bonding and cooperation of mature males. According to one early theorist, the function of bonding between the normally competitive males is to harmlessly dissipate the aggressions that developed when the males were active in defending the troop. The roles expected of individuals are determined largely by their age and sex; their position in baboon society governed by the requirements of reproduction (the role of females) or survivorship (male roles, for instance as manifested by the need protect the females and young). (As many authors have since pointed out, this conforms closely to the expected sex roles in western culture at the time this model was being developed.) Savanna chimpanzee models emphasize the idea that early hominids would bring the Darwinian features to this habitat: bipedalism, tool use, canine reduction, and the increased intelligence of chimpanzees. In various ways these models suggest how the Darwinian features would fundamentally alter the adaptations of early hominids occupying a baboon-like niche. Baboons are among the most successful of the living primates, especially compared with the dwindling relic populations of African apes. The implication of the various savanna chimpanzee models is that by combining the most successful aspects of both species, hominids are the most successful of all primates.

While the killer-ape model focuses virtually uniquely on hunting ability, the more recent savanna chimpanzee models of hominid origins emphasize the greater intelligence and behavioral flexibility of chimpanzees, and incorporate a much wider range of behaviors, with different models emphasizing different behaviors. What differences would a chimpanzee-like creature bring to a baboon-like adaptation? This can be examined by comparing how chimpanzees and human are similar, how early hominids and modern hunter/gatherers might be similar, or focusing on what is unique in the hominids. Well beyond Darwin's considerations, attention has been drawn to other unique or unusual hominid behaviors and how they may have functioned in a savanna adapting chimpanzee, such as the use of home bases, structured reciprocal food sharing, male provisioning of mates and offspring (eventually male parenting), scavenging, and concealed ovulation.

THE CHIMPANZEE REFERENT

The focus of savanna chimpanzee models is to try and understand how this species can be used to reconstruct the prototype from which hominids evolved, and what factors caused hominid behaviors, and subsequently morphology, to appear in it. It would seem obvious that the last common ancestors of hominids and chimpanzees were not the same as chimpanzees, any more than they were the same as modern humans. Yet, this assumption seems to underlie many of the attempts to use chimpanzees as a referent for modeling hominid origins, examining how chimpanzee behaviors and morphology might be expected to change with the shift to a terrestrial, savanna habitat. Another use of the chimpanzee in modeling hominid origins is a comparative one, finding the behaviors and morphology held in common between chimpanzees and humans, and then assuming that these were characteristic of the last common ancestor.

For example, N. Jablonski and G. Chaplin examine the likely responses of a chimpanzee-like early hominid group when encountering scarce seasonal resources at the end of the Miocene in East Africa. They argue that increased competition would raise the level of violence and aggression between group members. The solution to this problem they suggest is the increased use of an existing chimpanzee behavior in a new environment. The proposal is that an increased number of bipedal threat displays were effective in mitigating violence and allowing a smooth distribution of limited resources to develop. Like Mann in his explanation of canine reduction, they envisage this humanizing trend in terms of its effects on social control.

Comparative Behavioral Reconstruction

To try and reconstruct probable behavioral patterns of the prehominid prototype from both descendent species, M.P. Ghiglieri attempted a classic comparative analysis and arrived at a suite of shared social behaviors that link the two living species, and that the last common ancestor might therefore be expected to have

- Female **exogamy**
- Weak bonds between females
- Closed social groups
- Stable multi-male, multi-female communities
- Males active in territorial defense
- Males seek, attack, and may kill male rivals
- Polygynous mating system for at least some societies
- Both males and females travel alone
- Fission-fusion sociality common within communities
- Female associations primarily due to attraction to the same male(s)
- Male **endogamy**

- Communal territoriality common among males
- Mating competition between males of the same community mild relative to that between communities
- Sexual dimorphism moderate, males cooperate in alliances against rivals

Ghiglieri contends that the most critical features for hominid origins are female exogamy and male alliances, as this combination underlies the emergence of human social groupings and the resolution of the conflicting reproductive strategies of males and females:

- **Males** produce almost unlimited sperm but have offspring production that is limited by their access to females. Their maximum reproductive potential is to be widely distributed with respect to females.

- **Females** produce a very limited number of eggs and have an even more limited potential for live births. Because their offspring production is limited by their access to sources of energy, their maximum reproductive potential is to maximize their access to resources.

Yet, to be useful in modeling hominid origins, two basic problems with Ghiglieri's list of expected prehominid (the species that is the last common ancestor of hominids and chimpanzees, the same as prechimpanzee) behaviors and reproductive strategies must be resolved. First, it assumes that there is no significant ecological causation, or ecological or demographic constraints on these behaviors, so that their distribution can be hypothesized to reflect behavioral homologies. Ghiglieri argues the case of homology, as "communal breeding strategies by male kin are ... extremely rare among nonhuman primates". Second, the list ignores major aspects in which human (and by inference earlier hominid) social behaviors are unique and therefore potentially play an important role in hominid origins. For instance, one human uniqueness contrasts the sharing of chimpanzee females among males with the long term bonds between the sexes with no real promiscuity in humans. A second is the human pattern of much longer parental investment, and male parenting. This difference is related to the characteristically human division of labor.

Ghiglieri's use of the chimpanzees was all referential, as he declined to develop a conceptual origins model. Moreover, the assumption that shared social behaviors were characteristic of the common ancestor precludes a significant ecological basis for their variation. This would make the influence of a savanna shift on their expression and variation minimal, thereby undermining the basis of the savanna chimpanzee model - that chimpanzee-like behavior can be expected to change in prehominids or early hominids when their ecology changes. The same criticisms apply to a similar referential model developed by Wrangham, but using all of the African apes for establishing what is held in common. The fact is that even the most elaborate of attempts to find common features in ape and human behavior (c.f. Rodseth et al) have been descriptive, and therefore are examples of referential modeling. It is not even clear that many of the social behaviors can be validly compared as they exist in a human cultural context that can be quite different (see Chapter 3) from their context in chimpanzee society. A prime example is the comparison of primate communication and human language (see Chapter 4). Even the basic biological differences have a different meaning in the cultural context; gender rather than sex is a primary variable, and kinship is a social institution rather than a categorization of relationships due to common ancestry. As one of my colleagues quipped, these comparisons may be well below the common denominator.

Hunting

In fact chimpanzee data has been, at best, confusing as the referent for understanding human origins as the consequence of a savanna adaptation. Chimpanzee hunting is a case in point. As W. McGrew points out, chimpanzees could be used to outline the important developments in the hominid hunting adaptation by observing what they do *not* hunt: fast moving solitary prey, and mammals weighing more than 15 kg. The hunting model assumes that the hominids evolved from an anthropithecine with a chimpanzee-like hunting adaptation (the chimpanzee = primitive assumption of the model), but if we assume that ecological constraints are relevant to the expression of hunting variation, the prediction that chimpanzees in a more open habitat will be more hominid-like in their behavior is not met. For instance, C. Boesch and H. Boesch studied the details of hunting in a number of chimpanzee groups, ranging from forest to open woodland habitats. Their conclusion is that chimpanzee hunting is quite different from hunting by social carnivores.

- Group hunting in social carnivores responds to the defense potential of the prey whereas in the chimpanzees it does not.
- Chimpanzee hunting contrasts in its high level of coordination and cooperation

This suggests that referential models for hominid origins based on carnivore species (e.g. Schaller and Lowther, Thompson) are probably irrelevant. It is the chimpanzees that "hunt in the most elaborate way known for animal hunters." Yet, the ecologically-related differences in chimpanzee hunting patterns also make them poor models of hominid prototypes (table 5.1).

The conclusion that Boesch and Boesch drew from their comparisons was, foremost, that the forest chimpanzees are more efficient hunters than the savanna ones. They hunt more frequently, less opportunistically, and with a greater success rate. They hunt more often in groups, group size averages are larger, and the amount of hunting collaboration is much higher. In short, they are more like hominid hunters. Other more hominid-like behaviors include the apparent absence of cannibalism, the tendency to eat meat on the ground, the smaller number of participating females, and the patterns of sharing - males provision females more than other males, and there is some female provisioning of males (to the same extent that females provision each other). This comparison provides little in support of the "savanna" part of the savanna chimpanzee model. To the extent that ecology is hypothesized to explain why a chimpanzee adapted to the savanna would be expected to develop hominid social behaviors, Boesch and Boesch maintain that the hypothesis is incorrect as far as hunting is concerned.

Subsequent studies by C. Stanford and colleagues have blurred many of these differences. In particular, their work suggests that the Gombe (savanna-woodland) chimpanzees hunt as often and are equally successful, but the earlier observation that they do not cooperate has held up. Thus, the hypothesis that there is significant ecological causation for chimpanzee behaviors has grown weaker, even as this causation assumption has come to underlie increasingly complex models of social variation, as described below.

Table 5.1
Hunting in Three Chimpanzee Groups
from Boesch and Boesch (1989) and Stanford and colleagues (1994)

	Täi Chimpanzees (tropical rain forest)	Gombe Chimpanzees (savanna-woodlands)	Mahale Chimpanzees (savanna-woodlands)
Common prey species	Colobus monkeys (91%) other primates (9%)	Colobus monkeys (82%) other primates (3%) bushpig (8%) bushbuck (6%) other (1%)	Colobus monkeys (13%) other primates (19%) bushpig (8%) bushbuck (19%) other (34%)
Cannibalism observed	no	yes	yes
Age of prey: percent adult	50%	11%	22%
percent Colobus adult	47%	25%	33%
Opportunistic hunting	less often	more often	
Average hunts per month	10	8.6	1.6
Colobus prey success rate	55%	41%	
Solitary hunts	8%	64%	76%
Collaboration in group hunts	65%	19%	0%
Kills by females	18%	23%	29%
Meat sharing (in percent): owner-beneficiary			
adult male-adult male adult male-adult female adult male-subadult	21 38 13	38 41 10	
adult female-adult male adult female-adult female adult female-subadult	9 8 11	1 1 9	
Most common meat eating place	ground	trees	

Association patterns and the Social Matrix

Probably the most intricate conceptual model of hominid origins and the initial hominid adaptation developed from primate data came from R. Foley and P. Lee. They classify primate societies in a matrix defined by male and female sexual strategies and how these influence what the authors call their distribution states: the nature of associations between individuals of the same sex after they have reached maturity, often arising from patterns of residence or dispersal from the parental unit. Foley and Lee argue that there are only three options open to each sex

1. individuals can be solitary relative to others of the same sex
2. individuals can form associations with non-kin of the same sex
3. individuals can for associations with kin of the same sex

They use these options to define a matrix of possible social systems. The axes of the matrix are the male and female distribution possibilities, and the contents of each cell are the primate species that are described by the intersection of the two axes. Accepting the notion that ecological constraints are important in determining the form of primate social systems, they contend that the exact role played by these constraints is to define the pathway or pathways from one cell in their matrix to another. For instance, according to their analysis chimpanzee societies provide an example of male alliances with kin and female alliances with non-kin. These female alliances are advantageous when food resources are patchy, but large enough to be used by several individuals. Two or more females may cooperate to defend such a patch from other females. The pathway from this combination to the early hominid social system is constrained by their contention that early hominid females also aggregated in non-kin groups. Their argument is that as prehominids occupied drier and drier savannas, the patchy nature of the environment in combination with the decreasing density of dry season food sources supported smaller and smaller groups until the female dispersion state tended toward the solitary - there was just not enough food in any one place to support groups during the dry season. At the same time, social cohesion over widely dispersed subgroups was maintained by associations of related males, based on male kin alliances in the chimpanzee-like ancestors. Thus, Foley and Lee directly relate the origin of hominid social structure to the consequences of a chimpanzee adaptation to the ecologically different savanna, and therefore employ a specific chimpanzee analogy to reconstruct the position of hominids in their matrix of possible social systems. One could argue, as Stanford and Allen have, that this is so hypothetical as to be, in reality, another referential model for hominid origins based on chimpanzees. It is also so complicated that direct sources of data are unlikely to ever clarify the question of its validity; too complex, in other words, to be useful in making implications about the evolution of behaviors of extinct species.

The Pygmy Chimpanzee Model

We must wonder, in the end, how appropriate the chimpanzee *is* as a model to base theories of hominid origins? Perhaps the most detailed attempt to use this species to understand hominid origins and interpret early hominid adaptation and behavior is the Bonobo (pygmy chimpanzee) model, developed by A. Zihlman and her colleagues. They argue that the living pygmy chimpanzee is the best prototype for a hominid ancestor because of all primate species, it is most similar to humans. Bonobos were first described as a species apart from the common chimpanzee because of their different, face-to-face, copulating position, thought by the scientists observing them in the Frankfurt zoo to be more human-like. Zihlman and her colleagues argue that in comparison with the common chimpanzee, a number of other features are more human-like as well:

- Canine dimensions are smaller
- Facial size is smaller
- The upper body is more gracile
- Fore and hind limbs are closer together in size
- Sexual dimorphism is less, especially in the canines
- Bipedal locomotion is more common on the ground

From these they conclude that the pygmy chimpanzees are the most generalized of the living anthropithecines, and therefore are most like the last common ancestor. Moreover, they argue that in comparison with australopithecines "they are similar in body size, postcranial dimensions, and ... even in cranial and facial features". Parenthetically, they seem willing to derive this ancestral condition from "Ramapithecus", a species one would have thought should be totally precluded from anthropithecine ancestry if their phylogeny was correct.

B. Latimer and his colleagues consider this model to be invalid, contending that many of the comparisons with living humans are invalid, and that the fossil record fails to confirm the single prediction of the model - earlier hominid fossils should appear more like pygmy chimpanzees (the hypothesized generalized condition) in their anatomy. Citing F. Weidenreich's analysis, they argue that gracile features of the human and pygmy chimpanzee dentition and cranium are caused by the relatively large brain size in both, but this common cause has a *different evolutionary basis in the two species* - brain expansion in humans and **dentofacial** (the teeth, jaws, and face) reduction in the pygmy chimpanzees. The volume focused on this species that R. Susman subsequently edited is quite interesting in this regard, as Susman's own contribution shows that the postcranial anatomy and locomotor behavior of the Bonobos are best explained by their arboreal adaptations and are unlikely to be primitive retentions.

Latimer et al's strongest arguments, however, are paleoanthropological. The Miocene African hominoids were poorly known postcranially when they wrote, but in **dentocranial** (teeth, jaws, face, and cranial vault) anatomy they are quite unlike the Bonobos. Their teeth, jaws, and faces were very large, adapted to dietary items that require powerful and prolonged chewing. Hominids from the Late Miocene and Pliocene (Chapter 6) are most similar to the earlier anthropithecines in exactly these features. Furthermore, while Zihlman and colleagues make much of the measurements that show similarities between Bonobos and the early hominids, in most cases these compare the incomparable. What meaning could similarities in femur length and head dimensions have, when the comparison is between the most arboreal of the African apes and an obligatory biped? Finally, early hominids lived in very different habitats than the pygmy chimpanzees are found today, making any behavioral similarities based on hypotheses of similar ecological adaptations unlikely as well.

Are Chimpanzees a Valid Referent?

In their discussion of the pygmy chimpanzee model, Latimer and his colleagues conclude "it is dangerous to predict anatomy, behavior, habitat, range, distribution, ecology and adaptations of extinct early hominids through the use of comparative behavior, anatomy, and biochemistry in living primates." This stricture, if accepted, should give us pause for thought about any of the chimpanzee models for hominid origins. If the fossil record is the primary source of information about hominid origins, study of the pre-divergence (Chapter 3) and post-divergence (Chapter 6) anthropithecines suggests that living chimpanzees have evolved too far from the ancestral condition to be an appropriate referent for modeling this process. This record provides a variety of reasons to suggest that in behavior and morphology chimpanzees are not the primitive condition for the chimpanzee-hominid clade.

- **Ecological**: the habitats in which the earliest hominids are found differ from any habitat supporting chimpanzee populations today. No fossil apes have ever been recovered in regions where early hominid fossils occur, and the breadth of ecologically-based variation in the behaviors of living chimpanzees does not show that chimpanzees act or adapt more like hominids when they are found in environments that more closely resemble early hominid habitats.
- **Dietary**: unlike chimpanzees, Miocene anthropithecine and early hominid jaws are large and the molar teeth are expanded with thick enamel, while the incisors are small. These indicate very different dietary adaptations.
- **Locomotor**: there is no evidence in the hand remains of the earliest hominids to reflect a knuckle-walking stage in their immediate ancestry, and there is no reason to expect such evidence to have been lost as part of the hominid bipedal adaptation. Moreover, the number of lumbar vertebrae in early hominids is 6, compared with 5 in living humans and 3-4 in chimpanzees, suggesting at least some of the specializations for brachiation are lacking in the prehominids. In fact, as discussed in chapters 4 and 6, the arboreal activities of the earliest hominids are unlikely to have been much different from those of small living humans.

Today's chimpanzees are ecological generalists, according to C. Stanford, ranging widely across several African environments without substantial variation in their gross social organization. This contrasts with the more specific adaptations of the even wider ranging baboons, but undermines the ecological causality assumption necessary for most, perhaps all, of the various savanna chimpanzee models. Moreover, the success of chimpanzees as ecological generalists might reflect a quite different adaptive strategy than the early hominids, with their dietary and locomotor specializations. The fact is that chimpanzees are at least as altered from the common ancestral state, although in quite different ways, and it is reasonable to question whether they are any more valid as the basis of referential models for hominid origins than modern humans themselves would be.

THE !KUNG MODEL

The late G. Isaac drew on an analogy with recent hunter/gatherers, in particular the !Kung San of the northwest region of the Kalahari desert in southern Africa, for the referent to interpret the Late Pliocene archaeological evidence he was uncovering in East Africa, and to model human origins. His version of the savanna chimpanzee model posited very hominid-like behaviors as the immediate consequence of hominid origins. In what remains a very influential theory, he argued that the hunting hypothesis is inadequate as an explanation of critical elements found in contrasting human and ape features, as exemplified by comparisons of chimpanzees and living hunter/gatherers. According to Isaac, human hunter/gatherers are unique in the following ways:

- Because hunter/gatherers are bipedal they habitually carry around food, tools, and other possessions in their arms or in containers.
- Spoken language serves to exchange information about the past and future, and regulate social relations.
- Food acquisition is a "corporate responsibility in hunter/gatherer society, and family groups are the usual central focus for food sharing among adults and between adults and juveniles. Chimpanzees [at that time] were known only to share foods when males shared meat - a behavior that Isaac termed "tolerated scrounging". After Isaac's untimely death, F. De Waal reported unreciprocated food sharing in chimpanzees, and the patterns of sharing the spoils of hunting are shown in table 5.1.
- Hunter/gatherer social groups have a **home base**, a focus in space where individuals can expect to meet each other and engage in social and other activities.
- Gathered foods are not all eaten as they are obtained (i.e. snacking) but are brought back to the home base.
- Hunter/gatherers spend more time acquiring high protein resources [and, one could add, other high quality food resources], although chimpanzees do hunt cooperatively. Among the higher primates, only humans regularly take prey weighing over 15 kg, according to Isaac.
- Many foods are prepared outside of the mouth by grinding, crushing, cutting, and cooking.
- Hunter/gatherers have a much longer list of technological equipment for food acquisition, transport, and preparation, although chimpanzees do use modified sticks for termite and ant collection and for cleaning the marrow out of cracked bones, and they traditionally return to single immovable rocks for cracking nuts with a rock hammer (in some cases for generations), and may use clubs (at least in threat displays).

In listing these differences between chimpanzees and hunter/gatherers, Isaac argued that a hunting explanation alone is inadequate, and instead proposed that the fundamental hominid adaptation was a social one - food sharing. The two most important elements of his model are the postponing of food consumption until hominids return to a home base, and the sharing of food there. Isaac interpreted some of the East African hominid archaeological sites were he worked to show evidence of repeated use. However, not all sites were interpreted as home bases, some had no apparent pattern of organization reflected in the distribution of faunal remains or stone tools across their surface, others could only be identified as sites of hominid activities because of **manuports** (stones which, because of the geological circumstances or the material involved, must have been carried there from somewhere else). Manuports showed that tools were being transported. Other sites had hominid-made tools that showed signs of wear, evidence thought to show that foods were being processed there. He found, at one site, four hippopotamus legs and a scatter of tools, which he interpreted as a hippo butchering episode that ended with most of the meat being carried off, presumably to a home base. Bones of fauna at some sites showed cutmarks, which were taken to mean that they were butchered at the home base. Together, this provided Isaac with evidence that the two most important elements of his model appeared early - carrying tools and meat to a home base that was repetitively used implied food sharing.

To some extent this model was unraveled by two developments, each of which called the validity of the referent into question. First, L. Binford was able to show that many of the elements of the model that came from the excavations at Olduvai Gorge and Lake Turkana were patterned from faunal assemblages that were not debris of human hunting as had been assumed, but rather resulted from a mix of both human and carnivore hunting and scavenging activities. Moreover, he hypothesized that the human activities concerned were focused more on scavenging than hunting, a suggestion soon confirmed by R. Potts and P. Shipman, whose scanning electron microscope (SEM) study of bones from Olduvai Gorge showed them to be "covered with carnivore gnaw marks" and, most importantly, revealed that the cutmarks left by hominid tools were almost always superimposed over them. This showed that the gnawing came first, a sure sign of scavenging. Binford's further analysis of semi-complete animal skeletons, where bones and stone tools were found together, showed that the pattern of associations for the preserved bones (for instance, the common association of lower leg and head parts) on the Olduvai **"living floors"** (areas thought to be preserved hominid campsites) were the same as that left behind by large African predators and scavengers such as lions and hyenas.

Finally, he was able to isolate two components within the tool assemblages. In one, there are small tools, barely modified, found with the debris of their manufacture. For instance, the tool might be a pebble with a sharp edge, found with the flakes whose removal produced that edge (see figure 7.# pebble tool). The small tools form what he calls the "expedient component", and are the usual ones found with fauna dominated by lower limb and head associations. Very often, the limbs were broken open for the extraction of fat and marrow (the significance of this resource is explored in Chapter 9). In the other component, more patterned artifacts with greater complexity to their production are occasionally found. These are usually made of raw materials that are different from the small tools, and which often could only be found naturally far away. These transported tools often show more use-wear, and in one place a study by Isaac revealed the presence of plant material on them, indicating their use in plant processing (evidently pounding, as the tools are battered hammers). The distribution of the more complexly made component was also environmentally dictated, for instance the battered hammers are most often found with the plants (in this case a cattail-like aquatic plant). Other transported tools are associated with the remains of animal carcasses with meat-bearing parts that could be (and, judging from the cut marks probably were) exploited. Binford concluded that none of the tool sites were home bases. In many cases the implements were made on the spot of scavenging opportunities, and left there to be discovered by the archaeologists He argued that the "living floors" were actually activity areas, marked by collections of expedient tools that accumulated at the spot where they were used. At Olduvai these were often places where scavenging opportunities provided by carnivore activities presented themselves again and again, or where plants could be found and processed with predictable regularity. The highly visible sites at Olduvai Gorge are not the same as the highly visible living areas of recent hunter/gatherers, places where individuals could expect to meet each other and engage in social activities, especially reciprocal food sharing. With the loss of a valid basis for the "home base' interpretation, his analysis undermined the basis for Isaac's hypothesis that food sharing was the primary element of humanization.

Parenthetically, Binford raised one more point about these sites, which if valid has far-reaching implications for understanding early hominid behavior. The highly visible Oldowan sites were quite different than the preserved social areas of the recent past. The Oldowan sites were places where technology was used over and over again in coping with the environment, in reoccurring scavenging or food processing episodes. Given this interpretation, Binford questioned why so many unworn expedient tools were consistently found accumulated together. A "home base" explanation would account for tools accumulating in one place (especially curated tools, with use wear from continued activities), the tool accumulations after all were the basis for the "home base" interpretation to begin with, but at this point in his reasoning Binford had pretty much ruled this explanation out. Hominids seemed to go back to the same place over and over again, produce expedient tools that were used once, and leave them behind. Modern humans, he expected, would either curate the tools, carrying them away and using them until they dulled or broke, or would remember that many appropriate tools were already there to be used again when they returned. Binford's conclusion was that while tools were used in various aspects of early hominid adaptation, they were not part of any planned adaptive strategy.

Second, the validity of using the !Kung, and by implication other living peoples who seem to be hunting and gathering, as models for Plio-Pleistocene hunter gatherers is increasingly questioned. There were always problems in using people with the capacities of modern humans to model the behavior of hominids with one-third their brain size. Other difficulties stem from using living peoples displaced to very ecologically peripheral habitats, to model Plio-Pleistocene populations occupying much richer environments. But perhaps the most intractable problem is whether the !Kung, or any of the San, can be considered hunter/gatherers at all, in the sense of the common Pleistocene adaptation, and thereby whether they provide a valid basis for comparison. The issue is to what extent for most of the Holocene have !Kung groups been integrated by trade and individual mobility into a regional economy, which also includes local pastoralists. They have certainly been broadly integrated for the last several hundred years -- points raised by E. Wilmsen and argued in a number of publications, including focused discussions in a debate that swirled through the pages of the journal *Current Anthropology*, in papers by J. Solway and R. Lee, E. Wilmsen and J. Denbow, and R. Lee and Guenther, and the comments by a number of other authors that were published with them. For instance, when R. Lee worked among the !Kung at Dobe, gathering the data that Isaac subsequently used in his comparisons, 70% were involved in a mixed economy that included farming, herding, and foraging, while the rest were retainers on cattle posts. The extent of autonomy varies widely among the San. However, even the most autonomous groups were embedded in broad regional trade networks with other San and pastoralists and, simply put, they have not been fully dependent on their hunting and gathering for their subsistence in historic times if not for much longer. Besides trade, many !Kung San were employed as subsistence or wage laborers. These retained their ties with seemingly autonomous hunting and gathering San, usually through kin, and historically this increased the access of the least affected-appearing groups to trade goods. The Late Stone Age adaptations of these peoples, as with all other hunter/gatherers, was irreversibly altered by contact and subsequently institutionalized relationships with pastoralists and/or agriculturists. Certainly in this century they are part of the world system.

One final point about the !Kung model is a consequence of its reliance on the interpretation of early hominid archaeological sites. Over the years the analysis of the fauna and archaeological remains has gradually shifted from a hunting to a scavenging interpretation based on stone tool distributions and use-wear (discussed in Chapter 7). Yet, the fact that stone tools and archaeological sites span less than the last half of human existence makes the assumption that this adaptation (whether hunting or scavenging) was either a cause or immediate consequence of hominid origins very tenuous.

MALE PARENTING

In an extremely influential publication C.O. Lovejoy focused on the demographic consequences of adaptive trends in chimpanzees to provide insight into hominid origins. He argued that the living apes and their Miocene anthropithecine ancestors can be regarded as K-adapted (see Chapter 2), a slow reproduction strategy in which the females bear few young and spend a long time teaching them, preparing them for adult life. Much of this preparation is for the details of their social interactions, and an equally extended juvenile period provides the opportunity for practicing social behaviors in play, according to J.B. and C.S. Lancaster. The expanded period of child dependency determines the space between live births, a 5-6 year period (see table 3.2) that is greater in chimpanzees than in any other primate (although it can be matched in some human populations). Lovejoy argued that the behavioral complexity of chimpanzees in concert with their K-strategy reproductive adaptation led to a "demographic dilemma". Chimpanzees evolved one of the possible solutions to this problem - slow down the rate of maturation and thereby expand the learning period. In particular, the special importance of learning during the intense mother-infant relation before weaning, required long periods between births. But with first births averaging 13-14 years in the wild this creates a different adaptive problem, the expansion of longevity to assure a sufficient number of children and continued maternal care for their survivorship. The solution to one problem, in other words, created another.

Assuming that a chimpanzee-like life history characterized the last common ancestor, Lovejoy suggests that hominids might have originated when an anthropithecine group developed a different solution to the demographic dilemma. The hominids were able to couple maturational slow down with an increase in their rate of reproduction (the differential fertility of natural selection) by developing behaviors to help shorten the time between births without changing the time of infant dependency. A more rapid rate of reproduction would take the pressure off of the longevity requirement, and have the added advantage of allowing populations to quickly respond to a new or changing environment, or recover from natural catastrophes or diseases. In fact, because the same r-adapted behaviors also improved infant survivorship, these changes promoted population expansion in a species whose ancestors were "locked" into a very small potential for population growth because of its life history strategy.

Lovejoy, in focusing on reproduction, emphasized the importance of unique hominid features that played no role in Darwin's model. Hominids appeared and were successful because they altered this reproductive strategy to a more r-oriented adaptation, increasing their rate of reproduction without altering the focus on learning and the long period of child dependency; in fact, quite the opposite. The two elements that evolved to play a fundamental role in this change are

- behavioral - male parenting
- anatomical - obligate bipedalism

The leader of the group that developed our understanding of obligate bipedalism in the earliest hominids, he focused on the consequences of viewing bipedalism as the first of the Darwinian features to appear. Lovejoy's model expanded on the importance of the bipedal adaptation in the novel context of male parenting.

In Lovejoy's modeling of early hominid social behavior, terrestrial populations developed a search-intensive feeding strategy for obtaining high quality food resources (this contrasts with the feeding strategy of many other terrestrial primates such as gorillas and some baboon populations). Because the high quality food resources are widely distributed across the environment, systematically using them would select for increasingly complex mental mapping, as discussed in Chapter 4. C. Peters has emphasized high quality plant resources such as young leafs, shoots, tubers, and tough-rinded low canopy fruits that would be available where early hominids are found or likely to have been, on forest floors and edges, and lake and stream margins. A Mann suggests an additional emphasis on insects, annelids, eggs, amphibians, small reptiles, and invertebrates.

Lovejoy suggests that bipedal hominid males began to **forage** (scavenge, hunt, gather, or collect) high quality provisions and return with food for their pair-bonded females and young. He suggested that each male maintained a long term pair bonding, or **monogamous**, relation with a female, thereby specifically provisioning one mate and their young and promoting his own genes. The improved provisioning affected the female's diet enough to allow a shorter interval between births. This is because primates evolved a system of preventing ovulation during lactation by keying female fertility to their fat resources (these are dramatically depleted during lactation). Provisioning greatly improved fat resources and thus promoted an earlier return to fertility, with subsequent pregnancy and shorter birth interval. Moreover, with the provisioning of children the rate of reproduction was further increased because of their improved survivorship. A significant male parenting role is rare in primates, but where it does appear the effects are similar. For instance, males are important in infant care in many marmoset species, and unlike the other South American anthropoids the females in these populations consistently give birth to twins.

According to Lovejoy, the loss of external manifestations of seasonal fertility (estrus) and the change from seasonal to monthly periods of fertility removed a major disruption of long term pair bonds, and allowed for even shorter spans between births. This change was made possible by the continued, and predictable, provisioning of females by their mates. Periods of estrus and ovulation are not always coincident in primates, according to B. Sigmon, estrus occurring on a lunar cycle while ovulation more strongly controlled by the seasonality of the environment (offspring are born when their survivorship is most probable). This creates what she describes as "sexual activity out of proportion to ovarian activity", and therefore available to fulfill other social functions. This relationship of estrus and ovulation changes quickly in domestication (or captivity in zoos) when feeding is on a regular basis. Estrus and ovulation become coincident and breeding can take place throughout the year, when there is ovulation. Lovejoy's contention is that bipedalism was the key anatomical change allowing this adaptation; males needed it to carry foods to provision their mates and children, while females needed it to carry the multiple dependent young that must be the consequence of slow maturation plus shortened birth spacing (plus, as K. Gibson points out, the inability of these young to grasp the mother with their feet, lost as a consequence of the obligate bipedal behavior). Tool and weapon use play roles, as females could effectively use weapons to help defend the young that they cared for while males were away, and the simplest tools, ranging from digging sticks to rocks with sharp edges, would be of substantial aid in the foraging activities. Finally, the evolving changes in hominid sexual activities may have played an important role as well. Sigmon argues that the further development of female receptivity between estrus periods - even as these became coincident with ovulations - emphasized the importance of the non-reproductive roles that had evolved because of the excess of sexual energy over the energy required for reproduction. Sigmon, as well as S. Hrdy and others, suggest that these non-reproductive activities may have formed the basis for longer term pair bonding; not necessarily because of the lure or reward of sexual gratification, as authors such at K. Hill and S. Parker have suggested, but perhaps for more mundane reasons such as the continued familiarity of mothers (and their offspring) to males who they continually copulate with. The evolving complexities of social interactions as sexual activity came increasingly under social control, planning, and expectations for reciprocity over a broad range of behaviors, were important beginnings in the evolution of human intelligence.

The framework provided by Lovejoy's ideas has proven to be very influential, as indicated by the fact that at least five studies have elaborated on aspects of this model, or significantly overlap with it. P. Turke, for instance, expanded on the importance of concealment of ovulation, the monthly periods of fertility, the potential for (what male anthropologists continue to refer to as) "continual receptivity", and the group synchronization of the menstrual cycle, to maintain long terms pair bonds in small groups.

In a theory emphasizing the importance of sexual selection, S. Parker also focuses on the importance of male provisioning, which she terms "nuptial feeding". She assumes that there was a chimpanzee-like fission-fusion social organization because the prehominids "have a similar diet and live in similar habitats". As a consequence of their more extensively developed subsistence technology, Parker argues that prehominid males were able to access higher energy foods. Newly empowered by possessing these foods, "with 'courtship or nuptial feeding of estrus females, males could entice females to go away with them on 'safaris' or honeymoons." Bipedal locomotion is critical in this model, as it is in Lovejoy's, but mainly for the males. Parker recognizes the potential importance of bipedal carrying to obtain, transport, and defend the preferred foods, but there is more. Bipedalism, according to Parker, would also allow females to assess the size of the male, the size of the gift, and the size of his genitals (like Sheets-Johnstone, Parker hopes to explain the fact that hominid penis length is absolutely and relatively greater than any other pongid). She thereby regards bipedalism as part of the male reproductive strategy, and attributes its appearance to sexual selection. The canines reduced as smiling during courtship became more important than snarling at other competitive males.

Quiatt and Kelso discussed the importance of what they term 'household economics' in what they hypothesize was an emerging family system. Their focus is on the advantages of a dual subsistence economy, based on regular cooperation, reciprocal food sharing and a sex-based division of labor, as contrasted with individual foraging or the unreciprocated food sharing of chimpanzees. They argue that the primary driving force for the family, in comparison to the mother-plus-offspring units common to other species, was the number of contemporary dependent offspring in the early hominids. This makes a cause out of what Lovejoy regards as an effect, but the potential for positive feedback in this evolutionary process resolves the contradiction. Advantages of a household economic system include

- a greater consistency in dietary resources available to the household,
- a wider potential resource range provided by the sexual division of labor in food procurement, and
- the potential for biparental child care as well as incorporating older siblings (marmosets and tamarins do this as well, but their life history strategy and social context are each quite different).

The foundation of the household is a reproductive pair bond that "provides a continuing basis for exchange between individuals who labor together and apart, with built-in mechanisms for promoting reciprocity and parity". They regard the reciprocal exchange system as "bioculturally defined". While this is not a necessary part of their model, it fits with the speculations about kinship systems presented below.

J. Lancaster's focus has been on delayed maturation in early hominid children and the effects this would be expected to have on biological and social adaptations. Lancaster provides an intellectual link between Mann's (in his studies of early hominid delayed maturation) and Lovejoy's hominid origins theories. She argues that the fundamental "platform of hominid behavior" is the division of labor between male hunting and female gathering. This adaptation, in her model, focused on the problems created by the unique hominid pattern of delayed maturation and a long period of high level parental investment. Hominids are unique in this combination, which results in multiple dependent young of differing ages. The period of lactation puts females under significant stress. For instance, in a study of baboons she reports that the death rate doubles for lactating females. This is why apes are only able to have one nutritionally dependent child at a time. At the same time, prolonged maturation is an important consequence of the structural changes in the early hominid brain, discussed by R. Holloway (see below). Moreover, it may be connected to the requirements of the combination of extensive foraging techniques, food sharing, and as Darwin posited tool-use - a point developed further by Parker and Gibson. The hominid adaptation to this life history strategy is found in the long period of high level parental investment, a possibility created by the newly evolved paternal contribution as posited by Lovejoy. Lancaster contends that the contributions by both parents toward the survival of juveniles created a paternal partnership and an evolutionary bond was forged between them that decreased the effects of sexual selection, for instance as described in the Tanner or Parker models.

I examined the consequences of a nuclear family structure that evolved to provide for, socialize, and otherwise educate the young, for early hominids with their long maturation period but short life span. This began by determining the age at death for individuals on the basis of tooth wear. Once the period between successive tooth eruptions could be estimated from Mann's work (Chapter 4), the rate of tooth wear can be determined the following way. In australopithecines (and humans), when the second molar erupts the first molar has about five years of occlusal wear. When the third molar erupts, there is more or less ten years of wear on the first molar, and five years on the second. From these known degrees of wear (and others, from premolar eruptions), it is possible to form a fairly accurate picture of how long any tooth has been wearing. Adding this to the time of eruption provides an approximation for the age at death. I used this technique estimate ages at death for the Swartkrans australopithecine site at the PlioPleistocene boundary (see Chapter 7), because this collection has a reasonable chance of being a random sample, as far as age is concerned, and it has the largest number of juveniles (critical to the technique's accuracy) know for any early hominid collection. Some of their demographic characteristics can be estimated if one makes two assumptions.

1. Although Swartkrans is a random sample of many populations, we must assume that the ages in the sample are like the ages in an "average" real population and there was no long-term change in population size over the relevant time span.
2. We must assume that approximately one-fourth of those born died before the age of three but were not all fossilized because of the fragility of the bone in the very young (this figure comes from survivorship in recent hunter/gatherers, prior to contact with Europeans and the infectious diseases that evolved in their urban environments).

The average age at death at Swartkrans is between eleven and twelve years. Assuming that reproduction began at the age of 12-14, a figure that is high for chimpanzees and low for humans, and accepting K. McKinley's calculation that birth spacing averaged three to four years, we encounter the following situation at Swartkrans. If a mother gives birth to her first offspring at the age of 12-14, the odds are better than 50% that both parents will not survive until this offspring is old enough to reproduce. If her second offspring is born when she is 15-18, the parents have a 75% chance of not living until this second offspring is of reproductive age. They almost certainly would not live to see a third offspring reproduce. Because virtually no early hominids survived beyond 35, delayed maturation combined with a short life expectancy created the problem of raising numerous orphaned offspring (this is not as short lived as it might appear to westerners, the beneficiaries of 20th century medicine. In one well studied pre-Columbian American Indian population it was determined that very few lived beyond the age of 45).

With early adult deaths common and maturation therefore taking up a large percentage of total adult life span, orphaning would be quite common, especially for the later born children. This could have a significant potential effect on the evolutionary process as anthropithecine orphans, human or chimpanzee, have lower survivorship than other children. For instance, studies by both J. Goodall and G. Teleki show greatly heightened mortality among chimpanzee orphans, and M. Flynn reports this for living people, even when the orphans are adopted. Grandparent involvement in raising children would be an obvious way to meet this need with a social solution, as it has been in human societies, but the age structure of early hominids precludes this. I believe that extended families, requiring the recognition of lateral kin, is the direction that the solution took.

The issue of kin recognition is complex, as R. Alexander discusses. This is because kin often live near each other and their "recognition" may be no more than special behavior towards familiar individuals. Alternatively kin "recognition" may be phenotype matching of less familiar individuals to more familiar ones, as W. Holmes and P. Sherman suggest. There is a specialized region of the human brain that does this, in several steps, discussed in Chapter 13. A kinship *system* is different as it involves reciprocal role relations and expectations that are culturally defined. Kinship systems, what I posit here for the early hominids, are examples of a unique aspect of culture, as they incorporate culturally defined and delimited role expectations for functions and relationships originally of biological origin, discussed in Chapter 4. The extension of kinship laterally to include parents' sibs (aunts and uncles), relatives with the maximum potential for raising orphaned or partially orphaned children and with the most to gain from the viewpoint of genic level selection, requires cultural definitions (no matter how simplified the culture may have been). Alexander, who in his essay was not concerned with solutions to orphaning in early hominids, suggests a further and potentially even more important role for kinship recognition - the positioning of one's self in a socially defined network. This would bring together the three independent cognitive elements of human consciousness that he believes have independent origins: self awareness, the ability to imagine possible alternatives, and the ability to interpret the mental states of others (these are discussed in Chapter 4).

The origin of kinship systems in the early hominids meets a need unexpressed in any other higher primate species. Kinship systems are an important social adaptation to this early hominid life history strategy, and I believe that the process of adjusting to the requirements of long maturation with short life span became one of the initial critical foundations for the evolution of language and culture. This theory, then, suggests that the beginnings of culture can be expected as part of the hominid origins process.

THE GATHERING ADAPTATION

As discussed above G. Isaac, C.O. Lovejoy, and J. Lancaster, among others, argued that hominid origins involved a fundamental change in feeding strategy, based on reciprocal sharing and a sexual division of labor in which males and females obtained foods in different ways. There is, as well, a different view of how changes in feeding strategy might have set hominids on their unique course. This view emphasizes the importance of tools in foraging, obtaining and carrying foods, and the nature of the dietary regime that tool use opens to the hominids, already, as primates, eclectic eaters. In some variations on this theme it is argued that hominids originated as a consequence of focusing on exploiting a specialized dietary item; for instance small object eating for C. Jolly's theory, bone crunching as part of a carnivorous adaptation according to F. Szalay. In others the emphasis is on expansion of dietary range allowed by a simple foraging and carrying technology, for some of permutations of possible gathering models there is specific focus on the role of women in this positive feedback between technology and efficient gathering. G. Bartholomew and J. Birdsell were the first to combine a more complex consideration of body size, bipedalism, and tool use, with the wider range of resources that this adaptive complex would make available to the early hominids, in reconstructing the conditions of human origins and early evolution. Even a tool as simple as the digging stick, D. Coursey suggested, multiplied the range of usable savanna resources, and can be especially critical during the dry season. A. Mann pointed out that with the exception of roots and tubers (these are digging stick dependent), the potential dietary range for early hominids differs little from that exploited by chimpanzees, and for that matter by living hunter/gatherers. His argument is that the early hominids neither arose as specialized hunters nor uniquely as gatherers, but rather as diverse feeders who expanded their dietary range with simple tools.

The importance of these tools, however, should not be minimized. G. Teleki's observations indicate the importance of chimpanzee subsistence technology in expanding their range of usable resources, and make one additional point. Learning extractive foraging, as Parker and Gibson refer to it, requires a long period of apprenticeship. Increasing the importance of tool use in subsistence would lengthen the learning period, a change that would be in line with Mann's contention of maturation delay in the early hominids.

N. Tanner is perhaps the most influential of those scientists proposing separate gathering and hunting (or scavenging) adaptations as a cause or immediate consequence of hominid origins. She begins with a chimpanzee referent for reconstructing the behavior and ecology of the prehominids, and then asks what would cause this to evolve in the hominid direction. Following Zihlman's development of the "Woman the Gather" model, Tanner envisioned tool use as underlying an evolving savanna adaptation, the simple tools mainly used by female in foraging. Females were under the most nutritional stress because of their roles in bearing and nurturing offspring. There would be, in her model, little reason for males to change their foraging activities; significant male hunting, in her view, was precluded by their small body size although scavenging larger carcasses was a possibility. She argues that the males might have been adventurous, formed bonds easily both within and beyond the troop, and participated actively in the defense of females and the young, but that they made no direct contribution to their food supply.

Kinship recognition and kin-defined behaviors might have been characteristic of the early hominid females. In the living social primates, the mother-infant bond tends to be maintained through life, expressed later as differential behavior of offspring toward mothers and vice versa. Tanner suggests that such a **matrifocal** unit is probably the main stabilizing factor in primate groups. Moreover, females tend not to change groups, and if one does, the group itself is drastically altered since usually the entire matrifocal unit accompanies her. With more stable social units, and the likelihood of an entire lifetime spent in the same home range, the early hominid females may have carried the greater knowledge of environmental resources. Females, then, were more important than males in the formation of protocultural behavior during the early stages of cultural evolution, according to this model. Subsequent hominid evolution was oriented around the small matrifocal groups. Selection, in this model, would favor more intelligent females with enhanced abilities to carry. Females would be in a position to exercise sexual selection, picking mates who were friendly, sociable, and less aggressive, and thereby inadvertently selecting for males with reduced canines. This process would increase the complexity of communication and social bonding, in Tanner's model, until finally reciprocal relations could be established with males. Only later in human evolution, then, would the two roles have combined in a hunting/gathering adaptation based on food sharing, home bases, and the other elements implicit in schemes such as Isaac's. Tanner's model leaves it unclear as to when this might have occurred. Workers such as Binford (who, actually, drew the idea of separate foraging from an unusual interpretation of Lovejoy's writings) have indicated this might have been quite late in human evolution, perhaps only with the emergence of modern humans - ideas that will be discussed in Chapter 11. Whatever the case, the direction of hominid evolution was oriented by positive feedback between improvements in provisioning, socialization, and expanded cognitive abilities.

MENTAL EVOLUTION

The final focus discussed in this section involves models that give primary importance to the role in hominid origins of the last Darwinian feature, brain size expansion (in so far as it reflects mental evolution). T. Wynn has discussed hominid mental evolution, in so far as it is indicated in stone tools, which he interprets in accordance with Piaget's developmental interpretations. Fundamentally, his approach is to reconstruct the motor operations involved in manufacturing stone tools, assuming that this reflects the cognitive complexity of the tool makers. Wynn's work, however, provides little insight into hominid origins. Even if valid, the fact that he finds the makers of the earliest (2.6 myr) stone industry, the Oldowan, to be chimpanzee like in their mental abilities and the makers of the Acheulean, the next industry to appear (1.4 myr) to be indistinguishable from modern humans in their capacities, places all hominid mental evolution long after hominid origins, and makes it impossible to model as it seemingly happened all at once.

R. Holloway, whose work analyzing the endocasts of early hominids demonstrated their fundamental neural reorganization, focused on the brain, culture, and human evolution in his own modeling of the process. He suggested that the most important cortical changes in the neural reorganization were language-related (table 4.4), and therefore that language and culture were intimately connected with hominid origins. Holloway therefore argues that in the origins process, social changes are more important than technological ones: "it was not the tools themselves that were the key factor in successful evolutionary coping. Rather the associated social, behavioral, and cultural processes, directing such activities as tool-making, hunting and gathering were basic". Holloway took a structural approach to culture, an important precursor to the one I have attempted to develop here, in which he argued that we create our environment by imposing a structure on it; if this sounds familiar, it is because Bickerton's primary representational system as discussed in Chapter 4 is fundamentally the same idea. Humans, according to Holloway, generate this structure from their arbitrary symbol system. Therefore the norms for human behaviors, including those reflected in tool making, are social and arbitrary rather than innate. In this way his ideas link stone tools with Bickerton's secondary representational system, the framework for arbitrariness in human culture. If stone tools industries reflect shared secondary representational systems, according to Bickerton's model (written long after Holloway's work but quite complimentary to it) we would expect the tool maker to be a language user. This was Holloway's expectation, and was verified by his analysis of early hominid endocasts showing neural reorganization and other evidences of language ability. In Holloway's view, the process of becoming human was gradual and cannot be linked to any specific event, such as the hominid-chimpanzee split. The advantages of these mental changes were mainly organizational, helping to solve some of the social problems created by the maturational slow down that was itself a consequence of the increased learning required by neural reorganization. He was not interested in the specifics of food acquisition, being more concerned with the organizational consequences for hominid society such as sharing, planning, and communicating. Continued increasing brain size and increasing behavioral and organizational complexity follow each other through human evolution as parts of a positive feedback system, where neither is a clear cause or effect.

Hominids began their development along this line because of a combination of environmental and social complexity, according to the converging arguments that have been presented by A. Mann, J. O'Keefe, and R. Wallace. The former change, affecting several anthropoid primate species, was a consequence of successful adaptation to the developing environmental mosaics of Miocene eastern Africa (see below), and the latter mainly characterized the hominids because of their sexual division of foraging behaviors, the complexities of raising multiple children with overlapping periods of dependency, and the increasing importance of kinship relations. Complex environmental mapping came to incorporate social mapping as well, according to this model, and ultimately resulted in shared social maps encompassing kin and other special relations and providing a position for self in the social context. Shared representational systems, according to Bickerton (see Chapter 4), are the foundation of human language.

The Third Ape

Hominids are what many have called Darwin's third ape (J. Diamond reviews the history of this idea). Even a glance at the present distribution of apes across Africa shows that the early hominid sites fill in unoccupied regions and create, together, a total anthropithecine range which even exceeds that of terrestrial monkey species. An understanding of how this third ape originated will always be limited by the nature of the data we can hope to obtain. Perhaps as importantly, the boundaries for this understanding are dictated by how we approach it. Two important points about hominid origins were raised in this chapter.

First, if we are to model the process of hominid origins from our knowledge of evolution theory, as Tooby and DeVore contend, the model must be a conceptual one - sets of concepts and variables whose interrelationships are specified by potentially falsifiable theories. Second, the use of any referential models in elucidating this process is very questionable, except insofar as they help develop a conceptual one. This is mainly because the prehominids and early hominids were so unlike any living species that we cannot assume the present necessarily gives us insight into the past - a point made in several essays written over the past decade by L. Binford. Over and over again in the discussions above, both referential models that have been used in developing ideas about hominid origins, the chimpanzee and hunter-gatherer ones, have been insightful for some details but proven inadequate in the focus on causation. This doesn't mean that all referential modeling is wrong, because quite to the contrary much of our insight about the extinct hominids must come this way, but many of the expectations developed from comparisons with the living are contradictory and it is clear that they cannot all be right. The earliest hominids, and their immediate ancestors, are unlike any living species. It follows that a significant source of information about hominid origins must come from the remains of the hominids themselves. We cannot deny the weight of past theory, in particular the Darwinian one, on our expectations, but more than 100 years later Darwin may not be the best place to start. If nothing else, perhaps this will put a long-awaited end to the precept that "humans evolved from the apes."

MIOCENE MIDGET MODEL

What follows is, I believe, is an internally consistent melding of the evidence from the fossil record, comparative primate studies, and the better established contentions of socioecology, as I understand them at the moment. It is a narrative based on a model of hominid origins that is testable in two ways: through the hypotheses relating form and function, and through the predictions about the skeletal anatomy of as yet unknown Late Miocene hominids and their ancestors.

The Late Miocene prehominids were small primates living across a range of habitats not unlike that of living chimpanzees, although at the dry extreme perhaps extending into more open country than chimpanzees inhabit today. The earliest unambiguous association of hominids with open grasslands is at the Pliocene Tanzanian site of Laetoli, some 3.7-3.5 myr and long after the time of hominid origins. I have always been struck by an observation of the late Bill Bishop, that while the primate-bearing sites of the East African Miocene and Pliocene may not have appeared exactly as they do in the present, it would be possible standing at these sites today to have a habitat that closely resembled the ancient one within the field of vision. I also remember Bishop for composing and singing, in his deep baritone voice, a song at an international meeting to try and reconcile some of the antagonistic paleoanthropologists presenting their ideas - a far more daunting task than any attempted here. One of Bishop's contentions was that early hominids adapted to **ecotones** (boundaries between ecological zones, in this case between forest and grassland parches) more than to either the forest or the grasslands themselves. This has been a seductive hypothesis and is widely accepted, but may be flawed by the fact that because the fossilization process usual involves burial, fossils are often found at or near water and in East Africa sources of water are usually surrounded by trees in an often otherwise direr, treeless environment. Knowing where the animals die does not always reflect where the populations lived.

Late Miocene postcranial remains of the prehominids are unknown, but Middle Miocene sites such as Maboko suggest a very small body size - 23 to 30 kg. Focusing on a later sample, from the Pliocene, the earliest known hominid postcranial remains suggest a smaller body size average than living chimpanzees (table 5.2).

The evidence of comparative anatomy available to us strongly suggests that our ancestors passed through an arboreal stage, but the Miocene and Pliocene remains indicate it may have been characterized by no more than a climbing adaptation. This follows suggestions by J. Fleagle et al, J. Prost, and B. Senut (see Chapter 4), who find many preadaptations for bipedalism to be a consequence of an adaptation for climbing. Unlike them, however, I suggest that there were no specific morphological patterns that reflect special suspensory postures or activities. Arm hanging and brachiation, and even adaptations to the cautious quadrumanous branch climbing of orangutans, were never as well developed in these prehominids as in modern large bodied apes. Although this contention demands the interpretation that the arboreal below-branch behaviors and terrestrial knuckle-walking of the African apes are homoplasies, it is possible that there is a common basis for this, tied to their larger size. Anthropithecines the size of chimpanzees or larger may be restricted to below-branch adaptations while at a smaller size above-branch bipedalism is effective, as it is in gibbons (but this is the *only* aspect of the behavioral reconstruction I propose that could be called "Hylobatean"). For small species who could adapt either above or below the branches, the advantages of more highly desirable food resources that can be reached by a frugivore with a below-branch adaptation may be countered by the disadvantages of the inefficient terrestrial locomotion that this arboreal adaptation seems to require - knuckle-walking (table 4.1).

Arboreal bipedalism in a small anthropithecine has its own different set of advantages and disadvantages. It does not necessarily preclude brachiation; in fact, many theorists assume both above and below branch adaptations characterized the prehominids. However, I regard it as an alternative to the below-branch adaptations of the larger living apes, emphasizing vertical climbing and standing on branches to reach food that is most effective at a small body size. Small apes can use thinner supports and their arms can be more effectively used in balance when trunk is vertical, while in larger species the increased body mass makes this adaptation more difficult.

Table 5.2
Body Weights (kg) for Chimpanzees and Estimates for early Australopithecines
Modified after McHenry (1992), Jungers and Susman (1984), Uehara and Nisada (1987)

	Female Mean	Male Mean	Species Middle-Sex Average	Weight Dimorphism (M/F)
Australopithecus afarensis[1]	26.0[2]	44.6	35.3	1.7
Australopithecus africanus[1]	30.2	41.3[4]	35.8	1.4
Pan troglodytes[3]	36.5	47.9	42.2	1.3

[1] Estimated from the hindlimbs only, and whenever possible from articular surfaces, using a bipedal human regression model as is also preferred by McHenry.
[2] Includes the 3 Hadar females McHenry used for his estimate of 29.3 kg, and the diminutive ER 16002 femur
[3] Varies by population: female/male for a Mahale group is 35.2/42, Eastern Zaire 34.3/42.8, Gombe 29.8/39.5
[4] Includes MLD 46

The idea that hominids may have evolved from a small vertical climber and above-branch biped is hardly my discovery. Elements of the model can be traced throughout this century to Morton, Washburn, and Tuttle, and was most recently expressed by McHenry. Perhaps the most detailed proposal was made by T. Harrison on the basis of his studies of the *Oreopithecus* postcranial skeleton. He argues that the postcranial anatomy of this chimpanzee-sized hominoid reflects the ancestral condition for large hominoids (not that it is ancestral), with a pelvic anatomy adapted for vertical climbing. According to Harrison, the last common ancestor of humans and chimpanzees shard this anatomy, an exaptation for obligate bipedalism that implied this species was more capable of effective bipedalism than any living African ape. The basis for the argument is flawed, however, by the fact that it is the proconsul postcranial anatomy that is thought to be primitive in the hominoids, mainly because it is ubiquitous throughout the African Miocene species. Never the less, this is a reasonable prediction for the anthropithecines.

My proposal is somewhat different because it does not include the interpretation of significant below-branch behaviors in anthropithecine ancestry. This is one of the possible implication of B. Benefit and M. McCrossin's observation that no Miocene ape has the shoulder and upper arm morphology of modern apes (to the contrary, as C. Ward points out the *Sivapithecus* humeri are quite monkey-like in their shaft curvature and orientation). Like Tuttle, I accept the implication that hominids, because of their small size and the small or even smaller size that can be inferred for their prehominid ancestors, may have been arboreal bipeds and never have passed through a knuckle-walking stage. Also like Tuttle, I accept the implication that the phylogenetic split between hominids and chimpanzees may predate the obligate bipedalism by which hominids can be recognized in the fossil record - we just may never know. Unlike Tuttle, however, I find the paleoecological data and the implications of ape behavior to also suggest that there never was a purely or uniquely arboreal stage for the later Miocene anthropithecines. This means a reconstruction of locomotor abilities must include both their arboreal and terrestrial facets, and it seems clear that a form of knuckle- or fist-walking is required by the adaptations to below-branch behaviors in the large bodied apes (c.f. Tuttle). In this context I accept the implications of the absence of any knuckle-walking adaptations in the arm or hand remains of the earliest hominids to mean that before the differentiation of hominids and chimpanzees, the ancestral species was small, adapted to the vertical climbing and above-branch bipedalism that their diminutive size allowed (c.f. McHenry), and therefore *were not particularly adapted to brachiation or arm hanging*. Thus while Tuttle reconstructed the Miocene prehominid as large, chimpanzee sized or even bigger, the best evidence available now indicates that to the contrary, the Late Miocene prehominids were midgets among the African apes.

C. Ward argues that the pattern of African hominoid evolution may be based on differing specializations from a plesiomorphic anthropithecine Like Harrison she believes many of the ancestral postcranial traits resemble *Oreopithecus*, including a broad torso and pelvis that were moderately shortened relative to the *Proconsul* condition, and a long lumbar segment of the spine. She posits that the drastically shortened torso and lumbar segment (as well as certain hand and foot proportions) of the African apes, orangutans, and some New World monkeys are homoplasies that evolved to meet the requirements of their arboreal activities. As detailed earlier in this chapter, the strongest support for the absence of brachiating or significant arm-handing in these Miocene midgets is the combination of 6 number of lumbar vertebrae in the australopithecines and the complete absence of any brachiating specializations in the early australopithecine hand remains, at a time before the hand specializations for tool-making appeared (these might have hidden or eliminated evidence of earlier adaptations to hanging - for instance, the diagonal finger hook grip - or brachiating had there been any). Perversely, the Miocene hominoid best fitting this description is *Oreopithecus*, an enigmatic form related to the proconsuls and not the anthropithecines.

This contention would interpret the complex of below-branch behaviors and knuckle-walking in the chimpanzee and gorilla lineages as analogous adaptations of similar species to the same phenomenon; mainly, size increase. Similar adaptations in closely related species to a common cause is the best explanation for detailed homoplasies. I hypothesize that the underlying basis for gorilla differentiation was size, almost certainly reflecting a shift to terrestrial folivory. The subsequent differentiation between chimpanzees and hominids might have been size based as well, but both these species are much more eclectic eaters and is certainly possible that diet played a less important role. Hominid origins are also chimpanzee origins, and our constant search for understanding why the hominids originated may reveal a blind spot, as we focus on our own ancestors as the "new and different" ones.

The implications of this reconstruction are several.

- Hominids did not go through a pre-divergence stage in which significant arm-hanging and brachiation were part of their arboreal repertoire. This is almost certainly because the prehominids were so small.
- Chimpanzees developed their below-branch (and therefore knuckle-walking) adaptations after the split with hominids. Only the smallest of the Late Miocene anthropithecines would be potential last common ancestors.
- A mix of arboreal and terrestrial activities characterized the prehominids. Hominids did not simply change from an arboreal to a terrestrial species at the beginning of their unique evolutionary pathway.
- Prechimpanzees, by implication, did go through an arboreal bipedalism stage, and to this degree A. Kortlandt has been correct in his suggestions that chimpanzees were once much more like hominids
- Hominids changed from a mixed arboreal and terrestrial lifeway to a uniquely terrestrial one, because of the restrictions to arboreal behaviors that were a byproduct of the anatomical adaptations to obligate bipedalism; most importantly, the loss of grasping feet.
- Obligate bipedalism evolved from vertical climbing and arboreal bipedalism. The question is not why the hominids stood up, but rather why bipedalism became so important to them that they couldn't do anything else.

This focus on the origins of hominid bipedalism reflects the data base, and the realization that both Darwin's and Jolly's origins theories are wrong. The four unique hominid features that Darwin explained in his origins model did not evolve together as a package, while the anatomy reflecting a small object feeding adaptation that Jolly once posited as responsible for hominid origins is now known to characterize most of the Miocene African pongids. Moreover, there are a number of other unique hominid characteristics that an origins model might account for, although many of these are behavioral and therefore cannot be addressed with evidence from the fossil record.

The Changing East African Habitats

It seems likely that there were emerging interrelated ecological adaptations associated with hominid origins in the Late Miocene. While it has become fashionable to relate major evolutionary changes to significant climatic or environmental changes (c.f. M. Pickford, E. Vrba, and others), it is difficult to find a broad climatic culprit for hominid origins and a more local evolutionary model seems appropriate. D. Malone presents data from a variety of sources that show eastern Africa evolving from a homogeneous lowland tropical rain forest at the beginning of the Miocene to a heterogeneous patchy environment mixing forest, woodlands, and open grassland by the Miocene's end. He argues that the gradual fragmentation of the lowland forest and the spread of grasslands were due to the combined effects of the East African rifting process (the tectonic movements creating the continent-long rift valley) and increasing seasonality. This disruption, he suggests, produced "a mosaic of smaller, topologically, climatically and vegetationally more heterogeneous environments." A. Hill makes a similar but even more detailed case from the very well analyzed sequence of deposits in the Tugen Hills, west of Lake Baringo in Kenya. Rather than some kind of a replacement of forest by grasslands "forcing" the hominids to develop a bipedal adaptation, it was probably the patchwork of microhabitats that created multiple opportunities for the evolving anthropithecine and cercopithecine primate faunas.

One important aspect of these changes, affecting both cercopithecoids and pongids adapting to them, is the expanded capacities for spatial mapping that are required by seasonal environmental mosaics. This capacity has been linked to an evolving system of spatial and social mapping that is surely an important aspect of the complex social behaviors that characterize all of these species.

Late Miocene Cercopithecine Evolution

It is of some interest to examine the consequences of these changes on the cercopithecoids of East Africa. With the appearance of more fragmented wooded areas and increasing dryness where the rifting process created rain shadows for Indian Ocean storms, monkeys were able to exploit the leaves in the more thinly forested, drier areas. P. Andrews and L. Aiello hypothesize that the East African cercopithecoids evolved their essentially terrestrial adaptations to these conditions. As part of this adaptation many of the species evolved the ability to utilize very difficult food sources

- the sacculated stomach of colobines, in which protozoa and bacteria break down difficult to digest cellulose
- the shear ridges (lophs) in cercopithecine molars that allowed some grasses to be eaten, and their greater toleration for secondary plant compounds that opened their ability to eat unripe fruits

Late Miocene Anthropithecine Evolution

In the frugivorous anthropithecines, one of the opportunities created by the evolving patchwork of microhabitats was realized, in a response to seasonality and the dramatic variability it imposed on the quantity and quality of foods. The ancestors of gorillas, it would appear, adapted to the changing circumstances with increased body size and an emphasis on terrestrial folivory. This minimized the effects of both patchiness and seasonality, and avoided competition with monkeys. The smaller arboreal frugivorous species continued to widen the range of food resources it utilized, increasingly making low quality foods an important part of its diet for part of the year. I would assume that there were a number of speciations, responding to these changing circumstances in different regions, but the fossil record for this time span (9-6 myr) is the poorest for any period of anthropithecine evolution. Some of the behavioral adaptations I believe developed then include:

- an increasing importance of cooperative hunting
- food sharing between adults of both sexes
- the use of tools in foraging
- an increase in social complexity and its developmental price, including:
  - a further slowdown in maturation and a delay of the time of first birth into the teens
  - the extension of more neural circuitry development until after birth, where the developing brain can respond to learning (this is marked by more brain size growth after birth)

By about 6 million years ago this smaller prehominid anthropithecine evolved two differing adaptations - probably the result of a final speciation.

One species developed a suite of new adaptations and expanded its dietary range by further broadening its arboreal feeding range, evolving much larger incisors to deal with tough-rinded fruits, and emphasizing below-branch feeding using slow quadrumanous climbing and suspensory postures to reach foods at the branch-tips. J. Fleagle and his colleagues argue that most of the morphology we associate with brachiation, a short and stiff torso combined with a long pelvis and their unique hand and limb proportions, could have evolved for this purpose. It was an important enough adaptation to restrict terrestrial locomotion to quadrupedalism in the form of the notoriously inefficient knuckle-walking - a important restriction as the differentiated and seasonal environment dictated a diverse combination of wet forest and woodlands below-branch feeding and a considerable amount of terrestrial feeding and movement between forest patches. McHenry, in his modeling of this process, suggests that larger body size may also have played a role in this locomotor restriction.

The other species also increasingly emphasized terrestrial resources, making use of two important adaptations it already possessed that guided the adaptation to this habitat - bipedalism and a powerful masticatory apparatus. This increasingly efficient locomotor adaptation opened the possibility of a more complex feeding strategy based on carrying and cooperation - a sexual division of foraging that broadened the potential resource base and thereby provided a higher quality and more consistent diet, in the face of a patchier, seasonal environment. The efficiency of bipedalism, discussed in Chapter 4, is an important aspect of this adaptation, especially with the importance of daily foraging over wide ranges. Carrying was important for both weapons such as clubs and tools such as digging sticks. Moreover, here I agree with Lovejoy's reconstruction of events. With changes in the availability, quality, and consistency of food, birth spacing decreased and females contended with an additional carrying problem - multiple dependent offspring of different ages, just at the time when obligate bipedalism made it impossible for these offspring to use their feet in helping hold on to the mother. It was just these elements, efficiency of locomotion and carrying, that selected for *obligate* bipedalism in the already bipedal hominids, and the arboreal adaptation was lost.

In the context of highly differentiated environments of East Africa, and the tendency for the hominids to extend their range as populations expanded from the increased number of births, efficient bipedal locomotion brought some of the hominid foragers into drier environments than anthropithecines had thus far adapted to. They were able to successfully compete with the low-quality food adapted cercopithecoids by concentrating on different low-quality foods, their unique adaptations based on:

- using the power of grinding between large, thick enameled teeth, rather than shearing,
- using tools such as digging sticks and rocks for smashing and grinding to obtain foods unavailable to the monkeys
- relying on cooperation and sharing to lessen dependency on any particular resource at a specific time

Was there also competition between the two small anthropithecine species? It is a reasonable supposition, certainly one I made in the first edition of this book, but the fact is that to date they have never been found together. Indeed, the alert reader will remember that one of them, the chimpanzee ancestors, is yet to be found at all!

ORIGINS MODELS

The Darwinian Details

Of the four features Darwin linked together in his origins model, only obligate bipedalism has survived the more than 100 years of new discoveries and rethinking.

Bipedalism

Reviewing the discussions above, there are a variety of explanations that have been proposed for the early origin of obligate bipedalism in the hominids. According to R. Tuttle and colleagues (and modified by this author), these can be summarized as follows:

- **Upwardly mobile hypothesis**: before terrestriality, ancestral hominids were small bodied, long legged climbers, practicing limited (if any) suspensory behavior and above-branch feeding
- **Schlepp hypothesis**: selection from terrestrial carrying of food and dependent young who couldn't cling well with their modified feet
- **Peek-a-boo hypothesis**: bipedalism arose to allow peeking over tall grasses
- **Speak softly and carry a big stick hypothesis**: bipedalism arose as part of a threat display system to reduce aggressions and mitigate violence.
- **Trench coat hypothesis**: bipedalism allowed phallic display and inspection of provisions for the attraction of choosy females
- **Two feet are better than four hypothesis**: bipedalism resulted in energetically efficient walking and running, especially compared with the inefficient knuckle-walking imposed on the other pongids.

What is most interesting is the fact that these hypotheses are not particularly contradictory. Most elements of them could be correct. I find the reconstruction of a very small arboreal climbing biped as the ancestral condition to be most convincing. The hypothesis I have suggested is most like the upwardly mobility hypothesis, mainly differing for three reasons:

1. it recognizes the implications of the chimpanzee/human sister grouping in reconstructing the order of adaptive changes
2. it is cognizant of the newer data showing the very diminutive sizes of the earliest hominids
3. it incorporates the biomechanical analyses showing that most pongid skeletal adaptations thought to reflect brachiation and arm hanging may be a consequence of vertical climbing and quadrumanous motion through the trees

As discussed above, the **Miocene midget hypothesis** is based on the contention of a continuing anthropithecine adaptation to the evolving East African environmental mosaic. It accounts for both the comparative anatomy of the living African apes, the homoplasies in chimpanzee and gorilla locomotor adaptations, by the independent but necessarily similar consequences of larger size. The details of the earliest hominid locomotor and forearm anatomy may reflect the ancestral repertoire of locomotor behaviors, climbing and arboreal bipedalism, and it is the evolution of bipedalism as an *obligate* locomotion that can be tied to the hominid terrestrial adaptation. It will require Late Miocene postcranial remains to test the validity of this model.

Tool use

Tool use almost certainly predates the hominids, while stone tool manufacture and use is only known from the latter half or less of our time on Earth. Canine reduction is a complex issue; like tools there are both pre and post origins aspects to it. Some changes are probably tied to bipedalism and tool use. Simple tools that could be picked up and used came to replace canines in their various functions in displays and defense. In addition, breaking a pebble would produce a cutting edge for food preparation, animal skinning and dismemberment, and fighting, and the pebble (unlike canines) could be replaced. Minimal modification of pebbles surely preceded even the simplest recognizable stone tools.

Canine reduction

Greenfield's dual selection model suggests that with a decreasing role for large male canines, they would become disadvantageous for a variety of reasons (see Chapter 4). A shift in the balance of selection resulted from the advantages for both sexes of having smaller, incisor-like canines. With canines no longer needed for cutting and slashing, they are in an excellent position for gripping, holding, and pulling. Human canines are used for these purposes today, a function that became possible when they were incorporated into the incisor row, bringing the advantage of their larger curved roots; the size of incisor roots are limited by the space available between the palate and the nose, whereas the canine roots can continue along the side of the nose. Furthermore a curved root makes canines less likely to be lost during life than incisors, which have straight tapering roots.
As discussed in Chapter 6, the earliest hominid canines are reduced in size and feminized in form, in comparison with chimpanzees. However, even in Pliocene australopithecines, with their long history of obligate bipedalism, the canines show considerable functional variation; individuals at one extreme producing honing (sharpening) wear on the back of the canine by using them to cut, while at the other extreme the canines wear flat as they occlude with the other teeth in the thoroughly modern fashion. Later changes in hominid canines could not be a direct consequence of the bipedal adaptation. The final series of changes may be related to the appearance of stone tools at the end of the Pliocene.

Brain size

Finally there is the issue of increasing brain size. No evidence suggests that the earliest hominids had larger brains than other anthropithecines of their body size, although this mainly reflects the absence of evidence. However the question of brain structure, or organization, in the earliest hominids has proven to be a more divisive issue, to be detailed in Chapter 6. Many scientists have interpreted the very fragmentary endocasts of the earliest hominids to show some of the elements of neural reorganization, discussed in Chapter 4. The interrelated questions of language and culture are discussed below.

Hunting and gathering

Like Bartholomew and Birdsell, and later Mann, I just do not believe that hunting is an important issue. Animal protein was probably part of a wide range of foods the early hominids included in their diet over the course of a year, and some of it no doubt was obtained by hunting. However, this was not hunting with the social baggage evoked in the hominid origins models. The pattern of *hominid* hunting is for it to be an all-male activity, and part of a social system emphasizing reciprocal food sharing and long term bonding. There is no real evidence for these activities until much later. In fact, it is possible that the hominid pattern hunting and gathering is first associated with the Early Pleistocene origins of *Homo sapiens*, long after hominid origins. Nor do I believe that scavenging was a significant possibility until stone tools provided the ability to flesh and dismember carcasses and extract marrow, and this was so long after hominid origins that scavenging cannot have played a significant role.
Hunting/gathering, or scavenging/gathering are probably not accurate descriptions of early hominid foraging. I would suggest that "gathering/sharing" or "cooperative foraging" might better describe the early hominid strategy. Most of the recently proposed gathering models are surely correct in their

emphasis on this foraging strategy, but it is quite unlikely that there was a sexual division of food acquiring behaviors, as one would expect from the female involvement in raising multiple dependent offspring for the bulk of her adult life, but as part of an adaptation in which males and females fed themselves independently. Albeit in the absence of direct evidence, I believe that the alternative strategy of cooperation and sharing is to have been expected in these early hominids, and was probably an important part of their adaptation to the fragmented and dispersed seasonal food sources of the Late Miocene. This is a simple proposition to test. If there were separate male and female foraging strategies, without sharing, we can assume that there were some differences between male and female diets since the whole basis for the gatherer theories lies in sex-differences in mobility and technology. Dietary differences imply some differences in the rate and pattern of tooth wear, and here there is direct evidence for the absence of sex differences in the early hominids. While this does not prove that foods were shared, reciprocally or otherwise, it is important evidence against positing separate, different feeding strategies - a critical element in some of the gathering models discussed.

As to what was foraged, there are two types of answers. First, and probably most important, the advantage brought by the complexities and skills, tool using and otherwise, of both chimpanzees and hominids assures that the broadest possible range of food resources were used. In the hominids, the large thick enameled molars and powerful jaws provided the opportunity to extend this range to include foods that were difficult to masticate, or which took long periods to masticate effectively because of their low quality. This became an important part of their ability to expand their habitat into extremely dry areas.

C. Jolly developed his "seed-eaters" model to explain hominid origins. At this it failed, as the adaptations he isolated are now recognized to be the ancestral condition for the anthropithecines, and are common to many of the Miocene pongids. However Jolly's work, in concert with that of C. Peters and others, provides important insights for understanding the dietary advantages in seasonally utilizing grasslands resources for primates with the masticatory adaptations of the early hominids. These adaptations allowed them to extend their ranges into habitats where the resources are largely grasses and seeds. In reconstructing this habitat, he argues that most contemporary grasslands are wetter and have more resources on them. This is because modern grasslands are the artifacts of human agriculture, resulting in the clearing of large areas. Grasslands which might be expected to occur before human intervention are found today under extremely dry conditions, or where poor drainage causes periodic flooding, inhibiting the growth of trees and shrubs. In such areas there is a rich food supply in grasses and broad-leafed plants, as well as in roots and tubers. These habitats provide a concentration of high-energy yielding food resources for early hominids, able to take advantage of them through adaptations to the specific requirements of food collection and preparation, as well as defend themselves in treeless conditions.

The cereal grains, roots, tubers, and bean pods must be collected, and then prepared for digestion by being ground down into digestible particles. In modern people, this preparation is technological and takes place outside of the mouth. For the early hominids the preparation of cereal grains and other tough or low quality foods was oral. What these food sources require in common is the ability to apply powerful forces in chewing, and the ability to resist or slow down rapid tooth wear—in other words big jaws and teeth. Hominid postcanine tooth size, and possibly body size as well, expanded through the Late Miocene and Pliocene.

Life History, Language, and Culture

Certain life history changes in the hominids required social solutions. The change that came with pelvic alterations for bipedalism, from easy, solitary births to a more laborious process in which the mother was helpless, created the need for social birthing. Hominids were unique in combining the further maturational slowdowns required by learning increasingly complex information, with more offspring (from shorter birth spacing), so population sizes could persist and even expand without an extension of the total life span. The problem this combination raised was orphaning for many of the later born young, and I have suggested that the response to this was a kinship system, within which there was a very important role for lateral kin. The extension of kinship laterally to include parents' sibs, the relatives with the maximum potential for raising orphaned or partially orphaned children, requires cultural definitions. A kinship *system* involves reciprocal role relations and expectations that are culturally defined. In fact, they are examples of a unique aspect of culture, as kinship systems incorporate culturally defined and delimited role expectations for functions and relationships originally of biological origin. These expectations form equivalence structures (Chapter 4) that are simple and basic shared secondary representational systems. I contend, then, that even the least complex kinship systems are linked to a simple but never the less human form of language, and reflect the ability to form equivalence structures, an essential aspect of human culture.

The only direct evidence that addresses this speculation is to be found in the changes in the external form of the human brain that took place during this period. These have been found to lie more in the reflections of the brain's reorganization than in its size. As discussed in the next chapter, Pliocene hominid endocasts show marked structural differences from living pongids. The key to what took place probably lies in the amount of information that must be learned by the young. With increasing social complexity appearing and the importance of shared expectations and norms in guiding relationships, evolution would favor the ability to form more complex equivalence structures and improving the rate and accuracy with which they were learned. Thus brain changes in these hominoids probably reflect the development of more complicated neural models and increased connectivity between association and ordering areas in the brain.

Summary

A full understanding of why hominids originated is as much a problem today as it was in Darwin's time, but for quite different reasons. Darwin developed his very influential model in the virtual absence of evidence, while today far too much is known for a single comprehensive interpretation, given the limitations of the fossil record. The anatomy of Late Miocene prehominids and the earliest hominids converge on a reconstruction of the prehominids at the time of the chimpanzee-hominid split (there is no chimpanzee fossil record to help with this). The last common ancestor was a diminutive primate, with a mean body weight less than bonobos and chimpanzees. The dentocranial features include large jaws and postcanine teeth, with thick enamel, but small incisors (at least compared to *Pan*). The postcranial remains suggest that the prehominids were vertical climbers, quadrumanous above-branch feeders, and arboreal bipeds. Behaviorally their social life was complex and their subsistence technology may have included using manufactured tools in foraging - two ongoing behavioral developments that require a prolongation in the maturation process for additional learning.

Darwin's theorizing about hominid origins, in the last century, focused on the descent from the trees; we would say, today, the appearance of obligate terrestrial bipedalism and the associated loss of any specific climbing adaptations. He argued that hominids evolved to become terrestrial hunters, bipedalism freed the hands to manipulate and carry tool and weapons, the tools replaced canines which therefore reduced, and increased intelligence underlay these complex behavioral changes and communication assured they would be accurately passed from generation to generation.

In this century three groups of origins models developed from the Darwinian one. The **Killer-Ape** models focused on the combination of changes Darwin discussed, and emphasized the roles of male cooperation and the effects of males provisioning the more dependent child-rearing females. Some, although not all, of these models became "sex for meat" oriented but all were preeminently male-biased in respect to which sex most or all of the humanizing changes applied to. The **Savanna Chimpanzee** models are oriented around the proposition that hominids arose when a species similar to chimpanzees, or with chimpanzee-like abilities, adapted to dry open grasslands. Some of these models continue to emphasis the importance of hunting, others "baboonize" hominid origins by positing a baboon-like adaptation. Chimpanzee studies are used in two different ways in developing models in this group. Some emphasize the similarities between chimpanzees and humans in reconstructing the last common ancestor, while others emphasize the differences in trying to understand why hominids became a separate, more successful lineage. Two of the latter are Isaac's, assuming the early hominids are like San and differed from other primates because of their sharing of hunted and gathered foods at home bases, and Lovejoy's, based on the appearance of male parenting and their provisioning of females and dependent (related) young. The **Gathering** models emphasize the importance of foraging a broad range of seasonally abundant food sources, and the importance of technology in extracting and carrying the foods. Many, although not all, of these assume separate sex feeding strategies with little or no male provisioning of females and young. Others are more similar to Isaac's ideas, emphasizing reciprocal sharing.

The hominid origins narrative I present draws from many of these theories, and attempts reconciliation with the fossil record. I model the process as both hominid and chimpanzee origins, suggesting that the increasing fragmentation and seasonality of Miocene habitats forced a series of responses in the surviving African anthropithecines, terrestrial folivory and body size increase in the gorilla lineage, and later a split between the much smaller anthropithecine ancestor of chimpanzees and hominids. This species was adapted to vertical climbing and above-branch bipedalism, according to the reconstruction that best fits the anatomy of its immediate descendants. Chimpanzees developed below-branch feeding (and locomotion) adaptations to increased arboreal frugivory, and an inefficient terrestrial adaptation (knuckle-walking) which, however, had the advantage of allowing some carrying, to expand their eclectic feeding habits. The hominids evolved a much more efficient terrestrial adaptation as obligate bipedalism replaced the more generalized terrestrial and arboreal bipedal behaviors, and hominids were able to expand their range and occupy drier and more opened woodland and grassland environments because of their locomotor efficiency, enhanced carrying abilities, and subsistence tool use. I posit that the feeding strategy was not unisexual, but could best be described as "cooperative foraging". With mobility maximized and carrying an obvious potential for both sexes, subsistence was based on reciprocal sharing, and Lovejoy's and Lancaster's thinking about an early appearance and great importance for male parenting is probably correct. The life history consequences of these changes are more, better surviving children spaced closer together, longer maturation times for the children, but no substantial increase in life span. This insures an increase in orphaning and with the emphasis on learning I believe that in response kinship systems appeared that required elementary cultural behaviors and language, as described in the last chapter.

ANATOMY OF A CONTROVERSY

Women and Hominid Origins - The Bias of Fossil 'Man'

In 1966 R. Lee and I. DeVore organized a symposium entitled "Man the Hunter", with papers subsequently published as a book with that title in 1968. While the phrase "hunters and gatherers" appears in their introduction to the volume, the emphasis is best expressed by the title. Human evolution is seen as a positive feedback loop linking cultural and biological developments, the major cultural developments associated with hominid origins and evolution are oriented around hunting, and it is after all *Man* who is the hunter. The hypotheses focused on hominid origins and early evolution can be easily seen to reflect this bias. Men hunted. Men made and used tools for the hunt, providing selection for increased skill and intelligence. Men formed associations for cooperative hunting, thereby creating the basis for society. Men shared the spoils of the hunt with women, provisioning them. As for the role envisioned for women, as A. Zihlman put it "home bases seemed to be invoked as places for early hominid women to stay home. While there, they were loosing estrus in order to be continually sexually receptive."

This symposium was hardly the only example, male bias was all prevailing. Just consider the titles for some of the popular books from this time period dealing with these issues: *The Naked Ape, Men in Groups, The Territorial Imperative, The Imperial Animal.* Nor did the 1960's-1970's present the last examples. In the next decade D. Falk, in a review of brain evolution, pointed out that virtually all "prime mover" theories for hominid brain size increase usually biased in favor of males. Tooby and DeVore resurrected "Man the Hunter" in an almost original form. Lovejoy's 'Origin of Man' hypothesis (see pp. xx-xx) was widely regarded as male-biased (but not, I would expect, in comparison to Parker's theorizing about the role of male provisioning and its consequences). This case is less clear as the evolutionary focus is not uniquely on males, as Lovejoy's thinking was based on the importance of gathering (in contrast to hunting) *and* sharing in hominid origins; he envisaged complimentary interrelated roles for both sexes, and proposed that the humanization process affected each individually and as an bonded pair. While neither the title nor some of the language in this very influential essay was helpful, with regard to the question of bias, perhaps the most telling point is the very similar model of early hominid female reproductive strategy developed by J. Lancaster, a self-proclaimed feminist. Lancaster argues that from its very beginnings, during the process of human evolution women are uniquely confronted with:

- a high commitment to rearing multiple nutritionally dependent young of differing ages
- a tradeoff between the conflicting demands of production and reproduction
- a bargain often struck with males for assistance in rearing young in exchange for confidence in paternity

Although there were early reactions to *Man the Hunter,* for instance in a 1971 paper entitled "Woman the Gatherer" by S. Linton, it was mainly the students of the next generation, educated in this ethos, who began responding to sex bias as professional scientists. In the decade of the 1980's, no less than 3 influential papers in the *Yearbook of Physical Anthropology* and one in *Annual Review of Anthropology,* addressed the question of sex bias in theories and studies of human evolution. It is not coincidental that all were written by women.

These papers took several lines of attack. The first, and perhaps most important, was to point out that the problem is there. Zihlman was particularly effective at this, reviewing male-authored literature that *ignored* a "Women the Gatherer" role (for instance the Carrier study of hominid adaptations to running, discussed in Chapter 4), *dismissed* it with the assertion that one theory is as good as any other (such as in Cartmill's essay on the origins of bipedalism), or *co-opted* it in food sharing hypotheses such as Lovejoy's where, she contends, males are said to gather and therefore co-opted the gathering role of females. The second was to focus on a critical role for women in hominid origins, with the development of an alternative to "Man the Hunter". This first began with Linton's "Woman the Gatherer" (finally to culminate in a book of this title edited by F. Dahlberg). This theory is based on a chimpanzee referent; Zihlman, after all, is part of the group that created the pygmy chimpanzee model discussed on pp. xx-xx. Ironically, as L. Fedigan points out, the same symposium that so strongly established the "Man the Hunter" model also became the source of its alternatives. For instance, in his paper R. Lee argues that plant and marine resources are far more important than game animals, and J. Deetz expressed similar cautions. Several other implicitly female-oriented models of hominid origins emerged from this debate.

In her "Woman the Gatherer" model, Zihlman argues that the basic unique hominid adaptation is to obtain plant foods with tools. In her theory, bipedal locomotion and the invention of devices for carrying allowed women carrying babies to walk to distant food sources, and then carry the collected foods back to a safe eating place. Children had to be carried because the bipedal adaptation altered foot morphology so it could no longer be used for climbing, or in the case of children for clinging to the mother. Children, and in some versions of this model also men, are thereby provisioned. The model, as K. Gibson points out, links together the Darwinian features (bipedalism, tool use, canine reduction, brain expansion) in a female-oriented alternative to "Man the Hunter".

Another influential female-oriented model was presented by S. Hrdy. She sketches the evolution of women in an active, assertive, dominance-seeking context based on her analysis of female roles in non-human primates. She envisions the driving force of women's evolution as competition with other women, and denies the reality of the way women are sketched by other models of human evolution - the unaggressive image, bonded with other women, that Hrdy claims cannot be found among other primates and therefore cannot be validly hypothesized in human evolution.

The basic points raised by feminists such as Zihlman; mainly, that male and female researchers have tended to offer very different models of hominid origins, was once indisputably correct. This is no longer the case. For instance Tooby and DeVore, who have been justifiably criticized for male bias in their review of referential and conceptual modeling in reconstructing hominid behavioral evolution (especially as they resurrect the "Man the Hunter" model), have succinctly and accurately summarized the importance of an emphasis on gathering plant foods with tools and collecting them in containers in an accurate reconstruction of hominid origins. They admit that the "Woman the Gatherer" model provides an alternative pathway for understanding the positive feedback between technology and bipedalism, while at the same time bringing under scrutiny the theory that dietary change is a prime determinant in hominid evolution. Boesch and Boesch use the chimpanzee referent to undermine several aspects of male oriented hominid origins models. They point out that tool use in the forest adapted chimpanzees is predominantly a female activity. Moreover, tools are but rarely used in meat procurement, never as weapons although occasionally in marrow extraction. As Stanford and Allen observe, the combination of these facts is "clearly at odds with male-centered models of human social evolution". In fact, if the chimpanzee is a valid model for reconstructing the social behavior of prehominids (a contention examined at length in this chapter), data such as these dislink the three elements whose association is at the base of the male-centered hunting model for hominid origins -- the appearance of

1. a hunting (in contrast to a scavenging) focus for procuring meat
2. male cooperation during hunting
3. the use of tools and/or natural objects to aid in hunting

If these three cannot be combined as part of a hunting adaptation at the time of hominid origins, the use of hunting to account for the Darwinian features is no longer valid.

The modeling of human origins and evolution could never attain realism or accuracy without this debate and the deeper realizations it has brought. Yet, it would be a mistake to simply consider the fact that there is a controversy to reflect the resistance of male ignorance to female enlightenment. The strong reaction of Zihlman to Lovejoy's writing, for instance, must be seen in the context of their earlier engagement over the mechanisms and evolution of hominid bipedalism, as exemplified at the 1974 Wenner-Gren conference on "Early Hominids in Africa" and in the subsequent volume that C. Jolly edited from it. Moreover, it would be wrong to conclude that all origins theories tainted by sex-bias were developed by men. Women have played their part in creating this problem, and as we have seen all sex-biased theories developed by women are not female-biased. Feminism remains an important social issue and exists far beyond the boundaries of paleoanthropology. At times this means it generates more heat than light, as changes in attitudes and approaches within the paleoanthropological community are ignored in the broader context of male-bias in the sciences and society. Lancaster's complaints about the persuasiveness of the phrase "fossil man" in human studies, a point well taken, were made years after the first edition of this book which never once used it, and it is unreasonable to act as if the female perspective and the fact that women have always held up half the world has not yet been recognized by paleoanthropologists of both sexes.

Paleoanthropology is not the only discipline in which women have been fighting an uphill battle for recognition and equality, but it is unusual in that the battle concerns the importance of women in the topics studied *as well as* among those who conduct the studies. Although women still lag behind men in salary, employment, and access to higher ranked positions, women's status in the sciences has been improving, according to a review by B. Vetter, just as the importance of women in human evolution was "discovered" and has become an object of legitimate focus in paleoanthropology. Since it is largely women paleoanthropologists attaining positions of importance and respect who have compelled our discipline to make this change in perspective and focus, the two aspects of the uphill battle are linked. Science is not the purely objective recounting of reality we learned about in high school, but is an integral part of our social milieu. As L. Fedigan puts it, if we cannot free ourselves of our subjectivity, we must try and make sense of it.

REFERENCES AND FURTHER READINGS

ALEXANDER, R.D. 1990 Epigenetic rules and Darwinian algorithms: the adaptive study of learning and development. *Ethology and Sociobiology* 11:241-303.

ANDREWS, P., and L. AIELLO 1984 An evolutionary model for feeding and positional behavior. In D.J. Chivers, B. Wood, and A. Bilsborough (eds): *Food Acquisition and Processing in Primates.* Plenum, New York.

ARDREY, R. 1961 *African Genesis.* Dell, New York.

BAKER P.T. 1960 Climate, culture, and evolution. *Human Biology* 32:3-16.

BARTHOLOMEW, G. A., and J. B. BIRDSELL. 1953 Ecology and the protohominids. *American Anthropologist* 55:481-498.

BEACH, F.A. 1978 Human sexuality and Evolution. In S.L. Washburn and E.R. McCown (eds): *Human Evolution: Biosocial Perspectives.* Benjamin Cummings, Menlo Park. pp. 123-153.

BERTHELET, A., and J. CHAVAILLON (editors) 1993 *The Use of Tools by Human and Non-Human Primates.* Clarendon, Oxford.

BINFORD, L.R. 1987 The hunting hypothesis, archaeological methods, and the past. *Yearbook of Physical Anthropology* 30:1-9.

BISHOP, W.W. 1976 Pliocene problems relating to human evolution. In G.Ll. Isaac and E.R. McCown (eds): *Human Origins: Louis Leakey and the East African Evidence.* W.A. Benjamin, Menlo Park. pp. 139-153.

BLUMENSCHINE, R.J. 1991 Breakfast at Olorgesailie: the natural history approach to early stone age archaeology. *Journal of Human Evolution* 21(4):307-327.

BLUMENSCHINE, R.J., and J.A. CAVALLO 1992 Scavenging and human evolution. *Scientific American* 267(4):90-96.

BOAZ, N.T. 1994 Significance of the Western Rift for hominid evolution. In R.S. Corruccini and R.L. Ciochon (eds): *Integrative Paths to the Past. Paleoanthropological Advances in Honor of F. Clark Howell.* Prentice Hall, Englewood Cliffs. pp. 321-343.

BOESCH, C. and H. BOESCH 1983 Optimization of nut-cracking with natural hammers by wild chimpanzees. *Behaviour* 83:265-286.

___. 1984a Possible causes of sex difference in the use of natural hammers by wild chimpanzees. *Journal of Human Evolution* 13:415-440.

___. 1984 Mental maps in wild chimpanzees: an analysis of hammer transports for nut cracking. *Primates* 25:160-170.

___. 1989 Hunting behavior of chimpanzees in the Täi National Park. *American Journal of Physical Anthropology* 78:547-573.

BRAIN, C.K. 1985 Interpreting early hominid death assemblages: the rise of taphonomy since 1925. In P.V. Tobias (ed): *Hominid Evolution: Past, Present, and Future. Proceedings of the Taung Diamond Jubilee International Symposium.* Alan R. Liss Inc., New York. Pp. 41-46.

CARO, T.M. 1987 Human breasts: unsupported hypotheses reviewed. *Human Evolution* 2(3):271-282.

CARTMILL, M. 1983 Four legs good, two legs bad. *Natural History* 92:64-79.

CERLING, T.E. 1992 Development of grasslands and savannas in East Africa during the Neogene. *Palaeogeology, Palaeoclimatology, and Palaeoecology* 97:241-247.

COSMIDES, L., and J. TOOBY 1987 From evolution to behavior: evolutionary psychology as the missing link. In J. Dupré (ed): *The Latest on the Best: Essays on Evolution and Optomology.* MIT Press, Cambridge. pp. 277-306.

COURSEY, D.G. 1973 Hominid evolution and hypogeous plant foods. *Man* 8:634-635.

DAHLBERG, F. (editor) 1981 *Woman the Gatherer.* Yale University Press, New Haven.

DART, R.A. 1953 The predatory transition from ape to man. *International Anthropological and Linguistic Review* 1:201-218.

DARWIN, C. 1871 *The Descent of Man and Selection in Relation to Sex.* Murray, London.

DEVORE, I., and S.L. WASHBURN 1963 Baboon ecology and human evolution. In F.C. Howell and F. Bourière (eds): *African Ecology and Human Evolution.* Aldine, New York. pp. 335-367.

DE WAAL, F. 1989 Food sharing and reciprocal obligations among chimpanzees. *Journal of Human Evolution* 18:433-459.

DIAMOND, J.M. 1991 *The Rise and Fall of the Third Chimpanzee.* Hutchinson Radius, London.

DOBZHANSKY, Th., and F.J. AYALA 1977 *Humankind. A Product of Evolutionary Transcendence.* Raymond Dart Lectures Special lecture. Institute for the Study of Man, University of the Witwatersrand Press, Johannesburg.

DUNBAR, R.I.M. 1983 Theropithecines and hominids: contrasting solutions to the same ecological problem. *Journal of Human Evolution* 12:647-658.

EATON, S.B., and M. KONNER 1985 Paleolithic nutrition: a consideration of its nature and current implications. *New England Journal of Medicine* 312:283-289.

EISELEY, L. 1961 *Darwin's Century.* Doubleday Anchor, Garden City.

FALK, D. 1980 Hominid brain evolution: the approach from paleoneurology. *Yearbook of Physical Anthropology* 23:93-107.

FEDIGAN, L.M. 1986 The changing roles of women in models of human evolution. *Annual Review of Anthropology* 15:25-66.

FISHER, H.E. 1982 *The Sex Contract.* William Morrow, New York.

FLEAGLE, J.G., STERN, J.T., JUNGERS, W.L., SUSMAN, R.L., VANGOR, A.K., and WELLS, J.P. 1981 Climbing: A biomechanical link with brachiation and with bipedalism. In M.H. Day (ed): *Vertebrate Locomotion. Symposium of the Zoological Society London* 48:359-375. Academic Press, London.

FOLEY, R.A. 1985 Optimality theory in anthropology. *Man* 20:222-242.

FOLEY, R.A. and P.C. LEE 1989 Finite social space, evolutionary pathways, and reconstructing hominid behavior. *Science* 243:901-906.

FRISCH, R.E. 1988 Fatness and fertility. *Scientific American* 258(3):88-95.

GALDIKAS, B.M.F., and G. TELEKI 1981 Variations in subsistence activities of female and male pongids: new perspectives on the origins of hominid labor division. *Current Anthropology* 22(3):241-256.

GHIGLIERI, M.P. 1987 Sociobiology of the great apes and the hominid ancestor. *Journal of Human Evolution* 16:319-357.

GOODALL, J. 1986 *The Chimpanzees of Gombe: Patterns of Behaviors.* Belknap Press, Cambridge.

GREGORY, W.K. 1949 The bearing of the *Australopithecinae* on man's place in nature. *American Journal of Physical Anthropology* 7(4):485-512.

HAECKEL, E. 1876 *The History of Creation: Or the Development of the Earth and its Inhabitants by the Action of Natural Causes.* Appleton, New York

___. 1898 On our present knowledge of the origin of man. *Annual Report of the Smithsonian Institution* pp. 461-480.

HARAWAY. D.J. 1988 Remodeling the human way of life: Sherwood Washburn and the New Physical Anthropology, 1950-1980. In G.W. Stocking Jr. (ed): *Bones, Bodies, Behavior. Essays on Biological Anthropology.* University of Wisconsin, Madison. pp. 206-259.

___. 1989 Primate Visions. Gender Race, and Nature in the World of Modern Science. Routledge, New York.

HARRISON, T. 1991 The implications of *Oreopithecus bambolii* for the origins of bipedalism. In Y. Coppens and B. Senut (eds): *Origine(s) de la Bipédie les Hominidés.* Cahiers de Paléoanthropologie, Centre National de la Recherche Scientifique, Paris. pp. 235-244.

HATLEY, T., and J. KAPPELMAN 1980 Bears, pigs, and Plio-Pleistocene hominids: a case for the exploitation of below ground food sources. *Human Ecology* 8:371-387.

DE HEINZELIN, H. 1994 Rifting, a long-term African story, with considerations on early hominid habitats. In R.S. Corruccini and R.L. Ciochon (eds): *Integrative Paths to the Past. Paleoanthropological Advances in Honor of F. Clark Howell.* Prentice Hall, Englewood Cliffs. pp. 313-320.

HIATT, B. 1970 Woman the gatherer. In F. Gale (ed): *Women's Role in Aboriginal Society. Australian Institute of Aboriginal Studies* 36:2-8.

HILL, A.H. 1987 Causes of perceived faunal change in the later Neogene of East Africa. *Journal of Human Evolution* 16(7/8):583-596.

HILL, K. 1982 Hunting and human evolution. *Journal of Human Evolution* 11:521-544.

HOLLOWAY, R.L. 1969 Culture: a human domain. *Current Anthropology* 10:395-412.

___. 1975 The role of human social behavior in the evolution of the brain. Forty-third James Arthur Lecture on the Evolution of the Human Brain. American Museum of Natural History, New York.

___. 1981 Culture, symbols, and human brain evolution: a synthesis. *Dialectical Anthropology* 5:287-303.

___. 1989 On depiction and language. *Current Anthropology* 30(3):331-332.

HOLMES, W.G., and P.W. SHERMAN 1983 Kin recognition in animals. *American Scientist* 71(1):46-55.

HOOTON, E.A. 1947 *Up From the Ape*, revised edition. MacMillan, New York.

HRDY, S.B. 1981 *The Woman than Never Evolved*. Harvard University Press, Cambridge.

___. 1990 Sex bias in nature and in history: a late 1980's reexamination of the "biological origins" argument. *Yearbook of Physical Anthropology* 33:25-37.

HUXLEY, T.H. 1863 *The Evidence as to Man's Place in Nature*. Murray, London.

ISAAC, G.Ll. 1978 The food-sharing behavior of protohuman hominids. *Scientific American* 238(4):90-108.

___. 1981 Emergence of human behaviour patterns. *Philosophical Transactions of the Royal Society, London,* Series B, 292:177-188.

___. 1983 Aspects of human evolution. In D.S. Bendall (ed): *Evolution from Molecules to Men*. Cambridge University Press, London. pp. 509-543.

___. 1984 The archaeology of hominid origins: studies of the lower Pleistocene in East Africa, 1971-1981. In F. Wendorf and A.E. Close (eds): *Advances in World Archaeology*, Volume 3. Academic Press, San Diego. pp. 1-86.

ISAAC, G.Ll. and D.C. CRADER 1981 To what extent were early hominids carnivorous? An archaeological perspective. In R.S.O. Harding and G. Teleki (eds): *Omnivorous Primates. Gathering and Hunting in Human Evolution*. Columbia University Press, New York. pp. 37-103.

JABLONSKI, N.G., and G. CHAPLIN 1993 Origin of habitual terrestrial bipedalism in the ancestor of the Hominidae. *Journal of Human Evolution* 24(4):259-280.

JOLLY, C.J 1970 The seed eaters: a new model of hominid differentiation based on a baboon analogy. *Man* 5:5-26.

___. 1973 Changing Views of Hominid Origins. *Yearbook of Physical Anthropology* 16:1-17.

JUNGERS, W.L. and R.L. SUSMAN 1984 Body size and skeletal allometry in African Apes. In R.L. Susman (ed): *The Pygmy Chimpanzee. Evolutionary Biology and Behavior*. Plenum, New York. pp. 131-177.

KEITH, A. 1923 Man's posture: Its evolution and disorders. *British Medical Journal* 1:451-454, 499-502, 545-548, 587-590, 624-626, 669-672.

KOLATA, G.B. 1974 !Kung hunter-gatherers: feminism, diet, and birth control. *Science* 185:932-934.

KORTLANDT, A. 1986 The use of stone tools by wild-living chimpanzees and earliest hominids. *Journal of Human Evolution* 15:77-132.

KORTLANDT, A., AND E. HOLZHAUS 1987 New data on the use of stone tools by chimpanzees in Guinea and Liberia. *Primates* 28:473-496.

KROEBER, A.L. 1928 Sub-human cultural beginnings. *Quarterly Review of Biology* 3:325-342.

LANCASTER, J.B. 1975 *Primate Behavior and the Emergence of Human Culture*. Holt, Rinehart, and Winston, New York.

___. 1978 Carrying and sharing in human evolution. *Human Nature* 1:83-89.

___. 1991 A feminist and evolutionary biologist looks at women. *Yearbook of Physical Anthropology* 34:1-12.

LANCASTER, J.B., and C.S. LANCASTER 1983 Parental investment: the hominid adaptation. In: D.J. Ortner (ed): *How Humans Adapt*. Smithsonian International Symposia Series, Smithsonian Institution, Washington D.C. pp. 33-65.

LATIMER, B.M 1991 Locomotor adaptations in *Australopithecus afarensis:* the issue of arboreality. In Y. Coppens and B. Senut (eds): *Origine(s) de la Bipédie les Hominidés*. Cahiers de Paléoanthropologie, Centre National de la Recherche Scientifique, Paris. pp. 169-176.

LATIMER, B.M., T.D. WHITE, W.H. KIMBEL, D.C. JOHANSON, and C.O. LOVEJOY 1981 The pygmy chimpanzee is not a living missing link in human evolution. *Journal of Human Evolution* 10:475-488.

LAUGHLIN, W.S. 1968 Hunting: an integrating biobehavioral system and its evolutionary importance. In R.B. Lee and I. DeVore (eds): *Man the Hunter*. Aldine, Chicago. pp. 304-320.

LEE, R.B. 1992 Art, science, or politics? The crisis in hunter-gatherer studies. *American Anthropologist* 94(1):31-54.

LEE, R.B., and M. GUENTHER 1991 Oxen or onions? The search for trade (and truth) in the Kalahari. *Current Anthropology* 32:593-601.

LEE, R.B., and I. DEVORE (eds) 1968 *Man the Hunter*. Aldine, Chicago.

LEWIN, R. 1989 New views emerge on hunters and gatherers. *Science* 240:1146-1148.

LEWIS, O.J. 1972 Evolution of the hominoid wrist. In R.H. Tuttle (ed): *The Functional and Evolutionary Biology of Primates*. Aldine-Atherton, Chicago. pp. 207-222.

LINTON, S. 1971 Women the gatherer; male bias in anthropology. In S-E. Jacob (ed): *Women in Cross-Cultural Perspective*. University of Illinois Press, Champaign.

LOVEJOY, C. O 1981 The origin of man. *Science* 211:341-350, 217:304-305.

___. 1993 Modeling human origins: are we sexy because we're smart, or smart because we're sexy? In D.T. Rasmussen (ed): *The Origin and Evolution of Humans and Humanness*. Jones and Bartless, Boston. pp. 1-28.

MALONE, D. 1987 Mechanisms of hominoid dispersal in Miocene East Africa. *Journal of Human Evolution* 16(6):469-481.

MANN, A. 1972. Hominid and Cultural Origins. *Man* 7:379-386.

___. 1981 Diet and human evolution. In R.S.O. Harding and G. Teleki (eds): *Omnivorous Primates. Gathering and Hunting in Human Evolution.* Columbia University Press, New York. pp. 10-36.

MARZKE, M.W., K.L. WULLSTEIN, and S.F. VIEGAS 1992 Evolution of the power ("squeeze") grip and its morphological correlates in hominids. *American Journal of Physical Anthropology* 89(3):283-298.

MCGREW, W.C. 1979 Evolutionary implications of sex differences in chimpanzee predation and tool use. In D.A. Hamburg and E.R. McCown (eds): *The Great Apes.* Benjamin/Cummings, Menlo Park. pp. 441-464.

___. 1981 The female chimpanzee as a human evolutionary prototype. In F. Dahlberg (ed): *Woman the Gatherer.* Yale University Press, New Haven. pp. 35-74.

___. 1991 Chimpanzee material culture: what are its limits and why? In R. Foley (ed): *The Origins of Human Behavior.* Unwin Hyman, London. pp. 13-24.

MCHENRY, H.M. 1991 First steps? Analysis of the postcranium of early hominids. In Y. Coppens and B. Senut (eds): *Origine(s) de la Bipédie les Hominidés.* Cahiers de Paléoanthropologie, Centre National de la Recherche Scientifique, Paris. pp. 1133-141.

___. 1992a Body size and proportions in early hominids. *American Journal of Physical Anthropology* 87(4):407-431.

___. 1992b How big were early hominids? *Evolutionary Anthropology* 1:15-20.

McKINLEY, K. 1971 Survivorship in gracile and robust australopithecines: a demographic comparison and a proposed birth model. *American Journal of Physical Anthropology* 34:417-426.

MAREAN, C.W. 1989 Sabertooth cats and their relevance or early hominid diet and evolution. *Journal of Human Evolution* 18(6):559-582.

MORRIS, D. 1967 *The Naked Ape.* Dell, New York.

MORTON, D.J. 1927 Human origin, correlation of previous studies on primate feet and posture with other morphological evidence. *American Journal of Physical Anthropology* 10:173-203.

MUSONDA, F.B. 1991 The significance of modern hunter-gatherers in the study of early hominid behaviour. In R. Foley (ed): *The Origins of Human Behavior.* Unwin Hyman, London. pp. 39-51

MYERS, F.R. 1988 Critical trends in the study of hunter-gatherers. In B.J. Siegel, A.R. Beals, and S.A. Tyler (eds). *Annual Review of Anthropology.* Annual Reviews, Palo Alto. Volume 17:261-282.

NAPIER, J.R. 1960 Studies of the hands of living primates. *Proceedings of the Zoological Society of London* 134:647-657.

O'CONNELL, J.F., K. HAWKES, and N.B. JONES 1988 Hadza scavenging: implications for Plio/Pleistocene hominid subsistence. *Current Anthropology* 29(2):356-363.

O'KEEFE, J., and L. NADEL 1978 *The Hippocampus as a Cognitive Map.* Oxford University Press, New York (and subsequent review by various authors in *The Behavioral and Brain Sciences* 2:487-533 (1979).

PARKER, S.T. 1985 Higher intelligence as an adaptation for social and technological strategies in early *Homo sapiens*. In G. Butterworth, J. Rutkowska, and M. Scaife (eds): *Evolution and Developmental Psychology*. Harvester Press, Brighton.

___. 1987 A sexual selection model for hominid evolution. *Human Evolution* 2(3):235-253.

PARKER, S.T., and K.R. GIBSON 1979 A developmental model for the evolution of language and intelligence in early hominids. *Behavioral and Brain Sciences* 2:367-407.

___. 1990 *"Language" and Intelligence in Monkeys and Apes*. Cambridge University Press, New York.

PERPER, T., and C. SCHRIRE 1977 The Nimrod Connection: Myth and Science in the Hunting Model. In M.R. Kare and O. Maller (eds): *The Chemical Senses and Nutrition*. Academic Press, New York. pp. 447-459.

PETERS, C.R. 1987 Nut-like oil seeds: foods for monkeys, chimpanzees, humans, and probably ape-men. *American Journal of Physical Anthropology* 73(3):333-363.

PETERS, C.R., and E. O'BRIEN 1984 On hominid diet before fire. *Current Anthropology* 25:358-360.

PIAGET, J. 1971 *Structuralism*. Routledge and Kegan Paul, London.

PICKFORD, M. 1991 What caused the first steps towards the evolution of walkie-talkie primates? In Y. Coppens and B. Senut (eds): *Origine(s) de la Bipédie les Hominidés*. Cahiers de Paléoanthropologie, Centre National de la Recherche Scientifique, Paris. pp. 275-293.

PILBEAM, D. 1972 An Idea We Could Do Without—The Naked Ape. *Discovery* 7(2):63-70.

POTTS, R. 1984 Home bases and early hominids. *American Scientist* 72(4):338-347.

___. 1988 Ecological context and explanations of hominid evolution. O*SSA (International Journal of Skeletal Research)* 14:99-112.

POWER, M. 1991 *The Egalitarians, Humans and Chimpanzee*. Cambridge University Press, New York.

PROST, J.H. 1980 Origin of bipedalism. *American Journal of Physical Anthropology* 52:175-189.

QUIATT, D., and J. KELSO 1985 Household economics and hominid origins. *Current Anthropology* 26(2):207-222.

RENFREW, C. 1987 An interview with Lewis Binford. *Current Anthropology* 28(5):683-694.

RICHARDS, G. 1988 *Human Evolution*. Routledge Press, London.

SCHALLER, G.B., and G. LOWTHER 1969 The relevance of carnivore behavior to the study of early hominids. *Southwestern Journal of Anthropology* 25:307-341.

SCHICK, K.D., and N. TOTH 1993 *Making Silent Stones Speak: Human Evolution and the Dawn of Technology*. Simon and Schuster, New York.

SHEETS-JOHNSTONE, M. 1989 Hominid bipedality and sexual-selection theory. *Evolutionary Theory* 9:57-70.

SHELL, E.R. 1991 Flesh and Bone. *Discover* (12/91):37-42.

SIGMON, B. 1991 Evolutionary changes in the reproductive system and mating strategies after hominids became upright bipeds. In Y. Coppens and B. Senut (eds): *Origine(s) de la Bipédie les Hominidés*. Cahiers de Paléoanthropologie, Centre` National de la Recherche Scientifique, Paris. pp. 267-273.

SOLWAY, J.S., and R.B. LEE 1990 Foragers, genuine or spurious? Situating the Kalahari San in history. *Current Anthropology* 31(2):109-146.

STANFORD, C.B., and J.S. ALLEN 1991 On strategic storytelling: current models of human behavioral evolution. *Current Anthropology* 32(1):58-61.

STANFORD, C.B., J. WALLIS, H. MATAMA, and J. GOODALL 1994 Patterns of predation by chimpanzees on red colobus monkeys in Gombe National Park, 1982-1991. *American Journal of Physical Anthropology* 94(2):213-228.

STEIN, G.J. 1988 Biological science and the roots of Nazism. *American Scientist* 76(1):50-58.

STRUM, S.C., and W. MITCHELL 1987 Baboon models and muddles. In G. Kinzey (ed): *The Evolution of Human Behavior: Primate Models*. State University of New York Press, New York. pp. 87-104.

SUSMAN, R.L. (ed) 1984 *The Pygmy Chimpanzee. Evolutionary Biology and Behavior*. Plenum, New York.

SZALAY, F.S. 1975 Hunting-scavenging protohominids: A model for hominid origins. *Man* 10:420-429.

SZALAY, F.S., and R.K. COSTELLO 1991 Evolution of permanent estrus displays in hominids. *Journal of Human Evolution* 20(6):439-464.

TANNER, N.M. 1981 *On Becoming human*. Cambridge University Press, Cambridge.

___. 1987 Gathering by females: the chimpanzee model revisited and the gathering hypothesis. In W. Kinzey (ed): *The Evolution of Human Behavior: Primate Models*. Cambridge University Press, New York. pp. 3-27.

TANNER, N.M., and A. ZIHLMAN 1976 Women in evolution. Part I: innovation and selection in human origins. *Signs: Journal of Women in Culture and Society* 1:585-608.

TELEKI, G. 1973 *The Predatory Behavior of Wild Chimpanzees*. Bucknell University Press, Cranbury.

___. 1974 Chimpanzee subsistence technology: materials and skills. *Journal of Human Evolution* 3:575-594.

THOMPSON, J.M. 1993 Cultural diversity in the behavior of *Pan*. In D. Quiatt and J. Itani (eds): *Hominid culture in Primate Perspective*. University of Colorado Press, Boulder.

THOMPSON, P.R. 1975 A cross-species analysis of carnivore, primate, and hominid behavior. *Journal of Human Evolution* 4:113-124.

___. 1976 A behavioral model for *Australopithecus africanus*. *Journal of Human Evolution* 5:547-558.

TIGER, L. and R. FOX 1971 *The Imperial Animal* Holt, Rinehart, and Winston, New York.

TOOBY, J., and I. DEVORE 1987 The reconstruction of hominid behavioral evolution through strategic modeling. In G. Kinzey (ed): *The Evolution of Human Behavior: Primate Models.* State University of New York Press, New York. pp. 183-237.

TURKE, P.W. 1984 Effects of ovulary concealment and synchrony on protohominid mating systems and parental roles. *Ethology and Sociobiology* 5:33-44.

___. 1988 Concealed ovulation, menstrual synchrony, and parental investment. In E. Fisinger (ed): *Biosocial Perspectives on the Family.* Sage, Newbury Park.

TUTTLE, R.H. 1974 Darwin's apes, dental apes, and the descent of Man: normal science in evolutionary anthropology. *Current Anthropology* 15:389-398.

___. 1975 Parallelism, brachiation, and hominid phylogeny. In W.P. Luckett and F. Szalay (eds): *Phylogeny of the Primates.* Plenum, New York. pp. 447-480.

___. 1977 Naturalistic positional behavior of apes and models of hominoid evolution, 1929-1976. In G.H. Bourne (ed): *Progress in Ape Research.* Academic Press, New York. pp. 277-296.

TUTTLE, R.H., D.M. WEBB, and N.I. TUTTLE 1991 Laetoli footprint trails and the evolution of hominid bipedalism. In Y. Coppens and B. Senut (eds): *Origine(s) de la Bipédie les Hominidés.* Cahiers de Paléoanthropologie, Centre` National de la Recherche Scientifique, Paris. pp. 187-198.

UEHARA, S., and T. NISHIDA 1987 Body weights of wild chimpanzees *Pan troglodytes* schweinfurthii of the Mahale Mountains National Park, Tanzania. *American Journal of Physical Anthropology* 72(3):315-321.

VETTER, B. 1992 Women in science - Ferment: yes, progress: maybe, change: slow. *Mosaic* 23(1):34-41.

VRBA, E.S. 1985 Environment and evolution: alternative causes of the temporal distribution of evolutionary events. *South African Journal of Science* 81:229-236.

WALLACE, R. 1989 Cognitive mapping and the origin of language and mind. *Current Anthropology* I30(4):518-526.

WASHBURN, S.L. 1950 The analysis of primate evolution with particular reference to the origin of man. *Cold Spring Harbor Symposia on Quantitative Biology* 15:67-78.

___. 1959 Speculations on the interrelationships of the history of tools and biological evolution. *Human Biology* 31:21-31.

___. 1968 *The Study of Human Evolution.* Condon Lecture, Oregon State System of Higher Education, Eugene.

WASHBURN, S.L., and V. AVIS 1958 Evolution of human behavior. In A. Roe and G.G. Simpson (eds): *Behavior and Evolution.* Yale University Press, New Haven. Pp. 421-436.

WASHBURN, S.L., and F.C. HOWELL 1960 Human evolution and culture. In S. Tax (ed): *Evolution after Darwin: The Evolution of Man.* University of Chicago Press, Chicago. pp. 33-56.

WASHBURN. S.L. and C.S. LANCASTER 1968 The evolution of hunting. In R.B. Lee and I DeVore (eds): *Man the Hunter.* Aldine, Chicago. pp. 293-303.

WEIDENREICH, F. 1941 The brain and its role in the phylogenetic transformation of the human skull. *Transactions of the American Philosophical Society* 31:321-442.

WILMSEN, E.N. 1983 The ecology of illusion: anthropological foraging in the Kalahari. *Reviews in Anthropology* 10:9-20.

WILMSEN, E.N., and J.R. DENBOW 1990 Paradigmatic history of San-speaking peoples and current attempts at revision. *Current Anthropology* 31:489-524.

WILSON, P.J. 1980 *Man the Promising Primate*. Yale University, New Haven.

___ *The Domestication of the Human Species*. Yale University Press, New Haven.

WOLPOFF, M.H. 1978 Analogies and interpretations in paleoanthropology. In C.J. Jolly (ed): *Early Man in Africa*. Duckworth, London. pp. 461-503.

___. 1982 *Ramapithecus* and hominid origins. *Current Anthropology* 23:501-522.

___. 1991 Comment on "The human community as a primate society" by Rodseth *et al. Current Anthropology* 32(3):249.

WRANGHAM, R.W. 1987 The significance of African apes for reconstructing human social evolution. In W. Kinzey ed: *The Evolution of Human Behavior*. State University of New York Press, Albany. pp. 51-71.

WRANGHAM, R.W., and E. VAN ZINNICQ BERGMANN-RISS 1990 Rates of predation on mammals by Gombe chimpanzees. *Primates* 31:157-170.

WYNN, T. 1985 Piaget, stone tools, and the evolution of human intelligence. *World Archaeology* 17:31-43.

___. 1991 Archaeological evidence for modern intelligence. In R. Foley (ed): *The Origins of Human Behavior*. Unwin Hyman, London. pp. 52-66.

ZIHLMAN, A.L. 1978 Women and evolution. Part II: Subsistence and social organization among early hominids. *Signs: Journal of Women in Culture and Society* 4:4-20.

___. 1981 Women as shapers of the human adaptation. In F. Dahlberg (ed): *Woman the Gatherer*. Yale University Press, New Haven. pp. 75-120.

___. 1985 Gathering stories for hunting human nature. *Feminist Studies* 11(2):365-377.

___. 1987 Sex, sexes, and sexism in human origins. *Yearbook of Physical Anthropology* 30:11-19.

ZIHLMAN, A.L., and N. TANNER 1978 Gathering and the hominid adaptation. In L. Tiger and M. Fowler (eds): *Female Hierarchies*. Aldine, Chicago. pp. 53-62.

ZIHLMAN, A.L., J.E. CRONIN, D.L. CRAMER, and V.M. SARICH 1978 Pygmy chimpanzee as possible prototype for the common ancestor of humans, chimpanzees, and gorillas. *Nature* 275:744-746.

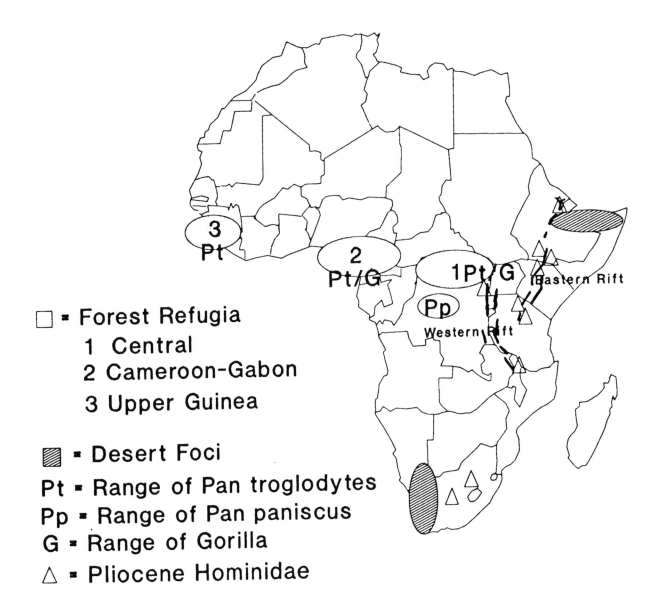

□ = Forest Refugia
   1 Central
   2 Cameroon-Gabon
   3 Upper Guinea

▨ = Desert Foci

Pt = Range of Pan troglodytes

Pp = Range of Pan paniscus

G = Range of Gorilla

△ = Pliocene Hominidae

Map 5.1 Living ape and Pliocene hominid distributions, after Boaz (1994). The known ranges are separated by the western rift.

FROM: Boaz, N.T. 1994 Significance of the Western Rift for hominid evolution. In R.S. Corruccini and R.L. Ciochon (eds): *Integrative Paths to the Past. Paleoanthropological Advances in Honor of F. Clark Howell.* Prentice Hall, Englewood Cliffs. pp. 321-343, figure 17.4.

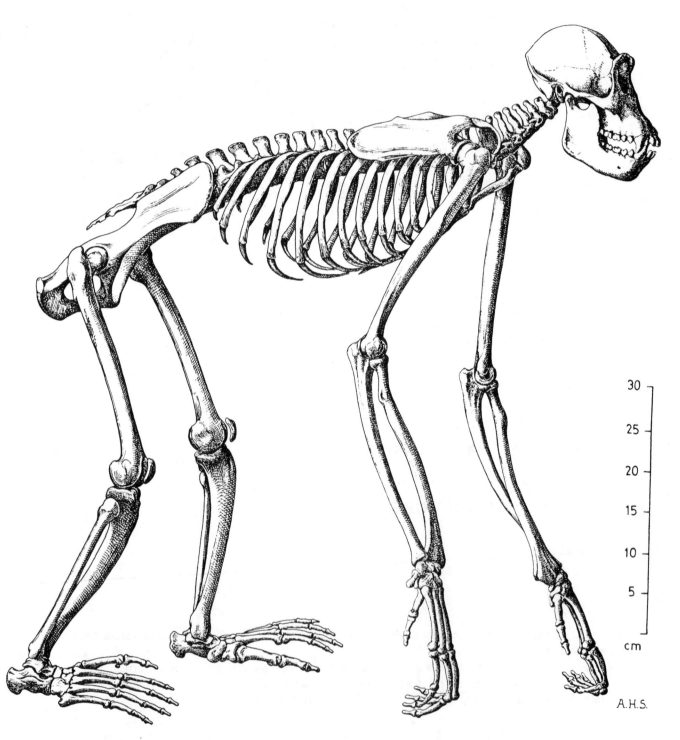

30

25

20

15

10

5

cm

A.H.S.

FIGURE 5.1 Skeleton of a chimpanzee in knuckle-walking posture, After Schultz (1969).
FROM Schultz, A.H. 1969 The skeleton of the chimpanzee. In G.H. Bourne (ed): *The Chimpanzee,* Volume
I. Karger, Basel. pp. 50-103.

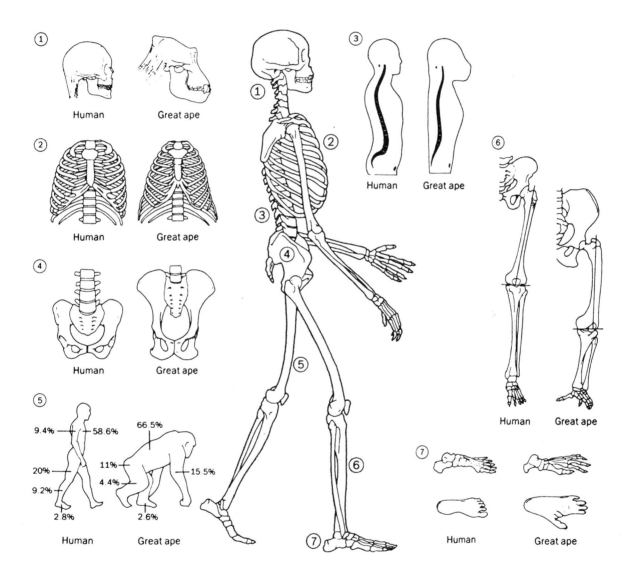

FIGURE 5.2 The main anatomical consequences of ape and human locomotor differences, adapted from Martin (1992).

FROM Martin, R. 1992 Walking on two legs. In S. Jones, R. Martin, and D. Pilbeam (eds): *The Cambridge Encyclopedia of Human Evolution.* Cambridge University Press, Cambridge. p. 78.

hominoid

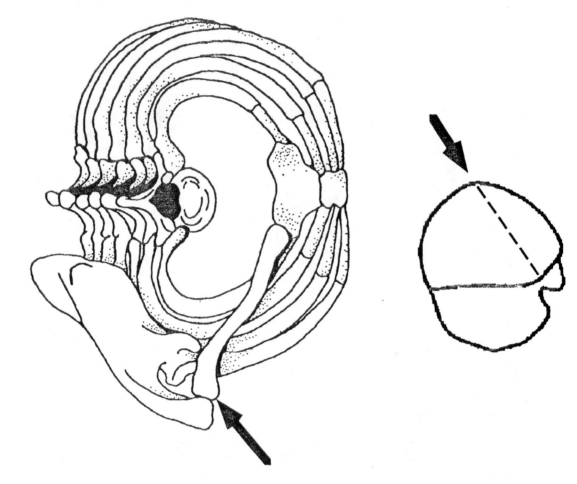

FIGURE 5.3 View of the chest from above, comparing different primates. Figure courtesy of C. Ward. The view shows the trunk shape and shoulder orientation differences, and their reflection in the orientation of the humerus head.

monkey

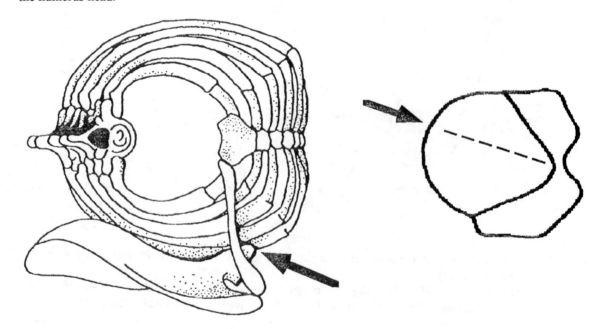

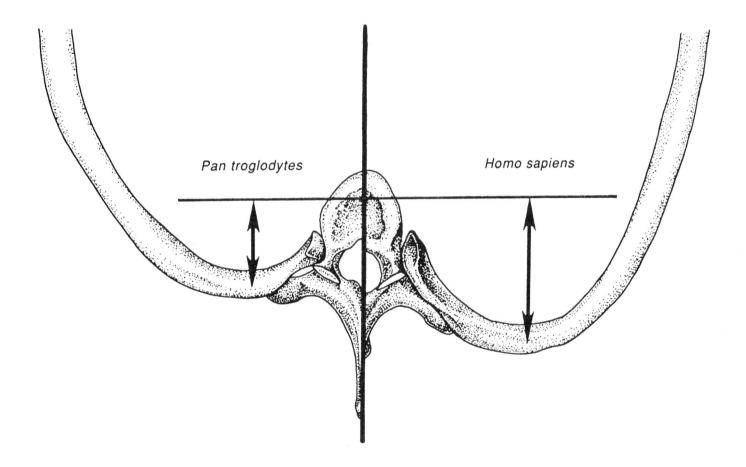

FIGURE 5.4 Chest shape as seen at the level of the 7th thorassic vertebra and the associated rib, from Jellema et al (1993). The human rib is more strongly angled and extends more posteriorly. It has a greater moment arm (arrows) than the chimpanzee rib and has more volume in the chest cavity (chimpanzee chests are more volumetric below, see figure 5.2)

FROM Jellema, L., B. Latimer, and A. Walker 1993 The rib cage of KNM-WT 15000. In R.E. Leakey and A.C. Walker (eds): *The Nariokotome Homo erectus Skeleon*. Harvard University Press, Cambridge.

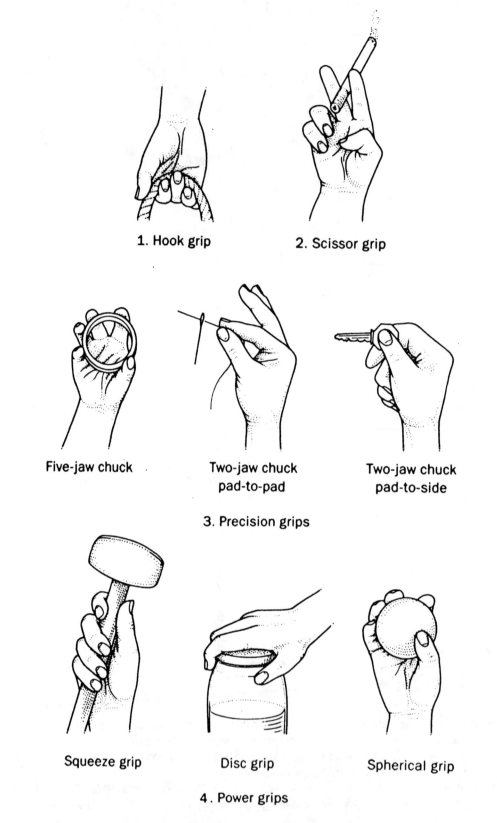

1. Hook grip   2. Scissor grip

Five-jaw chuck   Two-jaw chuck pad-to-pad   Two-jaw chuck pad-to-side

3. Precision grips

Squeeze grip   Disc grip   Spherical grip

4. Power grips

FIGURE 5.5 Human hand grips, after Trinkaus (1992).
FROM Trinkaus, E. 1992 Evolution of human manipulation. In S. Jones, R. Martin, and D. Pilbeam (eds): *The Cambridge Encyclopedia of Human Evolution.* Cambridge University Press, Cambridge. pp. 346-349.

CHAPTER SIX

Australopithecines: The First Hominids

The australopithecines of Africa are the earliest hominids, both phylogenetically and behaviorally. They are linked to humans in their morphological attributes and in at least some of what can be inferred of their behavior. "Australopithecine" is a term that once had taxonomic meaning because it referred to the subfamily Australopithecinae. The subfamily is no longer thought to be valid. It is now recognized that all of the species that were once in it can be subsumed in the genus *Australopithecus*, so the use of australopithecine has become an informal way to discuss the species in this clade (see figure 7.#). Our genus, *Homo*, is a descendent of one species of *Australopithecus*. To some extent australopithecine also refers to an evolutionary grade, describing a group of species of small brained hominids with a powerfully developed masticatory apparatus, large faces and mandibles, obligate bipedal adaptations with a rather long forearm/hindlimb ratio, large pelves with broad, elliptical birth canals, and other features described below. This grade characterizes hominids from the latest Miocene, Pliocene and earliest Pleistocene, but not uniquely hominids of the genus *Australopithecus* as at least one early *Homo* species (Chapter 8) has many characteristics of this grade as well. The taxonomy, of course, reflects clade and not grade.

The first australopithecine fossil to be found was the cranium, endocast, and mandible of a juvenile, from the debris left by a lime mine excavation into the remains of a cave near Taung in southern Africa (see Map). The fossils were first recognized as hominid by R. Dart, towards the end of 1924. Today, we date Taung to the later portion of the australopithecine time span (figure 6.1). Subsequent australopithecine discoveries, beginning in the 1930's, were mainly confined to R. Broom's collecting activities at other South African sites. The first adult specimens were discovered in 1936, in the **breccias** (consolidated cave fillings including rocks, windblown soils, and surface debris including animal bones that fell or had been swept into the cave opening) removed from the remnants of the Sterkfontein cave system during lime mining in the Transvaal region. Soon after, in 1938, australopithecines were found in the nearby exposures at Kromdraai, also the remnants of a prehistoric cave. The Transvaal caves, then and now, have provided the majority of all australopithecine discoveries.

There were also australopithecines discovered in East Africa during this decade but they were unrecognized or ignored. For instance, L.S.B. Leakey found what we now realize to be a much earlier specimen near the Tanzanian site of Laetoli in 1935 but he thought the canine he retrieved was a monkey - T.D. White first recognized it as an early hominid decades later. At the beginning of the second world war, some important discoveries and interpretations were made by German paleoanthropologists, but remained unknown to or were specifically ignored by scientists of the allied countries that were fighting the Germans. In 1939 L. Kohl-Larsen found several fragments in the same region of Tanzania visited by Leakey, but one, an occiput, was subsequently lost. A maxillary fragment he discovered near Laetoli, sometimes called the Garusi maxilla, was first classified by O. Abel as an australopithecine of the kind then being found at the Sterkfontein site in South Africa, but the classification that was accepted was published by H. Weinert, arguably one of the better pre-war German paleoanthropologists but with a reputation tainted by some of his activities, political as well as professional. Weinert allocated the specimen to an early Indonesian hominid genus, "*Meganthropus*", a classification supported by the well-known paleontologist A. Remane, and thus it somehow passed out of consideration as an East African australopithecine (details of the German East African expeditions and subsequent analysis are discussed at length by R. Protsch).

South Africa continued as the center of the next decade's discoveries, with caves at Swartkrans which is very close to Sterkfontein and Kromdraai (excavated first by Broom), and Makapansgat about 200 miles to the north, excavated by R. Dart. Early hominid research did not focus again on East Africa until the M.D. and L.S.B. Leakey discoveries at Olduvai Gorge in Tanzania began in the late 1950s. Olduvai was the first important East African source of numerous hominid remains, but other sites with large numbers of specimens began to be uncovered soon thereafter, discoveries that continue until the present. Further exploration in East Africa led to M.D. Leakey's systematic working of Laetoli, to the south of Olduvai

Gorge, and R.E.F. Leakey's discovery of extremely rich deposits to the east and later the to the west of Lake Turkana, formerly Lake Rudolf, in Kenya, F.C. Howell's discoveries north of the lake in southern Ethiopia, and M. Taieb's discoveries in central Ethiopia, followed by important finds by D.C. Johanson, T.D. White, and others.

Australopithecine sites (figure 6.1) begin in the terminal Miocene, extend through the Pliocene (approximately 5.2-1.8 myr, see table 1.3) and span most of the earlier portion of the Pleistocene. The dates for these sites range from being firm radiometric determinations to being pure guesswork, but no australopithecine forms appear to be younger than approximately 1.5 myr (figure 7.1). Moreover, while jaws and teeth that fit into the australopithecine range of variation appear outside of Africa in the later part of the Early Pleistocene, it is unlikely that these actually represent australopithecines; no definite australopithecine fossil is known from outside of Africa.

This chapter is concerned with the Late Miocene and Early Pliocene australopithecines of East and South Africa, dated to between 5.8 and 2.6 myr, which I believe are all of the genus *Australopithecus*. The various main sites (see Map) are discussed in a temporal sequence. The earliest of these are scattered individual specimens from northern Kenya and Ethiopia. These specimens are discussed in some detail, and they provide important insights into hominid origins and the earliest hominid adaptations because of their early dates. The reader is asked to remember that the best references to descriptions of all hominid specimens will be found in the **Paleoanthropology Bibliography**, and not necessarily in the publications listed at the end of the chapter which are concerned more with their interpretation and analysis. Subsequently dated, larger sites, are also from East Africa; Laetoli provides evidence of jaws and teeth as well as some footprints, and the somewhat later Hadar material adds details of the postcranial skeleton and cranial vault. The earlier of the South African sites follow the Hadar sequence in time. These have yielded the best samples of the crania of Pliocene australopithecines. Possibly contemporary with them, there are scattered remains of similar specimens in East Africa.

Miocene and Earlier Pliocene Australopithecines

There are only a few fragmentary specimens from the later Miocene and earliest Pliocene (figure 6.1). We focus on these mainly because of their unique importance in unraveling the details of hominid origins and early evolution.

LATEST MIOCENE

Only two Miocene primate fragments have been suggested as hominids (see the discussion of the Lukeino molar in Chapter 3) and only one of these is identified with certainty. The earliest hominid known at present is the Lothagam mandible fragment LT 329, from west of Lake Turkana, dated to between 5.8-5.6 myr according to A. Hill and colleagues. The specimen is only a posterior portion of a right **mandibular corpus** (the horizontal part of the body of the mandible, holding the teeth) with a worn first molar and sockets for the P_4 and other molars. Yet, because of this early date, attention seems riveted on this fragment. Found in 1967, and in spite of access to the original specimen in the National museums of Kenya, and casts easily available, it is only in the last eight years that there have been three major papers dealing with it. The T. White study draws no conclusions about the specimen's affinities, but Hill et al and, in a very detailed analysis A Kramer, conclude that Lothagam cannot be distinguished from the earliest named hominid species *Australopithecus afarensis*, in spite of the almost 2 million year span between it and the first large sample of this species, from Laetoli. Kramer systematically examined the relation of Lothagam to the four closest related taxa: the ancestral condition as reflected in the thick enameled medium sized dryopithecines; chimpanzees, the closest non-hominid; *A. afarensis*, the oldest named hominid species as represented at the later Pliocene sites of Laetoli and Hadar; *Australopithecus africanus* from Sterkfontein, the hominid species it was originally allocated to (Lothagam was found before *A. afarensis* was identified). Kramer unequivocally associates the specimen with *A. afarensis* on the basis of a metric and morphological analysis, while Hill and colleagues quite specifically liken it with the smaller of the *A. afarensis* mandibles from Hadar.

As Kramer points out, the synapomorphies shared with *A. afarensis* must give insight into the origins controversy, as they reflect early appearing features in the hominid clade. If the dryopithecine condition is taken as plesiomorphic, Lothagam and *A. afarensis* share the following derived features:

- the mandibular body is tall relative to the molar roots (the part holding the roots make up less than half the total height)
- the jaw is not as prognathic, in that it does not stick out as far in front of the articulation with the cranium at the mandibular fossa
- the part of the corpus with tooth sockets is wide and the mandibular body, as a whole, is thick (in its directly taken dimensions and relative to corpus height)
- the first molar is less elongated, more squared, in shape

Virtually all of these features reflect enhanced power and efficiency in molar grinding. The molars appear squarer, are better positioned under the masticatory muscles, and the jaw holding them is stronger. Given that the adaptation to powerful mastication is an anthropithecine, and even more ancient, adaptation, Kramer's suggestion is that the existing adaptation was enhanced at or near the time of hominid origins.

Figure 6.1

Stratigraphic Positions for Mio-Pliocene Early Hominid[α] Crania and Selected Mandibles[β]

From Afsaw et al (1992), Boaz (1988), Feibel et al (1989),
Haileab and Brown (1992), Hill et al (1992), McKee (1993)

Date (myr)	Omo	Turkana (KNM-ER and KNM-WT)	Other East African	South African (estimates)
2.2	*7-125, 74a-21,* *427-7,323-76-896*			⇑ Swartkrans (1)
2.3	*860-2* *57-41,*		*Uraha*	⇑ Sterkfontein (5)
2.4	338y-6, *44-2466*	*16005*	Chemeron BC 1	Gladysvale Sterkfontein (4)
2.5	345-11, 51-80 (dental)	17000 (Lomekwi)	KP 271 (Kanapoi humerus) ⇓	
2.6	*18-18,*18-31 (dental)			
2.7	*55s-33*	5431 (dental)		⇑ Taung ⇓
2.8				⇑ Makapansgat (3,4) ⇓
2.9			(Hadar Fm top)	
3.0	Usno Fm (dental)			
3.1			⇑ AL 438, 444 ⇓	
3.2		2602, *8556,* 16002 (femur)	AL 162, 288, 333	
3.3		*16006*		

3.4	2603, 2605, 2606 (dental)	AL 166, *198*, 199, 200, Maka
		LH 15 ⇑
3.5		LH 16
		Laetoli footprints
3.6		Laetoli (most specimens)
		⇓
3.7		Fejej ⇓
3.8		
		Belohdelie
3.9	Sibilot (radius)	
4.0	Allia Bay *20432* and dental	
4.1		
4.2		
4..3		
4.4		
4.5		
4.6		
4.7		
4.8		
4.9		
5.0		*Tabarin* (TH 13150)
		⇑
5.1		BC 1745 (Mabaget humerus)
5.2		
5.3		
5.4		
5.5		
5.6		*Lothagam* (LT 329)
		⇓
5.7		•
		•
5.8		•

α   Only major specimens are shown

β   Mandibles only are in italics

EARLIEST PLIOCENE

The Middle Pliocene hominids from Laetoli, Tanzania, are the first large early hominid sample and part of the basis for T.D. White and D.C. Johanson naming of the most ancient hominid species *A. afarensis*. The earliest hominids, from the Late Miocene, described above, can be linked to *A. afarensis* through just a few fragmentary specimens. Two of these are close in time, from the beginning of the Early Pliocene; the others are more than a million years later.

Chemeron hominids

Mabaget (5.1 myr) is a fragment of left humerus from the top of the bone, including the head (the articulation with the scapula), from the Chemeron Formation west of Lake Baringo in Kenya. As described by C.O. Lovejoy as part of a paper by M. Pickford and colleagues, BC 1745 is sub-adult. The humerus head is not completely joined to the neck by the growth process, but the fusion had begun at death and the bone would not have grown larger had the individual lived longer. The bone is very small; the shaft is some 10-15% larger than the Hadar female AL 288 ("Lucy") but markedly smaller than male humeri from Maka and the Hadar site. H. McHenry estimates the head size as close to Lucy's, and suggests a similar body weight in his reconstruction (about 28 kg). Based on the diminutive size, it is probable that the specimen is female. Several anatomical observations that reflect whether or not the forearm is used in locomotion, relate the specimen to other hominids and distinguish it from apes. These include the shape of the head (elliptical rather than spheroid as in living apes) and its orientation relative to the shaft. Ape arms are positioned more laterally, an important climbing adaptation but a major contributor to their lack of power and accuracy in aimed throwing. Although a subsequent study by B. Senut questions its hominid affinities, I am convinced by the assessments provided in Lovejoy's description.

Also from the Chemeron Formation, BC 13150 was found in a lake margin environment with locally variable savanna elements. The fragment from Tabarin (5.0 myr) is a piece of mandibular body from the rear of a right jaw preserving the first and second molar teeth. One of the important characteristics it shows is a consequence of powerful masticatory forces. The interpretation of powerful mastication is based on the form and angle of the molar roots. In these teeth the roots are divided into front (or mesial) and back (or distal) branches, and both branches angle toward the rear as they descend downwards from the crown, into the mandible. The serrate pattern, described for *A. afarensis* by S. Ward, combines a very large mesial molar root that is more vertically oriented with a smaller distal root angled both distally and in a buccal (outward) direction. Functional analysis published with S. Molnar relates this morphology to the requirements of powerful mastication. Ward and Molnar's experiments suggest that the large mesial root corresponds to the fact that the mesial half of each molar sustains more force during chewing than the distal half. The angled distal root reflects the strong component of lateral jaw movement during chewing, as a buccal orientation puts it in a position to best resist the downward motion during chewing. The taller rami of some later hominid mandibles act to more evenly distribute the **occlusal forces** during chewing, and this serrate pattern is subsequently lost, even among hominids who produce more powerful forces while chewing. Other evidence of powerful mastication in the Tabarin mandible, reflecting the ancestral condition, includes the thickened molar enamel and low molar cusps. However unlike thick enameled Middle Miocene pongids such as *Kenyapithecus*, its tooth wear suggests a stronger transverse component of jaw motion during chewing (and therefore perhaps less canine interlock because of canine reduction according to Ward and colleagues), and the hominid has a relatively broader occlusal surface.

LATER PART OF THE EARLY PLIOCENE

Allia Bay (3.95)

Following the earliest Pliocene is a gap of over a million years with no known hominid specimens. Subsequent to this gap, a (growing) sample, currently of 13 fragments, has been recovered in the ongoing excavations at site 261-1 at Allia Bay, on the east side of Lake Turkana. At the time the site was formed

Lake Turkana did not exist. The large Omo river flowed through the area, surrounded by gallery forest and floodplain grasslands, bordered in turn by dry thorn brush. According to K. Coffing and colleagues, who described the material, the condition of the hominid fossils suggests they came from habitats very near the river. If this is not where they lived, it is at least where they died.

Apart from the ER 20432 mandible, the specimens are all dental. This mandible, a left anterior fragment with the two premolars and a canine root, is somewhat larger than *A. afarensis* males such as LH 4 and like the Laetoli specimen it is male. The broken canine root is the largest known for an *A. afarensis*, 20% larger than the mean value. It evidently did not contact the P_3 (there was a diastema), because there is no interproximal facet caused by it in the front surface of the tooth. This premolar is sectorial, with a broad elliptical cross-section and a single large outer cusp. There is no wear on the occlusal surface that could have been caused by the upper canine honing against it.

Among the isolated teeth, ER 20422 is said to particularly resemble the Lukeino molar.

Sibilot Hill (4.0-3.8)

East of Allia Bay of Lake Turkana are deposits with several early hominid remains, including a virtually complete radius ER 20419. Comparable dimensions are quite similar to those of largest Hadar australopithecine male radii (see below) such as AL 333x 14. Its estimated length of about 27 cm would be expected in a heat-adapted human of approximately 1.75 m height (part of the hominid heat adaptation is to have long limbs relative to trunk size), but the height estimate for a shorter-legged, longer armed australopithecine species should be less, perhaps 1.65 m. A body weight of some 60 kg is suggested, using McHenry's procedures. This is above the Hadar male mean but the similarity to the size of AL 333x 14 shows it to be within their range. At the top of this range, it is quite large for an early hominid (especially in contrast to the Mabaget humerus described above). What supports the interpretation as a male and female within a single dimorphic species is the fact that a pattern of marked sexual dimorphism is already known for Pliocene hominids, from the large Hadar *A. afarensis* sample (within which both of these specimens would easily fit),

R. Heinrich and colleagues describe the bone as a hominid-like, not used in significant arm hanging or weight support but with several features reflecting a climbing adaptation. In particular, they focus on the shape and orientation of the distal **articular surface**, because this provides some information about the wrist. These scientists argue that the anatomy of the specimen allowed for increased wrist flexion, and interpret it (and several other features) to reflect a phylogenetic, and perhaps individual, history of vertical climbing. It is difficult to determine which history is relevant, since the development of obligate bipedalism would not be a source of selection against this wrist anatomy even though significant climbing activities were precluded by the loss of grasping feet. The details of the distal articular surface they describe are also found in orangutans, the most plesiomorphic of the apes, and in other early australopithecines. Subsequent changes in this region, they speculate, may be associated with the increased manipulative motions of the thumb that reflect its use in tool making. These changes do not appear in specimens until the end of the Pliocene. Unlike the orangutans but similar to living humans the neck at the proximal end of the radius is elongated. The short orangutan radius neck is taken to reflect suspensory activities in this species, and it is reasonable to conclude that the Sibilot Hill specimen climbed trees as a part of its adaptation but did not arm hang or brachiate.

Belohdelie (3.9-3.8)

The earliest hominid cranial remains are a large piece of frontal bone and 4 associated cranial fragments from the site of Belohdelie, Ethiopia. According to B. Asfaw the specimen is an adult. It is not complete, missing the center part of the bone with the top of the nose, but enough is present to show that the part of the bone that encloses the front of the brain, the squama, is the size of the frontal squama in many gorillas and chimpanzees. However, it differs from one or both African ape species in five ways:

1. The lateral corner of the supraorbital torus is vertically thicker than most common chimpanzees, and much thicker than all Bonobos

2. The roof of the supraorbital torus slopes evenly up to the frontal squama, rather than being separated from it by a deep groove, or **sulcus**, which is the common morphology for the African apes
3. The bone of the squama is thicker than virtually any African ape
4. The outside of the squama that forms the internal wall of the temporal fossa slopes inward toward the midline rather than being vertical as in the African apes, a slope that is caused by the convergence of the temporal muscles
5. The upper border of this sloping internal wall ends in a temporal line, marking the greatest extent of the temporal muscle attachment, that parallels the back of the supraorbital torus and then angles strongly toward the midline where the opposing lines meet at the back of the frontal bone. In the African apes the temporal line swings backwards at the outside corner of the supraorbital and does not parallel it.

The last two points, distinguishing the Belohdelie frontal from virtually all African apes, suggest that the anterior temporalis muscle was extremely well developed (this is supported by the fact that the lines almost meet at the back of the frontal bone) - an important component of the powerful mastication complex described in Chapter 4, anterior temporalis provides vertical forces to the teeth.

White finds the specimen very similar to the juvenile Laetoli (LH 21) vault pieces and the fragmentary female Hadar (AL 288) frontal (these later sites are described below), and Asfaw attributes it to their species *A. afarensis*. The minimum breadth of the frontal (between the internal walls of the temporal fossae) is large, similar to a male *A. africanus* (the most closely related species with complete frontals known for both males and females). Moreover, the thickness of the supraorbital is almost double that of the Hadar female. If these reflect sexual dimorphism in *A. afarensis*, as I believe, the implication that Belohdelie may be male is important in assessing the significance of the very small frontal bone size. It is possible that the Belohdelie hominid has the smallest male brain size known.

Fejej (3.7-3.6 myr)

Described by J. Fleagle and colleagues, this Ethiopian site from just north of the Kenya border yielded 6 heavily worn mandibular teeth (FJ-4-SB-1), and an unworn P_4 (FJ-4-SB-2) of a much younger individual. In size, morphology, and pattern of wear on the older individual's dentition the specimens are indistinguishable from *A. afarensis* dentitions.

Laetoli: The Earliest Large Australopithecine Sample (3.7-3.5)

At the Tanzanian site of Laetoli, some 50 kilometers south of Olduvai Gorge, paleontological discoveries began in 1935 with the first visit of M.D. and L.S.B. Leakey. An upper jaw fragment was found soon after by the German paleontologist Kohl-Larsen, and an isolated canine and incisor from the area were subsequently identified in fossil primate collections. The bulk of the hominid discoveries are the result of work by M.D. Leakey between 1974 and 1979, and have been described in detail in several papers by T.D. White. Most of the sample of 24 individuals is dated to about 3.6 myr; they span from 3.76 to 3.56 with LH 16 slightly later, and LH 15 later yet, younger than 3.46 myr. The hominid remains preserved are mainly jaws and teeth, and parts of a child's postcranial skeleton (LH 21, mentioned above). Laetoli was a savanna woodland with distinct seasonality - most of the rain fell in a single season. It is unclear from the geological circumstances whether the hominid occurrences were seasonal or whether the hominids were more broadly adapted to this environment's seasonality itself. In support of the latter, microwear studies on the teeth of later Pliocene hominids suggest both non-abrasive frugivory and consumption of hard, gritty foods such as roots, seeds, and rhizomes.

The best preserved specimen from the site, the LH 4 mandible (figure 6.2), was part of the basis for the definition of *A. afarensis* in the first description of the species by D. Johanson and T. White - a definition whose validity was hotly debated in the pages of a 1980 issue of the journal *Science* (207:1102-1105). This specimen, in many ways, exemplifies the dental and mandibular features characterizing the

Laetoli sample, if not indeed all of *A. afarensis*. The postcanine dentition is moderate in size for an early hominid, similar to Lothagam and larger than Tabarin. However, these teeth are quite large compared to chimpanzees. For instance, excepting the first molar length, the mandibular molar dimensions are much larger than the maxima for the large sample of chimpanzees compared in table 6.1.

Table 6.1
Laetoli Mandibular Tooth Size

	Chimpanzee Male Mean	Chimpanzee Female Mean	LH 2	LH 3	LH 4	LH 14	M 18773
I1 Length	8.3	8.1	8.0			5.7	
I1 Breadth	8.7	8.5	7.7	7.3		7.3	
I2 Length	8.8	8.7					
I2 Breadth	9.5	9.0				8.0	
C Length	13.5	11.0	9.5	9.7		8.7	8.1
C Breadth	11.6	9.6		12.1	10.6	10.6	10.3
P3 Length	8.8	7.6	9.2	9.8	10.0	9.9	
P3 Breadth	11.1	10.6	11.0	13.4	12.2	13.1	
P4 Length	8.1	7.9		10.9	9.4	10.8	
P4 Breadth	9.0	8.8		12.3	10.8	11.4	
M1 Length	11.0	10.8	14.3	13.5	12.0		
M1 Breadth	10.0	9.7	13.0	13.4	12.7	13.2	
M2 Length	11.1	11.0			13.9		
M2 Breadth	10.5	10.2			13.6		
M3 Length	10.4	10.1			16.3		
M3 Breadth	9.9	9.4			13.8		

The mandibular morphology reflects the consequences of the postcanine size expansion. The mandibular bodies are relatively thick, especially under the molar roots. The pattern of stress across the large front teeth is reflected in the rounded sloping symphysis, with its even curvature and two internal buttresses, or **mandibular tori**. As in Miocene anthropithecines, the lower buttress extends much farther backward than the upper one. The front of the mandible is broad and squared off compared with the narrow fronts of the "V" shaped Miocene anthropithecine toothrows and is similar to chimpanzees in this regard. In both chimpanzees and the Laetoli hominids this probably reflects an expanded size for the anterior teeth. By inference this would seem to be a pre-divergence adaptation, perhaps for dehusking fruits but the study of a Hadar maxilla's incisors (see below) suggests that they were also used for stripping leaves. One other point. The toothrows are further apart in LH 4 than in Miocene anthropithecines and most chimpanzees. It has been suggested that this expanded distance means a larger mouth size, perhaps for chewing more food at once. With expanded molar size and thick enamel, the low quality diet of at least some difficult to masticate foods indicated in the discussion of the Lothagam mandible would seem to characterize this sample as well.

The maxillary postcanine teeth are equally large (table 6.2), relative to the chimpanzees, and the observation I made many years ago, that the early hominids are essentially chimpanzee-sized creatures with gorilla-sized postcanine teeth, remains valid. Quite unlike gorillas, however, the enamel cap of the postcanine teeth is quite thick. Moreover, the postcanine teeth differ from both African apes, as well as their anthropithecine predecessors, in expanded breadths and more bulbous cusps.

Table 6.2
Tooth Size in the Best Preserved Laetoli Male and Female Maxillae

	Chimpanzee Male average	Chimpanzee Female average	LH 3 Male	LH 5 Female	LH 6 Female
I1 Length	11.9	11.9	11.8		
I1 Breadth	10.6	10.2	8.5		
I2 Length	9.3	8.9	7.8	5.5[1]	7.8
I2 Breadth	9.0	8.5	8.1	6.7	7.2
C Length	14.8	11.8	11.8	9.5	9.8
C Breadth	11.5	9.5	12.2	9.7	10.4
P3 Length	8.2	8.0	9.5	8.1[1]	9.6
P3 Breadth	10.5	10.2	13.7	12.5	13.0
P4 Length	7.5	7.3	9.9	8.5[1]	9.4
P4 Breadth	10.4	10.1		13.2	13.8
M1 Length	10.5	10.4	13.2	10.3[1]	12.3
M1 Breadth	11.1	11.0	14.8	13.3	14.1
M2 Length	10.2	10.0		11.5[1]	
M2 Breadth	11.0	10.7		14.5	
M3 Length	9.2	8.9		11.0	
M3 Breadth	10.1	9.9		13.7	

[1] Significantly shortened by interproximal wear.

STRUCTURE AND FUNCTION OF THE ANTERIOR TEETH

The Laetoli anterior dentitions are the earliest known for hominids (the Allia Bay mandible only preserved a large broken canine root) . The canines retain the anthropithecine condition of marked sex differences in their size and form. Male canines are easy to distinguish by their greater size and higher, more tapered crowns. Compared with later hominids, the canines are big relative to the posterior teeth and in many ways approximate chimpanzee canines in the projection of unworn teeth beyond the toothrow as well as in the basal dimensions of the teeth (we would expect the crown of the Allia Bay canine to be similar, had it not been broken). For instance, the maximum breadths of 3 out of 4 mandibular canines are midway between female and male chimpanzee means, and the fourth is above the male mean. Canine lengths, however, are less as the hominid canines of both jaws are shaped differently, being broader relative to their lengths. Mandibular incisors are large, the LH 2 central incisor also approximating chimpanzee size. Large front teeth in *A. afarensis* are also indicated by upper central incisors from Laetoli, some of which are among the largest known for any hominid and very similar to chimpanzees, although relatively narrower (the **labiolingual**, or tongue-to-lip, dimension). Unlike chimpanzees, however, the hominid maxillary incisors reflect the plesiomorphic condition in which the lateral incisor is much smaller than the central.

The LH 4 mandibular canine is broken so its occlusal details are unknown, but there was a diastema between it and the P$_3$ for the upper canine to fit (figure 6.2). Moreover the 4 P$_3$'s from the site, varying from unworn to heavily worn, also exhibit some aspects of this primitive morphology (like the Allia Bay tooth). Their crown form is elliptical in cross-section; the long axis of the ellipse is approximately transverse across the tooth, although the buccal side is displaced just slightly forward. They each have a dominant buccal cusp with a long, gradually sloping buccal face (a projecting upper canine would rest against this face when the jaws were closed), a weaker and (when unworn) much lower lingual cusp, and a ridge of enamel connecting the two. This archaic anatomy raises the question of whether the anterior teeth were used for cutting (there is no evidence for cutting in the earlier Allia Bay male). At least some of them were. The lower canine from the Laetoli beds collected by L. Leakey in 1935 (M 18773), clearly was used in anterior cutting. The back surface of the crown is highly worn, tip to base, and microscopic examination shows that the wear scratches are vertical. This means that the wear surface formed against the front face of what was presumably a large projecting upper canine, as the jaws closed together. Many chimpanzee lower canines are worn in a fully analogous manner, and the maximum dimension of the Laetoli tooth is between female and male chimpanzee means (but the length is barely within the chimpanzee range). The other lower canines are known in specimens showing several degrees of wear, ranging from the unworn LH 3 to the more moderately worn LH 14 and finally to the very worn LH 4 mandible, shown in figure 6.2. In their unworn form, these teeth are triangular in shape with a pointed tip and sharp edges on both leading and trailing surfaces (see Figure 6.LC). As they began to wear, the tip became blunted (or broken) to the level of the other teeth, and unlike M 18773 no honing maintained the sharp back edge on any of the other specimens. This behavioral variation, shown by the contrast of cutting in one specimen with its absence in two other worn ones, is not a consequence of age-at-death, and as for association with sex the specimen used for cutting is the *smallest* of the mandibular canines. If this means it is female, it is interesting that at the later *A. afarensis* site of Hadar the females also have a more ape-like aspect to their canine/premolar complex; in this case, as discussed below, a much higher frequency of P$_3$'s with single cusps.

On the smaller number of maxillary canines, the trailing surfaces wear against the occlusal surface and outside (buccal face) of the P$_3$, and a small diastema separates the premolar from the lower canine in LH 4 for the upper canine to fit (evidence of diastemata occur in 3 out of 4 Laetoli mandibular dentitions according to White). In the LH 5 maxilla (figure 6.5), a female, the trailing edge is sharpened. White points out that sharpening of this edge is maintained through a combination of thin (outer hard) enamel and expanded (inner softer) dentin. Once the dentin is exposed, a sharp enamel edge on the back of the tooth is maintained because the enamel flakes away as it is undercut by the more rapidly wearing dentin. This edge must wear as the lower premolar slides across it, so again it is the female specimen who seems to cut with her anterior teeth. L. Greenfield argues that this motion and the sharpening of the back of the upper canine is unrelated to the use of the teeth in cutting, but the dramatic wear facets found in some of the Laetoli (and Hadar, see below) canines indicates otherwise. In contrast, the small wear facet on the *leading* edge of the upper canine of LH 5 is flattened and dull, showing that unlike specimens such as the lower canine M 18773, there is no cutting between the lower canine and its upper counterpart in this elderly female.

ERUPTION PATTERN

Two of the Laetoli mandibles have incompletely erupted dentitions. Because of accidents of preservation these two, LH 2 and LH 3 (consisting only of isolated teeth), provide the best information there is about relative tooth development and eruption pattern in *A. afarensis*. Differences between the human and chimpanzee eruption patterns (and sources for the information) are discussed in Chapter 4. Using this information, table 6.3 compares the incompletely developed isolated mandibular dentition of LH 3 with chimpanzee and human data. LH 2 is not used as well because in the absence of CT scans it is better to use teeth no longer held in a jaw. CT based estimates of the development of unerupted teeth in mandibles have proven to be quite different than X-ray estimates, a point also discussed in Chapter 4.

Analysis of the two partially completed maxillary dentitions, LH 3 and 6, provides the same results. While it would be better to have several specimens at the same developmental age, and second molars for LH 3 and 6 to check the I2:M2 polymorphism, as much as can be told these Laetoli children fit the human developmental pattern and not the chimpanzee one. Especially significant is the relative canine development; in the chimpanzee pattern the crown develops later relative to first molar eruption and its eruption is further delayed by the late development of the canine root. The Laetoli mandibular canine has begun root formation at the time of first molar eruption. Incisor development also fits the hominid pattern; this is visible in the better preserved upper central incisor, which has a significant portion of its root. In sum, to the extent that dental development reflects general physiological development, the earliest australopithecine that can be analyzed show evidence of maturational delay, just as A. Mann and colleagues have claimed characterizes later australopithecines from South Africa.

Table 6.3
Relative Dental Development for Mandibles
when the First Molar has Just Erupted

	Cross Sectional LH 3[1] incompletely developed dentition	Longitudinal Chimpanzee sample [Anemone et al (1991)]	Cross Sectional Inuit sample [Trodden (1982)]	Longitudinal Modern European sample [several studies]
M2	No crown found	crown complete, no root	crown complete less than 1/4 root	Crown almost or fully complete
M3	No crown found	crown begun	crown absent	crown absent
P3 and P4	P3 crown complete, trace of root P4 crown complete trace of root	partly complete crowns	P3 complete with 1/4 root P4 complete	P3 crown complete P4 crown almost complete
C	crown complete trace of root	partly complete crown	crown complete 1/2 root	crown complete, varying root
I1	crown complete some root development	crown complete, slight root	crown complete root 3/4 complete	crown complete, partial root

[1] My assessments agree fully with those published by T. White. These differ markedly from those published by B.H. Smith (1989)

FOOTPRINTS AND LOCOMOTION

Also found at Laetoli was a sequence of some 15 overlapping ancient ground surfaces formed of freshly deposited volcanic ash. The unit, called the footprint tuff, dates to the later portion of the hominid span, about 3.56 myr. Each of the ground surfaces preserves the remains of a fairly wet, sandy region near what must have been a water hole. The ground surfaces were covered with footprints, ranging in size from those of small birds to elephants. Ash falls or other debris covered these surfaces, preserving the prints.

M. Leakey described and illustrated several sets of human-appearing footprints crossing some of these floors. The best preserved hominid trail, at site G, was formed at the end of the dry season. It is comprised of two sets of prints (numbers 1 and 2). According to T. White, there are two side-by-side trails made to two individuals walking bipedally. A third set, number 3, is from site A (see table 6.4). White finds a number of features in these prints that reveal a human-like anatomy and gait pattern, and several subsequent studies have confirmed their presence and found additional reflections of the very human-like nature of the ancient bipedality. These include:

- pronounced heel strike
- lateral transmission of force from the heel to the base of the lateral metatarsal
- well developed medial longitudinal arch
- adducted great toe, in front of the ball of the foot and parallel to the other digits
- a deep impression for the great toe commensurate with toe-off

The prints are 21.5 and 18.5 cm in length, leading to stature estimates for the individuals of 140-150 cm for the larger and 120-130 cm for the smaller if it can be assumed that the prints accurately reflect foot size, the specimens are adult, and the hominids who made the prints have the same foot-body size relation as small humans. McHenry estimates the average male statue of *A. afarensis* from Hadar at 151 cm, and "Lucy's" height is 105 cm, so these hominids are certainly in the right size range to have made the prints.

Table 6.4
Laetoli Footprint Trail Parameters
From Charteris *et al*

Footprint Trail $\Rightarrow$	1	2	3
Foot length (cm)	18.5	21.5	15.5
Stride length (cm)	77.5	94.5	62.0
Stature estimate (cm)[1]	120	140	100
Walking velocity (cm/s)	56	72	42
Cadence (steps/minute)	85	90	80
Foot-lengths per stride	4.2	4.4	4.0

[1] This is the minimum suggested by White, based on a Pygmy model with a foot length - stature ratio of 15.5%

J. Charteris and colleagues have attempted to ascertain forward velocity of the hominids from their stride length (the distance between two successive footfalls of the same foot), because they were able to show a direct relationship between forward speed and the length of the stride. The stride length is very short in all three trails, as judged by the relation of the stride length to the foot length (presumably a measure of body height, certainly the basis for its estimation). In fact, the 3 trails are very similar in approximating 4 foot lengths per stride. This is taken to mean that they were walking very slowly, a point confirmed by their estimated velocity. Their forward speed was within the range of customary human walking speeds but too slow for the locomotion to have been at the natural stride velocity (see Chapter 4); taking body size into account their forward speed was estimated at 50%-60% that of modern humans asked to walk at a "comfortable" or "preferred" speed. The Charteris study, and a similar one by Tuttle and colleagues, concludes that the hominids were :strolling" when they left their footprints behind for posterity and the deliberations of many future generations of paleoanthropologists.

These interpretations seemed straightforward, but they have not been without controversy. At one extreme is was suggested that the larger trail was made by two individuals, one walking in the tracks left by the other, while at the other extreme the suggestion is that some of the tracks were not made by hominids but by bipedal bears. It has been proposed that hominids with the foot bones found at Hadar (no foot bones are known from Laetoli but the widespread assumption is that the same species is present at both sites) could not have made the modern-appearing Laetoli prints, and it has been suggested that the short stride length and seemingly slow gait reflects that "fact" that their legs were too short.. It is difficult to be sure whether this disparity of opinions reflects real problems in understanding the prints, or the lack of paleoanthropological expertise and experience in interpreting footprint tracks.

While the preservation of the hominid trails ranges from poor to excellent, the total body of evidence shows that a small, bipedal striding primate lived in the area and sometimes strolled near the water hole locality. No other hominid species is known from this time period, and in my view it is likely that the footprint maker was *A. afarensis,* the same species whose skeletal remains were discovered nearby. Perhaps even more firmly than any skeletal remains that could be found, this establishes the mode of locomotion for this Middle Pliocene australopithecine sample. With the Maka femur, these prints show that obligate bipedalism clearly has a greater antiquity than either hominid canine form or significant brain size expansion (see below).

Maka (3.4)

Linking the Laetoli remains with the large, slightly later, hominid sample from Hadar are a number of specimens from Maka, near Belohdelie, including a proximal femur piece, two partial mandibles (and a mandibular ramus and several teeth), a bit of ulna, and a virtually complete humerus. T. White and colleagues describe an environment intermediate between the drier and more open Laetoli habitat and the more humid and forested situation at Hadar. The eroded portion of the top of a femur was found stratigraphically above the Belohdelie frontal and separated from it by a cindery tuff (CT) horizon. Additional specimens discovered later are numerically dated to 3.4 myr.

The partial femur fragment MAK-VP 1/1, a young adult according to White, preserves the top-quarter of the bone, but without its articular head. There is little doubt that the Maka femur represents the kind of individual who could have made the Laetoli footprints. It has a number of features that suggest a predominately or habitual bipedal form of locomotion.

1. The gluteus maximus attachment (see figure 4.2) is mostly on the back of the shaft, rather than on its side where it would be if it had functioned as an abductor
2. The femur neck is long (relative to the size of the shaft), a consequence of the lateral iliac flare described in Chapter 4
3. The neck (and upper shaft) is anterior-posteriorly flattened, making the neck relatively tall and thereby resistant to bending stresses during one legged support
4. While in general the outer cortex is small, the bone thickness on the anterior neck surface is expanded, a response to muscle force during toe-off and the force transmitted when the leg comes to the ground at the end of its swing
5. The neck-shaft angle is low

The size of the bone is moderately large for an early hominid, a 45 kg body weight can be estimated using McHenry's procedures. It is just above the middle of the range of variation of Hadar australopithecine body size estimates, and midway in the range of the earlier Pliocene specimens we are discussing as it is considerably smaller than the individual represented by the ER 20419 radius. VP 1/1 probably is male (45 kg is the average Hadar male weight).

Also large is VP 1/3, a mostly complete very stout humerus with the remnants of strong attachments for the muscles that flex the shoulder (bringing the arm toward the body) and rotate the lower arm. Its length was estimated at 296 mm, corresponding to a height of about 1.35 m and an estimated weight which is so similar to that of the Maka femur that they could well be the same specimen. Contributing to the stoutness is the thick outer cortex of bone (cortical bone) - some 8 mm on the inner surface at the middle of the shaft.

The Maka bone shows notable similarities to the humerus of the diminutive Hadar female "Lucy". Where its robustness contrasts with the Hadar female, there are parallels with sex-related differences normally found in humans, and the idea that these differences reflect sexual dimorphism is supported by a another humerus from Hadar (AL 137-5) that is virtually identical to Maka in size and anatomy (but more directly comparable to Lucy as it is closer in age and from the same site). The dimorphism suggested if Lucy is compared with either of these (80% for bone length, 62% for estimated weights) is well within the normal comparisons of males and females that can be found within gorillas, and would not be extreme (e.g. smallest female/largest male) for the much less dimorphic chimpanzees. Another way to look at Maka is that the bone is short relative to the prominence of its robust muscle attachments and shaft thickness and its shaft has a slight backwards bend - chimpanzee humeri of similar thicknesses are much longer, and their shafts are straighter. Moreover, Maka is not particularly chimpanzee-like in its joint-to-shaft proportions or in the pattern of muscle attachments. While there is little doubt that tree climbing was an important element in the behavior of this hominid, as J. Ohman and colleagues point out the upper limb of this individual was *very* strong, there are no indications of key chimpanzee-like specializations that would uniquely adapt it for their linked arboreal and knuckle-walking behaviors. Climbing was quite different than the arboreal activities of chimpanzees, with their prehensile feet in that it had to be accomplished in the context of other adaptations to obligate bipedalism. The pattern of humerus muscularity required by a climbing biped, lacking prehensile feet, would not only be useful in climbing, but in bludgeoning and digging as well.

It is quite likely that this large estimated body size is part of the normal range of variation in a sample that is quite like the much more numerous Hadar one. This is indicated by the range of variation within the small Maka dental sample. Included in it is an isolated molar larger than all but one of the comparable Hadar teeth (an M_2, VP 1/4), and another (VP 1/13) smaller than any from Hadar. Small individuals are also found in the postcranial remains - an ulna fragment VP 1/111 matches one of the smallest from Hadar.

VP 1/12, the most complete of 4 jaws, is in fact the most completely preserved *A. afarensis* mandible. Intermediate in size, it preserves the characters described in the more fragmentary materials described above. These include

- parallel postcanine tooth rows
- marked angle of the mandibular condyles long axis (this reflects the angle of the mandibular fossa on the cranial base)
- canine-premolar diastema
- large canines and incisors
- molars with ascending size order (first smallest)
- triangular third molar crown shape
- serrated molar roots

The mandible is very similar to the LH 4 male in size and shape. Its P_3 is moderately asymmetric, and like most of the Hadar males (see below) it has 2 cusps. With its third molars just erupted VP 1/12 is younger than LH 4, but in spite of its age there is arthritis on the surfaces of both of its condyles. This is the earliest evidence of this degenerative joint disease in the hominids.

Hadar (3.4-2.96)

A much larger sample of early hominids has been recovered from the Hadar, in the Afar triangle region of Ethiopia. M. Taieb first realized the potential of this region, and organized an international group to survey it in 1972. Hominid discoveries began in 1973, and have continued intermittently until present. The Hadar sample is now comprised of close to 300 pieces, representing from 40 to 100 individuals. It includes the usual multitudinous jaws and teeth, as well as a fairly complete face and several incomplete cranial vaults, portions of a child's skull, and most importantly postcranial remains (more than 60% of the sample), including much of a single associated skeleton.

The stratigraphic sequence spans dates from about 3.4 to slightly less than 3 million years ago. Hominids have been found from virtually all time levels (see table 6.5). The details of the anatomy for the sample discovered before 1981 were published in a single issue of the *American Journal of Physical Anthropology* (1982: volume 57, number 4) that was devoted to a description of the Hadar sample as it was as of 1977. The paleoecology suggests that most of the region was comprised of lakes, and their floodplains, intersected by streams and a few larger rivers. Analysis of the **paleosols** and the pollen sequence indicates a dry grassy woodland environment, ranging to gallery forest in some localities. Even though none of the fauna suggests dense forest, the contrast with today's desiccated environment is dramatic. Over the period of deposition the climate varied from more humid to drier and arid and back to more humid conditions again.

Table 6.5
Generalized Stratigraphic Relations of Hadar Hominid Sites[1]

Members	Selected Tuff and Basalt Horizons with Radiometric Ages	Hominid Localities
Kada Hadar (KH)	BKT 3	
	BKT 2$_L$ U=2.92 myr L=2.95 myr	
Upper		437,438 (associated partial skeleton with cranial fragments),439,440,444 (male skull 444-2)
	BK 1	
Lower		
	KHT (3.18 myr)	288 ("Lucy")
Denen Dora (DD)		58,161,162,176,188,207,241,293, 333 (possibly related individuals), 366,388
	TT 4 (3.22 myr)	
Sidi Hakoma (SH)	3.40-3.22	211,322
	Kadada Moumou Basalt (3.22)	
		128,129,137,145,166,198,199 200,228,249,266,277,311, 400,411,417 (417-1d female face),441,442
	SHT (3.4 myr)	

[1]   From Walter (1994)

THE DENTITIONS

There are three important questions addressed by the dental remains, as always the most numerous element in the samples:

1. How do the earlier (Laetoli) and later (Hadar) samples differ
2. What functional changes do the differences suggest
3. Can the sample be regarded as a single species, and if so what the dentitions reveal about its behavior

In most respects the Hadar dentitions are quite similar to those from Laetoli, although the larger sample size results in more variation. T. White, who compared the Hadar with the Laetoli dental sample, concludes that "surprisingly few" metric or morphological features distinguish them. In general the Laetoli dental sample can be subsumed in the range of the almost 10 times larger Hadar one. The degree of variation in these dentitions is not unusual, and can be attributed to a number of causes ranging from individual idiosyncrasies to marked sex differences. One collection from the Afar consists of the remains of at least 13 adults and children (2 juveniles and 2 infants) from the 333 locality who may have died together, as argued by J. Aronson and M. Taieb, quite possibly in the flood that buried them according to S. Radosevich and colleagues. The hominid bones are the only fossil mammals found in the very thin (20 cm) fossil-bearing layer. This collection has virtually the full range of variation found in the total Hadar sample, which suggests that marked variation was a normal populational characteristic of these early hominids.

Differences between the samples - form and anterior dental functions

Systematic differences in size and shape between the Laetoli and Hadar teeth are virtually non-existent. In fact, the samples both show some systematic variations, compared to later australopithecines, that reflect (perhaps primitive) uniquenesses in their adaptive patterns. For instance, the large size of the incisors and canines at both sites is a real distinction from subsequent hominids. The male canines, in particular, are unusually large while the central incisors are so big that these are the only hominids in which the lateral incisors are spread wider apart than the outer margins of the nose. As R. Kay notes, the large incisor size suggests an important role in food preparation.   One set of maxillary incisors, from AL 200-1, substantiates this. According to studies by A. Ryan, irregular wear across the entire front of the jaw seems to reflect a stripping function similar to gorillas, who are often observed to place a large leaf in their mouth and pull the stem out between their semi-clamped front teeth, using them to strip off the edible cellulose. The large canines often require a diastema between the lower canine and premolar, a very common feature at both sites.

Table 6.6
Wear Angles[1] for Maxillary Canines
From Greenfield (1990)

Taxon	Mean Angle (degrees)	Sample Range
Papio	79	70-88
Gorilla	86	71-95
Pan	87	71-93
Australopithecus afarensis		
LH 5	89	
AL 199-1	121	
AL 200-1	116	
AL 333-2	103	
AL 333x-3	117	
AL 400-1	121	

[1] The angle between the worn back edge of the canine and the opposite edge

The most significant difference between Hadar and the earlier Laetoli dentitions appears to be in anatomy and wear of the functionally interrelated canine and P_3, reflecting non-masticatory functions of the anterior teeth. Frequencies of features indicating the use of the canines in cutting appear to decrease between the samples. For instance, White reports that evidence of mandibular diastemata occur in 3 out of 4 Laetoli specimens, but only 6 of 16 from Hadar. He also notes that the wear on the canine distal face is lingual facing in the worn Laetoli specimen (LH 5) suggesting canine honing, while in the Hadar canines this facet faced distally and could better be described as blunting. Moreover, as Greenfield points out the crown outline of the LH 5 canine has very acute canine wear angle, similar to other primates, while the wear on the Hadar maxillary canines results in shallower angles, outside the ranges of the other primates (table 6.6).

The interpretation of the functional differences between maxillary canines is confused by the variation in their functional partners in canine cutting, the lower anterior premolars. There are variations in the morphology of these teeth that are, by in large, expressed differently in males and females. Some of the lower anterior premolars resemble the Laetoli form, a few even completely lack the secondary cusp. These teeth, with their asymmetric elliptical crown shape, closely resemble dryopithecine or early anthropithecine premolars, some of which have even better expressed lingual cusps that specimens such as AL 128-23 and 288-1 (Lucy).   However, variation in premolar morphology is continuous, and at the other extreme lie premolars that are more symmetric with almost equal-sized cusps (AL 333W-1a). Between these, a gradation of lingual cusp sizes can be found. W. Leonard and M. Hegmon attempted to quantify this premolar variation and assess its variation as a function of sex and time. Because the data were quantified, they were able to show that an *A. afarensis* premolar sample is morphologically more variable than either human or chimpanzee samples. The main source of variation was found to be sex (figure 6.3). In most cases the male teeth are significantly more **molarized** (molar-like in their morphology, in having a larger number of cusps or more equal sized cusps) in that they usually more closely approximate the bicuspid condition with cusps of equal size. The male premolars are also more rotated (table 6.7) in position (rotation is the angle that the line connecting the cusps makes with the jaw's midline - modern human premolars are most rotated as this line is virtually at right angles, while many primate sectorial premolars the rotation is much less so the long sloping outer surface will face towards the back of the maxillary canine rather than towards the cheek). Female P_3's more often have buccal cusp dominance or are just single-cusped (sectoral) as in the AL 288-1 and AL 417-1d mandibles (sex determination for these two is independent of the mandibles). It may seem unexpected that females of *A. afarensis* are more ape-like in premolar:

1. morphology (more often having a single cusp or a very dominant buccal cusp when there are 2)
2. rotation (with the sloping surface facing more forward than outward)

but *chimpanzee females and males vary exactly the same way*. Leonard and Hegmon found that chimpanzee females have less molarized and less rotated premolars as well. The pattern of sexual dimorphism is the same in these two, closely related species. It should be noted that these are average, or usual differences. There are exceptions for both sexes.

Table 6.7
Angle of the P_3 Relative to the Midline[1]
after Leonard and Hegmon

	Hadar	Chimpanzee
Female	39	39
Male	68	50

[1] See figure 6.3

These authors examined the question of whether there was variation in these anatomies through time. They found that the premolars of both sexes tend to increase their angulation, making them less suitable for shearing against the upper canine. However, the premolar crown morphology of the females appears stable over the *A. afarensis* time span, while the males evolved a more molarized form with equal sized cusps. The sex difference in morphology combined with the different evolutionary patterns suggests sex differences in function. Leonard and Hegmon propose that this may reflect feeding differences; for instance males may have eaten more lower quality foods during at least some times of the year, accounting for their marked sexual dimorphism in postcanine tooth size and their greater premolar moralization described above. Feeding differences could indicate that there were differences in the daily ranges of males and females, a possibility the authors hypothesize may reflect female responsibility for multiple dependent offspring.

While the range of Hadar premolar morphology incorporates that found at Laetoli, the functional evidence is somewhat different. At Laetoli there is evidence of transverse motion, bringing the top and as the jaws close the sloping buccal face of the premolar across the distal face of the maxillary canine, thereby creating honing wear at the back of the upper canine as discussed above. Greenfield makes a series of similar observations for the Hadar specimens. However, as White notes the wear on the Hadar canines is more blunting.

None of the Hadar specimens shows point-producing crown wear, honing wear facets on the upper canine, or the pattern of P_3 wear exhibited on Laetoli specimens (and on juvenile orangutans; their short deciduous canines and their bicuspid dm_1's, with a transverse ridge connecting the cusps, makes them an anatomical and functional analog for the Laetoli hominids). The wear on the Hadar anterior dentitions reflects the end of a series of behavioral changes in the hominids. The Hadar P_3 's are more often incorporated in the grinding complex, and the canine was not used in cutting. However, some of the canines still projected beyond the occlusal plane of the other teeth and show multiple flat wear facets as the result of incidental wear against the opposing mandibular teeth.

Therefore, the few functional differences between the Hadar and Laetoli dental samples may reflect the later date for Hadar. Within the much larger sample of Hadar specimens, the variation in size and morphology is marked, and much of it is probably the result of sexual dimorphism. The two samples quite clearly are time slices taken from the same evolving hominid species.

My, Grandma, What Big Teeth You Have!

The postcanine teeth are perhaps most distinctive in their size. If we compare the combined areas (lengths time breadths) of all the postcanine teeth to the estimated body weight, Lucy, the earliest grandma to leave a dentition and postcranial skeleton, "weighs in" with a ratio of 2.3%. This is more than double the 1.1% average for chimpanzee relative postcanine size, or the 1% modern human average (a .9% female and 1.1% male average for the central Australian Walbiri - see table 6.10). Similar results were obtained by McHenry. He uses an allometric analysis of African hominoids to show that Lucy's relative tooth size is some 2.8 times that expected for a hominoid of her estimated body weight

Dental Variation at Hadar - sex or species?

If the large dental sample at Hadar is unusual in any respect, it must surely be in its variation. The question many scientists have grappled with is whether this reflects

- taphonomy - circumstances of sampling and deposition in this death assemblage
- time span represented - especially if dental changes were taking place
- a biological cause such as
    - sexual dimorphism
    - different species with isolated, protected gene pools each varying its own way

T. White and colleagues have argued that much of this variation appears to be the result of an ape-like magnitude of sexual dimorphism. Size and canine morphology characteristics can be used to suggest the sex of many dentognathic remains, if we can assume that the same criteria apply to these ancient hominids that are used for sex determination in much more recent peoples. Should the sex determinations be correct, two of the most complete female and a male maxillas (AL-199 and AL-200, figure 6.5) show as much percentage dimorphism in their posterior teeth as living orangutans. While some of the male and female mandibles differ even more, the *average* postcanine dimorphism between male and female *samples* is similar to the more dimorphic apes, gorillas and orangutans (table 6.8). Dimorphism in the canines, while greater than in the other teeth, is much less than in the dimorphic apes, for instance gorillas. It is much more similar to the thick enameled fossil apes such as the European dryopithecines. The marked molar size dimorphism mentioned above is another similarity with these dryopithecines, which I take to reflect the ancestral (plesiomorphic) condition even though the Ravin dryopithecines are not (contra authors such as L. DeBonis and his colleagues) direct hominid ancestors. J. Kelley and D. Etler show a similar pattern of marked molar dimorphism in the Lufeng Sivapithecini, where they argue that although its magnitude greatly exceeds living apes species (others had argued that the molar variability reflected two species at Lufeng), the present is not necessarily a good guide for interpreting the past in this case. They conclude that only one primate species was present there, providing a sample that parallels Ravin in these patterns - almost certainly because the samples are large. I concur, and would add that the early hominids retain this ancestral pattern. It is the living apes with high canine and low molar dimorphism that have an unusual dimorphism pattern.

Table 6.8
Percent Sexual Dimorphism (100 × M/F)
adapted from Frayer and Wolpoff (1985) and McHenry (1991)

	Lower Canine Breadth	M$_2$ Breadth	Femur Length	Mandible Height
Gorilla	138	107	121	124
Pan	123	104	104	109
European dryopithecine (Ravin de la Pluie)	130	112		136
Australopithecus afarensis	128	111		118
Australopithecus africanus	117	109	121	119
European Neandertals	116	105	108	116
Zalavar (9-12 C Hungarian)	108	106	109	109

However, these comparisons could be invalid if the attributions of sex to the fossil specimens are incorrect. An alternative way to compare variation is to use the **coefficient of variation** - a measure based on the relative standard deviation (the ratio of the standard deviation to the mean, multiplied by 100). R. Kay has argued that when this coefficient is calculated for a sample including males and females, high values reflect a great degree of sexual dimorphism in the species. Therefore, the coefficient can be used to compare magnitudes of sexual dimorphism in a sample, even when the sexes of the specimens in it are unknown. This particular issue was also addressed because one of the scientists who believed that the Hadar sample was actually two species, T. Olson, cited 'too much tooth size variation' as one basis for his claim. Independent studies by T. Cole and F. Smith, and by W. Kimbel and colleagues, examined the coefficient of variations for *A. afarensis* teeth and compared these with other primates (table 6.9).

Simply put, both studies showed that the *A. afarensis* teeth have less relative variation than gorillas or orangutans, and the canines are considerably less so (table 6.9). These are the same conclusions that were drawn from comparisons based on the assumption that the individuals specimens had been correctly sexed, but in this case no specific sex determinations were made. The magnitude of dimorphism in the Hadar sample may be large compared with subsequent hominid species, but is not at all unusual for a pongid. However, as Cole and Smith point out the pattern is different, as it combines postcanine variation, and by implication dimorphism, as great as in the most dimorphic of the apes with a much lower magnitude of canine variation (although still the most variable of all the teeth).

Table 6.9
Variation[1] for *Australopithecus afarensis* and Dimorphic Ape Mandibular Teeth[2]

Mandibular Tooth	Australopithecus afarensis breadth CV	Gorilla breadth CV	Pongo breadth CV
I1	2.3	9.3	9.2
I2	8.4	10.6	9.9
C	11.9	17.6	20.0
P3	8.3	10.0	11.4
P4	7.7	8.2	9.5
M1	6.8	6.4	7.8
M2	7.7	7.0	8.1
M3	7.1	7.9	9.5

[1] Measured by the CV, or **coefficient of variation**, the standard deviation as a percentage of the mean

[2] Data from Cole and Smith (1987), similar comparisons for some of the teeth were published by Kimbel and colleagues

It is probable that the comparison of variation in the postcanine teeth and canines reflects two different aspects of sexual dimorphism. In the anthropoid primates, as in many other mammals, dimorphism is reflected in a large body size difference between males and females. This is almost certainly the cause of the postcanine tooth variation in the pongids compared here, since in human populations the postcanine tooth sizes are partially related to body size whether it is measured by height or weight. The australopithecine sample is similar in postcanine variation to the apes that average male body weight double that of females (table 6.10). It is quite credible that the same applies to these early hominids, and that the males were, on the average, close to twice the weight of females (I estimate a ratio of 1.7 for the species based on hindlimb weight determinations). A number of human populations have an average male/female weight ratios a quarter or less than that of the dimorphic apes (roughly 1.25 compared with 2.0). In any moderate sized group it is easy to find individual men who weigh twice as much as women. However, when a ratio of 2 (or, perhaps 1.7 like these early hominids) is the *population average*, variation in both sexes assures us that it will be easy to find individual men who weigh three or even four times as much as particular women, even in a fairly small sample. This goes a long way toward explaining some of the *A. afarensis* postcranial variation discussed below, especially when the smallest and largest specimens in the sample are compared.

Table 6.10
Body Weights (kg) for Dimorphic Apes[1] and a Human Group[2]

	Male Mean	Female Mean	Ratio	CV for M_1 breadth
Pongo pygmaeus	78.8	38.8	2.0	7.8
Gorilla gorilla	157.9	75.4	2.1	6.4
Australians[2]	59.6	47.4	1.3	5.0

[1] From McHenry (1992)
[2] Accurate and meaningful human data are harder to come by than one might gather, because obesity is so common in just those populations for which data can be easily found, and because weight can change so much during life. These figures are for a Central Australian tribe, the Walbiri, with good longitudinal data gathered over several decades by T. Brown, G. Townsend, and colleagues. The weights used were chosen from the longitudinal series for each individual and represents the weight at the age they stopped increasing in height.

CRANIA AND MANDIBLES

Apart from a few earlier fragments, the Hadar australopithecines provide the earliest hominid cranial remains, and they certainly are the earliest fairly complete ones. Focusing on the best preserved specimens, females are known from "Lucy's" (AL 288-1) fragments and a cranial rear, AL 162-28. Males include the largely complete AL 444-2 and a reconstitution T. White produced from most of a face (AL 333-1) and cranial rear (AL 333-45) of two different individuals, from somewhat lower in the sequence (table 6.5). In addition there is a fairly complete child, AL 333-105. These specimens suggest that the species is characterized by a fundamentally chimpanzee-like braincase combined with a much larger face reflecting numerous adaptations to powerful mastication. Comparisons by W. Kimbel and colleagues show that this combination of very small cranial vaults and large prognathic faces with a large postcanine dentition and widely flaring, well developed cheeks is unknown among living primates. Kimbel, White, and Johanson published a particularly complete comparative analysis for the specimens known as of 1984 and the discussion below relies heavily on it.

Several brain sizes can be estimated for this sample. Two adult values are shown in table 6.11; these are very small, fully within the chimpanzee range. However, the male and female sizes are each above the chimpanzee means. Given the fact that the chimpanzees seem to be somewhat heavier, these early hominid vaults are relatively as well as absolutely larger. Using the estimated body weights to determine ratios of brain to body weight suggests the difference in relative brain size is quite large, possibly as much as 50% for females and about half that for males (because of the dramatic sexual dimorphism the human tendency for females to have relatively larger brain size than males is exaggerated in the early hominids). The brain weight/body weight ratio seems high, especially for the female estimates which are similar to living human values. Body size here is much smaller than living humans, however, and the effects of allometry need be taken into account. When the two early hominid values are plotted on a primate allometric curve (figure 6.11), they show relatively larger brain size than similarly sized apes, but the expansion is not dramatic. We can conclude that even if the modern chimpanzees reflect the ancestral condition for brain size (i.e. that there has been no expansion during their evolution), by some 3 million years ago there has been some increase in hominid brain size. This is at a time when some specimens still preserve evidence of canine cutting, and it is earlier than the first known stone tools (see below).

Table 6.11
Cranial Capacities of Hadar Specimens and Chimpanzees[1]

	Hadar	Chimpanzee
Male		
cranial capacity (cc) (range)	485 (AL 333-45)[2]	399 (n=163) (292-500)
mean body weight (g)	44600	47900
percentage brain size	1.09	0.83
Female		
cranial capacity (cc) (range)	375-400 (AL 162-28)	371 (n=200) (282-460)
mean body weight (g)	26000	36500
percentage brain size	1.44-1.54	1.02

[1] Data from Tobias (1971), Holloway (1988), McHenry (1992), and table 5.2. Body weights in this and all subsequent comparisons are based on hindlimb articular surface analysis whenever possible, and always using the hominid limb-length to weight relationship.
[2] AL 444-2 is slightly larger - its exact capacity is unknown at the time of writing but it is probably more or less 500 cc. This is not enough difference to significantly change the percentage brain size.

The increased cranial capacity affects some parts of the brain much more than others, and can be taken as an indication of significant neural reorganization. One of the brain endocasts (AL 162-28) was studied by R. Holloway. He found evidence of neural reorganization in two anatomical areas (table 4.HW); the position of the lunate sulcus, reflecting the expansion of the secondary association area in the posterior parietal cerebral cortex at the expense of the visual area, and the expansion of the inferior parietal lobule. The parietal cortex increase, as discussed in Chapter 4, reflects the dramatic hominid expansion of this alternative association area that is involved in the integration of sensory information (i.e. cross-modal matching), not incoincidentally bypassing the limbic system. A. Mann suggests the expansion of the inferior parietal lobule is of particular importance as well. Its enlargement reflects expanded environmental (and Holloway adds social) mapping. He links the increased need to learn these representations to the extended period of maturation. Direct evidence for delayed maturation in the Hadar sample is unknown, as no subadult specimen preserves the appropriate teeth to analyze relative development. However, as discussed above there are several Laetoli children who can be analyzed and these provide evidence indicating a maturational delay within the normal human range.

Contrasting with the expanded brain size, many other features of the cranial vaults resemble chimpanzees. Especially at the cranial rear and on its base there are some features that reflect a pattern of muscle use that is not unlike those of closely related apes. For instance, the mandibular fossa is very flat -

there is little vertical distance between the resting place of the mandibular condyle (its position with the mouth closed), and the articular surface where the condyle is positioned during chewing (see Chapter 4 for a discussion of the chewing cycle). According to research by R. Hinton, the details of mandibular fossa form develop during life. This particular morphology reflects a predominance of **anterior tooth loading** - the regular use of the front teeth in clamping and pulling. This could mean aggressive biting, but just as well may reflect behaviors such as leaf stripping described above. An independent reflection of dominant anterior tooth use was noticed by T. White. At the front of the mandibular body there is a passage way (foramen) for the mandibular nerve to exit the bone. As the bone remodels around this opening, its orientation comes to face in the direction of the most remodeling. In chimpanzees, with their pronounced anterior tooth use, the passage faces anteriorly, while in most hominids (and especially robust australopithecines), with more emphasis on posterior loading, the foramen has a posterior orientation. In the Hadar (and Laetoli) hominids the foramen faces anteriorly. The opposite mandibular fossa morphology, a deep fossa with a marked inferior displacement for the mandibular condyle in its position during chewing, is according to Hinton a reflection of **posterior tooth loading** - the production of high force magnitudes between the postcanine teeth. Its appearance in later australopithecines is related to a decrease in anterior loading magnitudes and the expansion of the postcanine teeth, especially of the premolars which are best situated under the masticatory muscles such as masseter and the anterior part of temporalis (see Chapter 4).

A number of other features suggest that the nuchal muscles are very well developed, but are set onto the head at an angle that is closer to horizontal. The occiputs are very broad, two males exceeding the values for all other australopithecines in their breath dimensions. The **nuchal plane** is the part of the occiput below the **nuchal torus** (the ridge formed by the top of the nuchal muscles) where these neck muscles attach. In *A. afarensis* the length of the nuchal plane is less than in chimpanzees of similar head size, but he breadth of the nuchal plane is much greater than in chimpanzees (as one would expect from the broad occiputs). This shape difference in the nuchal muscle attachment is generally characteristic for early hominids, and reflects their emphasis on muscles important in lifting and pulling at the shoulder. The angle of the nuchal plane is quite different from chimpanzees. It is closer to the horizontal - for instance 50° in AL 162-28 and 45° in AL 333-45, as compared with a mean angle of 69° (56°-77°) in a chimpanzee sample. The greater horizontality reflects the consequences of bipedal stance, as does the anterior position of the **foramen magnum.** This foramen is not just the entry-way for the spinal chord into the braincase, but also is the pivot for neck rotation (the top vertebra or atlas articulation with the head) and the point there the weights and forces acting on the head must balance. The relative position of the foramen magnum is considerably more to the rear in chimpanzees; according to W. Kimbel and colleagues, the distance from the front of the foramen magnum to the back of the head, as a proportion of the total head length, is 51% in the 333-45 male (the chimpanzee average is 33%).

The nuchal muscles and their angulation reflect more than stance and head balance. They also respond to the forces generated in anterior tooth loading - forces thought to be prominent because of the large anterior tooth sizes. Another consequence of this tooth use pattern is the strong development of the posterior, more horizontally oriented, part of the temporalis muscle. It extends so far backwards that the lines marking the muscle attachment areas for the nuchal and posterior temporalis muscles meet at the back of the adult crania, forming a **compound temporonuchal crest** (a compound crest is a ridge of bone caused by the pull of two muscles working in different directions - in this case the nuchal muscles pulling downward and the temporal muscles pulling forward). As a whole this configuration at the base of the skull is very ape-like and was once thought to reflect an ape-like head carriage and the absence of true bipedalism in australopithecines (see S. Zuckerman, for instance). We now understand it to be a consequence of high magnitudes of force used in anterior tooth loading, superimposed on a small cranial vault - small enough for the neck and jaw muscles to meet at the rear. And, its details differ from the chimpanzee condition. The apes the compound crest comes virtually or completely to the center of the back of the head whereas in the hominids the compound crest is much less extensive and only at the outer corners.

The sagittal cresting pattern of *Australopithecine afarensis* is variable, but generally much more reminiscent of the apes than the cresting in the nuchal region. Its arrangement in the early hominids is of some interest. Following along the sagittal suture at the top of the skull, is a compound crest caused by the meeting of the temporalis muscles from each side. A sagittal crest appears whenever the combination of temporal muscle size and brain size allows the muscles to reach the midline at the cranium's top. Therefore it shows sexual dimorphism, since compared with body size male crania are relatively smaller than female crania (table 6.11), while there is no relative difference in temporalis size (larger bodies require proportionally more calories and consequently more chewing - the proportionality applying as long as male and female diets are the same). In gorillas all males and many females are crested, while in chimpanzees some males and no females have this crest. The African ape crests, when they occur, are usually posteriorly situated along the sagittal suture, a consequence of their emphasis on (and development of) the more horizontal, posterior, portion of the temporalis muscle that follows from their anterior tooth use. The female Hadar specimens described above lack sagittal crests, while the males AL 444-2 and AL 333-125 have them. This would seem to fit the chimpanzee pattern in which no females and only some males are crested. However, a penecontemporaneous specimen from the Lake Turkana region, ER 2602 discussed below, also has a sagittal crest and this vault is otherwise the size of the Hadar females. The presence of crests on some members of both sexes, but not others, suggests that populational polymorphisms in body size and diet also play roles in crest expression. This pattern of population variation is unlike chimpanzees (or other living apes).

The anatomical details of cresting vary markedly in the small sample. As B. Asfaw points out, AL 333-125 has an anteriorly developed crest which unlike any chimpanzee extends onto the frontal bone (actually, a plesiomorphic condition in the Pongidae - see Chapter 3). This suggests a much more powerful anterior temporalis development than the African apes ever show - an important component of the powerful posterior tooth loading complex found in all species of *Australopithecus*, and not a surprising morphology to be found in this earliest species with its large postcanine teeth compared with similarly sized apes. Yet, AL 444-2 has a crest that is only developed on the posterior part of the vault. The posterior aspect of the muscle is more expanded and chimpanzee-like in the AL 333-45 male as well. In these males the temporalis muscle extends onto the occipital, meeting the nuchal muscles and forming a compound temporonuchal crest on the outer parts of each side of the bone, as described above. The temporalis muscle, in sum, can be relatively large in both its posterior and anterior aspects, and the muscle-size to brain-size relation is similar to but probably larger than the chimpanzee condition (this is presumably why some females such as ER 2602 are crested). With brain sizes larger than chimpanzees, the different relationship reflects the consequences of the markedly bigger Hadar teeth.

The face of this species is a unique aspect of its anatomy, clearly reflecting the merging of the chewing adaptations described above. Known from only a few specimens, the top of the face is defined by a flattened forehead and distinct supraorbitals (browridges). In males such as AL 444-2 these can be moderately thick while in females such as Lucy they are defined as a poorly developed bar across the top of the orbits, offset from the **squama** (the flat part) of the frontal bone by the **temporal lines** (the lines or very low ridges on the bone formed by the edge of the temporalis muscle) as they converge toward the top of the skull. The supraorbitals are much more a part of the frontal bone than in chimpanzees, where they protrude in front of the squama like the overhang of a house's roof. In the chimpanzees, this protruding torus is separated from the frontal squama by a distinct angle, forming a broad trough at the torus-squama juncture known as a **supratoral sulcus.** The Hadar frontals are very similar to the Belohdelie specimen, in lacking the supratoral sulcus and in terms of their combination of greater breadth across the temporal fossa combined with their reduced sagittal length. Breadth between the temporal fossae in Belohdelie and AL 444-2, for instance, is greater than in most chimpanzees and any other australopithecine specimen. The similarities between these two frontals (as well as comparisons of earlier postcranials with Hadar) suggest to Kimbel and colleagues that *A. afarensis* provides "a persuasive body of evidence for prolonged stasis". But stasis must be established by comparing samples with many well-represented skeletal elements, not just a few individuals preserving largely different body parts.

Y. Rak describes the *A. afarensis* face as large and robustly developed, with some special structures buttressing the front where the anterior tooth roots are held. Faces from this sample have many chimpanzee-like features, such as the marked prognathism and the projection of the anterior of the palate (the part that holds the incisors) in front of the canine roots. He considers the main differences that distinguish this hominid from a chimpanzee-like ancestor to be

- retraction of the palate from a position in front of the face to under it
- deeper cheeks
- forward shift of the cheeks (zygomatic process of the maxilla, and zygomatic bone) and of the front of the masseter muscle
- expansion of the anterior part of the temporalis muscle
- structural changes in the jaws related to
  - expanding premolars and molars
  - incisor and (especially) canine reduction and decreased emphasis on anterior loading

These trends are an important component of early hominid evolution and continue through the Pliocene, their continued development serving to distinguish later hominids from *A. afarensis.* They continue to develop over time and as their expression becomes even more pronounced there is a morphological clade linking australopithecine species. For instance, later in time and in more pronounced form they distinguish Swartkrans robust australopithecines from *A. africanus.* Facial details, of course, are not the same in male and female Hadar specimens. Females such as AL 417-1 have shorter faces with less prognathism (especially less under the nose) and smaller canines.

A. afarensis is the most primitive of the hominids, least characterized by these trends. The front of the face is dramatically prognathic, a configuration shared with chimpanzees. Also resembling the African apes there two distinct contours to the face, as seen in side view. One of these is a fairly straight line formed by the flat nasal bones and extending down the prominent pillars enclosing the expanded canine roots. The other is formed by the prognathic upper jaw.

In both chimpanzees and the early hominids, the combination of large central incisors and a narrow nose usually brings the roots of the lateral incisors to the outsides of the margins of the nasal aperture. This places the canines far to the outside of these thin margins. The canine roots of both species are large (more massive, of course, in the apes), and act as anchors, or supports, in the face against the forces generated when the anterior teeth are used powerfully. Only one Hadar specimen differs somewhat from this anatomy. With its smaller anterior teeth, the AL 417-1 canines (rather than lateral incisors) lie on the outside of the nose, whose much thicker margins are therefore formed of the robust canine root buttresses. These root buttresses are enclosed in distinct pillars along the nasal edge in this specimen, which Rak refers to as **anterior pillars**.

Projecting in front of the flattened nasal region is a convex-shaped upper jaw, beginning its outward curvature just below the nose and enclosing procumberant incisors. The palate is narrow and shallow and its roof is thin. Above it, in the nasal opening, the insertion for the nasal cartilage is recessed into the nose, suggesting that the external nose had little or no projection, also like chimpanzees (figure 6.6). To the sides, the massive widely flared cheeks of the Hadar faces support prominent masseter muscles, positioned far to the outside of the mandible so as to give them a strong horizontal component of force - an important source of the side-to-side motion when the postcanine teeth are used in grinding. The masseter muscle begins its cranial attachment at a fairly posterior place that is near the level of the first molar as in the Miocene apes, and also like them the anterior of the muscle is positioned low, close to the tooth row (figure 6.7). The lower cheek border supporting this muscle extends toward the toothrow in a straight line so that there is solid bone between the toothrow and themasseter attachment, two places where strong forces act on these crania. Rak argues that with the anterior pillars, this **maxillary shelving** forms a structural frame for reinforcing the cheek below the orbits (figure 6.8). The deep, flaring cheeks that support this muscle also surround the temporal fossa, which must be large to enclose the bulky temporalis muscle described above. This masticatory-related complex is superimposed on what is otherwise a very chimpanzee-like middle and upper face (especially the nose and the features surrounding it).

The mandibles vary widely, ranging from specimens similar to Laetoli 4 to others, generally smaller, which have a narrower anterior region and more closely resemble the *Kenyapithecus* condition of straight, posteriorly divergent tooth rows. These variants in the shape of the toothrow may reflect differences in size, sex, or both. An even greater range of variation is suggested by the less complete fragments. Probably the greatest distinction from the Laetoli mandibles is at the symphysis. The Afar specimens tend to be more vertical on the external face. Internally, the two buttresses are more equal in size, and the lower buttress is more rounded and less shelf-like. These differences reflect the changing anterior tooth functions described above.

Generally, the other mandibular differences parallel those already discussed for tooth size, and it is likely that a major component in the variation is a size-related one resulting from a significant average difference between males and females. This is suggested by the fact that most of the total range of mandibular variation is expressed at the 333 site alone, where it is possible that the individuals sampled are closely related. The ramus is vertical and very large relative to the mandibular body. Its size reflects the size of the masseter muscle, while its vertical height tends to even out the occlusal forces across the toothrow, according to work by S. Ward and S. Molnar. There is a marked size and shape difference between the male and female rami. The male condition is an almost square structure - height and breadth are virtually identical - while the female morphology features a much lower ramus, about 3/4 of the diminished height. The variation in just two specimens is at the high and low extremes of the range for 10 chimpanzees. Analysis of the much larger sample of mandibular bodies (the corpus, or tooth-holding part) by B. Kimbel and colleagues shows a pattern (and range) of variation that most closely resembles gorillas. The main differences in mandibular dimensions are in corpus height. Corpus breadth is much more similar through the sample regardless of size. This means females will be more robust, in that they are relatively broader. In all, these are highly variable mandibles, largely due to the marked sexual dimorphism of the sample, with the ramus providing attachment for powerful masticatory muscles and the corpus supporting the well-developed postcanine roots (see the discussion of the Lothagam mandible's molar roots above) and moderate anterior teeth that were powerfully loaded in a variety of ways.

POSTCRANIA

More than 60% of the Hadar sample is comprised of postcranial remains, providing the first detailed glimpse of early hominid postcranial adaptations. Included in them are several individuals with multiple skeletal elements, a knee and an arm for instance, a possibly associated humerus and femur from the 333 site (AL 333-109 and 333-3), a partial upper limb skeleton (AL 438-1), and AL 288-1 (Lucy) - much of the skeleton of an extraordinarily small female (figure 6.9). The pelvis, lower limbs, and foot of this skeleton (and others) show a complete adaptation to the obligate, striding bipedalism that characterizes later hominids, and transformations in the pelvic inlet that suggest significant alterations in birthing (see Chapter 4) from the ape condition. However, proportion of arm bones and arm to leg length, and some of the pelvic dimensions, differ from living humans, and the hand morphology lacks certain features thought to reflect the specialized requirements of toolmaking and tooluse.

The postcranial skeleton, then, reveals some general differences between recent and living people and the Hadar hominids. One of these is size. Lucy was only some 105 cm (just under 3.5 feet) in height. Her weight - 27 kg or so, as calculated by McHenry, is very small and yet relative to her height it is a little on the heavy side (in comparison with living humans) according to L. Aiello. Lucy, however, is one of the smallest individuals from Hadar and other more fragmentary postcranial remains represent larger individuals. For instance, McHenry estimates a 40.4 cm length for the AL 333-3 femur, which is 1.5 times as long as the 27 cm length of Lucy's femur. She is not at all the smallest *A. afarensis* femur known (ER 16002, see below is ,markedly smaller), and even fragments of larger femora have been reported (and should not be unexpected, given the magnitude of sexual dimorphism). Dimorphism in upper limb remains is not as great, the AL 137-50 humerus or 438-1 ulna being about 25% longer than Lucy. Remembering that weight is proportional to the cube of height, the estimates discussed above suggest that males may have *averaged* between 1.7 times (postcranial based, see table 5.2) and 2 times (dentition based, see table 6.9) the weight of females. This estimate of dimorphism implies that males were about the size of Pygmy men, and females were much smaller than women in any living human group. Individuals, of course, can vary much more than this and as discussed above it should not be extremely difficult to find males that are 3-4 times as heavy as the smallest females, given this magnitude of *average* dimorphism. The most extreme femur length comparison clearly reflects the consequences of this prediction.

A second difference is in the bony features reflecting muscularity. It is clear from the size of the joint articulations, the morphology and buttressing of many of the bones (ranging from the fingers to the long bones), and the thickness of the limbs that the Afar hominids were muscularly powerful. Their strength was probably far more like that of a chimpanzee of similar size than that of much larger modern humans. Bony adaptations to strength come as the result of powerful and prolonged muscle use.

A third difference is in proportions. Lucy is an obligate biped, and for biomechanical reasons the only homologous comparisons of her locomotor elements are with other obligate bipeds; mostly, in other words, with living humans although there is another fairly complete australopithecine skeleton (STS 14), many skeletal elements of a *Homo habilis* specimen (OH 62), and an early *Homo sapiens* youth (WT 15000). The problem in this situation is that the tendency is to compare Lucy to these and then try to explain the differences; after all, we know a great deal about the function and mechanics of bipedalism in our own species. Yet this has it backwards, because it is *H. sapiens* (and the other later specimens) that came to differ from Lucy and not the reverse. With this in mind, perhaps the best generalization is that the proportions of Lucy are different. It is not just a matter of having relatively long arms (or short legs) as the humeral/femoral index of 84% suggests (table 6.12), because (among other things):

- limb shafts are relatively thick,
- there are 6 lumbar vertebrae, as in all early hominids with complete lumbar columns,
- the vertebrae and the sacrum are diminutive; specifically small are
  - the vertebral bodies and sacrum, and by implication the intervertebral disks between them
  - the vertebral canals, and by implication the spinal column they enclose
- the rear of the vertebrae (the part supporting the dorsal muscles of the back) are robust and well developed
- the pelvis is disproportionately large relative to the rest of the skeleton,
- and various dimensions of the pelvis are disproportionate to each other,
- the trunk may have been somewhat more funnel-shaped than cylindrical

The mean relative humerus length for the female Pygmies is 12%, the same as Lucy. The mean relative femur length for the female Pygmy is 17%, somewhat higher than Lucy although her value is well within the range of the small sample. Thus, compared to the trunk both of these limbs have relative lengths within the range of small humans, although no individual combines their exact proportions. This is because her legs are shown to be relatively short in this and other comparisons. A. Schultz's observes that relative upper limb length in living humans is much like that in the other large bodied hominoids - relatively long compared with monkeys, but shorter than the specialized gibbons. If human and ape arms are of similar relative lengths, and Lucy's arm length is similar to the mean Pygmy value, it is likely that Lucy's arms reflect the pre-divergence anthropithecine condition and that no selection altered their relative length. It follows that relative arm length has remained unchanged throughout human evolution.

The elongation of Lucy-length legs is the change that brought *A. afarensis* limb proportions to the modern human relationship. W. Junger's observation that further leg elongation is one of the major postcranial changes from *A. afarensis* to *H. sapiens* is correct, but he is wrong, I believe, in attributing this change to increased bipedal efficiency. Bipedal locomotion encompasses a broad range of locomotor behaviors under very different conditions, and morphological changes that adversely affect some of these are helpful for others. Moreover, R. Francicus and T. Holliday were able to demonstrate that Lucy's stride length and frequency were within the human range and not quantitatively distinct. Insofar as these parameters affect energy efficiency, Lucy's was within the modern range as well, but compared with the *average* for humans of all sizes she was not as efficient for long distance walking, although more efficient for running in short spurts. Her relative leg length, and many other aspects of her lower body anatomy (discussed below) such as the large joint sizes in her lower limbs that reflect the different mechanical requirements of obligate bipedalism, are quite different from chimpanzees.

Table 6.12
Comparison of AL 288-1 and a Small Pygmy Woman

	Lucy (AL 288-1	Small Pygmy Woman[1]
Height (cm)	105	123
Weight (kg)	27	30[2]
Cranial capacity (cc)	350-400	1072
Postcanine mandibular tooth area (P4-M2) (mm^2)	384	255
Humerus length (cm)	23.5	24.4
Humerus head diameter relative to length	11.5%	12.7%
Femur length (cm)	28	33
Femur shaft robustness (midshaft circumference relative to length)	25.3%	18.4%
Femur head diameter relative to length	9.6%	10.4%
Limb Proportions relative to the height of the 3rd lumbar vertebra[3] (comparison is with the range of female Pygmy values*)		
Relative humerus length	12%	10%-14%
Relative femur length	15%	14%-19%

[1]   Unless noted, Pygmy dimensions from McHenry
[2]   Estimated from Efé female weight-height regression to better estimate the expected value for this woman
[3]   The AL 288-1ak vertebrae used for this was identified as an L3 when first described. Subsequently D. Cook and colleagues argued that it is an L2. The Efé comparisons were also made relative to L2 height, with this possibility in mind, but there were no significant changes in the relative limb length ranges.
*   From Wolpoff (1983b)

There are three interdependent reasons why relative leg length increased in the course of human evolution, certainly by the first appearance of *H. sapiens.*

1. **Allometric**: larger individuals have longer legs relative to their forearm length
2. **Climatic**: body size changes will effect height, while girth can be expected to remain more constant in any particular climate, in spite of increasing body size, so larger individuals will have longer legs relative to their trunk.
3. **Locomotor**: long lower limbs are most efficiently used in long distance, low energy striding

In independent studies, C. Ruff, R. Franciscus and T. Holliday, and I have shown that leg elongation is an allometric consequence of increasing body size (figure 6.4). No *H. sapiens* is as small as AL 288-1 and other early hominid females such as STS 14 and OH 62, which is why there are no individuals with her relative arm/leg length ratio. Larger, human-size bodies will automatically have relatively longer legs because of their expanded size. For instance, the 333 association is from a much larger individual, 40% heavier in McHenry's estimated weights, based on femur size. The specimen's estimated humeral/femoral index is 78, at the top of the human range, according to C.O. Lovejoy, and Franciscus and Holliday estimate an elongated limb length/body weight ratio for the specimen. This confirms the allometric relation that several have suggested, but also indicates that the smaller *A. afarensis* lower limbs (and the lower limbs of other diminutive hominids) are relatively short. At least part of the reason *H. sapiens* has relatively longer legs is allometric - *H. sapiens* is bigger. However, there is probably more than size alone that is responsible for lower limb length increases.

In a different analysis, Ruff suggests that climatic adaptation also plays an important role in the changing pelvic and lower limb proportions that come with body larger size. Ruff focuses on the fact that tropically adapted mammals tend to maximize the ratio of their body's surface area to volume. Body heat is lost at the skin surface - a loss that is the goal of a tropical adaptation. There are two ways to achieve a maximum surface area to volume ratio, small body size and long limbs. Therefore, it is possible for heat-adapted populations to vary considerably in body size, the long limbs of larger bodies making up for the larger size, as far as this ratio is concerned. Ruff further illustrates that if the body is thought of as approximating a cylinder, changes in its cross-sectional diameter will affect the surface area to volume ratio, while changing height will not. Thus, Ruff contends, it is the trunk and pelvic diameters of human bodies that we can expect to remain constant in a given environment, while limb and trunk lengths can change in response to selection that is not related to climatic adaptation, as long as larger individuals have relatively longer limbs.

What would such selection be? Answers are suggested in the work of P. Wheeler, who contends that lower limb elongation in hominids reflects more intense grasslands utilization. He points out that leg elongation will increase the surface area to volume ratio for hominids, improving their ability to radiate excess heat and evaporate sweat. Longer legs also brings the body mass higher above the ground into a **microhabitat** where the air is cooler and more likely to be in motion. Larger hominids, he suggests, would dehydrate more slowly in open tropical environments. Simulating the **thermoregulatory** adaptations of equal weight hominids with australopithecine and *Homo sapiens* limb proportions, taking both water loss and stride length differences into account, Wheeler estimates a 20%-30% greater water requirement for the australopithecine-proportioned hominid.

In sum, within a given environment, the climatic and allometric analyses concur to predict that larger hominids will have relatively longer legs. The main cause of unusual early hominid limb proportions is their very small size. Subsequent increases in hominid body size involved relative leg elongation for both improvements in stride length and climatic adaptation, and these advantages no doubt played an important role in the body size increases. Conversely, these arguments imply that the adaptive advantages enjoyed by the midget-sized australopithecines may be found in less open, wetter environments. This is not dissimilar from the environmental reconstructons that have been developed for Hadar.

Pelvis and Lower Limb

Because the earliest known hominid pelvic remains are Lucy's, a considerable amount of detail is known about the details of the entire pelvis and lower limb. These details have laid to rest the long debate over the pattern of australopithecine locomotion, revealing the earliest hominids to be efficient obligate bipeds, as R. Dart and later C. Lovejoy claimed in all of their publications. Their analyses, accomplished on more fragmentary specimens before Lucy was discovered, have become one of the classic derivations of function from form in paleontology, and reflects the triumph of the deductive reasoning of biomechanical analysis over multivariate associations that distinguish measurements of the anatomy without providing insight into why the associations are distinguishable. Functional analysis suggests three main influences on hominid pelvic morphology:

1. locomotion,
2. climatic adaptation
3. birthing

The AL 288 innominate is fully adapted to obligate bipedalism and a striding gait, in the features and proportions corresponding to its functions in locomotion as detailed in Chapter 4. These anatomical details provide for the same muscle positions that are found in living humans and in fact all other known hominids. Apart from the increases in body size that occur near the beginning of the Pleistocene, the main causes of pelvic variation during human evolution are probably to be found in the second and third influences on pelvic variation, climate and birthing. The critical osteological features of Lucy's innominates are (figure 4.10):

- distinct anterior spines (superior and inferior)
- a greater sciatic notch

- an ilium that is
    short relative to its breadth
    rotated forward (as seen from above)
    flares dramatically outward above the hip
- a short ischium.

The AL 288-1 pelvic inlet is unusually broad. Major contributors to the broad pelvic inlet are the long pubic bones and the broad sacrum at its rear, in comparison with the narrow sacra of chimpanzees. The sacrum breadth also reflects the expanded size of the vertebral bodies, a function of their role in weight transmission in bipeds. Yet, sacrum breadth in Lucy (and STS 14) is small compared with later humans, with even larger pelvic inlets. Three elements contribute to the breadth of these early hominid pelves:

1. a broad birth canal (especially the inlet to the pelvic aperture) to provide room
    for wide shoulders
2. a broad pelvic rim for weight support (viscera because of the more conical trunk
    shape, and pregnancy-related changes in women)
3. broad hips to improve leverage for the balance-related gluteal muscles

Birth-related changes in the australopithecine pelvis indicate a transverse position for the head during the birth process (see Chapter 4, and below). Shoulder breadth, rather than the diminutive australopithecine head size, would appear to have been the limiting factor. C.O. Lovejoy, who reconstructed Lucy, suggests that her pelvic breadth reflects the broadening of the pelvic basin that is required to support the lower viscera during upright stance. Perhaps more importantly, Lucy and the other complete australopithecine pelvis are both females, and as L Hager points out early hominid women spent a considerable part of their adult lives pregnant. Much of Lucy's anatomy may be a response to pregnancy-related changes in weight support and weight transmission. There is a third, also non-contradictory explanation. Her limb proportions described above and her slightly longer trunk (the presence of 6 lumbar vertebrae, in contrast to the normal number of 5 in living people), combine to suggest that Lucy had relatively more of her skeletal and muscular mass in her upper torso and forelimb than in larger hominids of modern human proportions. In considering the requirements of lateral balance during stride (Chapter 4), the **moment** (the length of the lever arm times the mass) of the upper torso and forelimbs around her acetabulum was large for this reason. Another factor increasing this moment is the great distance between the acetabulum of her supporting leg and the acetabulum on the side of the swinging leg (a consequence of the broad pelvic inlet). Together these create considerable momentum around the supporting hip joint and provide a second explanation for the very efficient development of the lateral balance mechanism in Lucy, and other australopithecines, particularly as reflected in the great lateral flare to the hip (and consequent broad pelvis). If, as I believe, these anatomical details are primitive in the hominids, the balance mechanism must be quite ancient.

The birth canal, of course, is large enough to give birth to australopithecine-shaped heads, if not with ease at least without the **obstetric** difficulties that is common in our own species. In fact, shoulder breadth rather that head size may have been the main limiting factor, accounting for the unusually narrowed elliptical shape of the birth canal. The main locomotor constraint on the obstetric pelvis was the need to vertically align the weight bearing joints, the sacrum (bringing upper body weight to the pelvis) and the acetabula (continuing the transmission of weight to the leg). This was accomplished by minimizing the distance form the sacrum to a line between the acetabula, and tilting the pelvis forward so that the top of the sacrum is positioned above this line. These changes limit the anterior-posterior dimension of the pelvic inlet, but it remains more free to vary in its transverse dimension. Tague and Lovejoy argue that the AL 288 pelvis is spacious for the head if it can be assumed that during birth the fetal cranium rotates into a transverse orientation throughout its trip through the obstetric pelvis, without the second rotation that is normal during for modern human birth. However, even the first rotation would make the birth process a slow one, according to Rosenberg, and the ease of births was more shoulder than head-size related. Australopithecine births were more difficult than today's chimpanzees, although it is not clear whether they were difficult enough to require Midwifery. They probably were laborious and dangerous enough to be social rather than solitary events. The magnitude of birth-related problems (how slow, how difficult?) is unknown and this leaves the question unanswered of whether australopithecine infants were as atricial (see Chapter 3) as human infants are today.

One consequence of the broad pelvic rim is found in the shape of the trunk. The ribcage just above the broad pelvic rim is correspondingly broad. With the bulk of the chest volume near its base, the top of the ribcage is narrower because chest volume is closely related to body size (and not trunk shape). Combined these give the trunk a conical appearance, contrasting with the more barrel-like human trunk shape and more closely resembling the chimpanzee condition. However, the conical appearance of chimpanzee trunks is even *more* striking as these primates have even narrower upper trunks. This is a consequence of their combined locomotor behaviors. In arm hanging and brachiation the scapula blade is positioned along the back which faces the glenoid joint outwards, but according to B Latimer the narrow shoulders allow the scapula to re-orient and face the glenoid forward (toward the ground in the quadrupedal position) during knuckle walking. Even still, the clavicles are long enough to affect important anatomical constraints during the birth process.

Pelvic breadth, then, responds to constraints of locomotion and the birth process. There is a thrid factor. Ruff, as reviewed above, argues that pelvic width will tend to remain constant in a given climate, independent of height, giving very small individuals a relatively broad pelvis, and females a relatively broader pelvis than males..

The lower limb shows commensurate adaptations to striding. For instance, the neck of the femur (the connection between its head and the long shaft) is elongated to position the shaft under the laterally flared hip. This length creates the potential for considerable bending, especially if the trunk often swayed from side to side as would occur if climbing or arboreal acrobatics similar to chimpanzees were common. In fact, because of these trunk positions, even the much shorter chimpanzee femur neck has a thick layer of compact bone to reinforce it. Yet, the longer necked human femurs, and their australopithecine predecessors beginning with the Maka femur neck, have very thin compact bone. This shows that the only significant force passing through the femur neck came during toe-off or as a consequence of the balance muscles and body weight which both force the femur head and the hip socket together. If there is no significant bending or twisting, bone can resist compression such as this easily, without any special modifications of thickening - an anatomy that characterizes the femur necks of obligate bipeds who gave up any specific adaptations for climbing, bridging between branches, or under branch positioning.

A high **bicondylar angle** results from the combination of broad pelvic (including biacetabular breadth) and short legs. With the tops of the legs far apart because the broad pelvic inlet separates the acetabula, the femur is angled strongly outward above its base because the knees must meet at the midline of the body. This is necessary as the supporting leg must be as aligned as possible under the center of gravity. At the base of the femur the bone surface is flattened, a consequence of the force that passes through the joint in one-legged support during walking, when the leg is fully straightened out. Another reflection of bipedalism is found in the relative size of the two ridges on the front of the femur's end. These are positioned on either side of the **patella** (knee-cap). When the quadriceps muscle is active it pulls the patella upward, but because of the flared ilium the anterior spines are well outside of the shaft's axis. The quadriceps therefore tend to pull the patella over the lateral ridge and the ridge on the outer edge must be taller to prevent the patella from displacing. Finally, Lovejoy's analysis of motions that are possible at the knee indicates that the adaptation to bipedalism included the finer details that might be expected to have evolved after the major more basic changes described above.

Foot

The Hadar collection is unusual, as foot elements are very well represented. These include part of the AL 288-1 foot, associated with many other postcranial elements, and a single individual (333-115) found encapsulated in a small carbonate block. As discussed in Chapter 4, the foot is modified for bipedalism, with the development of a double arch on its base and the loss of all grasping ability. Although it is widely cited in secondary sources that the Hadar toes are long and curved, neither is the case if body size is taken into account. Instead, most of the digits are greatly shortened compared with those of similarly sized chimpanzees. The best evidence is for Lucy (table 6.13), as she preserves the only association of foot elements with other skeletal parts. Her toe bones are short and human-like (the singular exception to shorter human toe lengths is the big toe, which is greatly expanded in length and thickness and aligned parallel with the other toes, adapting it to produce maximum force during toe-off). The isolated AL 115 foot has longer digits, and most likely comes from a larger male (perhaps, for instance, the 40% heavier AL 333-3 individual). There is no way to calculate relative toe length or curvature as there is nothing to relate to these, but according to Latimer the differences in *relative* toe lengths and curvatures in chimpanzees are so far from the human range (their toes, after all, are longer and more curved while their body sizes are generally smaller) that the isolated Hadar foot could not lie within or even near the chimpanzee range.

Table 6.13
Length of Lucy's Proximal Foot Phalange Relative to Humerus Length[1]

Digit Number	AL 288-1	Modern Human Range[2] (n=14 for each digit)	Chimpanzee Range[2] (n=14 for each digit)
II	8.5	7.5-9.7	10.7-13.5
III	8.5	7.0-9.0	12.2-15.7
IV	8.5	6.5-8.5	11.0-15.2

[1]   Data are given as percent of humerus range. Since the chimpanzee humerus is long, this *shortens* the relative length of the chimpanzee digits. Never the less, the relative chimpanzee digit lengths greatly exceed humans (and the associated AL 288-1 finger) strongly emphasizing the dramatic difference in relative lengths.

[2]   The comparison is with the maximum range for each of the 3 digits the Hadar toe might represent (its identification is as either digit II, III, or IV).

Moreover, like human toes, the four lesser digits can **dorsiflex** to a angle as great as 75°, but are limited in their plantar flexion (the opposite of the chimpanzee ability, see table 4.2). These modifications extend to the ankle, which is altered to support the entire body weight. The metric and morphological differences between the foot elements at Hadar and those of similar sized chimpanzees are really quite dramatic. As J. Langdon and colleagues note in their study of the foot's weight conversion abilities and longitudinal arch, virtually every skeletal adaptation to bipedalism known for modern humans can be found in the Hadar foot remains and the AL 333-115 foot reconstruction.

Forearm

Some scientists have suggested that the orientation of the shoulder and the form of the elbow show evidence of a climbing adaptation in some of the Hadar australopithecines. According to J. Stern and colleagues, Lucy's shoulder joint (the glenoid joint on the scapula) has an usual upward orientation compared with the more outward facing joint in living humans. They take this to indicate an adaptation to climbing. However, Lucy's body size raises the possibility that the difference in orientation is a consequence of her small size. In fact, a study of size related variation within humans shows that the smaller individual tend to have more upward facing joints. It is also possible that shape differences in her upper trunk positioned the glenoid joint on the body in a less upward orientation. The scapula is one of the two bones whose position is determined by muscles and not an articulation with other bones, so its orientation is sensitive to the shape of the trunk that it rests on. Moreover, a functional interpretation of this anatomy is confused by the fact that Lucy's scapular angles fall with the observed range of variation in modern populations, making it difficult to argue that her joint orientation reflects more arboreal activity than living people engage in.

B. Senut contends that there are two morphological patterns in the sample of Hadar forearms, reflected in the detailed anatomy at the elbow. She identifies one humerus fragment as identical to modern people, and three others (including Lucy) as being more "chimpanzee-like". However, the "modern-appearing" specimen (AL 333-29) is substantially larger than the other three in the few dimensions that can be compared, and sexual dimorphism is a much more likely explanation of their variation. The anatomical differences of this much larger male are probably a consequence of allometric scaling. Allometry continues to play a role in these interpretations for two reasons:

1. many of the Hadar australopithecines are much smaller than living humans so that the affects of size must be considered in comparisons
2. the variation between males and females (and especially between the larger males and the smaller females) is so great that the affects of size must be considered in comparisons

B. Watkins and colleagues argue that the most obvious elements important in the arboreal adaptation of all the large apes, as well as gibbons and siamangs, are forelimb dominance (forearms longer than hindlimbs) and digital elongation (see below). Lucy's hindlimbs predominate her forearm; for instance her humerus is only 84% the length of her femur while in all apes the average humerus length is greater than femur length. Moreover, as B. Latimer has suggested, there are some very convincing reasons why a specialized climbing adaptation is an improbable interpretation of *A. afarensis* anatomy. Latimer's reasoning precedes from the fact that ape arborealism is dangerous, and that the foot adaptations are the most important element of their ability to climb.

Yet, Pliocene australopithecine lower limbs and feet had sacrificed all aspects of this anatomy in their adaptation to obligate bipedalism. This should make australopithecine climbing more difficult and require that it involve a human-like pattern of thickness and muscularity related changes in the forearm to compensate for the loss of grasping feet. Three observations do reflect such a pattern:

1. The humeri (for instance AL 137-30, Maka, and several AL-333 fragments) present a combination of relatively large size and marked robustness, in the form of thick forearm shafts and pronounced muscularity.
2. The ulnae are relatively long, for instance the Lucy ulna/humerus ratio is about 92%.
3. The curved shape of the AL 438-1 ulna reflects an adaptation to the forces generated in climbing.

These observations do not, however, indicate special changes for any other arboreal behaviors (especially for arm hanging or brachiation) and they do not indicate any compromises in the bipedal adaptations of the pelvis, hindlimb or foot. Moreover, powerful arms may also reflect other behaviors, from bludgeoning with simple clubs to forceful digging activities.

Hand

J. Stern and colleagues have argued that the Hadar fingers are more curved than humans and that this ape-like curvature reflects the consequences of arboreal activities including arm hanging. Yet, Latimer has pointed out that the orientation of the finger joints must also be taken into account for this assessment. In arm hanging apes the forces acting on the fingers combine force from the muscles on their palmar surface pulling them together, and the force of the branch on the fingers (this must be large as it totals to body weight). The joints, in this case, are at an angle to a line perpendicular to the shaft. If, however, the only forces were those of the muscles, oriented along the bone shafts, the articulations would be vertical to the shafts. He shows that the later is the case in the Hadar fingers, and interprets this to mean that the Hadar hands were very powerful and that their curvature responded to very active muscle use, but not the use of the hands in locomotion. Watkins and colleagues provide the basis for a similar argument. They detailed the substantial digital length reduction in living humans, compared with apes. Elongated digits are a critical aspect of the climbing vertical trunks or large diameter supports in clawless primates, and an integral element in the finger hook grip that apes use to grasp smaller supports. Hadar fingers are very short compared with any living large-bodied ape, whether absolute size or relative size is considered. In the 3rd digit (the only one fully preserved in the composite 333-115 Hadar hand), humans average 24%

shorter than chimpanzees, relative to body weight. These authors took the length of the Hadar 3rd digit and related it to the *smallest* Hadar body weight estimate, as this would give the *largest* possible ratio, and obtained a value almost identical to the human mean - 22% shorter than chimpanzees, relative to body weight. In the light of this shortening, issues about the extent of digital curvature at Hadar are irrelevant.

A number of studies have established beyond question that the Hadar hand remains show no evidence of a knuckle-walking in their ancestry. While these specimens lived long after any such knuckle-walking may have occurred (c.f. Chapter 3), in fact about half of all hominid evolution had already taken place by their time, there is no reason to expect traces of the behavior would be erased by subsequent adaptations. The basis for this conclusion is as follows. The short digits of human hands are not required by bipedal locomotion. One implication is that digital shortening and the increased dexterity of human hands is a consequence of selection associated with tool making and tool use. But had this selection left a significant mark on the Hadar remains? One very important contributor to the human power grip, or squeeze as described by M.W. Marzke and colleagues, is the elongated human thumb. B. Latimer has shown that the evidence of thumb size and morphology from Hadar shows the thumb to be intermediate in length - relatively short compared with modern humans but relatively long compared with apes. Moreover, the fingers lack the broad flattened tips characteristic of our hands (a point also noted by Stern and colleagues). Marzke and colleagues, and others, suggest that these characteristics combine to indicate that the Hadar australopithecines may not have been able of effectively anchor hand-held objects (clubs, tools). Supporting this assertion is their analysis that shows a lack of stresses in the bones of the palm. Together these combine in an interesting suggestion that the human power grip is a unique adaptation to tool use and not a remnant of the requirements of grasping during under branch activities. Chimpanzee grips, in fact, are quite different in anatomy and when applied to large objects their grip forces are much weaker unless they can use their overlapping finger grip. Weak grip is one of the reasons the bonobo in the tool making experiment described by Toth and colleagues (see Chapter 7) has so much trouble producing stone flakes by knapping. The Hadar hand lacks some of this human adaptive pattern, and as M Shrewsbury and A. Sonek suggest it may not be coincidental that no stone tools have been found as early as the hand remains at Hadar, or anywhere else. The implication of this is that technology did not alter Hadar hand morphology from the ancestral condition, and therefore the anatomy of this region might largely reflect the ancestral condition. This makes the absence of any anatomy associated with knuckle-walking much more significant. It also has certain implications for interpreting the use of the hands in other activities.

CLIMBING ADAPTATION

The idea that early australopithecines were proficient climbers and that this accounts for a number of their anatomical compromises in their locomotor system has become widely accepted, far beyond the ability of the data to sustain it. This is why it is discussed at length above. One research team promoting this suggestion has noted that (what they interpret to be) the climbing adaptations are better expressed on the small specimens than on the large ones, and conclude from this that females were more arboreal and less efficient on the ground than males. There are two good reasons why this interpretation is believable, if not seductive. First, it is reasonable to suppose that early australopithecines retain climbing adaptations from their ancestors, the midget common ancestors of chimpanzees and the human line, that were lost in subsequent hominid evolution. This rendition meets classic evolutionary expectations, in which a species that is intermediate between two different adaptations in time and different from each in morphology is hypothesized to be intermediate in behavior. Second, a hypothesized climbing adaptation provided a solution to a problem bothering many Paleolithic archaeologists. These scientists are committed to the precept that technology is critical to human adaptation and evolution. They have been bothered by the fact that these early bipedal humans successfully persisted in difficult environments without tools, and have tried to understand how. Climbing trees for safe sleeping places and to escape predation came to play an important role in many behavioral reconstructions, although they have been largely male-focused and the problems of how mothers holding dependent infants were able to climb, or what kept these infants and older babies lacking prehensile feet from ending up on the ground have never been explored.

No matter how compelling this interpretation is, the court of last resort must be found in the anatomy. The loss of a grasping foot in these bipeds requires conspicuous forearm and hand changes if chimpanzee-like behaviors were common - adaptations that reveal greater strength than chimpanzees of similar size. The climbing adaptations detailed above do not reflect a chimpanzee-like pattern. They are not part of a forearm adaptation that *also* includes arm hanging and brachiation, and they do not involve the use of the forearm in terrestrial locomotion. The ulna joint with the humerus (e.g. the ulna's contribution to the elbow) is too small and faces in the wrong direction for an effective weight-support adaptation on the ground. Once again, chimpanzees make poor models for early hominids. As L. Aiello puts it, the anatomy of the ulna and the heavily muscles and stocky humerus "would be ideally suited to a creature which climbed in the trees but also walked on two legs when on the ground". The pelvis and lower limb and foot anatomy in these hominids reflect efficient development of obligate bipedal locomotion and show no compromises with a climbing adaptation

Was there an important role for climbing in australopithecine adaptations? I believe the evidence of the forearms strongly supports this interpretation. The paleoecology at Hadar appears to have been forested, and both analogy with other primates and ecological reconstructions have emphasized the potential importance of trees as food sources (new leafs, fruits) and safe sleeping places for the early hominids. Climbing, then, could well have been of importance in this environment, but it was climbing *achieved in a human-like manner* and not the remnant of an earlier chimpanzee-like locomotor adaptation, if there ever was one. To understand this distinction it is important to consider the full locomotor repertoire of both species. Chimpanzees are fundamentally arboreally adapted in their locomotor anatomy, well suited for arm hanging, brachiation, and climbing. Their terrestrial locomotion developed within these anatomical constraints and is the most inefficient terrestrial adaptation known in the primates - knuckle walking. *A. afarensis* is an obligate, efficient terrestrial biped with all of the anatomical adaptations this locomotion requires. Their climbing adaptations developed within these anatomical constraints. The *A. afarensis* approach to climbing resulted in a muscular expansion for their arms that consummated in larger individuals with arm bones with thicknesses and prominent muscle markings that rival the anatomy of steel workers. The issue for understanding the differences between these species is not one of climbing *versus* not climbing, or even a question of which species climbed more often. It is the *full locomotor patterns* of these species that must be compared to understand the contrasts in what is only one element of this pattern: climbing. Pliocene hominid climbing is not a "left-over" behavior from pre-hominid ancestors, some 3 to 4 myr years in their past. Their climbing activities were an adjunct to their terrestrial commitment to obligate bipedalism, and required a unique anatomical pattern because of the restrictions imposed by this terrestrial locomotion.

CONTINUED WORK

After a hiatus of some 8 years, field research in Ethiopia has been continued. The promptly published discoveries at Fejej and at Maka, discussed above, are the first fruits of this change, and the discoveries of numerous important finds at Hadar have just begun to be announced in *Nature*, at national meetings, and discussed in private. Several of my colleagues have told me that the new specimens confirm their various earlier theorizations, but were unwilling or unable to provide the specifics. The reader is cautioned to remember that history shows when newly discovered specimens kept under wraps finally become available to the broader paleoanthropological community for their study, the enthusiastic claims of their discoverers and like-minded colleagues who are privy to the information about them do not always hold up.

The later Early Pliocene from around Lake Turkana (3.4-3.0 myr)

Scattered remains of *A. afarensis* have been found from the areas surrounding Lake Turkana in Ethiopia and Kenya. The dates and detailed provenience of these and all other circum-Turkana hominids from the Pliocene and early Pleistocene are given by C. Feibel and colleagues.

After the Allia Bay material discussed above, the oldest specimens from the region are the three broken teeth from the Tulu Bor Tuff at 3.4 myr. The ER 2602 calvarium is dated to between 3.35 and

3.06 myr, about the same as the WT 16006 (3.35 myr) and WT 8556 (3.26 myr) mandibles. WT 16002, much of the upper part of a femur, is 3.25 myr. It is likely that all of these specimens represent *A. afarensis,* but many are too fragmentary or incomplete to be sure. The fact is, however, that no other hominid species has been unambiguously identified in this time span.

The vault is from Koobi Fora, a region on the northern part of the east side of the lake, and the mandibles are from Nachukui Formation on the western side of the lake, both areas worked exhaustively by R.E. Leakey and his colleagues. The lake was formerly named Lake Rudolf, and the east side was extensively researched before the west. This is why specimens from Koobi Fora have the designation ER (East Rudolf). After the lake was renamed work began on the west side, and the specimens subsequently discovered are designated WT (West Turkana).

ER 2602 is most of the back and top of a vault, a piece of cheek bone, and a small piece of supraorbital. The vault is approximately the size of the Hadar females, somewhat thicker. There is a sagittal crest that extends across the top of the cranium. Toward the rear of the parietals it divides into two parallel lines which travel together onto the occipital, then diverge and sweep downward and outward to form compound crests with the nuchal lines. This ape-like condition shows that the posterior part of the temporalis muscle was very well developed (as discussed in Chapter 4, the posterior temporalis is expanded when the canines and incisors are used in forceful ways). It also reflects the high position of the nuchal muscles, important in anterior tooth loading. The cheek fragment is at the front of the temporal fossa, comprised of maxilla and zygomatic. It is strongly angled (from the flat outer face of the cheek to the backward projecting zygomatic arch), suggesting that the zygomatic arch did not flare dramatically outward as in some australopithecines where it must enclose massively developed temporalis muscles. The existing dimensions of the vault, with this evidence of less well developed masticatory muscles, suggests that the sagittal crest is present because of small brain size. This contrasts with the other crested *A. afarensis* specimen (AL 333-125), a fragment that is much larger and regarded as male.

The other significant piece from this time is the WT 16002 femur. According to A. Walker the specimen is definitely an adult. It is the smallest adult hominid known. Circumferences of its shaft taken at various comparable places are some 77% that of Lucy. If this is even roughly proportional to bone length we can expect the specimen was some 22 cm long, with an estimated body height of 81 cm, several inches under 3 feet! WT 16002 was not included in McHenry's estimates of the Hadar *A. afarensis* female weight, but is in the table 5.2 determination of a 26 kg average for the females of the species.

To the north there are 23 teeth from the 3.05 myr Usno Formation of the Omo region in Ethiopia, recovered by expeditions directed by Y. Coppens and F.C. Howell. They were discovered before *A. afarensis* was named, but are now recognized to represent this hominid. The Omo habitat was forested at this time.

Latest Early Pliocene South African Sites: Gracile Australopithecines

The South African australopithecines were the first to be discovered (LeGros Clark provides an excellent history of the discoveries and early interpretations). As they came to be accepted as hominids, and the full range of their variation became known, the interpretations of their relationships developed into J. Robinson's ecologically based scheme of a "gracile omnivore" and a "robust vegetarian" that continues to pervade early hominid studies. This "gracile vs. robust" dichotomy has been quite persuasive, but not necessarily correct.

Here, I have developed the early hominid discussion temporally rather than historically. From the vantage point of their earlier East African appearance, the extension of the australopithecine range into southern Africa is not unexpected. After all, they are found in the same habitats where baboons are found today, and the baboon range is much wider than the range over which we have sampled Pliocene hominids (suggesting, at least to this author, that the australopithecine range will ultimately be found to have been even broader). When relative counts are possible, it seems the hominids usually occurred in about the same density as the baboons that were contemporary with them in these areas.

The Transvaal cave sites of Sterkfontein, Makapansgat, and Gladysvale, and probably the more distant Taung, seem to date to the very end of the Early Pliocene (Figure 6.1). Makapansgat Member 3 (and possibly 4), the oldest of the three, is some 2.9 myr. This is slightly younger than the top of the Hadar formation and younger than the 3 myr Usno teeth from Omo. The Dart deposits (e.g. the cranium) at Taung, 2.8-2.6 myr, and Sterkfontein Member 4 (and Gladysvale) at 2.6-2.4 myr, are somewhat younger according to J. McKee, whose estimates are supported by a report of ESR dates from Sterkfontein Member 4. The linear uptake model age estimate from the older part of a sample of animal teeth is 2.4±.3 myr. This overlying Sterkfontein Member, which also has hominid remains (see Chapter 8), is younger yet but has proven to be problematic for two reasons. First, according to E. Vrba the faunal (and possibly hominid) fossil remains from it are heterogeneous, and appear to sample two different periods. One of these, she believes, is approximately 2 myr in age, but the other is near the Early/Middle Pleistocene boundary, less than half that age. Further confusing the hominid sample is a point raised by P. Tobias. Most of the specimens recovered during his tenure directing excavations at the site, which includes virtually the entire sample thought to come from Member 5 and many specimens attributed to Member 4, were found in an area of the cave where the complex stratigraphy makes proveniences uncertain. These STW specimens (STerkfontein, Witwatersrand), which include many but not all of these attributed to a robust australopithecine taxon (see below) may come from Member 4 *or* 5. Horse species of the modern genus *Equus*, also reported from Sterkfontein Member 4 where they would indicate a younger (<2.3 myr) age may also be mixed in from Member 5.

With this caveat in mind, most of these South African specimens are regarded as a single Pliocene species, first named at Taung by R. Dart as *A. africanus*, and they will be treated as a single sample here. There is no particular reason to believe that these australopithecines "spread" into southern Africa at this time. It is quite possible that earlier, perhaps considerably earlier, remains will yet be found in this region. Hominids earlier than 3 myr, of course, may not be *A. africanus.*

Table 6.14
Percentage body parts in South African Caves and East African Open Air Sites
Modified[1] and Updated after Wood (1988)

Parts Represented	South African Caves	East African Open Air Sites
1992 total number >	950	850
Cranial, facial, and mandibular	30	26*
Isolated teeth	53	44*
Postcrania	21	29*
Associated skeletal elements	1 (n=5)	1 (n=11)

[1] unmodified with 1993 and newer Hadar specimens.

The presence of australopithecine remains in the South African caves provides a source of evidence about habitat variability and preference that is different from the East African occurrences. The possible taphonomic biases from the water-related burials of East Africa include differences in body part representations (table 6.14) because of varying bone densities, as well as the problem of whether the habitat the hominids were found in is where they lived because of the potential for water transport - stream deposits can "associate" species that did not live in the same habitats. There are also taphonomic biases in the cave deposits, although they are different. The australopithecines and other fauna did not live in the caves, which were mostly shallow rock shelters or just holes with a large shaft opening into an underground chamber. At Sterkfontein and Swartkrans, two cave sites on opposite sides of a single small valley (the Kromdraai site is just a stone's throw from these), animals were washed or fell into the caves. C. Brain, when he was the Director of the Transvaal Museum in Pretoria and the excavator at Swartkrans, once wondered whether a similar process was taking place today. He climbed to the bottom of a modern vertical shaft opening into an underground chamber, similar to the australopithecine-bearing caves of the Pliocene, and discovered evidence of the same process by finding the remains of a cow that had fallen in about a week before. Finally, the South African australopithecines lived in a much more seasonal environment than their East African relatives, by virtue of being far from the equator (Taung is 27° S).

At Makapansgat, where the australopithecines are a very small proportion of the total fauna recovered, hyenas were the bone accumulating agents. They are almost always open country hunters and scavengers, who are known to carry their prey a considerable distance. According to work by R. Rayner and colleagues, when the Makapansgat valley was occupied by australopithecines there was higher seasonal rainfall and significant patches of subtropical forest. They reason that the low percentage of australopithecine remains, especially compared with baboons means that they normally lived in different habitats, the hominids occupying forest patches where the hyenas rarely hunt or scavenge. Occupation may have been seasonal, however. C. Peters and B. McGuire examined the present flora around the Makapansgat cave for insights into potential australopithecine habitat usage. A wide food range is available in the summer wet season, but winter resources are sparse and many such as the hard nuts and berries require a processing technology that is unevidenced for the South African australopithecines. They suggest the hominids may have moved to the more prolific lowlands during this season.

In contrast, the Taung fauna suggests a more open woodland or savanna, according to work by J. McKee. The contrast gains importance because Makapansgat Member 3 and Taung are quite close together in age, Taung probably lying between it and Sterkfontein Member 4 in age. Wooded grasslands which tend toward the drier side also predominate in Sterkfontein Member 4 times (the later Member 5 and Swartkrans Member 1 ecology is even drier, see Chapter 7). The elevation of the Transvaal provides a winter habitat that is extremely dry and can become quite cold.

Finding early australopithecines in this region clearly indicates that the Pliocene hominids were much more adaptable than one would infer from the East African occurrences alone. The Transvaal was by no means the hospitable environment that the East African lake shores must have been.   Lest we think of this as a purely tropical adaptation, the high veldt in the Transvaal is well south of the equator and is 5,000 to 6,000 feet above sea level. In the winter, the vegetation withers, and the temperature often falls well below freezing at night. In particular, far greater seasonal extremes in rainfall and temperature created a habitat that must have been uncomfortable during some portions of the year. The marked seasonality in environment and resources provided both opportunity and challenge for the australopithecines, as well as for the paleoanthropologists trying to ascertain their relationships to the more centrally located East African populations. These South African occurrences are more peripheral, ecologically and geographically, as well as more ecologically diverse. It may be that the effective generalized adaptation they developed to marked seasonality in resources for one area allowed the hominid to utilize a wider range of habitats without subsequent anatomical specializations.

POSTCRANIA

I have put the postcranial discussion first because with few exceptions, comparable parts are virtually identical to the Hadar remains; a point made by Lovejoy and colleagues, McHenry, and others. In particular, there is no evidence for significant changes in morphology, size, or in limb proportions. The small female Sterkfontein skeleton, STS 14, includes a pelvis, 2/3 of the thoracic and all of the lumbar vertebrae, the upper part of a femur (whose length can be reconstructed) and lower part of a radius. These show a large pelvis relative to the limbs and a relatively short leg. These proportions are confirmed by the much larger STW 431 partial skeleton, according to McHenry, and both specimens have proportions like those of Lucy.

Sterkfontein and Makapansgat provide five innominates; the two from Makapansgat (MLD 7/8 and 25) are juvenile, from Sterkfontein a third is a fragmentary adult (STS 65), the fourth is a very large adult male, part of the associated skeleton STW 431 that is similar in size to the largest limbs from Sterkfontein (or Hadar), and the fifth belongs to the partially complete female postcranial skeleton STS 14. In addition there are several large femoral fragments, although no complete bone has yet been found. These confirm the implications of the Afar skeleton, demonstrating a complete skeletal adaptation to bipedalism. In fact, this later material is even more modern appearing with its shorter ilium and deeper acetabulum. The larger specimen, STW 431, is the earliest male innominate known. As we could predict from general allometric considerations, it is much more human like in its iliac flare (the blade is not as dramatically curved outward as it is in the midget females), the anterior spines are quite prominent (the posterior surface is missing), and the acetabulum is relatively larger compared with the other dimensions of the bone. The relatively short legs in this specimen might suggest that allometry is not fully responsible for lower limb elongation in larger hominids. However, their length was reconstructed from the size of this acetabulum, and there is reason to believe that it is the acetabulum and not the legs that is relatively small compared with modern counterparts. The reason for this comes from Lovejoy's analysis of the biomechanics of the hip joint, one of his earliest works. Lovejoy showed that the more widely flared hips of the australopithecines gave the balancing muscles, the abductors, a long lever arm. Better leverage means that less force is required of these muscles and with less force passing through the hip joint it is smaller (this maintains the same pressure in the joint, the force divided by the area over which it is applied). The link between a smaller hip joint and shorter legs is tenuous, and the allometric question needs to be resolved with actual lower and upper limb remains from the same specimen.

In fact the postcranial resemblances of *A. afarensis* and *A. africanus* are quite remarkable. Both samples show 6 lumbar vertebrae - there are 3 lumbar columns from Sterkfontein, including one that was on display at the site for many years. The STW 431 humerus is very similar to the large Hadar specimens, and shares their anatomical peculiarities. According to McHenry an isolated capitate (a small bone in the wrist) is identical to the several found at Hadar, combining many human-like and some unique features. Marzke, it will be remembered, interprets these and other traits to imply that the Hadar hand did not have an efficient squeeze power grip, or a well developed precision grip (thumb opposing the four finger tips). These, it was posited, evolved in concert with hominid tool use, so the implication that the Sterkfontein capitate is part of a similar hand fits with the absence of tools in Member 4 of the site. D. Ricklan's analysis of the other isolated hand elements provides additional information. No thumb is preserved allowing the question of a precision grip to be addressed. He found the anatomy of the other digits and the bones of the wrist to reflect a wide range of stable, powerful grips that were very similar to human hands and quite unlike those of apes. While the anatomy he describes is similar to that Marzke attributes to the lack of an efficient squeeze power grip, Ricklan does not agree with her interpretation of these features and believes them more similar to modern humans.

Comparison of the two small females, AL 288-1 and STS 14, reveals both differences and similarities. They vary anatomically, in spite of their similar size. STS 14 has a shorter ilium, deeper acetabulum, and a narrower sacrum. The later contributes to what appears to be a more circular birth canal. However, crushing and distortion make an exact reconstruction of its shape uncertain (one reconstruction, by M. Abitbol, makes the STS 14 birth canal much more elliptical, and very similar to AL 288-1). Moreover, R. Tague estimates about the same pelvic inlet circumference for the two. Because he believes this circumference is obstetrically important, Tague concludes that births in STS 14 may have been faster and easier because of the more rounded inlet shape (if it is more rounded), maximizing the space available for fetal entry and passage through the birth canal. However, this conclusion rests on the assumption that fetal head size at birth is the same in the two species, and this is unlikely as *A. africanus* adult head size is larger. It is most reasonable to conclude that births in both species were slow and moderately difficult, and that the change in pelvic inlet shape was a response to increasing head size at birth.

Like the earlier Hadar female, the Sterkfontein female (STS 14) was very short, no larger than AL 288-1 she was about 3.5 feet. A larger postcranial sample, however, gives an idea of how height was distributed. Five individuals have an estimated average height of 115 cm for 3 females, and 138 cm for two males (the sample average of 127 cm is the same as the Hadar sample average for one male and female). The dimorphism in height, 20%, is probably a more accurate figure than the Hadar height dimorphism estimate because the sample size is larger (there is only one Hadar male and female). This magnitude is about double the human populational mean and similar to that of gorillas (see table 6.8 comparing average femur dimorphism).

The robustness of the limbs and the size of features that relate to muscular power (muscle attachments, relative joint areas) indicate that these hominids were heavier than modern people of the same height, the greater weight largely reflecting the added musculature. Estimates based on McHenry's work and several new specimens indicate a mean female body weight of 30.2 kg and a male mean of 41.3 kg (table 5.2). There is a significant decrease in the estimated sexual dimorphism (table 6.16), from males 1.7 times heavier than females to males 1.4 times heavier, as the female mean weight is greater than the Hadar estimate while the male mean is less. Yet, the averages for the two samples (based on the average of the male and female means) are the same. Body size, then, cannot account for the increasing brain size or the postcanine **megadontia** in this sample.

DENTITIONS

There are a large number of teeth in the South African *A. africanus* sample, although fewer complete or fairly complete dentitions compared to the Hadar australopithecines because of the fragmentation that takes place during events surrounding deposition in the caves where they are found. There is a considerable amount of metric and morphological overlap between the two australopithecine species. Some dentitions, such as STW 252, closely resemble their Hadar counterparts in size and anatomy; so much so that the phenetic basis for distinguishing the species has been blurred. Yet, it is the relation of the *samples* that attains importance in evolutionary studies and these are large enough to show some clear evolutionary trends. The one thing these trends probably do *not* reflect is a difference in body size.

Compared with *A. afarensis,* the *A. africanus* teeth show the following changes:

- postcanine teeth are larger, more bulbous cusped, and relatively broader (the size difference is greater in the later erupting teeth of each type), and may have somewhat thicker enamel, especially on the tooth walls.
- the anterior lower premolars are always bicuspid, usually with equal or close to equal sized cusps, and wear more similarly to the other premolars. Their enamel thickness is greater.
- comparing anterior teeth of the same sex, the *A. africanus* central incisors show no reduction but the other anterior teeth are usually smaller. The ranges almost completely overlap, however, and there are very large canines and incisors in both samples.
- no canines (permanent or deciduous) wear to have cutting edges, even though a few are large enough to project beyond the level of the other teeth (this is much more common in the *A. afarensis* sample).

Although the canines are reduced compared with the earlier Pliocene samples, their roots (especially of the maxillary teeth) are still long and robust. None of the canines were involved in cutting or slashing, canine-premolar diastemata are rare, and no premolar lacks two fairly symmetrically developed cusps. The canines wear more rapidly than those from Hadar, and the wear is invariably on their tip, reducing even the largest to the level of the other teeth in older age (i.e., 30's). The same marked sexual dimorphism characterizes postcanine tooth size differences (about the order of that in gorillas). While the canine size dimorphism is less than in any of the apes, it is greater than the dimorphism in other remaining teeth. Contrasting with the reduced dimorphism in the postcranial materials, no evidence shows a decrease in dental dimorphism compared with the earlier East African hominids.

Why the big teeth and the evolutionary trend for even further expansion? A. Walker suggests that the chewing pattern of these hominids was much like modern humans, and my research indicates that their rate of tooth wear was also similar to many more recent hunting/gathering populations - the molars and premolars seem designed to last a lifetime, the oldest individuals dying at about the time they have little or no crown areas left in their mouth (a maximum age of about 35). Since the teeth are so much larger than ours, this implies that the australopithecines produced the same pressure between their jaws, but over a much larger surface. One explanation for this adaptation is the seasonal use of very low quality food sources that require a great deal of chewing, but without high magnitudes of force. The same masticatory apparatus, however, could produce high force magnitudes, if the force is applied to small objects and not spread out across all the teeth. The thick enamel on the tooth walls clearly indicates that such compressive loads are normal, and that (what G. Macho and F. Thackery call) "puncture grinding" was used to masticate fibrous foods. Moreover, J. Wallace reports thick scratches on the occlusal surfaces that indicate dietary grit must have been regular, and therefore an additional source of wear.

Table 6.15
Maxillary Tooth Sizes for *Australopithecus*
from Kimbel and White (1988) and the author's data

	A. afarensis mean	CV¹	A. africanus mean	CV¹	A. robustus mean	CV¹	A. boisei mean	CV¹
I1 length	11.1		10.8	11.5	9.3	9.2	10.1	
breadth	8.4	7.9	8.3	6.6	7.5	6.1	8.1	
I2 length	7.7		7.0	9.8	6.4	4.7	7.5	
breadth	7.2	10.2	6.7	8.0	6.7	10.3	7.4	
Breadth of:								
C	10.9	10.1	10.2	9.3	9.6	11.5	8.9	8.5
P3	12.4	6.2	12.5	4.3	13.8	6.5	15.2	9.3
P4	12.1	5.0	13.0	6.8	14.9	6.7	16.2	10.1
M1	13.2	6.8	13.9	5.9	14.6	5.9	16.2	6.7
M2	14.7	4.6	15.8	8.2	15.8	6.1	18.1	8.1
M3	13.9	7.4	15.5	9.4	16.8	4.3	18.2	

¹ Coefficient of Variation for n>4

One possibility for reconciling these is to examine how these **biomechanical** reconstructions fit with the examination of **dental microwear**. Studies by F. Grine and R. Kay suggest that frugivory is the predominant source of microwear; an important food item being mature fleshy fruits, with the seeds and pulp swallowed whole. As discussed in Chapter 7, they also propose a frugivory adaptation for the robust hominids from Swartkrans, but with more emphasis on seeds and other hard objects crushed between the molars. Yet, as we will discuss, this appears to be contradicted by a strontium/calcium ratio analysis of the Swartkrans hominids. Walker has pointed to a "last meal effect" on microwear, as the patterns mainly reflect foods eaten near the time of death. For what I believe is the true solution to these different answers to the diet question, we must return to the precept (Chapter 3) that primates are eclectic feeders, and are likely to respond to seasonal differences by dramatically shifting their diet. Add to that the ability for detailed mental mapping of the environment we have posited for the earliest hominids, and the most likely conclusion is that all of the sources of dietary reconstruction are correct and reflect different aspects of a very broad, seasonally varied diet, as A. Mann suggested. The causes of microwear may not be the source of selection influencing jaw biomechanics, and rare food items (perhaps dirty) leaving chips may have influence on observed wear far beyond their importance in the diet, or in producing the overall wear rate.

I believe the best evidence suggests dietary seasonality, with emphasis on low quality resources for part of the year and, as Wallace put it, the need to prepare most foods in the mouth.

CRANIA

The earlier South African sites provide the first good sample of complete or fairly complete early hominid crania. These include a complete (but toothless) Sterkfontein female cranium, two fairly complete male crania of quite different size, also from Sterkfontein, and numerous more fragmentary faces and braincases (see figure 6.12). The specimens combine three categories of features: some are remarkably chimpanzee-like, others are the result of bipedalism and braincase expansion, and still others are adaptations to dietary items requiring prolonged and/or powerful chewing, as described above.

Facial variation

There is a set of primitive features seen in the combination of a large prognathic face and a small braincase, which creates a rather chimpanzee-like appearance. However, even without the Makapansgat specimens included the sample is quite variable and it is invariably a mistake to use one or two specimens to characterize it (for instance as with the foramen magnum position discussed below) as virtually all of the phylogenetic analyses do. Faces differ, sometimes dramatically, in features such as the alveolar prognathism, flatness of the palate roof, sharpness of the lower nasal border, and so on. With this caveat in mind, at the extreme, some faces closely resemble those of the Hadar hominids. Yet, on the average the faces differ from those of the earlier australopithecines, continuing the existing evolutionary trends. Compared with *A. afarensis,* the *A. africanus* faces express

- retraction of the palate from a position in front of the face to under it
- forward shift of the cheeks (zygomatic process of the maxilla, and zygomatic bone) and of the front of the masseter muscle
- expansion of the anterior part of the temporalis muscle
- broader nasal aperture
- anterior pillars extending above the canine roots of variable expression creating thickened lateral nasal margins
- structural changes in the jaws related to
  - expanding premolars and molars
  - incisor and (especially) canine reduction and decreased emphasis on anterior loading

The reduced anterior teeth of some specimens, and a expansion of nasal breadth, combine to make the canines lie at the nasal borders. Their root buttresses, which Rak calls anterior pillars, continue higher in the face than the canine roots themselves and form the sides of the nose, giving it thick lateral edges. Rak considered the anterior pillar a unique trait, according to him only appearing in South African australopithecines (*A. africanus* and at Swartkrans, but this was before a Hadar **midface** was found with well developed pillars). He believes this structure mainly responds to increased forces acting on the anterior premolars. However, McKee argues that the structure more directly responds to forces on the canines, and the fact is that the anterior premolars of the two species are very close to the same size. One of the Hadar faces has anterior pillars, but generally the feature is only found in later hominids, although not uniquely South African australopithecines as some *H. habilis* specimens (including OH 24, which has small premolars) and a number of modern humans show it as well, according to McKee. It is likely that the development of the anterior pillars and other related features of midfacial anatomy is influenced by both the forces applied to the face along the canine roots and the bone enclosing them, and the positioning of large root buttresses along the sides of the nose where one of their edges is bounded by an open space.

Cranial vault

Another Hadar-like feature is the occasional (inferred) appearance of sagittal crests. Cresting in this sample is more poorly evidenced than it is in the earlier *A. afarensis* remains, but this is more an artifact of preservation than one of presence or absence and there may not be a significant different in its frequency. Also resembling this earlier sample is the seeming lack of relation between cranial size and cresting. The best evidence for sagittal crests is in a small specimen (STS 17), one of the largest (MLD 1), and according to F. Thackery a CT scan made of the outer layer of bone that is from the top of the STS 5 head (a thin layer of bone pealed off of the top of the head, its top external surface is still embedded in matrix and the bone is too thin to remove it) seems to show a low crest extending into the matrix where it has been hidden from view.

Superimposed on these features is a second set, resulting from some of the more distinctive developing hominid adaptations. *A. africanus* shares some unique features with later hominids in the genus *Homo* that *A. afarensis* specimens often lack, or express more weakly. Perhaps most importantly is the brain size increase. If the averages based on these small samples are accurate, both male and female cranial capacity increases relative to the *A. afarensis* sample (table 6.16), males by 4% and females by about double that, giving a brain size increase of some 6% in a species with the same body size. Brain size, as a percentage of body size, increases (table 6.16). Percent sexual dimorphism in brain size is very similar, decreasing to 17% which is about the magnitude of difference in the more dimorphic apes such as gorillas. The most forward part of the braincase is better developed than in *A. afarensis* so that the forehead is somewhat more filled out. Other changes in the brain (discussed by Holloway) also affect cranial shape.

Table 6.16

Cranial Capacities in Pliocene *Australopithecus* species

Australo-pithecus species	Male			Female			Middle-sex		
	mean cranial capacity (n=)	body weight estimate	brain percent of body weight	mean cranial capacity (n=)	body weight estimate	brain percent of body weight	mean cranial capacity	body weight estimate	brain percent of body weight
afarensis	485 (1)	44600	1.09	400 (2)	26000	1.54	442.5	35300	1.25
africanus	505 (5)	40800	1.24	430 (4)	30200	1.42	467.5	35500	1.31
aethiopicus	415 (2)	84000	0.49						

Turning to the cranial base and rear, like the Hadar specimens the base is long and flat and the foramen magnum (see Figure 4.6) is often in an equally posterior position. However, there is a considerable range of variation in foramen magnum position, with STS 5 at one extreme, more posterior than the Hadar composite cranium, and STS 19/58 at the other, the position more anterior (W. Kimbel and Y. Rak attribute this to taxonomy and consider STS 19/58 to be an unnamed species of *Homo*). There are several intermediate specimens. Before complete pelves were known the rearward position of the foramen magnum in the best known specimen, STS 5, was taken as evidence of poor head balance and a reflection of an intermediate form of locomotion mixing bipedalism with forelimb weight support. However, the independent pelvic evidence for bipedalism and the footprints show that the position and angle of the foramen magnum does not correspond to a significant locomotor difference. If it is related to the cranial flatness, according to J. Laitman and colleagues it might correspond to a different adaptive difference - a high (ape-like) larynx position. This high position allows drinking and breathing at the same time, but is poorly placed for the resonating chamber formed by the palate and throat to produce many of the sounds used in human language. These authors infer limited vocal language abilities in the South African australopithecines. They posit that vocal language created sufficient selection to modify this throat configuration in spite of the selection against it, caused by the potential (often realized today) to inhale foods and choke on them, created by the crossing of passages to the lungs and stomach. To some extent these speculations coalesce with arguments linking the evolution of language and tool use (none evidenced in Sterkfontein Member 4).

The Hadar-like foramen magnum position is reflected in similar positions and angles formed by structures surrounding it. However in one case, behind the foramen magnum, the area for neck muscle attachment is more like subsequent *Homo* species - it is longer and at much less of an angle (i.e. more horizontal), but unlike *A. afarensis* it does not meet the posterior extension of the temporalis muscle to form a compound temporal/nuchal crest because the posterior temporalis is reduced in expression, a reflection of the decreasing use (and size) of the front teeth.

An additional set of features characterizing these crania results from the dietary adaptation. These are also one of the developing hominid adaptations as some of the subsequent *Homo* samples have an even better developed masticatory system, at least as far as postcanine tooth loading is concerned. The *A. africanus* posterior teeth are large compared with the size of the hominids. Tooth size falls within the range of variation of gorillas, although body weight estimates only a quarter or less of the gorilla average. Corresponding to the large teeth, the areas of both jaws holding the tooth roots are thick and deep. The ramus of the mandible is high and vertical (especially in the males; females have shorter faces and consequently a lower ramus). Buttresses appear across the inner face of the symphysis, responding to the powerful forces acting on the mandible during chewing (see Chapter 3). The position of the zygomatics is variable, but they tend to be forward (again especially in the males). An important difference in the temporal fossa reflects the evolving adaptation. The Hadar fossae are flattened, as in chimpanzees. This is the usual anatomy for primates that produce powerful horizontal forces between their anterior teeth. In *A. africanus*, as we have seen there is a shift away from this and toward more powerful vertical forces between the posterior teeth. The corresponding anatomy of the glenoid fossa at the mandibular articulation is to have a steep vertical separation between the roof of the fossa and the articular eminence in front of it, where the mandibular condyle rests when the jaw is at rest or when the joint is acting as a pivot.

In sum, the crania attributed to *A. africanus* are significantly advanced over the *A. afarensis* remains. The differences, in many cases, represent a continuation of trends evident in the Pliocene hominids if *A. afarensis* is thought to have evolved from a chimpanzee-like ancestor (however problematic the assumption). The evolving features make the species more closely resemble later *Homo* samples, and there is absolutely nothing about the crania, dentitions, or postcranial remains that would preclude *A. africanus* from the ancestry of subsequent hominids, including ourselves.

DENTAL ERUPTION, MATURATION, POPULATION AGE-AT-DEATH DISTRIBUTION

In Chapter 4 we discussed the many problems, and ongoing controversy, involved in determining the eruption times for the permanent teeth of australopithecine children. One example used was from Sterkfontein. It was shown that this individual (STS 24) fit a human pattern of relative dental maturation and eruption and could be readily distinguished from the expectations of a chimpanzee-like pattern. Perhaps the most heated controversy on this topic has been over the first australopithecine discovered, the Taung child. A. Mann interpreted the specimen as one of those reflecting a human-like maturational pattern based on his analysis of the X-rays. He determined an age-at-death for the specimen of 5-7. Years later when G. Conroy and M. Vannier took CT scans, they produced the first accurate and detailed information about the crown and root formation stages of the unerupted teeth. They focused on two aspects of their data, the lag of incisor eruption behind the first permanent molar, and the lag of canine eruption behind the second permanent molar (suggested by the relative development of the teeth, as they are far from eruption in this child). In both cases they argued that a significant lag is ape-like and not human-like, and meant that Taung was erupting molars early (relative to humans) and therefore maturing much faster (3.3 years was the estimated age-at-death). However Mann published an ancient Persian child with relative tooth development just like Taung, and a survey of human populational variation revealed it to be common to have these lags in some samples, although not in Americans - the source of so much of the dental eruption data. In fact, what the CT data showed is that Taung died at a younger age than had been estimated, 4.5-5.5 years (at the low end of the range of human population averages for individuals erupting their first permanent molar), and that the eruption pattern has human-like but un-American. There are a number of juveniles from the *A. africanus* sites and all fit a human pattern of dental maturation. In the context of the fact that this pattern can be recognized at Laetoli, a much earlier site representing an ancestral species, this should not be surprising.

Estimates of the age-at-death for children and juveniles provide the possibility for estimating the age-at-death for many other population members with dental remains, a procedure discussed in Chapter 5. Sterkfontein (or Sterkfontein and Makapansgat) are little different in their age-at-death distribution from the much larger Swartkrans sample described there, according to K. McKinley. With an average age of death in the low teens, and a maximum life span of 35-40 years, delayed maturation placed a significant adaptive strain on australopithecine parenting - one reason why Lovejoy and Lancaster's hypothesizing about an early male parenting role stands such a good chance of being valid. It also emphasizes the importance of the adaptive pay-off from the maturational delay, a pay-off that most surely was reflected in the advantages accrued from the almost certainly social, and perhaps also cultural behaviors (and behavioral expectations) that took so long a time to learn.

HOW MANY SPECIES?

Once again, with large samples from two of the sites, various authors have questioned how many species were there. It is always a possibility (however remote) that there have been two contemporary and sympatric human species throughout the span of human existence, and that these are most evident and distinguishable at sites where the number of individuals found is large. However there is another explanation. The persistence of this problem makes it tempting to suggest it is not so much based on the biology, a consequence of the pattern and magnitude of biological variation, as it is the result of the paleoanthropologists' expectations of how much variation there should be in a single species sampled with small numbers over time. The difficulty is often similar to the one W. Kimbel and T. White encountered in their analysis of *A. africanus*: the variation is too much to be attributed to sexual dimorphism alone, but the two species, if there are actually two, "are very similar morphologically and may be difficult to define unequivocally".

Beginning with R. Dart, several scientists have suggested a mixture of robust australopithecine features (or in some cases specimens) at Makapansgat. Focus was brought on the large postcanine teeth with rounded bulbous cusps on some of the specimens such as MLD 2. Similarly, R. Clarke believes a Sterkfontein specimen he reconstructed, STW 252, is part of a second species found there, a species directly ancestral to the South African robust australopithecines. Clarke considers traits in the Sterkfontein sample such as tooth size, or certain aspects of facial morphology, to be so highly variable that "different species seems to be the most plausible explanation". Yet the Sterkfontein teeth are much less variable than the Lufeng sample of fossil apes discussed by J. Kelley and D. Etler, and the variations in facial morphology, all which had been reported in earlier discovered parts of the sample, have been interpreted somewhat differently. Even before STW 252 was discovered, Y. Rak contended that the anatomical basis for robust australopithecine faces are found in the earlier Sterkfontein sample; in particular, in the males of that sample (this is perilously close to the argument once advanced by C. Brace, that the robust australopithecines were males and the gracile australopithecines females). Rak argued that there is an ancestral/descendent relationship between these two samples, even as I did a decade before. Of course, if there were no speciation events between them, populations on the same lineage are in the same species, according to the evolutionary species precept. We return to this question in Chapter 7.

There are also suggestions of a "*Homo*-like" species at the site. These center on the STS 19 cranial base and associated parietals (STS 58), found apart from the main deposits in a dump of lime left over from quarrying activities decades before australopithecines were found at Sterkfontein. The specimen may be from Member 5 instead of Member 4, according to R. Clarke. For those who believe there is *H. habilis* in this later member (not including this author, as discussed in Chapter 8) this would support the contention that it is *Homo* rather than *Australopithecus*. W. Kimbel and Y. Rak argue for this interpretation. The two parts of the cranium, when combined, provide the basis for R. Broom and J. Robinson's endocast reconstruction suggesting a 530 cc brain size, which would be one of the largest for the Sterkfontein+Makapansgat sample. Subsequently however R. Holloway reconstructed enough of the endocast from the cranial base alone to estimate brain size, and determined a 436 cc capacity, which does not support its attribution to *Homo*. Nor doe the for of the semi-circular ear canals - these are like the other australopithecines. While the specimen has a shorter cranial base and more transversely oriented petrous bone than the others, these make it more like *Homo*, but also more like *A. robustus*. Broom and Robinson noted the "human-like" proportions of the internal anatomy, while accepting it as an australopithecine, and C. Dean and B. Wood discussed this pattern of variation and concluded that it is a reasonable extension of the normal range of australopithecine variation.

Australopithecus africanus in East Africa?

The beginning of the Late Pliocene, 2.6 myr, and the time just before it, is the *A. africanus* span in South Africa. Hominids are very poorly represented in East Africa at this age. Yet, this is the period that should be the focus of the numerous discussions of whether *A. africanus* occurs in East Africa. The fact is that there are no cranial remains in East Africa from this, or any other, time with distinctive *A. africanus* features, and the mandibles of most early hominids have proven difficult to distinguish.

The Koobi Fora dental set ER 5431 is dated to 2.7 myr. This set of 8 teeth are the two sides of a single individual's P_3-M_2. The specimen has some resemblances to *A. afarensis,* and several scientists have included it in that taxon. However the teeth are broadened and the cusps more rounded and bulbous than is common in that species. A number of features closely resemble *A. africanus* specimens such as (but not uniquely) MLD 2. These include

- absolute size and proportions of the teeth (relative broadening)
- bulbous molar cusps
- proportions between the teeth, such as the predominance of second over first molar size
- pattern of asymmetry of the P_3 crown and the deep grooves on its buccal (external) surface
- deep cingulum on the mesiobuccal (outer-front) quadrant of both molars
- weakly developed remnants of extra cusps on the M_2

The teeth are evidence of an australopithecines species that it neither *A. afarensis* nor a hyper-robust variety known from East Africa. Its P_4 anatomy suggests that it is not a robust australopithecines of the South African variety either, and the specific resemblances to *A. africanus* cited above probably should be taken at face value. It may be relevant that this is the time that *A. africanus* lived in South Africa. Similar as these teeth are to *A. africanus,* by themselves (certainly, without cranial remains) they cannot prove the species existed in East Africa. However the absence of evidence is not evidence of absence and these teeth are, as some would say, very provocative.

Two other isolated teeth are relevant to this discussion, both diagnostic mandibular premolars from the Member C of the Omo Shungura Formation. Omo 18-33 (2.6 myr) and L 51-80 (2.5 myr) each show affinities to *A. africanus* according to G. Suwa, whose expertise is focused on premolar anatomy.

Can this mandibular dentition and the isolated teeth be interpretable as evidence for the early appearance of *Homo*? In Suwa's analysis the premolars also resemble some early *Homo* specimens and he is unwilling to decide between these two possibilities. In B. Wood's discussion of the ER 5431 dental set it is likened to a much later mandible attributed to an early *Homo* species, ER 1802. However, it is difficult to reconcile the resemblances he cites with the specimens' actual morphology. In fact, the later Turkana specimen lacks virtually all of the features that ER 5431 shares with *A. africanus* specimens. Affiliations with this South African hominid may be uncertain because they must be based on the dental comparisons alone, but special affiliations with later *Homo* remains are downright unlikely. In a word, the answer is no. If the teeth are regarded as anything, they should be allocated to the species that they resemble.

Summary

Hominid sites discussed in this chapter provide important information about the earliest hominids and the pattern of their evolution.

- Lothagam and Tabarin: enhanced powerful mastication; earliest hominid is *A. afarensis.*
- Mabaget: very small body size, no specific evidence of a climbing forearm adaptation
- Allia Bay: root of a very large canine (exceeding other *A. afarensis)* and sectorial premolar crown, but with no wear due to honing against the upper canine
- Sibilot Hill: radius of a very large specimen lacking adaptations to suspension or weight support
- Belohdelie: very small, thick vault with an expanded anterior temporalis muscle
- Laetoli: delayed maturation, footprint trails giving independent evidence of bipedalism, emphasis on anterior loading and retention of canine cutting, low quality diet

- Maka: femur indicating habitual bipedalism, humerus suggesting short but powerful arms, earliest evidence of degenerative joint disease
- Hadar: Cranial capacity expansion (relative brain size larger), neural reorganization, reduction or loss of canine cutting complex, extreme relative postcanine tooth size (compared with body size), postcranial anatomy showing bipedalism was *obligate* and all potential for foot grasping was lost, hand anatomy lacking grip related adaptation related to tool making
- East Turkana *A. afarensis*: female with sagittal crest, smallest individual body size known
- South African *A. africanus* sites (Makapansgat, Sterkfontein Member 4, Taung): Habitation of seasonal environments, broader habitat range without concomitant anatomical specializations, anterior reduction and loss of canine cutting, postcanine expansion and the appearance of true megadonty at the extreme end of the range, significant brain size expansion with gorilla-like dimorphism but reduced body size dimorphism
- A similarly aged East African specimen: ER 5431 is a 2.7 myr Koobi Fora dental set suggesting but not proving the presence of *A. africanus* in East Africa

This chapter traces the evolution of *A. afarensis* into *A. africanus   A. afarensis,* as presently understood, is a long lasting hominid species, extending as it does from 5.8 to about 3 myr. The species is characterized by very small body size, forearm length reduction (although not to modern proportions), and the continued development of a powerful masticatory apparatus adapted for both puncture-grinding and prolonged reduction of low quality foods. These late Miocene/Pliocene australopithecines are recognizably hominid, especially as evidenced by

- the ubiquitous presents of skeletal adaptations to obligate bipedalism and consequent changes in the shape of the birth canal and in the birth process,
- maturational delay,
- expanded brain size relative to body size,
- neural reorganization in the few endocasts known.

Yet, the earlier samples retain a surprising number of anthropithecine features. It is not a species in stasis, as significant evolutionary trends affect the anterior dentition and its functions.

A. africanus is the second of the ape-like hominids (the "ape-men", as the South Africans so appropriately call them). With its ancestor, these species span the first 2/3 of hominid evolution. They represent the long lasting pre-stone tool making hominid form. The form is fairly stable, but evolutionary change is not absent. The descendent species shows continued increases in the development of the masticatory apparatus. *A. africanus* also increases in brain size and decreases its anterior dentition, losing all reflections of a canine/premolar cutting complex. Even given the difficulties of ascertaining sexual dimorphism in small samples (the various aspects of this problem are weighed out by G. Armelagos and D. Van Gerven), it appears to be significantly smaller in this later species. Yet, the similarities with the earlier hominids are so great that some have suggested it may be no more than a geographically distinct subspecies. The pattern of phyletic evolution in the Late Pliocene hominids indicates otherwise, and raises the issues of homology and homoplasy in hominid evolution.

ANATOMY OF A CONTROVERSY
The Species Count: Safety in Numbers?

As is the case with virtually every large hominid sample known, some scientists have suggested there are more than one species at Hadar. Indeed, this was the first presumption of D. Johanson, who subsequently modified his view when joined by T. White. T. Olson focused on some details of the mastoid region at the back of the skull and the shape of the nasal bones (whether or not the maximum breadth measured across the bones is at their top or at their bottom) in arguing that two species are represented at Hadar - one ancestral to the robust australopithecines ("*Paranthropus*", according to Olson) and the other ancestral to *Homo*. The possibility that some of the details he reported might reflect sexual dimorphism is suggested by the fact that the distribution of the very dimorphic P$_3$ morphology differs between the two samples he identified: (what he termed) "*Paranthropus*" P$_3$'s show variable lingual cusp dominance while (what he called) *Homo* does not. However, studies by R. Eckhardt, and T. White and colleagues showed that these cranial details vary far too much to be useful in reconstructing phylogeny.

D. Falk also finds evidence of a unique link to the robust australopithecines in the sample. Her argument is based on the internal cranial morphology at the back of the skull. The large veins that drain blood from the rear of the brain through the **jugular foramena** leave a groove-like impression called a **sinus** on the internal surface of the rear of the cranium. Usually in living humans this sinus follows the middle of the occiput transversely (one branch in each direction), reaching the jugular foramena by way of the temporal. This pattern is common, although not unique. A second variant is for the drainage to follow the midline of the occiput vertically, until it reaches the foramen magnum where it divides into two branches on either side of the foramen, each reaching a jugular foramen. Falk calls this the occipitomarginal pattern, and reports that it characterizes all known *A. afarensis* crania, as well as *Australopithecus boisei*. This is why she links the two samples. However, once again there is too much variation in the morphology. Both patterns regularly occur in humans, as pointed out in a review by W. Kimbel. The importance of their variation is emphasized by the fact that specimens of both *A. afarensis* (AL 444-2) and *A. boisei* (ER 23000) each have both patterns, one on each side of the occiput. The functional meaning of the variation, if any, is unclear, but it is not sufficient to show multiple taxa at Hadar, or to uniquely link some or all of the specimens there with *A. boisei*.

Yet, the argument for a link with robust australopithecines of some sort is not without merit, especially given the likelihood that this sample is an immediate ancestor of an early robust Australopithecine species, *A. aethiopicus*. In fact, there are many resemblances between the most complete male, AL 444-2, and the best known cranium of this species (WT 17000), discussed in Chapter 7. The Hadar australopithecines are also ancestral to *A. africanus*, and the issue is not about these different ancestries, or the resemblances to various later australopithecines that they reflect, but rather is over the question of whether cladogenesis *had already occurred* and contributes to the variation in this sample.

The identification of two species in the Hadar sample is not uncommon. Not all of the interpretations suggest that a unique robust australopithecine ancestor is found there; several focus on a more fundamental distinction, between *Australopithecus* and *Homo*. Excepting C. Oxnard who believes that no australopithecines or australopithecine-like hominids are ancestral to *Homo*, the origin of our genus is invariably interpreted to be at Hadar. B. Senut, as mentioned above, argues that both *Australopithecus* and *Homo* were present in the postcranial sample (as does A. Zihlman). With C. Tardeau who studies the knee region, Senut argues that the *Homo* adaptation contrasts knee stability and elbow flexibility, while the *Australopithecus* adaptation contrasts knee flexibility with elbow stability. A functional explanation for the variation, however, is not widely accepted. P. Shipman suggests that the two species may have been inadvertently combined in the composite cranium reconstitution (the reconstructed male is made up of cranial and facial elements from 12 different individuals, but only Shipman has suggested they may represent different species). The discovery of a complete male AL 444-2 should have put this idea to rest, but according to a report by J. Shreeve both Shipman and Olson suggest that other specimens are too small to belong to the same taxon as this male. The ancestry for three species is found by Y. Coppens. He detects evidence for the base of lineages leading to *Homo, A. africanus,* and a third extinct species. Finally, according to a review by R. Tuttle, a "remarkable outlier" among those who find multiple species at Hadar is W. Ferguson, who classifies some of the specimens as pongid (in the sense of "ape"). Ferguson may have been influenced by Johanson's early description of Lucy as showing "provocative resemblances" to Miocene apes such as *Ramapithecus*.

On the other hand, T. White, W. Kimbel, O. Lovejoy, and their colleagues who worked on this sample over the past decade, retain the hypothesis of a single species because, as Tuttle concludes in his review, "critics of the single species hypothesis have not assembled adequate compelling evidence against it". A number of other authors not directly involved in describing this sample (W. Leonard and M. Hegmon, R. Eckhardt, T. Cole and F. Smith) have addressed the pattern of metric and morphological variation and concur with the conclusion that it is continuous and not extreme, and this in my assessment as well. For instance, Leonard and Hegmon point out that the range of P_3 morphologies that Olson attributes to "*Paranthropus*" at Hadar is so great that several of the specimens have P_3 's with the minimal amount of molarization (rather than maximum molarization as one would expect of a robust australopithecine), and they reiterate the fact that since the same pattern of variation describes chimpanzees males and females, it is unlikely that a variation reflecting sex difference in chimpanzees will reflect species difference in the early hominids.

The Hadar discoveries from the early 1990's greatly improve our knowledge about the differences between smaller and larger crania and support the single species interpretation, but perhaps the most telling evidence is found in the recent discoveries at Maka. They increase the sample of sites with several specimens and showing the same anatomical pattern of variation found at Hadar and Laetoli. White argues that three sites with smaller and markedly larger specimens are much more likely to be dimorphs of a single species, than very similar but differently sized hominids with overlapping ranges found together again and again (chimpanzee and bonobos are never found together in life, and are very unlikely to be found at the same site as fossils even once, let along every time). As Kimbel puts it:

> there is absolutely no doubt in our minds that the variation in these specimens
> is consistent with what you see between male and female apes ... it is
> completely harmonious with the hypothesis of sexual dimorphism.

According to the newspapers, where such discussions are most likely to be found these days, this evidence has come to convince even diehard splitters such as the cercopithecoid expert E. Delson.

REFERENCES AND FURTHER READINGS

ABITBOL, M.M. 1988 Evolution of the ischial spine and of the pelvic floor in the Hominoidea. *American Journal of Physical Anthropology* 75(1):53-67.

___. 1989 Sacral curvature and supine posture. *American Journal of Physical Anthropology* 80(3):379-390.

___. 1991 Ontogeny and evolution of pelvic diameters in anthropoid primates and in *Australopithecus afarensis* (AL 288-1). *American Journal of Physical Anthropology* 85(2):135-148.

AGUIRRE, E. 1970 Identificatión de "*Paranthropus*" en Makapansgat. *Crónica del XI Congreso Nacional de Arqueologia (Mérida) 1969*:98-124.

AIELLO, L.C. 1992 Allometry and the analysis of size and shape in human evolution. *Journal of Human Evolution* 22(2):127-147.

___. 1994 Variable but singular. *Nature* 368:399-400

ARMELAGOS, G.J., and D.P. VAN GERVEN 1980 Sexual dimorphism and human evolution: an overview. *Journal of Human Evolution* 9(5):437-446.

ARONSON, J.L. and M. TAIEB 1981 Geology and paleogeography of the Hadar hominid site, Ethiopia. In G. Rapp Jr. and C.F. Vondra (eds): *Hominid Sites: Their Geologic Settings*. AAAS Selected Symposium 63. Westview, Boulder. pp. 165-195.

BARTHOLOMEW, G.A. JR., and J.B. BIRDSELL 1953 Ecology and the protohominids. *American Anthropologist* 55:481-498.

BISHOP, W. W. 1976 Pliocene Problems Relating to Human Evolution. In G. L. Isaac and E. R. McCown (eds): *Human Origins: Louis Leakey and the East African Evidence*. Benjamin, Menlo Park. pp. 139-53.

BOAZ, N.T. 1988 Status of *Australopithecus afarensis*. *Yearbook of Physical Anthropology* 31:85-113.

BOGIN, G. 1990 The evolution of human childhood. *BioScience* 40:16-25.

BONNEFILLE, R. 1994 Palynology and paleoenvironment of East African hominid sites. In R.S. Corruccini and R.L. Ciochon (eds): *Integrative Paths to the Past. Paleoanthropological Advances in Honor of F. Clark Howell*. Prentice Hall, Englewood Cliffs. pp. 415-427.

BRACE, C.L. 1973 Sexual dimorphism in human evolution. *Yearbook of Physical Anthropology* 16:31-49.

BRAIN, C.K. 1972 An attempt to reconstruct the behavior of australopithecines: the evidence for interpersonal violence. *Zoologica Africana* 7:379-401.

___. 1985 Cultural and taphonomic comparisons of hominids from Swartkrans and Sterkfontein. In E. Delson (ed): *Ancestors: The Hard Evidence*. Alan R. Liss, New York. pp. 72-75.

BROEK, A.J.P. van der 1940 Das Skelett einer weiblichen Éfe-Pygmae. *Zeitschrift für Morphologie und Anthropologie* 38:121-169.

BROOM, R.A. 1925 On the newly discovered South African man-ape. *Natural History* 34:409-418.

___. 1949 The Ape-Men. *Scientific American* 181(5):20-24.

___. 1950a The genera and species of the South African fossil ape men. *American Journal of Physical Anthropology* 8:1-13.

___. 1950b *Finding the Missing Link.* Watts, London.

BROOM, R.A. and J.T. ROBINSON 1948 Size of the brain in the ape-man *Plesianthropus. Nature* 161:438.

BROWN, F.H. 1994 Development of Pliocene and Pleistocene chronology of the Turkana Basin, East Africa, and its relation to other sites. In R.S. Corruccini and R.L. Ciochon (eds): *Integrative Paths to the Past. Paleoanthropological Advances in Honor of F. Clark Howell.* Prentice Hall, Englewood Cliffs. pp 285-312

BUTZER, K.W. 1974 Paleoecology of South African australopithecines: Taung revisited. *Current Anthropology* 15:376-382 .

BUNN, H.T. 1991 A taphonomic perspective on the archaeology of human origins. In B.J. Siegel, A.R. Beals, and S.A. Tyler (eds): *Annual Review of Anthropology.* Annual Reviews, Palo Alto. Volume 20:433-467.

CHARTERIS, J., WALL, J.C., and NOTTRODT, J.W. 1982 Pliocene hominid gait: new interpretations based on available footprint data from Laetoli. *American Journal of Physical Anthropology* 58:133-144.

CLARKE, R.J. 1985 *Australopithecus* and early *Homo* in southern Africa. In E. Delson (ed): *Ancestors: The Hard Evidence.* Alan R. Liss, New York. pp. 171-177.

___. 1988 A new *Australopithecus* cranium from Sterkfontein and its bearing on the ancestry of *Paranthropus.* In F.E. Grine (ed): *Evolutionary History of the "Robust" Australopithecines.* Aldine de Gruyter, New York. pp. 285-292.

___. 1990 Observations on some restored hominid specimens in the Transvaal Museum, Pretoria. In G.H. Sperber (ed): *From Apes to Angels: Essays in Anthropology in Honor of Phillip V. Tobias.* Wiley-Liss, New York. pp. 135-151.

COFFING, E., C. FEIBEL, M. LEAKEY, and A. WALKER 1994 Four-million-year-old hominids from east Lake Turkana, Kenya. *American Journal of Physical Anthropology* 93(1):55-65.

COLE, T.M., and F.H. SMITH 1987 An odontometric assessment of variability in *Australopithecus afarensis. Human Evolution* 2(3):221-234.

CONROY, G.C. 1991 Enamel thickness in South African australopithecines: noninvasive evaluation by computed tomography. *Palaeontologia Africana* 28:53-59.

CONROY, G.C., and M.W. VANNIER 1987 Dental development of the Taung skull from computerized tomography. *Nature* 329:625-627.

___. 1988 The nature of Taung dental maturation continued. *Nature* 333:808.

CONROY, G.C., M.W. VANNIER, and P.V. TOBIAS 1990 Endocranial features of *Australopithecus africanus* revealed by 2- and 3-D computed tomography. *Science* 247:838-841.

COOK, D.C., J.E. BUIKSTRA, C.J. DeROUSSEAU, and D.C. JOHANSON 1983 Vertebral pathology in the Afar australopithecines. *American Journal of Physical Anthropology* 60(1):83-101.

COPE, D.A. and M.G. LACY 1992 Falsification of a single species hypothesis using the coefficient of variation: a simulation approach. *American Journal of Physical Anthropology* 89(3):359-378.

COPPENS, Y. 1984 Systématique, phylogénie, environnement et culture des Australopithèques, hypothèses et synthèse. In Y. Coppens (ed): *Les Australopithèques. Actes de Deux Séances de la Société d'Anthropologie de Paris sur le Thème Australopithèques. Bulletins et Mémoires de la Société d'Anthropologie de Paris* 10 (Série 13):273-284.

DART, R.A. 1925 *Australopithecus africanus*: the man-ape of South Africa. *Nature* 115:195-199; 116:462.

___. 1940 The status of *Australopithecus*. *American Journal of Physical Anthropology* 26:167-186.

___. 1949 The Predatory Implement Technique of *Australopithecus*. *American Journal of Physical Anthropology* 7(1):1-38.

___. 1955 *Australopithecus prometheus* and *Telanthropus capensis*. *American Journal of Physical Anthropology* 13:67-96.

___. 1956 Cultural status of the South African man-apes. *Smithsonian Report for 1955*, pp. 317-338.

___. 1957 The second adolescent (female) ilium of *Australopithecus prometheus*. *Journal of the Palaeontological Society of India* 2:73-82.

DART, R.A., with CRAIG 1959 *Adventures with the Missing Link*. Viking, New York.

DAY, M.H. 1985 Hominid locomotion - from Taung to the Laetoli footprints. In P.V. Tobias (ed): *Hominid Evolution: Past, Present, and Future. Proceedings of the Taung Diamond Jubilee International Symposium*. Alan R. Liss Inc., New York. pp. 115-127.

___. M.H. 1985 Pliocene hominids. In E. Delson (ed): *Ancestors: The Hard Evidence*. Alan R. Liss, New York. pp. 91-93.

DAY, M.H., and E.H. WICKENS 1980 Laetoli Pliocene hominid footprints and bipedalism. *Nature* 268:385-387.

DEAN, M.C., and B.A. WOOD 1981 Metrical analysis of the basicranium of extant hominoids and *Australopithecus*. *American Journal of Physical Anthropology* 54:63-71.

DE ARSUAGA, J.L., and J. ALONSO 1983 Sexual variability and taxonomic variability in the innominate bone of *Australopithecus*. *Zeitschrift für Morphologie und Anthropologie* 73(3):297-308.

DEMES, B., and N. CREEL 1988 Bite force, diet, and cranial morphology of fossil hominids. *Journal of Human Evolution* 17(7):657-670.

DUCHIN, L.E. 1990 The evolution of articulate speech: comparative anatomy of the oral cavity in *Pan* and *Homo*. *Journal of Human Evolution* 19(6-7)687-697.

DUNCAN, A.S., J. KAPPELMAN, and L.J. SHAPIRO 1994 Metatarsophalangel joint function and positional behavior in *Australopithecus afarensis*. *American Journal of Physical Anthropology* 93(1):67-81.

DURHAM, W.H. 1976 The adaptive significance of cultural behavior. *Human Ecology* 4:89-121.

ECKHARDT, R.B. 1987 Hominoid nasal region polymorphism and its phylogenetic significance. *Nature* 328:333-335.

FALK, D. 1988 Enlarged occipital/marginal sinuses and emissary foramina: their significance in hominid evolution. In F.E. Grine (ed): *Evolutionary History of the "Robust" Australopithecines*. Aldine de Gruyter, New York. pp. 85-96.

FEIBEL, C.S., F.H. BROWN, and I. McDOUGALL 1989 Stratigraphic context of the fossil hominids from the Omo group deposits: northern Turkana basin, Kenya and Ethiopia. *American Journal of Physical Anthropology* 78(4):595-622.

FERGUSON, W.W. 1984 Revision of fossil hominid jaws from the Plio/Pleistocene of Hadar in Ethiopia, including a new species of the genus *Homo* (Hominoidea: Hominidae). *Primates* 25:519-529.

___. 1989 Critique of "*Australopithecus afarensis*" as a single species based on dental metrics and morphology. *Primates* 30(4):561-569.

FISHER, A. 1988 The more things change . . . *Mosaic* 19(1):23-33.

FRANCISCUS, R.G., and T.W. HOLLIDAY 1992 Hindlimb skeletal allometry in Plio-Pleistocene hominids with special reference to AL-288-1 ("Lucy"). *Bulletin et Mémoires del la Société d'Anthropologie de Paris* 4(1-2):5-20.

GIBSON, K. 1991 Tools, language and intelligence: evolutionary implications. *Man* 26:255-264.

GREENFIELD, L.O. 1990 Canine "honing" in *Australopithecus afarensis*. *American Journal of Physical Anthropology* 82(2):135-143.

GREGORY, W.K. and M. HELLMAN 1945 Revised reconstruction of the skull of *Plesianthropus transvaalensis* Broom. *American Journal of Physical Anthropology* 3(3):267-275.

GRINE, F.E. 1985a Australopithecine evolution: the deciduous dental evidence. In E. Delson (ed): *Ancestors: The Hard Evidence*. Alan R. Liss, New York. pp. 153-167.

___. 1985b Dental morphology and the systematic affinities of the Taung fossil hominid. In P.V. Tobias (ed): *Hominid Evolution: Past, Present, and Future. Proceedings of the Taung Diamond Jubilee International Symposium*. Alan R. Liss Inc., New York. pp. 247-253.

___. 1987 The diet of South African australopithecines based on a study of dental microwear. *L'Anthropologie* 91:467-482.

___. 1993 Australopithecine taxonomy and phylogeny: historical background and recent interpretation. In R.L. Ciochon and J.G. Fleagle (eds): *The Human Evolution Source Book*. Prentice Hall, Englewood Cliffs. pp. 198-210.

GRINE, F.E., and R.F. KAY 1988 Early hominid diets from quantitative image analysis of dental microwear. *Nature* 333:765-768.

HAILEAB, B., and F.H. BROWN 1992 Turkana basin - Middle Awash Valley correlations and the age of the Sagabtole and Hadar Formations. *Journal of Human Evolution* 22(6):453-468.

HATLEY, T., and J. KAPPELMAN 1980 Bears, pigs, and Plio-Pleistocene hominids: a case for the exploitation of belowground food resources. *Human Ecology* 8:371-387.

HEIPLE, K.G., and C.O. LOVEJOY 1971 Distal femoral anatomy of *Australopithecus*. *American Journal of Physical Anthropology* 35:75-84.

HILL, A.H., S. WARD, and B. BROWN 1992 Anatomy and age of the Lothagam mandible. *Journal of Human Evolution* 22(6):439-451.

HINTON, R.J. 1979 Form and function in the temporomandibular joint. In D.S. Carlson (ed): *Craniofacial Biology*. Craniofacial Growth Series, Volume 1, Monograph No. 10. Center for Human Growth and Development, Ann Arbor.

HOLLOWAY, R. L. 1975 Early hominid endocasts: volumes, morphology, and significance for hominid evolution. In R. Tuttle (ed): *Primate Functional Morphology and Evolution*. Mouton, The Hague/Paris. pp. 393-415.

___. 1983 Cerebral brain endocast pattern of *Australopithecus afarensis* hominid. *Nature* 303:420-422.

___. 1985 The past, present, and future significance of the lunate sulcus in early hominid evolution. In P.V. Tobias (ed): *Hominid Evolution: Past, Present, and Future. Proceedings of the Taung Diamond Jubilee International Symposium*. Alan R. Liss Inc., New York. pp. 47-62.

HOLLOWAY, R.L., and W.H. KIMBEL 1986 Endocast morphology of Hadar hominid AL 162-28. *Nature* 321:536.

HOLLOWAY, R.L. and J.S. SHAPIRO 1992 Relationship of the squamosal suture to asterion in pongids (*Pan*): relevance to early hominid brain evolution. *American Journal of Physical Anthropology* 89(3):275-282.

HOWELL, F.C., and Y. COPPENS. 1976 An overview of hominidae from the Omo succession, Ethiopia. In Y. Coppens, F.C. Howell, G. L. Isaac, and R. E. F. Leakey (eds): *Earliest Man and Environments in the Lake Rudolf Basin*. University of Chicago Press, Chicago. pp. 522-532.

HYLANDER, W.L. 1979 The functional significance of primate mandibular form. *Journal of Morphology* 160:223-240.

ISAAC, G.Ll. 1976 Early stone tools: an adaptive threshold? In G. de Sieveking, I.H. Longworth and K.E. Wilson (eds): *Problems in Economic and Social Archaeology*. Duckworth, London. pp. 39-47.

JOHANSON, D.C., and EDEY, M.A. 1981 *Lucy, the Beginnings of Humankind*. Simon and Schuster, New York.

JOHANSON, D.C., M. TAIEB, and Y. COPPENS 1982 Pliocene hominids from the Hadar formation, Ethiopia (1973-1977): Stratigraphic, chronologic, and paleoenvironmental contexts, with notes on hominid morphology and systematics. *American Journal of Physical Anthropology* 57(4):545-604.

JOHANSON, D.C., and T.D. WHITE 1979 A systematic assessment of early African hominids. *Science* 203:321-330.

___. On the status of *Australopithecus afarensis*. *Science* 207:1104-1105.

JUNGERS, W.L. 1982 Lucy's limbs: skeletal allometry and locomotion in *Australopithecus afarensis*. *Nature* 297, 676-678.

___. 1994 Ape and hominid limb length. *Nature* 369:194.

KAY, R.F. 1982 Sexual dimorphism in Ramapithecinae. *Proceedings of the National Academy of Sciences, U.S.A.* 79:209-212.

___. 1985 Dental evidence for the diet of *Australopithecus. Annual Review of Anthropology* 14:315-341.

KELLEY, J., and XU QINGHUA 1991 Extreme sexual dimorphism in a Miocene hominoid. *Nature* 352:151-153.

KELLEY, J., and D. ETLER 1989 Hominoid dental variability and species number at the late Miocene site of Lufeng, China. *American Journal of Primatology* 18:15-34.

KIMBEL, W.H. 1984 Variation in the pattern of cranial venous sinuses and hominid phylogeny. *American Journal of Physical Anthropology* 63:243-263.

KIMBEL, W.H., and Y. RAK 1985 Functional morphology of the asterionic region in extant and fossil hominids. *American Journal of Physical Anthropology* 66(1):31-54.

___. 1993 The importance of species taxa in paleoanthropology and an argument for the phylogenetic concept of the species category. In W.H. Kimbel and L.B. Martin (eds): *Species, Species Concepts, and Primate Evolution.* Plenum, New York.

KIMBEL, W.H., and T.D. WHITE 1988a Variation, sexual dimorphism, and the taxonomy of *Australopithecus.* In F.E. Grine (ed): *Evolutionary History of the "Robust" Australopithecines.* Aldine de Gruyter, New York. pp. 175-192.

___. 1988b A revised reconstruction of the adult skull of *Australopithecus afarensis. Journal of Human Evolution* 17(5):545-550.

KIMBEL, W.H., T.D. WHITE, and D.C. JOHANSON 1984 Cranial morphology of *Australopithecus afarensis*: a comparative study based on a composite reconstruction of the adult skull. *American Journal of Physical Anthropology* 64:337-388.

___. 1985 Craniodental morphology of the hominids from Hadar and Laetoli: evidence of "*Paranthropus*" and *Homo* in the mid-Pliocene of eastern Africa? In E. Delson (ed): *Ancestors: The Hard Evidence.* Alan R. Liss, New York. pp. 120-137.

___. 1986 On the phylogenetic analysis of early hominids. *Current Anthropology* 27(4):361-362.

___. 1988 Variation, sexual dimorphism, and the taxonomy of *Australopithecus.* In F.E. Grine (ed): *Evolutionary History of the "Robust" Australopithecines.* Aldine de Gruyter, New York. pp. 175-192.

KRAMER, A. 1986 Hominid-pongid distinctiveness in the Miocene-Pliocene fossil record: The Lothagam mandible. *American Journal of Physical Anthropology* 70(4):457-474.

KYAUKA, P.S. 1994 Developmental patterns of the earliest hominids: a morphological perspective. In R.S. Corruccini and R.L. Ciochon (eds): *Integrative Paths to the Past. Paleoanthropological Advances in Honor of F. Clark Howell.* Prentice Hall, Englewood Cliffs. pp. 229-250.

LANGDON, J.H., J. BRUCKNER, and H.H. BAKER 1991 Pedal mechanics and bipedalism in early hominids. In Y. Coppens and B. Senut (eds): *Origine(s) de la Bipédie des Hominidés.* Cahiers de Paléoanthropologie, Centre National de la Recherche Scientifique, Paris. pp. 159-167.

LAITMAN, J.T. 1984 The anatomy of human speech. *Natural History* 93(8):20-27.

LATIMER, B.M., J.C. OHMAN, and C.O. LOVEJOY 1987 Talocrural joint in African hominoids: implications for *Australopithecus afarensis*. *American Journal of Physical Anthropology* 74(2):155-175.

LEAKEY, M.D. 1981 Tracks and tools. *Philosophical Transactions of the Royal Society, London*, Series B, 292:95-102.

LEAKEY, M.D., and R.L. HAY 1979 Pliocene footprints in the Laetolil beds at Laetoli, northern Tanzania. *Nature* 278:317-323.

LE GROS CLARK, W. E. 1947 Anatomy of the fossil Australopithecinae. *Journal of Anatomy* 81:300-333.

___. 1967 *Man-Apes or Ape-Men? The Story of Discoveries in Africa*. Holt, Rinehart, and Winston, New York.

LeMAY, M. 1977 Asymmetries of the skull and handedness. *Journal of the Neurological Sciences* 32:243-253.

LEONARD, W.R., and M. HEGMON 1987 Evolution of P$_3$ morphology in *Australopithecus afarensis*. *American Journal of Physical Anthropology* 73(1):41-63.

LEUTENEGGER, W. 1972 Newborn size and pelvic dimensions of *Australopithecus*. *Nature* 240:568-569.

LEWIN, R. 1983 Were Lucy's feet made for walking? *Science* 220, 700-702.

___. 1983 Ethiopia halts prehistory research: a tangled and unpleasant web of intrigue surrounding U.S. scientists has endangered the future of research in the fossil-rich territories of Ethiopia. *Science* 219:147-149.

___. 1984 Do ape-sized legs mean ape-like gait? *Science* 221:537-538.

___. 1985 Surprise findings in the Taung child's face. *Science* 228:42-44.

___. 1987a Four legs bad, two legs good. *Science* 235:969-971.

___. 1987b The earliest humans were more like apes. Science 236:1061-1063.

LOVEJOY, C.O. 1975 Biomechanical perspectives on the lower limb of early hominids. In R. Tuttle (ed): *Primate Functional Morphology and Evolution*. Mouton, The Hague. pp. 291-326.

___. 1984 The natural detective. *Natural History* 93(10):24-28.

___. 1986 Paleoanthropology today. *Science* 232:1026.

LOVEJOY, C.O. and K.G. HEIPLE 1970 A reconstruction of the femur of *Australopithecus africanus*. *American Journal of Physical Anthropology* 32:33-40.

___. 1972 Proximal femoral anatomy of *Australopithecus*. *Nature* 235:175-176.

LOVEJOY, C.O., K.G. HEIPLE, and A.H. BURSTEIN 1973 The gait of *Australopithecus*. *American Journal of Physical Anthropology* 38:757-780.

MACHO, G.A., and J.F. THACKERAY 1990 Computed tomography and enamel thickness of maxillary molars of Plio-Pleistocene hominids from Sterkfontein, Swartkrans, and Kromdraai (South Africa): an exploratory study. *American Journal of Physical Anthropology* 89(2):133-143.

MANN, A.E. 1988 The nature of Taung dental maturation. *Nature* 333:123.

MARTIN, R.D. 1983 *Human brain evolution in an ecological context.* 52nd James Arthur Lecture on the Evolution of the Human Brain. American Museum of Natural History, New York.

MARZKE, M.W. 1983 Joint functions and grip of the *Australopithecus afarensis* hand, with special reference to the region of the capitate. *Journal of Human Evolution* 12:197-211.

MARZKE, M.W., K.L. WULLSTEIN, and S.F. VIEGAS 1994 Variability at the carpometacarpal and midcarpal joints involving the fourth metacarpal, hamate, and lunate in Catarrhini. *American Journal of Physical Anthropology* 93(2):229-240.

McCOLLUM, M.A., F.E. GRINE, S.C. WARD, and W.H. KIMBEL 1993 Subnasal morphological variation in extant hominoids and fossil hominids. *Journal of Human Evolution* 24(2):87-111.

McHENRY, H.M. 1983 The capitate of *Australopithecus afarensis* and *A. africanus*. *American Journal of Physical Anthropology* 62:187-198.

___. 1986 The first bipeds: a comparison of the *A. afarensis* and *A. africanus* postcranium and implications for the evolution of bipedalism. *Journal of Human Evolution* 15(3):177-191.

___. 1991a Sexual dimorphism in *Australopithecus afarensis*. *Journal of Human Evolution* 20(1):21-32.

___. 1991b Femoral lengths and stature in Plio-Pleistocene hominids. *American Journal of Physical Anthropology* 85(2):149-158.

___. 1992 Body size and proportions in early hominids. *American Journal of Physical Anthropology* 87(4):407-431.

McHENRY, H.M., and R.R. SKELTON 1985 is *Australopithecus africanus* ancestral to *Homo*? In P.V. Tobias (ed): *Hominid Evolution: Past, Present, and Future. Proceedings of the Taung Diamond Jubilee International Symposium.* Alan R. Liss Inc., New York. pp. 221-226.

McKEE, J.K. 1989 Australopithecine anterior pillars: reassessment of the functional morphology and phylogenetic relevance. *American Journal of Physical Anthropology* 80(1):1-9.

___. 1991 Palaeo-ecology of the Sterkfontein hominids: a review and synthesis. *Palaeontologia Africana* 28:41-51.

___. 1993 Faunal dating of the Taung hominid fossil deposit. *Journal of Human Evolution* 25(5):363-376.

___. 1994 Palaeoecology and australopithecine adaptation at Taung and Makapansgat. In: *Four Million Years of Hominid Evolution in Africa: Papers in Honour of M.D. Leakey.* In press.

McKEE, J.K, and S.B. HELMAN 1991 Variability of the hominid juxtamastoid eminence and associated basicranial features. *Journal of Human Evolution* 21(4):275-281.

McKINLEY, K. 1971 Survivorship in gracile and robust australopithecines: a demographic comparison and a proposed birth model. *American Journal of Physical Anthropology* 34:417-426.

OLSON, T.R. 1985 Cranial morphology and systematics of the Hadar Formation hominids and "*Australopithecus*" *africanus*. In E. Delson (ed): *Ancestors: The Hard Evidence.* Alan R. Liss, New York. pp. 102-119.

OXNARD, C.E. 1984 *The Order of Man*. Yale University Press, New Haven.

PETERS, C.R., and B. McGUIRE 1981 Wild plant foods of the Makapansgat area: modern ecosystems analogue for *Australopithecus africanus* adaptations. *Journal of Human Evolution* 10:565-583.

PICQ, P. 1990 Tendances évolutives de l'articulation temporo-mandibulaire et phylogénie des Hominidés. *Comptes Rendus de L'Académie des Sciences* 310:831-836.

___. 1991 The diet of *Australopithecus afarensis*: an attempted reconstruction. In E. Delson, I. Tattersall, and J. Van Couvering (eds): *Paleoanthropology Annuals* 1:99-102.

PUECH, P-F., and H. ALBERTINI 1984 Dental microwear and mechanisms in early hominids from Laetoli and Hadar. *American Journal of Physical Anthropology* 65(1):87-91.

RADOSEVICH, S.C., G.J. RETALLACK, and M. TAIEB 1992 Reassessment of the paleoenvironment and preservation of hominid fossils from Hadar, Ethiopia. *American Journal of Physical Anthropology* 87(1):15-28.

RAK, Y. 1983 *The Australopithecine Face*. Academic Press, New York.

___. 1985 Sexual dimorphism, ontogeny, and the beginning of differentiation of the robust australopithecine clade. In P.V. Tobias (ed): *Hominid Evolution: Past, Present, and Future. Proceedings of the Taung Diamond Jubilee International Symposium*. Alan R. Liss Inc., New York. pp. 233-237.

RAYNER, R.J., B.P. MOON, and J.C. MASTERS 1993 The Makapansgat australopithecine environment. *Journal of Human Evolution* 24(3):219-231.

REMANE, A. 1954 Structure and relations of *Meganthropus africanus*. *American Journal of Physical Anthropology* 12:123-126.

RICKLAN, D.E. 1987 Functional anatomy of the hand of *Australopithecus africanus*. *Journal of Human Evolution* 16(7/8):643-664.

ROBERTS, N. 1984 Pleistocene environments in time and space. In R. Foley (ed): *Hominid Evolution and Community Ecology*. Academic Press, New York. pp. 25-53.

ROBINSON, J.T. 1952 Some hominid features of the ape-man dentition. *Official Journal of the Dental Association of South Africa* 7:102-113.

___. 1962 Australopithecines and the origin of man. *Smithsonian Institution Report for 1961*:479-500.

___. 1972 *Early Hominid Posture and Locomotion*. University of Chicago Press, Chicago.

ROMER, A.S. 1930 *Australopithecus* not a chimpanzee. *Science* 71:482-483.

RUFF, C. 1988 Hindlimb articular surface allometry in Hominoidea and *Macaca*, with comparisons to diaphyseal scaling. *Journal of Human Evolution* 17(7):687-714.

___. 1991 Climate and body shape in hominid evolution. *Journal of Human Evolution* 21(2):81-105.

RYAN, A.S., and D.C. JOHANSON 1989 Anterior dental microwear in *Australopithecus afarensis*: comparisons with human and nonhuman primates. *Journal of Human Evolution* 18(3):235-268.

SCHULTZ, A.H. 1937 Proportions, variability, and asymmetries of the long bones of the limbs and the clavicles in man and apes. *Human Biology* 9:281-328.

___. 1961 Vertebral column and thorax. *Primatologica* 4:1-66.

SCHWARCZ, H.P., R. GRÜN, and P.V. TOBIAS 1994 ESR dating studies of the australopithecine site of Sterkfontein, South Africa. *Journal of Human Evolution* 26(3):175-181.

SENUT, B. 1981 Humeral outlines in some hominoid primates and in Pliopleistocene hominids. *American Journal of Physical Anthropology* 56:275-284.

___. 1993 French contribution to the study of human origins. *Human Evolution* 7(4):15-24.

SENUT, B., and C. TARDIEU 1985 Functional aspects of Plio-Pleistocene hominid limb bones: implications for taxonomy and phylogeny. In E. Delson (ed): *Ancestors: The Hard Evidence*. Alan R. Liss, New York. pp. 193-201.

SHREEVE, J. 1994 'Lucy,' crucial early human ancestor, finally gets a head. *Science* 264:34-35.

SHREWSBURY, M.M., and A. SONEK 1986 Precision holding in humans, non-human primates, and Plio-Pleistocene hominids. *Human Evolution* 1(3):233-242.

SMITH, B.H. 1989 Growth and development and its significance for early hominid behaviour. OSSA (*International Journal of Skeletal Research*) 14:63-96.

STERN, J.T., and R.L. SUSMAN 1983 The locomotor anatomy of *Australopithecus afarensis*. *American Journal of Physical Anthropology* 60:279-317.

___. 1991 "Total morphological pattern" versus the "magic trait": conflicting approaches to the study of early hominid bipedalism. In Y. Coppens and B. Senut (eds): *Origine(s) de la Bipédie des Hominidés*. Cahiers de Paléoanthropologie, Centre National de la Recherche Scientifique, Paris. pp. 99-111.

SUSMAN, R.L., and J.T. STERN 1991 Locomotor behavior of early hominids: epistemology and fossil evidence. In Y. Coppens and B. Senut (eds): *Origine(s) de la Bipédie des Hominidés*. Cahiers de Paléoanthropologie, Centre National de la Recherche Scientifique, Paris. pp. 121-131.

SUSMAN, R.L., J.T. STERN JR., and W.L. JUNGERS 1984 Arboreality and bipedality in the Hadar hominids. *Folia Primatologia* 43:113-156.

___. 1985 Locomotor adaptations in the Hadar hominids. In E. Delson (ed): *Ancestors: The Hard Evidence*. Alan R. Liss, New York. pp. 184-192.

TAGUE, R.G. 1991 Commonalties in dimorphism and variability in the anthropoid pelvis, with implications for the fossil record. *Journal of Human Evolution* 21:153-176.

TREVATHAN, R.W. 1987 *Human Birth: An Evolutionary Perspective*. Aldine, Chicago.

TOBIAS, P.V. 1971 *The Brain in Hominid Evolution*. Columbia, New York.

___. 1980 *Australopithecus afarensis* and *A. africanus*: critique and an alternative hypothesis. *Palaeontologia Africana* 23:1-17.

___. 1985 Single characters and the total morphological pattern redefined: the sorting effected by a selection of morphological features of the early hominids. In E. Delson (ed): *Ancestors: The Hard Evidence*. Alan R. Liss, New York. pp. 94-101.

___. 1989 Hominid variability, cladistic analysis, and the place of *Australopithecus africanus*. Hominidae. Proceedings of the 2nd International Congress of Human Paleoanthropology. Editoriale Jaca Books, Milan. pp. 119-127.

___. 1980 Sterkfontein: crucial new light on hominid evolution. In S.L. Washburn and R. Moore (eds): *Ape into Human: a Study of Human Evolution*. Little Brown, Boston. pp. 112-117.

TUTTLE, R.H. 1985 Ape footprints and Laetoli impressions: a response to the SUNY claims. In P.V. Tobias (ed): *Hominid Evolution: Past, Present, and Future. Proceedings of the Taung Diamond Jubilee International Symposium*. Alan R. Liss Inc., New York. pp. 129-133.

___. 1988 What's new in African Paleoanthropology? In B.J. Siegel, A.R. Beals, and S.A. Tyler (eds): *Annual Review of Anthropology*. Annual Reviews, Palo Alto. Volume 17:391-426.

TUTTLE, R.H., D.M. WEBB, N.I. TUTTLE, and M. BAKSH 1990 Further progress on the Laetoli trails. *Journal of Archaeological Science* 17:347-362.

UNGAR, P.S., and F.E. GRINE 1991 Incisor size and wear in *Australopithecus africanus* and *Paranthropus robustus*. *Journal of Human Evolution* 20(4):313-340.

VALLOIS, H.V. 1965 Anthropometric techniques. *Current Anthropology* 6: 127-143.

VRBA, E.S. 1985 Early hominids in Southern Africa: updated observations on chronological and ecological background. In P.V. Tobias (ed): *Hominid Evolution: Past, Present, and Future. Proceedings of the Taung Diamond Jubilee International Symposium*. Alan R. Liss Inc., New York. pp. 195-200.

WALLACE, J.A. 1973 Tooth chipping in the australopithecines. *Nature* 244:117-118.

WALTER, R.C 1994 Age of Lucy and the first family: single-crystal ^{40}Ar/^{39}Ar dating of the Denen Dora and lower Kada Hadar members of the Hadar Formation, Ethiopia. *Geology* 22:6-10.

WALTER, R.C. and J.L. ARONSON 1993 Age and source of the Sidi Hakoma Tuff, Hadar Formation, Ethiopia. *Journal of Human Evolution* 25(3):229-240.

WARD, S.C. and S. MOLNAR 1980 Experimental stress analysis of topographic diversity in early hominid gnathic morphology. *American Journal of Physical Anthropology* 53(3):383-395.

WEIDENREICH, F. 1948 About the morphological character of the australopithecine skull. In A. du Troit (ed): *Robert Broom Commemorative Volume*. Royal Society of South Africa:, Capetown. pp. 153-158.

WHEELER, P.E. 1988 Stand tall and stay cool. *New Scientist* 1612:62-65.

WEINERT, H. 1950 Über die neuen Vor- und Frühmenschenfunde aus Afrika, Java, und Frankreich. *Zeitschrift für Morphologie und Anthropologie* 42:113-148.

WHITE, T.D. 1980 Evolutionary implications of Pliocene hominid footprints. *Science* 208:175-176.

___. 1985 The hominids of Hadar and Laetoli: an element-by-element comparison of the dental samples. In E. Delson (ed): *Ancestors: The Hard Evidence*. Alan R. Liss, New York. pp. 138-152.

___. 1986 *Australopithecus afarensis* and the Lothagam mandible. In V.V. Novotný and A. Mizerová (eds): *Fossil Man. New Facts, New Ideas. Papers in Honor of Jan Jelínek's Life Anniversary. Anthropos* (Brno) 23:79-90.

___. 1994 Ape and hominid limb length, a reply to Jungers. *Nature* 369:194

WHITE, T.D., and D.C. JOHANSON 1989 The hominid composition of Afar locality 333: some preliminary observations. In G. Giacobini (ed): *Hominidae. Proceedings of the 2nd International Congress of Human Paleoanthropology.* Editoriale Jaca Books, Milan. pp. 97-101.

WHITE, T.D., D.C. JOHANSON, and W.H. KIMBEL 1981 *Australopithecus africanus*: its phyletic position reconsidered. *South African Journal of Science* 77:445-470.

___. 1982 Dating of South African hominid sites. *South African Journal of Science* 78:301-302.

WHITE, T.D., and G. SUWA 1987 Hominid footprints at Laetoli: facts and interpretations. *American Journal of Physical Anthropology* 72(4):485-514.

WHITE, T.D., G. SUWA, W.K. HART, R.C. WALTER, G. WOLDEGABRIEL, J. DeHEINZELIN, J.D. CLARK, B. ASFAW, and E. VRBA 1993 New discoveries of *Australopithecus* at Maka in Ethiopia. *Nature* 366:261-265.

WOLPOFF, M. H. 1973 Posterior tooth size, body size and diet in South African gracile australopithecines. *American Journal of Physical Anthropology* 39:375-394.

___. 1974 Sagittal cresting in the South African australopithecines. *American Journal of Physical Anthropology* 40:397-408.

___. 1976 Some aspects of the evolution of early hominid sexual dimorphism. *Current Anthropology* 17(4):579-606.

___. 1979 Anterior dental cutting in the Laetolil hominids and the evolution of the bicuspid P_3. *American Journal of Physical Anthropology* 51(2):233-234.

___ 1983a Australopithecines: The unwanted ancestors. In: K. Reichs (ed.) *Hominid Origins.* University Press of America, Washington, D.C. pp. 109-126.

___. 1983b Lucy's little legs. *Journal of Human Evolution* 12:443-453.

___. 1988. The origins of Humanity. In F. Doig (ed): *Tracks Through Time. Australian Natural History* Supplement 2:16-25.

WOLPOFF, M.H., J.M. MONGE, and M. LAMPL 1988 Was Taung a human or an ape? *Nature* 335:501.

WOLPOFF, M.H., and M.D. RUSSELL 1981 Anterior dental cutting at Laetolil. *American Journal of Physical Anthropology* 55:223-224.

WOOD, B.A. 1985 A review of the definition, distribution, and relationships of *Australopithecus africanus*. In P.V. Tobias (ed): *Hominid Evolution: Past, Present, and Future. Proceedings of the Taung Diamond Jubilee International Symposium.* Alan R. Liss Inc., New York. pp. 227-232.

___. 1988 Hominid diversity in the Plio-Pleistocene. *OSSA (International Journal of Skeletal Research)* 14:19-31.

___. 1992 Early hominid species and speciation. *Journal of Human Evolution* 22(4/5):351-366.

WOOD, B.A., and A.T. CHAMBERLAIN 1986 *Australopithecus*: grade or clade? In B. Wood, L. Martin, and P. Andrews (eds): *Major Trends in Primate and Human Evolution.* Cambridge University Press, Cambridge. pp. 220-248.

ZIHLMAN, A.L. 1985 *Australopithecus afarensis*: two sexes or two species? In P.V. Tobias (ed): *Hominid Evolution: Past, Present, and Future. Proceedings of the Taung Diamond Jubilee International Symposium.* Alan R. Liss Inc., New York. pp. 213-220.

ZUCKERMAN, S. 1966 Myths and methods in anatomy. *Journal of the Royal College of Surgeons of Edinburgh* 11:87-114.

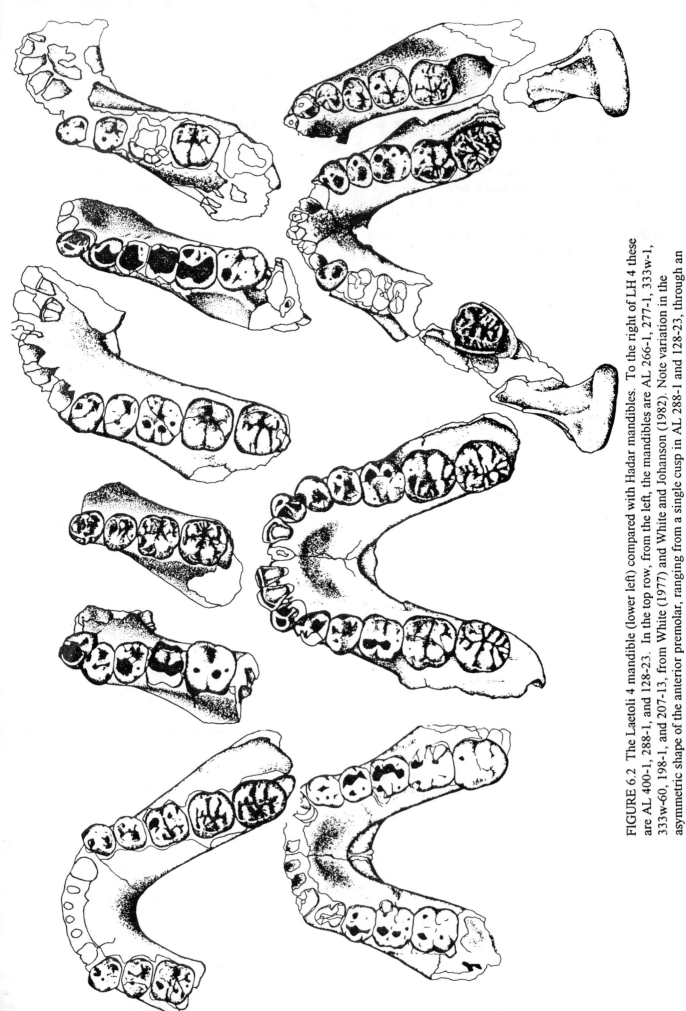

FIGURE 6.2 The Laetoli 4 mandible (lower left) compared with Hadar mandibles. To the right of LH 4 these are AL 400-1, 288-1, and 128-23. In the top row, from the left, the mandibles are AL 266-1, 277-1, 333w-1, 333w-60, 198-1, and 207-13, from White (1977) and White and Johanson (1982). Note variation in the asymmetric shape of the anterior premolar, ranging from a single cusp in AL 288-1 and 128-23, through an asymmetric shape with a dominant outer cusp and small inner one (LH 4), to equal-sized cusps (AL 333w-1). LH 4 has a clear diastema between the P_3 and the (broken) canine.

FROM: White, T.D. 1977 New fossil hominids from Laetolil, Tanzania. American Journal of Physical Anthropology 46:197-230; White, T.D. and D.C. Johanson 1982 Pliocene hominid mandibles from the Hadar Formation, Ethiopia: 1974-1977 collections. American Journal of Physical Anthropology 57:501-

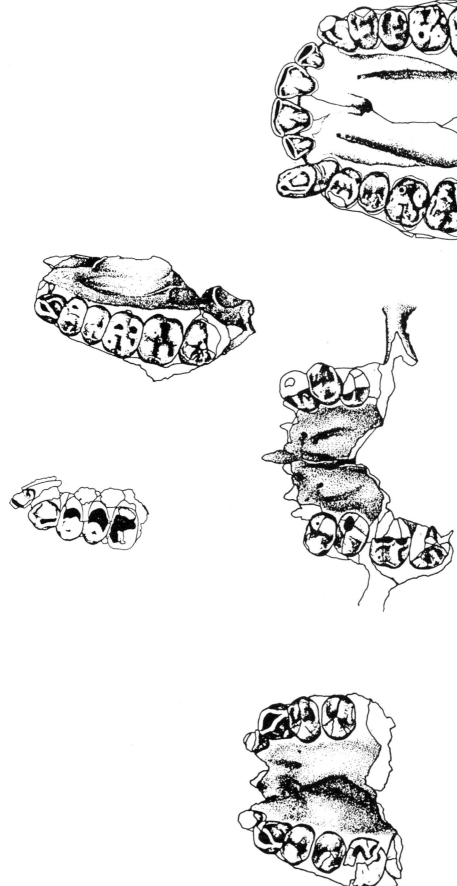

FIGURE 6.3   The LH 5 female maxilla (upper left) compared with Hadar maxillae, after White (1977) and Kimbel and colleagues (1982).   To the right is AL 199-1, another female, and below are three males, from the left AL 333-2, 333-1, and 200-1.   In the most complete specimen, AL 200-1, the right (reader's left) canine of the Afar maxilla is out of its socket, making it appear unusually projecting (a reconstructed form is shown in figure 6.5). The wear on the incisors is uneven; the heavier wear on the lateral incisors may have been due to their function in stripping. In both this specimen and LH 5 there is a diastema between the canine and incisor.

FROM: White, T.D. 1977 New fossil hominids from Laetolil, Tanzania. American Journal of Physical
 Anthropology 46:197-230; Kimbel, W.H., D.C. Johanson, and Y. Coppens 1982 Pliocene cranial
 remains from the Hadar Formation, Ethiopia. American Journal of Physical Anthropology 57:453-500.

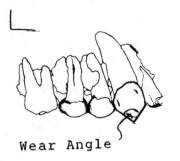

LH 5 Maxilla

Wear Angle

Labial   Distal

Mandibles:

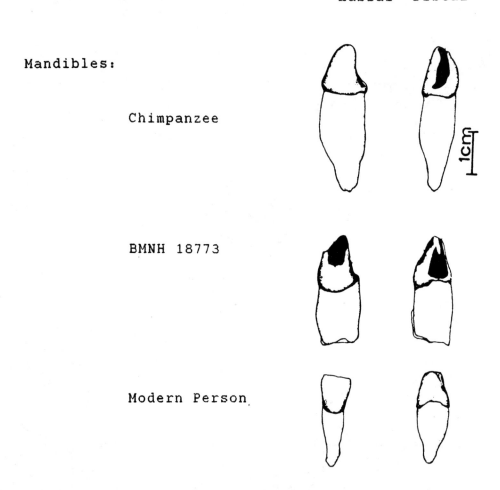

Chimpanzee

BMNH 18773

Modern Person

FIGURE 6.4 Canine wear in *A. afarensis,* after White (1977 and 1981). Below, the Laetoli hominid canine discovered in the monkey collection of the Natural History Museum of London is compared with a chimpanzee and human. Crown height and the distal sharpening wear is much like the chimpanzee. Above, the much less projecting LH 5 canine (also see figure 6.3) has a lower wear angle but none-the-less was sharpened during life.

FROM: White, T.D. 1977 New fossil hominids from Laetolil, Tanzania. American Journal of Physical Anthropology 46:197-230; White, T.D. 1981 Primitive hominid canine from Tanzania, Science 213:348-349.

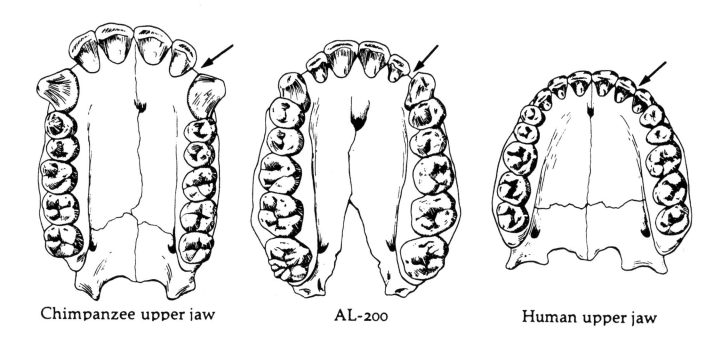

Chimpanzee upper jaw   AL-200   Human upper jaw

FIGURE 6.5 Comparison of a chimpanzee, human, and reconstructed AL 200-1 maxilla, after Johanson and Edey (1981).

FROM Johanson, D.C., and Edey, M.A. 1981 *Lucy, the Beginnings of Humankind.* Simon and Schuster, New York.

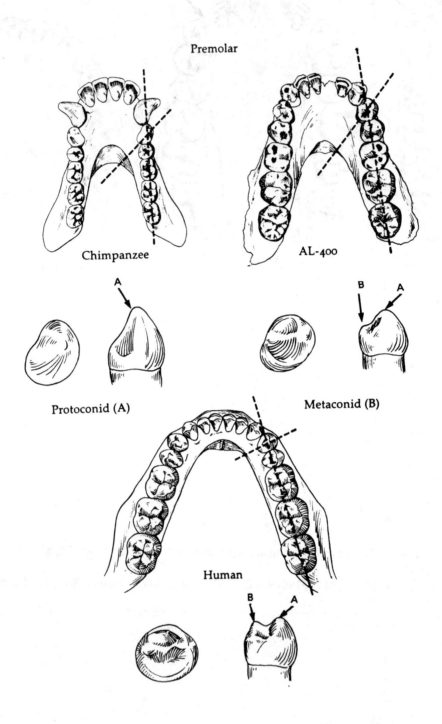

FIGURE 6.6 P₃ rotation in *Australopithecus afarensis* mandibles, showing the differences in angulation to the tooth row and the differing cusp heights, after Johanson and Edey (1981).

FROM Johanson, D.C., and Edey, M.A. 1981 *Lucy, the Beginnings of Humankind*. Simon and Schuster, New York.

FIGURE 6.7 Posterior view of chimpanzee (A), *A. afarensis* (B), and *A. africanus* (C) crania, after White and colleagues (1981). The Hadar cranium 333-45 and the chimpanzee have compound temporonuchal crests. They differ in height, the Hadar specimen being in the same position as the South African australopithecine, formed of a long posterior temporalis muscle rather than a high nuchal one.

FROM White, T.D., D.C. Johanson, and W.H. Kimbel 1981   *Australopithecus africanus*: its phyletic position reconsidered. South African Journal of Science 77:445-470, figure 10..

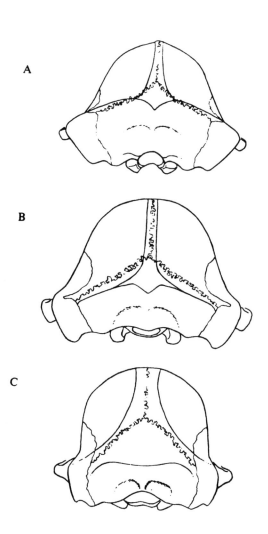

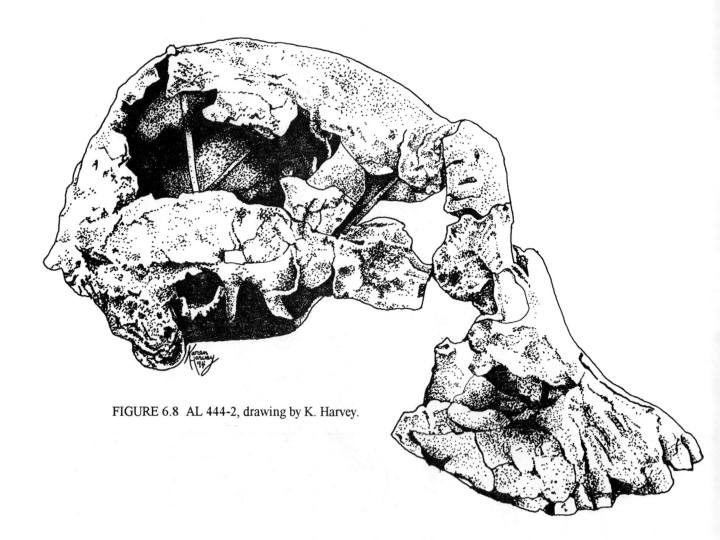

FIGURE 6.8   AL 444-2, drawing by K. Harvey.

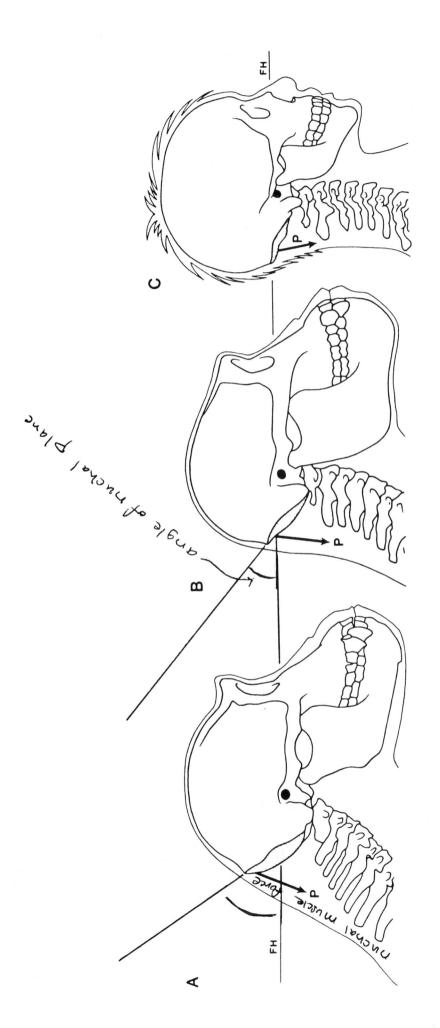

FIGURE 6.9 Head posture for a chimpanzee (A), *A. afarensis*, (B), and a modern human (C), after Jaanusson (1987). The angle of the nuchal plane with the Frankfurt Horizontal (FH) is shown. **FROM** Jaanusson, A. 1987 Balance of the head in hominoid evolution. *Lethaia* 20:165-176.

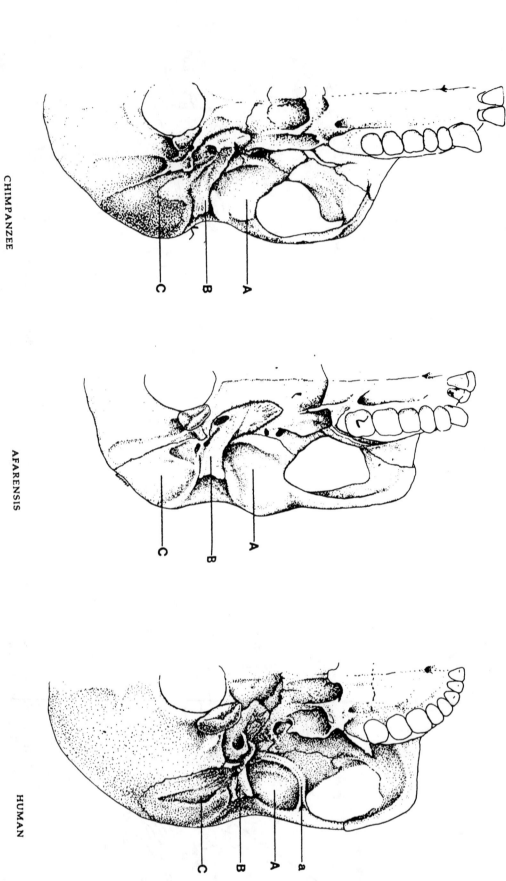

CHIMPANZEE

AFARENSIS

HUMAN

Figure 6.10 Comparisons of cranial base anatomy, after Johanson and Edey (1981). The figure shows the positions of the horizontal surface of the mandibular fossa (a), the sloping to vertical anterior wall of the fossa (A), the tympanic plate (B), and the mastoid process (C). The specimens are positioned with the foramen magnum in the same position.
FROM Johanson, D.C., and Edey, M.A. 1981 *Lucy, the Beginnings of Humankind.* Simon and Schuster, New York.

FIGURE 6.11 The AL-288 pelvis reconstruction, compared with a chimpanzee (above) and human (below), after Rosenberg (1992). The views of the three females compare the shape of the pelvic inlet and the hips. **FROM** Rosenberg, K.R. 1992 The evolution of modern human childbirth. *Yearbook of Physical Anthropology* 35:89-124, figure 5.

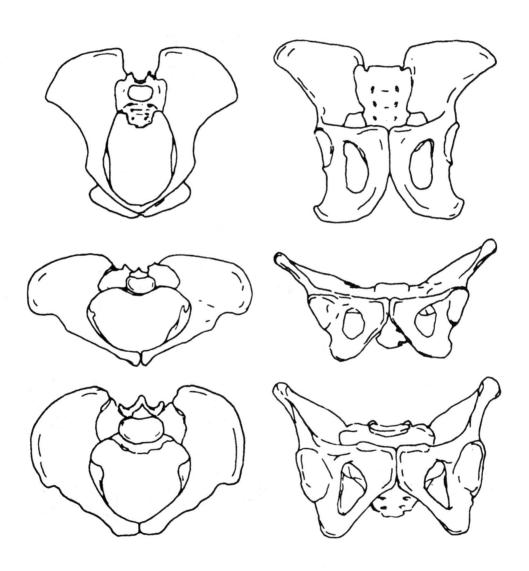

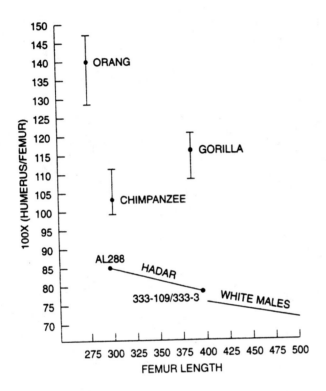

FIGURE 6.12 The relation of humerus and femur length in apes and humans (from Lovejoy 1993). The figure shows the allometry of this relation in the small (Hadar australopithecine) and large (European male) hominids, and emphasizes the relatively short arms in both species.

FROM Lovejoy, C.O. 1993 Modeling human origins: are we sexy because we're smart, or smart because we're sexy? In D.T. Rasmussen (ed): The Origin and Evolution of Humans and Humanness. Jones and Bartless, Boston. pp. 1-28.

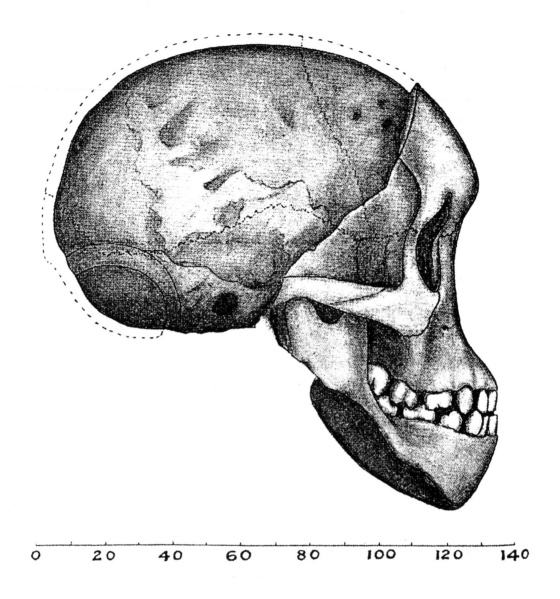

0   20   40   60   80   100   120   140

FIGURE 6.14   The Taung cranium, with its natural endocast positioned in the frontal bone, after Keith (1931).

FROM Keith, A. 1931 *New Discoveries Relating to the Antiquity of Man.* Williams and Norgate, London, figure 5.

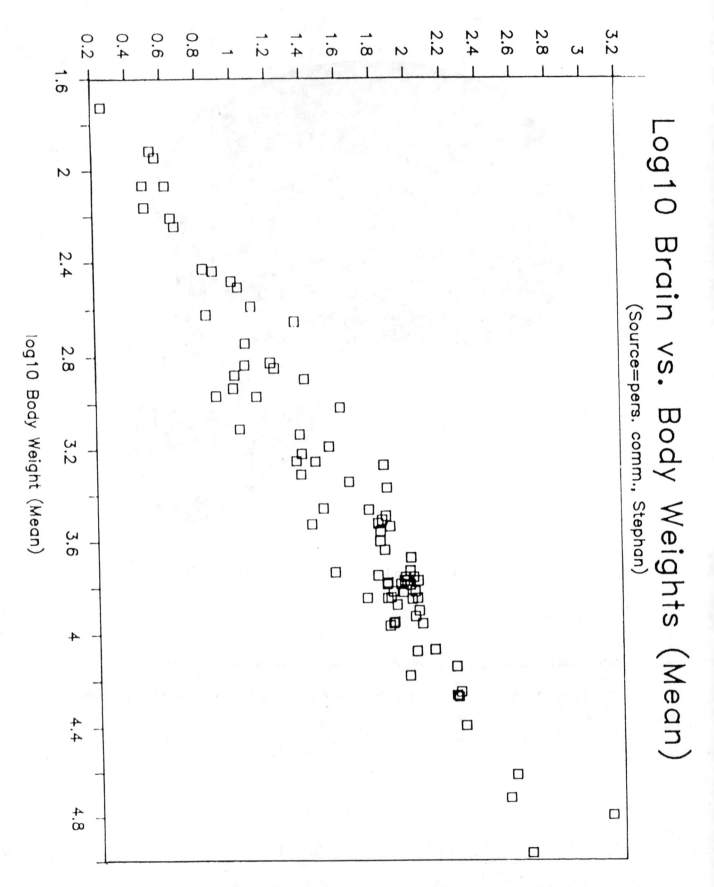

FIGURE 6.15 Relative brain size in primates. The allometric curve of brain and body weights is from Holloway (1988), who obtained species data from Stephan. Data are presented as base 10 logarithms, since an allometric curve plotted in log-log scale will appear as a straight line. Australopithecine data are from the text.

FIGURE 6.16 Lovejoy's reconstruction of the STS 14 pelvis and femur, showing a human-like biomechanical relationship and an adaptation to the problems created by one-legged stance. After Lovejoy and colleagues (1973).

FROM Lovejoy, C.O., K.G. Heiple, and A.H. Burstein 1973 The gait of *Australopithecus*. American Journal of Physical Anthropology 38:757-780.

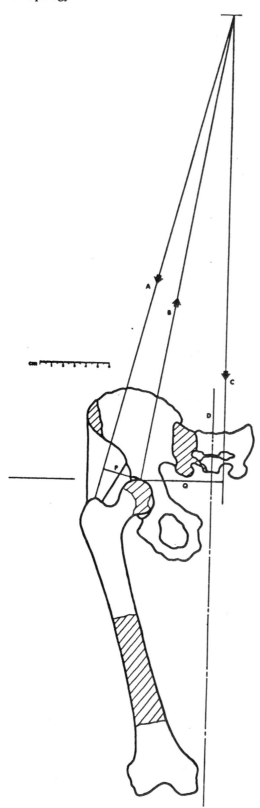

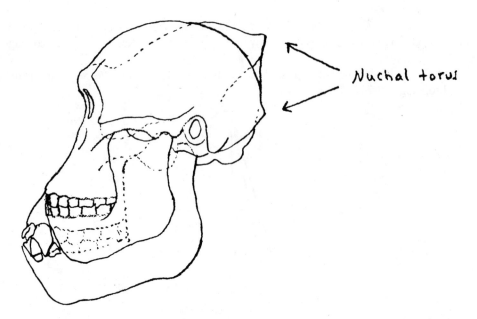

FIGURE 6.17 STS 5 compared with a female gorilla, possibly a match for postcanine tooth size but contrasting cranial form, face, and nuchal torus position.

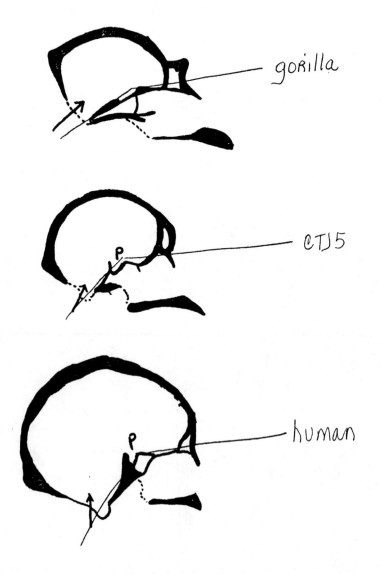

FIGURE 6.18 Flexion of the cranial base.

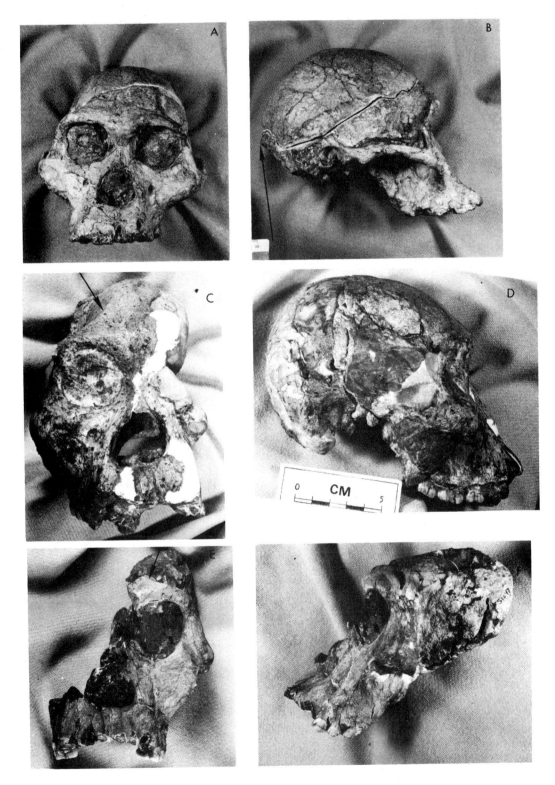

FIGURE 6.19 Sterkfontein fragmentary crania.

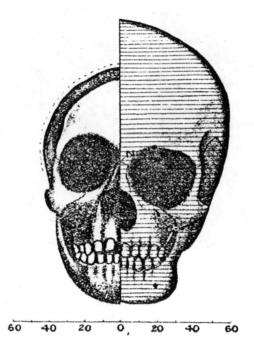

FIGURE 6.20 Ontogeny in *A. africanus.* Above, Taung is compared with a modern child of the same dental age (after Keith 1931), and below similar dental aged children of this australopithecine species and chimpanzees are compared with adults (after Rak 1983).

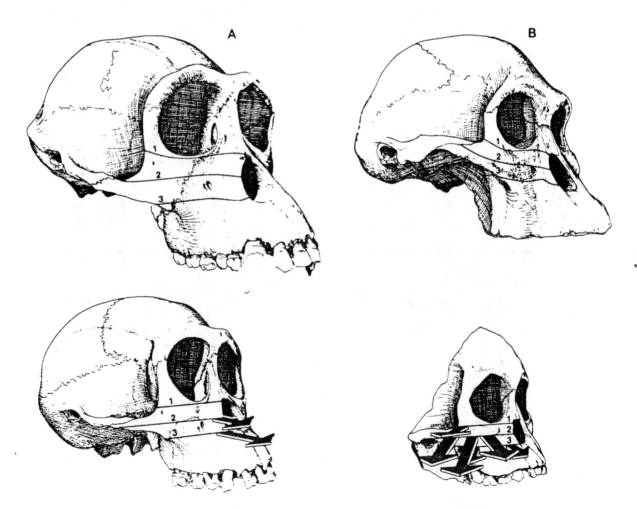

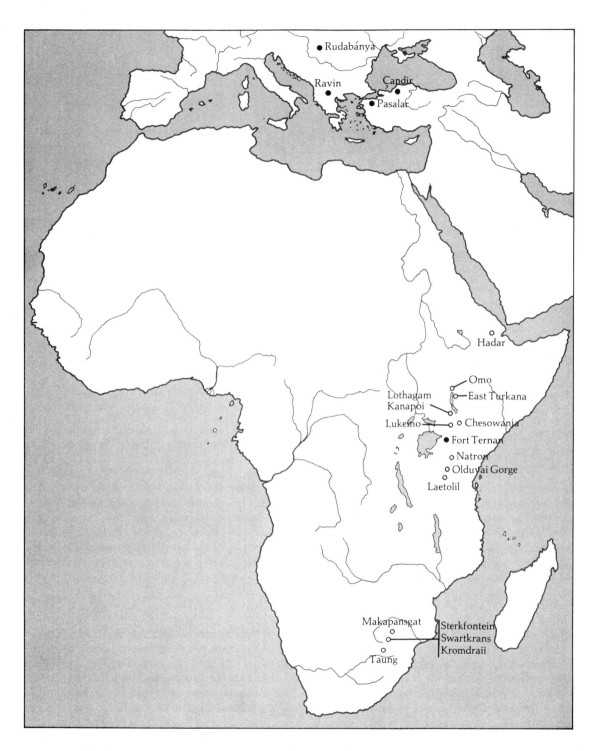

Map 6.1 Australopithecine sites.
FROM: First edition, Map 1.

PART THREE

DEVELOPMENT
OF THE
HUMAN
PATTERN

CHAPTER SEVEN

Evolution of the Robust Australopithecines

From 2.4 to 1.9 myr, there is a half-million year gap in the well-dated East African paleontological deposits, with very little hominid material of any kind (figure 7.1). This period is one of significant drying and the development of marked seasonality across Africa. It is possible, but far from certain, that there are hominid remains from South Africa spanning this gap. What we know of the populations of eastern Africa before this gap is that a very large, *Australopithecus afarensis*-like robust australopithecine, *Australopithecus aethiopicus*, was present. This species must have greater antiquity than the earliest specimen found, the so-called "black skull" would suggest as its lack of derived features shared with *Australopithecus africanus* indicates a divergence before *A. africanus* appeared. There are a few additional remains of *A. aethiopicus* scattered throughout the 2.4-1.9 myr span, and some fragmentary specimens that suggest other hominid populations.

At the end of this gap, the East African fossil record explodes with specimens and closely related taxa. Quite different hominid species groups had evolved by the time of the first large East African fossil sample, from the uppermost part of the Upper Burgi Member at Koobi Fora dated to just before the beginning of the Pleistocene at 1.88-1.90 myr. In this sample *A. aethiopicus* had been replaced with the smaller but even more megadont australopithecine species *Australopithecus boisei*, first known to appear at 2.25 myr. There is also a group of species in our genus, *Homo*, including the earliest *Homo sapiens*

When the East African discoveries first began to accumulate in large numbers in the early 1960s, attempts were made to interpret them within the framework of J. Robinson's **Dietary Hypothesis**, developed to explain the South African australopithecine variations. This pioneering hypothesis related the divergences in the South African australopithecines to ecological differences that were reflected in dietary adaptations. Robinson posited that the robust australopithecines found in South Africa were the primitive form of australopithecine, even though they were found later in time. They were thought to be associated with moist environmental conditions and adapted to the rich vegetation with their powerful masticatory apparatus, including large postcanine teeth. In Robinson's thinking, *A. africanus* evolved later, as the climate turned drier. This species perfected bipedalism and embarked on a savanna adaptation emphasizing omnivory and thereby taking advantage of a much wider range of resources. The postcanine teeth reduced in size but the canines expanded, according to Robinson as an adaptation to increased meat eating. It was *A. africanus*, in his scheme, that gave rise to later *Homo*.

Agreement was widespread but not universal. At one extreme there were those who like Robinson's predecessor, R. Broom, envisioned many more australopithecine taxa. On the other hand, E. Mayr had already proposed that all of the known australopithecines could (and should) be encompassed in the variation of a single species. I approached this question in a Popperian way, taking the **single species hypothesis** as simplest one and attempting to refute it. The basis for this hypothesis was my assumption that all hominids shared culture, since this was the "kickoff event" in hominid origins. Culture, I reasoned, would so broaden hominid niches that competition for limiting resources between species would be inevitable and lead to enhanced cultural abilities and further niche broadening. Only one of the competing species would be expected to persist. Extinction, rather than niche divergence, was the most probable outcome for the others This meant only one hominid species at a time could be expected.

L.S.B. Leakey with his wife, Mary, ultimately changed everything with their discoveries of first East African hominid cranial remains, at Olduvai Gorge in Tanzania. By virtue of being discovered first, the Olduvai material set the stage for the subsequent interpretation of East African hominids discovered later. When Louis and Mary Leakey first reported on the discovery of a massive cranium from Olduvai Gorge in 1959 (Olduvai hominid 5, or "the nutcracker man"), emphasis was placed on its human-like features (Figure 4.X). The later discovery of an individual with much smaller jaws and teeth but a bigger cranium (OH 7) provided a contrast between a large and small form of australopithecine-like hominid that was without equal in South Africa. These were soon placed in separate taxonomic categories: the larger was "*Zinjanthropus boisei*", the robust australopithecine of East Africa, and the smaller *Homo habilis*. It was generally felt that South African "*Paranthropus*" evolved into East African "*Zinjanthropus*" by continuing the trend for dental robustness. Through the succeeding decades and continuing at present a tremendous sample of this taxon has accumulated through the efforts of R. Leakey and his colleagues, mostly from the Koobi Fora region, the north east shore and inland area bordering Lake Turkana, and from the western side of the lake.

By the 1980's the South and East African robust australopithecines had already been placed in different species, if not different genera, and workers such as F.C. Howell and later F. Grine resuscitated R. Broom's much earlier contention that the Kromdraai and Swartkrans robust australopithecines were different species as well. WT 17000, the "black skull" as it was called, was discovered on the west side of lake Turkana in this decade and threw the taxonomy of the robust australopithecines into disarray. As luck had it, this was just as this taxonomy was to be featured during a workshop that F. Grine had sponsored for 1987 to discuss the natural history of the robust australopithecines and hopefully settle the outstanding issues in their systematics. Many attending that conference became renewed believers in **Murphy's Law**. Features reflecting its powerful masticatory system and the plesiomorphic aspects of its cranial capacity, cranial base anatomy, and anterior dentition seemed to place WT 17000 at the base of a robust australopithecine clade. If so, a problem was created by the fact that this clade must have developed numerous features in parallel with the other australopithecines. Conversely, should the black skull be unrelated to the later robusts, it would follow that the parallelisms are in the robust masticatory apparatus. Then, it would only be the masticatory complex that had to have evolved twice in the Pliocene. This would mean that robust australopithecine's are not a monophyletic group. In either case, the position of *A. africanus* was problematic, if not the position of the South African robusts as well - a position even further confused by the attribution to *Homo* of an isolated 2.4 myr temporal that resembles some of the South African robust australopithecines.

We focus here on several problems. Is *A. aethiopicus* ancestral to the later robust australopithecines? With the possibility of contemporary robust australopithecines varieties in southern and eastern Africa, another question is whether the geographic variation is at the subspecies or species level. Are these adaptive radiations or examples of geographic (or other sources of) racial variation in polytypic species? This is an important issue because it tells us much about the population dynamics and adaptive capabilities of hominids just at the origin of our species, *Homo sapiens*.

This chapter traces the evolution of the australopithecines through the Late Pliocene and Early Pleistocene, which is considered here to begin at 1.75 myr (see table 1.3), to their disappearance or extinction. It examines the evolution of the robust and hyper-robust australopithecine varities This relation is complex because it must contend with the question of whether there is an especially close phylogenetic relationship between *Homo* and one of the robust australopithecine species. It raises one of the most interesting issue of human evolution - the role of the robust australopithecines. The following chapter is concerned with the evolution of the australopithecine-like *Homo* species and the appearance of early *H. sapiens*.

Late Pliocene in East Africa

THE BLACK SKULL - A ROBUST VARIETY OF *AUSTRALOPITHECUS AFARENSIS*

The Late Pliocene begins some 2.6 myr ago. Slightly afterwards, in 2.5 myr deposits west of Lake Turkana, a very robust cranium that became known as the "black skull" because of the fossil's color, provided some surprises and created numerous problems in the interpretation of australopithecine evolution. The specimen, WT 17000 (or just 17K), combines numerous similarities with the Hadar remains with an extraordinary development of the masticatory apparatus and neck musculature. Unlike some remains it was published immediately after being discovered, and widely perceived to be the beginning of a clade leading to the later robust australopithecines of South Africa and the hyper-robusts of East Africa. Yet beginning with W. Kimbel and colleagues, a few paleoanthropologists pointed out that it shares virtually no unique features with these later species, and its main similarities to them are based on characteristics reflecting its masticatory adaptation.

The specimen is very similar to a male *A. afarensis,* but with a smaller cranial capacity (at 410 cc it is the smallest male hominid known), an even more powerful nuchal musculature, and an unusually well developed masticatory apparatus. The later is indicated by

- the large palate with a thick roof,
- the broken roots of large rooted (and presumably large crowned) molars and 4th premolar,
- the very anterior zygomatic process of the maxilla whose size and orientation creates a flat, flaring face (this puts the masseter attachment far forward and lateral, where its leverage in producing grinding motions is best).

While no teeth are preserved, the sizes of the roots and of the palate shows that both the anterior dentition and the postcanine teeth were quite large. Other specimens reveal thickened molar enamel, much like *A. afarensis.* With this combination of small brain and powerful mastication there is a not-unexpected well-developed sagittal crest with a rearward extension reflecting the consequences of anterior tooth loading. This crest meets the elevated nuchal crest to form an *A. afarensis*-like compound temporonuchal crest at the rear of the vault.

Other features uniquely resembling *A. afarensis* are numerous, and include (as described above for the earlier species):

- large anterior tooth sockets,
- flattened cranial base (and flattening of everything on it such as the flat, non-projecting articular eminence of the mandibular fossa and the shallow palate),
- posterior foramen magnum position and more sagittal orientation of the **petrous pyramid** of the temporal bone,
- extreme development of the nuchal muscles and the more vertical orientation of their attachment on the occiput
- extreme facial prognathism.

R. Holloway reports that besides its small endocranial volume, additional plesiomorphic features of the endocast not shared by other robust australopithecines include a narrow pointed frontal, low height of the posterior parietal lobes, and a chimpanzee-like form of the **cerebellar lobes** (these are reflected in the **cerebellar fossae** on the internal surface of the occiput). Unlike the later robusts, the specimen lacks the occipitomarginal sinus drainage.

The earliest known *A. aethiopicus* is probably the 2.7 myr L55s-33 mandible fragment from level C6 in the Omo deposits, north of Lake Turkana. L55s-33 is the front of a mandible. It exemplifies the difficulty of distinguishing hominid species based on mandibular remains alone, as most authors who have studied the specimen have been unwilling to allocate it. Comprised of a small piece of mandibular body with most of a worn P$_4$ crown, it was not considered to be the hyper-robust species *A. boisei* because this diagnostic tooth is too small, 83% the size of the smallest *A. boisei* tooth known. Yet G. Suwa, who has specialized in the analysis of australopithecine premolars, reported that the premolar is unusually thick enameled and has the squared-off shape of this hyper-robust species. Unable to choose which criterion was more important he, attributed it to an unspecified robust australopithecine taxon that is not *A. boisei*. He is probably correct, but he offered this suggestion just after the black skull was discovered and before *A. aethiopicus* was well understood. Turning to the specimen that *A. aethiopicus* was named after, according to S. Ward and B. Brown, the moderately sized 2.6 myr Omo 18-18 mandible possesses large (i.e. hyper-robust, or *A. boisei*-like) molar roots implanted in a serrate pattern that is characteristic of *A. afarensis* and described in Chapter 6. The thick, squat mandibular body has contours similar to *A. boisei*. Because of this combination of features it was this mandible that Y. Coppens used to describe the basis for the species "*A. aethiopicus*", before the 17K cranium was discovered. There are times when mandibles have proven to be misleading, but in this case the use of a mandible to define the species for a cranium would seem to have been valid.

AUSTRALOPITHECUS AFARENSIS AND *AFRICANUS*

At one time P. Tobias argued that *A. afarensis* and *africanus* were not different beyond the subspecies level, and that temporal and geographic variation would more than account for their differences. Even though there are clear evolutionary trends distinguishing the earlier and later species, with new discoveries in both taxa the ranges of variation have come to overlap even more and his arguments have become more compelling. Individual specimens such as STW 252 have similarities to the Hadar (and other *A. afarensis*) remains never before found in a Sterkfontein hominid - in this case the anatomy of the incisors and canines. At the same time, in phenetic terms, the later southern species is more similar to some subsequent populations of *Homo* than *A. afarensis* is, in having postcanine tooth expansion and concomitant changes in the bony part of the masticatory apparatus, as well as larger cranial capacity and a number of anatomical details. In other words, the lineage appears to be evolving in the direction of *Homo* - an interpretation that is even more compelling when the Member 5 crania are considered (see Chapter 8). Yet, the evolutionary species concept as used here is not delineated by phenetic variation but by branching. What, now, can we infer about the ancestry of *A. africanus* and its distinctions from the earlier Hadar australopithecines?

Assuming that *A. afarensis* is the common ancestor of both *A. aethiopicus* and *A. africanus*, was one of these later hominids the ancestor of the other? The numerous shared primitive features of *A. aethiopicus* and *afarensis*, especially in contrast with *A. africanus*, indicate that the South African australopithecine is very *unlikely* to have been an ancestor of *A. aethiopicus*. The other possibility is more credible, but the small brain size of the *A. aethiopicus* male makes it improbable as a direct *A. africanus* ancestor. The conclusion is that *A. africanus* and *A. aethiopicus* are both descendants of *A. afarensis*. *A. aethiopicus* populations survive longer than *A. africanus*, another source of evidence indicating that there has been a branching. With both species (*A. africanus* and later *A. aethiopicus*) descendants of the Hadar australopithecines, the South African species is defined at its beginning by a speciation event (see figure 7.5). Therefore, this reconstruction of the most probable phylogeny supports the species distinction of *A. afarensis* and *A. africanus*. Indirect evidence would suggest an approximate 3 myr date for this branching.

THE EARLIEST MEMBERS OF GENUS *HOMO*?

West of Lake Turkana, an isolated temporal bone was found in 1967, with matrix on the fossil which, according to A. Hill and S. Ward, relates it to a 2.4 myr level in the Chemeron formation. In what has come to be a controversial analysis, these authors attributed the fragment to the genus *Homo*. If correct, the BC 1 is the earliest known member - a half-million years older than any other cranial remains that can be attributed to *Homo*. They were able to clearly and unambiguously able show that it differs from both earlier hominid species, *A. afarensis* and *A. aethiopicus* (which are nearly identical in the temporal region), as well as from most apes, in 3 unique ways:

1. In these earlier species the large air-filled cells found in the **mastoid process** extend above the process into the flat portion (**squama**) of the temporal, an inflation of the bone called **pneumatization**. Chemeron lacks this inflation of the squama, in spite of its dramatically expanded mastoid
2. The lower surface of the **auditory tube** has a sharp **tympanic** (or as sometimes termed **petrosal) crest**
3. The mandibular fossa is very large and deep, but in spite of its size it is situated under the braincase. Its anterior face (the articular eminence) is steep and saddle shaped (curved convexly front-to-back, and concavely side-to-side).

They were also able to demonstrate Chemeron is not a hyper-robust australopithecine, of the sort found much later in East Africa. The hyper-robusts are among the few hominids with equally large and deep mandibular fossae, but these are positioned laterally to the cranial wall rather than being tucked under it, and lack a horizontal surface in front of the mandibular socket's anterior face which this specimen (like many other hominids) has.

Chemeron combines evidence of three adaptive systems. Powerful chewing forces are suggested by the large size of the mandibular fossa and the downward projection of the articular eminence (where the mandible's condyle rests when force passes through it, see discussion by R. Hinton). The saddle-shaped form of this eminence is important in the adaptation, as this shape is an alternative to the ball-and-socket type joint to allow turning motion, an important aspect of grinding as the condyle rests on the articular eminence when it pivots. A second system is implicated by the expanded, highly pneumatized mastoid process and its large rearward-facing posterior surface. Scientists such as R. Caspari have interpreted the rearward orientation of the posterior mastoid face to sometimes reflect the expansion of nuchal muscles that function in shoulder stabilization and powerful upper limb activities. Increased in size, these muscles attach over a broader area, extending onto the back of the mastoids. The third system is brain expansion. What Hill and Ward describe as the medial placement of the large mandibular fossa is actually a lateral expansion of the cranial wall over the fossa, indicating a relatively large brained hominid.

It proved to be easier to determine what the specimen *is not*, than to establish what it *is*. The evidence for cranial expansion would support the *Homo* diagnosis that Hill and Ward suggested. However only early *H. sapiens* has so large a mandibular fossa, and even the most robust specimens lack the lateral projection of the fossa and the backward projection of the mastoid; it extends so far from the wall of the vault that there is an actual shelf of pneumatized bone above it in Chemeron, while in early *H. sapiens* specimens such as OH 9 the back of the mastoid is level with the rest of the back of the head. All other early *Homo* samples, even those with large jaws and teeth such as ER 1470, have much smaller and shallower mandibular fossae (and also differ in the mastoid morphology described above). Chemeron is unlikely to be an early *Homo* species.

What it resembles most closely are South African australopithecines. Several *A. africanus* specimens have the sharpened petrosal crest and similar medial placement of the mandibular fossa (for instance, STS 19) and a few such as STW 505 appear to be almost as big (the mandibular fossa is only partially complete on this individual) but virtually none have the mastoid pneumatization or similar articular eminence projection or size which provides a steep vertical face for the mandibular fossa with a horizontal surface for the mandibular condyle to rest in front of it. It is among the South African robust australopithecines that the most similar morphology can be found. These samples, as discussed below, resemble the earlier *A. africanus* remains but are more robust and larger brained. Certain individuals such as TM 1517, the Kromdraai cranium and associated partial skeleton, are very similar to Chemeron in all these and other details.

Is Chemeron, then, the same species as TM 1517, and evidence of South African robust australopithecines in East Africa? Perhaps, but the South African robust australopithecines are distant in space and many believe them to be much younger in time (all other known *Homo* crania are younger in time as well). Moreover, at Kromdraai there are some specimens that have dental similarities with other robust australopithecines that cannot be examined in the Chemeron specimen. The resemblances between these two temporal bones could well point to an *A. africanus* affinity (and some authors view the

Kromdraai remains as anatomical intermediates between *A. africanus* and the later robust Swartkrans hominids). This would further substantiate the earlier dentognathic indications that this species was present in East Africa at the same time that it occurred in the south. The fact remains that a temporal bone may be too small a part of the cranium to be certain of its taxonomy. Once again the specimen could be described as provocative. It probably cannot be described as *Homo*.

At a slightly older age, the distal humerus from Kanapoi, on the west side of Lake Turkana, is dated to about 2.5 myr. This specimen is somewhat different from the Hadar distal humeri, more like recent hominids, according to H. McHenry and R. Corruccini who believe that the fragment has a number of modern features. B. Senut showed that it contrasts with the well-preserved Hadar specimens (she argues it may be similar to one very weathered fragment from the site, but since the similarities are based on the weak expression of features it is more likely that her conclusions are based on the bone's condition than on its anatomy). Senut subsequently suggested Kanapoi may represent an early species of *Homo,* and so it may, but it is also strikingly similar to the South African robust australopithecine distal humerus associated with the TM 1517 cranium. Kanapoi is a moderate sized bone, larger then TM 1517, with an estimated body weight of over 57 kg according to McHenry. Its main distinction from more recent specimens is in its internal anatomy. In human distal humeri, the shaft near the bottom end has a thin layer of compact bone and an internal cavity filled with lighter, spongy bone. This reflects the fact that the main forces that pass through the elbow are not of great magnitude and are mainly along the shaft. According to studies by A. Walker, the Kanapoi humerus has a very much thicker compact bone layer. This suggests that the forces acting on the elbow were markedly greater and had significant components of twisting (bending that close to a joint is unlikely).

In sum, there is no evidence for *Homo* in East Africa during the earlier portion of the Late Pliocene. There are a scatter of specimens, representing different anatomical parts, that show notable similarities to the robust South African australopithecines; enough to be suggestive, but not enough to be certain.

The Discovery of Stone Tool Manufacture

The Late Pliocene also sees the unprecedented and revolutionary discovery of how to make stone tools. The first tools were probably discovered by an australopithecine and are not particularly associated with any species of *Homo;* in fact, there is no reason to conclude *Homo* had yet appeared. We are not sure which australopithecine discovered them and which made the ones that have been found. The most likely candidates are all of the hominids as "monkey-see, monkey-do" pertains to hominids far better than to any monkey! Whoever first discovered and initially manufactured them, these tools must have been very important in the appearance and early evolution of *Homo sapiens*, as we have become the only species fully dependent on them for our survival and success. However, the fact is that while lithic artifacts are widely believed to be associated with the origin and/or early evolution of the genus *Homo*, between the first appearance of artifacts in the paleontological record and the first cranial specimens that can be attributed to *Homo* is more than a half-million years.

The earliest stone tools known are found in eastern Africa. At one time, an industry called "Kafuan" was thought to be the earliest one. However, it was found that the so-called Kafuan tools could not be distinguished from the results of natural fracturing. The earliest tools now recognized extend in range from the Hadar and the regions around Lake Turkana to as far west as the upper Semiliki Valley in Zaire where they overlap with the range of living chimpanzees. According to J. Harris they are dated to no earlier than 2.6 myr. These artifacts are divided into four basic types

1. **manuports**, rocks carried to a locality but not artificially modified (they are identified by the fact that they could not have been brought to the site by any process except hominid transport)
2. **hammerstones**, rocks used to strike against other rocks or hard objects
3. simple **cores**, the cobbles from which flakes are struck
4. unmodified **flakes** removed from cores by hammering

The main characteristics of these tools are their crudeness and their opportunistic forms. While the edges are sharp, they are far from straight. In addition, the so-called functional "types" that some archaeologists have identified may be more in the eyes of the beholders than in the intent of the australopithecines. Various tool types which are recognizable in later industries can be noted in the earliest **assemblages**. However, there is little evidence that these "types," including specialized woodworking tools like burins that have been reported, were intentionally shaped. Instead, the production of implements seems to have been a more haphazard activity. A number of attempts at production were likely made, and the most useful results utilized. One can picture an australopithecine picking through a pile of flakes for one or two that would be useful for a specific purpose—perhaps some long, thin flakes that could be used to cut the cartilage and tendons in a joint in order to dismember an animal. This is a very important behavior because it marks the beginning of associating form with function. However, it is quite another state of affairs to be able to *manufacture* a tool with the required shape in mind.

The study of lithic artifacts involves the means of manufacture or **technology**, including the raw material choice and the steps or decisions taken in its modification. Another important aspect, however, is the **land use pattern**. This refers to the study of how the traces of early hominid activities are distributed across the landscape, and the implications this has for reconstructing foraging behavior, habitat preference and seasonality, and food preferences. R. Potts provides a good background for readers unfamiliar with this archaeological terminology.

The earliest artifacts are very crudely made of quartz or finer grained volcanic lavas. The sites with lava tools have only a small number and a very low density. The quartz tools also occur at very low densities, of between 10 and 25 artifacts per square meter, at sites were a significant number of artifacts were found (quartz shatters more easily so that the same technology will lead to more identifiable artifacts). This can be contrasted with the intense scatters of the half million year later Oldowan Industry found at early Pleistocene sites such as Olduvai Gorge where the tools are 3 or more times denser. The Oldowan tool sites are typically assemblages (or collections) of stone cores and other utilized rocks, flakes, and manuports. Hundreds, even thousands, are typically found together in clusters of 50-100 m^2. The study of these sites formed the focus of G. Isaac's !Kung San analogy discussed in Chapter 5, and of L. Binford's criticisms of it.

J. Harris and colleagues interpret the earlier, pre-Oldowan tools as reflecting a simple understanding of the consequences of fracturing rocks to produce sharp-edged flakes, and the rudimentary skill to do so. Binford makes a distinction between

> **expedient tools**: tools that are made in response to an immediate need
> **curated tools**: tools that are kept for use in the future

Harris and colleagues find evidence that these earliest tools are uniquely expedient in their nature. They have further concluded that these earliest artifacts

- are found at or very near the natural sources of stone that can be modified into tools
- tend to be found along rivers bordered by strips of gallery forest
- are seasonal, and not made habitually throughout the year
- are probably part of the dry-season food procurement adaptation, when above ground plant foods are less abundant in seasonal East African environments
- are sometimes, but not at all invariably, found associated with bones

They believe that meat acquisition is a significant aspect of tool function. The focus on tools and meat is partially, but certainly not completely, a reflection of the 'Man the Hunter' precept discussed in Chapter 5. In a very influential demonstration, the late L.S.B. Leakey showed how easy it was to cut into and butcher goat-sized mammals with the simplest flakes - a source of food that would be unobtainable to a tool-less hominid lacking a powerful canine cutting complex. Microanalysis of some Early Pleistocene artifacts have identified bone fragments along the edge of a flake, and cut marks of a large tortoise shell suggest butchering.

Stone tools represent only a small part of the tool-making activity of early hominids. However, stone tools need no preservation to remain at a site, whereas to be found organic material must first be preserved, and often is not. Consequently, we know much more about stone tools than any made of wood or bone. Yet, there is some evidence of the vastly richer complex of non-lithic tools that were made and used. Even if the evidence for Dart's supposed prelithic Osteodontokeratic industry of tools made from bones, teeth, and horns is discounted, there are preserved bones at Olduvai, Sterkfontein and Swartkrans which are sharpened and scratched from their use in digging. In substantially later deposits in a South African cave, C. Brain showed that simple digging sticks he found, made of bone or antler, opened the possibility of a vast source of edible roots and rhizomes that could not be dug up with unaided hominid hands. Yet, in this chapter we will see that indirect evidence suggests only one of the hominid varieties in the Swartkrans cave was using the sticks to any significant degree. The requirements of this behavior may be much more complex than has been assumed. Studies of food residues on other possibly contemporary Early Pleistocene artifacts from East Africa have revealed plant remains as well. All of these occurrences are quite a bit later than the first tools known.

The most likely interpretation is that the earliest tools were used differently, intermittently and perhaps seasonally in butchering, bone smashing, and the gathering and preparation of visible plant foods. The implication is that early hominid tool use may not have been as ubiquitous or pervasive as many have assumed. The technology was simpler and cruder, even than that found at the famous Olduvai Gorge tool sites, a half million years later. If the tools were part of a dry season adaptation, as Harris and colleagues speculate, they might have arisen to meet the challenges of the newly developed seasonality in African climatic evolution at that time.

Table 7.1

Differences Between Chimpanzee and Early Hominid Artifacts

Abstracted from Wynn and McGrew (1989) and Brain et al (1988)

Chimpanzee	Early Hominid (Oldowan)
Known Tools	
wooden termite and ant probes	bone and horn digging sticks
marrow extraction sticks	flaked bone
leaf sponges	manuports
wooden hammers	stone hammers
stone hammers	stone anvils
stone anvils	flaked cores
tree-root anvils	unmodified stone flakes
wooden branches and clubs used in threat displays	modified stone flakes
Manufacturing Procedure	
Bitten to approximate length	modification by flaking
Other modifications by stripping, chewing	
Tool Transport	
	(at Olduvai)
hammers - 0.5 km	gneiss (rare) 6-13 km
probes - 1 km	quartzite 2-5 km
	lava <1 km

Of course, one might ask why so much is made of toolmaking. One of the reasons why 'Man, the Toolmaker' is no longer accepted is the fact that apes, especially chimpanzees, regularly make a wide variety of tools. As we have seen in the discussions of hominid origins (Chapter 5) and the controversies over interpreting the locomotor pattern of the earliest australopithecines outlined in the last chapter, there is a school of thought developed in the past decades that views early hominids as little modified apes.

While perhaps a justifiable reaction to Isaac's !Kung San interpretation of the earliest tool makers, there remains the question of whether this framework is justified by the data.

Attempting to take an ape's eye view of these early artifact assemblages, T. Wynn and W.C. McGrew concluded "at the most one can argue that the Oldowan pushed the limits of great ape adaptation; it did not exceed them." Their study compared a number of elements in the artifact related behaviors of chimpanzees and early hominids (but not the *earliest*, and for that matter not their earliest tool industries), and found them similar in three:

1. spatial concepts, particularly the concepts needed to modify natural objects, including:
   - proximity - as expressed in repeated modification to the same place on the object
   - boundary - early hominid tools seems to be designed with the configuration of the edges in mind, not the overall shape
   - order of activities that modify the object
2. standardization, superimposed in most cases by the nature of the natural materials used
3. design, both technologies were 'ad hoc', trial and error approaches for producing the desired artifacts

Surprisingly, in view of their conclusion of a basic similarity between the abilities of chimpanzees and the Oldowan tool makers, they reported a larger number of differences. These are reviewed in table 7.2, along with others suggested by an analysis of the Swartkrans cave bone tools which are probably of the same approximate age.

The question of chimpanzee abilities is addressed by the ongoing experimental studies of N. Toth and colleagues. Their attempts to teach a chimpanzee to manufacture stone flakes has provided considerable insight about what is unique in hominid tool making. Throughout this century chimpanzees have been observed manufacturing tools in captivity (there is the famous composite tool, made of piecing together bamboo rods, observed by W. Köhler). The Toth study, the most carefully designed and controlled that has yet been attempted, provides a most important piece of information in its failure to demonstrate hominid-like stone tool making abilities in this most human-like of the apes. The chimpanzee was given the problem of making a simple flake to cut a rope in order to obtain a piece of fruit. The animal quickly mastered the basic task of using a hammer-stone to strike flakes off of a core, but the abilities it demonstrated were very much different from those suggested by a study of the simplest australopithecine technology. In the experimenters' understated words, the chimp "exhibited a relatively low degree of technological finesse". Typically, the ape brought little force to its tool-making activities, in spite of the great overall strength of the animal. The flakes it made were very small and difficult to hold, and used only a narrow part of the edge of the core being held. These problems may be anatomical, involving the shoulder and the hand to the extent that the overlapping finger grip that chimpanzees can use to firmly grasp an object would be dangerous in the knapping procedure. Neuromuscular control played an important role as well. Yet, and perhaps equally importantly, there was no lack in understanding, or conceptualizing, the steps required to obtain the fruit. The chimpanzee finally learned to flake the stone core by throwing in on the hard floor (the experiments were outdoors). In an attempt to force a focus on knapping to produce flakes, the experimenters carpeted the floor, but the chimpanzee found it easier to rip up the carpet in order to continue the floor-smashing technology for flake production, than to effectively produce flakes using the hammerstone, as it was being taught to do.

It is difficult to agree with the conclusions of the Wynn and McGrew study. Perhaps most fundamentally, they ignore the basic difference between chimpanzees and the early hominids - the fact is that hominids make stone tools in large numbers and chimpanzees do not make any at all (and the experimental work suggests can not), in spite of all the potential advantages that the simplest cutting edges might bring. Stone tool manufacture did not come easily to our ancestors and it was clearly not a behavior of the first hominids. It characterized our line for considerably less than half of its time on earth! Long after tools were being made and used, only some hominids were able to master technology as seemingly simple as digging sticks. In these behavioral aspects the first hominid tool users were not, as Wynn and McGrew suggested, simply bipedal chimpanzees. This implies that the significant brain size expansion that the hominids of several lineages show in the Late Pliocene, beginning just before lithic technology is found and measured to the time of the Oldowan Industry and the first appearance of *Homo*, may well be linked to the evolution of lithic technology and the role it came to play in the hominid adaptive system.

East African Australopithecines

CONTINUED EVOLUTION OF *AUSTRALOPITHECUS AETHIOPICUS*

The Late Pliocene fossil record from East Africa is well dated, but unfortunately fragmentary. Before 1.9 myr, hominid remains are almost completely limited to the sites in the Omo River basin in southern Ethiopia, just north of where the river flows into Lake Turkana in Kenya. This region, following the cooling of 2.6 myr and thereafter, became a drier and more like a modern savanna than the earlier, more forested habitats. The river was flanked with gallery forest, in turn surrounded by dry-thorn savanna. The fossilization of the Omo specimens was not particularly good. Therefore, as they have become exposed to the open air and sun through erosion, the poorly fossilized bones quickly deteriorated, leaving usually only the hardest materials - teeth and a few jaws - to be found by the French and American expeditions that began working there soon after the first Olduvai discoveries (this is reviewed by N. Boaz). Numerous teeth, but only a few incomplete cranial or postcranial remains have been discovered.

Most of the diagnostic remains are of the hyper-robust australopithecine species *A. aethiopicus*. Following the earliest cranium (WT 17000, the black skull) and mandibles (e.g. Omo 18-18, the specimen that the species was named after) in time, there are several other crania and cranial fragments that can be associated with *A. aethiopicus*. Omo 338y-6 (2.39 myr) is an approximately 10 year old juvenile vault that lacks frontal bone and face. Even on a specimen this young, a number of features are expressed that reflect the development of a powerful masticatory system. These include temporal lines that meet at the middle in an anterior position (there would have been a sagittal crest had the youth lived longer), marked development of the **superior nuchal line** with a strong downward projecting **inion** at its center, and a large overlap of the temporal onto the parietal bone. Its cranial capacity is quite small (427 cc), although it must be within a few percent of its adult value. Holloway argued from a time long before the black skull was discovered that the 338y-6 brain endocast was unlike other robust australopithecines in size and morphology, lacking several features attributed to the robust australopithecine clade including an occipitomarginal sinus drainage. He now contends that in these characteristics it resembles the black skull. F.C. Howell and colleagues have suggested it be included in *A. aethiopicus* and they also attribute the scattered mandibular and dental remains of robust australopithecines from the earlier Late Pliocene of the Omo region to this species.

What appears likely is that at the beginning of the Late Pliocene the hyper-robust Omo species is *A. aethiopicus*. By its end australopithecine evolution in East Africa was continuing solely in the form of *A. boisei*. Based on the general resemblances of the crania it has seemed reasonable to assume that the earlier megadont species evolved into the later one, but this is almost certainly not the case. *A. boisei* shares a number of unique features with *A. africanus* that *A. aethiopicus* lacks. This supports the hypothesis that *A. africanus*, and not *A. aethiopicus*, is ancestral to this later robust species since *A. africanus* and *A. aethiopicus* are contemporaries and cannot both be ancestors. But in fact, and more importantly, as several paleoanthropologists such as R. Skelton, H. McHenry, and P. Tobias have shown *A. boisei* shares significant features uniquely with two even later species, the South African *A. robustus* and early *Homo*. Features linking *A. boisei* and *robustus*, and *Homo* crania include (but are not limited to):

- some structural brain differences reflected in the endocasts such as
    - greater frontal lobe breadth
    - expanded parietal cortex
    - increased cerebral height (high cerebral to cerebellar height)
    - cerebellar lobes "tucked in" (as defined by Holloway) and not projecting laterally or posteriorly

- increased flexion of the cranial base
- shortening of the cranial base and decrease in the angle of the **petrous** pyramids
- more anterior foramen magnum position
- deeper mandibular fossa with well delineated, projecting, articular eminence
- nearly horizontal orientation of nuchal plane
- expanded height of **occipital plane** of the occiput, with a concomitant low **inion** position
- decreased facial prognathism, especially **subnasal** (the maxilla below the nose)
- shortened distance between the toothrow and the mandibular fossa
- reduced posterior component of temporalis muscle
- weakly developed or absence of pneumatized bone in the temporal squama

Because of these many shared features, it is reasonable to propose that *A. boisei,* the South African robusts and early *Homo* have a much more recent, and *Homo*-like, common ancestor than *A. aethiopicus* (figure 7.5).

Thus *A. aethiopicus* is not ancestral to any of the later robust australopithecines and therefore played no role in the origin of the hyper-robusts who replaced them. The resemblances to these later hominids are based on homoplasies, mostly reflecting a common adaptation to dietary items requiring prolonged and powerful mastication in closely related hominid species. The differences between the two hyper-robust species can be best explained phylogenetically.

- *A. aethiopicus* is the consequence of an *A. afarensis* offshoot adapting to a niche requiring adaptation to dietary items needing prolonged and powerful mastication,
- *A. boisei* (in fact both subsequent robust species) is the consequence of an *A. africanus* offshoot, or the offshoot of an even later and more *Homo*-like descendent species, adapting to the same niche some half-million years later

If scientists persist in calling *A. aethiopicus* a "robust australopithecine" because of its masticatory adaptations, "robust australopithecines", like "apes", would cease referring to a monophyletic group.

The details of when and why the earlier megadont species gave way to the later are unclear, because it took place during the time span when the Omo contributes most hominid fossils, and these remains are mainly teeth. The few crania known such as L338y-6 are of *A. aethiopicus.* F.C. Howell and colleagues conclude that the isolated teeth not attributable to this taxon in Members E and F also do not represent *A. africanus.* The problem with teeth, even partially complete dentitions, is that most of them are undiagnostic for distinguishing the three robust australopithecine species, because they share so many details of crown size and shape and enamel thickness. For instance, F. Grine and L. Martin used Omo specimens to represent enamel thickness in *A. boisei* that almost certainly include the earlier species *A. aethiopicus.* In doing so they actually *under*estimated enamel thickness of *A. boisei,* as subsequent studies such as Ramirez-Rozzi's show its postcanine enamel thickness to be extraordinary, much thicker than *A. aethiopicus.*

Probably the best source of information for distinguishing robust species comes from a study of mandibular premolar variation by G. Suwa. Several P_3 features are generally shared by all of the robust australopithecine species, and he uses this anatomy to argue that the earliest appearance of a robust australopithecine species in the Omo deposits is the 2.6 myr L18-31P_3. Moreover, Suwa shows that the size and anatomy of P_4 was both diagnostic for robusts in general, and that one specific derived morphological pattern for the tooth could be uniquely associated with *A. boisei.* The P_4 of this species is very molar-like, expanded in size and square in shape (with a concomitant rearrangement of cusp positions). The more conservative (and presumably ancestral) P_4 form is characteristic of the South African robusts and most importantly also of WT 16005, a 2.41 myr mandible attributed to *A. aethiopicus* by Leakey and Walker, for a number of reasons independent of its premolar morphology. If we assume that the Late Pliocene robust australopithecine remains from Omo are only comprised of these two species, *A. aethiopicus* and *A. boisei,* the premolar anatomy can be used to trace their temporal distribution. Suwa concludes that below Omo Member G, prior to 2.3 myr, only the conservative P_4 morphology (meaning in the Late Pliocene, I believe, *A. aethiopicus*) is present, whereas after 1.90 myr only the derived P_4 morphology (meaning *A. boisei*) occurs. Within Member G (a stratum including the 2.20 myr Omo 323-76-896 *A. boisei* skull) both morphologies and by implication both species are preserved at Omo. Mandibles such as L427-7 (2.25 myr) and L74a-21(2.20 myr) have premolars with the derived morphology. Supporting this interpretation, Member G mandibles such as L7-125 (2.15 myr) and L74a-21 have very small anterior dentitions, which A. Bilsborough suggests may also be used to diagnose *A. boisei*. The earliest dates for A. *boisei* occurrences in East Africa are for these specimens, 2.25-2.15 myr.

The question of body size in *A. aethiopicus* is intriguing, and because there is a separation in time from the much later *A. boisei* remains we can attempt it. The results are surprising. There are six Late Pliocene postcranial bones from Omo that are older than 2.25 myr, including two **ulnas,** the proximal (shoulder) part of a humerus (L119-2718), and a large but otherwise *A. afarensis*-like **calcaneus** (heel bone), L33-896 that, according to B. Latimer, has all of this earlier species adaptations to the weight transmission requirements of bipedal locomotion. One ulna is complete, the 2.37 myr L40-19 specimen. It is a very long, relatively thin, and curved specimen originally attributed to *A. boisei* by F.C. Howell, and later by McHenry and colleagues on the argument that it shared features with both humans and apes but was generally unique. It is often assumed that anything "odd" and poorly understood could be attributed to the australopithecines, and because the McHenry study (and several others) was multivariate, functional questions about the anatomical differences were not addressed. Howell still considers it in that taxon, but its date places it squarely in a time span where the only robust australopithecine present is *A. aethiopicus*.

The ulna was not used in weight support, a fact clear from the orientation of its elbow articulation, from the small size of this articulation and its lack of buttressing, and from the very thin structure of the shaft itself. This anatomy conforms to Latimer's interpretation of the calcaneus in indicating the expression of obligate bipedalism, as is found in earlier and contemporary hominid species. We might view the ulna's length as the most important aspect of the bone. It is yet to be systematically compared with the Hadar ulnas, but no ulna from that site is as large (table 7.2). An ulna of this length would be expected in a >1.8 meter heat-adapted human (part of the hominid heat adaptation is to have long limbs relative to trunk size), but the height estimate for a shorter-legged, longer armed australopithecine species should be less, perhaps 1.75 m.

Table 7.2
Ulna Dimensions[1] for Pliocene and Early Pleistocene Hominids

	Omo L40-19	Hadar 333-119	333W-36	288-1 (R)	East Turkana 1500	Olduvai Hominid 13	62	Swartkrans Member 1 SKX 8761	Kromdraai TM 1517
Bone Length	313			(219)					
Trochlear notch height	24.2			17.6	16.5				
breadth	26.1			16.6	22.3	14.6			
Superior **olecranon** length	28.6			16.8	20.0	18.4			
minimum distance from posterior surface	21.1		13.5	12.7	14.3			14.1	14.7
breadth	28.6			16.7	20.0				22.2
Shaft below **radial notch** a-p	23.8	22.9	16.1	16.5			16.5		
m-l	24.0	18.7	14.0	14.5			16.0		

[1] See figure 7.2 for definitions of the dimensions used: "a-p" means anterior-posterior, "m-l" means medial-lateral

Should the Omo ulna represent a male *A. aethiopicus,* this was a very large species relative to other Pliocene hominids. For comparison the single *A. afarensis* male height estimate possible from a femur is for AL 333-3. This is 1.5 m (McHenry gives a maximum *A. boisei* height that is even shorter, under 1.4 m.). According to his studies the weight of AL 333-3 is about 50 kg., heaviest of the *A. afarensis* male hindlimbs. Taking these facts into account the expected weight for the L40-19 individual would be about double the *A. afarensis* mean, some 90 kg.

There are several somewhat smaller limb fragments older than 2.25 myr. Predicted body weight from the 2.43 myr L119-2718 proximal humerus is about 50 kg. B. Latimer estimates a similar weight for the L33-896 calcaneus. These bones, probably females of *A. aethiopicus* based on their much smaller size, are never-the-less the mean size of Hadar males. The middle-sex body weight estimate for the 3 specimens is almost double the *A. afarensis* value (table 7.3), but the sexual dimorphism in body weight is just about the same as in this earlier species (dimorphism in all other australopithecines is markedly reduced).

It is possible, perhaps likely, that the expanded masticatory apparatus for *A. aethiopicus,* compared with *A. afarensis,* is a consequence of this larger size. R. Caspari suggests that the large body size may account for some of the peculiarities in the adult males, such as the massive development of the nuchal muscles in WT 17K, as contrasted with all other known hominids. It would certainly account for the large masticatory apparatus. In fact, there would be little except for body size and its allometric consequences that distinguishes this hyper-robust australopithecine from its Hadar ancestor, were it not for the very small *A. aethiopicus* brain sizes that are thrown into even greater contrast given the large body size estimate. The estimated male *A. aethiopicus* percentage of brain weight to body weight is about half that of the Hadar males (table 6.11). This percentage is estimated from single, different individuals and needs be viewed very cautiously, but at the very least there is a dramatic contrast with *A. boisei,* and no tendency for brain size increase in *A. aethiopicus* is indicated.

AUSTRALOPITHECUS BOISEI

The bulk of the large remaining East African australopithecine sample begins in the terminal Pliocene, some 1.9 myr ago, and extends into the Pleistocene where the most recent specimens are about 1.4 myr. The earlier portion of the Pleistocene, called the Basal, Lower, or Early Pleistocene, is a million year span from 1.75 to 0.78 myr (table 1.3). Its definition was originally based on faunal changes (the appearance of modern genera of horse, elephant, and cattle) and later on the initiation of continental glaciations. Current definitions use the paleomagnetic stratigraphy (table 1.6), beginning with the pole reversal ending the Olduvai normal subchron and ending with the pole reversal that marks the beginning of the Brunhes normal chron. The australopithecine specimens come from several Rift Valley sites - the circum-Turkana deposits and Olduvai Gorge. Geographically between these are some additional find spots at which a smaller number of specimens have been recovered: Chesowanja and Natron. These *A. boisei* specimens are late in the sequence, dated to 1.6-1.5 myr. The most recent australopithecines are some very large isolated teeth from 1.4 myr Omo deposits. Whether by cause or by accident, the australopithecines do not survive beyond the appearance of the Acheulean industry, discussed in Chapter 10.

Like the earlier East African hominid habitats all these sites are in the immediate vicinity of lakes (if not actually on the lake shores) with nearby regions ranging from humid and heavily vegetated to the semiarid. However, a review by T. White revealed no habitat preference within the range of environments the australopithecines are found. At the Pleistocene's onset there is a significant faunal turnover. C4 plant dominance (Chapter 3) shows more wooded brushland and generally more aridity at the E African sites by 1.7 myr. Hominid artifacts are found at much higher densities, in drier, often much drier regions for the first time, and in upland areas well away from seasonal grasslands, according to J. Harris. The association of australopithecines with these earliest artifacts, however, has been and remains problematic

Figure 7.1
Stratigraphic Positions for Late Pliocene and Early Pleistocene Hominid[α] Crania and Mandibles[β]
From the same sources as figure 6.1, and Bilsborough (1992), Walter et al (1991, 1993), White et al (1982)

date (myr)	Olduvai	Omo	Turkana (KNM-ER and KNM-WT)	Other East African	South African (estimates)
1.4	9±	F203-1 (dental) **P996-17**		*KGA 10-1*[δ]	
1.5			*725, 729, 731, 733, 805, 992, 3892* **2592, 2595, 3883,16001**	Chesowanja	
1.6	16		*818, 820,* **1466,** *1468, 1817,* **15000** *3230*	*Peninj*	
1.7			*406, 727,* **730,** *732,* **801,** *807, 1170, 1506,* **1808,** *1820,* **1821,** *5429* *3891, 17400*		
1.8	5, 7, 62 24		*812,* 814, 1804, **3733,** *15930* 407, 805, *1477,* 1590, 1805, *1806, 3229,* 13750		
1.9		894-1	*1469, 1482, 1470, 1483,1500, 801,1802, 1812,* 1813, **2598,** 3732, 3735, 23000		
2.0		*75-14*			
2.1					
2.2		*7-125, 74a-21, 427-7, 323-76-896*			⇑ Swartkrans (1)
2.3		*860-2* *57-41,*		*Uraha*	⇑ Sterkfontein (5)
2.4		338y-6, 44-2466	*16005*	Chemeron BC 1	Gladysvale Sterkfontein (4)
2.5		345-11, 51-80 (dental)	17000 (Lomekwi)	KP 271 (humerus)	
2.6		*18-18* 18-31 (dental)			
2.7		*55s-33*	5431 (dental set)		Taung

Crania in bold face are unquestionably early *H. sapiens*

[α] Only major specimens are shown   [δ] Earliest Acheulean

[β] Mandibles only are in italics

Earliest Specimens

The only australopithecine species found in East Africa during the terminal Pliocene and later is *A. boisei*. The earliest occurrence of the species is from Omo Member G3 and does not exceed 2.25 myr. It persisted in the region for better than 3/4 of a million years. Omo L 323-76-896 (2.2 myr) is probably the earliest cranium known. It consists of parts of a cranial vault, several large postcanine teeth, and a very incomplete partial skeleton. The inside of the skull lacks occipitomarginal sinus drainage and it has been promoted by some paleoanthropologists as the latest surviving example of *A. aethiopicus*. Also similar to *A. aethiopicus* is the large canine size of the specimen, exceeding all later *A. boisei* canines. When describing it Y. Coppens and M. Sakka regarded the sex as male, in spite of the specimen's "gracility", and therefore recognized in it a different anatomical pattern than the *A. boisei* one. On the other hand, the mandibular fossa is neither flattened as in the black skull, nor like the South African *A. robustus* anatomy described below, but specifically resembles *A. boisei*. Moreover some of the A. *aethiopicus*-like features are not necessarily diagnostic. For instance, as mentioned in Chapter 6, one later hyper-robust specimen, ER 23000, has both sinus drainage patterns, one on each side of its head, making the pattern of sinus drainage a poor taxonomic indicator, as W. Kimbel argued.

A talus associated with the specimen suggests a body weight estimate of 49.5 kg, based on a regression analysis provided by B. Latimer. This is very similar to McHenry's estimates for a large Koobi Fora talus also attributed to *A. boisei*, 48.6 kg. Expressed as a deviation from the primate brain to body weight allometric curve (figure 6.11), brain size of this early *A. boisei* male is high for a hominoid primate and between the mean deviation for *A. africanus* males and *A. robustus* males. Relative postcanine tooth size, on the other hand, is much larger.

A second large early specimen is the L754-8 femur shaft which is somewhat younger, 2.12 myr from Submember G4. Since this is after the time of the earliest *A. boisei*, there really is no way to determine the taxonomy of the specimen except by size. McHenry estimates a body weight of about 50 kg for the femur, right in the area where the expected range of *A boisei* male size overlaps with *A. aethiopicus* females.

Postcranial Remains

Hyper-robustness, as the above suggests, does not apply to body size, as this species remains smaller than chimpanzees. Estimated body weight (table 7.3) averages only about 10% greater than the *A. africanus* mean (this is also evident in the comparison of the smallest female femora for each species, see table 8.2). With a 39 kg average, these australopithecines fit McHenry's description as "petite".

A. boisei averages only about 60% the size of the earlier hyper-robust species *A. aethiopicus*, the *boisei* males are below the mean weight of the *aethiopicus* females. With this much size difference, it is likely that body size plays a role in the species replacement, because the dietary requirements of the larger species were substantially greater. Another difference is in sexual dimorphism. The sexual dimorphism in *A. boisei* body weight (males 1.3 times heavier than females) is markedly less than the earlier species and instead resembles the other later australopithecines (*A. africanus* and *A. robustus*).

Table 7.3
Estimated Body Weights for *Australopithecus*

	A. afarensis[1]	*A. atheopicus*[3]	*A. africanus*[1]	*A. robustus*[2]	*A. boisei*[2]
Male mean	44.6	90	41.3	41.5	44.0
Female mean	26.0	50	30.2	31.9	34.0
Middle-sex average	35.3	70	35.8	36.7	39.0
Dimorphism	1.7	1.8	1.4	1.3	1.3

[1]   From Table 5.2
[2]   Modified after data in McHenry (1992), and given in the text
[3]   One male and one female (of the 3 total) are based on forelimbs, the other samples are based on hindlimbs only

The *A. boisei* weight estimates, it should be emphasized, are based on a very small sample size - one 1.89 myr associated fragmentary female skeleton (ER 1500 - not to be confused with the WT 15<u>000</u> early *H. sapiens* youth), the lower leg remains (OH 35) associated with OH 5 and attributed by researchers such as P. Tobias to that specimen, the Omo L 323 talus, and some incomplete material found at a 1.70 myr

East Turkana site (area 6A, Ileret) where only *A. boisei* was recovered. The details of the lower limb remains reveal *A. boisei* to be an obligate biped. Although there are many other isolated postcrania that could belong to this species, it has proved difficult to unambiguously identify which postcranial remains are *A. boisei* for two reasons:

1. the isolated postcranial remains of all the Late Pliocene/Pleistocene hominid species are very similar anatomically
2. in the regions inhabited by *A. boisei* postcranial remains are usually either found without associated jaws or teeth, or with the associated elements of both *Australopithecus* and *Homo*

Even still, McHenry arrived at similar male and female weight estimates for *A. boisei* by taking the averages for additional specimens that various authors have attributed to the species. Moreover, similar weight estimates are also obtained for the species when there is sorting of the Koobi Fora femora based on size clusters (this would add the ER 3728 femur, following Franciscus and Trinkaus). I believe that in spite of these problems, the mean weights are not likely to be far off.

H. Grausz and colleagues compared the skeletal elements of the ER 1500 *A. boisei* female with other small hominoids, including AL 288 (after some uncertainty about its correct taxonomy, ER 1500 was recognized as an example of *A. boisei* because of the striking similarities found between a toothless piece of its mandible and a largely complete *A. boisei* mandible discovered much later, ER 16005). They concluded that she has the same limb proportions, which would make her relatively shortened legs similar to both earlier species where the proportions can be determined (as well as to *A. robustus,* see below).

Dental Remains

A. boisei is the preëminent hyper-robust australopithecine as far as the masticatory apparatus is concerned. Posterior teeth and the associated cranial and mandibular structures quickly became more massive in this form than in any previous hominid. Table 8.1, for instance reveals OH 5 to have extraordinary posterior tooth size, easily matching gorillas with close to 10 times the body weight. The posterior teeth continue to increase in size over the span of the species existence.

The *A. boisei* dentitions combine the extraordinary size of the largest known posterior teeth of any hominid species with moderate to small anterior teeth. It is an oversimplification to claim, as many have, that the canines and incisors reduce even as (and according to some, because) the postcanine teeth expand. In fact, *A, boisei* incisors are close to the same size or larger than their *A. africanus* counterparts (table 6.15). It is the canines that reduce in this species, whether considering the average size or the size for each sex separately. In some of the later specimens, like the WT 17400 female, the canines are small enough to approach the size of deciduous teeth! Several studies have shown that hominid canine-posterior tooth size allometry is negative. This means that specimens with larger postcanine dentitions will tend to have smaller canines, holding sex constant. Thus to some extent the small canines of the species may be a consequence of their large postcanine tooth size. This notion is supported by the fact that the canines continue to reduce through the time span of the lineage, even as (and perhaps in part because) the posterior teeth increase in size. However, the complexity of the problem is seen in the fact that the South African robust australopithecines, discussed below, are only 10% smaller in body size and also have large postcanine teeth but do not have smaller canines (comparing males to males and females to females) than their *A. africanus* ancestors. In these comparisons, different patterns of selection are important in understanding the variation.

In any event, the postcanine tooth size of this *A. boisei* has become the benchmark for megadonty, and relative to body size these are the largest teeth known for any primate. According to A. Walker's SEM studies, microscopic molar wear consists of a pattern of occasional deep pits (quite different from the high pitting frequencies of the Swartkrans hominids) and coarse scratches most like the molars of chimpanzees and mandrills, which implies frugivory. However these teeth are much larger than those of chimpanzees, 2-3 times the occlusal area and for some specimens even above the gorilla range, even though the average body weight is less than that of the chimpanzees. If their size is an adaptation to the kinds of foods frugivorous chimpanzees eat, there must be a very large (perhaps seasonal) component of low-quality items such as bark and mature leafs ingested to account for this difference in the context of the microwear similarities. Walker suggests that a major component of low-quality foods for at least some times of the year would have played an important role in limiting their body size, as the amount of time required to chew and ingest low quality foods rapidly approaches 24 hours per day at body sizes much larger than these postcranially-petite hominids attained.

Facial Anatomy

The most obvious distinctions of *A. boisei* are facial, and clearly the consequences of the dietary adaptations reflected in the postcanine teeth discussed above. Our understanding of the *A. boisei* face comes largely from the insightful work of Y. Rak. In this species the requirements (and biomechanical consequences) of prolonged and powerful posterior tooth loading result in massively developed wide cheeks, to enclose the large temporalis muscles within the **temporal fossa** that is bounded by the cheeks and zygomatic arches, and to provide the masseter muscle with a strong horizontal force component (see Chapter 4). Relative to the teeth, which is to say the palate, the cheeks are so far anterior that the nose is recessed behind them and *A. boisei* faces pass the pencil test - a pencil placed so it spans between the cheeks passes in front of the borders of the nose. Enclosed in this massively developed bone, there are no anterior pillars along the sides of the nose (this might also be related to the canine reduction in the species, as discussed above). Rak calculates that the masseter covers between 50% and 57% of the palate in the two complete males (OH 5 and ER 406). In contrast, in male gorillas the coverage averages 15%. This extreme anterior position of the cheeks, and of the masseter forces, create a facial shape resembling a diamond, as the outer and upper rims of the orbits are pulled downward and the great breadth across the cheeks is accentuated. Rak describes the thin **supraorbital** structure as a freestanding arch; it is not supported by the braincase, as the frontal sweeps upward behind it rather than above it. With the masseter muscle forces pulling this arch downward and outward, a thick glabellar eminence at its center acts like a keystone in structural arches, supporting the supraorbital arch by resisting bending and localized tension in the bone. This juxtaposition of forces in the glabellar region may account for the unusual nasal shape. *A. boisei* nasal bones are broadest at their top and narrow toward their bottom, where they form the roof of the narrow nasal opening.

While *A. boisei* resembles *A. aethiopicus* (and other australopithecines) in some details of its robustly developed masticatory system, it is quite distinct from the earlier hyper-robust species as well as from *A. africanus* in a number of other features. *A. boisei* cranial bases are shorter, less **prognathic**, and more flexed with their toothrows considerably below their large, deepened mandibular fossae (another difference). These differences, bringing the teeth into a vertically lower position that is horizontally closer to the mandibular fossa, are uniquely shared with the other robust australopithecines and Early Pleistocene *Homo* species. T. Bromage measures this flexion as an angle, formed between a line from the ear to the top of the nose, and a line between the ear and the last molar tooth. As the teeth change their position to a lower and more rearward one the angle opens up (becomes larger). Values for (what Bromage calls the "meatus angle") are:

> **46°-49°:** apes, *A. afarensis* and *A. aethiopicus*, some *A. africanus* (STS 5)
> **52°-53°:** other *A. africanus* (SS 71), *A. boisei*, habilines of both varieties (ER 1470, 1813)
> **66°:** early *H. erectus* (i.e. *H. sapiens* as used here)

Coincidentally, the resemblance of one male *A. africanus* (STS 71) to robust australopithecines such as *A. boisei* in the meatus angle conforms to similar observations about the similarities in the midfacial skeletons of male *A africanus* and robust australopithecines made by Y. Rak, discussed in Chapter 6. Increased flexion also makes *A. boisei* (and the other species) better masticators. As discussed in Chapter 4, masticatory forces are more efficiently and more evenly applied to teeth in this lower and more posterior position.

J. Laitman and colleagues have related this anatomy to a lowered larynx position and subsequently angled vocal chamber. He argues that the lowered position marks the evolution of the ability to produce the kinds of sounds that human use in speech. They make these hominids potential language-users as well because the disadvantage that comes with this lowered larynx position is the familiar crossing of the esophagus and trachea; the loss of the ability to drink and breath at the same time, and the real potential for inhaling foods and choking to death. The masticatory and vocalization explanations are neither contradictory nor mutually exclusive of each other.

In spite of the reduced sexual dimorphism in cranial capacity (see below) and body weight, there are strong contrasts in male and female facial anatomy. The relation of facial size and head size differs, females having much more lightly built and markedly smaller faces. The differences are dramatic, and resemble those between male and female gorillas. As R. Leakey has discussed, the *A. boisei* specimens have been very important in determining the pattern and magnitude of sexual dimorphism in early hominids, and played an important role in establishing sexual dimorphism as a valid and important cause of variation. One consequence of these dimorphism patterns is that males of the terminal Pliocene and Early Pleistocene hominid species differ much more dramatically than females; for instance, compare female *A. boisei* and *H. habilis* specimens ER 732 and OH 24.

Brain Size and other Cranial Characteristics

The crania of *A. boisei* contrast large, massively constructed faces and modest, thin boned cranial vaults with prominent muscle attachments. The sex differences in facial size and architecture strongly contrasts with the more similarly sized heads. The main cranial differences are in the musculature and its effects on vault anatomy. For instance, males of this species are heavily crested while the female crania lack cresting and have much more lightly built crania.

Mean brain size (table 7.4) is some 5% greater than *A. africanus*. Relative to body size, brain size for the species deviates from the allometric expectations more than *A. africanus*. The brain/body weight ratio is about the same but allometric changes in brain size are not proportional to body size (the ratio gets smaller as body size gets larger), so in the larger *A. boisei* the *same ratio* means *greater deviation*. This also suggests a mean relative brain size expansion. At the rear of the braincase occipital support for the nuchal muscles is oriented more horizontally and the occiput above it is relatively expanded. These differences reflects some differences in the development of the back of the brain which R. Holloway relates to continued neural reorganization. In particular, the posterior parietal areas of the brain are expanded, the anatomy of the cerebellar region is modern, and the hemispheric asymmetries - a left occipital/right frontal petalial pattern (see Chapter 4) - reflect handedness.

The sexual dimorphism in brain size for this species appears to be markedly smaller than in other australopithecines. For instance, the South African australopithecines, *A. africanus* and *robustus,* have male/female brain size ratios of 17% and 20% respectively, while the *A. boisei* male brains average only 9% larger than the females. The meaning of this difference is unclear, because its range is similar to a sample of modern populations, where Tobias found the range of dimorphism in brain size to be from 5% to 18%.

This hyper-robust masticatory apparatus has certain other consequences on the anatomy of the crania. The mandibular fossa is large and deep. The **articular eminence** drops steeply in front of the fossa, forming its anterior wall, but does not flatten out to provide a horizontal surface for the loaded condyle to rest. (As discussed in Chapter 4, the loaded mandibular condyle is the one with force passing through it, on the side of the mouth that is opposite the side with food between the teeth). Instead the loaded condyle rests on an angled, fairly vertical surface. This shows that the major forces acting on the condyle during chewing must be perpendicular to that surface. These forces, as L. DuBrul points out, are mainly caused by the contractions of the powerful masseter muscle. He further notes that the masseter's internal partner, the lateral pterygoid muscle, must have provided a large but mainly transverse component of force, on the grounds of the purely transverse orientation of the anterior fossa face and the size of the **pterygoid plates**. The forces passing through the mandibular fossa drive the temporal squama above it to slide over the parietal, where these meet along a beveled edge (the temporal on the outer side and the parietal on the inner where they overlap). Rak argues that this bevel (the amount of overlap) is especially broad in *A. boisei* because of the movement during powerful chewing.

These descriptions of *A. boisei* craniofacial anatomy are idealized, and there are significant variations found in each element. For instance, B. Brown and colleagues describe a different supraorbital shape for

ER 23000, a specimen that contrasts with others such as OH 5 in having a more anteriorly positioned sagittal crest and thicker cranial bone.

Evolutionary Trends

The *A. boisei* adaptive complex was not static over time. Beginning with the earliest specimen, Omo L 323's larger canine and small cranial capacity (estimated at 490 cc by B. Brown and colleagues) mark the beginning of evolutionary trends decreasing canine size and increasing cranial capacity in *A. boisei*. The increases in brain size are marked and significant, as B. Brown and colleagues have shown . The other major change is in the masticatory apparatus, as posterior teeth and mandibular body size continue to increase during the evolution of the lineage. Sagittal cresting patterns change as well, with crests no longer appearing in all the large males. This is because of the significant brain size expansion. The brain size expansion is disproportionately greater than the masticatory apparatus size increases. In a purely allometric relation the masticatory apparatus responds much more strongly to body size increases than brain size does, and larger specimens have relatively larger jaws and teeth. If the A. boisei increases were due to body size alone we would expect to have higher cresting frequencies and not lower ones in the later specimens, but the opposite is the case. Thus, body size increases, if there were any - a point that remains unknown - cannot account for the brain size expansion. Moreover, the earlier brain sizes in this lineage were already greater than the ancestral condition of *A. africanus*.

In fact the two latest-occurring crania, the Chesowanja juvenile female and the ER 733 male, show significant brain size evolution. In the case of the partial Chesowanja vault, this can be easily seen by trying to place one of the earlier robust australopithecine endocasts in it, for instance the natural Swartkrans endocast SK 1585 or the endocast of the reconstructed OH 5 vault. Chesowanja has both the frontal and temporal poles (depressions that enclose the frontal and temporal lobes) preserved and these 530 cc endocasts are much too small to fit the specimen. Moreover, Chesowanja has very small canines, reflecting a trend for canine size decrease in *A. boisei*. The even more fragmentary Turkana specimen ER-733 may have been similar, at least based on its enlarged frontal dimensions. ER-733 resembles some early *H. sapiens* specimens in its thickened cranial bone, and browridge and forehead anatomy including the lack of a sagittal crest. This suggests a different and more *Homo*-like pattern of masticatory stress distribution that results from the cranial architecture that comes with the expanded brain case. even given the posterior tooth size expansion in this lineage.

A dietary explanation for the dental expansion might lie in an improved adaptation to semi-arid conditions. Such an adaptation could have become possible with the technological innovations of the late Pliocene, which produced recognizable lithic artifacts. Sharper digging tools and better cutting edges might have allowed the more effective collection and preparation of difficult-to-chew foods, resulting in expansion into more seasonally arid habitat and selection for jaws and teeth with increased chewing capacity. Unfortunately, what remains uncertain is the identity (or identities) of the East African tool maker.

With significant evolutionary trends in expanding posterior tooth size and cranial capacity, *A. boisei* is not by any means a species in evolutionary stasis. Even if these changes are partially a consequence of increasing body size, the greater magnitude of brain size changes show that more than body size alone was involved. Combined with the degreasing canine size, these trends show that the evolution of this lineage parodies the directional changes in *Homo* that are regarded, in our ancestors, as the consequences of an increasingly effective cultural adaptation. A full understanding of the later changes in *A. boisei* must await the recovery of more complete dated specimens, but the possibilities are intriguing.

Extinction

The extinction of *A. boisei* probably does not require special explanation. It is, after all, the fate of all species to become extinct. However, *Australopithecus* and *Homo* are much more often than not found in the same habitats, often at the same sites, and the potential for competition between these similar hominid species suggests a role for it in the evolution of both. In support of the relevance of competitive exclusion principle in explaining the pattern of evolutionary change, I believe that some of the changes late in the evolution of the lineage may be the result of a niche expansion allowed by an increasingly efficient adaptation for powerful chewing in *A. boisei,* perhaps encouraged by intensified competition with *Homo.* Adaptive breadth is indicated by some research of T. White. He found that while habitats where *A. boisei* and a *Homo* species are found together in death differed widely, neither showed any habitat preference. G. Isaac suggested that the changing adaptations that are marked by the origin and spread of the Acheulean may have been the final straw for these late australopithecines, and beyond their capacity to either mimic or adjust to. Competition over certain limiting resources such as dry season foods, rather than a prey-predator relation (as some have suggested), probably accounts for the hyper-robusts' eventual extinction. The successful lineage expanded into their niche, reducing the same foods to edibility through technology rather than with powerful teeth and jaws. At the same time, we can always wonder what would have happened had there been no competition between the hominid species of the Early Pleistocene. Would the broad adaptive patterns, complex social organization, and enhanced technological abilities of early *Homo sapiens* ever have emerged to play important roles? Or, in the absence of competition with what was surely a successful australopithecine adaptation, would the *Homo* species have continued to develop the suite of australopithecine adaptation that had already proven to be successful through the changing environments of the Pliocene? One cannot help speculating about the role that these robust australopithecines have played in human evolution.

Robust Australopithecines: Later South African Sites

The later South African robust australopithecine sites are Swartkrans and Kromdraai. The larger of these sites is Swartkrans. The sample there is probably the biggest from any hominid site that predates the appearance of modern people. The understanding of this cave and its contents has been the lifelong focus of C.K. Brain, who's multidisciplinary monographal treatment (*Swartkrans, A Cave's Chronicle of Early Man*) stands as a paradigm. T. White suggests that the hominid density in the cave may result from the fact that the australopithecines used the trees around the entrance as sleeping sites, where as Brain showed, they were preyed on by leopards and their body parts fell into the cave to be preserved. While several scientists (particularly F.C. Howell and F. Grine) believe that the Kromdraai remains sample a different, albeit closely related, species, I do not concur and will treat both samples together. They are very close to Sterkfontein in space - just across a shallow valley - but an unknown length of time away. Their dates are especially critical, as they impinge on the relation of the East and South African robust australopithecine varieties, and on the origin of the genus *Homo.*

"MISSION IMPOSSIBLE": DATING THE SOUTH AFRICAN SITES

We can divide the dating problem into two questions, how long a time is represented at Swartkrans, and how old are the two sites. As for the first, E. Vrba believes that the most recent of the three lower members, which contains *A. robustus,* may be as recent as 1.5 myr. If so, this would be as young as the latest surviving *A. boisei,* indicating a long span for the Swartkrans australopithecine accumulations. However, studies by three paleoanthropologists suggest a long span is incorrect:

1. C. Brain finds that each of the Swartkrans members seems to represent a short depositional period from his studies of the cave sediments
2. R. Klein points out that Members 1 and 3 are not very distinguishable on artifactual and faunal grounds
3. E. Delson suggests that the three lower members may encompass no more than 100 kyr from his studies of the cercopithecoid remains

The dating of the site is even more uncertain, because it must depend on calibrating the rates of local evolution for different species, or on faunal comparisons with other sites that are thousands of miles away and ecologically different. When changes in the poorly represented pigs found at the South African sites are calibrated, their study suggests there may be a time span of up to a million years between the *A. africanus* and the robust australopithecines. Yet, the zebra-like horse species associated with grasslands,

Equus capensis (= *Equus olduvaiensis*) is found in Swartkrans Member 1, and first appears in the Omo sequence at 2.3 myr. This would put a much older upper cap on the beginning date of Swartkrans Member 1. A calibration of rates of change in the numerous hominid teeth also indicates only a few hundred thousand years between *A. africanus* and the robust australopithecines, and as discussed above the similarities of the robust australopithecines and the *A. boisei* remains from East Africa also suggest an earlier date. Moreover, *H. habilis* appears in Swartkrans Member 1, a species that is not documented in East Africa earlier than 2.25 myr (see Chapter 8). In sum, should the morphology of the hominids be used to contribute to the **biostratigraphy**, a 2.3-2.0 myr age would fit best.

Perhaps the best evidence for dating the South African robust australopithecines comes from the reinterpretation of the Swartkrans Member 1 climate. Original work on soil particle size by C. Brain led to the reconstruction of a wet habitat which, when contrasted with the supposedly dry climate at Sterkfontein was the underlying basis of Robinson's dietary hypothesis that envisaged the robust australopithecines as vegetarians. However, Vrba's subsequent analysis of the **bovid** species at these sites showed a significant turnover of bovid taxa between them. She uses the Swartkrans Member 1 bovids as the basis for the claim that the region was cooler, drier, and more seasonal beginning with the earliest levels at Swartkrans. If this faunal turnover corresponds to the global climate changes as Vrba believes, it places Swartkrans and Kromdraai at a date in the younger part of the 3-2 myr span. Bearing in mind the possibility that the three Swartkrans lower members may in total represent a short time span, such a date would:

- conform to the identification of the 2.4 myr Chemeron temporal as similar to South African robust australopithecines (it couldn't change the morphology but at least they would be contemporary)
- suggest that the **morphocline** Rak proposes for the evolution of robust australopithecine faces - *Australopithecus africanus* → *robustus* → *boisei* - may be an actual evolutionary sequence.

The much more limited Kromdraai remains present equally formidable dating problems, and depending on which parts of the fauna are used it has seemed uncertain whether this small sample of specimens predates, postdates, or is contemporary with the Swartkrans Member 1 remains. The most wide-ranging faunal analysis to date, by J. McKee and colleagues, firmly places Kromdraai (both excavated and earlier hominid-bearing sites) between the earlier elements in Sterkfontein Member 5, and Swartkrans Member 1.

It is unclear whether the earliest parts of these sites are prior to the *A. boisei* remains from East Africa, which would support the notion that some of these australopithecines were ancestral to the East African variety. The most conservative approach, I believe, is to treat most known fossils of *A. robustus* and *boisei* as contemporaries, but examine the implications of the possibility that the *A. robustus* variant may have evolved first. Resolution of the conflicting interpretations will probably require a numerical dating technique.

CRANIA

A. robustus crania are well represented. Many fragmentary specimens and a few fairly complete ones were recovered, their condition is generally not as good as that of the earlier crania. Cranial capacity is known for only one specimen, SK 1585, a natural endocast of a young individual with a capacity of 530 cc. In his analysis of the endocast, Holloway concluded that the distinctively hominid features were better developed than in the earlier South African specimens. The features uniquely shared with later *Homo* species and *A. boisei* are described above, in the discussion of *A. boisei*, and can be characterized by modernity in overall shape, expansion of the upper part of the parietal cortex, and the shape and position of the cerebellum. Furthermore, the South African crania show significant expansion in size compared with *A. africanus*, perhaps even more so than their East African relatives (table 7.4), although the OH 5 relative brain size (table 8.1) suggests there may be more similarity than the comparisons of means indicate. When regression analysis is used to estimate the cranial capacities for a number of other incomplete specimens, a 15% increase over the *A. africanus* average is suggested. Males and females are equally effected and the 20% sexual dimorphism is about the same as the earlier species.

The *A. robustus* brain expansion is not a result of body size differences, as relative brain size increases as well by about 12%. The body size difference from *A africanus* (see below) is, in any event, minimal. If **encephalization** is regarded as the deviation from the expectations of allometry (figure 7.3), the difference clearly suggests that the South African robust australopithecine variety is more encephalized.

The Swartkrans crania show a remarkable amount of variation in form (see Figure 7.4) yet a number of features characterize many of them. Some of this range is due to sexual dimorphism (see table 7.4). For instance, males have larger faces and braincases, and sagittal cresting is more common. Cresting is quite common in the females as well. However, other elements are more variable. There are larger and smaller females and larger and smaller males, suggesting that like the earlier sites, Swartkrans represents samples from many different populations that inhabited the area over the centuries that the cave deposits were formed. These populations were probably not identical in their adaptations to the region.

Table 7.4
Cranial Capacities in Pliocene *Australopithecus* species

	Male			Female			Middle-sex		
	mean cranial capacity (n=)	body weight estimate[1]	brain percent of body weight	mean cranial capacity (n=)	body weight estimate	brain percent of body weight	mean cranial capacity	body weight estimate	brain percent of body weight
africanus	505 (5)	41300	1.22	430 (4)	30200	1.42	467.5	35800	1.31
robustus	587 (4)	41500	1.41	490 (4)	31900	1.53	538.5	36700	1.47
boisei	510 (5)	44000	1.16	470 (3)	34000	1.38	490.0	39000	1.26
aethiopicus	415 (2)	90000	0.46		50000			70000	
Homo habilis[2] from Olduvai	590 (1)	31700	1.86	501 (1)	27000	1.86	545.5	29350	1.86

[1]   In all cases except *A. aethiopicus* (discussed above) the body weight estimates are McHenry's hindlimb determinations based on bipeds, or others calculated from his formulae.

[2]   Based on one male, OH 7, and one female, OH 13 allowing estimates for all three variables

Compared with the Sterkfontein specimens, crania tend to be more robust, with better developed muscle markings, more prominent tori and thicker buttressing structures. Like the earlier specimens, these robust features are superimposed on thin cranial vaults. Some males (for instance SK 52) have vertically thick **supraorbital tori**. Cranial bases differ insofar as they can be studied - only the juvenile female SK 47 has a base well-preserved for most observations about the structures on or near the midline. This 11 year old specimen, and the few observations possible on some others, suggests that the Swartkrans hominids tend to have broader and usually shorter (more *Homo*-like) bases with a more anterior foramen magnum position and a petrous bone that is more transversely oriented. These similarities, of course, must be tempered by the effects of SK 47's age. The extent of these are unclear as most of the brain growth was complete (the estimated 495 cc capacity is close to the female mean) and it is unlikely that there would have been significant changes in the positions of the basal structures. Sample sizes for the outer rim of the cranial base are much better, showing that the Swartkrans hominids have larger mastoid process and greater pneumatrization of the surrounding cranial bone, and larger, deeper mandibular fossae with a distinct surface for the mandibular condyle to rest on when it is out of the socket, supporting the forces that result from chewing (see Chapter 4). Another cranial base modification reflecting mastication forces is found in the inner ear. Rak analyzed one of the inner ear bones of SK 848, an incus, and discovered it to differ from its closest extant relatives, humans and chimpanzees. He argues against phylogenetic and functional explanations and proposes that the variation may be a pleiotropic consequence of changes in selection acting on the mandibles (this is supported by the fact that the **ear ossicles** and mandible have a common embryological and evolutionary origin). More obviously related to mastication is the compound temporonuchal crest. This reflects the large temporalis muscle, extending backwards to meet the nuchal muscles (early in the history of australopithecine discoveries, before there was a complete specimen, S. Zuckerman interpreted this crest just the opposite, as expanded nuchal muscles indicating a quadrupedal stance). The expanded posterior temporalis muscles cannot be for large anterior teeth - these are notably smaller than their *A. afarensis* counterparts - so it must reflect posterior tooth loading. Another osteological reflection of an expanded posterior temporalis muscle is found at its mandibular attachment. Robinson points out that he **coronoid process** of Swartkrans adults is angled unusually backwards as the result of the intense muscle pull.

There may be some additional differences in cranial shape. J. Robinson thought that the adult Swartkrans vaults were lower in the front, but higher toward the rear. The sad fact is that no specimen is complete and undistorted enough to be sure of this. Especially with the new Sterkfontein discoveries, it is evident that most of the individual features found in the Swartkrans robust australopithecines also occur at Sterkfontein, but their frequencies differ and the average tends toward larger size and greater robustness. This is why many authors have characterized the hominids at these two sites as variations on a single theme. Yet with only a 3% increase in estimated average body size, as F. Grine has suggested these variations must be based on dietary differences and not on allometry as many authors (including this one) had supposed. The surprising nature of these dietary differences are discussed below.

The Kromdraai skull (TM-1517) appears to be similar to some of the larger Swartkrans females. While it shares an anterior foramen magnum position with the Swartkrans females, the cranial base is longer. Although too incomplete for a regression determination, comparisons with other specimens and endocasts suggest it is possible that Broom's 650 cc estimate was close to correct. If so the Kromdraai female may have had a capacity markedly larger than the Swartkrans females. McHenry suggests a size of 34.4 kg based on the talus, in line with the Swartkrans female body sizes. This would give a brain-body weight ratio of 1.89% (table 8.1) for this *individual* specimen (virtually all the ratios are based on mean weights and mean cranial capacities that are almost invariably for different individuals), larger than the *A. robustus* average. The male OH 5 ratio, 1.65%, is about as much less as males are generally less than females, and it is reasonable to suppose that these two specimens actually have very similar relative brain sizes.

FACES

Derived as is from *A. africanus,* the later South African sample continues the trends that distinguished their ancestors from the even earlier australopithecines. Faces reflect the fact that there are larger postcanine teeth, an even more powerful masticatory apparatus, and the associated structures to support it and improve its efficiency. In some respects the Swartkrans faces are structured similarly to the earlier *A. africanus* ones, and as a number of scientists have noted some of these earlier faces fully replicate the details found commonly later at Swartkrans (and are distinct from *A. boisei*) Most specimens of the *A. africanus* and *A. robustus* samples:

- are equally prognathic,
- have nasal bones that are the same size and shape,
- have distinct anterior pillars that border the nasal aperture, extending upward from the buttresses for the canine roots
- have a lower border of the cheek that is virtually a straight line from its origin on the side of the palate, extending to the base of the zygomatic arch, which is the widest part of the face

Y. Rak describes a kind of "A frame" found in both species, formed by the anterior pillars and the flat front surface of the maxilla below the nose (subnasal area), and set off from the rest of the face by a shallow fossa that runs along the pillars outer edges. This frame, he believes, acts as a support for the front part of the palate. The straight border of the lower cheek is also related to the masticatory system, as it provides a strut connecting the outer cheek region where the masseter creates force and the front of the posterior tooth row where chewing forces are supplied - the same region supported by the "A frame". *A. boisei* specimens, it may be noted, lack many of these structural details. They appear to have been submerged by the large size and anterior position of the cheeks, whose bulk serves similar functions.

Where the Swartkrans faces differ is largely in the position and development of the cheeks. They are significantly more anterior and the nose is recessed within them as described for *A. boisei* and characterized for both species as **facial dishing**. In most cases the anterior nasal spine is recessed behind the cheeks , but a few specimens such as the Member 2 maxilla SKX 265 have a more anterior spine that overlaps in anatomy with some *A. africanus* and early *Homo*. Because the foramen magnum is, on the average, more anterior in the Swartkrans hominids, the posterior dentition is closer to it. There is increased basal flexion as in *A. boisei,* and with the tall mandibular rami this puts more force through the postcanine teeth and distributes it more evenly (the postcanine teeth are more even in size, as discussed below).

DENTITIONS

The large Swartkrans sample shows a development of megadonty beyond what body size increases can explain, although far from the extent of *A. boisei*. The posterior teeth are absolutely *and* relatively larger than their already large toothed ancestors (table 6.15). The increases are greater in the premolars and the last molars, and their main effect is to provide both bigger and more evenly sized postcanine teeth. Because the dental sample is so large, it is possible to demonstrate that these changes are average changes, reflecting frequency differences in the underlying gene pools. In the ranges of variation, size and form overlap almost completely among the earlier and later samples. The process of size expansion involves the more frequent appearance of larger teeth and the less frequent appearance of smaller ones.

The anterior teeth contrast in having smaller mean sizes. The observed difference, however, depends somewhat on the sex ratio. There are more females than males represented in the Swartkrans teeth. Because the canines show the greatest amount of sexual dimorphism, this affects their comparison most. The magnitude of dimorphism is the same in the two samples, and when each sex is compared separately, the canine sizes are the same. Incisors, however, show size reduction even after taking the uneven sex distribution into account. Both central and lateral teeth are reduced; the lateral upper incisors are quite small, and uniform in anatomy. It is the smaller incisors of this sample that result in the flatter anterior palates, and contribute to the impression of flatter faces. This is a different pattern of anterior tooth reduction than *A. boisei* shows, where the canines are significantly smaller but the incisors appear less reduced or unreduced. The size reduction, while significant, does not reflect so much change that considerable overlap with other hominids is eliminated. Comparisons of individual specimens (for instance table 8.4) shows incisor sizes, even in the larger females, which march or exceed early *Homo* males.

Functionally, in the Swartkrans australopithecines the canine/premolar cutting complex completes its decomposition, most of the canines becoming **incisiform** and the bicuspid anterior lower premolar incorporated into the grinding complex. Grinding, however, is most efficient in the middle of the tooth row, and as G. Suwa discusses the P_4, is more affected by these evolutionary changes (and shows the least overlap between earlier and later samples).

Teeth and life history

Swartkrans teeth, like those of their ancestors, erupt in a human-like schedule. The order of eruption even more closely resembles some modern populational means as canines appear somewhat earlier than they do in the ancestral species and the lag-time between first molar and incisor eruptions is less. All the evidence points towards the interpretation of slowed maturational processes; indeed, this is the sample whose analysis first led to the discovery that maturational slow down characterized australopithecine children. With a good idea of when teeth erupted, age at death can be estimated for many of the teeth (see Chapter 4). The large sample size allows estimation of the average lifespan (11-12 years) from these data and a good appraisal of birth spacing, 3-4 years according to K. McKinley. These demographic parameters only validly describe an actual australopithecine population if the sample in the cave validly reflects their pattern of death (and see cautions expressed by J. Wood and colleagues). Predation accounts for many of the australopithecine remains, and it is unclear whether predators sampled sleeping hominids at random. Yet, my research shows similar death distributions among other australopithecine samples, some not from caves at all, and it is possible that these parameters (albeit inaccurately) reflect an average populational age-at-death distribution. If so, the combination of extended periods of maturation and short lifespans probably made orphaning common and suggests the early importance of an extended family, as discussed in Chapter 5. The relatively short birth spacing, compared with apes, was a distinct hominid advantage. It is credible to believe that the shortened birth spacing was made possible by sociality, and may have fostered increasingly complex social behaviors by promoting social interactions and lifelong bonds in the overlapping dependent offspring.

The crania with teeth reveal one other interesting facet of the early hominids. Relative to dental age, the cranial sutures (contacts between the separate cranial bones) close quite early. In people today the sutures remain open until maturity and first begin to fuse together significantly at a time of life when most australopithecines would already be dead. While living populations vary, and individuals even more so, generally brain growth is complete by the age of eighteen (although most of the growth takes place much earlier in life). After growth is completed, the cranial sutures begin to close and eventually fuse with each other at an advanced age (35-70+). In the australopithecine crania, suture fusion is already underway at the time of third molar eruption. This suggests that brain growth ceased much earlier than in living humans. It is possible that australopithecine children were born relatively more maturely, and that there was less brain growth to take place after birth. An alternative explanation is that they had a shorter learning period. Interestingly, several decades ago, Weidenreich suggested that earlier suture closure was the case for some specimens of Middle Pleistocene humans he was studying from the Zhoukoudian cave near Beijing, China. This idea was ignored, because no brain cases could be clearly associated with dentitions. It now appears that his interpretation was probably correct. These data suggest that there has been considerable change in the pattern and rate of development and maturation over the course of Pleistocene human evolution.

Teeth and diet

The evolutionary changes in tooth size and proportion are related to diet, and the simple hypothesis is that the dietary differences between this and the earlier australopithecines are responses to the environmental changes taking place across Africa. But what dietary changes are responsible for the dental differences? Several means of examining this question have been developed.

Enamel thickness in the postcanine teeth of this sample is quite great, especially on the crown walls and at the cusp tops. Only the East African australopithecines are more extreme, according to Grine and Martin who worked on broken or artificially sectioned tooth crowns. Analysis of CT scans that examine many more specimens shows no important differences in enamel structure or thickness in a large South African australopithecine sample of both species, according to Macho and Thackery. They point to the combination of thick occlusal and tooth wall enamel in both the *A. africanus* and *robustus* samples, and argue that substantial forces from puncture-crushing as well as grinding characterized both. Within this general description, however, there is systematic variation. The distribution of enamel on the occlusal surfaces of the teeth from Swartkrans suggests more crushing force and mastication of a more fibrous diet to these researchers. The four Kromdraai teeth they examined resemble *A. africanus* in these details.

Microwear analysis of the dental remains have been used in several attempts to reconstruct diet from the effects of foods on the molar enamel surface. Kay and Grine used a scanning electron microscope to examine a combination of pits, and scratches and their orientation, on the occlusal surface of molars. The *A. robustus* teeth showed a combination of more pits and broader scratches that these authors attribute to eating more hard food items. Yet, Grine has argued that "microwear may not be indicative of diet *per se*", and A. Walker's demonstration of a "last meal" effect raises the question of how typical the wear data for the hominids preserved in the South African caves may be. The caves may sample a seasonal occupation of the region and preserve evidence of dietary items that where neither common nor particularly important over the yearly adaptive cycle.

In fact, quite different conclusions were drawn from the chemical analysis of fossil bone and teeth. In a pioneering study, A. Sillen examined the ratio of strontium to calcium found in Swartkrans Member 1 bones. In general there is more calcium than strontium in the environment, but they are differentially accumulated in metabolic processes. Thus, the ratio of these in bone can reflect the foods that were eaten over long periods of time. For instance, animal products introduce a lower strontium/calcium ratio while roots, rhizomes, and edible grass parts such as seeds introduce an elevated one. The ratio also varies within food-types, so that leaf eaters will have a lower ratio compared with seed eaters. Thus, accurate analyses depend on comparisons with fauna with known diets from the same site.

Sillen's study showed the robust australopithecine remains to have low strontium/calcium ratios. Since their ratio lies between the values obtained for Swartkrans leopards and baboons, an eclectic, omnivorous diet of the sort suggested by A. Mann and C. Peters (but few others because of broad acceptance for Robinson's dietary hypothesis) is strongly implicated. Supporting this hypothesis is information from carbon isotope studies of the dental enamel. Research by J. Lee-Thorpe and colleagues suggests that while *A. robustus* ate primarily C3 foods, there was a significant C4 contribution that had to come from either eating grasses or (more likely) eating grazing animals who were eating the grasses. These studies combine to indicate that meat must have been a significant source for C4 foods with a low strontium ratio in the robust australopithecine diet. An adaptive scheme like the one R. Blumenschine developed for the Olduvai Bed I hominids could well apply here. He posits an active, confrontational dry season scavenging adaptation for these hominids, based on minimal cooperative organizational abilities and a technology no more complex than the use of hammerstones to break open bones for their fat and marrow. Robinson's dietary hypothesis, in the end, was wrong, and Grine's contention that robust australopithecines and early *Homo* in South Africa were able to avoid competition by dietary divergence because they were at different trophic levels is without basis. By any meaning of the word, the robust australopithecines were omnivorous, and as Sillen suggests, it is more appropriate to characterize their dietary range as *including* hard objects instead of *consisting of* them.

One final aspect relating diet and the dentition was revealed in research by T. White. He examined the frequency of enamel **hypoplasias**, areas of interrupted enamel development visible on the crown surface. Enamel development can be stopped by periods of high fever or malnutrition during infancy and childhood when the teeth are forming. White found that 17% of the Swartkrans teeth showed evidence of hypoplasia, compared with half this percentage at Sterkfontein. The dietary link is not direct as some Neandertal samples show much higher frequencies and it is ubiquitous in recent agriculturists, but in the context of other high frequencies this information suggests a high level of predictability for food resources available to growing children. .

POSTCRANIA

Swartkrans and Kromdraai have yielded a number of additional postcranial remains, some discovered decades ago (mostly summarized in J. Robinson's monograph *Early Hominid Posture and Locomotion)* and others described more recently by R. Susman and colleagues. The published interpretations of many of the earlier-discovered specimens need to be viewed in historic context. These postcranial remains are the first australopithecine ones found for many skeletal elements, at a time when no complete limbs or partial skeletons were known. In accordance with Robinson's evolutionary scheme it was assumed that the robust australopithecines were primitive, and the gracile ones (e.g. those from Sterkfontein and Makapansgat) were so *Homo*-like that *Homo* could be used to model their (then unknown) remains (see comments on the STS 14 innominate reconstruction below). Thus, the seemingly small heads and long necks on the Swartkrans proximal femur fragments were interpreted to mean an inefficient bipedal gait - one scientist even suggesting that the robust australopithecines couldn't walk but were forced to alternatively run forward and rest on their knuckles, while another worker analyzed the bones to show that they lumbered forward with their center of gravity always in front of their supporting leg (if the reader thinks this is easy, try it!). The debates over whether the femur heads were small or the femur necks long were endless, and of course unresolvable until a complete femur was found. One good example of the problems created by the incomplete remains and their inappropriate analyses is found in a thumb metacarpal from Swartkrans (SK 84). The shape of the bone was unusual for a hominid because of a beak-like projection on one of the articular surfaces. There were no other metacarpals known for any early hominids at that time, so it was compared with other primates, but not in a functional or biomechanical framework. When subjected to a multivariate analysis, it was found to be unlike all of the hominoids compared, and this was interpreted to mean that the thumb functions were limited and restricted, that a precision grip was not possible, and therefore that the bone belonged to a robust australopithecine incapable of tool using and not to a species of *Homo* thought to also be represented in Member 1, albeit in very low number. Then later, the same bone was found in the hand remains from an early *H. sapiens* skeleton from Lake Turkana, WT 15000. This bone is identical to the Swartkrans one, and it is quite likely that virtually everything that had been written or assumed about SK 84 was misleading, or downright wrong. In fact, in the context of today's knowledge, the incomplete robust australopithecine postcranial remains reveal sizes and proportions, anatomical and metric, that closely resemble the other australopithecine species and reflect the same pattern of obligate, efficient bipedalism.

Portions of the pelvis are known from both sites. One badly crushed Swartkrans innominate, SK 50, is quite large and is similar to the Sterkfontein male innominate. The SK 3155 juvenile female innominate is only slightly larger than the Sterkfontein female, according to McHenry. The Swartkrans female looks quite different and when there were fewer innominates known this was once thought to have functional significance (or in one case attributed to pathology). However, the differences are now recognized to be the result of the fact that the Sterkfontein female pelvis was badly crushed and because it was the first australopithecine pelvis found it was mistakenly reconstructed to look more like a modern human innominate than it did in life. The shape and curvatures of the undistorted Swartkrans specimen provide a much more accurate idea of what both specimens were like before fossilization, and show the consequences of a broad pelvic inlet and small hip-joint forces that are a consequence of the dramatic flare at the hips that characterizes all australopithecines. The several femurs known combine thick shafts and rather elongated and vertically tall necks, again because of the combination of broad hips and narrow inlets—the neck must be longer to reach from the shaft to the hip socket, and its extended length results in more bending and accordingly a greater neck height to resist it. Using McHenry's estimates of body weights based on these hindlimb and pelvic remains, the amount of sexual dimorphism seen in the *A, robustus* sample (table 7.3) is very similar to that in the earlier australopithecine species. The male/female mean weight ratio is not unlike some human samples (table 6.10).

Swartkrans generally has more complete bones, but several fragments associated with the Kromdraai female TM 1517 appear to be upper and lower limb remnants of the same individual. According to McHenry these have similar proportions to the other australopithecine remains, with hindlimbs (in this case represented by a talus) a little short relative to the forelimb. As mentioned above he estimates a body weight of 34.4 kg from the talus. The TM 1517 forelimb distal humerus and ulna fragment (see table 7.2) have none of the oddities found in the *A. afarensis* forearm or STW 431, and are indistinguishable from the remains of more recent small humans.

Some important hand remains were recovered from Member 1. R. Susman has argued that these represent the robust australopithecines from the site and with C. Brain has drawn behavioral conclusions from their anatomy that are important in how we regard the capacity of this species. Yet, E. Trinkaus and J. Long attribute them to a different species and the issue remains unresolved. The specimens are discussed in Chapter 8 with the Swartkrans remains attributed to *Homo*.

Robust Australopithecine Phylogeny

SOUTH AND EAST AFRICAN ROBUST AUSTRALOPITHECINE RELATIONS

The unique similarities of the South and East African robust australopithecines are many. They are mostly tied to the extraordinary development of the masticatory apparatus, including

- large, thick enameled postcanine teeth
- molarization of the fourth premolars
- Emphasis on the anterior temporal muscles, regularly creating what P. Tobias calls a **frontal trigone** (a flat or concave area within the triangle formed by the temporal lines and the back of the supraorbitals as a base, as the lines sweep up the frontal converging toward the middle)
- flat cheeks, so anteriorly placed that the face is dished and the nose recessed between them

Other similar features, Holloway, Grine and others point out, are unrelated to the masticatory apparatus and include

- the specifics of the expansion in the parietal lobes of the brain , configuration of the cerebellar lobes, and other details of neural reorganization reflected in the endocasts
- high placement of the top of the nose (it is close to the middle of the supraorbitals)
- high frequency of occipitomarginal sinus drainage

The obvious question is whether these very similar sister taxa are distinct species, or geographic subspecies in a wide ranging human-like polytypic hominid. To raise this issue is dangerous at a time when some paleoanthropologists argue that Swartkrans and Kromdraai robust australopithecines are different species, others find several species in the *H. habilis* remains, and even early *H. sapiens* is a focus of attention as some wish to create a different species for the earliest specimens. With so much splitting, reactions to the issue of polytypism range from "its the single species hypothesis again", to more simply "absurd". But ridicule, some say, is the weapon of the defeated and it might be better to judge this issue on it merits. There are very different definitions of species that underlie much of this discussion, but bringing the evolutionary species precept to bear does result in some evidence that the species are distinct. The strongest case comes from the distinct evolutionary pathway taken by *A. boisei*. While the earliest specimens (e.g. Omo L 323 and others) closely resemble the South African robust form, the lineage increasingly diverges from this condition.

Given that they are distinct species, this leaves a second question. Do they stand in an ancestor-descendant relation or are they sister species that evolved from a common ancestor, presumably *A. africanus*? First, do the South African robusts play a role in the origin of *A. boisei*? The hypothesis that a variety of *A. robustus* is the ancestor of *A. boisei* can be based solely on two points: an early date for at least some of the South African robusts (and/or verification of their close relation to the 2.4 myr Chemeron temporal), and the morphological intermediacy of *A. robustus* between *A. africanus* and *boisei*. Y. Rak has long argued (as have I) that the robust australopithecines tended toward an increasing hypertrophied masticatory apparatus over the course of their evolution (which he regards as quite specialized), and that *A. boisei* is the extreme reflection of this trend. For instance, while the height of the face increases by about 10% between the earlier and later South African samples, between the South African robust and *A. boisei* this increase is 30%. The lower portion of the face expands more than the upper, a result of the larger posterior tooth roots and the greater forces exerted on them. Areas of the cranium and face where muscles attach are particularly well developed and buttressed in the hyper-robusts, and as Rak describes it the profile is transformed into a visor-like frame in response to the masticatory forces. In his analysis of the large Olduvai male (OH 5), P. Tobias recognized these relations and concluded that the hyper-robusts represented an extreme version of the evolutionary trends in South Africa, and that what he and many others regard as successive South African australopithecine species were more closely related to each other than either was to the more extreme East African *A. boisei*.

However, an alternative hypothesis is that the two robust species are descendants from an *A. africanus* common ancestor. There is more to evolution than teeth and the smaller relative brain size of the earlier *A. boisei* specimens must be explained in any model of robust australopithecine evolution. It is possible that the relatively and absolutely larger brain size and other ways in which *A. robustus* differs from *A. boisei* and *africanus* evolved after an *A. boisei/A. robustus* split. This could require the interpretation that the expanded brain size of *A. robustus* is a homoplasy, paralleling expanded brain size in *Homo, unless* we posited that the ancestor of the subsequent *Homo* species was an early population of *A. robustus* (see below and Chapter 8). The homoplasy interpretation should not be difficult to accept as *we have already seen that significant brain size expansion within the A. boisei lineage alone must parallel* <u>Homo</u> no matter how the phylogenetic questions discussed here are resolved.

Supporting the sister species contention for *A. robustus* and *A. boisei* would be a date for Kromdraai that is earlier than Swartkrans. The Kromdraai sample, especially TM 1517, is more plesiomorphic (e.g. *A. africanus*-like) than the Swartkrans robust australopithecines, and therefore a credible model for the last common ancestor of these australopithecine species. According to F. Grine, specimens from Kromdraai resemble the *A. africanus* remains more than those from Swartkrans do in a number of ways, including the pattern of molar enamel thickness, microwear on permanent and deciduous teeth, and as Dean and Wood point out some anatomical variations of the female cranium such as its long cranial base. Should Kromdraai be earlier than Swartkrans Member 1, as Vrba suggests, it would support this hypothetical reconstruction. Since the earliest East African appearance of *A. boisei* is at 2.25 myr, this interpretation would be supported if Kromdraai was at least that age or older. These speculations put renewed focus on the similarities of the 2.4 myr Chemeron temporal and TM 1517.

But if *A. boisei* is an early branch off of the robust hominid lineage so well known in its later aspects from the South African sites, positioned in time between the Sterkfontein *A. africanus* and the Swartkrans *A. robustus* occurrences, this would have a definite taxonomic implication for the South African lineage. That is, the South African australopithecine lineage must necessarily be divided into two species by the *A. boisei* branch. The two Pleistocene robust australopithecines would also necessarily be different species in this interpretation of their phylogeny, in spite of their similar adaptations and close phenetic relations (although tooth wear shows the adaptations are far from identical, and differences such as those reflected in relative brain size show that the taxa are far from the same in other ways as well). Moreover, *A. boisei* may not be the only branch in this lineage, or the hominid populations in East African related to it.

ROBUST AUSTRALOPITHECINES AND THE ORIGIN OF *HOMO*

What are we to make of the detailed and in some cases unexpected similarities these robust australopithecines share with early species of *Homo*? Compared with earlier varieties such as *A. africanus,* these robusts and *Homo* are unique in a number of ways:

- encephalization: marked brain size expansion
- anterior foramen magnum position
- short, broad cranial base
- increased flexion of the cranial base and an open meatal angle
- deep mandibular fossa with a clear distinction between its tall anterior face and the articular surface for the mandibular condyle to rest and rotate during chewing,
- the not infrequent appearance of vertically thick supraorbital tori
- certain behavioral similarities including an omnivorous, seasonally varied diet with significant amounts of animal protein

The most likely explanation for these unique similarities is that these are shared with *Homo* because of either direct ancestry or a recent common ancestor; that is a primitive robust australopithecine of some sort is the ancestor of *Homo* (and other robust australopithecines) - the exact taxonomy dependent on the splitting order, as discussed below. What features would the last common ancestor be expected to have? McHenry and R. Skelton reconstruct the features expected in this last common ancestor based on the shared characteristics of *H. habilis* and the robust australopithecines; they assume that the *Homo* split away from a primitive robust australopithecine occurred earlier than the *A. boisei* split from an even more primitive species. They also assume that the earliest *Homo* species was *H. habilis* (but see Chapter 8). The ancestor they describe is *A. robustus* in virtually all features but one, the continued development of the generalized australopithecine powerful masticatory apparatus. In fact these authors might well have reached the conclusion that the postcanine teeth and the facial structures related to their use were expanded as well, had they focused on the more megadont varieties of early *Homo* in their comparisons, as argued by workers such as B. Wood. Tobias, in a similar exercise, also predicted the last common ancestor would be an unspecialized robust australopithecine. He promoted the Taung child for this position, as he has long argued that Taung would have grown up to be *A. robustus*-like.

The Swartkrans robust australopithecines can be ruled out as direct ancestors. This is because they are most likely too late, and detailed in Chapter 8 several Member 1 and 2 specimens are regarded as a contemporary *Homo* species by a number of scientists. A less specialized robust australopithecine-like variety similar to the Kromdraai remains (already posited as a basal robust australopithecine) could share enough unique features with Swartkrans and the *Homo* species to provide a credible model for their post-*A. boisei* split last common ancestor. However, Kromdraai *per se* may have too many specializations (particularly in the deciduous dentition, as described by Grine and others) to be this ancestor. Moreover, the ancestral population could not be *A. robustus*, as this species can only be a valid entity with the cladogenesis of the lineage into the two sister species *A. boisei* and *A. robustus* and according to this model (figure 7.5) this postdates the origin of *Homo*. Wouldn't it be interesting if there was a population with specimens that lack these particular specializations but otherwise resemble the Kromdraai remains. In fact there are two candidates for this:

1. one is comprised of several specimens in Sterkfontein Member 4 sample such as STW 252 and 505, that are said to represent an early *A. robustus* or its immediate ancestor,
2. the other is the Chemeron temporal, which is in the right place and at the right time and on the absence of evidence to the contrary could be posited as a more generalized Kromdraai-like form.

It is ironic that the very evidence that makes Chemeron unlikely to be an early *Homo,* increases the probability that it is a direct predecessor and a representative of the population that is the last common ancestor for *Homo* and the robust australopithecines.

Adaptive Variation

The presence of adaptively different contemporary hominids in the terminal Pliocene and earliest Pleistocene reflects the increasing abilities of the hominids to expand their resource base and make more effective use of seasonal environments. The rate of hominid speciations is unknown, but the *successful* ones seems to have clustered between 3 and 2 myr, resulting in two different clades, each with at least two species. Why then? Even at their maximum number, hominids never presented more than a miniature adaptive radiation. How widespread the species of these clades were is uncertain since some cases of evidently different species may actually be evolutionary change in the same species. The problem is that decently dated specimens from this critical period are known only from East Africa. The South African robust australopithecine sites are uncertain enough in age that one or both of them could be earlier than the appearance of either *A. boisei* or *Homo*. On the other hand, they could be of the same age or even somewhat younger. Whatever the case, geographic isolation of some late Pliocene populations resulted in the development of genetic isolation, leaving several lineages free to establish their own evolutionary tendencies, but where or exactly when, or even how many times this happened remains unclear.

The adaptive differences between the clades could suggest rapid evolutionary change after speciation, perhaps the consequence of competition since populations of these clades are often found at the same site in both South and East Africa. Of course this does not mean that they lived there at the same time of year, but the potential for competition between these similar hominid species must have been high, at least for some parts of the year. It is also possible that a punctuated equilibrium model may best explain the process, with the isolated populations at the periphery and the extreme end of the adaptive range, thus under selection to change quickly as genetic isolation was established. However, speciation-related changes and dramatic population replacement is not a necessary alternative to a more gradual evolutionary interpretation in this case. More than enough time is involved to account for the accumulating differences between the lineages, and both process may have been important.

The comparisons discussed above show that at least two demonstrable differences were involved in the distinct adaptive patterns. One of these was associated with diet and food preparation. Changes in the robust and hyper-robust australopithecines involved adaptations to dietary items requiring both powerful and prolonged chewing. Both force and pressure (force/area) was emphasized in their postcanine dentitions. A body size increase may account for the continued development of this adaptation in *A. boisei,* with the larger, later hominids requiring more food. Unfortunately, while numerous isolated postcranial remains have been found at the East African sites, there are few associations of skull and body parts, and no associations with a later *A. boisei* specimen. The postcranial remains of the australopithecines and at least one of the early *Homo* species cannot be separated into functionally different groups. This is not surprising given the complete adaptation to striding bipedalism in the Pliocene australopithecines, but it does not help the problem of determining which isolated postcranial remains belong with which clade.

The hyper-robust species also shows significant increases in brain size. Selection to increase the differences in adaptation almost certainly was in part the result of competition between the forms, a consequence of competitive exclusion. Species of the two genera are consistently found at the same levels at a number of sites, and a review by T. White clearly shows that no difference in habitat based on their places of death can be demonstrated. Competition for at least some limiting resources between culture bearing, tool-using, intelligent hominids could be expected to have been intense, but were species in both clades culture-bearing and tool using? I have long argued that if one of several contemporary hominid populations was a tool-user, they all were. "Monkey-see, monkey-do" must surely apply to any hominids far better than it applies to monkeys! Moreover, the evidence for tool use in robust australopithecines is reasonably good, given the probability that we are unlikely to uncover one clutching an artifact in death.. This evidence includes

- expanded brain size in all species in the robust australopithecine clade
- continued significant brain size changes in *A. boisei,* where the fossil record over a long period of time is good
- the several tool sites in East African where only *A. boisei* is found
- the fact that all of the Swartkrans terminal phalanges have finger-tip broadening and other hand remains reveal tool-making adaptations (see Chapter 8 - the numerous hand remains must belong to a number of individuals, some of whom were robust australopithecines)

It may also include the indirect suggestion of an increased range of vocalizations, *if Laitman and colleagues are correct in assuming that the flexion of the cranial base is related to the position of the larynx in the throat.* This is because the lowered position implied by the flexed cranial bases of *A. boisei* and *A. robustus* would mean these species could inhale foods and choke on them just as we do, a disadvantage that one would expect to be offset by the advantage of this larynx position in greatly expanding the range of vocalizations.

But tool use and culture are different issues. Culture is not to be taken for granted in the first tool-using hominids. There was not, as G. Isaac supposed, an adaptive threshold for stone tools, with their discovery followed by an explosion of lithic technology and adaptive change. To the contrary, the distinctions that J. Harris and his colleagues have recognized between the simple, seasonally limited pre-Oldowan cases of tool making (discussed above) and the Oldowan industries of the Terminal Pliocene and Early Pleistocene (Chapter 8) denote real adaptive changes that were missed as long as technology was the focus of studies. These changes are in distributional patterns at sites and broader land use patterns. The pre-Oldowan tool use may have been more of an adaptive response to certain seasonal requirements encountered in dry habitats, than an adaptive strategy that subsequent tool use became as it evolved as part of a cultural system. The former was ubiquitous across the hominids - the basal technology that was the object of hominid-see, hominid do - and the later may have been sophisticated enough to only be in the behavioral repertoire of early *Homo.*

In sum, the evidence as I interpret it suggests that the hominid clades, with their differing adaptations, were successful because of a number of technological and social changes that allowed them to effectively utilize seasonal habitats in both overlapping and differing ways. It is quite likely that tool use was of critical importance, perhaps even as the fundamental basis for these expanding adaptations. But the capacity for tool use, and the functions of this behavior, may not have been the same in all of the hominid species. To fully explore the implications of these ideas we need to include the other contemporary species in our discussions, early *H. sapiens*.

Summary

The Late Pliocene saw the appearance of three australopithecine species, all characterized as "robust australopithecines", one (or some say two) species of australopithecine-like *Homo,* and the first evidence of early *H. sapiens* - the topic of the next chapter. Stone tools were invented. At first there were crudely made sharp-edged flakes occurring only at low densities, found near the raw material sources, along rivers bordered by strips of gallery forest. They may not have been habitually made and only seem to have been seasonally important.

Of these hominids from the Late Pliocene and earlier Pleistocene, *A. aethiopicus* stands out as an exception, a relatively gigantic (double the size of the other species), highly dimorphic variant of the primitive *A. afarensis* that left no descendants. As far as we have the appropriate data to tell, the other australopithecine and australopithecine-like *Homo* samples share most or all of the following features:

- encephalization, shown by markedly expanded brain sizes, and neural reorganization resulting in endocast anatomy that closely resembles *H. sapiens*
- powerful masticatory apparatus and supporting structures of the jaws and middle face
- a suite of middle-face details such as
    - narrow nasal aperture
    - narrow nasal bones absolutely and relative to the aperture
    - small, unprojecting anterior nasal spine sometimes recessed behind the walls of the aperture
    - flat nasal bones lacking any internasal peaking
    - flat middle face, lacking nasal projection
- very small body size, averaging 35-39 kg (middle-sex average) which is under chimpanzee mean body weight
- reduced dimorphism (a ratio of 1.3-1.4, compared with 1.7 in earlier species and *A. aethiopicus*)
- several postcranial features differing from *H. sapiens*, including
    - relatively short leg length
    - small vertebrae (both bodies and vertebral canals)

All of the australopithecines of this period are the of the variety. They are not directly descended from *A. aethiopicus,* but rather share *A. africanus* if not a more recent group as their last common ancestor. The less specialized variety, *A robustus* appears in South African after *A. africanus*, but is poorly dated. *A. robustus* is probably in South Africa by 2.3-2.2 myr. According to F. Grine, there are no temporal trends for the *A. robustus* material trough the Swartkrans sequence. This may reflect stasis in the species, or result from Swartkrans sampling a very short time span. In East Africa the 2.4 myr Chemeron temporal, although attributed to *Homo*, is similar to this form and numerous isolated teeth from Omo deposits dated between 2.4 and 2.2 myr also resemble it.

The East African variant, *A. boisei,* is sampled over a very long time period (2.25-1.4 myr) and shows significant trends for increasing brain size and posterior tooth size, while canine size decreases. It is somewhat more specialized, with relatively larger postcanine teeth and masticatory structures that produce stronger chewing forces in a more efficient manner. Microwear studies suggest dietary differences and indicate that the *A. boisei* adaptation may emphasize very low quality but not particularly abrasive food items, at least seasonally. Their adaptation, in other words, is for prolonged chewing of tough items, but not requiring powerful crushing or breaking small objects. The *A robustus* diet is much more eclectic and includes significant amounts of meat.

These australopithecines are almost invariably found with one or another *Homo* species. Just as the anatomy reflects a close phylogenetic relation with *Homo*, this ecological observations emphasizes close adaptive ones. It is likely that there were significant aspects of competition between these differently evolving hominids that affected the evolutionary pathways of both.

ANATOMY OF A CONTROVERSY
Climate Changes and Hominid Evolution

Studies of three climatically sensitive indicators, the oxygen isotope record, the long record of faunal evolution from central Europe, and the loess (wind-blown soil) sequence from central China, suggest a significant change in worldwide climate at or near the beginning of the Late Pliocene, approximately 2.5 myr at the Gauss/Matuyama paleomagnetic boundary (table 1.4). E. Vrba and colleagues contend that there is a significant shift from the globally warm early Pliocene climates to the cooler, more rapidly oscillating climates of the late Pliocene - what they call a "window of climatic deterioration" between 2.8 and 2.5 myr. Widely dispersed phenomena occur at this time, including a marked cooling of Antarctic ice, and more significantly the onset of the continental glacial cycle (some have proposed that this should be used to mark the beginning of the Pleistocene - a definitional question - since this epoch is widely understood to be the glacial period). Vrba, in what she calls the **Pulse Hypothesis**, links a number of evolutionary events in the hominids to these climatic changes that occurred during this interval as they affect local conditions in Africa. Because she accepts the Punctuated Equilibrium model (see Chapter 2), Vrba relates all evolutionary changes to speciations and extinctions and during a period of climate change the rates of speciation and extinction would be expected to accelerate, creating a turnover pulse of rapid evolutionary change. Such a pulse, she contends, should be marked by an unusual number of first and last appearances of unrelated species in a limited time span. This is Vrba's climatic causation hypothesis.

The African paleontological record at close to 2.5 myr unquestionably reflects cooling and drying (aridification), as evidenced by changes in pollen as well as vertebrate fossils. In East Africa there is

- a major change in the Omo vertebrate faunas at about 2.6-2.4 myr, which Vrba interprets to mean "increased grasslands and hence aridity"
- the appearance of European immigrants, argued to reflect the equatorwards spread of temperate habitats, and therefore cooling
- a shift of microfauna to species reflecting arid and open conditions by 2.5-2.4 myr
- pollen changes at 2.5-2.4 myr indicating grassland expansion and a decline of wooded savanna
- a marked increase in seasonality

Continent-wide changes in vertebrate faunas seem to accelerate at about this time, although the expected complimentary pulse of accelerated extinctions is less well established. First noticed in South Africa by C. Brain, subsequent research established two patterns of change. According to A. Turner and B. Wood, in the large mammals there are incursions of new, grasslands adapted species about 2.5 myr and over the following half million years many species underwent parallel changes as they adapted to tougher and more abrasive dietary items. For instance, the grassland-adapted horse genus *Equus* immigrated into eastern Africa and this is when *Elephas* dominated in proboscidean evolution, a genus with high-cusped molar teeth. The most megadont of the baboon-like species also appeared at this time. They suggest that the trend, or parallel trends, for megadonty in the hominids began at this time as well. In this case the evidence is not clearly behind the hypothesis, as the evolution of megadonty in the South African gracile australopithecines (and their East African counterparts) from an *A. afarensis* ancestry precedes these changes. Even still, megadonty continues to evolve in the hominids and characterizes different species in *Australopithecus* and the emerging genus *Homo*.

These faunal changes seem to correspond to continent-wide climatic evolution. They are reflected in increasing aridity and more pronounced seasonality; albeit, more of a trend than a focused dramatic change. They can be seen in the South African sequence, where however the lower resolution makes precise dating impossible. They are also reflected in the sea core record, where a study of the sediment composition of cores from the South Atlantic, off the coast of West Africa, suggests that Africa became increasingly arid at about 2.5 myr. The evolving African climate heralded conditions that led to the onset of the fluctuations of the Pleistocene.

Four events are said to occur in hominid evolution, closely bracketing this short period about 2.5 myr ago. These are:

1. The first hyper-robust australopithecine adaptation
2. Dramatic increases in brain size in the South African hominids
3. The origin of the genus *Homo*
4. The first stone tools that can be recognized, whether identified as manuports or because of their artificial modification

The question of interest, of course, is whether the events can be linked to the changing climate, apart from what might just be a coincidence of dates. One way to approach this question is to examine how increased aridity and seasonality effects living primates with broad enough geographic ranges to potentially reflect climatic variation. R. Foley points out that when there is dry season stress, primates either tend to specialize all year around on abundant low quality foods, or adopt seasonally varied foraging strategies, that provide at least some higher quality resources. One potential source of high quality food is, as so many have argued, found in the meat, marrow, and fat of animal carcasses. These two patterns characterize the main differences between the subsequent Pleistocene adaptations of robust australopithecines and *Homo.*

We must entertain the hypothesis that the climate changes at the onset of the Late Pliocene may have been causal in the appearance of *Homo.* Perhaps the best support for this hypothesis is the proposal that many other mammalian species change at this time as well, in a wave of extinctions and the appearance of new species (Vrba's wave hypothesis). Moreover, the appearance of stone tool technology at this time, if the dates hold (there is always a question of whether the oldest has been found when an argument is based on 'the earliest appearance of ...') indicates a very important change in hominid adaptation. Yet, several environmentally sensitive African mammal species do not become extinct at this time and the main anatomical changes that characterize hominid evolution is the appearance of the first of several species to specialize in the food resources promoted by aridity. The question is whether one of these is the earliest *Homo* The evidence here is not all in yet, but the anatomy of *Homo* species at the terminal Pliocene, does not seem to appear a half-million years earlier, when the dramatic climate changes (pulses, waves, or whatever) were occurring. Moreover, the fact is that for climate changes to be recognized as causal for anatomical changes, as R. Blumenschine argues, the link must be more than a correlation. It must involve a hypothesis of cause and effect.

In his "Ecological theory for the origin of *Homo"*, S. Stanley suggests such a causal hypothesis, based on assumption of climatic changes as discussed above. He argues that in response to the deteriorating climatic conditions (at least from the vantage point of early hominids), beginning with *H. rudolfensis* (what he calls the earliest *Homo* species) there were significant behavioral changes as a more human-like pattern of intelligence evolved. For direct evidence he asserts that the combination of expanded adult brain size and distinct pelvic morphology shows that atricial births (see Chapter 3) characterized *Homo.* Early *Homo* brains, he suggests, grew like modern ones with the very rapid fetal rate of expansion extending through the first year of life. Drawing on work by R. Martin, he posits that helpless infants with the potential for rapid learning are the biological innovation for *Homo*, made possible by the "fact" that this was the first hominid species to totally abandon (what he calls) obligate arboreal activity and become fully terrestrial. The reader can appreciate that the serious problems with this elegant hypothesis are in:

- the absence of any data suggesting that earlier hominids engaged in obligate arboreal activities,
- the lack of evidence showing that the pelvic and brain size changes occurred at this time (the only pelves and cranial capacities known for *Homo* comes from the latest Pliocene, at the end of its span) changes,
- the lack of evidence showing that these can be linked to increasing atricial births

Yet, there are no other specific hypotheses linking the origin of *Homo* and the appearance of the earliest stone tools to each other *and* to the climate changes, and Stanley raises a number of valid issues in developing his hypothesis. These will be explored more fully in Chapter 8, with the discussion of the early *H. sapiens* specimens.

There is, however, one other hypothesis of causal links between species-level hominid evolution and climate change. This is R. Foley's idea that extinctions rather than speciations can be related to climatic changes. In fact, Foley finds no relationship at all between climatic variations and the first appearance of hominid species. An interesting idea, this one creates unusual difficulties in relating to data, as the last appearance of a species is very difficult to distinguish from the absence of evidence that could come from just bad luck (people who died in the wrong place, paleoanthropologists who looked in the wrong place). Another complicating factor in this analysis is the plethora of hominid species Foley identified to be able to generate his extinction statistics; 15 in all, of which all but one became extinct. This is far in excess of the number that Foley had earlier predicted should have occurred in the hominids - 3 to 11 with a mean expectation of under 6.

There may well be a causal link between the Late Pliocene climatic changes and the diversifying hominid adaptations, but it need not be in a wave of speciations and extinctions that respond to a sudden, dramatic climatic change. The interpretations of the oxygen isotope record have become more equivocal, and suggest a gradual 3-2 myr climatic cooling instead of a specific "2.5 myr event". A. Hill suggests than none of the faunal evidence from East Africa has insufficient resolution to test the "pulse hypothesis", and it is unsupported by the hominid fossil record. While the first known *A. aethiopicus* is dated to the right time to be a consequence of a "2.5 myr event", indirect evidence suggests that the origin of this species is considerably earlier. Moreover, it is unclear whether its masticatory-associated features reflect a dietary change, a dramatic body size increase, or, or course, both. Not all these possibilities necessarily reflect increasing aridity. The subsequent mini-adaptive radiations in the two hominid clades of the terminal Pliocene are considerably later, first evidenced just prior the Pleistocene's beginning. There is no theoretical reason to posit an origin for *Homo* before this, and as mentioned above no evidence that *Homo* was actually present earlier. Thus, the events in hominid evolution begging explanation because they seem to be associated, turn out to be partially or completely *un*associated. There are no special data from hominid evolution for the "pulse hypothesis" to address.

The case for a climatic influence on hominid evolution cannot be disproved, but the specific hypothesis linking australopithecine extinctions, the discovery of stone tool making, the appearance of the robust australopithecine adaptation, and the origin of *Homo* to worldwide climate changes (or for that matter to each other) are without basis. A 1993 conference called to focus on the question of climatic influence on human evolution by one of its most prominent supporters did not result in its convincing demonstration, in spite of the fact that for the most part only those who were favorably disposed to the idea were invited. T. White cautions that as more continent-wide or worldwide climatic events come to be recognized, some are bound to coincide with events in hominid evolution without being the causes of the evolutionary changes.

REFERENCES AND FURTHER READINGS

BEHRENSMEYER, A.K. 1976 Taphonomy and paleoecology in the hominid fossil record. *Yearbook of Physical Anthropology* 19:36-50.

BEYNON, A.D., and B.A. WOOD 1986 Variations in enamel thickness and structure in east African hominids. *American Journal of Physical Anthropology* 70(2):177-194.

BILSBOROUGH, A. 1986 Diversity, evolution, and adaptation in early hominids. In G.N. Bailey and P. Callow (eds): *Stone Age Prehistory.* Cambridge University Press, New York. pp. 197-220.

BINFORD, L.R. 1981 *Bones: Ancient Men and Modern Myths.* Academic Press, New York.

BLUMENSCHINE, R.J. 1989 A landscape taphonomic model of the scale of prehistoric scavenging opportunities. *Journal of Human Evolution* 18(4):345-371.

BOAZ, N.T. 1982 American research on australopithecines and early *Homo.* In F. Spencer (ed): *History of American Physical Anthropology (1930-1980).* Academic, New York. pp. 239-260.

BRAIN, C.K. 1980 Some criteria for the recognition of bone-collecting agencies in the African caves. In A.K. Behrensmeyer and A.P. Hill (eds): *Fossils in the Making: Vertebrate Taphonomy and Paleoecology.* University of Chicago, Chicago pp. 108-130.

___. 1981 The evolution of man in Africa: was it a consequence of Cainozoic cooling? Alex L. du Toit Memorial Lecture 17. *Transactions of the Geological Society of South Africa.* Annex to 84:1-19.

___. 1993a Structure and stratigraphy of the Swartkrans Cave in the light of the new excavations. In C.K. Brain (ed): *Swartkrans. A Cave's Chronicle of Early Man.* Transvaal Museum Monograph 8:23-33.

___. 1993b A taphonomic overview of the Swartkrans fossil assemblages. In C.K. Brain (ed): *Swartkrans. A Cave's Chronicle of Early Man.* Transvaal Museum Monograph 8:257-264.

BRAIN, C.K., and P. SHIPMAN 1993 The Swartkrans bone tools. In C.K. Brain (ed): *Swartkrans. A Cave's Chronicle of Early Man.* Transvaal Museum Monograph 8:195-215.

BROMAGE, T.G. 1992 Faces from the past. *New Scientist* (January 11):38-41.

BROOM, R.A. 1938 Pleistocene anthropoid apes of South Africa. *Nature* 142:377-379.

___. 1939a The dentition of the Transvaal Pleistocene anthropoids, *Plesianthropus* and *Paranthropus.* *Annals of the Transvaal Museum* 19:303-314.

___. 1939b A restoration of the Kromdraai skull. *Annals of the Transvaal Museum* 19:327-329.

BROOM, R.A. and J.T. ROBINSON 1950 Note on the skull of the Swartkrans ape-man *Paranthropus crassidens.* *American Journal of Physical Anthropology* 8(3):295-300.

___. 1950c Notes on the pelvis of the fossil ape-men. *American Journal of Physical Anthropology* 8(4):489-494.

BROWN, B., A.C. WALKER, C.V. WARD, and R.E. LEAKEY 1993 A new *Australopithecus boisei* cranium from east Turkana, Kenya. *American Journal of Physical Anthropology* 91(2):137-159.

CAVALLO, J.A., and R.J. BLUMENSCHINE 1989 Tree-stored leopard kills: expanding the hominid scavenging niche. *Journal of Human Evolution* 18(4):393-399.

CHAVAILLON, J. 1976 Evidence for the technical practices of Early Pleistocene hominids. In Y. Coppens, F.C. Howell, G.Ll. Isaac, and R.E. Leakey (eds): *Earliest Man and Environments in the Lake Rudolf Basin*. University of Chicago Press, Chicago. pp. 565-573.

CLARKE, R.J. 1994 Advances in understanding the craniofacial anatomy of South African early hominids. In R.S. Corruccini and R.L. Ciochon (eds): *Integrative Paths to the Past. Paleoanthropological Advances in Honor of F. Clark Howell*. Prentice Hall, Englewood Cliffs. pp. 205-222.

COPPENS, Y. 1978 Evolution of the hominids and of their environment during the Plio-Pleistocene in the lower Omo Valley, Ethiopia. In W.W. Bishop (ed): *Geological Background to Fossil Man*. Scottish Academic Press, Edinburgh. pp. 409-506.

___. 1980 The differences between *Australopithecus* and *Homo*: preliminary conclusions from the Omo research expeditions studies. In L.K. Königsson (ed): *Current Arguments on Early Man*. Pergamon, Oxford. pp. 207-225.

CORRUCCINI, R.S. 1994 How certain are hominoid phylogenies? The role of confidence intervals in cladistics. In R.S. Corruccini and R.L. Ciochon (eds): *Integrative Paths to the Past. Paleoanthropological Advances in Honor of F. Clark Howell*. Prentice Hall, Englewood Cliffs, pp. 167-183.

DAEGLING, D.J. 1989 Biomechanics of cross-sectional size and shape in the hominid mandibular corpus. *American Journal of Physical Anthropology* 80(1):91-106.

DAEGLING, D.J., and F.E. GRINE 1991 Compact bone distribution and biomechanics of early hominid mandibles. *American Journal of Physical Anthropology* 86(3):321-340.

DAVIS, D.D. 1964 *The Giant Panda: A Morphological Study of Evolutionary Mechanisms. Fieldania: Zoological Memoirs* 3:1-339.

DAY, M.H. 1981 Fossils and concepts in hominid paleontology: the W.C.O. Hill memorial lecture. *International Journal of Primatology* 2(2):105-120.

DEAN, M.C. 1986 *Homo* and *Paranthropus*: similarities in the cranial base and developing dentition. In B. Wood, L. Martin, and P. Andrews (ed): *Major Trends in Primate and Human Evolution*. Cambridge University Press, Cambridge. pp. 249-265.

___. 1988 Growth processes in the cranial base of hominoids and their bearing on morphological similarities that exist in the cranial base of *Homo* and *Paranthropus*. In F.E. Grine (ed): *Evolutionary History of the "Robust" Australopithecines*. Aldine de Gruyter, New York. pp. 107-112.

DEAN, M.C., and B.A. WOOD 1982 Basicranial anatomy of Pliopleistocene hominids from East and South Africa. *American Journal of Physical Anthropology* 59:157-174.

DEEMS, B., N. CREEL, and H. PREUSCHOFT 1986 Functional significance of allometric trends in the hominoid masticatory apparatus. In J.G. Else and P.C. Lee (eds): *Primate Evolution*. Cambridge University Press, Cambridge. pp. 229-237.

DELOISON, Y. 1985 Comparative study of the calcanei of primates and *Pan-Australopithecus-Homo* relationship. In P.V. Tobias (ed): *Hominid Evolution: Past, Present, and Future. Proceedings of the Taung Diamond Jubilee International Symposium*. Alan R. Liss Inc., New York. pp. 143-147.

DENIRO, M.J. 1987 Stable isotopy and archaeology. *American Scientist* 75(2):182-191.

DuBRUL, E.L. 1977 Early hominid feeding mechanisms. *American Journal of Physical Anthropology* 47(2):305-320.

FEIBEL, C.S., F.H. BROWN, and I. McDOUGALL 1989 Stratigraphic context of the fossil hominids from the Omo group deposits: northern Turkana basin, Kenya and Ethiopia. *American Journal of Physical Anthropology* 78(4):595-622.

FOLEY, R.A. 1991 How many species of hominid should there be? *Journal of Human Evolution* 30(5):413-427.

___. 1994 Speciation, extinction and climatic change in hominid evolution. *Journal of Human Evolution* 26(4):275-289.

GIBBONS, A. 1990 Paleontology by bulldozer. *Science* 247:1407-1409.

GOULD, S.J. 1987 Bushes all the way down. *Natural History* 87(6):12-19.

GRAUSZ, H.M., R.E. LEAKEY, A.C. WALKER, and C.V. WARD 1988 Associated cranial and postcranial bones of *Australopithecus boisei*. In F.E. Grine (ed): *Evolutionary History of the "Robust" Australopithecines*. Aldine de Gruyter, New York. pp. 127-132.

GRINE, F.E. 1981 Trophic differences between "gracile" and "robust" australopithecines: A scanning electron microscope analysis of occlusal events. *South African Journal of Science* 77:203-230.

___. 1986 Dental evidence for dietary differences in *Australopithecus* and *Paranthropus*: a quantitative analysis of permanent molar microwear. *Journal of Human Evolution* 15(8):783-822.

___. 1988a New craniodental fossils of *Paranthropus* from the Swartkrans formation and their significance in "robust" australopithecine evolution. In F.E. Grine (ed): *Evolutionary History of the "Robust" Australopithecines*. Aldine de Gruyter, New York. pp. 223-243.

___. 1988b Evolutionary history of the "robust" australopithecines: a summary and historical perspective. In F.E. Grine (ed): *Evolutionary History of the "Robust" Australopithecines*. Aldine de Gruyter, New York. pp. 509-520.

GRINE, F.E., and L.B. MARTIN 1988 Enamel thickness and development in *Australopithecus* and *Paranthropus*. In F.E. Grine (ed): *Evolutionary History of the "Robust" Australopithecines*. Aldine de Gruyter, New York. pp. 3-42.

HANNAM, A.G., and W.W. WOOD 1989 Relationships between the size and spacial morphology of human masseter and medial pterygoid muscles, the craniofacial skeleton, and jaw biomechanics. *American Journal of Physical Anthropology* 80(4):429-445.

HARRIS, J.W.K. 1983 Cultural beginnings: Plio Pleistocene archaeological occurrences from the Afar, Ethiopia. *African Archaeological Review* 1:3-31.

HARRIS, J.W.K., and S. CAPALDO 1993 The earliest stone tools: their implications for an understanding of the activities and behaviour of Late Pliocene hominids. In A. Berthelet and J. Chavaillon (eds): *The Use of Tools by Human and Non-Human Primates*. Clarendon, Oxford. pp. 196-224.

HILL, A.H. 1984 Hyaenas and hominids: taphonomy and hypothesis testing. In R. Foley (ed): *Hominid Evolution and Community Ecology*. Academic Press, New York. pp. 111-128.

___. 1987 Causes of perceived faunal change in the later Neogene of East Africa. *Journal of Human Evolution* 16(7/8):583-596.

HILL, A.H., S. WARD, A. DEINO, G. CURTIS, and R. DRAKE 1992 Earliest *Homo*. *Nature* 355:719-722

HOLLOWAY, R.L. 1972 New australopithecine endocast, SK 1585, from Swartkrans, South Africa. *American Journal of Physical Anthropology* 37(2):173-186.

___. 1981 The endocast of Omo juvenile L338y-6 hominid: gracile or robust *Australopithecus?*. *American Journal of Physical Anthropology* 54(1):109-118.

___. 1988 "Robust" australopithecine brain endocasts: some preliminary observations. In F.E. Grine (ed): *Evolutionary History of the "Robust" Australopithecines*. Aldine de Gruyter, New York. pp. 97-105.

HOWELL, F.C. 1976 Overview of the Pliocene and earlier Pleistocene of the Lower Omo basin, Southern Ethiopia. In G.Ll. Isaac and E.R. McCown (eds): *Human Origins: Louis Leakey and the East African Experience*. Benjamin Cummings, Menlo Park. pp. 227-268.

HOWELL, F.C., P. HAESAERTS, and J. DeHEINZELIN 1987 Depositional environments, archaeological occurrences, and hominids from Members E and F of the Shungura Formation (Omo basin, Ethiopia). *Journal of Human Evolution* 16(7/8):665-700.

HYLANDER, W.L. 1988 Implications of *in vitro* experiments for interpreting the functional significance of "robust" australopithecine jaws. In F.E. Grine (ed): *Evolutionary History of the "Robust" Australopithecines*. Aldine de Gruyter, New York. pp. 55-83.

ISAAC, G.Ll. 1985 The archaeology of hominid origins: studies of the Lower Pleistocene in East Africa, 1971-1981. *Advances in World Archaeology* 3:1-87.

JUNGERS, W.L., and F.E. GRINE 1986 Dental trends in the australopithecines: the allometry of mandibular molar dimensions. In B. Wood, L. Martin, and P. Andrews (eds): *Major Trends in Primate and Human Evolution*. Cambridge University Press, Cambridge. pp. 203-219.

KAY, R.F, and F.E. GRINE 1988 Tooth morphology, wear, and diet in *Australopithecus* and *Paranthropus* from southern Africa. In F.E. Grine (ed): *Evolutionary History of the "Robust" Australopithecines*. Aldine de Gruyter, New York. pp. 427-447.

KEELEY, L.H., and N. TOTH 1983 Microwear polishes on early stone tools from Koobi Fora, Kenya. *Nature* 293:464-465.

KIBUNJIA, M., H. ROCHE, F.H. BROWN, and R.E. LEAKEY 1992 Pliocene and Pleistocene archaeological sites west of Lake Turkana, Kenya. *Journal of Human Evolution* 23(5):431-438.

KIMBEL, W.H., T.D. WHITE, and D.C. JOHANSON 1988 Implications of KNM-WT 17000 for the evolution of "robust" *Australopithecus*. In F.E. Grine (ed): *Evolutionary History of the "Robust" Australopithecines*. Aldine de Gruyter, New York. pp. 259-268.

KIESER, J.A., and H.T. GROENEVELD 1988 Allometric relations of teeth and jaws in man. *American Journal of Physical Anthropology* 77(1):57-67.

KLEIN, R.G. 1988 The causes of "robust" australopithecine extinction. In F.E. Grine (ed): *Evolutionary History of the "Robust" Australopithecines*. Aldine de Gruyter, New York. pp. 499-505.

VON KOENIGSWALD, G.H.R. 1967 Evolutionary trends in the deciduous molars of the Hominidea. Journal of Dental Research 46:779-786.

___. 1979 Observations on the trigonid of the last lower deciduous molar (m_2) of man and some higher primates. In D.C. Johanson (ed): *Festschrift Albert Dahlberg. OSSA (International Journal of Skeletal Research)* 6:157-162.

KÖHLER, W. 1959 *The Mentality of Apes.* Second, Revised Edition. Vintage, New York.

KORTLANDT, A. 1986 The use of stone tools by wild-living chimpanzees and earliest hominids. *Journal of Human Evolution* 15(2):77-132.

LAITMAN, J.T., and J.S. REIDENBERG 1987 Advances in understanding the relationship between the skull base and larynx with comments of the origin of speech. *Human Evolution* 3(1):99-109.

LEAKEY, L.S.B. 1960 Recent discoveries at Olduvai gorge. *Nature* 188:1050-1052

LEAKEY, R.E. 1976 Hominids in Africa. American Scientist 64:174-178.

LEWIN, R. 1985 Paleoclimates in Southern Africa. *Science* 227:1325-1327.

___. 1986 New fossil upsets human family. *Science* 233:720-721.

LICHTMAN, D., J.W.K. HARRIS, M. KIBUNJIA, and H. ROCHE 1993 Experimental analysis of inorganic residues on early Pleistocene stone artifacts. *Nyame Akuma*

LOVEJOY, C. 0. 1978 A biomechanical review of the locomotor diversity of early hominids. In C.J. Jolly (ed): *Early Hominids of Africa.* Duckworth, London. pp. 403-429.

MARTIN, R.D. 1988 Evolution of the brain in early hominids. *OSSA (International Journal of Skeletal Research)* 14:49-62.

MARTIN, R.D., and A, M. MacLARNON 1985 Gestation period, neonatal size, and maternal investment in placental mammals. *Nature* 313:220-223.

MAYR, E. 1950 Taxonomic categories in fossil hominids. *Cold Spring Harbor Symposia on Quantitative Biology* 15:108-118.

McCOLLUM, M.A. 1994 Mechanical and spatial determinants of *Paranthropus* facial form. *American Journal of Physical Anthropology* 93(2):259-273.

McCOWN, T.D. 1950 The genus *Paleoanthropus* and the problem of superspecific differentiation among the hominidae. *Cold Spring Harbor Symposia on Quantitative Biology* 15:87-94.

McHENRY, H.M, H.M. 1991 Petite bodies of the "robust" australopithecines. *American Journal of Physical Anthropology* 86(4):445-454.

___. 1992 How big were early hominids? *Evolutionary Anthropology* 1(1):15-20.

McHENRY, H.M., and R.S. CORRUCCINI 1975 Distal humerus in hominoid evolution. *Folia Primatologia* 23:227-244.

McHENRY, H.M, H.M., R.S. CORRUCCINI, and F.C. HOWELL 1976 Analysis of an early hominid ulna from the Omo basin, Ethiopia. *American Journal of Physical Anthropology* 44(2):295-304.

McKEE, J.K., J.F. THACKERAY, and L.R. BERGER 1994 Faunal assemblage seriation of southern African Pliocene and Pleistocene fossil deposits. *American Journal of Physical Anthropology*

MERRICK, H.V. and J.P.S. MERRICK 1976 Archeological Occurrences of Earlier Pleistocene Age, from the Shungura Formation. In Y. Coppens, F.C. Howell, G.Ll. Isaac, and R.E. Leakey (eds): *Earliest Man and Environments in the Lake Rudolf Basin.* University of Chicago Press, Chicago. pp. 574-584.

OXNARD, C.E. 1975 The place of the australopithecines in human evolution: grounds for doubt? *Nature* 258:389-396.

PETERS, C.R. 1981 Robust vs. gracile early hominid masticatory capabilities: the advantages of the megadonts. In L.L. Mai, E. Shanklin, and R.W. Sussman (eds): *The Perception of Human Evolution.* University of California Press, Los Angeles. pp. 161-181.

POTTS, R. 1993 Archaeological interpretations of early hominid behavior and ecology. In D.T. Rasmussen (ed): *The Origin and Evolution of Humans and Humanness.* Jones and Bartless, Boston. pp. 49-74.

PRENTICE, M.L., and G.H. DENTON 1988 The deep-sea oxygen isotope record, the global ice sheet system, and hominid evolution. In F.E. Grine (ed): *Evolutionary History of the "Robust" Australopithecines.* Aldine de Gruyter, New York. pp. 383-403.

PICQ, P. 1990 *L'Articulation Temporo-mandibulaire des Hominidés: Bioméchanique, Allométrie, Anatomie Comparée et Évolution.* Cahiers
de Paléoanthropologie No. 7. C.N.R.S., Paris.

RAK, Y. 1978 The functional significance of the squamosal suture in *Australopithecus boisei. American Journal of Physical Anthropology* 49:71-78.

___. 1985 Australopithecine taxonomy and phylogeny in the light of facial morphology. *American Journal of Physical Anthropology* 66(3):281-287.

___. 1988 On variation in the masticatory system of *Australopithecus boisei.* In F.E. Grine (ed): *Evolutionary History of the "Robust" Australopithecines.* Aldine de Gruyter, New York. pp. 193-198.

___. 1994 The middle ear of *Australopithecus robustus.* Does it bear evidence of a specialized masticatory system? In R.S. Corruccini and R.L. Ciochon (eds): *Integrative Paths to the Past. Paleoanthropological Advances in Honor of F. Clark Howell.* Prentice Hall, Englewood Cliffs. pp. 223-227.

RAK, Y. and W.H. KIMBEL 1991 On the squamosal suture of KNM-WT 17000. *American Journal of Physical Anthropology* 85(1):1-6.

RAMIREZ-ROZZI, F.V. 1993 Tooth development in East African *Paranthropus. Journal of Human Evolution* 24(6):429-454.

RIGHTMIRE, G.P. 1972 Multivariate analysis of an early hominid metacarpal from Swartkrans. *Science* 176:159-161.

___. 1993 Did climatic change influence human evolution. *Evolutionary Anthropology* 2(2):43-45.

ROBINSON, J.T. 1954 The genera and species of the Australopithecines. *American Journal of Physical Anthropology* 12:181-200.

___. 1963 Adaptive radiation in the australopithecines and the origin of man. In F.C. Howell and F. Bourliere (eds): *African Ecology and Human Evolution. Viking Fund Publication in Anthropology* 36:385-416.

SCHAFFER, W.M. 1968 Character displacement and the evolution of the Hominidae. *American Naturalist* 102:559-571.

SENUT, B. 1986a Long bones of the primate upper limb: monomorphic or dimorphic? In M. Pickford and B. Chiarelli (eds): *Sexual Dimorphism in Living and Fossil Primates.* Il Sedicesimo, Firenze. pp. 7-22.

___. 1986b Distal humeral osseous anatomy and its implication for hominoid phylogeny. In V.V. Novotný and A. Mizerová (eds): *Fossil Man. New Facts, New Ideas. Papers in Honor of Jan Jelínek's Life Anniversary. Anthropos* (Brno) 23:3-14.

SEPT, J.M. 1992 Was there no place like home? A new perspective on early hominid archaeological sites from the mapping of chimpanzee nests. *Current Anthropology* 33(2):187-207.

SHIPMAN, P. 1986 Baffling limb on the family tree. *Discover* (September):87-93.

___. 1989 The gripping story of *Paranthropus. Discover* (April):66-71.

SILLEN, A. 1992 Strontium-calcium ratios (Sr/Ca) of *Australopithecus robustus* and associated fauna from Swartkrans. *Journal of Human Evolution* 23(6):495-516.

SILLEN, A. and SMITH, P. 1983 Strontium calcium ratios reveal weaning age in a skeletal population. *American Journal of Physical Anthropology* 60:253-254.

SKELTON, R.R., and H.M. McHENRY 1992 Evolutionary relationships among early hominids. *Journal of Human Evolution* 23(4):309-349.

STANLEY, S.M. 1992 An ecological theory for the origin of *Homo. Paleobiology* 18(3):237-257.

SUSMAN, R.L. 1988 The hand of *Paranthropus robustus* from Member 1, Swartkrans: fossil evidence for tool behavior. *Science* 240:781-794.

SUWA, G. 1988 Evolution of the "robust" australopithecines in the Omo succession: evidence from mandibular premolar morphology. In F.E. Grine (ed): *Evolutionary History of the "Robust" Australopithecines.* Aldine de Gruyter, New York.. pp. 199-222.

SUWA, G., B.A. WOOD, and T.D. WHITE 1994 Further analysis of mandibular molar crown and cusp areas in Pliocene and early Pleistocene hominids. *American Journal of Physical Anthropology* 93(4):407-426.

TOBIAS, P.V. 1965 Early man in East Africa. *Science* 149:22-33.

___. 1972 Dished faces, brain size, and early hominids. *Nature* 239:468-469.

___. 1988 Numerous apparently synapomorphic features in *Australopithecus robustus, Australopithecus boisei* and *Homo habilis*: support for the Skelton-McHenry-Drawhorn hypothesis. In F.E. Grine (ed): *Evolutionary History of the "Robust" Australopithecines.* Aldine de Gruyter, New York. pp. 293-308.

___. 1993 Earliest *Homo* not proven. Nature 361:307.

TOTH, N. 1987 The first technology. *Scientific American* 255(4):112-121.

TOTH, N., K.D. SCHICK, E.S. SAVAGE-RUMBAUGH, R.A. SEVCIK, and D.M. RUMBAUGH 1993 Pan the tool-maker: Investigations into the stone tool-making and tool-using capabilities of a Bonobo (*Pan paniscus*). *Journal of Archaeological Science* 20:81-91.

TURNER, A., and B.A. WOOD 1993 Comparative paleontological context for the evolution of the early hominid masticatory system. *Journal of Human Evolution* 24(4):301-318.

VRBA, E.S. 1988 Late Pliocene climatic events and hominid evolution. In F.E. Grine (ed): *Evolutionary History of the "Robust" Australopithecines.* Aldine de Gruyter, New York. pp. 405-426.

___. 1993 The pulse that produced us. *Natural History* 102(5):47-51.

WALKER, A.C. 1976 Remains Attributable to *Australopithecus* in the East Rudolf Succession. In Y. Coppens, F.C. Howell, G.Ll. Isaac, and R.E. Leakey (eds): *Earliest Man and Environments in the Lake Rudolf Basin.* University of Chicago Press, Chicago. pp. 484-489.

___. 1981 Diet and teeth: dietary hypotheses and human evolution. *Philosophical Transactions of the Royal Society, London,* Series B, 292:57-64.

___. 1984 Extinction in human evolution. In M. Niteki (ed): *Extinctions.* University of Chicago Press, Chicago. pp. 119-152.

WALKER, A.C., and R. E. F. LEAKEY 1988 The evolution of *Australopithecus boisei.* In F.E. Grine (ed): *Evolutionary History of the "Robust" Australopithecines.* Aldine de Gruyter, New York. pp. 247-258.

WHITE, T.D. 1978 Early hominid enamel hypoplasia. *American Journal of Physical Anthropology* 49:79-84.

___. 1988 The comparative biology of "robust" *Australopithecus*: clues from context. In F.E. Grine (ed): *Evolutionary History of the "Robust" Australopithecines.* Aldine de Gruyter, New York. pp. 449-483.

WILLIAMS, L.R. 1985 A critical reappraisal of the enigmatic "Zinjanthropus" (OH 5) profile. *Canadian Review of Physical Anthropology* 4:101-110.

WOLPOFF, M.H. 1971 Competitive exclusion among Lower Pleistocene hominids: the single species hypothesis. *Man* 6:601-614.

___. 1974 The evidence of two australopithecine lineages in South Africa. *Yearbook of Physical Anthropology* 17:113-139.

___. 1976 Multivariate discrimination, tooth measurements, and early hominid taxonomy. *Journal of Human Evolution* 5:339-344.

___. 1977 A reexamination of the ER 733 cranium. *Zeitschrift für Morphologie und Anthropologie* 68:8-13.

___. 1978 Some aspects of canine size in the australopithecines. *Journal of Human Evolution* 7:115-126.

___. 1980 Morphological dating of the Swartkrans australopithecines. In R.E. Leakey and B.A. Ogot (eds): *Proceedings of the 8th Panafrican Congress of Prehistory and Quaternary Studies.* The Louis Memorial Institute for African Prehistory, Nairobi. pp. 169-170.

___. 1988 Divergence between early hominid lineages: the roles of competition and culture. In F.E. Grine (ed): *Evolutionary History of the "Robust" Australopithecines.* Aldine de Gruyter, New York. pp. 485-497.

WOOD, B.A. 1988 Are "robust" australopithecines a monophyletic group? In F.E. Grine (ed): *Evolutionary History of the "Robust" Australopithecines.* Aldine de Gruyter, New York. pp. 269-284.

___. 1992 Old bones match old stones. *Nature* 355:678-679.

WOOD, B.A., and S.A. ABBOTT 1983 Analysis of the dental morphology of Plio-Pleistocene hominids. I. Mandibular molars: crown area measurements and morphological traits. *Journal of Anatomy* 136:197-219.

WOOD, B.A., S.A. ABBOTT, and S.A. GRAHAM 1983 Analysis of the dental morphology of Plio-Pleistocene hominids. II. Mandibular molars - study of cusp areas, fissure patterns, and cross sectional shape of the crown. *Journal of Anatomy* 137:287-314.

WOOD, B.A., and A.T. CHAMBERLAIN 1987 The nature and affinities of the "robust" australopithecines: a review. *Journal of Human Evolution* 16(7/8):625-641.

WOOD, B.A., and M. ELLIS 1986 Evidence for dietary specialization in the "robust" australopithecines. In V.V. Novotný and A. Mizerová (eds): *Fossil Man. New Facts, New Ideas. Papers in Honor of Jan Jelínek's Life Anniversary. Anthropos* (Brno) 23:101-124.

WOOD, B.A., and C.G. STACK 1980 Does allometry explain the differences between "gracile" and "robust" australopithecines? *American Journal of Physical Anthropology* 52:55-62.

WOOD, B.A., and H. UYTTERSCHAUT 1987 Analysis of the dental morphology of Plio-Pleistocene hominids III. Mandibular premolar crowns. *Journal of Anatomy* 16:625-641.

WOOD, J.W, G.R. MILNER, H.C. HARPENDING, and K.M. WEISS 1992 The osteological paradox: problems of inferring prehistoric health from skeletal samples. *Current Anthropology* 33(4):343-370.

WYNN, T., and W.C. McGREW 1991 An ape's view of the Oldowan. *Man* 24:383-398.

Figure 7.5
Plio-Pleistocene Australopithecine and early *Homo* Phylogeny
Modified* after Skelton and McHenry

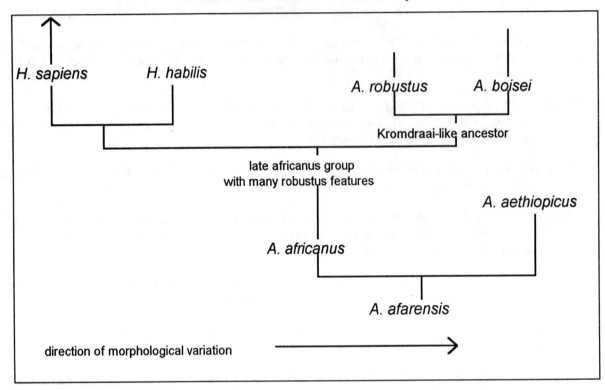

* The basic relations are similar those reflected in the Skelton and McHenry (1993) analysis, but as modified to reflect the temporal relations of the species shown in figure 7.1. This paper, and Grine (1993) have good discussions of alternative phylogenies.

FIGURE 7.2 The proximal end of an australopithecine ulna (ER 1500) and two of early *Homo sapiens*, courtesy of B. Senut, with descriptions of the measurements in table 7.2 and other tables using ulna dimensions.

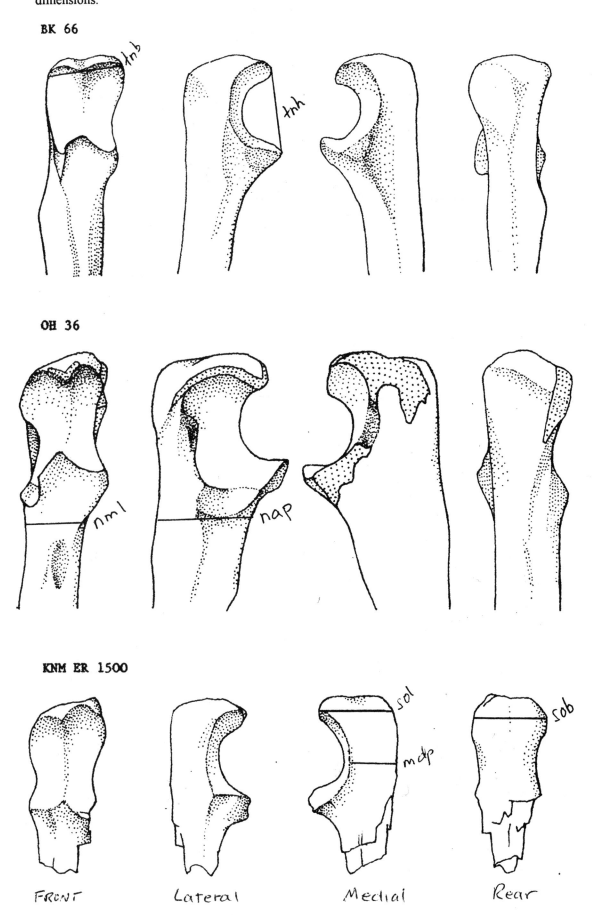

BK 66

OH 36

KNM ER 1500

FRONT   Lateral   Medial   Rear

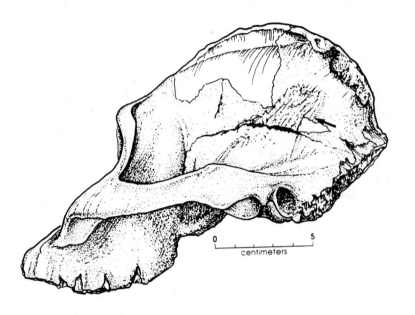

FIGURE 7.3 Lateral view of the WT 17000 vault, after Rak and Kimbel (1991).
FROM Rak, Y. and W.H. Kimbel 1991 On the squamosal suture of KNM-WT 17000. *American Journal of Physical Anthropology* 85(1):1-6.

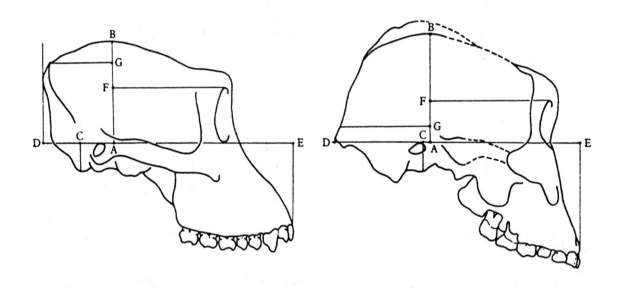

FIGURE 7.5 Female gorilla (left) and OH 5, comparing differences in proportion for the cranial height (FB/AB) and foramen magnum position (DC/DE), after Tobias (1967).
FROM Tobias, P.V. 1967 Olduvai Gorge, Vol. II. The Cranium and Maxillary Dentition of *Zinjanthropus* (*Australopithecus*) *boisei*. Cambridge University Press, London, figure 3.

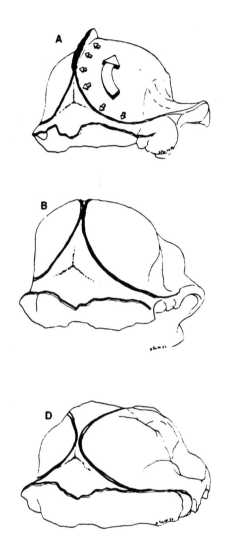

FIGURE 7.6 Posterior cresting patterns of *A. afarensis* (D), *A. africanus* (B) and *A. boisei* (A), after Rak (1983).
FROM Rak, Y. 1983 The Australopithecine Face. Academic Press, New York, figure 42.

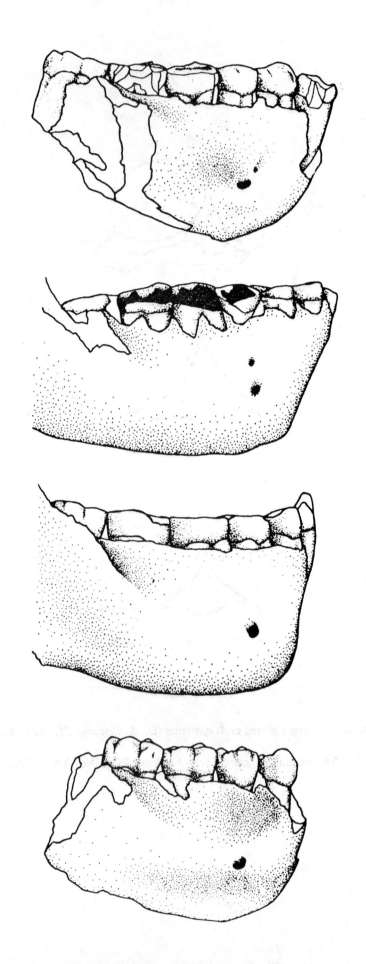

FIGURE 7.7 Comparison of australopithecine mandibles: LH 4 (above), STS 7, Natron, and ER 1802, after White and colleagues (1981). The *A. boisei* female from Natron has a mental protuberance that is a homoplasy with the mental eminence of recent humans.
FROM White, T.D., D.C. Johanson, and W.H. Kimbel 1981 *Australopithecus africanus*: its phyletic position reconsidered. South African Journal of Science 77:445-470, figure 12.

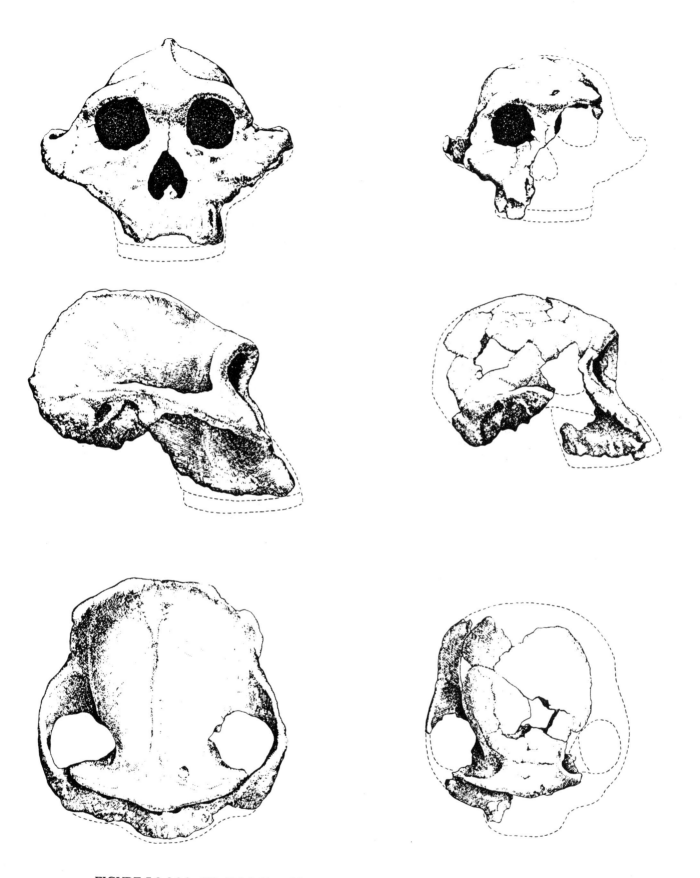

FIGURE 7.8 Male (ER 406, left) and female (ER 732) *A. boisei* specimens from the Koobi Fora region, after Walker and Leakey (1978).

FROM Walker, A.C., and R.E. Leakey 1978 The hominids of East Turkana. Scientific American 239(2):54-66.

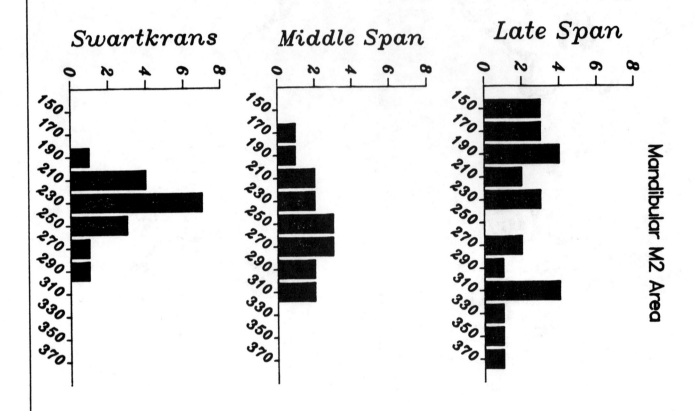

FIGURE 7.9 Evolution of molar size, showing the gradual distinction of the expanding *A. boisei* postcanine dentition. Prior to the later span, the *boisei* postcanine teeth overlapped with other australopithecines.

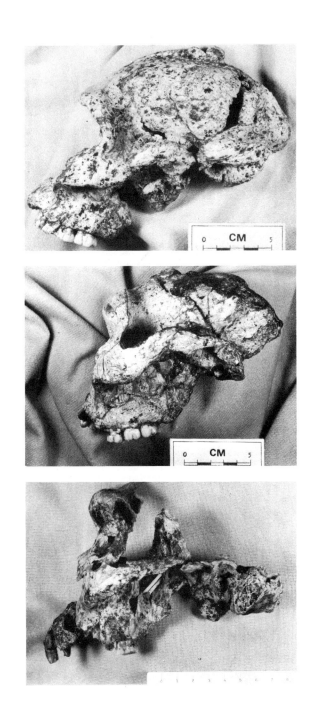

FIGURE 7.10 Swartkrans crania.

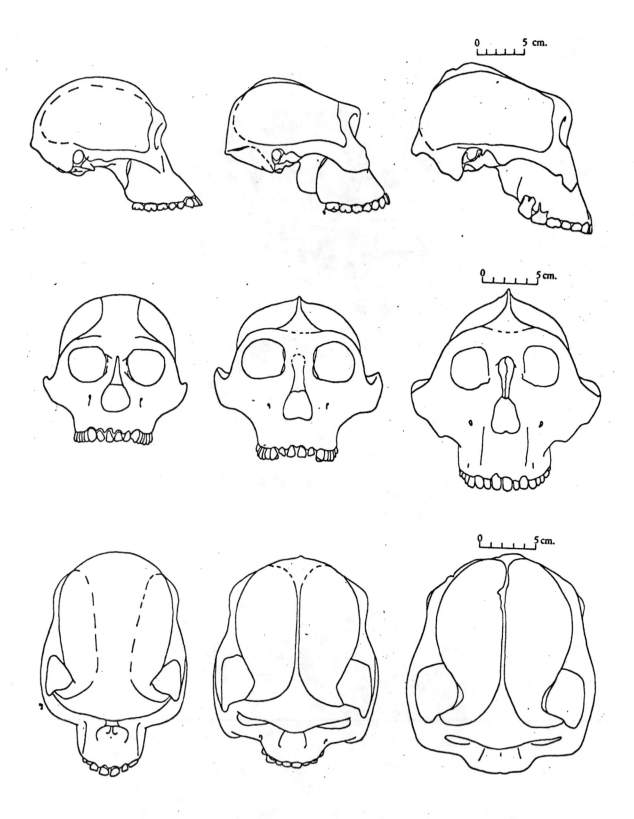

FIGURE 7.11 Allometric relation of three australopithecine species, represented by STS 5 (left, *A. africanus*), SK 48 (center, *A. robustus*), and OH 5 (right, *A. boisei*), after Tobias (1967). The cause of the allometry is in dietary difference as body sizes do not expand correspondingly. Allometry is not the full explanation of the differences between these species.

FROM Tobias, P.V. 1967 Olduvai Gorge, Vol. II. The Cranium and Maxillary Dentition of *Zinjanthropus* (*Australopithecus*) *boisei*. Cambridge University Press, London, figures 1,2, 21.

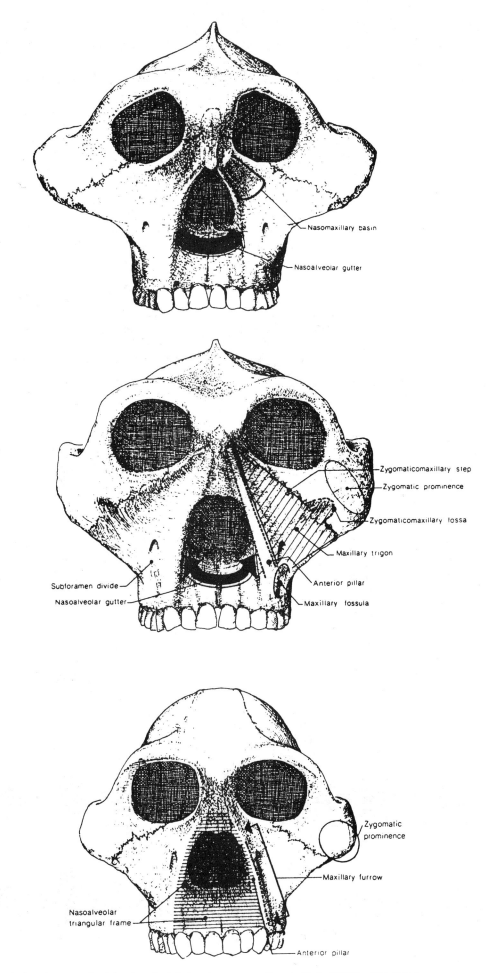

FIGURE 7.12 Systematic variation in australopithecine facial structure, according to Rak (1983). ER 406 is compared with SK 28 (middle) and an idealized *A. africanus*. Rak's terminology for midfacial structures is shown.

FIGURE 7.13 Comparison of palates of *A. afarensis* (AL 200-1, above), *A. africanus* (STS 17, middle), and *A. robustus* (SK 48, below).
FROM White, T.D., D.C. Johanson, and W.H. Kimbel 1981 *Australopithecus africanus*: its phyletic position reconsidered. South African Journal of Science 77:445-470, figure 9.

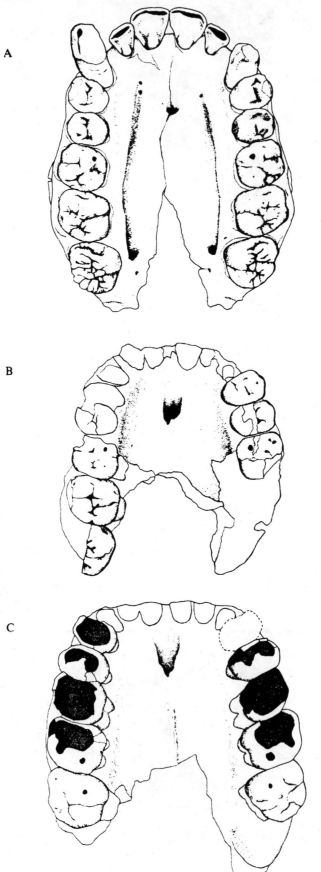

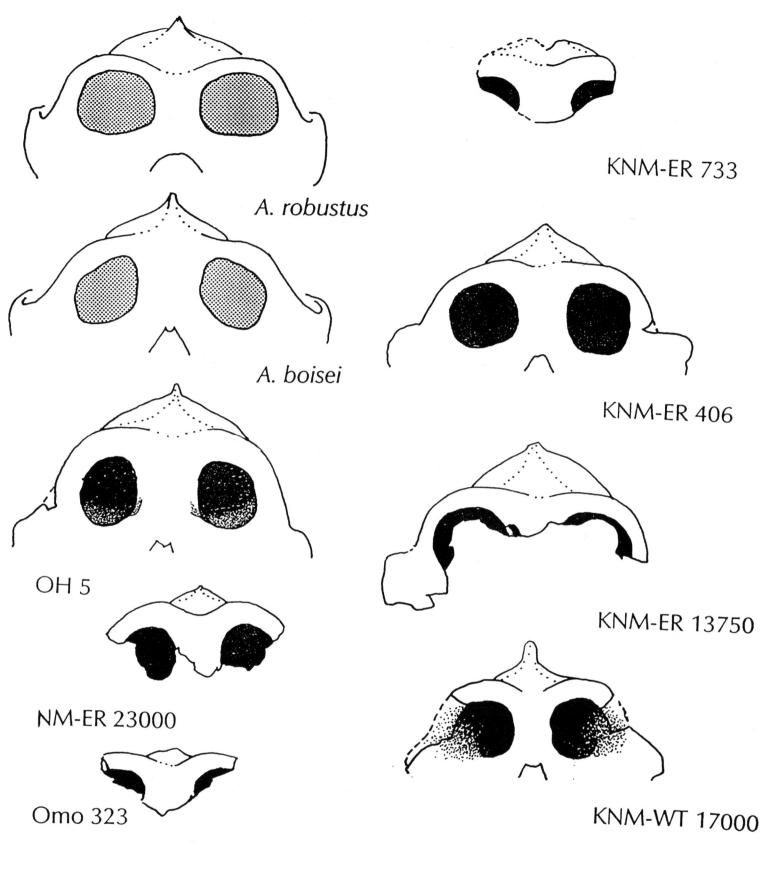

KNM-ER 733

A. robustus

A. boisei

KNM-ER 406

OH 5

KNM-ER 13750

NM-ER 23000

Omo 323

KNM-WT 17000

FIGURE 7.14 Facial views of robust australopitthecines, after Brown and colleagues (1993), showing variation in orbits and supraorbital anatiomy. All specimens are male except for the *A. robustus* face, based on the SK 48 female.

FROM Brown, B., A.C. Walker, C.V. Ward, and R.E. Leakey 1993 A new *Australopithecus boisei* cranium from east Turkana, Kenya. *American Journal of Physical Anthropology* 91(2):137-159, figure 11.

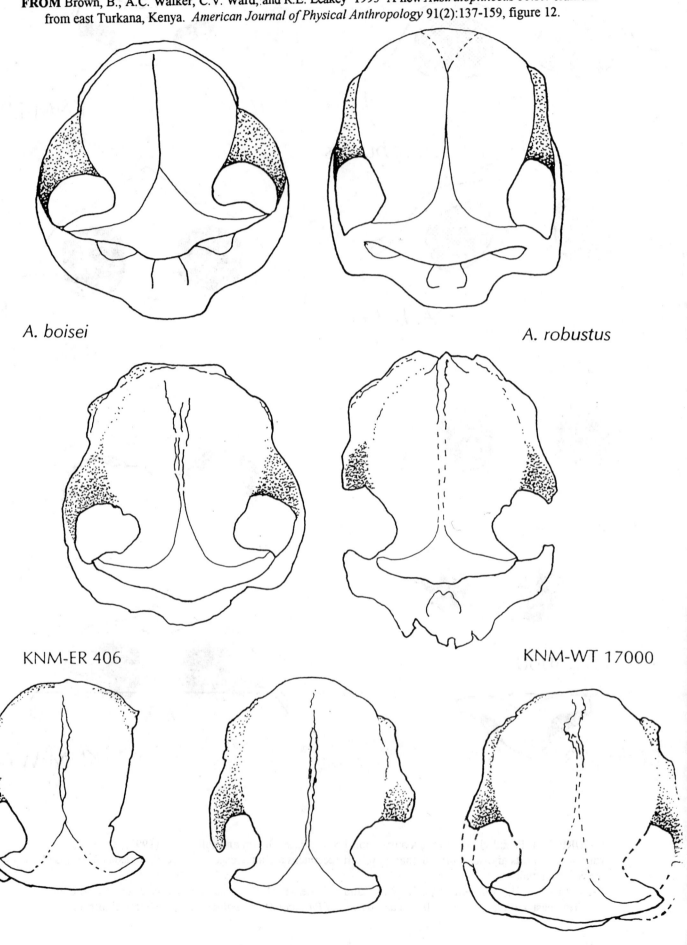

FIGURE 15 Superior views of rubust australopithecine crania, all male except for the SK 48 female *A. robustus*. After Brown and colleagues (1993).

FROM Brown, B., A.C. Walker, C.V. Ward, and R.E. Leakey 1993 A new *Australopithecus boisei* cranium from east Turkana, Kenya. *American Journal of Physical Anthropology* 91(2):137-159, figure 12.

A. boisei

A. robustus

KNM-ER 406

KNM-WT 17000

KNM-ER 13750

KNM-ER 23000

OH 5

CHAPTER EIGHT

Australopithecine-like <u>Homo</u>

In the large sample from the uppermost part of the Upper Burgi Member at Koobi Fora are the cranial remains of two, possibly three *Homo* species. This proliferation is not only the greatest number of *Homo* taxa found together, it is also the earliest known appearance of *Homo* crania. How much earlier the genus might have appeared is suggested by some isolated jaws and teeth, and a few postcranial remains that most likely are also *Homo*. They date to no older than 2.25 myr. These non-cranial skeletal elements cannot easily (if at all) be attributed at the species level, which means that on the available evidence we have no firm basis for positing which *Homo* species came first and is potentially ancestral to the others.

This chapter focuses on the appearance of *Homo*. The australopithecine-like varieties from East Africa (*Homo habilis* and possibly *Homo rudolfensis*) are discussed. Following this is a review of the more confusing anatomical evidence from South Africa, with some behavioral implications based on the ongoing analysis of the Swartkrans site.

Historic background

When the East African discoveries first began to accumulate in large numbers in the early 1960s, attempts were made to interpret them within the framework of J. Robinson's dietary hypothesis, developed to explain the South African australopithecine variations in an adaptive context. Louis and Mary Leakey's discovery of the first juvenile *H. habilis* specimen (OH 7) set the stage for the interpretation of what was then viewed as a smaller jawed, larger vaulted East African gracile australopithecine variety. The question was immediately raised of how this related to the gracile australopithecines of South Africa. It was generally appreciated that the South African specimens were earlier but it was unclear how much time difference was involved. The first East African crania were found soon after the discovery of Potassium/Argon, and the beginnings of numerical dating for these and other deposits and it took a long time for the results of the new chronological yardstick to be digested. Moreover, the South African australopithecine sites were poorly dated by any yardstick.

Most of the evolutionary models proposed were variants of the dietary hypothesis, the idea being that South African *Australopithecus robustus* evolved into East African *Australopithecus boisei* by continuing the trend for dental robustness, while *A. africanus* evolved into *H. habilis* by continuing the trend for encephalization (expansion of cranial capacity relative to body size). But there were also questions raised about whether *Australopithecus africanus* and *H. habilis* were really distinct, this was a phenetic issue then and its resolution seemed to depend on how much difference there was between the samples (as the East African specimens continued to accumulate). There was virtually no doubt about the immediate role that the specimens allocated to *H. habilis* somehow played in the origin of our lineage. This successive lineage was regarded as two sequential species, *Homo erectus* evolving into *H. sapiens*.

A. africanus played a pivotal role in this framework, as the last common ancestor of the two clades, widely (if inaccurately) termed the robust australopithecines and *H. habilis*. Its marked phenetic similarities to the later South African robusts (the source of the single species hypothesis) as well as to *H. habilis* in East Africa could be easily explained this way. Looking back from the much greater evolutionary complexity and taxonomic diversity we recognize at the end of the Pliocene today, it is difficult to recapture why there was so much controversy in those simpler times.

This model of taxonomic distinction for both East African forms was first proposed by L.S.B. Leakey and vigorously supported by P. Tobias, the South African anthropologist-anatomist who over the subsequent 30 years wrote the descriptive monographs on the Olduvai hominid remains. It was Tobias who created and doggedly championed *H. habilis* as an intermediate stage in human evolution. J. Robinson disagreed with the distinctions said to separate the two East African taxa from their South African counterparts, instead suggesting that the robust specimens represented "*Paranthropus*". He explained the sample which Tobias has described as *H. habilis* in the following way, the specimens from Olduvai Bed I were *A. africanus,* and from Olduvai Bed II were *H. erectus.* To clarify his phylogenetic interpretation, Robinson later proposed that *A. africanus* be renamed *Homo africanus* to emphasize its human-like adaptations and its phyletic position at the base of the *Homo* clade.

With a few prominent exceptions, most workers seemed to agree with Robinson's judgment. The exceptions were mainly

- those who from the onset had never supported the interpretation of an ecological (and phenetic) distinction between *Paranthropus* and *Australopithecus* in South Africa
- Tobias and a growing number of followers who regarded *H. habilis* as a separate, unique taxon showing more advanced features than the *A. africanus* sample from South Africa.

Questions about the validity of *H. habilis*, and the general difficulties in classifying a recognizably transitional form, provided the meat for what was the major anthropological debate concerning early hominids during the 1960s and early 1970s. In retrospect, what seems to have kept this debate going was the lack of really well preserved remains and the general disregard of the time difference between *H. habilis* in East Africa and *Australopithecus* to the south.

The next specimens to be discovered were the few better preserved remains found at Omo. These were placed in three taxa: *A. africanus, H. habilis,* and *Paranthropus.* The subsequent discoveries at nearby East Turkana were made by the Leakeys" son, Richard. The region proved to be prolific and generic sorting into *Australopithecus* and *Homo* was attempted for many of the specimens. As at Olduvai, the larger-brained *Homo* form was earlier. In fact, a misdating of an important marker-bed, the KBS tuff (the secondary volcanic ash deposit at Koobi Fora that overlays the earliest *Homo* specimens) made these hominids seem very early indeed. By the mid-1970s, it was clear that the various taxonomic names were being used differently by different workers and that there were at least three distinct views of how the samples were related phylogenetically:

1. The simplest view was the single species hypothesis: all the specimens represented geographic, temporal, or sex-based variants of a single variable lineage.
2. A second view argued for two distinct lineages; however, the composition of these varied depending on the worker concerned. The two lineages corresponded to the omnivore and vegetarian of the dietary hypothesis.
3. The third view proposed three (or more) distinct lineages. Again, their composition varied with the author concerned. Some saw *A. africanus-H. habilis* as one lineage, with *Paranthropus* and *Zinjanthropus* representing the other two. Others saw the gracile species as separate lineages and combined *Paranthropus* and *Zinjanthropus* in one

After the mid-1970s, three things happened that substantially altered the entire interpretive picture. First, some dating problems were resolved. There was accumulating evidence of a 1.88 myr date for the KBS tuff at Turkana. This eliminated the problems (and the need for their explanation) caused by what had appeared to be evidence of a 2.6 myr appearance of *Homo.* Better date estimates, based on a combination of faunal comparisons and paleomagnetism, were developed for at least some of the South African sites and in spite of the morphologists' battle cry ("the relationships anatomy shows are independent of samples or their dates"), this helped resolve a number of problems as well. Second, the clear association of early *H. sapiens* (then called *H. erectus*) crania with hyper-robust australopithecines by 1.5-1.6 myr was established at Lake Turkana. In a seminal paper, R. Leakey and A. Walker ended the single species hypothesis and raised the possibility of three contemporary clades at the beginning of the Pleistocene:

1. *Australopithecus (Zinjanthropus) boisei,*
2. *H. sapiens (erectus),*
3. a third gracile form variously regarded as *A. africanus* or *H. habilis.*

Third, the discovery and naming of *A. afarensis* created the possibility of a different, earlier, last common ancestor for the Pleistocene clades. This forced the need for decision about where to put *A. africanus*: on the *Homo* clade because of its resemblances to *H. habilis* or on the robust clade because of its resemblances to the South African robust australopithecines. Placing it on the robust clade was, perhaps, the final influence of the single species hypothesis as it recognized the importance of the similarities linking South African australopithecine species. This was the "new" part of the "new family tree" promoted by T, White and his colleagues. On the other hand, Tobias and a number of others (including myself, ironically the founder of the single species hypothesis) were unconvinced that *A. africanus* was displaced by this more primitive species as the *last* common ancestor for the East African groups. The very features that distinguished *A. africanus* from *A. afarensis*, made *A. africanus* more like *H. habilis* and other *Homo* species.

The 1980 were a decade of dedicated splitting, but this solved little and there was real phylogenetic confusion. V. Alexeev suggested that the earlier Plio/Pleistocene *H. habilis* specimens be placed in a distinct species, *Pithecanthropus rudolfensis,* and B. Wood used this division in a somewhat different way, to separate contemporary samples of *Homo*. This resulted in the recognition of three contemporary *Homo* species. as the reanalysis of circum-Turkana dates by C. Feibel and colleagues (figure 6.1) at the end of the decade clearly showed early *H. sapiens* as contemporary with the other two. All three species appear in the earliest large Koobi Fora sample, dated to the Terminal Pliocene.

Australopithecus-like Homo: a Tale of Two species?

By the terminal Pliocene, some 1.9 myr, at least two and possibly three species of *Homo* are present in the East African fossil record. One of these is our own, *H. sapiens*. Its anatomy and the adaptive changes it reflects will be detailed below. The other one or two are much more australopithecine-like. They are contemporary in the earliest large hominid sample from the eastern edge of Lake Turkana, from the top part of the upper Burgi Member, dated between 1.90 and 1.88 myr. An Omo Member G cranium from Submember G-28 falls within this span, and specimens just below (from G 14 and above) are quite close to it.

The precept of three different *Homo* species comes from two factors:

1. the unambiguous identification of specimens with distinct and unique early *H. sapiens* features in the terminal Pliocene sample
2. the perception that the other contemporary *Homo* species, *H. habilis,* contains too much variation to validly be a single species

First, some of the earliest remains from this span are clearly and definitively early *H. sapiens*. This taxon was once regarded as a separate one, *H. erectus* - an immediate and unique ancestor of *H. sapiens*. Some paleoanthropologists continue to use this species name for the specimens while others, in a flurry of what I consider excessive taxonomizing, use yet a different appellation to distinguish the earliest African humans from *Homo erectus* - *Homo ergaster*. *H. sapiens* and *H. ergaster* are the same, as far as the set of criteria for distinguishing them from other *Homo* species is concerned. Further, most paleoanthropologists seem to agree that by whatever name, these specimens are the direct ancestors of living humanity.

The second factor has to with the amount and pattern of variation in the species first named at Olduvai Gorge, *H. habilis*. While some scientists such as P. Tobias attempted to define *H. habilis* phylogenetically and phenetically (in terms of its genealogical position and morphology), others used it as a garbage bag to place East African hominids whose important characteristic was that they were not robust australopithecines. At first the gracile, larger brained specimens from Olduvai were placed in the species *H. habilis,* and the main focus of attention was over whether this species was sufficiently unlike *A. africanus* to be valid. Because of the very fragmentary nature of these early discoveries, and the then unresolved problem of the South African dates, there was continuous argument as to whether the East African specimens were anything more than a variant of *A. africanus*. J. Robinson was a particularly vocal supporter of this, lumping what he considered to be similar variations of early humans into a single taxon with geographic variation. To emphasize this point but at the same time recognize the transitional nature of the sample and its direct ancestry of *H. erectus*, he proposed renaming the combined species *H. africanus*. While the basic similarities that Robinson saw still exist, the arguments about *H. habilis* are somewhat different today because

- There is a larger sample and more variation, but also a better idea of average differences
- *A. africanus* is recognized to be much earlier in time than these East African remains
- Classic *H. habilis* from Olduvai (see below) is later than the first East African appearance of *Homo*

THE OLDUVAI REMAINS

With a much larger and more complete sample now available, coupled with the appreciation that the South African australopithecines were earlier in time by a half to a full million years, the argument that these late australopithecine-like hominids should be distinguished from them is enhanced. The fact that between the South African *A. africanus* remains and the Olduvai specimens there is a branching, of one or more robust australopithecine lineages, *requires* different species identifications. *H. habilis,* as classically defined at Olduvai Gorge, consists of both male (OH 7, 16) and female (OH 24, 13) specimens from Beds I and II. spanning a period of 150 kyr or slightly greater (table 8.3). The hominids are found in an earlier and later time period within this span. According to R. Walter and colleagues, these are wet, densely vegetated times with high lake levels, separated by a 10,000 year period of hotter, drier climate with lowered lake levels and more alkaline water. The *H. habilis* remains, in other words, are all associated with humid climatic conditions and high lake level at Olduvai. The morphology of these specimens has been reviewed numerous times by P. Tobias, most recently in his definitive monograph. Not only is this the first sample of *H. habilis* to be identified, but some researchers such as C. Groves and A. Chamberlain believe it is the only sample that should be placed in the species. For others, as we will discuss, the situation is somewhat more confused.

OH 7, a 12-13 year old boy, was the first *H. habilis* discovered. The specimen consists of two partially complete parietals, associated cranial fragments, mandible, much of a hand, and most of the foot (with the toes gnawed off). The parietals only partially preserve equivalent areas, and cannot actually be joined with a bone-to-bone contact anywhere. This has created numerous uncertainties in reconstructing his cranial capacity, arguably his most important characteristic, which would be problematic enough even if the parietals had been complete. I have reconstructed his cranial capacity at some 590 cc. In his Olduvai monograph Tobias claims a capacity of 647 cc, and other estimates have been above 700 cc. A large capacity is one of the three things that Tobias used to set *H. habilis* apart, as a transitional hominid species between *A. africanus* and early *H. sapiens* (then called *H. erectus*).

1. expanded cranial capacity
2. reduced postcanine tooth size
3. the precision grip, providing the anatomical basis for tool making ("*H. habilis*" after all means "handy man").

Tobias set out the details of his transitional species interpretation in a seminal paper written with the eminent paleontologist G. von Koenigswald. He has continued to develop the particulars of this argument over the subsequent decades, culminating in his extraordinary 2-volume monograph on the *Homo habilis* remains from Olduvai. From the beginning Tobias and von Koenigswald noted the many similarities of the OH 7 dentition and the dental remains of a large-jawed Indonesian hominid then called "*Meganthropus palaeojavicus*". J. Robinson had considered these "*Meganthropus*" remains (all jaws then) as Asian australopithecines, even renaming them "*Paranthropus palaeojavicus*", but von Koenigswald and others rejected this claim. Tobias and von Koenigswald convincingly demonstrated that the hominids could be arranged in series of grades, beginning with *A. africanus*, and through *H.*

habilis and "*Meganthropus*" evolving into (what they called) *H. erectus*. Subsequent work by A. Kramer has convincingly shown that all the Indonesian specimens can be subsumed in one species, *H. sapiens*.

There is some average postcanine tooth size reduction in OH 7 and the other Olduvai *H. habilis* remains compared with *A. africanus,* and more so compared with the more megadont australopithecine ancestors I have posited for *Homo* (table 8.4). Differences are especially apparent in

- P_3: a smaller and more asymmetric tooth
- P_4: much more similar to the P_3
- generally more narrow postcanine teeth.

A few specimens allow tooth size and body size, and their all-important relationship, to be observed (table 8.1). These show the two Olduvai specimens to be quite similar to the robust australopithecine female TM 1517. Clearly there is a considerable overlap of ranges for the relative size of the grinding part of the dentition. The Olduvai *H. habilis* remains are, on the average, the smallest of the earliest hominid species and although the differences among them are not great (excepting, of course, for the very large *A. aethiopicus* specimens), they need be taken into account when considering the magnitude of postcanine tooth size variation.

Associated with this 12-13 year old male child are the remains of a foot. It seemed to be older than the cranial pieces because of some arthritis, but according to R. Susman and colleagues this resulted from an earlier traumatic injury and not advanced age. These scientists show that the foot suffered carnivore gnawing and the ends were eaten off of some of its **metatarsals**; yet, others seem to be unfused which would suggest an age equivalent to the other parts of the OH 7 specimen. It shows a full adaptation to obligate bipedalism, including

- digital shortening,
- enlargement of the first digit and orientation with the others,
- a full double arch to the lower surface,
- efficient weight transmission at the ankle

There is a complete loss of any grasping ability, an important point in view of interpretations that have been placed on the OH 62 postcranial skeleton (discussed below). The talus provides a weight estimate of 31.7 kg, according to McHenry. This gives a brain/body weight ratio of 1.86%. The would be even somewhat bigger if a larger capacity estimate were accepted for the isolated parietals, but even still it is the largest for any early hominid male discussed thus far (table 8.1). This relative brain size is virtually the same as the Kromdraai female relative brain size (1.89%), both of course, estimates. Females, as noted in Chapter 7, have larger relative brain sizes than males, all other things being equal, so this comparison does not contradict the contention that on the average, *H. habilis* has larger relative brain size than *A. robustus* (table 7.4). Like the postcanine reduction, there is an average difference in brain size but considerable individual overlap. Compared with the expectations of primate allometry, if we consider the relationship a cluster rather than a thin line (that virtually every specimen *must* deviate from) OH 7 brain size is at the top or the range of allometric expectations (figure 8.1).

The OH 7 hand suggests a powerful but extremely small individual. The interpretation of the hand was thwarted for many years because of the mix-up of adult bones from a large colobine monkey with the hominid remains, leading to interpretations of tree-climbing in the early hominids that predated discovery of the Hadar remains, and set the stage for their interpretation. Now it is recognized that the OH 7 hand (if not those from Hadar) shows no special adaptations to grasping tree branches. It has the flattened finger tips that come with the range of human grips that seems to evolve with stone tool use, and articular surface modifications that suggest a very strong thumb, similar to those of very powerful archaic humans from the Late Pleistocene according to E. Trinkaus. These are important structural elements that are attributions of hands that can develop strong grasps in spite of short digits. When J. Napier first defined the precision grip, which he argued was unique only to specimens in the genus *Homo*, he used the anatomy of the OH 7 hand as an example of this grip and believed it marked its earliest appearance. It seems clear that as in the case of the Swartkrans hand remains that might be attributed to *Homo* (see below), the anatomy of OH 7 reflects the consequences of tool making and tool use.

Table 8.1
Estimated Brain and Tooth Size Ratios for Individual Specimens

Specimen	Taxon and sex	Weight estimate (kg)	Cranial capacity (cc)	Postcanine tooth size: P3-M2 area (mm^2)	Relative brain size (percent)	Relative postcanine tooth size (percent)
AL 288-1	*A. afarensis* female	27.3	380	439	1.43	1.61
Omo 323 (2.25 myr)	*A. boisei* male	49.5	490	(875)	1.00	1.77
OH 5 (1.77 myr)	*A. boisei* male	32.1	530	1032	1.65	3.21
TM 1517	*A. robustus* female	34.4	650	642	1.89	1.87
OH 7	*H. habilis* male	31.7	590	594	1.86	1.87
OH 13	*H. habilis* female	27.0	501	470	1.86	1.74

[1]   This is a minimum figure as the advanced age of STS 7 has resulted insignificantly shorter tooth lengths, reducing the grinding area.

Soon after OH 7 was found, two specimens from Bed II were discovered (table 8.3). These extended the anatomical and temporal range of the species. A 15-16 year old male cranium, OH 16, was complete when it was first seen but inadvertently crushed and fragmented by a herd of cattle before it could be excavated. It comes from the lowest part of Bed II and has thin cranial bone, moderately projecting but thin supraorbitals, and a cranial capacity slightly larger than OH 7. OH 16 has serious caries on one side of its jaw, and preferred to chew on the other side. The temporalis muscle on the side opposite the favored one puts its force through the side that is used (Chapter 4). The opposite side muscle is much larger; as I have reconstructed the specimen its temporal line extends all the way up to the sagittal suture, while the other temporal line is lower on the cranial vault, reflecting a more weakly developed muscle. The most interesting aspect of this young man is that his anatomy is quite different from ER 1470, a larger vaulted Lake Turkana male(discussed below) often regarded as the male corresponding to females such as OH 13 and ER 1813. There has been much concern about how both males can be accommodated in the same species (perhaps more concern than the differences really warrant).

The other specimen, the very fragmentary OH 13, is a 15-16 year old female combining a small vault (I estimate the capacity as just over 500 cc) with an even smaller body size, as determined from the small piece of proximal ulna reported in table 7.2. The ulna is similar in size to Lucy's, and the same body weight gives OH 13 a relative brain size the same as that of OH 7 (table 8.1). Coming from the middle part of Bed II, OH 13 is younger than 1.66 myr and thereby the most recent *H. habilis* known. These two specimens were allocated to *H. erectus* (now early *H. sapiens*) by Robinson, a determination that would have more merit if the cranial capacities had been as large as first thought (as an unusual illustration of uncertainty, one reconstruction of the OH 13 endocast is actually larger than another reconstruction of the entire skull, including reconstructed browridges). The cranial bone is markedly thinner than early *H. sapiens*, and there are dramatic differences in the tori at the front (supraorbital torus) and rear (nuchal torus) of the cranial vault. As L.S.B. Leakey noted soon after their discovery, OH 16 and 13 are quite distinct from *H. erectus* as found at Olduvai, and elsewhere.

The most australopithecine-like *H. habilis* cranium is "Twiggy", the badly damaged female that is the earliest vault from Bed I. OH 24 has a delicate face with a relatively large, anteriorly positioned cheek. Anterior pillars bound the sides of the narrow nasal opening, and the nasal bones are flat and lack any projection in front of the face. This is the australopithecine condition and contrasts with the anatomy of the region in early *H. sapiens* and some *H. habilis* specimens as described by Y. Rak. According to R. Franciscus and E. Trinkaus, Koobi Fora *H. habilis* specimens such as ER 1813 have the following features that OH 24 lacks:

- a salient anterior nasal spine (this spine is topped by a trough that holds the cartilage sheet at the center of the projecting nose - its presence shows that the nose projected significantly in front of the face).
- broad nasal bones
- nasal bone "peaking" formed by an angle between the nasal bones (**internasal angle**)
- projection of the middle and top of the nose away from the face, shown by expanded and outward projecting maxillary bones (the part of the maxilla between the nose and the orbit) to its sides (**maxillary pillar eversion**)

The low OH 24 forehead is depressed, even concave, just behind the thin supraorbitals. South African faces such as Makapansgat (MLD) 6 match this specimen quite well and although it is the most complete of the Olduvai *H. habilis* crania, there are those who would follow Robinson in emphasizing the resemblances to australopithecines. However, certain features are quite unlike the South African remains. For instance, the cranial base is short and broad, and the foramen magnum anteriorly positioned. The cheeks are less convex and bulging and more vertically oriented that the South African specimens, and their lower border has a distinct **maxillary notch**, that contrasts with the maxillary shelving - the straight line along the bottom of the cheek between the masseter attachment and the tooth row - described for all of the South African australopithecines in Chapters 6 and 7. Brain size seems quite large, although the vault is so distorted that Holloway's 590 cc determination is considered by several paleoanthropologists (including this one) to be an overestimate (see D. Lieberman and colleagues). Many of the features resemble the more complete Koobi Fora *H. habilis* specimens described below, but greatly extend the range of variation of specimens attributed to the taxon and blur the phenetic distinction between it and *A. africanus*. At least one scheme dividing the *H. habilis* remains into two *Homo* species places OH 24 and ER 1813 in different ones.

OH 62, so-called "Lucy's Daughter", is a much less complete specimen than her many times removed great grandmother, but none-the-less presents the first association of many skeletal elements with fragmentary cranial and dental remains attributable to *H. habilis*. Although the diagnostic portions of the face and cranium are incomplete and fragmentary, details resemble specimens such as OH 24. Like some other *H. habilis* specimens the maxillary borders of the nose are slightly everted along the maxillary pillars, suggesting some upper nasal projection - an important aspect of differing adaptation in *Homo* that is discussed in Chapter 9. Much of what had been surmised from the OH 7 postcrania was confirmed, and a wealth of new information was developed. All of the limbs are fragmentary and it is possible that their lengths of none can be reconstructed. Never the less, there has been quite some debate over her limb proportions.

OH 62 was widely publicized by D. Johanson, and colleagues allowed to examine the specimen, as having long arms - even relatively longer than Lucy's. The evidence for this is actually rather contradictory. Comparing OH 62 and AL 288, they are very similar in overall size but when limb elements can be compared, they do not always match. The partial ulnas are closest in size, while the OH 62 humerus is smaller. The femora have different bone shapes at the upper ends, where they can be compared (table 8.2). The shaft of the fragmentary Olduvai femur is less flattened than Lucy's - its front-to-back dimension (anteroposterior length) is greater but the side-to-side dimension (transverse breadth) is less. Realistically, length estimates from small proximal (upper) shaft fragments with different shapes are bound to be inaccurate and given the different forearm element sizes the safest conclusion is that the OH 62 proportions cannot be distinguished from AL 288. What is most puzzling is why this claim was made to begin with. The estimated femur length obtained by taking the midpoint of the range of estimates suggested by Johanson and Shreeve, 31.5 cm (table 8.2), gives an OH 62 humeral/femoral index identical to Lucy's - 83.8%.

The differences in femur shaft shape reflect differences in behavior. The OH 62 shaft is distinctly rounder. The markings for the attachment of the gluteus maximus (the major hip extensor, important in running and climbing, see Chapter 4) are weaker as well. These two facts might be related, as more powerful muscle use is thought to result in transverse expansion of the femur shaft. The OH 62 condition could reflect a species difference, of course, but the much older individual age of the specimen raises the possibility that normal consequences of aging may have come into play as well as what appears to be a life history of less activity. An analysis of OH 62's arm strength relative to her leg strength by C.O. Lovejoy and colleagues shows this strength ratio to be similar to living people, and therefore diminished as well. This suggests that her arms were not used in unusual activities requiring great strength, such as climbing - the widely accepted but anatomically unlikely activity often posited to explain the arm/leg proportions of the early hominids. In fact if OH 62 engaged in significant climbing the strength ratio for her upper arm would have to be unusually high, rather than low, even compared with brachiating apes. This because her bipedal-adapted feet could not be used to grasp, and the need for strong arms would be even greater. The analysis of arm and leg strength do not support the idea that OH 62 was a climber.

Table 8.2
Femur dimensions for some of the Smallest Hominid Females Known

	Just below the **lesser trochanter** (**platymeric** dimensions)			Mid-Shaft Circumference	Estimated Length[1]
	A-P diameter[2] (mm)	M-L diameter[3] (mm)	Approximate cross-sectional area (mm²)	(mm)	(cm)
ER 16002 A. afarensis	16	22	352	55	21.0
OH 62 H. habilis	21	21	441	62	31.5
STS 14 A. africanus	19	24	456		28.5
AL 288-1 A. afarensis	18	27	486	71	28.0
ER 1500 A. boisei	22	27	594		31.0

[1] From McHenry, or using his formulae, and with the exception of ER 16002 *not* based on the dimension in this table.
[2] Anterior-posterior
[3] Medial-lateral

What is also interesting is the sex usually attributed to the specimen. The very small size (McHenry estimates a 24 kg weight based on the femur shaft size) has always suggested female, but the OH 62 canine is quite large, and the postcanine teeth are bigger than those of the OH 13 female, raising the possibility that it might be a very small male. There are, after all, specimens such as ER 16002 that are considerably smaller (table 8.2). In fact, all of the front teeth were probably large, a point suggested by the great breadth between the incisor sockets (table 9.3). The front of the palate is much like STS 71, flattened across the snout with prominent anterior pillars bordering a slightly convex subnasal area. The palate itself is relatively short and broad, the length corresponding to the shortened teeth that come with OH 62's advanced age (late 20's), but the breadth is important as well. It coincides with the marked nasal breadth of the specimen, which is greater than that of any australopithecine, even broader than the other *H. habilis* specimens, and fully within the early *H. sapiens* range. However, as mentioned above many of the other facial details resemble OH 24 and some such as the recess of the lower nasal margin slightly behind the outer borders of the nose resemble South African australopithecines. OH 62 brings yet a different mix of features to *H. habilis*.

In fact, what might be most important in the comparison of these two is their minuscule size, and even then neither is by far the smallest of the known hominid postcrania (table 8.2). The midget sizes of the early hominids characterized at least one species of our genus as well. Size is clearly an important part of early hominid adaptation.

Table 8.3
Temporal Relations[1] of Olduvai *Homo habilis* with the
Earliest *Homo* Crania from Turkana

Age	Olduvai Tuff	Olduvai Specimens (OH)	Turkana Specimens (ER)
			⇧
1.66	IIA		**1466**[2]
1.67		16	
1.68		⇩	
1.69			
1.70			**730, 1808, 1821**
1.71			
1.72			
1.73			
1.74			
1.75	IF		
1.76	IC and ID		
1.77		⇧	
1.78		7, 62	**3733**
1.79		⇩	
1.80	IB		
1.81		24	
1.82		⇩	
1.83			
1.84			
1.85			1590, 1805
1.86			
1.87			
1.88			⇧
1.89			1470, 1813, 3732 **2598**, 3735
1.90			⇩

[1]   From Feibel *et al* and Walter *et al*
[2]   Specimens in boldface are early *H. sapiens* and are discussed in Chapter 8.

Some *H. habilis* specimens and even more *H. habilis* features are quite similar to *A. africanus*. When the remains were first reported, authors such as T. Bielicki pointed to the consequences of these facts and argued that their differences were not unexpected in an evolving hominid species in which members at one extreme will resemble the ancestral form while at the other they will resemble the descendent. J.

Robinson, as discussed above, viewed the problem in a similar manner, arguing that what Tobias called *H. habilis* was actually a mixture of earlier *A. africanus* and later *H. erectus* remains. Yet, subsequent discoveries in all of the samples have established that as a group, the Olduvai *H. habilis* remains contrast with *A. africanus* in their combination of reduced postcanine dentitions and expanded brain sizes. While earlier estimates of the differences were overly optimistic, the *combination of* changing brain and postcanine tooth size still distinguishes them from the earlier australopithecine species. This difference is particularly important in view of the other australopithecine-like characteristics of the *H. habilis* remains, such as their midget body size and relatively short legs. **Multivariate regression** predictions for the brain sizes of these incomplete specimens still shows them to have absolutely and relatively larger brain sizes than this *A. africanus*. However, the comparison with *A. robustus* is somewhat different. OH 7 relative brain size does not differ (or may not differ much) from the Kromdraai female estimate. A similar estimate may be obtained for the diminutive *H. habilis* female OH 13. Her fragmentary proximal ulna is very similar to Lucy's in size (table 7.2). If we assumed the same body weight, once again the same relative brain weight of 1.86% is obtained. At best, middle-sex brain size is only some 3% larger than the *A. robustus* middle-sex average. Thus, the Olduvai *H. habilis* brain sizes may be larger than some of their robust australopithecine predecessors, but they are not extraordinarily so. Those who find this conclusion unexpected, and who are fortunate to be able to access casts of the OH 7 parietals and SK 46 cranial vault, will be surprised when placing the former next to (or over) the later.

The postcanine dentitions are not only smaller, especially taking sex into account in the comparisons, but also relatively narrower. None of the specimens show the P_4 expansion and molarization seen in many of the Swartkrans hominids. Unworn cusps on the molars lack the bulbous expansion of the australopithecines and are more sharply edged. Some of the P_3's, for instance OH 7, have stronger buccal cusp dominance than is usual in *A. africanus*, although none are sectorial like many *A. afarensis* remains and no cases of canine/premolar cutting are known. Canines and incisors resemble the *A. robustus* condition in their absolute size, many elements of anatomy, and their diminution relative to the postcanine teeth (for instance, canine is so reduced in size that the ratio of canine to premolar dimensions in OH 13 is like that which Robinson attributed to the robust australopithecines).

THE KOOBI FORA REMAINS

But just as Olduvai *H. habilis* was widely perceived as being a valid species, even if more australopithecine- like than once thought, its interpretation was confused by the recognition of a potentially more complex situation stemming from the discovery of relatively complete remains in the Koobi Fora deposits that are earlier than the Olduvai occurrences (see table 8.3). While Tobias immediately accepted the large-brained specimens such as ER 1470 as examples of the species he named, *H. habilis*, A. Walker likened its anatomical features and masticatory adaptations to *Australopithecus*. Later, With R. Leakey he suggested that two different hominid varieties were represented in the Koobi Fora sample that Tobias regarded as *H. habilis*. This ultimately undermined the interpretation of *H. habilis* as a transitional species, because at Koobi Fora it is contemporary with specimens that some paleoanthropologists regard as a similar species that may be another candidate for the position. To refer to these two, whether they are different species, sexes, populations, or just normally varying samples, I will use the term "**habiline**". Like "australopithecine" or "ape" it is a non-taxonomic (N_2) term whose use is meant to avoid unneeded taxonomic controversy.

The oldest cranial *sample* at Koobi Fora is from below the KBS tuff, in the upper Burgi Member (figure 6.1). In this sample are crania ER 1470, 1813, 3732, and cranial fragments with an associated postcranial skeleton ER 3735. Each (and in some cases all) of these have been attributed by at least one paleoanthropologist to *H. habilis*. Another similar specimen from this narrow time range of 1.90-1.88 myr is Omo L894-1. Slightly later, but still preceding the Olduvai remains, is ER 1590 and the enigmatic specimen ER 1805 which has been likened to virtually every East African hominoid including *H. erectus, A. robustus,* and *Gorilla*! It may, or may not, be significant that all of these Koobi Fora remains attributed to *H. habilis* are earlier than the Olduvai occurrences. It is helpful that they are numerous, complete, and for the main part undistorted.

ER 1470 is a very large cranium (752 cc according to Holloway), painstakingly pieced together from hundreds of fragments by A. Walker. Other similar specimens are the 8 year old ER 1590 (with a capacity of over 700 cc) and the somewhat smaller, perhaps female ER 3732 (I estimate the capacity of this large fragment of vault and upper face at 545 cc). ER 1470 combines a very large face with an expanded cranial vault. The outer surface of the bone was weathered away before the specimen was fossilized, and most muscle attachments and cranial thickness cannot be accurately established, but the size of the head and the large root socket for the canine (no teeth remain) indicate male sex. The frontal lobes of the brain are expanded, and Holloway regards them as showing evidence of reorganization. He also believes that some of the speech areas can be discerned on the endocast, and the left occipital and right frontal petalias are very well developed. Other marked distinctions from the australopithecines include a broad, short cranial base with an anterior position for the foramen magnum and an expanded occiput behind it - both the nuchal muscle attachment and the occipital plane above it are large. The frontal lobes of the brain are wide, and the breadth of the frontal just behind the orbits is expanded outwards, a condition never found in the australopithecines.

However, as A. Walker has long emphasized (and his reconstruction clearly shows) the shape of the braincase and the large flat face are very similar to late Pliocene australopithecines; in fact, in some of B. Wood's cladistic analyses the most probable solutions group the specimen with *A. boisei*. These resemblances are based on features such as the neck muscles and the torus above them which are not well developed, the forehead is low and slopes evenly onto the back of the thin supraorbitals that do not overhang the orbits, and the cranial bone appears to be thin. The face is the most australopithecine-like aspect, with its small orbits and narrow upper facial region. The midface contrasts with the upper part in that it is massive and broad with tall and widely flared cheeks - they must be flared to enclose a large temporal muscle that is itself displaced laterally by the broad frontal lobes. The cheeks are positioned so anteriorly that they enclose the sides of the nose. Correctly reconstructed, (some of the earlier photographs incorrectly positioned the face in the vault) the face is dramatically prognathic, and as a whole the cranial and facial shape and proportions are quite similar to the much smaller STS 5. Yet, all of the face is not so australopithecine-like. The upper part of the nasal region is least like australopithecines of all the faces attributed to *H. habilis,* according to Y. Rak, R. Franciscus and E. Trinkaus. Franciscus and Trinkaus attribute to it nasal bone projection in front of the flattened cheeks and a slight internasal angle between the nasal bones (a peak extending along the **internasal suture**).

To try and resolve these conflicting interpretations, F. Thackery undertook a metric analysis in which he plotted a series of cranial and facial measurements for pairs of specimens against each other, comparing two specimens at a time. He found that specimens in the same australopithecine species generally resulted in a distribution of plotted points (each representing a measurement, taken on both specimens) that approximated a straight line. This suggested that they were, by in large, proportional to each other. Using OH 5 as a standard for comparison, ER 1470 was found to be proportional to it, the pairs of measurements distributing in a straight line. In contrast, ER 1813 and OH 24 were not found to be proportional to OH 5. Thackery focuses on the likelihood of common genes as an explanation for this similarity, which surely implies a recent common ancestor.

ER 3732, although somewhat smaller and less complete, confirms many of these details and ER 1590 shows that other specimens have an even larger cranial capacity, in spite of its 8 year old age (the pattern of the erupting and incompletely developed teeth best match a human child of that age, according to A Mann and colleagues). It also suggests that the large tooth roots remaining on the ER 1470 palate validly imply that there had been large teeth, since the ER 1590 tooth sizes are substantially bigger than the Olduvai habilines - even 17% larger in postcanine area than the OH 16 male. Among the Olduvai habilines, OH 24 is perhaps most similar to these specimens in shape, although unlike at least 2 of the 3 it is clearly a female. Sex determination for ER 3732 is uncertain, but in size and preserved details of the forehead and zygomatic it is very similar to OH 24, and like it the Turkana specimen is most probably female.

An overlapping but different combination of features is found in ER 1813 (and L 894-1 which is very similar to it). A generally much smaller brain case is associated with a cranial base and frontofacial region that is so similar to early *H. sapiens* that authors such as T. White include ER 1813 in the same taxon (for him this is *H. erectus*). ER 1813 is widely, and I believe correctly, regarded as a female, whichever taxon is correct. She died at about 15, with her third molar just coming into occlusion; in fact, a surprising number of individuals died at just this age, it may be a period of unusual physiological or perhaps social trauma. Her cranial sutures are knit together on both the inside and outside. This is surprising for an individual so young (it is a middle age condition in living humans), and suggests that brain growth - the main reason why human sutures are unfused for so long, ceased much earlier in these hominids than it does today.

According to M. Dean and B. Wood the cranial base is very similar to ER 1470, short and broad with a strong petrous angle and a very forward foramen magnum. The occiput is expanded and the nuchal plane lengthened. Together these put the mandibular fossa and ear opening closer to the center of the skull (as seen from the side) than ever occurs in the australopithecines. The frontofacial region is quite different from 1470. The dentitions of this specimen and others similar to it such as L 894-1 are dramatically smaller, indistinguishable from many early *H. sapiens*. These two are probably females, and have similar cranial capacities of about 500 cc (like the Olduvai habiline female OH 13). The vaults are thin and generally weakly muscled, although one of their early *H. sapiens*-like features on the cranial base is the development of the mastoid process and the broad groove that sets it off from the cranial base, the **digastric sulcus**. The supraorbitals are moderate, or even small, but are set in front of the forehead. To do so, the front of the forehead (frontal squama) and the top of the supraorbitals form the sides of a broad sulcus which is also characteristic of early *H. sapiens*. The temporal fossa is small and the breadth from one of its inner walls to the other (the **postorbital constriction**) is relatively expanded. These faces are small and delicate, and more vertically oriented (**orthognathic**) than the other *H. habilis* specimens. Cheeks, in particular, are smaller, posterior in position, and more vertically oriented than australopithecines (or the habilines described above). Their lower border is horizontal, and it forms a sharp maxillary notch to merge with the sides of the palate. The middle-face is not as broad as the upper face. The top of the nose also resembles early *H. sapiens*; the maxillary bones surrounding the top of the nose projects outward, showing that the nose projected away from the face in what Franciscus and Trinkaus describe as a decidedly *un*australopithecine manner. Yet, like the australopithecines the nasal bones (and nasal aperture) are quite narrow and while there does appear to have been a anterior nasal spine, it was not prominent.

A third Turkana cranium from this date range, ER-1805, was found in a somewhat higher stratigraphic position. With ER 1590 it is approximately 1.85 myr. The face was broken away from the cranium and the browridge area lost. Otherwise the cranium is fairly complete and there is an associated mandible. The specimen shows some closer resemblances to the australopithecines than do most of the habiline remains, and yet I believe the functional pattern indicates that it is best interpreted as an early *Homo*. Some australopithecine-like features include

- small cranial capacity (582 cc)
- long and low vault,
- combination of long cranial base and anterior foramen magnum position,
- long sphenoid base,
- size of the face relative to the braincase,
- flat, narrow nasal bones
- only a trace of an anterior nasal spine
- presence of a sagittal crest

However, there are significant contrasts with the normal australopithecine condition. The broad frontal suggests a narrow temporal fossa; the moderate sized postcanine teeth also indicate reduction in masticatory power and preclude it from being classified as *A. boisei*. The relatively great length of the cranium and the fact that the sagittal crest is in a posterior position both show that it was the posterior rather than the anterior aspect of the temporalis muscle that was emphasized. Finally at the rear of the skull, the mastoid region and the deep groove for the digastric muscle just inside of it are very much like early *H. sapiens*.

The whole cranial base is expanded due to an extraordinary development of spongy bone (pneumatization), and the nuchal muscle attachment area is expanded outward, forming a shelf over and behind the ears. Moreover, the temporal lines meet the nuchal torus at the rear of the vault and form a compound crest, helping even further extend the shelf at the back of the cranium and over the mastoids and ear openings. These latter features most closely resemble *A. afarensis*.

The importance of this cranium is its mix of australopithecine and early *Homo* anatomy, reflecting behavioral changes. Now known to be contemporary with early *H. sapiens*, it less likely to be a variant of it as F.C. Howell and I had supposed. The reader can imagine how this specimen might give new meaning to the phrase "taxonomic nightmare".

PLIO/PLEISTOCENE POSTCRANIA

A large number of postcranial remains are known from the Lower Pleistocene in East Africa, mainly from the Lake Turkana deposits but a few also from Olduvai and Omo. While at Olduvai there are associations with the OH 5, 7, 13, and 62 crania, only three specimens from the Turkana region are associated with cranial or dental materials which would allow one to determine which lineage it represented. Two of these are *A. boisei* specimens, discussed above. The third is ER 3735.

ER 3735 is in the oldest of the Koobi Fora groups, 1.90-1.88 myr in age. It consists of 50 pieces of badly eroded cranial vault and a number of postcranial fragments, that comprise the only association of crania and postcrania for a Pliocene occurrence of *Homo* at Koobi Fora. The cranial fragments include portions of frontal, zygomatic, and temporal with mandibular fossa that reveal it to be similar in shape to Koobi Fora specimens such as ER 1813. Several of the cranial fragments also resemble this Koobi Fora female in size; for instance the length of the temporal bone is 65 mm, similar to ER 1813's 63 mm and much smaller than ER 1470's 74 mm. It is tempting to regard ER 3735 as female, and the gracility of the vault and small supraorbital tori support this. However, the dimensions of the mandibular fossa are greater than two female crania, ER 1813 and L894-1 (in some dimensions they exceed ER 1470, according to Wood), and the zygomatic bone is very thick. These features reflect the masticatory apparatus and their variation suggests the specimen is a male. This is not the only male to resemble the ER 1813 cranial anatomy, OH 16 does so as well. McHenry gives a 37 kg estimate of body weight from the humerus (a larger weight is estimated from the radius head, but this is reconstructed and radius heads give weight overestimates in other specimens with several skeletal elements). Leakey and colleagues predict a 39 kg weight by assuming that ER 3735 is male and that it is as much larger than the OH 62 female (which they weigh in at 25 kg) as can be predicted for sexually dimorphic primates of this body size. These estimates are surprisingly similar. The weight is almost 20% greater than OH 7. However, it is very much smaller than the size of other isolated Koobi Fora postcranial remains that have been attributed to *H. habilis*. The question is whether these attributions are correct.

In their discussion of these postcranial fragments, Leakey and colleagues emphasize the size and strength of the forearm elements. For instance the **spine of the scapula** is very thick, easily exceeding modern humans with double or more the body weight. They infer from this that the **trapezius** (a muscle the stabilizes the scapula and brings it upward) and the **deltoid** (a muscle that cross the **glenoid joint** and moves the arm up (figure 8.2)) muscles are very large. The lever arm for the **biceps brachii** attachment on the radius is long, which they take to indicate great force in bending the elbow. They argue that these features reflect an enhanced climbing ability. Yet, comparison with archaic and recent humans from the Pleistocene who were not climbers, in some cases inhabiting Arctic tundra regions where there were no trees to climb, reveals similar features and suggests that non-locomotor explanations may also be appropriate.

In the report on the limb length ratios of ER 3735 that could be estimated from the postcranial fragments, R. Leakey and colleagues suggest the legs may be even relatively shorter than Lucy's. But, the two hindlimb fragments are not complete enough to be certain of this. There is enough evidence to suggest that the hindlimbs are relatively short. The most certain conclusion is that the limb proportions cannot be shown to differ from Lucy's.

The postcranial remains of the australopithecines and at least one of the early *Homo* species (Olduvai *H. habilis*) cannot be separated into functionally different groups. Perhaps this should not be surprising given the complete adaptation to striding bipedalism in the Pliocene australopithecines, but it does not help the problem of determining which isolated postcranial remains belong with which clade. Earlier, really large postcrania are associated with *A. aethiopicus* (Chapter 7), and large postcranial remains appear for the second time, in the terminal Pliocene beginning with the 1.95 myr ER 3228 innominate, but it is uncertain whether this belongs to any of the australopithecines, or australopithecine-like *Homo* species, or to early *H. sapiens* (this is discussed in more detail in Chapter 10, pp. xx-xx). Furthermore, with these large postcranials known through most of the later *A. boisei* span, the question of whether or not there was a size increase in this species will remain unknown until associated skeletal elements are discovered. We only know that an early male, Omo l 323, is the size of males in the other small early hominid species. Limb associations would help to solve a second problem, the question of why specimens attributed to *H. rudolfensis* are both large brained and megadont. Larger body size *could* account for it, but in the absence of associated skeletal elements, whether it *does* cannot be determined. The fact is that the large postcranial remains from Koobi Fora could belong to the *Homo* species not yet discussed, early *H. sapiens*. If so, and if the specimens attributed to the so-called *H. rudolfensis* are the same size as the other early hominid species, with a middle-sex body weight average of 35-39 kg, their large relative brain and postcanine tooth sizes would:

1. make them the most credible ancestor for early *H. sapiens*
2. show that early *H. sapiens* evolved from a megadont, large and flat faced robust australopithecine-like ancestor.

But this is all speculation. There is, of course, a hypothesis implicit in this discussion; that there is a second distinct habiline species, and that one of its significant differences, perhaps the most significant as it may contribute to the others, is larger body size. To test it would seemingly require associated postcranial remains. There may be another way.

HOW MANY SPECIES?

Paleoanthropologists as diverse as A. Chamberlain, W. Kimbel, Y. Rak, C. Stringer, I. Tattersall, and B. Wood have come to argue that the variation in *H. habilis* is too great to be encompassed by a single species because of the way that species was defined - as the gracile or non-*boisei* specimens from East Africa. Perhaps the most colorful description is Tattersall's: "little more than a convenient recipient for a motley assortment of hominin fossils from the latest Pliocene and earliest Pleistocene". Tattersall, as usual, leaves the details to his colleagues, and their numerous arguments have centered on whether a consistent internal division into two groups within *Homo* could be made. This has been a difficult task, for as P. Rightmire admits (1993:30) in a thoughtful review of the problem (which, by the way, concludes that there are two species in this sample):

If two species of early *Homo*, rather than just one, or three or more, are recognized at Olduvai and Koobi Fora, it should be acknowledged that the morphological difference between them is not especially great. The two are more similar to each other than either is to *H. erectus* [e.g. early *H. sapiens*]

Yet, the idea that there are two species is pervasive, and attempts to discuss otherwise do not engender replies but rather meet with reactions that range from "its the single species hypothesis again", to more simply "absurd" - the Greek Chorus for Plio/Pleistocene paleoanthropology.

The treatment of ER 1470 and 1813 is a mirror for how the two australopithecine-like *Homo* groups are considered. Some paleoanthropologists (including P. Tobias and myself) emphasized the similarities of these specimens and considered them to be *H. habilis*, and the source of the variation a combination of sexual dimorphism and body size difference. Yet, these two specimens, both from the upper Burgi Member, encapsulate the basis of distinguishing two *Homo* species. ER 1470 is very australopithecine-like, even robust australopithecine-like, in its teeth and frontofacial architecture - a point clearly shown by Thackeray's research - but has a very large brain size. ER 1813 is very similar to, really indistinguishable from, early *H. sapiens* in its teeth and frontofacial architecture but has a much smaller brain size. Yet in retrospect, one of the great weakness in the two species approach has been a lack of agreement on which specimens comprise the two groups. For instance, Stringer would include ER 1470 in *H. habilis*, but not ER 1813. Wood proposes just the opposite. Some authors restrict *H. habilis* to only mean the Olduvai material, while others include some of the Turkana specimens as well and some of these exclude certain Olduvai specimens. Moreover, there is really no point in detailing the schemes of different scientists, as minds seem to change with regularity.

As for the name of the second species, there is more regularity because naming is based on precedent. In 1986, V. Alexeev proposed to place the large-brained Turkana specimens in the genus he used to represent "the first true men" - "*Pithecanthropus*" - as a species apart from the later, Pleistocene, representatives of *Pithecanthropus* which he called "*rudolfensis*". He recognized ER 1813 as a female of *Pithecanthropus rudolfensis* because of "similar structural features", but one, perhaps, in a population "with a tendency to dwarfishness". He clearly distinguished these from the classic *H. habilis* found at Olduvai Gorge. The Olduvai remains, in Alexeev's view, were too australopithecine-like to be distinguished from other australopithecine taxa, and he proposed their renaming as *Australopithecus* or *Paranthropus habilis*.

The question is how much variation is there in this sample, and how can it be explained. There are a number of possible explanations of the variation, none of which are really mutually exclusive

1. time
2. body size
3. sexual dimorphism
4. taxonomy (within or between species)

The question of time is relevant because all of the Turkana specimens are earlier than all of the Olduvai specimens (see table 8.3). Those schemes (e.g. V. Alexeev, C. Groves, A. Chamberlain) that restrict *H. habilis* to mean only the Olduvai sample could rely on this fact to help explain the differences. Confusing this explanation, however, is the fact that the larger brained specimens are earlier. Moreover, most other assessments that conclude *H. rudolfensis* is valid interpret the Upper Burgi sample to include both *H. rudolfensis* (ER 1470) and *H. habilis* (ER 1813, 3735).

A critical problem is the lack of knowledge about body size in the larger brained specimens. It could be assumed, and most often has been assumed, that specimens such as ER 1470 have larger brain sizes, and a robust dental and facial size and morphology that is quite similar to australopithecines, because the individuals are big. Limbs such as the ER 1472 and 1481 femora are often attributed to these larger crania, suggesting dramatic allometric differences. However B. Wood questions whether the postcranial remains of habilines such as represented by OH 62 can be accommodated within the taxon represented by these large femoral remains from Koobi Fora? [According to McHenry the estimated OH 62 femur length is 31.5 cm, and the ER 1472 length is 40.1 cm]. He means this query to support the notion of two valid species among the habilines, yet it seems to me that this reflects a mistaken expectation for normal variability. For instance the two Hadar femora that McHenry reconstructs have lengths of 28.3 and 40.4 cm (and these are not the largest and smallest specimens in the species). In samples of small modern Africans the minimum and maximum femur lengths in a small pygmy sample is close to this difference, 32.6 and 39.2 cm, and comparing nearby populations the mean difference between Ugandan pygmy women and Nilohamatic men is even greater. Thus literal answer to Wood's question must surely be "yes", this much difference *can be expected*. Ironically, demonstration of a size difference would undermine, and not support (as some have presumed) arguments that different species are represented, because it would provide a different explanation than phylogeny for the cranial and dental variations. We know that markedly different body sized human populations can effectively adapt to the tropics and there is no reason to assume that these earlier hominids were less polytypic.

However, not one postcranial specimen is *actually associated* with remains attributed to *H. rudolfensis*. There is a very strong possibility that some of the larger (but not the largest, see the discussion of early *H. sapiens* postcrania below) limbs are those of habilines, but the issue is which crania correspond to these limbs. We just do not know if body size is an explanation for the cranial and dental variation said to characterize *H. rudolfensis* (the Koobi Fora medium size limbs are the size of Pygmies). The potential effects of allometry on differences in postcranial anatomy and limb proportions also remain unknown. Yet, the likelihood that some of the larger limbs are habiline suggests that this explanation might be relevant.

A similar question concerns the role of sexual dimorphism. Some of the taxonomic schemes (for instance R. Leakey and colleagues and P. Rightmire) seem to segregate samples that are predominately males and females. Many of the problems here are related to those of body size effects, but with the following proviso. Sex differences are recognizable in other early hominid species, in some cases such as *A. afarensis* and *A. boisei* they are quite dramatic. One way to approach the question of whether sexual dimorphism is a valid explanation of the variation is to examine whether there really is "too much variation"? Some who assert this make the same assertion about all hominid taxa, and the question must really revolve on the evidence. D. Lieberman and colleagues approached the question in a direct way. Without making any assumptions about the causes of variation, they asked whether specimens as different as ER 1470 and 1813 could be expected to be found in populations of highly dimorphic primates such as gorillas. They chose 20 gorillas from a single population and repeatedly sampled it to determine the probability of finding two specimens as different as ER 1470 and 1813. They conclude this is very unlikely, and that the two specimens most probably represent different species, unless they are more dimorphic than gorillas (actually, they generalize this conclusion to "all living higher primates"), or follow a different *pattern* of dimorphism.

The second possibility is supported by some research of B. Wood. He examined the multivariate relation of these two crania. While he found them quite distinct, he discovered that the same multivariate analysis shows them much more similar to each other than ER 406 is to 732, although these are two *A. boisei* crania thought to be a male and female of the same species. It is possible that hominids *do* have a different pattern of dimorphism than the dimorphic apes, certainly this would not be their only distinction from them! J. Miller also examined this question. He showed that considering the entire putative *H. habilis* sample together instead of focusing on only two crania does *not* reveal "too much variation" for it to represent a single species. Far from it!

While none of this proves that *H. habilis* is a single valid species of midget to pygmy sized populations that incorporate all of these remains, it does serve to show that the more conservative refutatory approach to this question fails to reveal sufficient evidence to reject the single species interpretation. My opinion is that this entire question will remain in the suspense account until postcranial remains are found associated with the larger brained sample, and the issue of variation in the sample can shift from one of probabilities to one of explanation. In the meanwhile, if there are two species here, they are sister species with little consistent means of distinguishing between them. Particularly important, in my view,

- different sorting criteria result in different sample compositions for which specimens are supposed to make up the species,
- no consistent set of criteria can characterize the differences between the samples no matter how they are sorted.

With its usual perversity, the fossil record has provided no consistent pattern of morphological differentiation between these samples that overlap in time and are found in the same Upper Burgi deposits. Cranial capacity, cranial base, nasal, and central facial anatomy, premolar root variation, each give a different, conflicting, pattern of variation and sort the specimens differently. While the idea that there might have been two australopithecine-like early *Homo* species remains viable, a more likely explanation for this pattern of variation is that of numerous closely related populations with similarities and differences that reflect adaptation, genic exchange, and body size. Polytypism, so common in wide-ranging primates and ubiquitous through the course of subsequent human evolution, might be the best explanation for these relatively small habiline variations.

LATEST PLIOCENE: *HOMO* FROM OMO?

The earliest definitive evidence of a *Homo* species at Omo is the fragmentary L894-1, dated to the same narrow interval as the first Turkana occurrences (1.90-1.88 myr). The fragmentary cranium is quite similar to the Olduvai *H. habilis* remains according to N. Boaz and F.C. Howell. One might expect that the first occurrences of *H. habilis* were just prior to this specimen, but this determination must depend on jaws and teeth which are notoriously inaccurate indicators. In Member G strata are postcanine teeth very similar to the *H. habilis* dentitions in the more distinct smaller and relatively narrow end of their range. However, *H. habilis* and early *H. sapiens* jaws and dentitions can be identical. This means that some of the smaller, narrow isolated teeth from Omo Member G (in or above Submember G4 at 2.12 myr) could be early *H. sapiens*. None of these are earlier than the first appearance of *A. boisei*, some 2.25 myr.

What about the larger habiline? These teeth are harder to identify in isolation. Even complete jaws are problematic. For instance in the Turkana sequence, the ER 1802 mandible from the upper Burgi Member is widely regarded as a male of early *Homo*. B. Wood, in fact, describes it as one of the several mandibles he is willing to place in *H. rudolfensis*. According to Wood the diagnosis of mandibles in this *H. rudolfensis* includes:

- broad postcanine tooth crowns (they are narrow in *H. habilis*),
- a large P_4 **talonid** (this extra area on the back of the tooth acts to make it squarer in profile and is a robust australopithecine characteristic according to Suwa),
- double rooted P_4's and sometimes P_3's (these teeth are single rooted in *H. habilis*)

R. Leakey and A. Walker attributed a very similar specimen from the KBS Member, ER 15930, to *A. boisei*, as a putative female However, comparing it to ER 1802, the specimen attributed to *H. rudolfensis*, J. Miller has shown a marked similarity between these mandibles and their teeth. This could reflect how similar isolated dentognathic elements of these species are, or alternatively reflect our need for better criteria for distinguishing them. In any event it definitely shows that caution needs be applied to the problem of identifying *Homo* at Omo (or anywhere else) from jaws alone, and cautions against attempts from isolated teeth (for an exception, see the discussion of Suwa's analysis of the mandibular premolars, above).

A mandible and cranial fragments dated to 2.02 myr, Omo 75-14, is as good a potential representative of the larger *Homo* variety as there is at the moment. Its premolar morphology is not robust australopithecine of any flavor, according to Suwa, while its tooth sizes are markedly larger than OH 16, the biggest Olduvai *H. habilis* male, and except for the M_3 even larger than ER 1802 (table 8.4). Thus, the larger *Homo* variety may have close to the same antiquity as the smaller one at Omo, and these data do not clearly resolve which, if either, came first. On the other hand, it may mean that *H. habilis* has always had the range of variation it shows in the Koobi Fora samples.

What of the potentiality for finding the immediate ancestors of *Homo* among the hominid samples from below Submember G4 (2.12 myr, and below the definitive *Homo* teeth)? In a review of specimens from Members E and F (2.40-2.33 myr), Howell and colleagues attribute 3/4 of the specimens to *A. aethiopicus* and the remainder to "aff. *Homo* sp.", an unnamed taxon with affinities to a species of genus *Homo*. The 13 *Homo*-like specimens, all isolated teeth, are said to "deviate from the range of australopithecine morphologies", but in fact they were only compared with *A. africanus* - the species that Y. Coppens affiliated the teeth with! My experience with these teeth suggest that they fall within the range of Swartkrans robust australopithecines in their size and anatomical characteristics. Perhaps more complete specimens would have inter-dental proportions unlike those of the Swartkrans hominids, but the specimens present do not refute the hypothesis that the second East African species in the later Pliocene is a robust australopithecine similar to the South African variety - a hypothesis suggested by the analysis of the Chemeron temporal. None of this, in my view, contradicts Howell's description of the teeth as having affinities to a species of *Homo* - a description that is also valid for many of the Swartkrans dental remains.

The fact is that there is a blind-spot as far as looking for robust australopithecines that are not *A. boisei* in East Africa is concerned. Scientists are sure, perhaps too sure, that because there already *is* a robust australopithecine species there, specialized as a vegetarian according to Robinson's dietary hypothesis, the hypothesis of a second similarly adapted one is not likely enough to warrant testing. Perhaps with

- the new dietary information published for the Swartkrans hominids,
- the robust australopithecine similarities in the Chemeron temporal,

- and the potential for an unspecialized robust australopithecine-like hominid as the last common ancestor of *Homo* and the more specialized varieties of the robust australopithecine clade,

the hypothesis that there is a second Late Pliocene East African australopithecine that is *both* similar to *A. robustus* and has affinities with (or is directly ancestral to) *Homo* will be considered more seriously.

Table 8.4
Comparison of Mandibular Tooth Dimensions

	Olduvai *H. habilis* female OH 13	Olduvai *H. habilis* male OH 16	Omo L75-14	Kromdraai female TM 1517	Swartkrans female SK 858	Swartkrans male SK 876	Turkana *H. rudolfensis*[2] female ER 1801	Turkana *H. rudolfensis* male ER 1802
I1 L[3]		6.3			5.6[1]			
I1 B[3]		7.1			6.9			
I2 L		7.7			6.6[1]			
I2 B	5.3	7.6			7.6	8.0		
C L	7.6	10.0		8.9	8.8	8.9[1]		
C B	7.5	10.1		9.3	7.9	10.8	8.5	(11.5)
P3 L	8.7	10.0	11.3	10.3	10.2	8.7[1]		10.4
P3 B	9.6	11.5	12.3	12.5	(11.5)	12.7		12.5
P4 L	8.8	10.1	11.4	11.3	11.1[1]	10.8[1]	9.2	11.1
P4 B	9.9	11.2	12.7	13.4	13.9	13.5	10.8	11.8
M1 L	12.6	14.6	15.6	13.9	13.7[1]	14.1[1]	13.1	14.7
M1 B	11.4	12.8	14.1	13.1	14.4	14.6	13.3	13.1
M2 L	13.3	15.6	17.5	14.4	15.9	16.1	14.2	16.7
M2 B	11.8	14.8	15.4	13.9	15.0	16.0		14.1
M3 L	14.7	15.9	15.1	16.2	16.8	18.3	16.5	17.5
M3 B	12.1	14.3	14.1	14.1	14.1	15.7	14.5	14.0

[1] Significantly shortened by **interproximal wear**
[2] As defined by B. Wood

I believe that these specimens support the contention that *Homo* may have evolved from an ancestor resembling the South African robust australopithecine, perhaps the species so poorly represented in the Omo sequence. One could argue the Omo evidence also suggests *H. rudolfensis* and *H. habilis* branched first, before *H. sapiens*. However:

1) each of these varieties shares a set of different important elements with early *H. sapiens* so it is unclear which would make the "better" ancestor
2) it is far from certain that they are different species
3) the hypothesis that some of the isolated teeth are those of early *H. sapiens* cannot be precluded, so *neither* might be earlier

In sum, the Omo remains confirm the ecological ties of early *Homo* and *A. boisei*. They first appear together, and as at Olduvai and Koobi Fora they persist together through the terminal Pliocene and into the Pleistocene. The last common ancestor of these two clades is probably not much older than their first appearance together, and as discussed above and in Chapter 7 this ancestor may have resembled a generalized robust australopithecine, not dissimilar to those found at the earliest South African robust site, Kromdraai. The specimens from the Shungura Formation, Omo, are very important because they span the time period when *H. sapiens* might have first appeared. However, because of their fragmentary nature they provide no insight as to which of the australopithecine-like *Homo* varieties - if any - is ancestral to *H. sapiens*.

THE GEOGRAPHIC RANGE OF EARLY *HOMO*

From the latter part of the later part of the Early Pliocene australopithecines are found in both eastern and southern Africa. Habilines are found across this range as well, and in at least one additional area. A mandible attributed to *H. rudolfensis* similar in age to the Omo Member F hominids was found in the Malawi Rift Valley, potentially along a corridor that could link these eastern and southern hominid populations. The climate was somewhat cooler and drier than today, and some have suggested that this links the emergence of *Homo* species to the late Pliocene climatic change (an argument that would be more convincing if there was better than a general date assessment based on faunal comparisons, and if we could be certain which *Homo* species is represented). The Uraha Hill mandible is very similar to a Koobi Fora habiline mandible, ER 1802. As discussed above, some paleoanthropologists place this robust specimen in *H. rudolfensis*.

Later South African Sites

Specimens of a *Homo* species are said to come from both Sterkfontein Member 5 and Swartkrans Members 1 and 2. Perhaps the most important factor linking these members is that they contrast with the earlier, australopithecine-bearing levels at both sites in being much drier and more seasonal. There are partial crania, as well as dental, gnathic, and postcranial remains. The most diagnostic of these, Sterkfontein (STW 53) and Swartkrans (SK 80/847), are not particularly similar to each other except, according to an analysis by F. Grine and colleagues, in characters they both share with australopithecines such as narrow nose, narrow frontal bone, broad middle-face, and other features reflecting a powerful masticatory system with a well-developed anterior temporalis. Their dates are, at best, only poorly approximated. What can be said definitively is that neither is early *H. sapiens*. What is less clear is whether either is *H. habilis,* or a related species. Differences in time, in geography, and possibly in other factors has created a situation in which their relationships are far from obvious - reflected in the fact that both have been allied with *Homo* by some authors and with *Australopithecus* by others.

For instance, STW 53 has weak anterior pillars, as does OH 24, and projecting supraorbitals similar only to OH 16 and ER 1813. SK 847, like most other habiline remains, lacks the anterior pillars but shares the (markedly larger) projecting supraorbitals. It has semicircular canals of the inner ear proportions and projecting nasal bones that are similar to early *H. sapiens*. As an example of the taxonomic confusion that reigns for these crania, the upper premolars of both specimens are 3-rooted. This is a feature which, according to B. Wood, clearly separates *H. habilis* from *H. rudolfensis* and would make both of these South African specimen *H. rudolfensis*! Yet, few of the other criteria for this species are met by the specimens, their faces are quite unlike ER 1470, and they especially contrast in their notably smaller brain size estimates.

STERKFONTEIN MEMBER 5

Member 5 at Sterkfontein has proven to be very problematic. Geologic and sedimentary indicators suggest the habitat was very dry, like SK 1, but the fauna (including the hominids) more closely resembles Sterkfontein Member 4 than any other site. As discussed in Chapter 7, because of the circumstances in the cave, it has proven difficult to distinguish Sterkfontein Member 4 and 5 specimens in many parts of the deposits that have been excavated over the past 2 decades, and E. Vrba has expressed concern that even if the Member 5 remains could be clearly delineated, they may include a span of up to a million years. A series of ESR dates of animal tooth enamel from Member 4 have two peaks in their distribution. H. Schwarcz and colleagues suggest this might mean there is a mixture of Member 5 fauna into the sample, but if the Member spans a long time, the mean age of 1.7 myr for the younger animal teeth provides little information about the age of the Member 5 australopithecines. Indicative of these problems is R. Clark's observation that while both Sterkfontein Member 5 and Swartkrans Member 1 (see below), sites directly across the valley from each other, are supposed to contain (what in his view are) *H. habilis* remains, the predominant hominids at Swartkrans are the robust australopithecines, while no robust australopithecines are found in any of the Sterkfontein members. Until a direct series of Member 5 ESR ages are attempted, these environmental and faunal data are the only basis for assessing the age of the Member 5 hominids. To me these data suggest that the Sterkfontein Member 5 specimens lie between Member 4 and the later Swartkrans Member 1 remains, and perhaps most importantly that Members 4 and 5 are probably quite close together in time.

This contention is supported by the hominid remains in a way that resolves the contradiction Clark raises. In my view, the case for *H. habilis* in Sterkfontein Member 5 is weak and unconvincing, even accepting the attribution of the most complete example to a level later than the bulk of the *A. africanus* sample. The face of the Member 5 putative *H. habilis* female, STW 53, is said to closely resemble other *H. habilis* remains such as OH 24 and 62. It actually most closely resembles certain of the other earlier Sterkfontein specimens. Including OH 24 in the *H. habilis* range (not all paleoanthropologists are willing to do this) extends it to encompass many *A. africanus* features, but even this is not sufficient to establish a good case for STW 53 as *H. habilis*. And if the data for the relative proportions of the inner ear's semi-circular canals are to be taken seriously, it is so unusual that it has been likened to a large monkey, with "less adaptation to bipedalism than the australopithecines" according to F. Spoor and colleagues. The study the is based on makes many assumptions, and depends of knowledge of body size for its proportions which, for STW 53, is unknown. It does point up the marked differences between the absolute dimensions of these canals in the Sterkfontein specimen and the much more *Homo*-like SK 847 discussed below.

STW 53 is very much like STS 71 in the cranial rear, including the shape and proportions of the occiput, the size and details of the mastoid process (flattened rear, digastric sulcus, and broad shelf of pneumatized bone above it that extends over the ear and is continuous with the broad gutter over the mandibular fossa). The forehead profile behind the supraorbitals is like STS 5. The mandibular fossa and the shallow articular surface in front of it are also quite similar in STW 53 and STS 71. It resembles STS 19 in the breadth of the cranial base and the foramen magnum position. It is like STS 52 in its marked prognathism of the nose and lower face, prominent anterior pillars, and the distinct, although unprojecting nasal spine (holding the cartilage of the mid-nose and suggesting some projection of the fleshy part of the structure). The nose is similar to these australopithecines, in combining flat, unprojecting, and narrow nasal bones and the lack any sort of an internasal angle where they join each other, with a narrow aperture. The palate appears to be broad relative to its length, but this is actually a consequence of the very broad postcanine teeth (an australopithecine feature). It is broad if the measurement is taken across the outer borders of the teeth, but as narrow as the others when the measurement is taken between the inner borders. In other words, STW 53 combines the features that are found in Member 4 australopithecines.

The case for *H. habilis* is based on only one part of the anatomy - the upper face/anterior frontal. The greatest similarities to *Homo* are in the frontal bone, as Tobias pointed out. An early *H. sapiens*-like **frontal keel,** or **torus,** runs down the middle of the frontal **squama,** and the thin supraorbitals extend more anterior to the frontal. In the upper part of the face, the top of the nasal aperture projects slightly in front of the orbits, Otherwise, there are few if any distinctions that can uniquely link it with other specimens attributed to *H. habilis*. Do these similarities demonstrate that the species is present, or that this is a late *A. africanus* sample evolving in the *H. habilis* direction? I tend toward the later interpretation and believe that the similarities the mastoid region and the area above it share with Chemeron are significant. Chemeron is more robust, however, as it has a much larger mandibular fossa and larger and more projecting articular surface for the mandible articulation during chewing (figure 8.3) - a feature it share with robust australopithecines and some early *Homo* species..

THE UNENDING ENIGMA OF SWARTKRANS

Some 3% of the Swartkrans Member 1 specimens have been attributed to *Homo*. The best evidence for *Homo* is the composite Swartkrans cranium that R. Clarke reconstructed from a midface and cranial base which J. Robinson attributed to "*Paranthropus*" (SK 847) and a maxillary fragment (SK 80) Robinson had used to name a new genus, "*Telanthropus*". Emphasizing the anatomy of the middle face, I and a few others were unwilling to separate it from the robust australopithecines, whose variation at Swartkrans, even without this individual, was and remains underappreciated. Indeed, a multivariate analysis of frontofacial features attempted by A. Bilsborough and B. Wood associated it with the female *A. boisei* cranium ER 732. However, a different multivariate analysis by G. Clark and **nonmetric traits** considered by T. Olsen seem to position it with *A. africanus,* but C. Dean and B. Wood report that the cranial base resembles anything but this group, and is closest to robust australopithecines or to *Homo*, and the absolute sizes of the semi-circular canals are said to link it with *Homo*. The question is whether the problem here lies with the specimen or the technique used to analyze it!

SK 80/847 is often attributed to *H. habilis,* although Robinson changed his allocation of the maxillary fragment from "*Telanthropus*" (a genus he named to describe the maxilla's uniqueness) to *H. erectus* and at one time Clarke indicated his belief that the composite skull he reconstructed (SK 80/847) may be *H. erectus.* This is a suggestion that is supported by McCollum's analysis of the subnasal morphology, Franciscus and Trinkaus' discussion of anterior nasal projection, and Robinson's original observation of the distinct anterior nasal spine. He realized that the spine, which supports the cartilaginous wall along the center of the external nose, projects in front of the lower nasal border and thereby positions the trough holding the nasal cartilage forward enough to show that there were a true projecting external nose and not a flat one as in apes, and most australopithecines. Clarke more recently made a third taxonomic assessment and suggested SK 847 is even "more advanced" than *H. erectus* and may be a direct ancestor of *H. sapiens*. This, of course, assumes the validity of a theory proposed by L. Leakey toward the end of his career. This theory is based on three assumptions:

1. *erectus* and *H. sapiens* are different species (see Chapter 9)
2. *erectus* is a side-branch, not an ancestor of *H. sapiens*
3. *habilis* evolved directly into *H. sapiens*

These considerations are difficult to reconcile with the implications of the large portion of a parietal found associated with SK 80/847 and usually attributed to it. With the cranial base, the dimensions of this fragment suggest a cranial capacity of under 500 cc.

F. Grine and colleagues attempted a multivariate analysis to resolve the issue, comparing it to early *H. sapiens* females (ER 3733) and two females they attributed to *H. habilis*: ER 1813 and STW 53. These are specimens that had not been found or could not be studied for the earlier multivariate analyses. A "multivariate yardstick" was developed from variation in several extant populations. Based on it, the differences between the Swartkrans skull and the *H. habilis* sample were found to be on the order of normal within-population variation, and they attribute the Swartkrans specimen to this taxon. The mastoid size, flat nasal bones and narrow nose, masticatory biomechanics, and I would add small cranial size and orbit dimensions, and remnants of diminutive anterior teeth, make it an unlikely early *H. sapiens*.

The late differentiation of *Homo* and the robust australopithecines from a hypothesized ancestor sharing the unique similarities of these two clades would go a long way towards explaining why problem specimens like this one (and see the discussion of ER 1805 above) are found, as well as what may be interpreted as the habiline-like variations in the earlier Sterkfontein specimen STW 53. The similarities of these clades are much greater than often credited, and in discussing specimens such as these, focus must be brought on the few features that clearly differentiate them. Yet, these morphological signals have proven confusing, a reflection of the closeness of the taxa being distinguished.

The other Swartkrans cranial specimens attributed to *Homo* are the Member 1 juvenile specimens SK 27 and 47. Besides being young, both crania are similar in that they were crushed flat as pancakes and best preserve details of the cranial base. According to M. McCollum and colleagues, the recessed nasal margin and anterior nasal spine of SK 47 affiliate it with the other Swartkrans robust australopithecines. The problem is that there are no juvenile cranial bases of early *Homo* to compare them with. Also attributed to *Homo* are mandibles such as SK 15 (without certain provenience) and SK 45 which is said to come from Member 1 but which was recovered by R. Broom and neither excavated nor found in place. Broom, at the end of his career, is said to have carried specimens around, sometimes for days, before reporting them and recording the details of their discovery at the Transvaal Museum (J. Robinson was originally hired by the museum to reform this practice). Because of its very modern anatomy, I believe it is a Late Stone Age *H. sapiens* mandible, mistakenly confused to come from this early member because of some small breccia particles adhering to it. C. Brain admits that it may not even come from the Swartkrans cave.

There are some attributions to *Homo* that use dental criteria, either enlarged incisors (meaning dimensions about a millimeter larger than incisors found in some of the robust australopithecine crania) or little worn upper molars that are longer than broad. The minute differences often make the taxonomic exercise very unconvincing, and these teeth fall within the actual or expected range of Swartkrans robust australopithecines. However, G. Macho and F. Thackery examined the enamel of one Swartkrans Member 2 molar attributed to *Homo*: SKX 268, a M^1. They concluded that while the thickness of the occlusal enamel cap was comparable to the other Swartkrans specimens, the sides of the tooth were thinner than most other molars examined from the site and it is clearly separated from the other teeth in a multivariate analysis. They inferred that this individual was best adapted to include in its diet abrasive food items that did not require powerful forces during mastication.

It is quite possible that there are *Homo* specimens in the provenienced Swartkrans Member 1 and 2 hominid remains. With hindsight, it seems that much of the basis for the debate over whether SK 847 is *Homo* or an australopithecine variety can be found in the very close relation between *A. robustus* and *Homo*. The issue of what species of that genus it and other specimens represent is more complex. I believe that whatever the alleged early *Homo* specimens are, there is no convincing evidence to link them to early *H. sapiens* similar to the 1.9 myr and younger remains from East Africa. This, in turn, has implications for the interpretation of certain postcranial remains and the tools found at Swartkrans.

Swartkrans hands

In his analysis of the more recently discovered Swartkrans remains, R. Susman focused on some features of the foot and hand remains that seem to differ significantly from the *A. afarensis* condition. The metatarsal of the big toe was described as extremely similar to humans in foot posture and the range of dorsiflexion (figure 4.6). A number of the remains are handbones. Their analysis reveals certain contrasts with the Hadar hand remains (and possibly those few hand bones from Sterkfontein discussed in Chapter 6):

- the thumb is relatively longer
- the saddle-shaped joint at the base of the thumb is relatively larger, showing that more force passed through it
- the attachment for the flexor muscles at the end of the thumb are large and well developed
- finger tips are larger and particularly broader

Susman argues that the Swartkrans hominids had a well-developed precision grip and could hold objects in their hands tightly. Moreover, details of a radius with a well preserved distal end, SKX 3602, show a wrist anatomy that reflects an expanded range of thumb motion. These are the details that authors such as

M. Marzke attributes to the effects of tool use on hand evolution. But, the question is *which* Swartkrans hominid?

The implication which Susman and colleagues draw is that *A. robustus* was the tool maker and tool user. Their assessment rests on two grounds:

1. the vast majority of Member 1 specimens are *A. robustus*
2. there are two anatomically different thumb metacarpals and one of them closely resembles the West Turkana early *H. sapiens* specimen WT 15000; by implication the other, more "modern appearing", was attributed to *A. robustus*

However E. Trinkaus and J. Long question both of these points. They argue that the taphonomy of relative sample sizes does not allow one to attribute either or both of the hand bones, and they demonstrate that the metacarpals' differences in size and anatomy are not sufficient to show that different species are represented, when these are compared to within-population variation today.

Because of the unique resemblances of the SK 84 thumb bone to an early *H. sapiens* specimen (WT 15000), the null hypothesis is probably that the human-like hand remains should be attributed, albeit tenuously, to *Homo*. *The* SKX 3602 radius has a reconstructed length of about 23.5 cm, suggesting a height of about 1.6 m (or shorter, if it is a species with australopithecine-like proportions). While not a proof, the fact that it is below the range of early *H. sapiens* in east Africa (see Chapter 10) suggests what the anatomy of the SK 847 skull also implies - the *Homo* species is *H. habilis*.

Swartkrans Tools

Stone tools have been known from the Swartkrans cave for some time. They were first thought to only come from Member 1 but it is now recognized that there are numerous occurrences in the three lower members. The tools are made of quartz, quartzite, and the easier flaking chert. The quartz and quartzite tools were modified by a **bipolar technique**, in which the core is placed on a rock and hit on its upper end with another stone, called the hammerstone (none of these were found), to produce flakes with sharp edges. The Swartkrans Members 1 and 2 "industries" are the debris from activities around the opening of the shaft leading to the cave that were washed into it. This process sorted them by size and shape, and makes it difficult to compare these tools with others. They are mostly simple cores that were used to produce flakes (few flakes were found), and in some cases subsequently used in bashing. The distribution of tools in Member 3, however, suggests that the cave (then a gully leading to an open fissure) may have been occupied. It is here that evidence of fire has been found (see below).

Some 68 bone tools were found in the three members. They are mostly made of large flakes from animal limb shafts and horncore pieces. According to C. Brain three categories of tools have been recognized

1. bones whose pattern of wear and details of scratching suggest they were used as digging tools
2. similar bones whose worn areas are as described above but also covered with a fine polish
3. awl-like tools only showing wear on their tips

The digging tools taper to a smooth point, where the wear is rounded. They are covered with numerous long scratches, with occasional prominent cross-striations. Two aspects of their use were established by C. Brain and colleagues by experiment - similar tools were systematically used to dig up edible lily bulbs on the stony Swartkrans hillside. It was found that the longitudinal scratching and end wear came from repeatedly plunging the tool into the ground, and the cross-stria from its encounters with stones. A full day of digging failed to reproduce the number of longitudinal scratches usually found on these tools, and Brain and colleagues concluded that the tools were **curated**, in that they were kept and used for several days before being discarded. Supporting this interpretation are the tools covered with fine polish. In discussing a similar bone tool from Sterkfontein Member 5, J. Robinson had suggested the polish might have come from rubbing the tool with a soft substance such as leather. Again relying on experiment, Brain and colleagues found they could replicate the polish by carrying the tools in leather bags, and they suggest this was their means of transporting and curating the objects. They further posit that the awl-like tools may have been used in punching holes in soft material like leather. Finally, the persistent, unchanging tool collections in each of the three members suggests that even given the shortest Swartkrans chronology, digging on this hillside was a long lasting, seasonally specific, tradition for hominids.

A related finding in the Swartkrans cave concerns the possible use of fire. C. Brain and A. Sillen report finding burnt animal bones in Swartkrans Member 3. This is the only member of the three in which all of the small number of hominid remains found thus far are robust australopithecine, which continues the confusion of whose activities are preserved. The long lasting digging tool tradition found through this member indicates a very long time span for it. The digging tools are directly associated with burnt bone in this Member. This suggests that a hominid population may have used the hillside seasonally for a long time. The fact that evidence for fire use is only in Member 3 would indicate that the hominid traditionally using the hillside may have discovered or learned about it then, according to the train of logic of these authors. According to Brain, the vertical distribution of burnt bones suggests that "the fires had been tended repeatedly in the Member 3 gully during its period of infilling." Moreover, some of the Member 3 faunal remains show cut marks (none are found on earlier materials). Whether these are behavioral innovations that characterized robust australopithecines or other hominids, for instance *Homo,* occasionally visiting the area, is very problematic because of the circumstances and cannot be determined from the tools alone.

Planning, the ability to project and organize future action, is an outgrowth of the hominid facility in mental mapping and can be linked to various aspects of cognition and perhaps communication in the context of culture (c.f. Gibson and Milbrath). Some Swartkrans hominid left behind four elements that reflect on its cultural capacity:

1) A bone and horn core culture based on the carrying and curation, perhaps in leather bags, of digging tools that were used for several days before being discarded.
2) Indirect evidence that this culture encoded a regular seasonal activity as a long lasting tradition

and later in the Member 3 span of traditional occupation of the rock shelter over the cave

3) The manipulation of fire at heats intense enough to show the occurrences were artificial and not smoldering debris on the cave floor.
4) The application of stone tools in defleshing animals

The Sillen Solution

A. Sillen proposes a solution to the question about who owns the Swartkrans hands and tools and who made the fire, that seems most satisfactory. In his ongoing Strontium/Calcium research he was able to analyze a fragment of *Homo* bone - from the SK 847 composite skull. This specimen has a much higher Sr/Ca ratio than any of the 8 *A. robustus* specimens. The geophytes (lily bulbs) that grow on the Swartkrans hillside have a very high Sr/Ca ratio. Sillen posits that at least some of the *Homo* populations were using the bone points for digging tools to obtain these roots, thereby expanding their niche to intensely collect enough of these underground resources to leave a distinct chemical marker (another specimen attributed to *Homo,* the 8 year old SK 27 boy, has a lower Sr/C ratio, but this might still reflect the influence of his mother's milk). This would implicate a *Homo* species as the tool user, and provide a good argument to support the contention that the hand bones showing adaptations to tool making and use were those of *Homo* as well. This reconstruction also fits the data developed for the molar crown enamel thickness pattern, as the geophytes are greasy and chewy, rather than hard. The requirements for chewing them would account for the combination of thick enamel cap and thin walls on a Swartkrans *Homo* tooth reported by Macho and Thackeray. The sample sizes are too small for this to be more than a hypothesis, but it is the only one that fits a range of data from a variety of sources.

The idea that an omnivore might reduce its meat input and successfully expand its niche to encompass significant underground plant resources turns some of the assumptions of "Man the Hunter" upside down, but makes good sense in a seasonally dry environment. Dry seasons, when most above-ground plant resources have disappeared, is when omnivory might be most important during the hominid yearly cycle. Yet, J. Speth has shown that the use of animal resources towards the ends of dry seasons is prohibited by the fact that fat is required to digest animal protein, but the fat resources for both hominids and their potential prey are minimal at this time in strongly seasonal environments. Early hominids shifting to hunting, or more likely to scavenging, during this time of the year would encounter the strongest potential for food resource limitations on population size, between the lack of predictability, the fluctuating uncontrolled supply of scavengable foods, and the danger of spending more than is gained by eating fat-depleted meats. The invention of digging sticks to obtain the nutritionally rich underground tubers and roots, the structures plants use to store their resources, would be particularly advantageous.

If it is true that only *Homo*, and not one of the australopithecines, was able to invent this simple technology, it reflects significant limits to the adaptability and depth of australopithecine mental processes in spite of the brain size increases shown in several australopithecine clades.

- It would imply that this seemingly simple Oldowan technology was beyond the mental capabilities of australopithecines to learn or copy.
- It would support C. Gamble's contention that *hominid* technology became a social behavior.
- It would strongly suggest that the lithic technology from East African Oldowan sites was the product of *Homo* populations.

Thus there is reason to believe that the capacity for tool use, and the adaptive functions of this behavior, may not have been the same in all of the hominid species. The differences are not clearly apparent in the technology or tool types, but the Swartkrans evidence suggests that curation and traditions might have differed and we can look at land use patterning and other related behavioral reflections in the archaeological record as well. To fully explore the implications of these ideas we need to include the other contemporary species in our discussions, early *H. sapiens*.

Summary

The Late Pliocene saw the appearance of one (or some say two) species of australopithecine-like *Homo*, and the first evidence of early *H. sapiens*. Habilines, the australopithecine-like forms, vary in body size from the midget-sized *H. habilis* to larger Pygmy or San-sized specimens that some call *H. rudolfensis*. In general they show cranial size expansion from the earlier australopithecines such as *A. africanus*. The difference is greatest for some specimens such as ER 1470, but these also show posterior tooth size expansion and facial features and proportions that resemble the robust australopithecines. Some of the classic *H. habilis* specimens from Olduvai are more like early *H. sapiens* in posterior tooth size and facial features including the form of the supraorbital region, nasal projection and breadth, and details of the anterior palate. However, their brain size is markedly smaller, body size is in the Midget range like most of the australopithecines, and body proportions also resemble these diminutive hominids.

Many scientists working on the habiline problem are uncomfortable with the amount of variation in specimens attributed to this species and seem to be in agreement that there are two distinct groups in this collection. However, the distinguishing features of these so-called species have never been satisfactorily established; various paleoanthropologists sort the sample into the two species differently, and the sorting criteria must be based on combinations of features as all the individual variants of particular features appear in both. This is an unacceptable situation. The pattern of variation suggests an alternative explanation, that subspecies or racial variation based on different adaptations reflected in body size (and its consequences) is a better interpretation. If we assume that the larger crania and faces with powerful postcanine dentitions (and their structural consequences) of specimens such as ER 1470 reflect body size differences, much of the variation between specimens such ER 1470 and ER 1813 can be explained by the fact that they are different sexed individuals in different sized populations. The fact is that there *are* medium sized postcranial remains, larger than the midget habilines and smaller than those associated with early *H. sapiens*, that *might* be those of a larger habiline sample. However, there are no crania or jaws associated with them.

Postcranial remains, in fact, are only *directly* associated with the midget habilines, revealing them to be the same diminutive size as other australopithecines and with most of the same postcranial features and proportions. Even still, analysis of the foot remains reveal adaptations shared with *H. sapiens* and the fingers share hand adaptations for tool use, including thumb elongation, expanded joint size, and broad finger tips. In fact, many features of early *H. sapiens* can be found in the habiline sample, and the habilines would make a quite convincing ancestor but for the fact that the earliest definitive specimens are younger than the earliest *H. sapiens*. Habilines probably are ancestral, but at the moment it is unclear whether the smaller or larger form, or perhaps a different earlier variety, played the role of the last common ancestor for the *Homo* species.

The South African specimens attributed to *Homo* are either poorly differentiated australopithecines or specimens related to the habilines. There is no definitive evidence of early *H. sapiens* in the later members of the Transvaal caves. The implications of this interpretation is that the archaeological and other evidences of complex behavior can be associated with this extinct species. The contextual data show that habilines used and made stone tools, and their anatomy reflects the consequences of it.

The ancestry issue is confused by the fact that **early *H. sapiens* is the earliest *Homo* species found in the Upper Burgi Member sample**, also containing the first of the definitive habiline crania (both small and large varieties).

ANATOMY OF A CONTROVERSY
The Riddles of the Olduvai Sites

Beginning some 2 myr ago and for a brief period of some 250 kyr, hominids left behind the remnants of their activities on or near the shore of an ancient East African lake, to be preserved as the Bed I Oldowan sites. The climatic conditions changed from wetter to hotter, drier and more open during this span. All of the Bed I hominid remains are attributed to either *A. boisei* or *H. habilis* and most are found between Tuffs IB (1.80 myr) and IC (1.76 myr). This is the period of densest vegetation, wettest conditions, and highest lake levels. There are two widely debated questions about the Oldowan that need to be viewed from both the archaeological and the biological perspective:

1. who made the tools ?
2. what is the adaptive pattern they are part of ?

The Oldowan assemblages, as found at Olduvai, include large numbers of densely distributed crude, amorphous, flakes and the cores they were struck from. Other elements are the hammerstones that were used to produce the flakes, and unmodified manuports (an unmodified cobble or large pebble known to have been carried to the site because it could not have occurred there naturally). Regularity or symmetry, when it is found, seems more by accident than by design. The artifacts were modified by direct percussion, as the hammerstone was used to hit the core, breaking off flakes. It was first thought that the cores were the tools, the object of hominid activities, and the flakes were the debris. Usewear studies (examining the artifacts for microscopic scratches and breaks) suggests that the opposite was usually the case, and it was the flakes that were the focus of activities. The main impression left by these tools is that they are expedient - manufactured to meet immediate requirements. As to who made the tools, any hominid living at the time potentially could have but let us examine the indirect evidence.

- The only hominid species found at Olduvai during this period are the classic *H. habilis* remains and the robust australopithecine *A. boisei*.

- Similar bone and stone tools are found in Member I at Swartkrans, where the only hominids found are either attributed to the small variety of *H. habilis* or the robust australopithecine *A. robustus*.
- The *Homo* species and *A. boisei* show brain expansion compared with the ancestral condition found in *A. africanus*.
- Of the three only *H. habilis* is known to have the hand modifications that have been associated with and seem to be a consequence of tool use.
- Early *H. sapiens* is found during this time span, but not clearly at either of these two sites (if it was present, it was rare there). *H. sapiens* has a larger brain size, and long legs and a very much larger body size than the other hominids.
- Stone tools were being made before any species of *Homo* is known to have lived.

If we posit that a species of *Homo* made the tools at these two places, and indeed that tool making was an important element in the appearance, early evolution, and success of *Homo,* the question of which species made the tools at these two particular sites remains important because one is just about double the size of the other and this difference has significant adaptive consequences. I find it unreasonable to posit that *H. sapiens* was the tool maker, or at least the only tool maker, at these sites. The antiquity of stone tool making and the anatomy of *H. habilis* hands suggests at least one other suspect. Yet, if there are differences between the terminal Pliocene/earliest Pleistocene industries of these closely related species, they are yet to be established because:

- no archaeologist has examined the question of lithic variation with the potential explanation of two different tool-making *Homo* species in mind - raw materials or different activities are usually proposed as the causes of whatever variation is found
- no tool site from this time period is unequivocally and uniquely associated with early *H. sapiens*

The potential for two different tool making hominid species with sophisticated potentials and very different body sizes could be the key to resolving the second particularly intractable question - were the tools part of a hunting or a scavenging adaptation? The former was championed by the late G. Isaac and some of his students. In their analysis of Olduvai Bed I sites such as the area where the OH 5 cranium and OH 35 tibia and fibula were found, called the FLK site (this yielded some 2500 artifacts and more than 60,000 animal bones), H. Bunn and E. Kroll suggest that hunting rather than scavenging was the main source of animal protein. From their analysis they conclude that "substantial" quantities of meat and marrow were consumed, that there was significant hunting or aggressive scavenging of large animals, and that there was "cooperative food sharing on a scale unknown to modern primates". The bases for their interpretation are threefold:

1. Theoretical - early humans would find it difficult to compete with other scavengers for access to fresh carcasses
2. Distributional - they initially interpreted the faunal remains to be mainly prime-aged adults (rarely available to scavengers because the carnivores are more likely to take the very young, or past-prime individuals)
3. Artifactual - their study of cutmarks left on bones (many more were at the center than on the ends, near the joints) suggested that meat removal rather than disarticulation was the primary focus of hominid activities. Disarticulation would be important for carrying parts of a carcass off If the early hominids scavenged, they argued, there must have been very early access to freshly killed animals.

However, A. Turner points out that through the Pleistocene the eating habits and resource utilization of East African carnivores left more than ample opportunities for scavenging. Moreover, in a reanalysis of the Olduvai fauna age structure, Bunn and Kroll found that many of the individuals they originally interpreted as prime age were actually past prime. This would mean that hunting and scavenging could not be distinguished. The cutmark analysis, too, was problematical (as all cutmark analyses are problematical). There is continued controversy over the criteria for identifying cutmarks and distinguishing them from carnivore tooth marks and scratches from trampling. The carnivore gnawing problem is particularly damaging to their case. Shipman found that the many of the Olduvai bones were gnawed, and that the gnaw marks tended to be on meat-bearing bones whereas many of the cutmarks were on non-meat-bearing bones. L. Binford was particularly critical of their case for this reason.

Scavenging had been regarded as a significant potential dietary resource for hominids by a number of paleoanthropologists studying early hominid anatomy and diet. Subsequently, archaeologists such as Binford, as discussed in Chapter 5, came to regard scavenging as the main element in the Olduvai hominid bone accumulations because of his study of associations among the faunal remains. He focused on the use of stone tools in breaking open limb shafts for marrow and fat. These resources, largely ignored in many of the scavenging discussions, are actually critical for utilizing lean meats that were undoubtedly common during the dry season. This is because without a source of fats, digesting low fat meats requires hominids to burn their own body fats just at the time when they are in most need of these reserves. Binford argued that fat and marrow were probably the resources that most of the scavenging activities focused on.

P. Shipman put forth a case for scavenging from the archaeological perspective, based on the consistent overlay of cut marks on top of carnivore canine tooth scratches on Olduvai bones. Working with R. Potts, her cutmark analyses seemed to preclude a hunting explanation for those faunal remains that were the debris of hominid meals. In retrospect, however, she has probably placed too much emphasis on the consequences of a perceived adaptive shift to meat eating, especially when the Swartkrans evidence seems to show that a dry season lean meat eating adaptation might be replaced and bettered by the effective use of roots and tubers that digging sticks allow.

R. Blumenschine examined the potential for scavenging in the early Pleistocene of East Africa, arguing that the factors making it a potentially effective adaptation for hominids (seasonality, carcass availability, predator behavior) existed then. He contends that while scavenging may be an erratic source of food, it can be a predictable one with minimal organization of hominid activities and technology no more complex than hammerstones that can be used to break open bones for marrow. Blumenschine accounts for the Bunn and Kroll data, and Shipman and Potts cutmarks observations, with the hypothesis that hominid scavenging was not passive but confrontational, as hominids threw stones and waved and banged sticks to discourage others interested in the carcass. He argues that coordinated, cooperative efforts allowed hominid groups to access freshly killed carcasses.

I find it quite credible to suppose that the diminutive *H. habilis* populations developed effective, but passive, dry season scavenging adaptations as part of their adjustment to the increased seasonality of the changing East African environment. Yet, it may be significant that most of the Olduvai hominid and archaeological site occurrences discussed in this debate are from the wettest period of the Bed I time period, when the requirements of seasonality are eased. It is also true that the large body size and the long legs of early *H. sapiens* are clearly adaptive for hunting. Other early *H. sapiens* adaptations to long distance, diurnal walking and running are respiratory, and these are reflected in the nasal anatomy of this large *Homo* species. It is quite credible to suggest that perhaps *H. habilis* is the Olduvai scavenger, while rarer evidences of a somewhat different *hunting **and** gathering* adaptation were left by early *H. sapiens*. Large body size would be particularly adaptive for the requirements of several different economic roles within this adaptive arrangement, and would facilitate confrontational scavenging as well. Seemingly contradictory archaeological arguments may reflect this adaptive dichotomy, and it is now possible to contend that all of the archaeological interpretations are more correct than not.

And what of *A. boisei*? The anatomical characteristics and the direction of their change, if not the "hominid-see, hominid-do" precept of early hominid behavior, strongly suggest this species was a tool maker and user as well, and any technology would be useful for its habitat utilization. If, as I believe, their abilities are reflected in the lithic remains and distributions of the pre-Oldowan industries described in Chapter 7, these would become archaeologically invisible once the Oldowan was widely made. Any evidence of *A. boisei* activities would be submerged in the Oldowan occurrences, or interpreted within their framework. Moreover, it is possibly that imitation led to a more sophisticated technology in the behavioral repertoire of these hominids, although the Swartkrans evidence argues against this.

REFERENCES AND FURTHER READINGS

ALEXEEV, V.P. 1986 *The Origin of the Human Race.* Progress Publishers, Moscow.

BEHRENSMEYER, A.K. 1984 Taphonomy and the fossil record. *American Scientist* 72(6):558-566.

BEHRENSMEYER, A.K., K.D. GORDON and G.T. YANAGI 1986 Trampling as a cause of bone surface damage and pseudo-cutmarks. *Nature* 319:768-771.

BIELICKI, T. 1966 On *Homo habilis. Current Anthropology* 7:576-578.

BILSBOROUGH, A. 1984 Multivariate analysis and cranial diversity in Plio-Pleistocene hominids. In G.N. van Vark and W.W. Howells)ed): *Multivariate Statistical Methods in Physical Anthropology.* D. Reidel, Dordrecht. pp. 351-375.

BINFORD, L.R. 1984 Butchering, sharing, and the archaeological record. *Journal of Anthropological Archaeology* 3:235-257.

___. 1988 Fact and fiction about the *Zinjanthropus* floor: data, arguments, and interpretations. *Current Anthropology* 29(1):123-135.

BLUMENBERG, B. 1985 Population characteristic of extinct hominid endocranial volume. *American Journal of Physical Anthropology* 68(2):269-279.

BLUMENBURG, B., and A.T. LLOYD 1983 *Australopithecus* and the origin of the genus *Homo*: aspects of biometry and systematics with accompanying catalog of tooth metric data. *Biosystems* 16:127-167

BLUMENSCHINE, R.J. 1987 Characteristics of an early hominid scavenging niche. *Current Anthropology* 28(4):383-407.

___. 1988 Reinstating an early hominid scavenging niche: a reply to Potts. *Current Anthropology* 29(3):483-486.

BLUMENSCHINE, R.J., and F.T. MASAO 1991 Living sites at Olduvai Gorge, Tanzania? Preliminary landscape archaeology results in the basal Bed II lake margin zone. *Journal of Human Evolution* 21(6):451-462.

BRAIN, C.K. 1993 The occurrence of burnt bones at Swartkrans and their implications for the control of fire by early hominids. In C.K. Brain (ed): *Swartkrans. A Cave's Chronicle of Early Man.* Transvaal Museum Monograph 8:229-242.

BRAIN, C.K., C.S. CHURCHER, J.D. CLARK, F.E. GRINE, P. SHIPMAN, R.L. SUSMAN, A. TURNER, and V. WATSON 1988 New evidence of early hominids, their culture and environment from the Swartkrans cave, South Africa. *South African Journal of Science* 84:828-835.

BRAIN, C.K., and A. SILLEN 1988 Evidence from the Swartkrans cave for the earliest use of fire. *Nature* 336:464-466.

BROOM, R.A. and J.T. ROBINSON 1950 Man contemporaneous with the Swartkrans ape-man. *American Journal of Physical Anthropology* 8(2):151-155.

BUNN, H.T. 1986 Patterns of skeletal representation and hominid subsistence activities at Olduvai Gorge, Tanzania, and Koobi Fora, Kenya. *Journal of Human Evolution* 15(8):673-690.

BUNN, H.T., and E.M. KROLL 1986 Systematic butchery by Plio/Pleistocene hominids at Olduvai Gorge, Tanzania. *Current Anthropology* 27(5):431-452.

___. 1988 Fact and fiction about the *Zinjanthropus* floor: data, arguments, and interpretations. *Current Anthropology* 29(1):135-149.

CHAMBERLAIN, A.T. 1989 Variations within *Homo habilis*. In G. Giacobini (ed): *Hominidae. Proceedings of the 2nd International Congress of Human Paleoanthropology.* Editoriale Jaca Books, Milan. pp. 175-181.

CHAMBERLAIN, A.T., and B.A. WOOD 1987 Early hominid phylogeny. *Journal of Human Evolution* 16:119-133.

CLARK, G.A. 1981 Multivariate analysis of "*Telanthropus capensis*": implications for hominid sympatry in South Africa. *Quaternaria* 22:39-63.

CLARK, J.D. 1993 Stone artifact assemblages from Members 1-3, Swartkrans Cave. In C.K. Brain (ed): *Swartkrans. A Cave's Chronicle of Early Man.* Transvaal Museum Monograph 8:167-194.

CLARKE, R.J. 1977 A juvenile cranium and some adult teeth of early *Homo* from Swartkrans. *South African Journal of Science* 73:46-49.

___. 1988 Habiline handaxes and paranthropine pedigree at Sterkfontein. *World Archaeology* 20(1):1-12,

CLARKE, R.J., and F.C. HOWELL 1972 Affinities of the Swartkrans 847 cranium. *American Journal of Physical Anthropology* 37:319-336.

COPPENS, Y. 1978 Evolution of the hominids and of their environment during the Plio-Pleistocene in the lower Omo Valley, Ethiopia. In W/W. Bishop (ed): *Geological Background to Fossil Man.* Scottish Academic Press, Edinburgh. pp. 409-506.

DAVIDSON, I., and S. SOLOMON 1990 Was OH 7 the victim of a crocodile attack? In S. Solomon, I. Davidson, and D. Watson (eds): *Problem Solving in Taphonomy. Tempus* 2:229-239

DAY, M.H. 1976 Hominid postcranial material from Bed I, Olduvai Gorge. In G.Ll. Isaac and E.R. McCown (eds): *Human Origins: Louis Leakey and the East African Evidence.* W.A. Benjamin, Menlo Park. pp. 363-374.

ECKHARDT, R.B. 1976 Observed and expected variation in hominid evolution. *Journal of Human Evolution* 5:467-476.

GRINE, F.E. 1985 Was interspecific competition a motive force in early hominid evolution? In E. Vrba (ed): *Species and Speciation. Transvaal Museum Monograph* 4:143-152.

GRINE, F.E., B. DEMES, W.L. JUNGERS, and T.M. COLE III 1993 Taxonomic affinity of the early *Homo* cranium from Swartkrans, South Africa? *American Journal of Physical Anthropology* 92(4):411-426.

HOLLOWAY, R.L. 1976 Some problems of hominid brain endocast reconstruction, allometry, and neural reorganization. In P.V. Tobias and Y. Coppens (eds): *Les Plus Anciens Hominidés.* Centre National de la Recherche Scientifique, Paris. pp. 69-119.

HUBLIN, J-J. 1984 Les superstructures occipitales chez les prédécesseurs d'*Homo erectus* en Afrique: quelques remarques sur l'origine du torus occipital transverse. In Y. Coppens ed. *Les Australopithèques.*

Actes de Deux Séances de la Société d'Anthropologie de Paris sur le Thème Australopithèques. *Bulletins et Mémoires de la Société d'Anthropologie de Paris* 10 (Série 13), pp. 303-312.

ISAAC, G. Ll. 1980 Casting the net wide: a review of archaeological evidence for early hominid land-use and ecological relations. In L-K. Königsson (ed): *Current Argument on Early Man. Report from a Nobel Symposium.* Pergamon, Oxford. pp. 226-251.

___. 1989 Cutting and carrying: archaeology and the emergence of the genus *Homo*. In J.R. Durant (ed): *Human Origins.* Clarendon Press, Oxford. pp. 106-122.

JOHANSON, D.C. 1989 A partial *Homo habilis* skeleton from Olduvai Gorge, Tanzania: a summary of preliminary results. In G. Giacobini (ed): *Hominidae. Proceedings of the 2nd International Congress of Human Paleoanthropology.* Editoriale Jaca Books, Milan. pp. 155-166.

JOHANSON, D.C. and J. SHREEVE 1989 *Lucy's Child. The Discovery of a Human Ancestor.* William Morrow, New York.

KENNEDY, G.E. 1983 A morphometric and taxonomic assessment of a hominine femur from the Lower Member, Koobi Fora, Lake Turkana. *American Journal of Physical Anthropology* 61:429-436.

KOREY, K.A. 1990 Deconstructing reconstruction: the OH 62 humerofemoral index. *American Journal of Physical Anthropology* 83(1):25-33.

LEAKEY, L.S.B. 1961 The juvenile mandible from Olduvai. *Nature* 191:417-418.

___. 1964 Very early African Hominidae and their ecological setting. In F.C. Howell and F. Bourliere (eds): *African Ecology and Human Evolution. Viking Fund Publication in Anthropology* 36:448-457.

LEAKEY, L.S.B., P.V. TOBIAS, and J.R. NAPIER 1964 A new species of the genus *Homo* from Olduvai Gorge. *Nature* 202:7-9.

LEAKEY, R.E. 1976 An overview of the Hominidae from East Rudolf, Kenya. In Y. Coppens, F.C. Howell, G.Ll. Isaac, and R.E. Leakey (eds): *Earliest Man and Environments in the Lake Rudolf Basin.* University of Chicago Press, Chicago. pp. 476-483.

___. 1988 Human origins: current topics of relevance and interest. OSSA (International Journal of Skeletal Research) 14:11-18.

LEAKEY, R., A.C. WALKER, C.V. WARD, and H.M. GRAUSZ 1989 A partial skeleton of a gracile hominid from the upper Burgi Member of Koobi Fora Formation, East Lake Turkana, Kenya. In G. Giacobini (ed): *Hominidae. Proceedings of the 2nd International Congress of Human Paleoanthropology.* Editoriale Jaca Books, Milan. pp. 167-173

LEE-THORPE, J., and N. VAN DER MERWE 1993 Stable carbon isotope studies of Swartkrans fossils. In C.K. Brain (ed): *Swartkrans. A Cave's Chronicle of Early Man.* Transvaal Museum Monograph 8:251-256.

LEWIN, R. 1983 Man the scavenger. *Science* 224:861-862.

___. 1987 The earliest "humans" were more like apes. *Science* 236:1061-1063.

LEWIS, O.J. 1980 The joints of the evolving foot. Part III. The fossil evidence. *Journal of Anatomy* 131:275-298.

LIEBERMAN, D.E., D.R. PILBEAM, and B.A. WOOD 1988 A probabilistic approach to the problem of sexual dimorphism in *Homo habilis*: a comparison of KNM-ER 1470 and KNM-ER 1813. *Journal of Human Evolution* 17(5):503-511.

MacARTHUR, R.H., and R. LEVINS 1967 The limiting similarity, convergence, and divergence of coexisting species. *American Naturalist* 101:377-385.

MANN, A.E. 1970 "*Telanthropus*" and the single species hypothesis: a further comment. *American Anthropologist* 72:607-609.

MARZKE, M.W., and M.S. SHACKLEY 1986 Hominid hand use in the Pliocene and Pleistocene: evidence from experimental archaeology and comparative morphology. *Journal of Human Evolution* 15(6):439-460.

MILLER, J.A. 1991 Does brain size variability provide evidence of multiple species in *Homo habilis*? *American Journal of Physical Anthropology* 84(4):385-398.

PARKER, S., and C. MILBRATH 1993 Higher intelligence, propositional language, and culture as adaptations for planning. In K. Gibson and T. Ingold (eds): *Tools, Language, and Cognition in Human Evolution*. Cambridge University Press, New York. pp. 314-334.

POTTS, R. 1984 Hominid hunters? Problems of identifying the earliest hunter/gatherers. In R. Foley (ed): *Hominid Evolution and Community Ecology*. Academic Press, New York. pp. 129-166.

___. 1987 On butchery by Olduvai hominids. *Current Anthropology* 28(1):95-96.

___. 1988 *Early Hominid Activities at Olduvai*. Aldine, Chicago.

POTTS, R., and P. SHIPMAN 1981 Cutmarks made by stone tools on bones from Olduvai Gorge, Tanzania. *Nature* 291:577-580.

PUECH, P-F., H. ALBERTINI, and C. SERRATICE 1983 Tooth microwear and dietary patterns in early hominids from Laetoli, Hadar, and Olduvai. *Journal of Human Evolution* 12:721-729.

RAK, Y. 1985 Systematic and functional implications of the facial morphology of *Australopithecus* and early *Homo*. In E. Delson (ed): *Ancestors: The Hard Evidence*. Alan R. Liss, New York. pp. 168-170.

RIGHTMIRE, G.P. 1993 Variation among early *Homo* crania from Olduvai Gorge and the Koobi Fora region. *American Journal of Physical Anthropology* 90(1):1-34.

ROBINSON, J.T. 1960 Affinities of the new Olduvai australopithecine. *Nature* 186:456-457.

___. 1961 The australopithecines and their bearing on the origin of man and of stone-tool making. *South African Journal of Science* 57:3-13.

___. 1965 *Homo habilis* and the australopithecines. *Nature* 205:121-124.

___. 1966 The distinctiveness of *Homo habilis*. *Nature* 209:957-960.

___. 1967 Variation and the taxonomy of the early hominids. In T. Dobzhansky, M. Hecht, and W. Steere (eds) *Evolutionary Biology* 1:69-100. Appleton-Century-Crofts, New York.

___. 1972 The bearing of east Rudolf fossils on early hominid systematics. *Nature* 240:239-240.

SABAN, R. 1984 *Les veines méningées moyennes des Australopithèques.* In Y. Coppens (ed): Les Australopithèques. Actes de Deux Séances de la Société d'Anthropologie de Paris sur le Thème Australopithèques. *Bulletins et Mémoires de la Société d'Anthropologie de Paris* 10 (Série 13): 313-324.

SEPT, J.M. 1986 Plant foods and early hominids at site FxJj 50, Koobi Fora, Kenya. *Journal of Human Evolution* 15(8):751-770.

SCHICK, K.D., and N. TOTH 1994 Early Stone Age technology in Africa. In R.S. Corruccini and R.L. Ciochon (eds): *Integrative Paths to the Past. Paleoanthropological Advances in Honor of F. Clark Howell.* Prentice Hall, Englewood Cliffs. pp. 429-449.

SHIPMAN, P. 1986a Scavenging or hunting in early hominids: theoretical framework and tests. *American Anthropologist* 88(1):27-43.

___ 1986b Studies of hominid-faunal interactions at Olduvai Gorge. *Journal of Human Evolution* 15(8):691-706.

SHIPMAN, P., and A.C. WALKER 1989 The costs of becoming a predator. *Journal of Human Evolution* 18(4):373-392.

SILLEN, A. 1994 Strontium calcium ratios (Sr/Ca) and strontium isotopic ratios (87/86Sr) of *Australopithecus robustus* and *Homo* sp. from Swartkrans. *Journal of Human Evolution* (in press).

SILLEN, A., and T. HOERING 1993 Chemical characterization of burnt bones from Swartkrans. In C.K. Brain (ed): *Swartkrans. A Cave's Chronicle of Early Man.* Transvaal Museum Monograph 8:243-249.

SPETH, J.D. 1987 Early hominid subsistence strategies in seasonal habitats. *Journal of Archaeological Science* 14:13-29.

___. 1989 Early hominid hunting and scavenging: the role of meat as an energy source. *Journal of Human Evolution* 18(4):329-343.

SPOOR, F. 1993 *The Comparative Morphology and Phylogeny of the Human Bony Labyrinth.* Cip-Gegevens Scientific Publishers, The Hague.

STRINGER, C 1986 The credibility of *Homo habilis.* In B. Wood, L. Martin, and P. Andrews (eds): *Major Trends in Primate and Human Evolution.* Cambridge University Press, Cambridge. pp. 266-294.

___. 1987 A numerical cladistic analysis for the genus Homo. *Journal of Human Evolution* 16(1):135-146.

___. 1992 *Homo habilis* closely examined. *Current Anthropology* 33(3):338-340.

SUSMAN, R.L 1988 New postcranial remains from Swartkrans and their bearing on the functional morphology and behavior of *Paranthropus robustus.* In F.E. Grine (ed): *Evolutionary History of the "Robust" Australopithecines.* Aldine de Gruyter, New York. pp. 149-172.

___. 1991a Who made the Oldowan tools? Fossil evidence for tool behavior in Plio-Pleistocene hominids. *Journal of Anthropological Research* 47(2):129-151.

___. 1991b Species attribution of the Swartkrans thumb metacarpals: reply to Drs. Trinkaus and Long. *American Journal of Physical Anthropology* 86(4):549-552.

SUSMAN, R.L., and N. CREEL 1979 Functional and morphological affinities of the subadult hand (O.H. 7) from Olduvai Gorge. *American Journal of Physical Anthropology* 51:311-331.

SUSMAN, R.L., and J.T. STERN 1982 Functional morphology of *Homo habilis*. *Science* 217:931-934.

TATTERSALL, I. 1992 The many faces of *Homo habilis*. *Evolutionary Anthropology* 1(1):33-37.

TOBIAS, P.V. 1966 The distinctiveness of *Homo habilis*. *Nature* 209:953-957.

___. 1976 African hominids: dating and phylogeny. In G.Ll. Isaac and E.R. McCown (eds): *Human Origins*. Benjamin, Menlo Park. pp. 377-422.

___. 1978 The earliest Transvaal members of the genus *Homo* with another look at some problems of hominid taxonomy and systematics. *Zeitschrift für Morphologie und Anthropologie* 69:225-265.

___. 1987 The brain of *Homo habilis*: a new level of organization in cerebral evolution. *Journal of Human Evolution* 16(7/8):741-761.

___. 1989 The status of *Homo habilis* in 1987 and some outstanding problems. In G. Giacobini (ed): *Hominidae. Proceedings of the 2nd International Congress of Human Paleoanthropology*. Editoriale Jaca Books, Milan. pp. 141-149.

___. 1994 The craniocerebral interface in early hominids. Cerebral impressions, cranial thickening, paleoneurology, and a new hypothesis on encephalization. In R.S. Corruccini and R.L. Ciochon (eds): *Integrative Paths to the Past. Paleoanthropological Advances in Honor of F. Clark Howell*. Prentice Hall, Englewood Cliffs, pp. 185-203.

TOBIAS, P.V., and G.H.R. VON KOENIGSWALD 1964 A comparison between the Olduvai Hominines and those of Java, and some implications for hominid phylogeny. *Nature* 204:515-518.

TOTH, N. 1986 The Oldowan reassessed: a close look at early stone artifacts. *Journal of Archaeological Science* 12:101-120.

TRINKAUS, E. 1984 Does KNM-ER 1481A establish *Homo erectus* at 2.0 myr BP? *American Journal of Physical Anthropology* 64(2):137-140.

___. 1989 Olduvai hominid 7 trapezial metacarpal 1 articular morphology: contrasts with recent humans. *American Journal of Physical Anthropology* 80(4):411-416.

TRINKAUS, E., and J.C. LONG 1990 Species attribution of the Swartkrans Member 1 first metacarpals: SK 84 and SKX 5020. *American Journal of Physical Anthropology* 83(4):419-424.

TURNER, A. 1988 Relative scavenging opportunities for East and South African Plio-Pleistocene hominids. *Journal of Archaeological Science* 15:327-341.

WALKER, A.C. 1981 The Koobi Fora hominids and their bearing on the origins of the genus *Homo*. In B.A. Sigmon and J.S. Cybulski (eds): *Homo erectus. Papers in Honor of Davidson Black*. University of Toronto Press, Toronto. pp. 193-215.

___. 1991 The origin of the genus *Homo*. In S. Osawa and T. Honjo (eds): *Evolution of Life: Fossils, Molecules, and Culture*. Springer, Tokyo. pp. 379-389.

WALKER, A.C., and R. E. F. LEAKEY 1978 The hominids of East Turkana. *Scientific American* 239(2):54-66.

WALLACE, J.A. 1975 Dietary adaptations of *Australopithecus* and early *Homo*. In R. Tuttle (ed.): *Paleoanthropology, Morphology and Paleoecology*. Mouton, The Hague. pp. 203-223.

WALTER, R.C, P.C. MANEGA, R.L. HAY, R.E. DRAKE, and G.H. CURTIS 1991 Laser-fusion ^{40}Ar/^{39}Ar dating of Bed I, Olduvai Gorge, Tanzania. *Nature* 354:145-149.

WILLIS, D. 1989 *The Hominid Gang*. Penguin, New York.

WOLPOFF, M.H. 1968 "*Telanthropus*" and the single species hypothesis. *American Anthropologist* 70:447-493.

___. 1970 The evidence for multiple hominid taxa at Swartkrans. *American Anthropologist* 72:576-607.

___. 1981 Cranial capacity estimates for Olduvai hominid 7. *American Journal of Physical Anthropology* 56:297-304.

WOOD, B.A. 1989 An interview with Phillip Tobias. *Current Anthropology* 30:215-224.

___. 1993a Early *Homo*: how many species? In W.H. Kimbel and L.B. Martin (eds): *Species, Species Concepts, and Primate Evolution*. Plenum, New York.

___. 1993b Four legs good, two legs better. *Nature* 363:587-588.

___. 1993c Rift on the record. *Nature* 365:789-790.

WYNN, T. 1993 Layers of thinking in tool behavior. In K. Gibson and T. Ingold (eds): *Tools, Language, and Cognition in Human Evolution*. Cambridge University Press, New York. pp. 389-406.

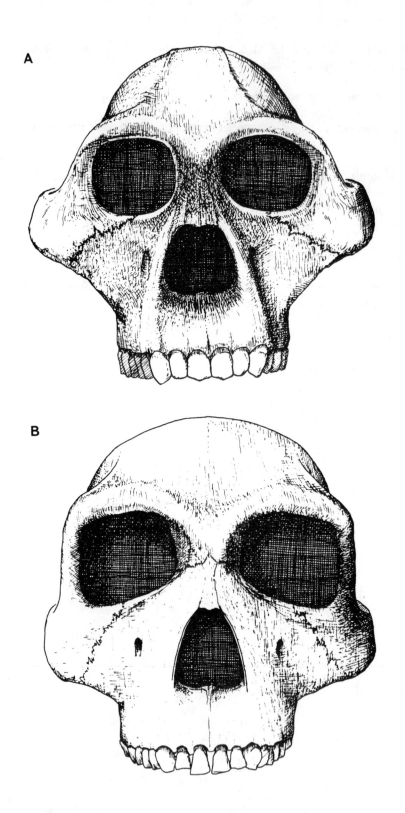

FIGURE 8.4 Rak's (1983) idealized comparison of an australopithecine (above) and *H. habilis* face.
FROM Rak, Y. 1983 The Australopithecine Face. Academic Press, New York, figure 7.

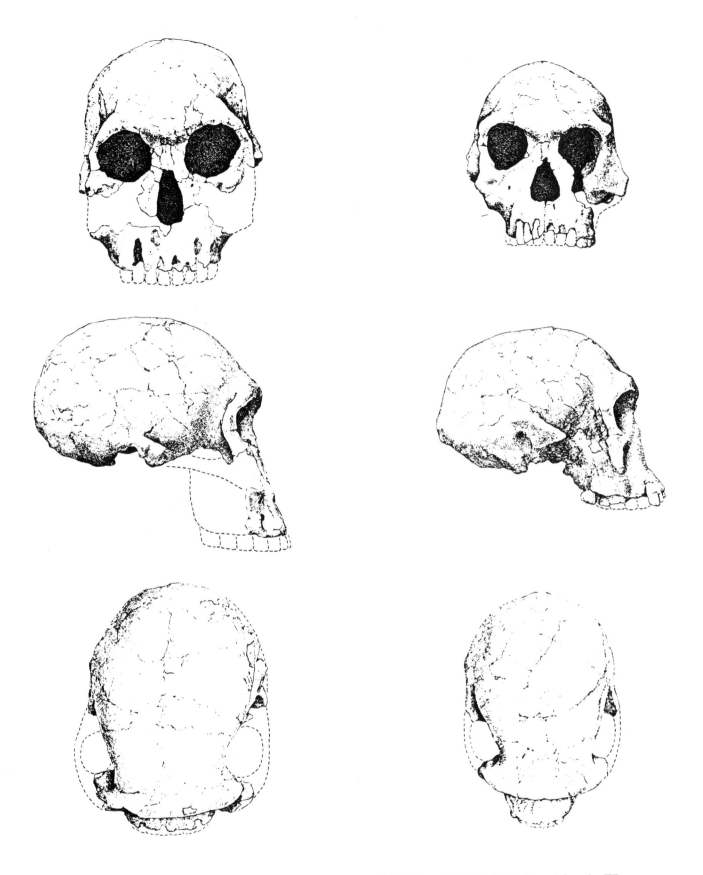

FIGURE 8.5 Comparison of crania often regarded as a *H. habilis* male (ER 1470, left) and female (ER 1813), after Walker and Leakey (1978).

FROM Walker, A.C., and R.E. Leakey 1978 The hominids of East Turkana. Scientific American 239(2):54
66.

FIGURE 8.6 Idealized variation in the facial structure of 4 Pliopleistocene species compared with a
chimpanzee (A), after White and colleagues (1981). B is *A. afarensis*, C is *A. africanus*, D is *A. robustus*,
and E is *H. habilis*

FROM White, T.D., D.C. Johanson, and W.H. Kimbel 1981 *Australopithecus africanus*: its phyletic
position reconsidered. South African Journal of Science 77:445-470, figure 8.

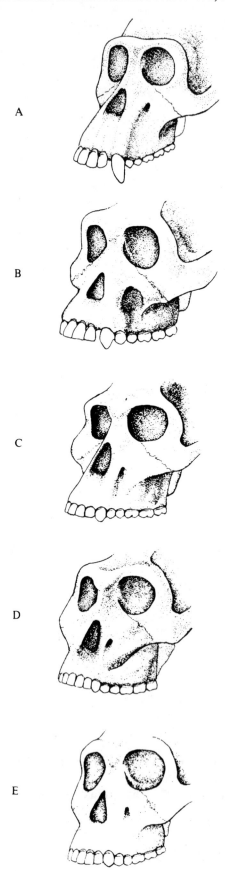

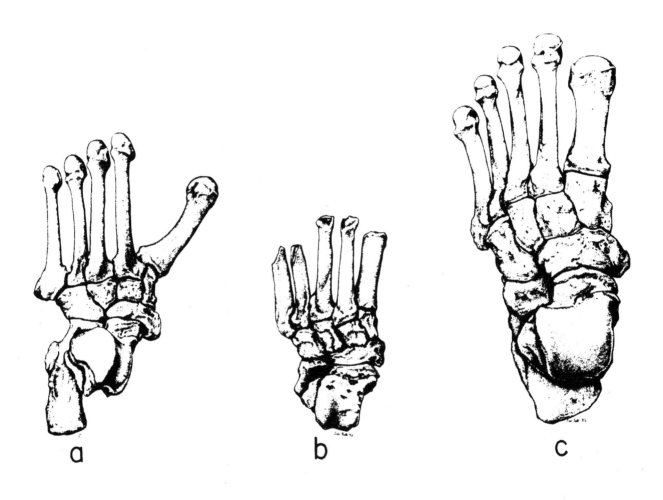

FIGURE 8.7 The Olduvai 8 foot (center) compared with a chimpanzee (left) and human, after Sussman. **FROM** Susman, R.L. 1983 Evolution of the human foot: evidence from Plio-Pleistocene hominids. Foot and Ankle 3(6):365-376, figure 2.

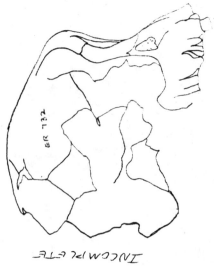

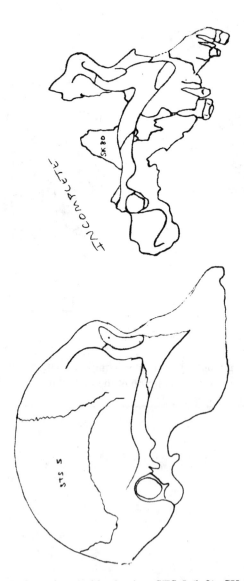

FIGURE 8.8 Three female crania of approximately equal brain size: STS 5 (left), SK 80/847 (center), and ER 732.

CHAPTER NINE

The Origin of <u>Homo</u> sapiens

In the plentiful sample of hominid crania from the latest part of the Upper Burgi Member (1.90-1.88 myr) at Koobi Fora, is found a large fragment of an unequivocal early *Homo sapiens* cranium. The specimen in question, and the species it represents, has been and still is by many regarded as *Homo erectus*, an extinct hominid species directly ancestral to *H. sapiens*. However, a number of scientists including this author have come to believe that *H. erectus* is not a valid species name. This is because according to the interpretation that *H. erectus* and *H. sapiens* are ancestral and descendent species on a single lineage

- there is no cladogenesis at the Middle Pleistocene origin of *H. sapiens* from *H. erectus*
- there is no distinct anatomical boundary separating the ancestral *H. erectus* from the descendent *H. sapiens*
- there is no single worldwide diagnosis that distinguishes so-called late *H. erectus* from subsequent samples of early *H. sapiens*
- relative to the ancestral condition there are virtually no apomorphies that are unique to *H. erectus.*

The problem is not in the interpretation of evolution but in the naming of species in accordance with evolutionary species criteria. Its solution is to cease distinguishing the earlier specimens as *H. erectus*, instead including them in *H. sapiens*, and this is the practice that will be followed here. For the sake of convenience and the clear identification of samples, I will follow the convention of dividing *H. sapiens* by criteria of time and geography.

- **Early *H. sapiens***: the earliest specimens, from the later Pliocene and Early Pleistocene (all of these were traditionally *H. erectus)*
- **Middle Pleistocene *H. sapiens***: the Middle Pleistocene specimens, only the earlier of which were traditionally *H. erectus* according to some authors although others would place virtually the entire sample in this taxon
- **Late Pleistocene *H. sapiens***: the Late Pleistocene specimens, including Neandertals *although this term is not synonymous with Neandertal*
- **Recent *H. sapiens***: the post-Pleistocene remains
- **Living *H. sapiens***: living and very recently (for instance historic) humans

Given the definition of evolutionary species (Chapter 2) and because *H. sapiens* is a widespread polytypic species, these divisions cannot be made solely on anatomical grounds. No set of criteria can uniquely distinguish most (let alone all) members of one of these from the others. The subdivisions can no more be exclusively categorized than can "anatomically modern *H. sapiens*" - a term in wide use today that has not been (and cannot be) validly defined.

Africa is the only place from which the earliest *H. sapiens* remains are known, and indeed was the sole continent inhabited by the species for at least its first half million years of existence. The first African *H. sapiens*, of course, must have appeared even earlier than the first specimens that have been found, or at least identified. It is possible that some of the Omo dental remains spanning 2.25-1.90 myr may belong to it as well, but this cannot be determined. It is interesting that while speculation abounds, the hard facts are that no species of *Homo* can be shown earlier than any other based on clearly diagnosed cranial remains. As to which *might have been* earlier, it is credible, perhaps probable, that early African *H. sapiens* evolved from an australopithecine-like *Homo* species, but since this would have to be earlier than the identified remains of *Homo habilis*, and for that matter earlier than the identified remains of

"*Homo rudolfensis*" (for those who prefer to believe this appellation describes a biologically valid species), it is unnamed.

The evidence for the earliest *H. sapiens* is framed in the adaptive context that distinguishes this species from all other hominids. The chapter concludes with a model of the origin of the early *H. sapiens* morphological complex. The role of lithic technology in the origin and early evolution of *Homo* is discussed, with focus on a series of subsequent behavioral and physiological changes that accompanied the evolution of a an adaptation based on gathering, scavenging, and hunting.

Earliest *Homo sapiens* Crania

The earliest known clearly diagnosed *H. sapiens* cranium is a 1.90-1.88 myr cranial fragment from East Turkana: ER 2598, a big, thickened occipital piece extending from the top of the bone below to the base of the nuchal torus, with detailed unique similarities to other, later, early *H. sapiens* specimens. There is a vertically thick and backwards projecting **nuchal torus** with a deep and broad sulcus below it emphasizing its rearward projection. Another distinction is the flexed occipital angle - between the occipital and nuchal portion of the bone is only about 108°. Inion, the highest point for nuchal muscle attachment, lies on the base of the nuchal torus and is well above the internal projection where the transverse and vertical ridges separating the right and left **cerebral** depressions (fossae) and the right and left **cerebellar** fossae (these are the depressions corresponding to the cerebral and cerebellar lobes of the brain, see figure 9.1) meet. This point, called **endinion**, is often used to gauge whether the nuchal muscles are expanded. Large nuchal muscles bring inion to a much higher position (for instance as in early *H. sapiens*), while smaller ones leave inion in a lower position that is usually coincident with the internal endinion position. In most australopithecines and australopithecine-like *Homo* (and in recent and living humans) inion and endinion are coincident. This is probably the case on your head, if you could see inside of it. ER 2598, by this measure, has expanded nuchal muscles, as inion lies some 15 mm above endinion. Another early *H. sapiens* feature is the transverse curvature of the back of the head as seen from above. With the flexed occipital angle this emphasizes the backwards projection of the nuchal torus. The bone is rather thick, and like most other early *H. sapiens* specimens it is the in dense outer cortical layer and not the spongy internal structure (**diploë**) where most of this thickening occurs. Internally the cerebral fossa is deeply excavated and shows little asymmetry, the left cerebellar fossa might be slightly larger. While fragmentary, there is no doubt that this specimen is an early *H. sapiens*.

The best preserved of the early *H. sapiens* crania is the 1.78 myr ER 3733 female, dated to the same age as the habiline specimens OH 7 and 62. This cranium (see figure 9.2) gives evidence of numerous features contrasting with the australopithecines; although varying in frequency and development, much of the same complex still characterizes this lineage over a million years later.

The virtually complete skull has a capacity of 848 cc, combined with a posterior dentition of moderate size and large anterior tooth sockets (table 9.3) suggesting incisors of ER 1590 size, similar to or larger than the habilines. This combination, however, is quite different from that found in habiline specimens. In the habilines large anterior teeth are part of all-around large dentitions and thus are usually found in palates with sizable posterior teeth (e.g. OH 16, ER 1590). Posterior dentitions of the smaller ER 3733 size are only found in small specimens, associated with habiline cranial vaults barely greater than 50% the ER 3733 capacity. For instance, the habiline female ER 1813 (figure 8.#) has a posterior dentition of about ER 3733 size but a cranial capacity of just over 500 cc. A male, ER 1590, with a cranial capacity only 150 cc less than ER 3733 has a posterior tooth area 32% larger. Thus, while these individual features of ER 3733 are within the habiline range, the combination is not!

The thickness of the cranial bones falls within the habiline range, and many cranial features individually resemble these more australopithecine-like hominids. ER 3733 is most like habiline females in some of her facial features, including posterior tooth size and morphology, development of the robust zygomatic bones, reduced prognathism of the lower face, the broad distance between the orbits, and the thin vertical dimension of the browridge. Moreover, the face is narrow relative to its (not insubstantial) height. These contrast with the larger, more prognathic faces of the australopithecines, with their broader and more prominently developed anterior cheeks, recessed and poorly developed nasal spines, and indistinct nasal margin and undifferentiated subnasal area. One would assume that the unique features shared by all *Homo* species evolved in the last common ancestor after branching from the australopithecines, but as discussed above we really know nothing of this hypothesized taxon.

Despite the similarities, grade differences from the late australopithecines and contemporary habilines are substantial. It could be said that in general early *H. sapiens* differs more from the habilines than these do from the earlier australopithecines, although as noted above many (perhaps most) of its individual features are found in the habiline sample . Most fundamental is the dramatically larger cranial capacity, and there are proportional differences in the vault dimensions. These are mainly greater relative length, greater breadth of the frontal bone just behind the orbits (i.e., less postorbital constriction), and greater backward extension of the cranial rear behind the foramen magnum so that the ear openings are closer to the center of the head and the foramen magnum position is in a more anterior position relative to the other structures on the cranial base. The forward projection of the browridges in front of the face of the frontal squama gives the brow ridges a real "top" and there is a deep groove (**supratoral sulcus**) where this horizontal top meets the sloping anterior face of the frontal squama. Its depth is accentuated by a bulged area at the middle of the forehead called the **frontal boss**, giving the front of the forehead a more vertical orientation. The supratoral sulcus separates the brow ridges from the forehead.

The temporal lines (marking the edge of the temporalis muscle) rise high on the cranial sides, but they approach each other most closely toward the center of the cranium rather than in the more forward position common in habilines. Between them, along the midline, is a **sagittal keel**. Another contrast is the small size of the temporal fossa which suggests a reduced temporalis muscle. The gutter for the lowest part of this muscle to lie in, over the top of the mandibular fossa, is the root of the zygomatic arch. Its top is where the fibers of the rear-most posterior temporalis lie. Like the temporal fossa. this gutter is also considerably smaller than in all but the smallest habilines. Yet, the mandibular fossa is large and deep. It is poorly divided into the fossa proper, and a convex articular surface for the mandibular condyle to rest on, in front of it, that is actually the front wall of the fossa. Behind it, the mastoid processes are small (this is a female characteristic) and separated from the enlarged cranial base by a very broad and deep groove for the digastric muscle (this muscle is important in opening the mouth and bringing the jaw backwards during chewing, and raising the hyoid bone at the top of the trachea, just above the larynx). Finally, there is a thick nuchal torus and significant expansion in the area available for the attachment of the neck (nuchal) muscles below it. The torus is similar to other early *H. sapiens* females such as ER 730. It is much smaller than ER 2598, a specimen - probably male - with a vertically thicker torus that extends out from the cranium much more strongly and is prominently developed across most of the cranial rear rather than just in the central region. The 3733 torus is in a high position on the rear of the cranium as indicated by the distance between inion and endinion (about 23 mm, but even this is less than their separation in another early *H. sapiens* female cranium ER 1808 [see below]). This shows that the nuchal muscles are expanded in size and take up more attachment area.

Facial differences include a facial breadth that is small relative to the frontal breadth. This contrasts with the dramatic expansion of the orbit size and nasal aperture. There is a broad nasal opening (table 9.3) with a distinct lower border (rare in habilines), and a distinct, projecting anterior nasal spine. The flat, even concave, subnasal area is set off from the palate by a marked angle at the nose's lower margin. The breadth across the nasal bones is expanded, even relative to the broad nasal aperture, and nasal bones project in front of the faced because of their flexed internasal angle (peaking). Adding to the projection is the maxillary pillar eversion, bringing the nasal aperture border well in front of the orbital margins. Franciscus and Trinkaus assert that "this volumetric expansion with an externally projecting nose has important implications for nasal respiratory physiology".

Initial descriptions of the ER 3733 vault suggested a marked resemblance to the 0.5 myr Middle Pleistocene female from the Zhoukoudian cave, near Beijing (see Chapter 11), reconstructed by F. Weidenreich. This similarity is more apparent than real and is seen mainly in the side view. Even in this view, one can see the much smaller vault, less bulging forehead, and much larger face of the earlier African female. There are other differences in robustness, vault thickness, and some details of the occipital bone that some have interpreted to reflect the differences in their ages and the geographic areas they come from.

Slightly later than ER 3733 is an extremely similar but much more fragmentary female specimen, ER 730 (1.70 myr). The anatomy of the specimen confirms details of the only moderately thickened supraorbitals (about the size as the ER 3883 male, discussed below), weakly developed occipital torusing, and only moderately thickened cranial bone. The vault fragments are associated with a mandible with molar teeth worn down onto the roots, an unusually aged condition for an early hominid that suggests she died at about 35.

Much later (at 1.57 myr) ER 3883 is the best preserved early adult male, characterized by a vault slightly smaller than ER 3733 (cranial capacity is minimally 804 cc) and a detailed replication of most morphological features. The vault is somewhat thicker, although unlike ER 3733 there is no special bone thickening, or sagittal keel. The forehead flatter and less of a supratoral sulcus separates it from the top of the supraorbitals, mastoids are much larger, and the nuchal torus is slightly better developed (all male features), but the most dramatic differences are in the face. Only the middle and upper portions of the face are preserved in ER 3883, but enough remains to show that sexual dimorphism is best expressed here. Supraorbitals are markedly thicker, especially in the middle of the face, and project further in front of the forehead. The torus is continuous, not interrupted by a groove over the nasal bones as in ER 3733. The facial region below clearly is larger as well, more anteriorly projecting, and more massive. The breadth across the middle face is some 13% greater, and indications are that the difference in facial height would be even greater. Some evidence suggests masticatory differences as well. The mandibular fossa is much deeper and has a steep anterior face. This anatomy is associated with increased molar use (see Chapter 4, pp. xx) because it is most efficient for chewing forces between the postcanine teeth while the jaw is open. Another indication of the same is the broad gutter on the zygomatic root, formed by the top of this mandibular articulation. While not nearly as broad as in the robust australopithecines, there were clearly a large number of fibers and this part of the muscle was important in mastication and perhaps other dental functions.

WT 15000 - The Skeleton of a Boy

The anatomy of a juvenile male is preserved by the "stripling youth", the 1.60 myr skeleton discovered in 1984 at Nariokotome on the west side of Lake Turkana. Described in what must be record-breaking time in a monograph edited by A. Walker and R. Leakey, WT 15000 (or WT 15K) has provided a goldmine of information about the earliest aspects of *H. sapiens* evolution. This 11 year old boy died and was buried in a swamp with shallow water (there is no evident cause of death). According to A. Walker his corpse was carried by the slow current for a short distance and came to rest in a muddy area where it was quickly buried, preserving most of the skeleton.

His age at death was determined by the incomplete eruption of his dentition. The second molars were just coming into occlusion and the permanent upper canine had not yet erupted. The condition of the 3rd molars shows that they were soon to erupt, probably at about 15, the age of last molar eruption for most Early and Middle Pleistocene humans (as well as Pliocene hominids). The eruption of this last tooth marks the end of most long bone and cranial growth; for instance, the cranial sutures begin to fuse in early *H. sapiens* at this time (brain growth in living people continues for longer and the sutures of the skull do not begin their fusion until the middle 20's). This may explain an observation made by B. Smith in her analysis of the boy. She notes that his skeletal maturation seemed more advanced than the dental maturation of his more anterior teeth. At 160 cm, he was closer to his final adult body size (about 188 cm according to Ruff and Walker) than most 11 year old boys would be today. For instance, fusion of the limb elements is about as advanced as a modern 13 year old. My research shows that the slowdown of adolescent growth, as marked by the more leisurely pace of molar eruptions in today's populations (and most likely of skeletal maturation as well) did not become established until the later part of the Late Pleistocene (this undermines studies by authors such as G. Sacher that attempt to directly link changes in human growth and maturation to brain size expansion, as fully modern brain size is attained by the *beginning* of the Late Pleistocene, if not earlier).

Like the limb fusions, the face is also advanced in maturity. Sinuses, the large open spaces enclosed by bone, in the maxilla between the orbits and tooth roots and in the frontal behind the brow ridges, had begun to form at a much earlier age than would occur today. The face was already large, very prognathic, and robustly developed. WT 15K resembles females such as ER 3733 in the anatomy of his facial features, just as children today have more feminine features than adults. This is because the **secondary sexual characteristics** develop largely at puberty and later, and males can develop their robust skeletal characteristics such as brow ridges, cranial tori and muscle markings, and thickened bone, even later in life. WT 15K's perceived femininity, in other words, reflects the absence of maturing male features. Walker speculates that as an adult he may have been extremely robust, perhaps significantly more so than the ER 3883 male and approaching specimens such as the 1.4 myr Olduvai early *H. sapiens* specimen OH 9 (see Chapter 10). Even as a juvenile, though, he shows the unique early *H. sapiens* features discussed above, including the large orbits, anterior supraorbital projection, projecting nose and nasal bones, great nasal breadth, and so on.

In sum, there is no doubt that the maturation rate of this boy was slowed, but it seems likely that the earlier growth periods were more lengthened by this process than the later ones. Independent support for this assessment is found in the analysis of the youth's endocast. D. Begun and A. Walker show that rapid fetal brain-growth rates extended beyond birth in this specimen, in a very human-like pattern. While this responds to problems created by large brain size at birth (see below), by increasing the period of infant dependency it contributes to maturational delays.

With an estimated adult brain size of 909 cc, according to Begin and Walker, and based on Ruff and Walker's adult body weight estimate of 68 kg, he is the earliest individual to have a relative brain weight that is significantly above the curve of primate allometry (figure 9.3) *in spite of his elevated body weight.* Early *H. sapiens* is truly the first large brained hominid. The endocast studies provide some suggestions about what behaviors the expanded brain size might have most strongly affected. Perhaps unsurprisingly, one of the structural asymmetries in Broca's area (see Chapter 4) is in a region important in muscular coordination of both tongue and hand movements. Combined with other evidence this supports the contention of an early appearance for complex vocalizations, presumably part of an evolving language system, and strengthens the evidence for a link between the evolution of language and stone tool manufacturing first and most prominently argued by R. Holloway.

Table 9.1
Relative Limb Lengths[1] and Climate

	Brachial Index (radius/humerus)	**Crural Index** (tibia/femur)	Humeral/Femoral Index	Pelvis Breadth/ Stature
WT 15000[3]	80	88	63	.144
Living Africans	76-79	82-86	71-72	.148-.174
Living Europeans	73-74	78-83	70-73	.160-.188
European Neandertals	73.6	77.2	71.5	.187[2]

[1] Population means, from Ruff and Walker, and Trinkaus
[2] Western Asia Neandertal (Kebara 2)
[3] Adult length estimates

WT 15K's postcranial remains are of great interest. They are one of the only two known to belong to early *H. sapiens*, and the second (ER 1808, see below) is severely **pathological**. In spite of being sub-adult and lacking some of the anatomical features that develop later in the growth process, they provide a key for identifying *H. sapiens* skeletal remains. The skeletal parts are, for the most part, modern and the limb proportions are also like those of living humans - compared with the australopithecines the lower limbs are longer and the pelvis smaller relative to body size. In particular, his height (185 cm estimated for adult height) and proportions (table 9.1) are those of living *tropical* humans, with relatively long distal limb segments (tibia compared with femur, radius or ulna compared with humerus) and a trunk that is long compared with its breadth. This fits the **Bergmann/Allen rule** for tropical adaptation - the ability to expel body heat is maximized when the trunk is elongated and limbs are lengthened, especially those limbs furthest from the trunk. As discussed in Chapter 6, Ruff has argued that climatic adaptation is mainly attained by changes in the body's breadth (for instance, as measured by the breadth between the hips), and not variation in height. This, he contends, explains why WT 15K has a pelvic diameter very similar to the (expected) male australopithecines, but also why there is a much lower ratio of this diameter to stature. The much greater height is achieved by leg elongation, bringing the proportions of the youth into the modern range. This height is not an adaptation *to* tropical climate but an adaptation *within* that climate. In this context, WT 15K leg length is *very* long indeed. For instance, the humeral/femoral index is very far below the range of any known African population, and this in spite of the fact that the African indices are already small because leg lengths are so long. The causes of these relative and absolute dimensions must be sought among the advantages of larger size and longer legs.

There are some other significant differences from the modern human condition. For instance, in their study of the vertebrae Latimer and Ward show:

- the vertebral bodies and sacrum are very small and australopithecine-like
- also like australopithecines there are 6 lumbar vertebrae
- the **neural canals** of the vertebrae that enclose the spinal cord are small, especially in the neck and mid-back region
- **vertebral spines** are large and erect

Thus, while some distinctions from modern humans (such as leg length) are unique, others are resemblances to the australopithecines. Additional similarities to the australopithecines include

- the thumb metacarpal is beaked and unusual in shape (this is discussed with the Swartkrans hominids, where a similar bone is found)
- femur necks are elongated (they need to reach more toward the midline because of the relatively narrower breadth across the acetabula)

Some of these distinctions have behavioral implications. Latimer and Ward argue that the large, horizontally oriented vertebral spines (in living humans these spines are oriented more downwards) support muscles whose more posterior position is required by the wide curvature of the ribs. In the bipedal condition the vertebral column is positioned deeper into the ribcage, the backs of the ribs thereby extending further behind the vertebrae and leaving less room for the muscles that extend the back (their importance is reflected in the fact that they are the source of most muscular back-aches). These ribs show that the trunk is more barrel-shaped than australopithecine trunks (best known for AL 288). The lower portion of the ribcage is close to the same breadth as the australopithecines (corresponding to similar breadths at the top of the pelvis), but in so much larger an individual this is effectively a narrowing at the base of the ribcage. All other things being equal this narrowing would have reduced chest cavity volume (it must scale to body size), but the volume is actually expanded in this early human. The increase is accomplished by an expansion of the upper trunk, creating the modern-appearing barrel-shape and at the same time requiring some structural changes in the shoulder (especially in the scapula) that, perhaps not coincidentally, improved the potential for powerful aimed throwing.

Perhaps the variation in the neural canals has the greatest potential importance. In her analysis, A. MacLarnon argues that the small size of the spinal cord in the thoracic region is caused by the lower level of muscular activity in the **intercostal muscles**, which cause movements of the rib cage and anterior stomach wall and provide fine muscle control of breathing. She believes that this fine muscle control, by implication missing in the youth, is related to spoken language production and infers that these hominids did not speak. However, a substantive comparative analysis by C. Childress supports a rather different and I believe more likely explanation that is one of Walker's first explanations for the small neural canals. He proposed, and Childress subsequently verified, that the main nerves affected by the diminished spinal cord size were those that control finger movements and coordination. Childress believes that early *H. sapiens* did not have the finer points of control and coordination, and that this accounts for much of the "crudeness" found in the artifacts of the later Oldowan (and indeed of other early Pleistocene lithics)

Walker claims that the limbs are very similar to modern humans. The arms show the development asymmetries that result from right hand preference; right handedness is also indicated by asymmetries in other paired limb bones, especially the anatomy of the clavicles, and by endocast asymmetries. Walker also comments on the anterior-posterior narrowness of the reconstructed pelvis (the inlet shape is elliptical, a very australopithecine-like form). He suggests that the narrow pelvic inlet shows that cranial capacity at birth was not the half of adult size that characterizes ape infants, but rather the relatively reduced one-quarter to one-third of modern humans - a cause of motor skill atriciality as discussed in Chapter 3 and a marker of dramatic brain growth (and associated learning changes) after birth. Ruff believes that the pelvic outlet is narrow as well, indicating the birth process was australopithecine-like and did not involve a second rotation to bring the baby into the sacrum-facing position of today's births. He reasons the broad, elliptical shape of the pelvic aperture reflects the continued dominance of the clavicles as a source of problems during the birth process - fetal heads had not attained the size to influence size and shape constraints and select for the changes in aperture shape that characterize women today (and in the Late Pleistocene). These are seductive speculations which might well be valid, but in this case I would agree with K. Rosenberg's assessment - the specimen is too fragmentary to draw any conclusions about the pelvic aperture's basic shape and proportions, let alone use this juvenile boy to assess the birthing characteristics of adult women.

Mandibles and Teeth

Many of the larger early *H. sapiens* mandibular corpus dimensions and proportions are well within the australopithecine range, and the ramus seems to have been broad and tall. This fact, plus the virtually complete overlap in dental dimensions, makes it difficult to distinguish all but the most complete dentognathic material from the habilines, during the time period when they overlapped. For the **edentuous** specimens (jaws without any teeth remaining or preserved) there is even a potential for confusing male mandibles of early *H. sapiens* with the smallest mandibles of *A. boisei*, a possibility made all the more worrisome by the low number of obviously male early *H.* sapiens specimens. The small sample that can be unambiguously attributed to early *H. sapiens* includes a number of moderate- to small-toothed specimens, mostly from east of Lake Turkana, such as ER 730 (associated with the cranial fragments described above) and 992. Even in the case of ER 992, one of the most complete specimens from East Turkana, some scientists intimately familiar with the sample, such as P. Rightmire, focus on the resemblances of this specimen with the OH 13 mandible and wonder, with some justification, if it is actually a habiline. Further confounding the issue, this particular individual is the specimen after which *H. rudolfensis* (see Chapter 8) was named. Yet there are mandibles associated with cranial remains that are clearly early *H. sapiens*. Apart from the WT 15K juvenile most of these are females of early *H. sapiens* (e.g. ER 730, 1808). There are some larger, more robust specimens, smaller than the contemporary *A. boisei* mandibles with teeth, that probably represent the corresponding adult males. If so, combined in a single sample, these mandibles reflect a degree of sexual dimorphism that is similar to that found in *A. africanus* and the robust australopithecine species. Cranial size dimorphism in the entire early Pleistocene African sample, is similar to these earlier species as well (see Chapter 10).

The mean size of the posterior teeth in the early *H. sapiens* specimens is reduced compared with the latest australopithecines, although like the mandibular bodies many specimens fall within the australopithecine range. Reduction is greatest in the middle of the posterior tooth row. Relatively, the second and third molars are less reduced than the first; the fourth premolar is diminished and is generally equal to or smaller than the third. However, similar to the australopithecine condition, the premolars are broad relative to the molars. Morphologically, the molars show the same multiple cusps that were found in the australopithecines, and particularly like the habilines the unworn molars are relatively long. Also resembling the habilines, the P_4 is not especially molarized and more closely resembles P_3. Canines and incisors are also within the australopithecine range, but in this case in the upper end. These teeth, if correctly allocated, are most like the habilines and it is possible that large anterior teeth may be a linking factor for all of the early *Homo* species. Some of the upper incisors have weakly developed **marginal ridges** along their lingual (inner) edges. Their crowns have moderately curved occlusal surfaces and at the crown base there is a small lingual **tubercle**. The virtually unworn WT 15K incisors provide a good example of this morphology. These three manifestations of **shoveling** are similar to that found in some australopithecines, and as discussed in Chapter 11 quite different from the shoveling morphology of Asians - the geographic area best known for the highest frequencies of prominently expressed incisor shoveling. In subsequent populations different combinations of these elements become better or more poorly expressed. One striking dental difference from the australopithecine condition is the lack of significant cusp addition in the posterior aspect of the dm_1 of the Turkana juvenile ER 820.

According to A. Walker, the early *H. sapiens* teeth from Koobi Fora "show very coarse microwear, scratches and pits very much like those seen in bush pigs" (these are omnivorous pigs that eat roots, carrion, and insects, and spends much of their time digging). Such a difference would markedly contrast with the tooth wear normal for the East African australopithecines, but *H. habilis* wear remains poorly reported and comparisons are not possible. The wear variation suggests dietary differences, and as the discussion of the Swartkrans hominids shows their direction may be unexpected.

Other Postcrania

A large part of the isolated postcranial sample from Koobi Fora has remained undiscussed because it is unclear what hominid or hominids it represents. Now it is time to return to this issue. As discussed above it is widely presumed that the larger terminal Pliocene postcranial remains are those of the habilines of the variety some describe as *H. rudolfensis*. This assumption is taken as support for the argument that there is a second habiline species, although ironically demonstration of a large body size for these specimens would *undercut* the species interpretation of their variation by providing a different explanation for it. However, there is not one association of a postcranial fragment with this variety, and the fact is that all other hominid species of this time are very small.

There are, however, two associations of the large postcrania with cranial materials and both of these are with early *H. sapiens*: WT 15000 (described above) and ER 1808 - a large female specimen with many skeletal elements. The cranial, mandibular, and dental fragments resemble ER 730 and even more closely 3733 (especially in the very thin supraorbital torus). Female sex is suggested by these resemblances and in particular the low mandibular body (even lower than the ER 730 female), small canine, thin supraorbital, and some details of the pelvic fragments. In a characteristic early *H. sapiens* pattern the nuchal torus is well developed and extends across the back of the vault. It projects well behind the occiput and is bordered where the torus and upper part of the bone meet by a shallow sulcus. The vault thickness is relatively and absolutely greater than the other two females.

Postcranial bones are quite long. Ruff estimates a 48 cm femur length and a body height of 173 cm for this adult woman. She had a very unusual disease, according to Walker and colleagues a form of hypervitaminosis A, a consequence of ingesting too much vitamin A in a short time period. This disease, really a metabolic disturbance, causes hemorrhaging along bone surfaces, and subsequent irregular formation of bone there. As a result of the additional bone her limbs quickly doubled in thickness, no doubt a painful cause of death. Two sources with concentrated vitamin A in her environment are raw carnivore liver and the eggs, pupae, and larvae of bees.

Because of these two associations and the fact that no early *H. sapiens* cranial remains are associated with small postcranials, the simplest explanation is that the large Koobi Fora postcranial remains are those of early *H. sapiens*. When all of the actual or estimated lengths from Koobi Fora are plotted (figure 9.4), they fall into three groups. The smallest is comprised of 6 specimens that range from ER 1500 (a female *A. boisei*) to ER 993, a reconstructed specimen almost always attributed to *A. boisei*. It also includes ER 738, 1463, 1503, and 1809. Some of these could be the small habiline, as the estimate for the OH 62 femur length (31.5 cm) is right within this range. It is reasonable to assume that neither of these small species is represented in the large group, but both might be found in the middle group. For instance, F.C. Howell attributes ER 3728 to *A. boisei*. This specimen, reconstructed at 39 cm, is the smallest specimen in the middle group and has a reconstructed weight, according to McHenry, of 45.2 kg. This is almost exactly at the *A. boisei* male mean - 44 kg (table 7.3).

The large group, comprised of 5 specimens, includes the early *H. sapiens* female ER 1808, the adult estimation for the male WT 15K, as well as ER 1592, the estimated length of the femur that would be expected to fit the ER 3228 innominate, and the very much more robust "broomstick femur" ER 736 (since WT 15K is an 11 year old, this might be the robustness characteristic of an adult early *H. sapiens* male). Because this set includes the only known early *H. sapiens* male and female specimens, the minimal interpretation is early *H. sapiens* is very large - perhaps the most striking feature of the species. While G. Kennedy suggests that ER 1481, one of the middle sized femora, is also early *H. sapiens* (*H. erectus* in her terminology), this would have to be a much smaller female than ER 1808 (60% the weight) and Trinkaus shows that this phylogenetic assertion is not justified by the specimen's anatomy. Are there any reasons besides their unusual lengths to believe that these femurs represent a distinct species? Some years ago, Kennedy suggested an anatomical criterion to help identify early *H. sapiens* femurs. She reasoned that virtually all of the femurs known to be associated with this taxon later in time, for instance at the approximately 0.5 myr Chinese site of Zhoukoudian where there is a sample of 6, have an unusual shaft shape. At the middle of the shaft there is expanded flattening from side to side. The transverse dimension is much greater than the anterior-posterior dimension, a relationship expressed in the **pilastric index** which divided the later by the former

$$\text{Pilastric index} = 100 * (\text{anterior-posterior diameter})/(\text{transverse diameter})$$
dimensions taken at the center of the shaft, or midshaft

She suggested that low pilastric indices might be expected to distinguish the same species much earlier in time, for instance in the taxonomically mixed-up sample in the East African Plio/Pleistocene where known australopithecine femurs are more rounded at the midshaft and thus have higher pilastric indices (this was subsequently found to also be true for the small habilines). This criterion works, but not as unambiguously as hoped. If we examine this index, many but not all of the early *H. sapiens* femurs identified by length meet her criterion and have lower pilastric index values, meaning more flattened femur midshafts. Another way to put this is that not all of the early *H. sapiens* femurs have flattened midshafts, but all of the femurs with flattened midshafts are early *H. sapiens* . This average tendency is expressed even more distinctly in later specimens (see Chapter 10). The cause of this shape is linked to another feature of most early *H. sapiens* femurs (and other limb bones) - the cortical bone of their shafts is quite thick (some 1½ times the australopithecine value). Thick cortical bone characterizes the larger habiline femurs as well, but early *H. sapiens* differs in that shaft thickness is by far the greatest on the medial wall, contributing to the flattened shape of the bone described above. This distribution of cortical bone responds to a somewhat different pattern of forces during locomotion. In particular, according to work by C. Ruff and colleagues it suggests that there was probably more running, especially over rough ground where there is a greater tendency for the trunk to sway from side to side. The pelvic mechanisms to stabilize the body during these and other activities were not as efficient as in the australopithecines because pelvic width is the same absolute size as in these early hominids, but relatively very much narrower.

The loss of efficiency is effected by the maintenance of an elliptical shape for the pelvic inlet, as Ruff reconstructs it for the ER 3228 pelvis. Bearing in mind that the specimens concerned are males, inlets of this shape are very australopithecine-like and as suggested above this might reflect the a similar affect of a shoulder-size dominance over head size constraints during birth (small heads at birth support the interpretation of significant atriciality in these children). However at this large size the leverage for the balance muscles is reduced and they must work with more force. Consequences of this greater force include a very strong **acetabulo-cristal buttress** on the side of the (otherwise thin) ilium to strengthen the bone against it, transverse expansion of the femur shaft (this is the direction of the force) making it more pilastric, and the cortical thickening of the femur shaft as described above.

According to Ruff and Walker, the sizes of the two most certain early *H. sapiens* specimens are:

- ER 1808 female: 173 cm, 59 kg
- WT 15000 male: 185 cm, 68 kg

The Ruff and Walker estimates are based on a somewhat lower weight-to-height relationship than McHenry uses for the australopithecines. This is justified because the australopithecines are relatively stockier. S. Molnar reviews weight/height relationships in human populations and finds that both climate and body size play important roles. Using data he presents, weight estimates based on tall African populations are substantially lower (88%) than the Ruff and Walker determinations, which therefore seem to take the elevated muscle mass of these early humans sufficiently into account.

Middle sex weight, 63.5 kg, if we can assume it approximates the population mean, is more than double that of the Olduvai habilines (29.4 kg), strongly suggesting that size difference is one way that the two species avoided competition. It is a significant expansion, just about an 80% increase from the *A. africanus* condition, if this is taken to be ancestral. The contrast with the small contemporary habilines is extraordinary, not at all like a Masai-Pygmy comparison (it is the *large* habilines who are Pygmy-sized, a point discussed below) but more in line with the "biggest in the world" and "smallest in the world" that one might expect to see in a small town carnival.

Ruff and Walker seem quite justified in their assertion that no subsequent average body size increases occur in human evolution. Quite to the contrary. If the few remains we have accurately estimate the population mean, early *H. sapiens* is *larger* (certainly taller) than the average height in most living populations, virtually all living African populations. Only the biggest Africans on record are taller, and they are not heavier. The mean Nuer body height is 185 cm, and mean weight is 62 kg.

Figure 9.4
Koobi Fora Femur Lengths[1]

[1] Actual or estimated (from McHenry) length in centimeters

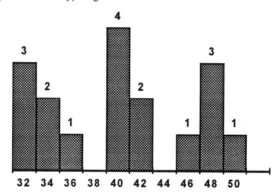

The early *H. sapiens* weight dimorphism of 1.15 is smaller by half than that of the less dimorphic australopithecine species (table 7.3). Once again if we can assume that these two earliest specimens are indicative of the average population values, their dimorphism is not unusual, in the context of modern variation; for instance, it is exactly the same as the percentage dimorphism in Turkana living in this region, west of Lake Turkana, today. This dimorphism in body weight estimates, and the magnitude of femur length dimorphism, are within the ranges of human population values and not far from the mean for many populations. It is not clear how significant of a change the reduction from the australopithecine condition represents, as the range of average dimorphisms for living populations is substantial - at its maximum even including populations as dimorphic as some australopithecine species.

The interpretation making fewest assumptions is that the middle sample of Pygmy-sized specimens includes no early *H. sapiens* (because the large sample has a female). At the same time it is possible that the large sample has other species in it. This would have to be males of the larger habiline variety. The main point is that *these data suggest that there is a larger habiline variety*, for what else could the bulk of the middle group be? The middle group includes specimens such as ER 1471 and 1482, which as Walker suggests do show a morphological complex that differs from australopithecines and small habilines, and Franciscus and Trinkaus also regard them as large habilines. Others in the sample such as ER 737 and 803 have been similarly regarded by Day and colleagues and it might just be that these educated guesses have been right all along. Supporting this interpretation are the combination of two elements in these limbs:

1. shaft shape
2. cortical bone thickness

At their centers, and indeed along their length, the femur shafts are more rounded. The anterior-posterior and transverse diameters are similar and the pilastric index is higher than the average for early *H. sapiens,* a high index is a more australopithecine-like condition. Yet like early *H. sapiens* the cortical bone on the shaft walls is quite thick, actually thicker than the early *H. sapiens* mean, relative to shaft size. None of this, of course, indicates *which* crania are associated with the Pygmy-sized bodies, but the temptation to suggest that they are the large-brained ones is irresistible.

If this logic is valid, it implies that a set of footprints found on the east side of Lake Turkana, and other very large unassociated postcranial remains from around the lake are also probably those of early *H. sapiens*. Outstanding among these is the virtually complete ER 739 humerus from high in the sequence, dated to 1.53 myr. Missing only the head (shoulder articulation), its length is estimated at 355 mm which suggests a body height of 178 cm, again using the proportions of long limbed Africans. The specimen is unusual for its very prominent muscle markings and thick shaft. Muscles providing strength in motions at the shoulder and elbow are particularly well developed, at the base of the bone there are indications of powerful hands as well. According to H. McHenry, the ratio of the circumference around the bone at its midshaft to bone length is so large that it not only exceeds modern human averages, it is almost outside the range of variation for gorillas. While several multivariate studies were interpreted to show these features reflected special adaptations to climbing and even arm hanging, the likelihood that the specimen is early *H. sapiens* supports alternative suggestions that they reflect strength in behaviors that are unrelated to the trees. This interpretation is supported by an analysis of the **olecranon fossa**, the deep pit at the base of the humerus in which the hook-like projection on the top of the ulna (**olecranon process**) fits to form the elbow. This fossa is deep and has a very steep side on its lateral margin for joint stability in the climbing and arm hanging apes. In ER 739 the fossa is shallow and has a sloping margin, both human-like characters. Powerful forces applied at the shoulder and elbow more likely reflect carrying heavy objects or strength in motions such as clubbing and thrusting.

Lastly, this makes the ER 3228 innominate out to be an early *H. sapiens*, a point already accepted by several authors who have noted its similarities to the early Middle Pleistocene innominate from Olduvai Bed IV, OH 28 (see Chapter 10). In fact, as the oldest of the Upper Burgi specimens, the 1.95 myr date leaves ER 3228 as the first evidence of early *H. sapiens* and the oldest of any *Homo* specimen from Lake Turkana deposits. It is a male, somewhat smaller than the adult size estimated for WT 15K. McHenry gives an estimated weight of 61.6 kg. There is considerable resemblance of the specimen to the youth's innominate, but it is much more complete and easier to analyze and compare with other innominates since it is adult. ER 3228 is distinct from the australopithecines, and yet shows a number of australopithecine-like features:

- flared iliac blade set at an angle to the lower part of the hip bone and widely angled relative to the body
- strongly projecting anterior superior spine
- small anterior-posterior opening to the broad pelvic inlet
- elliptical inlet shape (as reconstructed by Ruff)

Other characteristics of the innominate may be an allometric consequence of the large body size. These differences are allometric and not simple proportional expansions of the australopithecine anatomy because of the limitations imposed by climatic adaptation. These limitations imply that pelvic widths will differ little in spite of variation in body size. The biomechanics of a large, relatively narrow bipedal male pelvis requires more joint pressure (larger acetabulum) and more forces on the relatively thin upper blade of the innominate because many of the balance muscles have reduced leverage and consequently must produce stronger forces. These changes require better developed buttresses such as the acetabulo-cristal one extending to the iliac crest with a very prominent tubercle where this abductor-resisting structure reaches the top of the bone (and increased size of the same muscles have consequences for the shape of the femur shaft, helping to explain its medial-lateral expansion). These indeed are its main anatomical differences from the smaller australopithecine hip bones.

Therefore, the pelvic features that differ from australopithecines are unlikely to reflect locomotor differences. In fact, they may indicate similar obstetric mechanisms, expressed at a larger body size, in which a small brained **neonate** with large shoulders was born in a transverse orientation (this is described in Chapter 4). Australopithecine births involved some difficulties, according to R. Tague and C.O. Lovejoy, and the maintenance of a similar birth process in the much larger species suggests that these difficulties continued to be offset by the advantages of this pelvis form. It was only with much larger-brained neonates that birth-related selection altered pelvis shape, with adverse consequences in the locomotor-related biomechanics. The implications of this pelvis shape, however, are somewhat different than for the australopithecines, as early *H. sapiens* adult brain size is considerable larger. If we can assume that this anatomy is also found in the females, it implies what A. Walker suggested from his analysis of the less complete WT 15K pelvis - that births were premature compared with other primates. Drawing on data from his pelvis analysis with C. Ruff, as well as the WT 15K endocast studies made with D. Begun, he contends that early *H. sapiens* infants were atricial, and had the very rapid fetal rate of brain growth through their first year of life, just as human children today (with all the implications that immature births and intensive first-year learning have for the evolution of society). That this unique, modern pattern of development seems to have appeared in the earliest *H. sapiens* is a powerful argument in favor of the taxonomy used here.

The Ancestry Issue

Simply put, the ancestry of early African *H. sapiens* is unknown, beyond the likelihood that this ancestry is African as it is here that all other early hominids are found. As B. Wood notes, there simply is no definitive evidence of any *Homo* species earlier than 2 myr. In general, as mentioned above, it is most probable that an as yet unidentified early habiline is the immediate ancestor of our line. The early *H. sapiens* remains resemble the small form most closely in facial structure and the dentition, but are most similar to the larger form in brain size. P. Tobias favors the first, and A. Walker the second, but the possibility of an ancestor that is not a habiline (and thus a common ancestor of *H. sapiens* and the habilines) cannot be easily dismissed. No putative ancestor combining both sets of features is known, and if discovered it would most likely be diagnosed as early *H. sapiens* in any event. This issue is not likely to be resolved soon.

The Adaptive Pattern of Early *Homo*

Based on the present evidence, it seems likely that populations recognizable as *H. sapiens* appeared in Africa toward the end of the Pliocene, before 1.9 million years ago. Their link to the earlier australopithecines is unquestionable. Features ranging from the shape of the first metacarpal to the small vertebral sizes to thin supraorbitals, contrast with recent living people and closely resemble these diminutive hominids. In fact many individual features of the sample overlap with australopithecines, but their combinations are different. However, other characteristics, beginning with the obvious - brain size and body size expansion - are quite distinct and on the whole early *H. sapiens* represents a real acceleration from the more slowly changing rate of australopithecine evolution -- a change that might be linked to the australopithecines by an intermediate group similar to the large brain and body sized habilines, but not any of the *known* habilines because even if they are large enough, they are too late. Early *H. sapiens* is a new grade of organization. The differences are greater than those that distinguish any of the earlier or contemporary hominid species, and on the more than reasonable assumption that *H. sapiens* evolved from an australopithecine ancestor, the distinctions of the species probably indicate dramatic changes in the direction of selection acting on human populations at the end of the Pliocene. The possibility also exists that *H. sapiens* evolved in a different area and replaced the Turkana australopithecine populations during the latest Pliocene, but if so its ancestors are either australopithecines as well or we must posit that in spite of the wealth of Pliocene evidence, a still unknown hominid species gave rise to our own.

In my opinion the changes are unquestionably linked to behavior. It has become the vogue to explain brain size expansion virtually any way except behaviorally. As P. Shipman points out, everything from home range to life span to diet has been implicated. The role of diet has been most thoroughly examined. T. Clutton-Brock suggested that leaf eating and other folivorous primates have relatively smaller brains because their stomachs are expanded as part of their adaptation to low quality, difficult to digest foods. Frugivores and faunivores may need larger brains for more complex mapping of the environment, since their food sources are widely and unevenly distributed. But larger brains have their cost. R. Martin, W. Leonard and M. Robertson, and others focus on the metabolic costs of a large brain (in humans this organ that is 2% of the body weight uses some 20-25% of its metabolic energy - in other primates that figure is under 10%). Martin emphasizes two facts:

1. maternal metabolic output, through pregnancy ad lactation, largely determines adult brain size since most brain growth occurs prenatally or just after birth
2. energy requirements are exaggerated during a *human* baby's first year, when the infants are most susceptible to varying nutritional intake, because their brain grows at an extraordinary fetal rate.

Thus, in his thinking brain size evolution in the hominids is tied to their metabolism. If the exaggerated growth rate of the first year is linked to brain size expansion, this becomes a positive feedback loop as the expanding brain size demands the improvement of the behavioral changes that provided the possibility for expansion. How can hominids afford this metabolic drain? Many have suggested that a significant dietary change to richer, high quality food resources was accomplished as animal foods were obtained by hunting. L. Aiello and P. Wheeler treat brain evolution as a "zero-sum game". Since a big brain requires massive amounts of metabolic energy, and there is just so much that the body can produce, they reason that the brain must have expanded at the expense of some other organ. They believe that the size of the human intestines is relatively small compared with other primates, and it is here that they propose an evolutionary trade-off has been made. Large brains, they argue, require a high quality diet - meat and fruit. Because the large brains have expanded at the expense of the gut, at its reduced size, they can't digest anything else.

Yet Sillen's interpretation of the Swartkrans hominids and their behaviors, and the analysis of hominid activities at Olduvai, suggest that the behavior of early *H. sapiens* is distinct and dramatically more complex and insightful than earlier and contemporary hominids that do not deviate from the primate allometric curve. Language and related aspects of social behavior (c.f. Chapter 4), in particular, require size related organizational changes in the brain. Two anatomical sources suggest these were taking place at this time. First, research by J. Laitman and colleagues indicates that early *H. sapiens* cranial bases show changes that reflect an angled vocal tract - an important element of human sound production (this point is discussed in more detail in Chapter 13). The vocal tract changes compliment comparative neuroanatomical studies by both R. Holloway and D. Falk that suggest distinct language-related areas can be found on the endocasts of early *H. sapiens*. Second is the evidence for premature birthing and the extension of the fetal growth rate over the fist year of life, derived from studies of the pelvic remains. As discussed in Chapter 3, this combination of physical atriciality is linked to social precociality and is a hallmark of intense social learning. Expanded brains and the evolution of complex behaviors are socially oriented in humans. The behavioral explanation, the obvious one that bigger brains are there because of what big brains do, mainly learn, remember, and think better, fits the available data from a variety of sources and should be disproved before other, more esoteric, explanations need be advanced.

Equally, perhaps even more important is the dramatic change in body size and the elongation of the legs. Body size increases are not uniquely for the purpose of affecting an allometrically larger brain, as some have suggested. To the contrary, the earliest *H. sapiens* crania have significant relative brain size expansion and as pointed out above are the first hominids to deviate significantly above the primate allometric curve. For some time prior to 1.9 myr, numerous australopithecine populations had been changing in a direction which ultimately led to the great increase in the frequency of features described in the discussions of early *H. sapiens* morphology. I believe that the behavioral changes underlying this pattern of morphological evolution were a consequence of the development of new gathering and food preparation techniques that relied on some basic technological innovations that were beyond the capabilities of earlier hominids, and of a consistent and predictable diurnal scavenging and hunting adaptation to the lowland savannas of Africa. Two sources of evidence are important in understanding how this new grade of organization was achieved:

1. direct behavioral evidence from the archaeological record
2. the linking of behavioral and anatomical changes

SOME HELP FROM ARCHAEOLOGY

The tools found during this period are described as part of the Oldowan Industry (or, as some archaeologists prefer, Oldowan Industrial Complex). They have been discovered in large numbers, often in dense concentrations. Oldowan tools generally are polished bones and antlers, and modified pebbles, or flakes struck from pebbles with relatively simple fracturing. The Oldowan includes hammerstones and numerous crudely made, irregular cores. Many of these are not tools at all, but only blanks left over after the removal of flakes. Two things distinguish them from rocks with natural fracturing. First, the flaking is bifacial - it occurs on both sides of an edge. Naturally fractured rocks are usually flaked on only one side. Second, the tools are often manufactured using manuports, types of stone not normally found at the site or even in the nearby area. At Olduvai in Bed I, for instance, the main sources of materials for the stone tools were the river beds, whose cobbles included easily workable volcanic rock washed down from the highlands. These sources varied in distance from the Olduvai activity sites by 2 to 12 km. R. Potts argues that some of the better cobbles for tool making were left in catches, at convenient spots were the hominids returned later for various activities including tool making. These interpretations of the activity areas suggest that the tools, and the materials used in making them, were in L. Binford's terms curated, and not simply an expedient response to the needs of the environment.

N. Toth has shown that the main cause of artifact variation in shape comes from the shape of the initial blank, and not an idea or precept about the final form that the maker might have held in his or her mind. The utilized flakes were often modified as they were resharpened when they became dull. This also altered their shape and is an important element in the so-called "tool types". In fact, there really are no "types" in the Oldowan, in the sense of tools made in accordance to a regular pattern. The artifacts are crudely made and without regular form, facts that suggest they are mainly the debris left behind from rock-smashing activities whose main focus was to produce sharp flakes. This indiscriminate smashing aspect of the Oldowan distinguishes these tools from simple Oldowan-like artifacts made later in time, even today as reported by archaeologists such as B. Hayden.

Binford has further suggested that the Oldowan technology was directed toward scavenging activities, arguing that the cores were used in breaking open bones for their internal fat and marrow and relying on data about the juxtaposition of gnaw marks and tool-produced scratches on bone developed by R. Potts and P. Shipman to argue that some of the flakes were used for dismemberment after the bones were gnawed on by carnivores. Considerable insight has come from the microscopic study of the artifacts. Wear on flakes has been attributed to cutting meat and grass stems or reeds, and to sawing or scraping wood. It is clear that these sharp flakes were used in activities that left cut marks found on animal bones at the Oldowan sites. According to Shipman some of the bone artifacts were used to dig and others to cut or scrape animal skin. The significance of the later activity is that when combined with evidence provided from the study of animal bone cutmarks indicating that skins were being removed, there is a strong indication that the hominids were using the skins, for instance in making skin bags for carrying.

The Pliocene and Early Pleistocene was not a period of technological stagnation. Tools undergo a recognizable evolution into the Oldowan, first found at about 2 myr in the Lake Turkana basin. According to J. Harris and colleagues, the industries at Olduvai and Koobi Fora differ from their simpler predecessor in the following ways

- much higher number and density of artifacts
- activity areas identifiable, often far from raw material sources
- not restricted to a particular season and widespread spatially
- improvements in flaking technology, suggesting a better knowledge of
  - particular material's flaking properties
  - the effects of percussion strength and angle

One of the most important aspects of Oldowan tools is that they have been found together in large clusters. These were first interpreted as **living floors** (excavated camp sites). It was assumed that the excavated surface represents the place where hominids once lived, and in some cases the content and patterning of the debris on the surface was taken to be the result of hominid activities. For instance, at one of the Olduvai Bed I sites, a pattern was found in the distribution of animal bones. There is a central circle in which all of the bones are smashed into very small pieces. Surrounding this circle there are also animal bones. These, however, are whole. The types of bones inside the circle have marrow, while the unsmashed bones outside have little or no marrow. The interpretation was that there were area-specific functional activities. In one area, bones containing marrow were smashed and the marrow extracted, while outside of this area other bones were discarded. The hominids seemed to be making maximum use of marrow-yielding bones in a habitual place and manner.

But were these accumulations the results of hominid activities, as the earlier enthusiastic interpretations assumed? This question has been the focus of a major, and very long lasting, debate in paleoanthropology. These accumulations could potentially be:

1. The consequences of normal taphonomic processes that accumulate patches of stones and bones
2. The fortuitous overlay of hominid-modified stones and carnivore-modified bones that accumulated at different times
3. Places where hominids carried artifacts (or blanks to make artifacts) and bones as part of their food

Distinguishing these has proven to be difficult. However, over the course of the debate a general agreement has developed that many of the stone-bone associations are activity related, and therefore that some sites reflect the activities of hominids even if not their campsites. That some of these activities focused on eating there is no doubt, but the issues remain of whether hunting or scavenging was the mode of food acquisition, and whether there was food sharing or individual snacking (this issue was discussed in Chapter 5). Realistically, both of these are false dichotomies - extremes at the ends of a continuum of inseparable behaviors.

Of course, some hunting must have occurred - we could gather that from chimpanzee studies, although as discussed in Chapter 5 chimpanzee hunting is ecologically variable and contextually different than any recognizably human pattern. It tells us little about hunting in the early hominids except for its likelihood. Hunted game was probably restricted to very small, young, or slow animals - especially if the midget hominids were the hunters. Hunting in modern human groups has four important aspects:

1. When it occurs, it is a consistent and role specific behavior.
2. Opportunism is reduced because hunting activities are planned and learned.
3. Game larger than the hominids is regularly hunted.
4. It is an inseparable part of a complex adaptation for predictably obtaining foods that is focused on gathering and depends on a sex-based division of labor

The question is when each of these began to characterize hominid hunting. A related question is how the various elements combined in the food-obtaining activities of the different species of *Homo*.

The behavioral changes revealed by the archaeological studies continue through the earlier Pleistocene. Only several hundred thousand years after the earliest appearance of the Oldowan, or Oldowan-like industries, a better-made tool assemblage called the Karari industry is found in the circum-Turkana region. The Karari is characterized by modifications of the flakes and an increasingly recognizable number of tool forms. Similarly, the so-called "Developed Oldowan" of Bed I and lower Bed II seems to be the same industry with different raw material sources. A comprehensive study by M. D. Leakey shows that considerable changes distinguish it from the earlier tool-making activities. By lower Bed II times the evidence provided by the activity areas differs in three important respects.

1. As already mentioned, a greater variety of tool types can be distinguished, and the tools generally appear to be better made (more symmetric forms, straighter edges, etc.).
2. There is a wider variety of different types of sites. This suggests that hominids were beginning to conceive of making different sets of tools for different functional activities, perhaps such as killing, butchering, collecting, and so on.
3. Remains representing all the body parts of large animals are found in higher frequency in the activity areas, and the bones are more fragmented.

These accumulations may not be the result of carnivore kills, but instead have a better chance of representing the hunting or active, confrontational scavenging activities of the hominids themselves, and suggest an improved ability to utilize both meat and marrow.

As to who made the tools, it has been widely perceived that the answer is probably "everybody". The evidence is that at least two species of *Homo* were manufacturing the Oldowan at the beginning of the Pleistocene (see Chapter 8) and there is probably an invisible spread of simpler industries that the Oldowan, by virtue of its ubiquity and density, covers up. With Isaac's idea of an initial technological explosion followed by stasis seemingly incorrect, and the potential not just for different tool-making hominids, but different tool-making species of *Homo* that varied in brain size as well as body size and leg length, the possibilities of species-specific differences in technology and the role of tools in adaptation must be explored. With *H. sapiens* present through the span of the Oldowan, and the evidence provided by studies of chimpanzee tool use and from Swartkrans revealing just how difficult even the simplest technological innovations seem to have been, we must also consider the possibility that there was only one tool-user who contributed to the continued changes that developed within the Oldowan

THE EVOLUTION OF HUNTING/SCAVENGING/GATHERING, AND ITS CONSEQUENCES

If Binford is correct in asserting that scavenging and bone marrow acquisition were the main foci of Oldowan activities, we know that at least at Swartkrans these were supplanted by the dietary advantages of underground resources accrued by digging sticks. The question of diet in the early *Homo* species is far too complex to be framed as "scavenging vs. hunting". The human adaptation is a hunting/scavenging *and* gathering one, and both theoretical reconstructions and direct evidence suggests that we must begin to view the past in this framework.

Combining the archaeological evidence with the evolutionary direction taken by early *H. sapiens* strongly implies that it was the evolution of hunting, confrontational scavenging (as Blumenschine describes it), gathering, and the associated organizational changes, that accounted for their successful adaptation. This change in adaptation was more opportunistic than reactive to any particular climate change, originating with the niche expansion made possible by the late Pliocene technological and organizational innovations. Understanding it requires several anthropological myths to be shed. In particular it is probably incorrect that in the emerging adaptation of early *Homo*

- meat was a significant proportion of the diet during any season
- meat was necessarily obtained by organized hunting
- meat was invariably the main aim of hunting or scavenging activities
- tools were a male possession because their main purpose was to aid in killing and butchering

P. Shipman once asked what it takes to be a meat eater. Her answer was phrased in terms of metabolic cost, position of a carnivore on the ecological pyramid, and the advantages of high quality resources. Yet, humans did not simply, or even particularly become meat eaters - they evolved a very efficient hunting, scavenging, and gathering adaptation whose advantages have been not in specialization on one particular resource (single resource focus is a Neolithic strategy), but rather on the exploitation of the broadest range of resources. The early Pleistocene hunting/scavenging/gathering adaptation is not a particularly *modern* one - even if it incorporates all of the individual elements found in modern approaches to food procurement. The organization of these in successful strategies is an aspect of early Pleistocene food acquisition that is not easily observable from archaeological evidence, but is as important as the individual elements.

The Importance of Gathering

Significant hominid hunting or scavenging is impossible at virtually any level of technology without an effective gathering adaptation in place, and associated social constructs that provide for a division of labor and systematic sharing and mutual provisioning. A scavenging and hunting adaptation requires more calories than a more sedentary pattern based on collecting. According to C. Peters, the difference in calorie requirements is substantial regardless of body size, approximately 33%. Moreover, gathering is more productive and less risky. Even among modern hunter/gatherers (albeit peoples in marginal environments) women gathering is some 67% more productive than male hunting. It is quite likely, argues J. Lancaster, that male hunters can only afford to risk so much subsistence time because of "the greater extractive efficiency of women" - a point also raised in the first edition of this book. This gathering efficiency is obtained at an energetic cost, however. G. Bentley points out that foraging and gathering imposes a heavy workload, and is a source of selection for increased body size.

It is unlikely that hunting could have become a very important activity until hunting techniques became relatively efficient, as measured by the calories obtained compared with the energy expended. Moreover, the potential importance of hunting as a dry season adaptation was limited by access to fats. Hunting during the dry season requires hominids to spend their diminishing body fat resources to digest lean meats. Meat eating could not be a particularly effective dry season adaptation without supplemental sources of fat. Later Pleistocene human populations solved this problem in a variety of innovative ways.

The Role of Technology

Ironically, one very successful adaptive innovation of early *Homo* may have been the replacement of meat by underground resources during the dry season, a replacement made possible by the invention of digging sticks. An alternative way of solving the problem was suggested by Binford who argues that a main focus of Oldowan technology was to obtain marrow and fats by smashing bones. Whether underground resources or bone smashing, the problems raised by dry season dietary fat deficiencies may have engendered solutions that were dependent on a simple technology - one that it is increasingly clear all early hominid species did not share. Even at this earliest time, and in this simplest sense, some hominids had become dependent on technology for their survival. Many, including this author, believe that a hominid dependence on technology presages a dependence on culture.

The important technological innovations were not wholly or perhaps even significantly related to hunting and scavenging. The technology required for effective gathering and mutual provisioning is much more complex. The use of digging sticks is a case in point, extending the range of critical resources during the season when foods are most difficult to obtain. Moreover, some very important changes appeared in the evolution of technology for food preparation (if not in the improvement of stone tool manufacturing skills). These were probably a causal factor in the increasing number of tool types within the Olduvai sequence. The later (Developed) Oldowan sites coexist in areas with sites with a tool kit little different from the earlier Oldowan. Whether this reflects differing cultural adaptations of *Homo* species with different behavioral potentials or function-specific tool kits made by the same species is unclear. Whatever the case, Developed Oldowan tool kits include some new tool types, such as a crudely pointed chopper-like tool and small scraping tools. A roughly circular tool usually showing evidence of battering greatly increases in frequency. The battering on these spheroids is thought to result from pounding foods to make them easier to chew. If so, this was a marked improvement in food preparation. Every increase in the amount of cutting, chopping, or smashing of foods before they were chewed would have decreased the need to maintain a masticatory complex that produced powerful forces and stood up to excessive wear for a long time.

Even more formidable problems are met when the object of gathering shifts from snacking to food sharing as collected foods that are very difficult to carry such as small grains, roots and tubers, insects, and so on must be separated, cleaned, and transported. Technology played a more critical role in the evolution of these and related activities than in the evolution of hunting and confrontational scavenging *per se;* implements are extremely important in both obtaining and preparing plant foods, while containers are critical for carrying them once the pattern of eating all foods at their source is left behind. The three critical inventions of the Lower Paleolithic are, in my view,

1. flakes for cutting
2. digging sticks
3. containers for carrying

Viewing these early hominids through our jaded eyes, with the expectation that they are little different from ultra-primitive humans and that the ancestral condition as represented by chimpanzees is near-humanity in any event, we tend to forget that these were difficult hominid inventions. They are not part of the chimpanzee behavioral repertoire, and the best evidence suggests that hominids attained the intellectual capacity and behavioral complexity to invent and effectively use them only for the last third of their evolution. Big deal? They are a much bigger deal than one might have supposed.

The containers are ever so more complex than the other two, but absolutely critical for collecting and transporting foods that are small or time-intensive to obtain in large numbers. Containers play another role in this adaptation. The innovation of containers may have been one of the factors resulting in the dramatic body size increases that characterized the earliest *H. sapiens* populations. Carrying a water supply provided the opportunity for long distance diurnal walking, an important element in many hunting strategies as well as in landscape scanning for scavenging possibilities. This is because of the hominid emphasis on sweating as the major heat-loss mechanism, discussed below. Moreover, in the absence of sufficient water in arid areas, it is necessary to maximize the ratio of body surface area to body weight to improve heat loss through radiation. This ratio is most effectively maximized when body size is small. It is possible that by providing sufficient water during daily activities, containers helped remove the earlier small-size limitation on hominids adapted to arid or semi-arid regions. Through allowing activities that are best accomplished by long legged hominids, and removing one of the body size limiting factors, the invention of containers may be one of the earliest cases in which a technological innovation affects behavioral adaptations and ultimately leads to morphological change.

In fact, w*ithout containers there would be no hunting. scavenging, and gathering adaptation.* Their early invention, however, is not just speculation. It is almost astonishing that there are indications of containers at this early time. This evidence, discussed above, is provided by the leather-polish on the Swartkrans digging sticks (they must have been curiated as the number of use-wear scratches requires several days of use), and the bone cutmarks in positions denoting the detachment of skin tendons.

Changing Adaptation and Diet

There are numerous implications involved in this adaptive shift. The obvious dietary one is the decrease in the amount of low quality foods in the diet. These items, the most difficult and time consuming to masticate, provided the main source of selection that maintained a variable but large masticatory apparatus in all early hominid species. Humans today have a much higher quality diet than other primates of similar size, or even than one might expect from their metabolic needs at rest, according to W. Leonard and M. Robertson. One main source of nutritionally denser foods is meat, and the physiological adaptations to meat eating are evident in the human intestines (evidence for this is reviewed by K. Milton). Most evidence suggests that the nutritional changes responded to the metabolic demands of increasing brain size, and as noted above it is probable that the emergence of *H. sapiens* was intimately connected to these nutritional changes. Higher quality food sources became more prevalent because of

- the wider range of usable foods in each habitat that sharing allowed.
- food preparation technology,
- the ability to carry large amounts so that all individuals need not invest collecting time,
- more regular access to fats and marrow during the dry season
- the improved predictability of scavenged and hunted protein

The effects of these changes spread across many aspects of hominid morphology, but were perhaps most immediately evident in the reduction of the australopithecine or australopithecine-like masticatory apparatus in early *Homo*, and especially early *H. sapiens*.

Body size

Perhaps the most spectacular distinction of the earliest *H. sapiens* is the increase in body size and change in proportions. The body height estimates are close to double those of the smaller *H. habilis* variety. Weight differences are even greater. Weight should vary with the cube of height all other things being equal. All other things are not equal, however, as early *H. sapiens* is more linear

- Ruff shows that pelvic widths are more constant in a given environment than limb lengths, so taller individuals have relatively narrower trunks and therefore relatively less body mass
- Limb elongation is an allometric consequence of increased body size - heavier individuals will tend to change in proportion and have relatively longer limbs
- The maximization of body surface area relative to mass (heat adaptation) is accomplished by limb elongation

As Ruff and Walker point out, early *H. sapiens* is about the same size as the tallest of today's linear sub-Saharan Africans. Moreover the increased linearity has implications beyond heat adaptation, which is to say that the body size increase was for more reasons than to adapt to the tropics. After all, hominids had lived there for a long time, and as Ruff points out their shorter, wider bodies were also effectively adapted to open and dry environments, The question is "why now?".

Table 9.2

Water Loss Parameters Relative to Body Size for Active Sweating Hominids
in a 35-40° C Environment[1]

Weight (kg)	Surface area Relative to Weight (m^2/kg)	Sweat Loss Relative to Weight	Total Water Loss Relative to Weight	Water Consumption (kg/12 hr)	Range (km. at 4% dehydration tolerance)
35[2]	.034	2.36%	3.71%	1.30	11.5
61[3]	.028	1.90%	3.10%	1.88	22.0

[1] From Wheeler (1992); he gives data for a number of weights but only two are reproduced here
[2] Middle sex *A. africanus* weight is 35.5 kg, the smaller *H. habilis* mean slightly less
[3] Mean for the earliest *H. sapiens* male and female is 63.5 kg

A number of scientists have suggested that the reason for the body size increase and limb elongation is a behavioral rather than a habitat change (c.f. R. Foley and others) - a contention that makes sense as early *H. sapiens* is found in the same habitats as much smaller hominid species. A. Sinclair and colleagues suggest that limb elongation would improve stride length and make it easier to follow migratory herds. P. Wheeler shows that even if similar proportions are assumed, larger bipeds are more efficient in hot and arid conditions when water resources are limited. Comparing two of the body sizes he analyzes (table 9.2), the two that happen to approximate the mean weights of *A. africanus* (or *H. habilis*) and early *H. sapiens*, Wheeler's data show that the relative surface area is smaller at the larger body size - this is purely geometric, he assumes the body proportions are the same regardless of size. At larger sizes the sweat loss relative to body size is smaller and the total water requirement relative to body weight is less. Wheeler estimates the maximum daily range - this almost doubles at the approximate early *H. sapiens* size. even though body weight is only 76% greater.

If larger sized bodies of the same proportions are more efficient in water usage and have markedly greater ranges, the reader can imagine that the actual situation, proportionately longer legs in the larger bodies, would make an even greater difference. Wheeler argues that a diurnal arid grasslands-activity adaptation requires proportional changes as well as increased body size because this

- lengthens stride (more distance for the same energy),
- increases surface area/mass ratio (with increased efficiencies discussed above)
- makes the whole body more linear, improving both radiation and evaporation heat loss
- places more of the trunk in a microhabitat away from the ground, minimizing plant cover and exposing the naked skin to more breezes and cooler air.

In modeling the effects of the proportional changes, he shows that at the extremes, comparing the body build of early *H. sapiens* and australopithecines, water loss in early *H. sapiens* is reduced to 70-80% the value for a similarly behaving australopithecine (or habiline) of the same weight.

This reasoning has been misconstrued to be an explanation for the development *of* bipedalism (c.f. B. Wood), but it is not. Wheeler's contention is that bipedalism is a *necessary exaptation* for diurnal mobility in an arid tropical setting. What Wheeler clearly shows is that the postcranial changes in early *H. sapiens* greatly increase mobility and the efficiency of diurnal activity in arid habitats.

There is one other aspect of the body size increase that can be explored. Hunting has only rarely been observed in primates. When the adaptation appears in a primate species, the particular characteristics shared by primates are used to develop a pattern of both behavior and morphology unlike that of most other hunting animals (this is reviewed in Chapter 4). Since early hominid hunting and confrontational scavenging was almost certainly diurnal, this would accrue another advantage because most carnivores hunt at dawn or dusk and therefore would provide little direct competition (if not danger). In addition, there is every reason to believe that the early hominids were extraordinarily social, even for primates. Thus the inference is that hominid hunting was a social activity. In Africa today, the only diurnal social hunter besides ourselves is the wild dog. These carnivores prefer game weighing approximately 55 kg or less. Therefore, it is possible that a niche for a social diurnal hunter and confrontational scavenger focused on larger prey was open in the earliest Pleistocene, and that it was occupied by the first hominid hunter-scavengers.

The Respiratory System

Early *H. sapiens* faces are distinguished by broad, prominent noses, with the base of the nasal aperture greatly expanded and the nasal bone breath increased in size even relative to the base. The noses markedly project in front of the maxillary pillars surrounding them, and the pillars themselves project in front of the rest of the middle face. Combined, these changes reflect a much more voluminous nasal chamber in early *H. sapiens*. R. Franciscus and E. Trinkaus relate this to important changes in nasal respiratory physiology. The changes have two functions:

1. increasing the volume of inspired air
2. helping retain internal humidity by retrieving moisture during expiration

A large nasal chamber encourages nasal inhalation and provides for the possibility of humidifying the air. Proper lung function requires virtually 100% internal humidity, and high activity levels in arid environments would rapidly dry the nose and have serious metabolic consequences if the air is not moistened. Franciscus and Trinkaus argue that a large nasal chamber with downward facing nostrils creates a turbulence in air that is expired through the nose because it must change the direction of its flow and thereby slow significantly. Promoted by the turbulence, and allowed by the fact that the internal nose is cool relative to the body core (where the air was at 100% humidity), moisture condenses on the inner surface, where it is used for humidifying the next breadth when dry air requires this. Franciscus and Trinkaus regard these as adaptations to high activity levels in an arid environment. These changes can be related to the requirements of high levels of diurnal activity. Like so many other aspects of early *H. sapiens* anatomy, they reflect changes that D. Carrier (see Chapter 4) ascribes to an important role for running, and combine to suggest an increased emphasis on that role at this time.

Sweating and the Loss of Body Hair

There are certain physiological requisites for diurnal activity in the tropics. It is of great advantage for heat-adaptations to allow intense activity during the hottest part of the day. If mobility then is important, inactivity is no longer a viable alternative and the physiological adaptation must be for getting rid of excess heat. Modern people are well adapted for this, and it is likely that these adaptations originated with the hunting/scavenging/gathering adaptation. What are these adaptations? One, body size, is discussed above. But the idea that large, long limbed hominids are heat adapted because they are large and long limbed presupposes that sweating is the main mechanism of heat loss, a point made by Ruff and Walker in their discussion of WT 15K.

If Pliocene hominids followed the pattern of most primates, they were probably covered with body hair. Body hair itself can be a heat adaptation if metabolic heat is not particularly high. Hair creates a dead-air space between the skin and the outside of the hair, and air is an excellent insulator. Thus in an animal that is relatively inactive during the day, solar radiation heats up the outside of the hair while the skin is insulated from the heat. Many modern desert-dwelling people use a similar adaptation, substituting loose robes for body hair (these are lightly colored and also reflect a significant amount of heat). In primates covered with thick hair, inactivity during the hotter parts of the day is a requisite for this adaptation to work. There is much to be said for insight in that Noel Coward song that goes, "*only mad dogs and Englishmen go out in the noon-time sun*". In a hominid that insists on activity during the day, the problem is to effectively get rid of excess metabolic heat. In this case, an insulator surrounding the skin is not helpful.

Basically, there are two ways of getting rid of heat, radiation and conduction. Radiation is a process in which heat is emitted from a warm object in the form of infrared waves. Conduction occurs when a warm object is directly connected to a cooler medium that can transmit heat away from it. The efficiency of radiation depends on the *difference* in temperature between the object radiating (a hot person) and the surrounding medium (air). In hot areas, where air temperature is as high as body temperature, if not higher, radiation is not effective. Modern people get rid of excess heat through the process of conduction by the mechanism of sweating. There are four types of human perspiration: diffusion water (from the skin and lungs), thermal sweating (from sweat glands), palmar-sole sweating, emotional sweating (especially from the **axillary** region and the forehead). Of the two types of sweat glands, apocrine glands which are deep within the skin and hair-related, and eccrine glands which are closer to the skin surface and each open to it through a pore, the eccrine glands are the main source of diffusion and thermal sweating in humans. This is because they are densely (150-340 per cm^2) and fairly evenly distributed over the body. As G. Folk and H. Semken point out this distribution is not as necessary consequence of hairlessness, as other hairless mammals such as elephants and rhinos lack it. It must, they reason, be a specific human adaptation to diurnal activity in the tropics.

Extensive body hair both acts as an insulator and makes sweat-drop formation and therefore dripping easy, thus reducing the amount of sweat that evaporates. As sweat drips off a body, along body hairs for instance, each drop carries away a certain amount of heat. However, if a drop of sweat *evaporates,* raising its temperature by 1 degree when it changes its physical state from liquid to gas uses over *250* times as much heat as it takes to raise the temperature of the same drop 1 degree without evaporation. In other words, evaporation of sweat is an extremely effective way of getting rid of metabolic heat, and is much more easily attained then there is hair loss. Moreover, Wheeler's studies show that while inactive but hair-covered hominids would be cooler than hairless ones, even low levels of activity reverses the situation. Once metabolic heat rises significantly above the resting body temperature it quickly exceeds the cooling capacity of hair-covered hominids. For hairless hominids, cooling is significant for high activity levels, even in very hot temperatures, in part because with high activity the eccrine glands produce much more sweat (in humans eccrine sweating is 5 or more times the rate of apocrine sweating in horses, according to Folk). A third advantage of hair loss as part of a sweating adaptation to diurnal tropical activity comes from the consequences of the insulating properties of hair in cooler temperatures. Hair loss allows radiation to cool the body when the air is cooler, lowering the drinking requirements of hominids, for whom water quantities available through the day are a significant limiting resource.

For these reasons, the hominid adaptation to the tropics involved significant reduction in the number and size of hair follicles (with their associated apocrine glands) and the development of eccrine glands all over the body. This combination allows the effective heat-loss mechanism of sweat evaporation to operate efficiently. Even today, some tropical hunters can kill their prey by literally walking them to death. Most (but not all) mammals can be exhausted by forced activity during the heat of the day; since they lack as effective a heat loss mechanism when metabolic heat gets too high, they overheat sooner than the human chasing them. In this regard, the human stride mechanism is particularly effective, since it allows fairly rapid locomotion over long periods with only minimal use of the largest hip muscle—*gluteus maximus*. Human stride keeps the metabolism operating at a lower level, while sweating provides an effective heat-loss mechanism. They combine in a unique hominid adaptation to tropical diurnal activity.

There are two important results that stem from this adaptation. First, it makes hominids water dependent. A sweating hominid is a thirsty hominid. Most early hominid sites are found adjacent to or near water. Of course, this is partly due to the fact that preservation is more likely. However, the generalization is also true for archaeological sites without preserved bone. By indicating that a water supply was important, this suggests an early beginning for selection leading to the effective hominid diurnal adaptation. Moreover, the opportunities for scavenging are predictably best near water since this is a favored spot for carnivores to take their prey. However, hunting and scavenging cannot always take place in the vicinity of water, especially when it becomes increasingly less opportunistic. Reflecting these activities, increasing numbers of Karari and Developed Oldowan tool clusters are found away from the immediate vicinity of water. Carrying water depends on one of the most basic human inventions, and one unfortunately not commonly subject to preservation—the container. The innovation of containers was one of the most important human cultural adaptations, and probably one of the critical factors that led to the development of effective organized hunting and confrontational scavenging as a predictable source of food. Of course, long before this development, containers had been incorporated into gathering strategies, making the collection and transport of foods an effective alternative to snacking.

Skin Color

The second important result of the diurnal mobility heat adaptation involves skin color. A variety of skin colors occur in chimpanzees and probably also occurred in earlier hominids. This is because no particular selection acts on skin color in a primate covered with body hair. However, the loss of body hair led to specific skin color selection in humans as the result of two independent selective pressures: vitamin D synthesis (see Chapter XX) and skin cancer.

The substance giving pigmentation to the skin, melanin, is produced by **melanocytes**. These pigment-producing cells occur in the bottom portion of the epidermis (the outer layer of skin). There are no population differences in numbers of melanocytes, although their activity in producing melanin, and consequently average populational pigmentation, can vary considerably. Melanin acts to limit the amount of ultraviolet radiation that can penetrate the skin. Extensive ultraviolet penetration has two effects that are disadvantageous in the tropical adaptation discussed. First, even mild sunburn resulting from ultraviolet penetration significantly reduces the rate of sweating, and of course severe sunburn is extremely painful. Second, sufficient penetration leads to skin cancer. Together, these result in selection favoring dark skin as part of the hominid adaptation to tropical diurnal activity.

Possible Social Changes

We may also consider the question of what changes a shift to this hunting/scavenging/gathering economy might have caused, and how they might have been reflected in the structure of hominid society. Virtually every model of *hominid* origins, certainly those focused on behavioral commonalties with the social primates, imply that long term bonds between males and females, and a complex of role differences, had evolved long before the economic changes posited here. We cannot, in other words, posit that these adaptations formed the basis for human society. However, they may well have been focal in some of the important aspects of human social evolution. One area of change was surely in the maternal relationships, as the period of accelerated postnatal brain size increase, perhaps as long as a year, was linked to accelerated learning and required a stable input of high quality nutrition that mean the mother's metabolism must also have been elevated. With a significant expansion of food sources, increased reliance on shared foods collected during the day created the required background for these changes, and at the same time provided the basis for more complex social relationships. New approaches to the potential limitations of dry season resources placed a premium on numerous and potentially different dietary adaptations, with the one common aspect of broadening the range of resources that populations regularly used. The key social adaptations were cooperation and organization, and information exchange was as important as exchanging foods.

One might expect greater formalization of role-specific behaviors to accompany these changes, especially because regular socially defined expectations are an excellent means of encapsulating past experiences and preserving them for the benefit of the future. Formalization, and ultimately ritualization of the quantity, quality, and appropriate conditions for sharing, development of strategies requiring communication and cooperation between females and between males, and attempts at long-range planning for the yearly cycle are additional associated cultural behaviors that might be expected to become increasingly important. As J. Speth points out, food sharing in living hunter/gatherers is complex and multidimensional, involving not only the mutual benefits discussed above but also food taboos, inequality of access to nutritionally important foods (especially to women), and the control of fertility. The emphasis on formalization and ritualization is not misplaced, as these are ways of regularizing expectations that allow the cultural system to begin functioning as an extrasomatic means of transmitting information from generation to generation - one of its most important roles in human evolution. Sharers, after all, share much more than food.

The pattern of differential food gathering activities depends on the earlier appearance of certain social behaviors: using a home base, developing sharing as an expected behavior, and evolving communication capabilities at least complex enough to allow displacement. The interpretation of these behaviors from the archaeological remains of the early hominids has been one of the most significant achievements of 20th Century archaeology. I believe that G. Isaac was quite correct in his expectations that these were important aspects of hominid organization in the early Pleistocene. The problem, and much of the ensuing debate about these interpretations, is that we are not viewing the remnants and reflections of a *human pattern* of sharing, a *human* home base, or *human* language. Like virtually all workers in the decades of the 1970's and 80's, Isaac assumed that interpreting these and other behaviors from archaeological remains could be patterned after modern human hunters in peripheral environments. The most significant contribution that L. Binford made to the debate was to show this is not a valid approach. If the interpretation of the past cannot be assumption-free (Binford's claim is that it *must* be, but many believe that is neither possible nor necessarily desirable), it must begin with explicit assumptions that have a realistic basis. The second important realization is the extent to which human biology and behavioral capacity must be taken into account.

Ultimately as these behaviors became more complex and sophisticated they increased in importance and became incorporated into the human behavioral system as structured, learned behaviors that were expressed in contexts reflecting stratification based on sex, age, and differential access to resources ranging from foods themselves to knowledge about them. As particular bands more effectively utilized the resources of their environments, they occupied wider ranges and were constantly moving throughout these ranges, depending on the distribution of food and water sources at any particular time. It is likely that under these conditions more contact between widely dispersed populations occurred, and therefore there was more genic exchange. Increased contact between populations probably also led to the development of more complex social relations. The range of role relations and other formalized behaviors depending on individual expectations would have to expand greatly with increased contact between populations. It is possible that regular mechanisms to formalize relations between groups evolved. In the ethnographic present, such mechanisms can be as diverse as extended kinship, complex trade systems (including trading potential mates), and warfare. In a word, the long term results of these activities is human culture, and perhaps with the appearance of a hunting/scavenging/gathering adaptation some 2 myr ago we have a glimpse of its beginnings.

The implication I wish to draw is that the adaptive shift involved is much wider reaching in its consequences than a simple dietary change or resource utilization strategy might suggest. I believe that this shift led to the development of far more complex, socially defined interactions both within and between groups. Such interactions involve the development of more detailed behavioral expectations and their associated neurological models. There are two pieces of direct evidence that could reflect these neurological changes. One is the significant expansion of brain size in early *H. sapiens*. Probably nothing takes up more neurological circuitry than these complex models and the importance of communication within their framework. Second, more gradually and somewhat later there is a reflection in the tools themselves - direct evidence suggesting the evolution of complex neurological models organizing social (and other aspects of) reality are found in a singular technological innovation. Mainly, with the appearance of the Acheulean (Chapter 10) tools take on recognizable, repeated form. Probably second only to the invention of technology itself this is the singularly most important development in the material culture of the early Pleistocene.

Archaeologists have been slow to realize the significance of these developments, quite possibly because by "humanizing" our interpretation of chimpanzees (and some of the other primates), we have humanized the way we look at our own ancestors to a point far beyond the actual behavioral sophistication they achieved. It has been poorly realized how fundamental the beginnings really were, the extent to which smashed stone and digging sticks were difficult achievements of extraordinary magnitude. L. Leakey once defined hominids as the primates who "made tools in a set and regular pattern", a description that does not particularly characterize any of the artifacts, or the opportunistic stone-smashing aspect of their production, we have been discussing. But within the Oldowan, and related lithic industries, specific forms do come to regularly characterize tools. The "tool types" at the earliest Oldowan sites that appear to be more in the eyes of the beholder, scrapers, borers, polyhedrons, bifaces, and the like, are found with consistency of form and regularity of the reduction process creating them, only a half million years later. Once I heard the renowned African archaeologist J.D. Clark quip "if *Homo erectus* could talk, he must have said the same thing over and over again." My understanding of the first million years of human technology is quite different.

Morphological Changes in early *Homo sapiens*

There are a number of ways in which the early *H. sapiens* remains differ from other early hominids. These can be dramatized in several different comparisons. The contrasts with *A. africanus* compare with the best known clearly identified ancestor of the species. Comparisons with the habilines reflect differences from a "more advanced" australopithecine-like contemporary whose contrasts may reveal ecological and adaptive differences. Many of the similarities and differences with these two species are quite similar, and the differences between the comparisons are more often than not in magnitude than in direction.

Fundamentally, the most important anatomical distinction of early *H. sapiens* is that the specimens are significantly larger than ancestral hominids or contemporary *Homo*. There is relative limb elongation that is partially allometric, partially mobility related, and partially adapted to energetic diurnal activities in an arid tropical climate - three explanations which are *not* mutually contradictory. The robustness and internal structure of the postcranial remains indicate elevated activity levels, according to C. Ruff and colleagues. Most early *H. sapiens* distinctions in the postcranial skeleton are caused by, or at least prominently related to, the differences in size and consequences of increased diurnal activities. I view four interrelated complexes of changes at the very beginning of this species:

1. increasing cranial capacity,
2. adaptations to changing dental functions,
3. adaptive changes affecting midfacial structures (visual, water retention)
4. strengthening of the cranial vault.

CHANGES RELATED TO BRAIN SIZE

One important cause of cranial differences lies in the expanding cranial capacity. The full extent of actual expansion remains unclear since some of the brain size increase is due to larger average body size. However, even if we think of primate allometry (figure 9.3) as a cluster of relationships rather than a thin line reflecting the average tendency WT 15K is the earliest hominid specimen to deviate significantly from the expectations of primate allometry, thereby showing significant brain expansion beyond the requirements of size.

Early sapiens crania are not simply "blown up" australopithecine crania, as for instance the large habilines such as ER 1470. Disproportionate changes are due to both the expansion of specific areas within the brain and the changing balance of masticatory forces acting on the skull (to be discussed below) as well as certain other adaptive changes. There are associated increases in the basic cranial dimensions of length, breadth and height. Cranial length expansion is most marked, possibly because it represents consequences of three different changes:

1. increasing vault size to enclose a larger brain
2. differential expansion in the posterior parietal association area
3. an increased horizontal component to the direction of posterior temporalis muscle and a longer nuchal plane (both of which are masticatory-related)

The combination of these changes affect the posterior aspect of the vault, and this is where most of the length expansion takes place. Thus, when considered relative to cranial height the relative distance from the ear to the front of the vault basically remains unchanged while the relative distance from the ear to the back of the vault greatly expands - the ear is in a more central position. Another source of differential expansion is in the frontal bone. The **postorbital breadth** (breadth across the postorbital constriction, the minimum across the frontal measuring the distance between the inner walls of the temporal fossae), and the **frontal bone breadth** at the **coronal suture** (maximum breadth across the frontal bone) both increase out of proportion to the other changes. But the postorbital breadth increases more, reflecting expanding frontal lobe breadth at the expense of the size of the temporal fossa. This places the outer borders of this fossa, the zygomatic arches, in a more lateral position - a change that has masticatory consequences (see below). This in part accounts for the expanded middle faces of early *H. sapiens*, a consequence of the lengthening of the zygomatic bone in order to enclose the more laterally positioned temporal fossae. These, then, are the main changes in the cranial vault associated directly or indirectly with the specific pattern of endocranial morphology and volumetric changes.

CHANGING DENTAL FUNCTIONS

A second set of interrelated changes combines new variations in diet and food preparation. It is reflected in changing dental function - the trend for posterior dental reduction and incisor expansion - and in some of the consequences of the changing cranial dimensions discussed above. This complex pattern is influenced by three things:

1. the decreases in posterior tooth size
2. changes in the masticatory cycle
3. changes caused by the consequences of cranial capacity expansion described above.

The reduction of the posterior teeth is one of the two most dramatic trends weaving through the human evolutionary process. This reduction is classically gradual in that it involves shifts in frequency distributions. Thus, while early *H. sapiens* has smaller posterior teeth than *A. africanus*, there is great overlap between the distributions. Associated with this reduction is a decrease in molarization, especially in dm_1 and P_4. In an related change, the **mandibular corpus** (the horizontal, tooth-bearing, part of the mandible) decreases in robustness, and a different relationship of height and breadth develops. The height of the mandibular corpus does not decrease, if anything it increases. Since mandibular corpus height is closely related to body height, this reflects the marked average body size increase in early *H. sapiens*. Because of the breadth reductions, the mandibles are significantly thinner. As some authors consider the relative breadth of a structure a measure of its *robustness,* these changes make the mandibles less robust. The significance of the posterior dental reduction, comparing *A. africanus* and early *H. sapiens*, can be gauged by the fact that it is about as rapid as the cranial capacity increase.

While the size of the postcanine dentition decreases (especially the later erupting teeth in each dental field), the changes are more complex than simple use reduction (i.e. the teeth reduce because they are not used as much) would suggest. The mandibular fossa increases markedly in size, and a broad articular eminence extends in front of the distinct anterior wall. This eminence is the resting place of the mandibular condyle with the force passing through it (the opposite side as the teeth with food between them) and the broad, flat platform is important for the movements during grinding. No reduction here! There are, in fact, a number of related changes in the teeth and (albeit rare) faces of early *H. sapiens.*

1. reduction in enamel thickness on molar walls, while the enamel cap stays thick
2. decreased temporal fossa size
3. greater horizontal component to the posterior temporalis muscle force
4. more lateral force in chewing, reflected in the temporal fossa anatomy and position, and the larger and broader cheeks

Many, perhaps most, of these changes reflect differences in diet and food preparation that change masticatory mechanics. For instance there is the molar enamel thickness that reduces in the enamel walls much more significantly than the thickness of the enamel cap. The upper part of the face expands at the expense of the lower. This is partly due to the increased size of the orbits and nose, discussed below, which help the positioning of the zygomatic arches further apart, but it is also influenced by the fact that in spite of the temporal fossae shrinking in size as the temporalis muscles change, the expanding frontal lobes position them further apart. The decreasing cross-sectional area of the temporal fossa reflects both a changing magnitude and a different pattern of posterior tooth functions. The expanded zygomatic bones (they are almost 20% larger than in *A. africanus*, table 9.3) are partially a result of the more lateral position of the temporal fossa, but they show an increased base for the masseter muscle attachment, and its more lateral positioning. This suggests that the masseter muscle increases in size, and with the reduced facial prognathism there would be improved ability to bring forces through the molar row. More importantly, in its more lateral position (because of the facial breadth changes), it contributes more strongly to the lateral grinding component of chewing. Combined with the greater horizontal component for the posterior temporalis muscle that comes from the longer crania, these changes create a more marked lateral thrust during the chewing cycle (motion of the jaw to one side is created by both the masseter and the posterior part of the temporal muscle on that side, see Chapter 4, pp. xx-xx). Yet, other changes such as the decrease in the total size of the temporalis muscle, especially its anterior component, show that the vertical force expended in grinding decreases. The reduction of vertical force is not an unexpected observation, given the parallel evidence for decreasing posterior tooth size.

These changes reflect the development of a different pattern for reducing foods, jaw motions with more of a transverse component emphasize the forces of a well-angled masseter muscle and a significant horizontal temporalis component in the mastication cycle. The evolution of what might be thought of as a greater emphasis on grinding and a reduced emphasis on crunching that these masticatory muscle changes seem to suggest is reflected in some dramatic changes in the microscopic tooth wear of this species. A Walker shows that a smooth wear pattern on enormous teeth changes to an eclectic pattern of deep grooves and scratches on somewhat smaller teeth. Dietary changes involved less use of low quality, low abrasion, but tough (physically difficult to break down) foods such as leaves and bark, and probably also reflect changes in food preparation which could have introduced grit and other non-dietary abrasives into the mouth (meat would do this as well).

There is a second set of changing features that reflect increased use of the anterior teeth. These include:

- increases in anterior tooth size
- the expansion of the nuchal plane
- the prominent thick supraorbitals that contrast early *H. sapiens* with the habilines and australopithecines.

The size increases especially affect the crowns and roots of the lateral maxillary incisors but the central incisors increase as well. Larger incisors are reflected in the expanded size of the subnasal region (lower facial size), the distinct angle between this region and floor of the nose, and the increased distance between the central roots (see table 9.3). Structural changes in the incisors include their shoveling; a morphology causing the upper incisors to resemble sided shovels such as coal shovels, formed by development of ridges along the margins of the internal face, curvature of the tooth from side to side, and prominence of the internal tubercle (bump) at the base of its internal face.

Increased use of the anterior teeth is probably not for mastication but rather food preparation (for instance in husking fruits) and other aspects of environmental manipulation. Holding something between the front teeth and using the neck muscles to pull it creates both vertical and horizontal forces between the teeth, the former from holding the object in place and the latter as the result of the pull (see Figure 9.5). The front of the mouth is a convenient position for powerful gripping, pulling, and twisting. The dramatically expanded incisors of apes, compared with their Middle Miocene ancestors, reflect mainly dietary adaptations, husking fruits and stripping leafs between these teeth. Observed uses of this "third hand" in humans, even more proficient environment-manipulators, include holding bone drills, straightening wood spear shafts, stripping hides, and loosening rusted gasoline drum covers. The much larger front teeth and related muscles in early *H. sapiens* suggest a much wider range of manipulating activities, as they appear at a time when technology is beginning to substantially replace the teeth in preparing foods for mastication.

The consequences of expanded anterior tooth use are clearly seen in musculature changes. Gripping and pulling with the front teeth requires both increased *horizontal* and *vertical* components to the anterior bite force (Chapter 4). The horizontal forces (figure 9.6)are associated with expanded neck muscles, nuchal torus development, cranial lengthening to increase the horizontal component of the posterior temporalis, and an expansion of the posterior temporalis muscle in size. In particular, horizontal forces acting on the mandible are provided by an increased horizontal orientation for the expanded posterior temporalis muscle (described above), while horizontal maxillary components are increased through the expansion of the nuchal muscles and are reflected in the anatomy of the nuchal plane and in the development of the nuchal torus.

The vertical aspect of this force (figure 9.7)is perhaps most dramatically reflected in the supraorbital torus expansion in even the earliest members of the taxon, an expansion that according to M. Russell is predictable from the combination of increasing anterior tooth use and the acute frontofacial angles (figure 9.9). She shows that vertical bite forces can be expected to more strongly affect the bone in the supraorbital area when the forehead is poorly positioned to help reinforce the region. Reinforcement is best when the forehead is aligned with the face (a straight frontofacial angle) and poorest when the angle is acute. Russell's modeling of the region has been examined in a series of macaque experiments by W. Hylander and colleagues. They confirmed the hypothesized *pattern* of bone deformation, but found that its magnitude was lower than expected (because the functional theory is wrong, or because the browridges were succeeding in their functions?). They also showed that any masticatory force, not just anterior, could strain the area, and that peeling and chewing foods such as apples and dried apricots resulted in fairly small amounts of supraorbital deformation. Their studies suggest that far more powerful forces than apple eating were affecting the supraorbital region of early *H. sapiens*, and show the difficulties involved in modeling a complex structure, and gauging the success of its functions.

With both strong anterior tooth loads and acute frontofacial angles in early *H. sapiens*, the expanded supraorbital torus buttresses the abutment of the frontal bone and face and reduces the strain (deformation of bone) caused by the masticatory-related stress (force on bone). That much of this stress comes from anterior tooth use is suggested by other details of early *H. sapiens* anatomy, not the least of which is the indirect evidence of greater anterior tooth use and reduced vertical forces acting on the posterior teeth discussed above. In early *H. sapiens* the supraorbital torus is markedly larger than all other earlier or contemporary hominids (table 9.3). It is both dramatically thicker (75% greater than *A. africanus*) and has a long, distinct top surface that projects in front of the forehead part of the frontal bone. The angulation between the torus and forehead is quite strong; a deep groove across the front of the skull called a supratoral sulcus marks this angle - characteristic of all early *H. sapiens* crania.

These changes are reflected in the details of the nuchal torus and expanding nuchal region of the cranium, the plane on the lower part of the occiput where the neck muscles attach, with related variation in the spines of the cervical vertebrae. The development of spongy bone across the back of the cranial base, from the region over the mastoid processes and in the form of a distinct torus all the way across the cranial rear, provides support for the increased forces of the expanded neck muscles. Indeed, changes associated with better-developed nuchal muscles are one of the most dramatic aspects of early *H. sapiens* crania. The occipital bone becomes much larger; part of this expansion reflects the brain-related changes, but the nuchal part comes to predominate the upper, or occipital part and the nuchal plane is almost twice as big as the *A. africanus* mean. That these changes are a result of anterior tooth functions, and not facial size (some thought that big neck muscles were needed to balance big faces) or posterior tooth use, can be seen in the fact that the nuchal planes greatly exceed *A. boisei* as well as the other australopithecines and habilines. The expanded nuchal plane and nuchal torus, and the posterior extension of the occipital bone described above, are part of the posterior cranial lengthening that places both the foramen magnum and the outer ear openings in a relatively more anterior position.

OTHER ADAPTIVE CHANGES IN THE MIDDLE FACE

Two unrelated but important differences characterize the middle face. One of the dramatic midfacial changes is the expansion of orbit size. While the orbit dimensions of the other *Homo* species is very close to the *A. africanus* mean (table 9.3), early *H. sapiens* is markedly larger. For instance the area enclosed within the orbits averages almost 40% greater and is above the range of all australopithecines and habilines (although ER 1470 is close). Ape eyeballs are much smaller than human ones, raising the possibility that the increase in orbit size was to facilitate an increase eyeball size. If so, and I believe this is the most likely explanation, this change reflects an increased number of rods and cones and thereby suggests higher visual resolution and greater visual acuity.

The other factor significantly affecting facial form is the complex of significant nasal changes discussed above. The broadening of the nasal opening and even greater broadening of the nasal bones, the increased volumetric capacity of the internal nasal chamber, and the turbulence-creating external nasal projection combine to suggest important changes in respiratory function that better adapt hominids to diurnal activity in tropical arid conditions. Anterior palate and subnasal differences such as the marked angle between the nasal floor and the subnasal plant reflect a combination of these changes and the reduction in facial prognathism.

Table 9.3
Some Early Hominid Facial Dimensions[1]

	Nasal Breadth	Breadth across Central Incisor Roots	C-M^3 Length	Orbit Breadth	Orbit Height	Cheek Size (length along zygomatic-maxillary suture)	Central Supraorbital Thickness (vertical height)	Central Supraorbital Length (frontal squama to edge)
A. afarensis								
AL 200-1	20.8	18.7	62.7					
AL 333-1	21.5					35.0		
A. africanus								
STS 5	26.5		56.4	37.4	30.6	31.0	8.4	13.5
STS 17	24.3	16.5	57.9		31.5		8.1	9.5
STS 22	19.9	15.9	53.8					
STS 52	25.1	18.3		35.9		32.6		
STS 53	21.5	15.7	57.4					
STS 66	34.0	16.9						
STS 71	26.8	15.5	61.1	36.3	31.4	31.2	4.8	14.2
STW 13	26.3	16.2						
STW 505	30.0	16.0			37.5	35.5	9.0	13.8
TM 1511						36.0	8.7	16.9
H. habilis								
?STW 53	24.0	16.0	58.8			30.0	4.4	13.9
OH 16							6.1	19.0
OH 24	26.1	17.3	55.0	36.6	31.5	33.5	7.7	15.0
OH 62	39.5	19.2	57.2					
ER 1813	23.9	17.0	55.9	32.3	30.7	32.0	9.6	18.5
Omo L894							6.5	15.0
ER 3735							6.9	11.5
ER 1470	26.5	18.5		43.0	35.0	41.6	9.2	20.5
ER 3732				36.5	30.5	37.7	8.4	16.2
ER 1805	32.5	18.0	62.3					
SK 847	22.0	14.2	55.5	35.0	32.0	35.5	7.2	15.7
early *H. sapiens*								
ER 3733	36.8	23.0		44.2	36.2	35.8	9.7	23.2
ER 3883				42.0	36.4	42.8	14.2	21.1
ER 730							13.0	20.0
ER 1808							11.2	
OH 9				42.8			19.4	27.0

[1]   See figure 9.8 for definitions of these measurements.

THE CRANIAL BUTTRESSING SYSTEM

The remaining changes occur in the thickness of the cranial bones (table 9. 4) and the system of buttresses. The average thickness of each cranial bone is much greater in early *H. sapiens*. Two of the buttresses, or tori, extending transversely across the cranium (the supraorbital and nuchal torus) are discussed above, and there are other thickened buttresses such as the torus along the temporal lines, along the top of the cranium, and along its sides just above the mastoids and ears (figure 9.10). These changes come as a result of two factors, the structural consequences of increased vertical and horizontal forces due to anterior tooth use (discussed above) and more general strengthening of the cranial vault.

Table 9.4
Cranial Bone Thickness[1]

| | Parietal[3] thickness at | | | | | | | | occipital thickness | |
| | Bregma | | Lambda | | Asterion | | Bone center | | Nuchal torus center | |
	male	female	male	female	male	female	male	female	male	female
A. africanus[2]	6.8		7.1		7.6		6.5		12.8	
H. habilis[2]	6.4		7.5		8.2		6.7		14.8	
African early *H. sapiens*	9.6	8.2	9.1	7.6	13.0	9.9	10.6	8.8	18.3	17.5
Modern human population maximum	8.4	6.9	8.3	8.0	8.3	6.5	6.4	6.6	14.6	13.4
Modern human population minimum	6.7	5.8	7.5	6.6	6.6	5.7	5.5	5.8	12.6	11.8

[1]   Population data are averages from Brown, fossil hominids from my data
[2]   Sample of both sexes
[3]   Definitions of the points on the parietal bone where these measurements are taken are found in figure 10.#

F. Weidenreich regarded the thickened cranial bone and marked torus system of Middle Pleistocene *H. sapiens* populations as means to strengthen the cranial vault. It has been widely speculated that such an adaptation might result from blows to the head received while hunting large mammals with weapons effective only at close range. Reports of healed scars on many Early and Middle Pleistocene *H. sapiens* crania support this idea. The increases in cranial thickness that comes with the appearance of early *H. sapiens* is more problematic to interpret. This is because it precedes what little evidence of hunting that the archaeological record suggests, and most cases of violence reflected in cranial injuries.. Moreover, it must be explained in the context of the fact that cranial vault bone thickness continues to expand through the Early and Middle Pleistocene evolution of the species. I view it, along with the expanded cranial buttressing system that appears particularly well expressed in the Asian populations, as related to (and perhaps responding to) the high level of healed cranial injuries that seem almost ubiquitous in early *H. sapiens* crania of both sexes. The causes of these injuries remain speculative, perhaps hunting accidents reflecting the inability to kill at a distance play a role, but the predominance of injuries on female crania reported by Stoner suggests that many are a result of elevated magnitudes of interpersonal violence. Several authors have used observations on Australian Aborigine tribes, some of whom can have high levels of interpersonal violence, to help understand the link between cranial vault thickness and healed cranial injuries in the past. M. Meggett reports persistent violence (including head-bashing) between women as they talk while they collect foods - their digging sticks turned from implements to weapons. Many of the wounds inflicted were serious. P. Brown reviews evidence of selection to maintain cranial vault thickness from the ethnographic present, that may explain the pattern of variation and its link to healed cranial fractures in the past. He points out that the traditional method for settling aggressive disputes in many communities is "to use a substantial wooden implement to strike towards the head of their opponent". The principle that the present should be used to interpret the past suggests that the injuries on *H. sapiens* crania beginning with the earliest sample, and the cranial changes that respond to them, are multicausal.

POSTCRANIAL CHANGES

Postcranial evolution in this early sample involves large body size and its consequences, the affects of a changing locomotor pattern, and the maintenance of small head size at birth in spite of the expanding adult cranial capacity.

Body height in these early hominids is extraordinary, just about as tall as the tallest African populations found today. Estimated weight is even heavier because of the greater amount of muscular development and some differences in trunk shape. Proportionally the legs are relatively long, so much so that when taken as a ratio to leg length the arms seem relatively short. These legs are characterized by thickened shaft walls, especially on the medial side of the femur which helps give many specimens an unusually low pilastric index. There are similar changes in the tibia. The question is why? The strength of bone differs according to what forces it is asked to resist. For instance, under compression, the strength of a femur is simply a function of the cross-sectional area of the cortical bone in its shaft. When subjected to bending or twisting (**torsion** is the most common cause of long bone breaks), bone strength depends on the distribution of the cortical bone as well as the amount. This distribution makes the early *H. sapiens* limbs more resistant to twisting. It also makes them particularly resistant to bending in a transverse direction. Bending to the side is a problem and a not uncommon cause of breaks because of the leverage of body weight around the supporting limb and the affects of an increased amount of force that is created when locomotion is rapid.

This later aspect of locomotion may have helped act as a limitation to further pelvic broadening in early *H. sapiens* (a broader pelvis creates a longer lever arm), and as discussed in Chapter 6 there is also a climatic affect on pelvis size. None the less, it seems unlikely that the birth canal in early *H. sapiens* was held to a narrow diameter for reasons of climate and locomotion alone, given its potential affects on the birth process and the state of maturity of the newborn. More likely, the relative immaturity of early *H. sapiens* newborn was the *goal* of selection and not its *victim*, the consequent fetal rate of rapid brain growth during the first year of life a neurological adaptation to the requirements of intense learning. What else could lead to, as P. Turke puts it, the combination of physical atriciality and social precociality in which children who cannot jump off the ground with both feet can control and manipulate every adult they come in contact with?

SEXUAL DIMORPHISM

The magnitude of sexual dimorphism in early *H. sapiens* body size is unclear. The existing sample for body size (n=2) suggests an unremarkable magnitude of dimorphism, not unlike the average dimorphism in populations inhabiting the same east African regions today. This is a conclusion which however uncertain (because of minuscule sample size) is not unexpected given that the later australopithecines already expressed magnitudes of dimorphism within the human populational range. Yet, the dimorphism in early *H. sapiens* cranial proportions and anatomical details remains greater than is usual for human populations. This suggests that some, perhaps many, of the secondary sexual characteristics that are dimorphic do not simply respond to body size differences. A similar pattern of dimorphism, contrasting marked cranial differences with unremarkable postcranial ones, is evident in much larger samples later in human evolution (c.f. Chapter 11) and therefore may be a valid interpretation of this much smaller, earlier data set.

The idea of different patterns of selection resulting from different activities in men and women was regarded as the single best explanation for changes in the pattern of sexual dimorphism in human evolution in a review by D. Frayer and myself, although it was also concluded that sexual dimorphism in human populations is multicausal, and may respond to variation in a number of different environmental and social variables. In the suggestions made here about social changes that might have characterized these early humans, in spite of role differences there is a premium on large body size in both sexes. A shared basis for this is the requirements of diurnal activity in an arid tropical environment. Moreover, women may have come under additional selection for increased body size because of the energetic requirements of their gathering activities. Thus, indications of a reduced level of body size dimorphism can fit the pattern of social behaviors reconstructed here.

Summary

Early *H. sapiens* (*née H. erectus*) is a good example of a genetic reorganization and a major adaptive shift. The earliest *Homo sapiens* specimens are found in the Upper Burgi Member sample at Koobi Fora, where it is the first of the *Homo* species to appear. Its ancestry is uncertain, but is most likely an as yet unfound or unidentified early habiline. This species is very distinct, with a dramatically larger body size and marked encephalization as indicated by the fact that even the earliest crania have the first relative cranial sizes deviating significantly from the other primates, in spite of a body weight that is 80% greater than *A. africanus* and more than double that of the Olduvai habilines. Evidence from a variety of both behavioral and anatomical sources indicates that populations of this species are the makers of the Oldowan industrial complex.

Three categories of changes are revealed in the crania of these early humans:

- brain size related (larger, especially longer vault, with broad frontal bone and an expanded parietal association area)
- changing dental functions (more anterior tooth use, greater emphasis on grinding and less on crunching),
- the development of a cranial buttressing system to strengthen the vault, including bone thickening and prominent tori

These combine in easily identifiable crania that are posteriorly elongated with a more centrally placed mandibular fossa, broader and more vertical face with markedly larger cheeks, thick and projecting supraorbital and nuchal tori, and an expanded nuchal plane. Other changes include the marked expansion of the orbits and the alteration of the nasal anatomy to promote moisture retention, with a larger nasal chamber and a broader, much more projecting external nose.

The postcranial changes are equally dramatic. Legs are relatively elongated compared with the smaller hominid species, reflecting a combination of allometry, climatic adaptation, and diurnal activity in a tropical arid climate. With some of the nasal modifications, these changes suggest an important role for diurnal running. Interestingly, the neural canals of the vertebrae in the upper part of the trunk are quite small. This may show somewhat less neurological control of the fine motions of the hand, a hypothesis that is supported by the crudeness of the tools found with these early humans. Before the extraordinarily complete Turkana youth, WT 15K, was found, I argued in the first edition of this text that the evolution of manipulative skill was every bit as important as the evolution of behavioral complexity in the Pleistocene hominids, and there is even more to link neurological and archaeological developments now.

There are certain changes evident in the life history parameters. One of these is the implication of the osteological limitations to birth canal size. This anatomy resembles the australopithecine condition, in spite of the expanded adult brain size. The inference is that early *H. sapiens* had the very rapid postpartum growth period that our children enjoy, actually an extension of the fetal rate, that means

- births were relatively premature (physical atriciality)
- early learning was particularly intense (perhaps implying social precociality)

A second change is found in the evidence of survivorship older than virtually any australopithecine. Two specimens in particular, ER 730 and OH 9 (discussed in Chapter 10), underwent age related anatomical changes that are almost never seen in the generally shorter-lived australopithecines.

Details of the legs, nose and dramatically expanded orbits confirm the interpretation of a tropical arid diurnal adaptation; it is likely that this is when humans became hairless, black skinned, and what R. Newman described as "a sweaty and thirsty animal". While the Oldowan "industry" consists of little more than bone or antler digging sticks, bashed rocks, and utilized flakes, learning to use these was a critically difficult invention with the most profound adaptive consequences. Many of the utilized stone implements were directed at gathering and scavenging activities, but the distinction between confrontational scavenging and hunting can often only be poorly made in the archaeological record. Aspects of the archaeological evidence suggests utilization of animal resources (marrow, fat, and meat) and provides evidence that containers were made. These are critical in the shift from snacking to gathering, and the independence from water sources necessary for the hominid adaptation to diurnal activities in arid tropical conditions. An important new adaptation evolves from the snacking and scavenging habits reflected in the opportunistic Oldowan. Based on technology-enhanced gathering, hunting, and confrontational scavenging, its emerging organizational characteristics are dependent on containers for carrying collected foods and water. This was a broad adaptive shift, much further reaching than the changes in diet and resource utilization strategies might suggest, leading to the formalization of complex, socially defined, interactions within and between groups. Not coincidentally, this is when the first regularized tool forms appear, presaging the Acheulean industry and the hominid expansion out of Africa.

ANATOMY OF A CONTROVERSY
Homo ergaster?

Several authors have chosen to distinguish these early *H. sapiens* specimens as a distinct species. No, I do not mean *H. erectus,* the old appellation for this earliest part of the *H. sapiens* clade, but a species even distinguished from that! *H. ergaster* was proposed by C. Groves and V. Mazak to describe ER 992, an isolated mandible. Using a phylogenetic species definition, authors such as B. Wood and C. Stringer have since supported the contention that this species distinction may be justified by unique features of the cranial sample they attributed to it (especially ER 3733, 3883, and 730). What is important about these features is the claim that they are more like living *H. sapiens* than are the later Middle Pleistocene remains from Sangiran (Indonesia)and Zhoukoudian (China) - the classic populations used to define *H. erectus. H. ergaster*, by this criterion, could be a unique ancestor for living humans while the above mentioned Asian forms are not.

According to B. Wood, the features resembling Late Pleistocene and living humans and distinguishing *H. ergaster* from other early *H. sapiens* include:

- increased cranial breadth across the parietals (in early *H. sapiens* the breadth across the cranial base is substantially greater than the breadth above it, across the parietals)
- increased occipital bone length
- broader nasal bones
- broader nasal opening
- shorter cranial base
- greater development at the base of the front of the mandible (**symphysis**)
- narrower M_1 and lower canine

However the list does not fit well with the observations of other researchers (including this author), and the separate species interpretation has not been widely accepted. For example take the claimed ergaster-recent sapiens synapomorphy of broader nasal bones. If the breadth across the nasal bones is taken at their lowest part, where they are widest, the 19.2 mm value for ER 3733 (putative *H. ergaster*) is not substantially different from the 20 mm value for the later Indonesian specimen Sangiran 17, a Middle Pleistocene *H. sapiens* cranium. On the available evidence this feature is *not* unique in *H. ergaster* and recent *H. sapiens*, to the exclusion of early *H. sapiens*. If the breadth across the top of the bones is used (the samples for this are much better as the area is more often preserved), the nasal bones are narrow and australopithecine-like, not broader. ER 3733 and 3883 have upper nasal breadth values (6.9 and 6.7 mm) that are *less* (not more, as Wood contends) than later African specimens such as OH 9 (11.2 mm) or the Sangiran hominids (10.1 and 12 mm), and these in turn are markedly less than the even later Zhoukoudian sample (16.7, 17, and 17.3 mm). Is it different species (albeit on the opposite criterion to the one that Wood proposed), or is it more likely that this expansion is a temporal trend that extends across the Early and Middle Pleistocene?

At best, the "unique features" appear to be relatively minor and evolutionary biologists expect some variation in samples of a species removed in both time and space. A. Bilsborough points out than even this short list is actually shorter than it seems, as several of the features are interrelated and mutually dependent in their expression. In a classic comparative analysis G. Bräuer and E. Mbua demonstrate that the alleged synapomorphies with recent and modern humans are actually shared with some members of the above-mentioned Asian populations of Middle Pleistocene *H. sapiens*. Most tellingly, A. Kramer developed a sophisticated analysis for examining the variation in Early and Middle Pleistocene *H. sapiens* (including the putative *H. ergaster* remains). He compared the magnitude and pattern of variability in the entire early sample with two groups:

- a sample of modern humans (one species) and
- a mixed sample of the three Koobi Fora hominid species from 2.0-1.7 myr (several species)

Kramer found the Early and Middle Pleistocene *H. sapiens* sample to be most similar to the single species - modern humans - in both magnitude and pattern of variation. In sum, there is no valid basis for distinguishing *H. ergaster* from early *H. sapiens*.

REFERENCES AND FURTHER READINGS

BEHRENSMEYER, A.K., and H.B.S. COOKE 1985 Paleoenvironments, stratigraphy, and taphonomy in the African Pliocene and early Pleistocene. In E. Delson (ed): *Ancestors: The Hard Evidence*. Alan R. Liss, New York. pp. 60-62.

BEHRENSMEYER, A.K. and L.F. LAPORTE 1981 Footprints of a Pleistocene hominid in northern Kenya. *Nature* 289:167-169.

BENTLEY, G.R. 1985 Hunter-gatherer energetics and fertility: a reassessment of the !Kung San. *Human Ecology* 13(1):79-109.

BILSBOROUGH, A., and B.A. WOOD 1988 Cranial morphometry of early hominids: facial region. *American Journal of Physical Anthropology* 76(1):61-86.

BINFORD, L.R. 1985 Human ancestors: changing views of their behaviors. *Journal of Anthropological Archaeology* 4:292-327.

BRÄUER, G., and E. MBUA 1992 *Homo erectus* features used in cladistics and their variability in Asian and African hominids. *Journal of Human Evolution* 22(2):79-108.

BROWN, J.K. 1976 An anthropological perspective on sex roles and subsistence. In M.S. Teitelbaum (ed.): *Sex Differences*. Anchor Books, Garden City. pp. 122-137

BROWN, P. 1987 Cranial vault thickness in northern Chinese, European, and Australian Aboriginal populations. *Acta Anthropologica Sinica* 6(3):184-189.

BUNN, H.T., and R.J. BLUMENSCHINE 1987 On "theoretical framework and tests" of early hominid meat and marrow acquisition: a reply to Shipman. *American Anthropologist* 89:444-448.

BUNN, H.T., and J.A. EZZO 1993 Hunting and scavenging by Plio-Pleistocene hominids: nutritional constraints, archaeological patterns, and behavioural patterns. *Journal of Archaeological Science* 20:365-398.

DANIELS, F., P. W. POST, and B. E. JOHNSON. 1972. Theories of the role of pigment in the evolution of human races. In V. Riley (ed): *Pigmentation: Its Genesis and Biologic Control*. Appleton-Century-Crofts, New York. pp. 13-22.

CLARK, J. D. 1993 The African tinder-box: the spark that ignited our cultural heritage. In A.J. Almquist and A. Manyak (eds.): *Milestones in Human Evolution*. Waveland, Prospect Heights. pp. 167-182.

CLUTTON-BROCK, T.H. 1980 Primates, brains, and ecology. *Journal of Zoology* 190:309-23.

DAY, M.H. 1976 Hominid postcranial remains from the East Rudolf succession, In Y. Coppens, F.C. Howell, G.Ll. Isaac, and R.E. Leakey (eds): *Earliest Man and Environments in the Lake Rudolf Basin*. University of Chicago Press, Chicago. pp. 507-521.

___. 1978 Functional interpretations of the morphology of postcranial remains of early African hominids. In C.J. Jolly (ed): *Early Hominids of Africa*. Duckworth, London. pp. 311-345.

DEAN, M.C. 1988 Another look at the nose and the functional significance of the face and nasal mucous membrane for cooling the brain in fossil hominids. *Journal of Human Evolution* 17(7):715-718.

EATON, S.B., and M. KONNER 1985 Paleolithic nutrition. A consideration of its nature and current implications. *The New England Journal of Medicine* 312(5):283-289.

ECKHARDT, R.B. 1987 Was Plio-Pleistocene hominid brain expansion a pleiotropic effect of adaptation to heat stress? *Anthropologischer Anzeiger* 45(3):193-201.

FISCHMAN, J. 1994 Putting a new spin on the birth of human birth. *Science* 264:1082-1083.

FOLK, E.G., and H.A. SEMKEN, Jr. 1991 The evolution of sweat glands. *International Journal of Biometeorology* 35:180-186.

FOLEY, R.A. 1984 Early man and the Red Queen: tropical African community evolution and hominid adaptation. In R. Foley (ed): *Hominid Evolution and Community Ecology.* Academic Press, London. pp. 85-110.

___. 1991 How many species of hominid should there be? *Journal of Human Evolution* 30(5):413-427.

FRANCISCUS, R.G., and E. TRINKAUS 1988 Nasal morphology and the emergence of *Homo erectus.* *American Journal of Physical Anthropology* 75(4):517-527.

GORDON, K.D. 1987 Evolutionary perspectives on human diet. In F.E. Johnston (ed): *Nutritional Anthropology.* Alan R. Liss, New York.

GOULD, S.J. 1976 *Ontogeny and Phylogeny.* Harvard University Press, Cambridge.

___. 1985 The most compelling pelvis since Elvis. *Discover* 6(12):54-58.

GOULD, R.A. 1981 Comparative ecology of food-sharing in Australia and northwest California. In R.S.O. Harding and G. Teleki (eds): *Omnivorous Primates. Gathering and Hunting in Human Evolution.* Columbia University, New York. pp. 422-454.

GROVES, C.P., and V. MAZAK 1975 An approach to the taxonomy of the Hominidae: gracile Villafranchian hominids of Africa. *Casopis pro Mineralogii a Geologii* 20:225-247, reprinted in W.E. Meikle and S.T. Parker (eds): *Naming our Ancestors: An Anthology of Hominid Taxonomy.* Waveland, Prospect Heights. pp. 107-125 (1994).

HABGOOD, P.J. 1989 An investigation into the usefulness of a cladistic approach to the study of the origin of anatomically modern humans. *Human Evolution* 4:241-252.

HAYDEN, B. 1979 *Paleolithic Reflections: Lithic Technology and Ethnographic Excavation among Australian Aborigines.* Humanities Press, Englewood Cliffs.

HILL, A.H. 1983 Hippopotamus butchery by *Homo erectus* at Olduvai. *Journal of Archaeological Science* 10:135-137.

HOLLOWAY, R.L. 1978 Problems in brain endocast interpretation and African hominid evolution. In C.J. Jolly (ed): *Early Hominids of Africa.* Duckworth, London. pp. 379-402.

___. 1983 Human brain evolution: a search for units, models, and synthesis. *Canadian Journal of Anthropology* 3:215-230.

HOWELLS, W.W. 1981 *Homo erectus* in human descent: ideas and problems. In B.A. Sigmon and J.S. Cybulski (eds): *Homo erectus. Papers in Honor of Davidson Black.* (combined bibliography at end of volume). University of Toronto Press, Toronto. pp. 63-85.

HYLANDER, W.L., P.G. PICQ, and K.R. JOHNSON 1991 Masticatory-stress hypotheses and the supraorbital region of primates. *American Journal of Physical Anthropology* 86(1):1-36.

ISAAC, G. Ll. 1981 Stone age visiting cards: approaches to the study of early land use patterns. In I. Hodder, G. Isaac, and N. Hammand (eds): *Patterns of the Past.* Cambridge University Press, New York. pp. 131-155.

ISAAC, G.Ll. and D.C. CRADER 1981 To what extent were early hominids carnivorous? An archaeological perspective. In R.S.O. Harding and G. Teleki (eds): *Omnivorous Primates. Gathering and Hunting in Human Evolution.* Columbia University Press, New York. pp. 37-103.

ISAAC, G.Ll., J.W.K. HARRIS, and D. CRADER 1976 Archeological Evidence from the Koobi Fora Formation. In Y. Coppens, F.C. Howell, G.Ll. Isaac, and R.E. Leakey (eds): *Earliest Man and Environments in the Lake Rudolf Basin.* University of Chicago Press, Chicago. pp. 533-551.

KENNEDY, G.E. 1983 Some aspects of fossil and recent hominine femora. *Journal of Human Evolution* 12:587-616.

___. 1985 Bone thickness in *Homo erectus. Journal of Human Evolution* 14:699-708.

KLEIN, R.G. 1987 Reconstructing how early people exploited animals: problems and prospects. In M.H. Nitecki and D.V. Nitecki (eds): *The Evolution of Human Hunting.* Plenum, New York. pp. 11-45.

KRAMER, A. 1993 Human taxonomic diversity in the Pleistocene: does *Homo erectus* represent multiple hominid species? *American Journal of Physical Anthropology* 91(2):161-171.

LAITMAN, J.T. 1985 Later Middle Pleistocene hominids. In E. Delson (ed): *Ancestors: The Hard Evidence.* Alan R. Liss, New York. pp. 265-267.

LATIMER, B., and C.V. WARD 1993 The thoracic and lumbar vertebrae. In A.C. Walker and R.E. Leakey (eds): *The Nariokotome Homo erectus Skeleton.* Harvard University Press, Cambridge. pp. 266-293, 442-443.

LEAKEY, L.S.B. 1966 *Homo habilis, Homo erectus* and the australopithecines. *Nature* 209:1279-1281.

LEAKEY, M.D. 1980 Early man, environment, and tools. In L-K. Königsson (ed): *Current Argument on Early Man. Report from a Nobel Symposium.* Pergamon, Oxford. pp. 114-133.

LEAKEY, R.E. and A.C. WALKER. 1976. *Australopithecus, Homo erectus* and the Single Species Hypothesis. *Nature* 261:572-574.

___. 1985 *Homo erectus* unearthed. *National Geographic* 168(5): 624-629.

LEONARD, W.R, and M.L. ROBERTSON 1994 Evolutionary perspectives on human nutrition: the influence of brain and body size on diet and metabolism. *American Journal of Human Biology* 6:77-88.

LOVEJOY, C.O., A.H. BURSTEIN, and K.G. HEIPLE 1976 The biomechanical analysis of bone strength: a method and its application to Platycnemia. *American Journal of Physical Anthropology* 44:489-506.

MARTIN, R.D., and A, M. MacLARNON 1985 Gestation period, neonatal size, and maternal investment in placental mammals. *Nature* 313:220-223.

McARTHUR, A.J. and J.A. CLARK 1987 Body temperature and heat and water balance. *Nature* 326:647-648.

McBREARTY, S., and M. MONIZ 1991 Prostitutes or providers? Hunting, tool use, and sex roles in earliest *Homo*. In D. Walde and N.D. Willows (eds): *The Archaeology of Gender.* University of Calgary Archaeological Association, Calgary.

McHENRY, H.M. 1973 Early hominid humerus from East Rudolf, Kenya. *Science* 180:739-741.

MILTON, K. 1987 Primate diets and gut morphology: implications for hominid evolution. In M. Harris and E.B. Ross (eds): *Food and Evolution: Toward a Theory of Human Food Habits.* Temple University Press, Philadelphia. pp. 93-115.

MOLNAR, S. 1992 *Human Variation: Races, Types, and Ethnic Groups.* Third Edition. Prentice Hall, Englewood Cliffs.

NEWMAN, R.W. 1970 Why man is such a sweaty and thirsty animal: a speculative review. *Human Biology* 42:12-27.

OAKLEY, K.P. 1961 On man's use of fire, with comments on tool-making and hunting. In S.L. Washburn (ed): *Social Life of Early Man.* Aldine, Chicago. pp. 176-193.

O'CONNELL, J.F., K. HAWKES, and N. BLURTON-JONES 1988 Hadza hunting, butchering, and bone transport and their archaeological implications. *Journal of Anthropological Research* 44(2):113-161.

PICQ, P.G., and W.L. HYLANDER 1989 Endo's analysis of the primates skull and the functional significance of the supraorbital region. *American Journal of Physical Anthropology* 79(3):393-398.

POTTS, R. 1991 Why the Oldowan? Plio-Pleistocene tool making and the transport of resources. *Journal of Anthropological Research* 47(2):153-177.

RICHTSMEIER, J.T., and A.C. WALKER 1993 A morphometric study of facial growth. In A.C. Walker and R.E. Leakey (eds): *The Nariokotome Homo erectus Skeleton.* Harvard University Press, Cambridge. pp. 391-410, 446-447.

RIGHTMIRE, G.P. 1992 *Homo erectus:* ancestor or evolutionary side branch? *Evolutionary Anthropology* 1(2):43-49.

ROBERTS, D.F. 1953 Body weight, race, and climate. *American Journal of Physical Anthropology* 11:533-558.

RUFF, C.B. 1989 New approaches to structural evolution of limb bones in primates. *Folia Primatologia* 53:142-159.

____. 1993 Climatic adaptation and hominid evolution: the thermoregulatory imperative. *Evolutionary Anthropology* 2(2):53-60.

RUFF, C.B. and A.C. WALKER 1993 Body size and body shape. In A.C. Walker and R.E. Leakey (eds): *The Nariokotome Homo erectus Skeleton.* Harvard University Press, Cambridge. pp. 234-265, 441-442.

RUSSELL, M.D. 1985 The supraorbital torus: "a most remarkable peculiarity". *Current Anthropology* 26(3):337-360; 27(3):259-260.

SABAN, R. 1986 Veines Méningées et Hominisation. In V.V. Novotný and A. Mizerová (eds): *Fossil Man. New Facts, New Ideas. Papers in Honor of Jan Jelínek's Life Anniversary. Anthropos* (Brno) 23:15-33.

SACHER, G.A. 1975 Maturation and longevity in relation to cranial capacity in hominid evolution. In R. Tuttle (ed): *Primate Functional Morphology and Evolution*. Mouton, The Hague. pp. 417-441.

SCHULTZ, A.H. 1960 Age changes in primates and their modification in man. In J.M. Tanner (ed): *Human Growth*. Pergamon, Oxford. pp. 1-20.

SHIPMAN, P. 1988 An evolutionary tale: what does it take to be a meat eater? *Discovery* (September):39-44

___. 1993 On the origin of races. *New Scientist* (16 January) 34-37.

___. 1994 Brains versus brawn. *New Scientist*

SINCLAIR, A.R.E., M.D. LEAKEY, and N. NORTON-GRIFFITHS 1986 Migration and hominid bipedalism. *Nature* 324:307-308.

SKINNER, M. 1991 Bee brood consumption: an alternative explanation for hypervitaminosis A in KNM-ER 1808 (*Homo erectus*) from Koobi Fora, Kenya. *Journal of Human Evolution* 20(6):493-503.

SPETH, J.D. 1990 Seasonality, resource stress, and food sharing in seasonal "egalitarian" foraging societies. *Journal of Anthropological Archaeology* 9:148-188.

STRINGER, C 1984 The definition of *Homo erectus* and the existence of the species in Africa and Europe. In P. Andrews and J.L. Franzen (eds): *The Early Evolution of Man, with Special Emphasis on Southeast Asia and Africa. Courier Forschungsinstitut Senckenberg* 69:131-143.

___. 1992 Evolution of early humans. In S. Jones, R. Martin, and D. Pilbeam (eds.): *The Cambridge Encyclopaedia of Human Evolution*. Cambridge University Press, New York. pp. 241-251

TOBIAS, P.V. 1991 The environmental background of hominid emergence, and the appearance of the genus *Homo*. *Human Evolution* 6(2):129-142.

TOTH, N. 1987 Behavioral inferences from early stone artifact assemblages: an experimental model. *Journal of Human Evolution* 16(7/8):763-787.

TRINKAUS, E. 1987 Bodies, brawn, brains, and noses: human ancestors and human predation. In M.H Niteki and D.V. Niteki (eds): *The Evolution of Human Hunting*. Plenum Press, New York. pp. 107-145.

TURNER, A. 1990 The evolution of the guild of larger terrestrial carnivores in the Plio-Pleistocene of Africa. *Geobios* 23:349-368.

TURNER, A., and A. CHAMBERLAIN 1989 Speciation, morphological change, and the status of African *Homo erectus*. *Journal of Human Evolution* 18(2):115-130.

WALKER, A.C. 1993a The origin of the genus *Homo*. In D.T. Rasmussen (ed): *The Origin and Evolution of Humans and Humanness*. Jones and Bartless, Boston. pp. 29-47.

___. 1993b Perspectives on the Nariokotome discovery. In A.C. Walker and R.E. Leakey (eds): *The Nariokotome Homo erectus Skeleton*. Harvard University Press, Cambridge. pp. 411-430, 447-448.

WALKER, A.C., and R.E. LEAKEY (editors) 1993 *The Nariokotome Homo erectus Skeleton.* Harvard University Press, Cambridge.

WALKER, A.C., M.R. ZIMMERMAN, and R.E. LEAKEY 1982 A possible case of hypervitaminosis A in *Homo erectus. Nature* 296:248-250.

WEIDENREICH, F. 1940 The *torus occipitalis* and related structures and their transformation in the course of human evolution. *Bulletin of the Geological Society of China* 19:480-546.

___. 1947 Some particulars of skull and brain of early hominids and their bearing on the problem of the relationship between man and anthropoids. *American Journal of Physical Anthropology* 5:387-418.

WHEELER, P.E. 1985 The influence of bipedalism on the energy and water budgets of early hominids. *Journal of Human Evolution* 21(2):117-136.

___. 1991a The loss of functional body heir in man: the influence of thermal environment, body form, and bipedalism. *Journal of Human Evolution* 14:23-28.

___. 1991b The thermoregulatory advantages of hominid bipedalism in open equatorial environments: the contribution of increased heat loss and cutaneous evaporative cooling. *Journal of Human Evolution* 21(2):107-115.

___. 1992 The influence of the loss of functional body hair on the water budgets of early hominids. *Journal of Human Evolution* 23(5):379-388.

___. 1993 The influence of stature and body form on hominid energy and water budgets: a comparison of *Australopithecus* and early *Homo* physiques. *Journal of Human Evolution* 24(1):13-28.

___. 1994 The thermoregulatory advantages of heat storage and shade-seeking behaviour to hominids foraging in equatorial savanna environments. *Journal of Human Evolution* 26(4):339-350.

WOLPOFF, M.H. 1976 Multivariate discrimination, tooth measurements, and early hominid taxonomy. *Journal of Human Evolution* 5:339-344.

WOOD, B.A. 1989 Hominid relationships: a cladistic perspective. *Proceedings of the Australasian Society for Human Biology* 2:83-102.

___. 1992 The origin and evolution of the genus *Homo. Nature* 355:783-790.

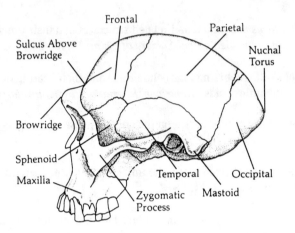

FIGURE 9.2 Early African *Homo sapiens* cranium ER 3733, showing the vault bones and some other features common in these early specimens.

FROM: First edition, figure 8.4

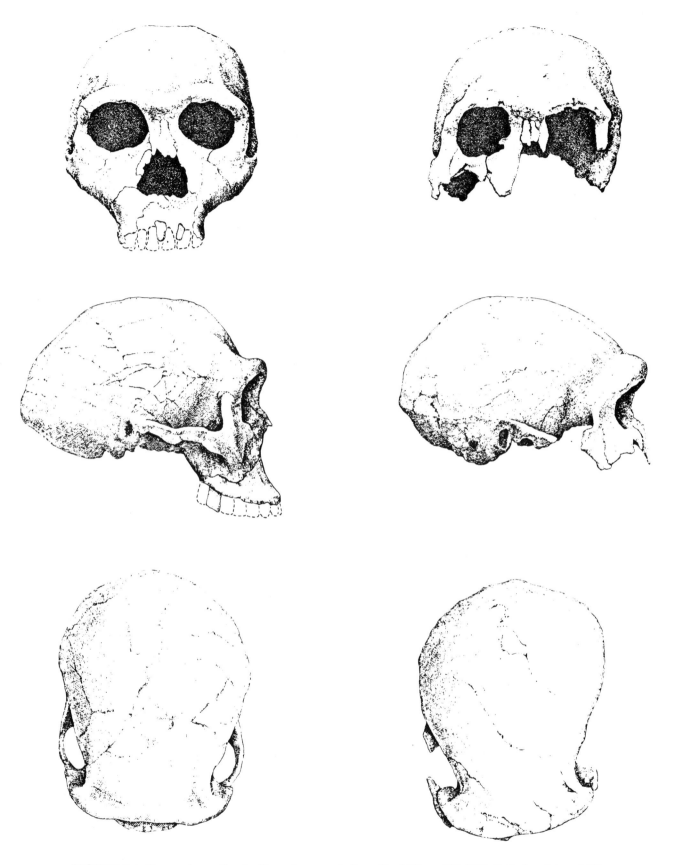

FIGURE 9.4 Comparison of early *H. sapiens* crania from Koobi Fora, ER 3733 (left, female) and ER 3883 (male), after Walker and Leakey (1978).

FROM Walker, A.C., and R.E. Leakey 1978 The hominids of East Turkana. Scientific American 239(2):54-66.

FIGURE 9.5 The size difference of early *H. sapiens* is indicated by the comparison of this modern human, about the height of early *H. sapiens* females, compared to the Hadar female "Lucy", after Wood (1992).

FROM Wood, B.A. 1992 Evolution of australopithecines. In S. Jones, R. Martin, and D. Pilbeam (eds): *The Cambridge Encyclopedia of Human Evolution.* Cambridge University Press, Cambridge. pp. 231-240.

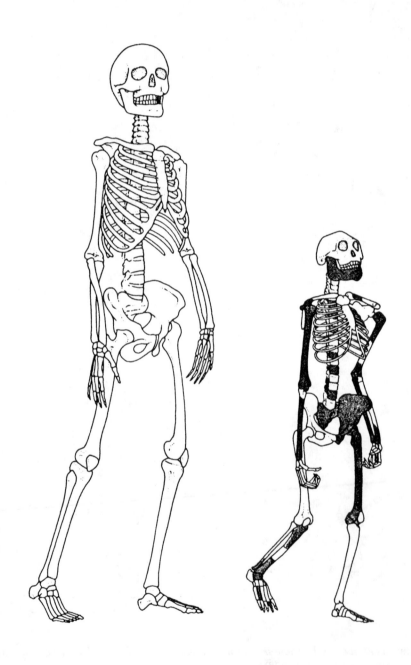

FIGURE 9.7 Views of the ER 993 femur, after Walker (1973), showing the positions of measurements for the platymeric and pilastric indexes.
FROM Walker, A.C. 1973 New *Australopithecus* femora from East Rudolf, Kenya. *Journal of Human Evolution* 2:545-555.

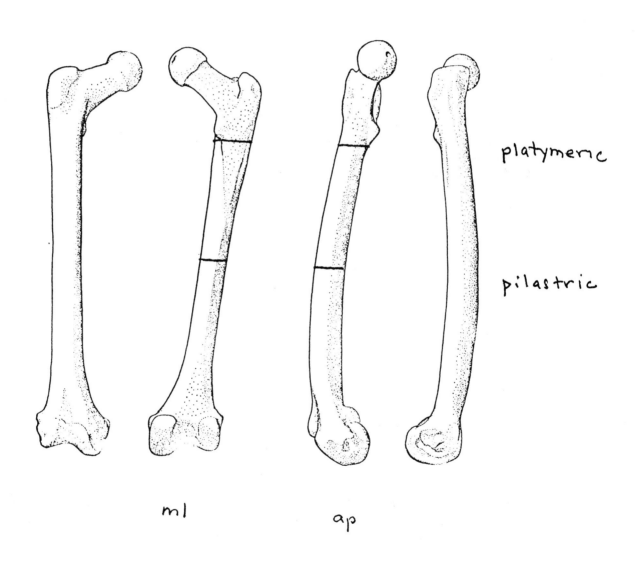

platymeric

pilastric

ml   ap

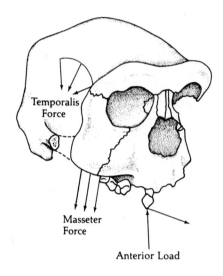

FIGURE 9.8 Drawing of Sangiran 17, a Middle Pleistocene Indonesian, showing a load on the anterior teeth (canine in this case) with its horizontal and vertical components (vertical from the force of the mandible), and the directions of the large muscles generating that mandibular force.
FROM: First edition, figure 8.6.

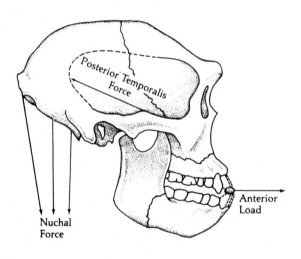

FIGURE 9.9 F. Weidenreich's reconstruction of the Indonesian late Lower Pleistocene cranium Sangiran 4 and the Sangiran I mandible. The drawing shows the horizontal portion of anterior load, shown as an outward facing arrow applied to the canine, and summarizes the main forces of the muscles that resist it.
FROM: First edition, figure 8.7

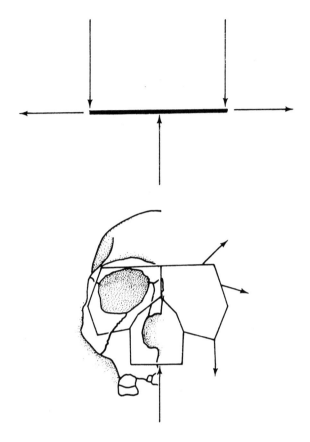

FIGURE 9.10 Simplified model of the ER 3733 face showing the vertical components of anterior load. The model is derived from Endo's facial stress analysis. A simplified model of the reaction of the face to vertical anterior loads, based on a drawing of the ER 3733 face. The model is derived from B. Endo's facial stress analysis. The upward-pointing arrow represents the force of an object between the teeth. This force is provided by the force of the mandible on the object. Therefore, the muscles closing the mandible also produce forces on the face. These are represented by the arrows on the right, and the main lines of facial resistance to these forces are represented by a simple beam model. The lower (downward pointing) arrow represents the masseter force, and the upper ones the anterior temporalis force. The actions of these forces meet in the area above the eyes. Their effects in this area can be reduced to a simpler model by representing the region above the eyes by a beam (shown above). On this beam, a central force acts

upward, and the forces to the sides act to bend the beam downward and pull it outward. It is the concentration of bending and tensile (producing tension) forces on the beam (supraorbital region) that creates the necessity for strengthening. In early hominids with low foreheads, the strengthening takes the form of a buttress, or torus, called the supraorbital torus or the browridge

FROM: First edition, figure 8.8

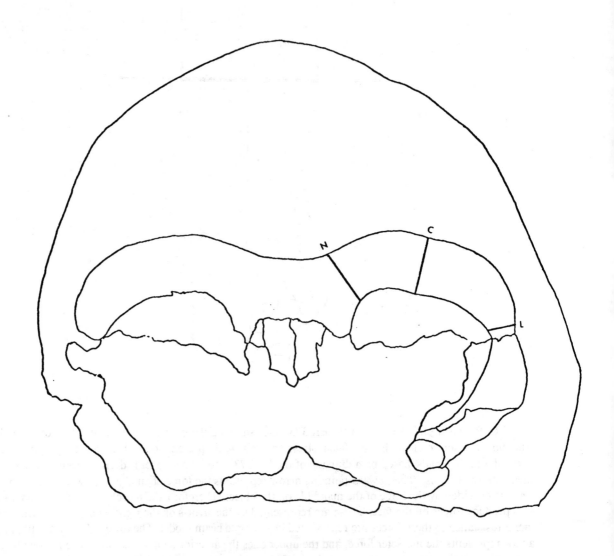

FIGURE 9.11 Facial measurements used in table 9.3. The ZKT L3 face is used to show measures of the supraorbital torus, and the reconstructed Kromdraai face, TM 1517, shows the other measurements.

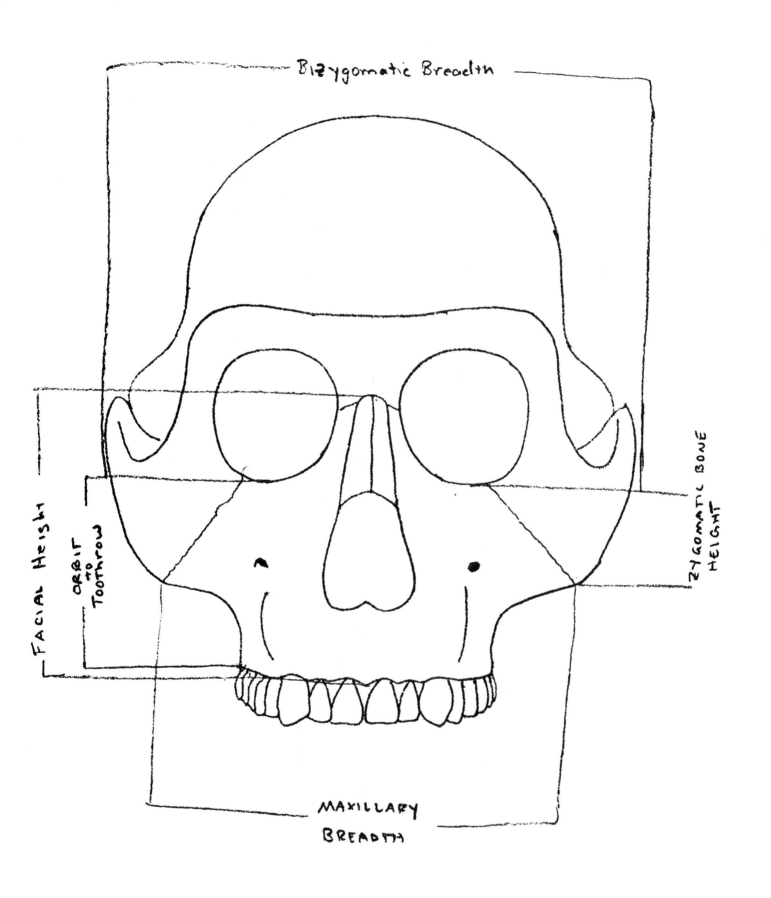

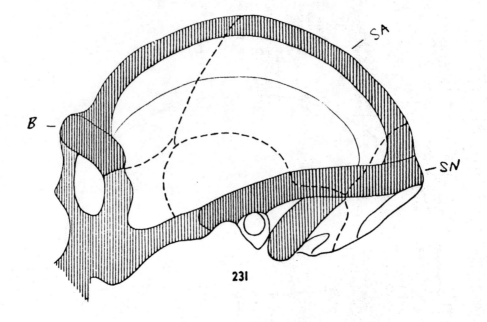

231

FIGURE 9.13 Cranial buttresses, after Weidenreich (1943).

FROM Weidenreich, F. 1943 The skull of *Sinanthropus pekinensis*: A comparative study of a primitive hominid skull. *Palaeontologia Sinica*, n.s. D, No. 10 (whole series No. 127), figures 231, 232.

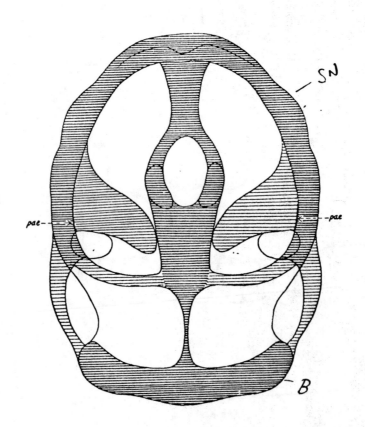

CHAPTER TEN

The Spread of Humanity

One of the most important consequences of the adaptive shift involved in *Homo sapiens* origins was habitat expansion. Humans, in a phrase, became a **colonizing species** during the last quarter of their career, as populations expanded their ecological range into arid and highland-to-mountainous habitats, and eventually moved out of Africa to spread across the tropical and subtropical regions of the Old World (see map 10.X). During this time many regional differences appeared, and populations at the edges of the human range developed distinctions that in some cases have persisted into the Late Pleistocene and even recent and modern times.

Why did hominids leave Africa? An important prerequisite was clearly the initial *H. sapiens* adaptive complex reflecting important differences in mobility - size, long legs, and other adaptations that reflect improved water retention and effective sweating. Additional mechanisms that have been proposed range from the ultimate consequences of population expansions that follow from the adaptation to food acquisition by hunting/scavenging/gathering evolving as early *H. sapiens* first appeared, to the idea that the Sahara acted like a pump, drawing in populations when it was wet and fertile and spitting them out (presumably right out of Africa) when the climate returned to the aridity of today. Certainly, the adaptive changes that are reflected in the large bodies and long legs of early *H. sapiens* may have been the initial impetus. Yet, these changes were in place and the mechanisms functioned before significant hominid colonizations began. The difference, as C. Gamble argues, also lies in the changes in human social behavior. What we do know is that by some half million years after the species appeared, there were significant adaptive changes that were associated with the spread of the Acheulean industrial complex. These were:

- more effective habitat utilization,
- additional food resources available through
  - ◊ organized hunting
  - ◊ confrontational scavenging
  - ◊ improved techniques for collecting and preparing gathered foodstuffs.

It seems likely that a sexual division of labor allowed groups to simultaneously use different resources, thereby increasing the carrying capacity of the regions they inhabited and allowing groups to expand into new and more difficult habitats. Groups adapting by hunting, scavenging, and gathering required a wider yearly **home range** to take best advantage of seasonal resources. These increased ranges brought groups into contact in regular, predictable manners and from these contacts and the mate exchanges that must surely have followed, broad social networks developed. Combined, these improved the knowledge base necessary for populations to incorporate new habitats, and made them less dependent on the distribution of particular resources. As Gamble argues, opportunities could be advantaged with fewer risks, and the spread of *H. sapiens* out of Africa, beginning by a date as early as 1.8 myr and certainly by 1.4 myr ago was the result. Human populations had begun to successfully inhabit other regions in significant enough numbers to leave archaeological and fossil records by this time. Populations inhabited the tropics of South and Southeast Asia (including Indonesia, connected to the continent during periods of low sea level), and ranged eastward into central China and as far west as the western edge of Asia.

The chapter begins with a discussion of the Acheulean industrial complex, which appeared about 1.4 myr and lasted at least as long as the Oldowan complex. The development of the Acheulean is tied to the adaptive capabilities of early Pleistocene *Homo sapiens* populations, and its evolution parallels and intertwines with the morphological changes in the lineage as there are elements of mutual causation. Following this is an examination of the earliest human populations outside of Africa, and a discussion of the evolutionary processes that led to the pattern of anatomical differentiation and the formation of geographic varieties, or races, at that time.

Appearance and Importance of the Acheulean Industrial Complex

A recognizable change in hominid adaptation, in part reflected in their stone tool industries preceded the initial geographic spread out of Africa. The changes had clear adaptive consequences and, more indirectly, helped orient the direction of morphological evolution. They can be best documented in East Africa, where the archaeological record has enough time depth for us to trace their origin and subsequent development. By the time of middle Bed II at Olduvai, a more complex, better-made tool set was being manufactured (figure 10.1- in this and other discussions of archaeological data the reader will find R. Klein's *The Human Career* most helpful). The Acheulean Industrial complex is a description of the archaeological industry that begins at this time and spans more than a million years, ultimately found across the inhabited world. It is, in the words of the late L.S.B. Leakey, the first attempt to manufacture artifacts in "a set and regular pattern". Often lumped together with the Oldowan as the "Early Stone Age", or "Lower **Paleolithic**", the later Oldowan (called "Developed" Oldowan) and Acheulean greatly overlap in both the **technology** and the **typology** of the artifacts. However the real distinction may lie between the Oldowan and the Developed Oldowan; unlike the Oldowan, the forms of Acheulean tools appear to have been preconceived by their makers, and the concept of "tool types" can be validly applied to some of the artifacts. In fact one tool type, **the handaxe**, is the defining characteristic of the Acheulean. Handaxes are **bifacially flaked**, pear-shaped, pointed general-purpose tool of vastly varying sizes. The most common tools, however, remain the amorphous and ubiquitous utilized flakes.

Many Acheulean tools were made from large flakes that were first struck from cores. Some workers have suggested that it was this innovation of producing *large* flakes to be worked into tools that underlay or stimulated the technological developments that followed. It is probable that the Acheulean developed from the Oldowan industry. Moreover, later Oldowan is also characterized by bifaces, although cruder in manufacture technology (i.e. the skill in producing the final form) and lower in frequency. Contemporary with the early Acheulean, it is probably a functionally different variant of the same industry.

The handaxe is an interesting and important tool. Once it appears, like the earlier Oldowan pebble chopper, it continues to be used right up to the present time. Its shape, and the few observations of living people who use similar tools, suggest that the handaxe was essentially a Paleolithic boy scout knife: an all-purpose tool used for cutting, digging, chopping, wedging, drilling, and possibly as an aerodynamic projectile (although this author does not find the projectile interpretation particularly convincing). Variations on handaxe size appear to be allometric, attempts were clearly made to produce the same shape at different sizes and in different size-related proportions. For instance, at one African site R. Crompton and J. Gowlett showed that even across a large size range the larger tools were similarly shaped but relatively thinner. They suggest that the tools were not a happenstance result of flake production, and the consistency in their shapes are not a simple consequence of retouch, as some archaeologists have proposed. Perhaps more subject to experiment and analysis than any other piece of Paleolithic technology, it has been manufactured in a variety of ways (P. Jones), used in butchering (N. Toth and K. Schick), thrown (E. O'Brien), and had its microwear analyzed (L. Keeley) to find plant residues.

Moreover, the tool has been used as a mirror to help understand the mind of early *H. sapiens*. Its form underwent considerable change and refinement over its long history, and even the technology of its manufacture changes dramatically. These refinements are probably tied to the evolution of hand-and-eye coordination in hominids, and provide a clear reflection of its evolution. G. Isaac suggests that the complexity of design and the precision with which it is executed can help indicate both the level of technological capability and the complexity of rule systems. T. Wynn finds importance in the two concepts he believes distinguish handaxes and other Acheulean implements from Oldowan tools, symmetry and what he calls spatial quantity (identification of geometric properties such as diameters and parallel sides). These are important, in his view, because they are not coincidental consequences of the reduction process but clearly indicate the intent of the toolmaker. If these ideas are valid, the modeling in the minds of the toolmakers (perhaps an extension of the earlier hominid capabilities for mapping) and their skill in translating this into forms that can be replicated, underwent considerable change and refinement during the Acheulean span, extending into the Middle Pleistocene. There is much to be said for the ideas of workers such as Wynn who believe that handaxe evolution is a reflection of significant mental changes incorporating generalization and conceptualization into the realm of human abilities.

The Acheulean complex is characterized by far more than the development and increasing frequency of the handaxe. Numerous new types of tools appear. In the earlier assemblages, the vast majority of the tools are unmodified flakes; retouch (or reworking) becomes much more common later. Many Acheulean tools reflect more concentrated periods of workmanship during their manufacture, and were resharpened after being used. H. Dibble points out that resharpening, the consequence of the **retouch** process, can significantly alter the shape of tools and make them seem to change from one "tool type" into another. Perhaps most importantly, the retouch process shows that people were insightful about the characteristics that tools needed to have to work effectively, and recognized the advantages of taking care of and curating the tools that they made. Large cutting implements form the largest single functional category of tools, although chopping tools and spheroids are also common.

More important than the expanded range of tool types is the appearance of standardization and consistent refinement of form. The Acheulean tools differ from the haphazardly shaped Oldowan tools in the development of clearly established intent, greater skill, and a more complex set of rules. Another source of variation is raw materials. With a regularization of patterns, variations are more evident and their explanation is a major goal of paleolithic archaeology. Apart from idiosyncrasy and personal preferences, there are three sources of variation that have been identified:

- raw material limitations
- functional influences
- geographic variation, perhaps because of differing traditions

Differences between the material cultures of different geographic regions become established during the Acheulean.

The relationship of the early *Homo sapiens* specimens and the Acheulean industry has long plagued east African prehistory. Two hypotheses are probably *incorrect*:

1. *Homo sapiens* evolved in another region and migrated to east Africa, bringing along this distinctive industry (e.g. M. Leakey, who recognized the hominid as "*Homo erectus*").
2. Acheulean was invented by earlier hominids, presumably *Homo habilis* and the consequential changes in selection resulted in early *Homo sapiens* morphology evolving.

Instead, what is most likely is that the evolving abilities of early *H. sapiens* led to changes in behavior, technology-related anatomical developments, and increasingly efficient use of resources that combined to characterize the Acheulean *culture*. Critical to this idea is the age of the Acheulean's beginning. According to B. Asfaw and his colleagues, the earliest clearly dated Acheulean is from the Konso-Gardula site in Ethiopia, where its age is 1.4 myr. This is more than a half million years later than the first appearance of *Homo sapiens*, and these authors therefore suggest the two are not linked. They comment on the sudden appearance of the industry in east Africa, and the "surprising control over raw material and tool form" shown by its earliest manifestation there.

While announcing a mandible associated with the Acheulean at Konso-Gardula (KGA 10-1), Asfaw and colleagues commented on climatic causation hypotheses -- attempts to causally link hominid evolutionary events to changes in global climate (see Chapter 7). In particular they discuss a suggestion made by E. Vrba: "changes to open and arid conditions may have triggered the origin of *H. erectus* and of his characteristic tool kit ...", and "the period around 0.9 myr may also coincide with the earliest massive expansion of any hominid". They are very skeptical of this claim, especially as the first appearance of "his characteristic tool kit" comes long after the species appears, and as we will discuss below, the first dispersals of hominids out of Africa are much earlier than 0.9 myr. In fact, they may belong to the period just after the Acheulean first appears.

Therefore, the possibility of a link between the early phases of the colonizing portion of human evolution and the sudden appearance of the Acheulean in east Africa is suggestive. This is because habitat expansion within Africa was an immediate consequence of the social and adaptive changes that were occurring. It is at this time that the drier peripheries of the East African lake basins were utilized for the first time, according to J. Harris, with highland occupations soon following. The occupied range expanded into the southernmost and northernmost parts of Africa, and as R. Klein points out, dispersals out of Africa were an inevitable consequence. The evidences of hominids across the warmer regions of Asia are found soon thereafter (figure 10.15).

The Africans

Numerous Oldowan, Developed Oldowan, and Acheulean sites from the Early Pleistocene, up to the time of the Middle Pleistocene's beginning, are found in a variety of different habitats across the African continent. The earlier of these sites are generally found near water—along rivers or streams and on the shores of lakes. Subsequently evidence of hominid activities appear in drier habitats, in regions characterized by dry grasslands because they were in rain shadows or higher up. There is no evidence for a true forest habitation at this time. Human populations lived in areas where the greatest concentration of game is likely to have been found, and their dependence on water is not unexpected given the hominid pattern of diurnal confrontational scavenging and hunting.

Occupation of the Konso-Gardula basin, findspot of the earliest dated Acheulean, spans the later time range of the Lake Turkana basin fossils, and the hominids and industry are roughly equivalent in age to the Chari tuff there. In that Kenyan time range, 200 km to the south, the Acheulean is unknown and an industry similar to the Developed Oldowan, the Karari, predominates. However at Olduvai, in middle Bed II which is the approximate age of Konso-Gardula, both Developed Oldowan and Acheulean are present. Since early *H. sapiens* occurs at all three sites at a time which postdates the latest occurring habilines, the cause of this archaeological variation must be ecological, functional, traditional, or most probably some combination of these. Asfaw and colleagues suggest that the key difference is the proximity of Konso-Gardula to raw material sources. In any event, circumstances conspire to make it clear that early *H. sapiens* populations were responsible for these industries. It is most likely, in fact, that a group of *H. sapiens* invented the Acheulean, developing it out of an earlier variety of the Oldowan. Its sudden appearance in East Africa does not resolve the question of whether it was developed elsewhere, or whether it was quickly developed locally.

The Konso-Gardula artifacts are quite densely scattered, and unlike other famous cases of very dense Acheulean accumulations such as Olorgesailie (about half this age), they were not concentrated by water transport. Roughly made bifaces and more sharply tapered picks are made from both cores and flakes, and attain lengths of as much as 27 cm. The picks are widely regarded as digging tools, and Asfaw and colleagues report both cutmarks and evidences of bashing on the associated fossilized bones of large mammals.

THE HOMINID SAMPLE

As mentioned above a mandible was found at the earliest dated Acheulean site, Konso-Gardula, and there are several other specimens that come from just about the time the Acheulean appeared, at or during the beginnings of the first and only real exodus - the colonization of the empty or near-empty Old World tropics. Besides some other mandibular remains and isolated teeth, a male cranium, some cranial fragments, an ulna and a fragmentary humerus comprise this sample.

The Konso-Gardula mandible (KGA 10-1) is one of the largest known for early *H. sapiens*, too big to fit the ER 3733 female and possible large enough for OH 9 (see below). The mandible is anatomically similar to Turkana specimens such as the 1.5 myr ER 992, although it is bigger, the corpus is more robust, and the molars do not have the elongation of earlier *H. sapiens* mandibular teeth. The latter, however, is probably a consequence of age, as its tooth wear is marked (teeth become shorter and more squared off with advanced age as interproximal wear reduces their length). There are artificial groves worn between several of the teeth, below the crown level and into the gum (of the living individual). Similar grooves have been called **"toothpick grooves"** by several researchers, who hypothesize that they result from cleaning between the teeth with thin abrasive implements. Toothpick grooves are not at all unique to early *H. sapiens*, as other hominids such as the Omo L 894-1 cranium have them.

Olduvai hominid 9 was found on the surface in a place where it could have only eroded out of the upper part of Bed II. With a date for Tuff IId below it, at 1.48 myr, and the base of Bed III above at 1.33 myr, the specimen can be firmly bracketed to just about the time that the Acheulean industry first appears. OH 9 is a massive faceless cranium (see figure 10.3) with the largest capacity (1067 cc) of all the early specimens. It differs from ER 3733 in many of the same ways that the earlier male ER 3883 does, but the differences are invariably more exaggerated. It is most probable that OH 9 is an aged male. Sex determination comes from its size and massiveness. The age is more difficult to estimate, because there are no teeth known for the specimen and these are the most reliable indicators of age-at-death. However, here there is a hint. On the cranial base, just to the inside and in front of the mastoid process, is a small projecting open cylinder called the **vaginal process**. Inside it rests a long spur of bone called the **styloid process**, the seat of attachment for the **stylohyoid ligament** which extends from the cranial base to the hyoid bone, lying just above the **larynx** and attached to it. The styloid process only fuses to the inside of the vaginal foramen well into adulthood. If the individual dies before this fusion the styloid is usually lost as it will fall out of the vaginal foramen as the bone dries. For instance, styloid processes are virtually unknown in the australopithecines - a condition sometimes taken to be phylogenetic (it would presumably be an autapomorphy) but actually a reflection of their young ages at death. In OH 9 the base of the styloid process in fused to the vaginal process, suggesting that he lived longer than most australopithecines were able to.

The browridge is the thickest known for *any* hominid and projects dramatically in front of the moderately sloping forehead, separated from it by a shallow supratoral sulcus. Contrasting with this anatomy, the flat parts of the cranial bones (squama) are moderate to thin, seemingly a characteristic of most early African *H. sapiens,* and there is no frontal keel. The temporal line is in the form of an edge, raised above the bone surface not covered by the temporalis muscle. At the back of the posterior temporalis muscle attachment, where the line marking the furthest backward extent of its fan-shaped fibers almost reaches the lambdoidal suture and then angles downward and forward, there is a raised and thickened ridge called the **angular torus** (figure 9.10, showing angular torus). The cranial base is broad, with heavy buttressing where muscles attach. The spongy structures above the mastoids assume massive proportions so that the more perpendicular parietals of the ancestral australopithecine condition become an evenly inward-sloping cranial wall, a difference easily visible when crania are seen from the rear view. While the mastoid processes and the area of the vault around them are broad and well developed, the nuchal torus contrasts with the mastoid development and with the supraorbital torus. It is not strongly raised, except across its middle portion, and does not project backward strongly.

Like the earlier males ER 3883 and 15K the OH 9 mandibular fossa is broad and deep, only more so. A fossa of this size reflects powerful masticatory forces. Which muscles produced these forces remains unknown in the absence of the face, but some evidence suggests that the posterior part of temporalis (the muscle used when the anterior teeth are loaded, and when the jaw is brought to the side during rotary grinding), was important.

Several details suggest that the missing portions of the specimen were more australopithecine-like than one might expect. Analysis by W. Maier and A. Nkini indicate that the cranial base was very flattened, a condition resembling *A. africanus*. Moreover, P. Rightmire suggests that the position of the back of the nasal chamber, seen on the cranial base, is so far anterior that a "forwardly positioned facial skeleton" (i.e. marked prognathism) is to be expected.

Besides these crania, there are bits and pieces of fragmentary cranial vault scattered over this time range that show the same distinct features. Omo specimen P996-17 is a thick-vaulted parietal fragment, considerably exceeding all of the Turkana and Olduvai specimens. At the open air site of Gomboré II, along the Awash river at Melka Kunturé, Ethiopia, an equally thick cranial vault fragment is very broadly bracketed between 1.20 and 0.78 myr. The thickness differences between these specimens and the Olduvai and Turkana remains is really dramatic. For instance, in the middle of the parietal bone the Gomboré II specimen has a thickness of some 15 mm. This is 1.6 times as thick since the mean thickness for the Olduvai and Turkana specimens is 9.4 mm, n=9). With samples so small it is unclear whether the thickness differences represent a temporal trend (some of the Middle Pleistocene Africans are thick vaulted as well) or geographic variation.

This sample also includes some postcranial remains. OH 36 is a virtually complete ulna, a surface find from upper Bed II that was almost certainly eroded out of Tuff IId, 1.48 myr in age. The length, of approximately 290 mm, corresponds to a height of 176 cm in living Africans. It is a robust bone with prominent muscle attachments and marked curvature along its shaft. Like its slightly older counterpart, the ER 739 humerus, the OH 36 shaft is very thick relative to its length (table 10.1). Joint anatomy at the elbow is unusual. The surface areas are relatively small; for instance, the height of the trochlear notch, the surface corresponding to the rounded distal end of the humerus, is quite small and yet the bottom of that notch, the **coronoid process**, projects far more than similarly sized ulnas of later archaic humans. These contribute to joint stability when the joint is **loaded** (i.e. forces pass across it) while it is flexed. Should the preponderance of these features indicate male sex, as I believe, OH 36 is shorter than the earlier males.

At Gomboré Ib, also near Melka Kunturé, there is a distal humerus fragment of very similar age. It is somewhat smaller than the slightly older ER 739, and is not as robustly developed. The articular anatomy (the upper part of the elbow) is said to be "more modern", but variation between these specimens is much like that among the humeri from Hadar, and is unlikely to be of taxonomic significance.

Table 10.1
Robustness and Articular Surface Trends in Large Archaic Adult Ulnas (in millimeters)

	Ulna Length from base (L)	Trochlear Notch Gape[1] (G)	Relative Gape (Height) (G/L%)	Coronoid Process Projection (P)	Relative Projection (P/L%)	Midshaft Circumference (C)	Robustness (C/L%)
OH 36	287	18.7	6.5	38.0	13.2	54	18.8
Baringo	275	19.3	7.0	27.5	10.0	41	14.9
Shanidar 1	273	25.0	9.2	30.0	11.0	42	15.4
Kebara	274	20.3	7.4	29.3	10.7	50	18.2
Skhul 4	294	25.2	8.6	34.2	11.6	45	15.3

[1] This is the height (along the bone's long axis) of the articular part of the notch, taken at its middle - figure 7.2

OH 34 is a specimen comprised of a fragmentary femur and even more fragmentary tibia from the JK2 site, near the top of Bed III, bracketed in age to between 1.33 and about 0.92 myr. H. McHenry estimates the bone length for the femur at 432 mm, which is rather short for one of the early *H. sapiens* specimens but even at this length it is longer than any femur attributed or attributable to a habiline. However, the cortical bone of the shaft is very thin and while this might be the result of erosion after the specimen was fossilized, some workers have suggested that the individual suffered from a pathology that may have affected bone length. Let it suffice to say that the M. Day and T. Molleson paper discussing these possibilities is aptly entitled "The puzzle from JK2".

OTHER SPECIMENS FROM THE EARLY-MIDDLE PLEISTOCENE BOUNDARY

In Africa, even through the end of the Early Pleistocene early *H. sapiens* specimens are known mainly from eastern and northern parts of the continent. They are contemporary with the earliest human remains in Asia (figure 10.15).

Other than a few fragmentary remains from the Swartkrans cave (the best preserved of these is the SK 15 mandible, possibly from Member II), the most southern of the early *H. sapiens* sites is Olduvai Gorge. The Swartkrans mandible resembles smaller australopithecines in many respects, but only robust australopithecines and *Homo* are known from the cave and with this choice of affiliation the latter is more likely. It is small, short (with the upper and lower margins of the corpus approximately parallel), and thick, with a low **ascending ramus** that suggests a somewhat reduced face. Its proportions (including the broad **dental arcade**) and size resemble the ER 730 female. A number of isolated teeth and other fragments from the site may well represent a *Homo* species as well, but which one (or whether there is only one) is unclear. Even still, given the behavioral capacities we have hypothesized (discussed in Chapter 9), the evidence of fire in Member 3 suggests that early *H. sapiens* is one hominid who was there.

More from Olduvai

The Bed IV deposits encompass the beginning the Middle Pleistocene sequence (the actual boundary is just below Tuff IIb, at the approximate middle of the Bed). Bed IV spans some 200 kyr and is dated to between 920 and 720 kyr, the age of the Kabuh Formation hominids from Indonesia. Although the Bed IV sample is small, it includes crania, mandibles, and postcrania.

Olduvai hominid 12 was found on the surface in lower Bed IV. It is a fragmentary female specimen with many resemblances to the much earlier ER 3733, although with an estimated cranial capacity of 727 cc it is even smaller. Other features similar to the earlier female include the thin vault bones and rounded posterior cranial contour. The contrast with OH 9 in sex-related features such as the size and expression of the browridge, mastoid process, or temporal lines could hardly be greater. Yet other features resemble the Olduvai male, such as the weak nuchal torus development (it is only prominent near the midline) and the low position of the torus on the cranium, the lack of a sharp parietal angle, and absence of distinct keels along the midline of the frontal bone or the sagittal join of the parietals.

OH 22 is the most complete of the Olduvai early *H. sapiens* jaws, found in the lower part of Bed IV, near the junction with Bed III. The mandible is preserved on most of the right side and has a relatively thick corpus of only moderate corpus height. The corpus **robusticity**, which is the height of the body divided by the breadth, is lower than virtually any another early *H. sapiens* mandible. Like most of these specimens the upper and lower borders of the corpus (that is, the alveolar margin and base) are close to parallel. The third premolar has anomalous form, unusually elongated from back to front where it tapers to a narrow end. Body thickness is greatest at the symphysis, where their are two distinct internal tori and an elongated extension of bone behind the incisors which (like the corpus robustness) is quite similar to the smaller habiline mandibles such as OH 13.

OH 28 is an associated femur shaft (McHenry estimated its length at 456 mm) and most of an innominate, found on the surface of an Acheulean site in the upper part of Bed IV. The innominate is quite similar to ER 3228, as detailed below, and almost identical in size (McHenry reconstructs and estimates (respectively) femur lengths for these specimens that indicate a body height of 169 cm for both). The acetabulum is relatively large, and the distance between it and the sacroiliac joint is short (this is the region where weight is transferred from the trunk to the lower limbs and where forces acting around the acetabulum come into play). C. Ruff reconstructs the pelvic inlet shape as elliptical. However, details that vary with sex indicate that unlike the earlier Turkana specimens, OH 28 was probably female. In spite of the fact that the hip bone had been chewed, probably by a crocodile, it can be seen that the ilium has marked fare, and a thickened pillar extending from the acetabulum to the top of the bone attests to powerful abductor forces. The orientation of this buttress is somewhat more rearward than in many recent pelves, and the anterior spines are quite prominent as a result (prominent spines on a more rearward positioned bone places the muscle attachments in the same position as smaller spines on a bone with a more forward orientation). This orientation, shared with ER 3228, suggests that early *H. sapiens* pelves probably had long pubic bones. Another reflection of the pattern of bipedal gait is the small lever arm for the hamstrings on the ischium. The femur shaft is markedly flattened, more so than any of the earlier *H. sapiens* specimens just under the lesser trochanter (**platymeric** index) and at the shaft middle (**pilastric** index). While linking it with other early *H. sapiens* femurs, the trend toward continued flattening in the Africans (especially with the earliest specimens) suggests an ongoing behavioral change.

Other East Africans

To the west, a very eroded and weathered frontofacial fragment (figure 10.4) was discovered in the vicinity of Lake Chad, associated with fauna from the end of the Early or beginning of the Middle

Pleistocene . The characteristic features of the face include its marked breadth (especially nasal breadth and the distance between the orbits) combined with reduced facial height, relatively large orbits, and a frontal bulge above the (eroded) browridge. What remains of the lower face suggests an australopithecine-like prognathism. The profile of the region below the nose is actually concave, similar to much earlier crania such as STS 5.

North Africans

Oldest of the North African sites is from Algeria. Ternifine, or Tighenif, is faunally dated to the beginning of the Middle Pleistocene, about the age of Olduvai upper Bed IV. When the humans lived there the area at the site was a shallow lake or swamp, surrounded by an open, arid environment. Three fairly complete mandibles (see figure 10.5), a parietal, and some isolated teeth together constitute an Acheulean-associated sample that combines a brain size estimated to be larger than any early Pleistocene hominid and great variability in the mandibular sample.

The parietal is that of a juvenile, its thinness is probably a result of the individual's youth as might be the weak expression of a sagittal keel and the absence of an angular torus. The dimensions are quite large and reconstruction suggests that the parietal represents a large cranial vault. A cranial capacity of about 1300 cc has been estimated.

The dental sample includes virtually complete mandibular dentitions (lacking representation of only the central incisor) plus a number of isolated teeth. Posterior tooth size is similar to the early Pleistocene Africans. Like them, the third molar is consistently smaller than the second. The anterior teeth are very large and the sample shows clear evidence of canine and incisor expansion compared with earlier remains. There is a considerable amount of **differential wear** on these teeth, quite heavy relative to the wear on the posterior molars.

There appears to be no relation between the size of the mandibles and the size of the teeth. In fact, the mandible with the largest body (Ternifine 3) has one of the smaller dentitions. Never the less, the tall, thick coronoid process attests to a significant development of the temporalis muscle. Considered together, the three mandibles have a number of features in common, such as parallel sided corpuses that are very high, although not particularly broad, and symphyses are flattened and have a marked posterior angulation and no trace of a chin. Only Ternifine 3 has any indication of a double buttressing system on the internal surface and this is quite reduced compared with OH 22. The ramus is complete, or virtually complete, in Ternifine 2 and 3. In the former the ramus is broad and low, while in the latter it is even broader and markedly higher (figure 10.6). This high ramus is thought to correspond to a large face. Ramus height in Ternifine 3 exceeds all other early *H. sapiens* mandibles. It is so tall that it is too big to fit on large faced male crania such as Kabwe.

THE EARLY AFRICANS

As a whole the Pliocene and early Pleistocene *H. sapiens* sample from Africa, spanning the first million years of *H. sapiens* evolution, has some interesting attributes. Even taking the long time span it represent into account, one of these is marked variation and the other is considerable uniformity over time.

A good example of the variation in this sample can be found in the supraorbitals. Nowhere else can supraorbital differences as great as the contrast between OH 9 and the female crania, whether the comparison is with ER 3733 (one of the earliest) or with OH 12 (the latest). There is marked variation in the mandibular fossa (deep as in OH 9 and ER 3883 *vs* shallow as in ER 3733) and other structural features as well. Variation in cranial bone thickness is discussed above. The African mandibles in this sample are also characterized by marked morphological and dimensional variability. The difference in size between SK 15 from South Africa and Ternifine 3 from the north marks the maximum extent of the known early *H. sapiens* range. Even in the small postcranial sample similar variation can be found. For instance, the elbow anatomy (as seen in the humerus distal articular surface) varies between ER 739 and the Gomboré humerus as much as it does within any hominid group.

A second attribute is uniformity. An analysis of brain sizes by E. Trinkaus and myself shows no tendency towards increase over this time span. Body size is also quite uniform over this period, not changing significantly over time and ranging only between 168 and 185 cm while averaging 174 cm for the 9 specimens that can be reconstructed. This is the average height for several of the tall and linear tribes that live in East Africa today, although far less variation than the adults in such tribes reflect (a difference that cannot be totally ascribed to the sample size of 9). Certain anatomical structures seem quite similar throughout the sample. For instance, the nuchal torus development is surprisingly constant, given the variation in time and other marked difference due to sex. The tori all seem to be developed only over the middle third of the skull, and the details of

- their marked midline vertical height
- their projection away from the cranial surface,
- the anatomical details of their external structure such as the form of inion,

are surprisingly uniform, in comparison to the variation found in other samples. In the mandibles, many (although certainly not all) of the specimens have robust mandibular bodies (that is, the ratio of breadth to height is high) with parallel sides (alveolar margin and base) and a smooth, backwards sloping symphysis. The postcanine teeth are moderate in size and also show no significant variation over time. In all, while the sample is really too small to be certain or to establish statistical validity, at the moment it does appear that the first million years of *H. sapiens* evolution in Africa is rather static. Whether this is the consequence of a small sample size spread over a long time span or a real reflection of the evolutionary process remains unclear.

However, some of the seemingly static features begin to change toward the end of this period, as hominids begin the dispersal process and spread widely. Most significantly, when the cranial capacity estimated from the Ternifine parietals is included in the sample, there is significant increase over time, suggesting that the dramatic trend for increasing cranial capacity spanning the rest of the Pleistocene begins about then. There is much to be said for the idea that the subsequent acceleration in human evolution was related to the dispersal itself, the behavioral changes that underlay the habitat expansions, and the new circumstances brought by the emerging polytypism affecting the entirety of this colonizing species. From the viewpoint of evolutionary theory, what may be most interesting about all of this is that *it is not related to a speciation event.*

Taken as a whole this is the most australopithecine-like of all *H. sapiens* samples:

- brain sizes partially overlap into the australopithecine range,
- sexual dimorphism in cranial capacity for the 3 males and 2 females is similar to the dimorphism expressed in australopithecine species and the Olduvai habilines (males average about 18% larger than females, at 927 cc and 788 cc respectively),
- many of their anatomical details, not known in either the crania or the postcranial remains of later humans, resemble the australopithecines

Yet, early African *H. sapiens* is overwhelmingly unique and in many respects quite human.

The First Indonesians

Controversial dates thought to be related to several Indonesian crania suggest that the first occupation of this area was latest Pliocene. The bulk of the evidence shows that humans spread to other continents somewhat later, during the Early Pleistocene. These indications are both paleontological and archaeological, being based on discoveries of fossil hominids and/or their tools. This dispersal was more than an increase in geographic range, as evidence shows new habitats were being occupied both in African and beyond. Thus human artifacts are found for the first time well out of the lowland savannas, region of the earlier successful early *H. sapiens* adaptations. Evidence of human occupations appear in relatively arid regions of North Africa and the Ethiopian highlands, in the temperate environments of northern China, and from the lowland rain forests to the higher, more open woodlands of Indonesia and presumably elsewhere in Southeast Asia.

The Indonesian woodlands were home to some of the earliest humans fond outside of Africa. Hominid remains from the Pucangan Formation, possibly as much as 1.8-1.6 myr, are the earliest found there. Interestingly, this is the first place where pre-modern fossil human remains (i.e. "missing links") were actively sought. Much of the theorizing of the time led to the expectation that humans may have arose in south Asia and E. Haeckel actually named the fossil that he presumed would be found there "Pithecanthropus"—the ape (Pithec) man (anthropus). Influenced by these expectations, E. Dubois, a young physician and lecturer at Amsterdam University, joined the Dutch overseas army in order to be posted to the island of Java where he was sure he could find early human remains. He was in Sumatra first, between 1887 and 1890 where his efforts were unsuccessful, but moving to Java in 1891 and 1892 his excavations near the Village of Trinil, along the Solo river, resulted in the discovery of an archaic appearing skull cap and then a femur of modern human form. To be more precise, the excavations of the laborers he hired led to these discoveries, an important point given the later questions of whether these two are truly of the same age. In any event, he believed in their association and ultimately named them "*Pithecanthropus erectus*", the erect ape-man. Some half century later this taxon was renamed as "*Homo erectus*", and even more recently merged with our own species *H. sapiens*. These were only the first of many specimens, ranging from the early Pleistocene to modern times, to be discovered on the island of Java, which was once connected to mainland Asia.

Table 10.2
Stratigraphic Positions of the Indonesian Hominids[1]

Formation	Level	Horizon	Date	Crania	Mandibles
Kabuh (Bapang)	Upper		0.58^t		
		Upper Tuff	$<.78^m$ myr		⇑
	Middle			S10	Ardjuna 9 Hanoman 13
		Tektite	0.71^t-0.78^t		⇓
		Middle Tuff			
	Lower			S2,3, 12, 17	S21
		Lower Tuff			
	Lowermost			Trinil skull	Kedungbrubus
	Grenzbank Zone		0.98^m myr at base		↑ ↑ ↑ S8
Pucangan (Sangiran)				S4,13a,15a,26 (27[2],31[2], Mojokerto[3])	S5,6,9,22
	Tuff 11		1.05^m myr		↑
					S1
	Tuff 10				

[1]   from Hyodo and colleagues (see table 1.6 for paleomagnetic column)
[m]   paleomagnetic-based date
[t]   fission track date from tektites
[2]   these may be 1.65 myr if the tuff dated by C. Swisher and colleagues is associated with them
[3]   this may be 1.81 myr in age if the tuff dated by C. Swisher and colleagues is associated with it

The stratigraphic sequence on Java is broken into three broad horizons, mainly on the basis of faunal differences. Each horizon represents a great time range. The earliest of these, the Pucangan formation with its Djetis fauna, is Early Pleistocene in age. One series of radiometric dates suggests that the base of the formation may extend into the Pliocene. The exact positions of the hominids are unclear. Mojokerto is the only specimen collected under somewhat controlled conditions (the others were retrieved by local people and reported or sold to paleoanthropologists), and even for this specimen the exact location and level were it was found is uncertain. It was found in 1936 near the village of Perning, and while there were attempts to relocate the findspot some 40 years later it is not completely clear that its actual origin has been established. Of the recent attempts to ascertain ages for the material, one study positions the hominid fossils are from the very top of the Putcangan, and another has them spread more evenly throughout. With the lack of provenience information and the absence of a stratigraphic exposure spanning the period, this will be a problem for the foreseeable future. Above the Pucangan lies the Kabuh horizon with Trinil fauna. Also in the Early Pleistocene, its age is bracketed by the end of the Jaramillo event and the beginning of the Middle Pleistocene (.98-.78 myr). Between these is the so-called Grenzbank, a boundary layer within the Jaramillo event from which many of the fossils (especially mandibles) were recovered. Finally, atop the Kabuh lies the Ngandong formation, which is also hominid-bearing (see Chapter 12). During the Early Pleistocene the faunas in the Trinil and Sangiran region were predominantly open woodlands, according to J. DeVos and colleagues. Their evolution, and perhaps that of the hominids as well, was strongly influenced by the fluctuating sea levels, alternatively connecting the island to South Asia and allowing faunal migrations and exchanges, and then isolating it for some period of time. The effects of isolation periods on the hominids have never been fully explored, but one suggestion has been that these resulted in the relative homogeneity that is found in the human remains. This possibility, and others, are discussed more fully below.

In any event, the lack of precise stratigraphic information is very worrying, but not completely catastrophic. This is because there is a fundamental difference in fossilization and fossil coloration between the Kabuh and the layers below. At least the specimens can be divided into an earlier and later sample.

At present, the remains of at least twelve hominids have been reported from the black clays of the Pucangan formation or the Grenzbank just above it at the Sangiran site. The fact that many of these are in a region of normal paleomagnetism either tightly dates them to the within the Jaramillo event (1.05-0.98 myr), or to the Olduvai event (<1.75 myr), see table 1.4. The latter interpretation would match the radiometric dates said to relate to the Mojokerto cranium and Sangiran 27 and 31. The uncertainties in the ages of these specimens are encapsulated in the attempts to relate Mojokerto to the dated volcanic tuff. On the one hand the geologists claim that the dated tuff is the only one from the region. Yet on the other the chemical analysis of tuffaceous materials adhering to the skull show similarities but not identity to the *in situ* tuff. As R. Potts put it, "they've done a great job of dating [the tuff] and a poor job of dating the hominids". Two differences may be telling: the ranges of mineral concentrations in the *small sample* of skull tuff are greater than the ranges in the *large sample* from the *in situ* tuff, and as G. Pope points out there are shells and other materials within the skull tuff. These suggest that the skull may have been rolled (for instance in transport by water) and its cranial cavity filled with materials including pieces of a tuff much older than the specimen. F. Brown suggests that Mojokerto may have settled into soils containing much older volcanic materials. Even more fatal to the association, in his review of the circumstances surrounding Mojokerto's finding, J. DeVos concludes the particulars of discovery are unclear (for instance at one time G. Von Koenigswald states it was found on the surface but later he said it was excavated), and that the locality where it was discovered is unknown. Thus while the dates are widely accepted as accurate, it is difficult to find fault with the conclusion of geologists such as Brown who are cautious about their association with the specimen. The relationships of the dates to the other specimens, of course, are much more problematic. They can only be associated with dated tuffs on the basis of their color or the (as yet unanalyzed) dark matrix adhering to them. No stratigraphic position is known for them.

Mojokerto, or Perning, is the skullcap of a child some 6-8 years of age, on the basis of the development of the external auditory meatus. It has a very small capacity, 650 cc or less, which would have been only slightly larger had the child survived to adulthood. Even at its young age, the early *H. sapiens* characteristics such as a browridge, nuchal torus, and spongy bone development at the cranial base (figure 10.7) had all begun to appear.

There are, in addition, at least four adult crania from the formation, in various states of preservation. Considering the three best specimens, Sangiran 4 (figure 10.8) consists of the rear of a vault and associated palate (a tooth once thought to be an associated incisor is actually a canine from another individual.) The front of the palate is very wide; the canine projected below the other teeth in life so that there are two different, flat, occlusal facets on its surface. R. Holloway estimates a 908 cc cranial capacity for it. There are strong buttresses extending along the sagittal suture and at the temporal lines. The nuchal torus is especially marked, and extends backwards so strongly that there is a sulcus above it where its to meets the occipital bone. Sangiran 27 is most of a cranium and face, in a very crushed and distorted condition that is as yet unreconstructed but appears quite similar to Sangiran 4 where the same portions are preserved. The supraorbital torus is the size and shape of African males: more rounded to follow the orbital contours, thinner and more projecting than its later Indonesian counterparts. The root of a very large canine is preserved and the front of the palate is flat. Facial details, however, are more like the later Indonesians - the nose is narrow (and its lower margin rounded like Sangiran 17 and differing from Sangiran 4 which has a sharp margin), the face is short, and the cheeks shelve down onto the maxilla in a low position. Its large mastoid process closely resembles Sangiran 4. Finally, Sangiran 31(figure 10.9) is a low, broad, very robust and somewhat distorted cranial rear that has been reconstructed by D. Tyler. It has the most strongly developed torusing of any Indonesian specimen, the thick nuchal torus extending across the entire rear of the vault and the temporal lines virtually reach the midline where they form parallel temporal crests (or one could say a divided sagittal crest) along the top of the skull. The torus and the crest, of course, are contrasting anatomies. The torus is a buttress created by the effects of muscle forces on certain bone shapes. For instance, a nuchal torus develops more readily on an angled occiput (one with a flexed occipital angle, between the nuchal and occipital portions of the bone) just as a sagittal torus develops more readily on an angled face (one with an angle between the face and forehead). The crest is a more direct consequence of muscle action, as it is a raised edge along the muscle's extension. Its presence reflects the combination of powerful temporalis contractions and a relatively small vault for the muscle to attach. In Sangiran 31 the torusing and cresting suggest that the missing face must have been very large, especially broad with massive cheeks in the early *H, sapiens* pattern. It is a good match for the more robust of the Sangiran mandibles, such as Sangiran 6 discussed below.

As a sample, these crania are clearly linked to the African early *H. sapiens* remains, sharing:

- similar sized cranial vaults (cranial capacities near or above the maximum *Homo habilis* brain size thus far reported, of 750 cc);
- anteriorly projecting and continuously developed supraorbital tori of various thicknesses [but including some thinner specimens matching OH 12 and ER 3733] separated from the frontal squama by a sulcus, or groove, of varying depth;
- flattening of the frontal squama broken by a bulge at its center (**frontal boss**) and in some cases presence of a sagittal keel;
- broadening and lowering of the face - specifically, expansion of the midface (**zygomaxillary** region and nose) and orbital size coupled with reduction of the lower face;
- lateral nasal aperture **eversion**;
- expanded nasal aperture breadth;
- angulation of the nasal bones in the sagittal plane (they meet at an angle) and expansion of their breadth relative to the breadth of the nasal aperture;
- position of the maximum breadth - across the parietals at their posterior rear, at the **mastoid (or asterionic) notch**;
- thickening of the flat cranial vault bones, involving both cortices and diplöe;
- **kyphosis** (flexion) of the cranial base;
- presence of an **occipitomastoid crest** and **digastric sulcus** on the cranial base, inside the mastoid processes;
- a distinct **nuchal torus** across the rear of the skull, projecting backwards to overhang the **superior nuchal line** and marking the place where there is a strong angulation between occipital and nuchal planes of the occiput;
- wide occiput with an expanded nuchal muscle attachment area;
- dominance of sagittal length of the nuchal plane over the length of the occiput above it (this also reflects the expanded nuchal muscles);
- coincidence of **inion** at the top of the nuchal muscle attachment and **opistocranion** (the most posterior point on the skull);

- wide separation of inion and endinion, with the inion position much higher;
- relative size reduction in the later erupting premolars (P4) and molars (M3<M2), even as all the posterior teeth reduce;
- lateral maxillary incisor expansion relative to the central incisors (this can mainly be seen in the root sockets of the Sangiran 4 and 27 palates)

Yet, at the same time the Indonesians show the dramatic expression of certain characteristics only foreshadowed on the earlier African specimens (OH 9 and the Turkana remains). For instance, at the most rearward position of the temporal lines, where their directions angles downward and forward, there is a well developed angular torus, a raised ridge only known on one of the earlier African crania. Vault thickness is greater in virtually all positions, especially more toward the cranial rear (table 10.3) but also at its center. Additional but less dramatic thickening of the vault occurs along the midline, where a keel runs lengthwise along the top of the skull. There is also a parietal buttress, a lengthwise thickening along the middle of the parietal where it can be seen to angle between the bone's more vertical side and its more horizontal roof. There is often a line or in some cases a ridge in this position, along the parietal buttress, marking the uppermost attachment of the temporalis muscle (figure 9.10). This temporal ridge, a well developed temporal line, is not to be confused with the buttress as they may not be in the same position. For instance, Sangiran 31 has a thickened buttress along the middle of the bone at its angle, a second buttress which is the sagittal keel along the sagittal suture, and a sagittal crest formed of convergent and parallel running temporal lines along the sagittal suture. Together, these buttresses almost certainly are present to provide additional strength to the vault.

Table 10.3
Mean Thickness of the Parietal Bone in Early *H. sapiens*[1]

Thickness at:	bregma	lambda	asterion	bone center
African	8.9	7.8	11.2	9.5
Indonesian	8.9	11.3	15.0	10.8

[1]   See figure 10.2, dimensions in millimeters

The nuchal torus is more laterally extensive, crossing the whole of the occiput and projecting more strongly behind the skull. The center structure, a downward pointing triangle of thickened bone called inion, is associated with the attachment for the strong ligament extending down the back of the neck (*ligamentum nuchae*). Sangiran 31 shows the most dramatic expression of these occipital features, including vault thickening, spongy bone development at the cranial base, a flexed angle at the back of the skull, and at this angulation a thick backward-projecting nuchal torus developed well away from the midline as well as near it. However, exactly the same features are seen on Sangiran 4 where they are more weakly expressed. Sangiran 4 has been known since F. Weidenreich's 1945 description and its robustness and large somewhat projecting canine led to the widely accepted conclusion that it is male. Now the discovery of Sangiran 31 suggests either that this interpretation is wrong and that women in the early *H. sapiens* sample from Indonesia have numerous masculine features which are similar to but more weakly expressed than in males, or that there is substantial variation in male robustness. I believe the second is more likely, and that female crania have not been recovered from the Indonesian deposits in this time range. The potential for substantial gracilization in (the as yet undiscovered) female crania may be reflected in the dramatic mandibular variation discussed below.

The two palates, Sangiran 4 and 27, are archaic in a number of respects. Large canines projected below the level of the adjacent teeth in Sangiran 4, while in Sangiran 27 the roots for the canine teeth are so large that the thick pillar enclosing them extends from the sides on the nose down to the toothrow where it creates a prominent bulge. There is a diastema between the Sangiran 4 canines and the (lost) lateral incisors. The latter is not an unusual feature since, of the six isolated canines known from the

Pucangan , the lack of wear facets between them ands the adjacent teeth (**interproximal facets**) shows that two did not actually touch the incisors. A slightly later large Middle Pleistocene male, Sangiran 17, also has this feature. Yet other features of the palate contrast with the australopithecine condition. Although the anterior teeth were prognathic, the prognathism is much reduced compared with that in the earlier hominids. The lower face is shortened, but both the palate and the nasal opening are greatly broadened. The palate is very large relative to the size of the teeth. The base of the broad cheeks is in a posterior position (over the anterior molars), giving the maxilla anterior to it a snout-like appearance.

Table 10.4

Early *H. sapiens* Occipital Dimensions[1]

	Occipital Plane Length (lambda to inion)	Nuchal Plane Length (inion to **opisthion**)	Relative Nuchal Plane Length	Biasterionic Breadth	Nuchal Torus Vertical Height	Nuchal Torus Thickness (backwards projection)
Africans	**45.8**	49.5	**107.3%**	116.0	21.9	17.3
Indonesians	49.1	54.7	110.8%	118.0	19.9	21.5

[1]   For definitions see figure10.12, linear dimensions in millimeters

Pucangan Mandibles

The mandibles, with the exception of Sangiran 1, may be associated with either the Pucangan or perhaps the Grenzbank just above. Only Sangiran 1, ironically the most gracile of the specimens, can be unquestionably allocated to the Pucangan. Some of the adult mandibles are also quite robust, and all of them, even the most gracile Sangiran 1, have a weakly developed inferior torus across the inside of the symphysis.   Specimens such as Sangiran 6 are both tall and thick, while Sangiran 1 is only tall. The premolars of all the specimens, even those with the most robust mandibular bodies, are quite unlike australopithecines with similar corpus robustness in that their premolars lack molarization. Unworn or lightly worn lower molars are elongated as in many other early *H. sapiens* and *H. habilis* molars. Sangiran 1 is the most contrasting specimen, also having a tall body but a much thinner one with a very thin lower margin of the mandibular corpus. In more robust specimens this lower margin can be very much thicker, and rounded rather than sharp. Following the pattern established at many of the australopithecine sites, adult mandibles are found with both large and small teeth and bodies, in the most robust cases the mandibular bodies varying well into the *Australopithecus boisei* range (figure 10.13).

Two aspects of the mandibular sample are of interest. First is the possibility that the marked size differences may correspond to a pattern and magnitude of sexual dimorphism as great as in the australopithecines. Second, like the Pucangan crania, the sample as a whole is the largest and most robust of any hominids found outside of Africa. Indeed, many of the mandibles exceed the African sample in size and robustness (although this may be a consequence of mistakenly allocating some of the toothless Turkana specimens to *A. boisei* - these are fragments of mandibular bodies that are similar to the Sangiran remains). That the Indonesian specimens are also among the earliest found out of Africa is probably not a coincidence, but the seemingly equally early remains from western Asia (see below) are quite contrasting in this regard.

Pucangan Dental Remains

A large number of isolated teeth were collected by the late G.H.R. von Koenigswald. He believes that it is possible to distinguish the earlier specimens from the Pucangan from the later specimens from the Kabuh on the basis of their color and fossilization. The dental sample attributed to the Pucangan , including the teeth in the jaws discussed above, features very large posterior tooth size. Their average size is about the same as that for both *H. habilis* and early *H. sapiens,* and like these earlier hominids the unworn molar teeth are relatively elongated (this is also the case for early teeth from China). The anterior teeth are also large, especially in breadth. Several upper incisors are shovel shaped, the straightness of the central incisor crowns, weakly expressed marginal ridges, and moderate tubercle expression following what appears to be an early south Asian pattern according to T. Crummett (shovel shape anatomy is discussed with the Zhoukoudian remains, in Chapter 11). They differ from the plesiomorphic condition in African specimens such as ER 15K by the straighter crowns of the central incisors and more curved crowns of the laterals. They also differ in being distinctly smaller in size.

Of the three deciduous teeth described by F. Grine, an upper canine and lower first molar lack any definitive characters for diagnosing their taxonomic affinities. However a deciduous second lower molar from the Pucangan is particularly elongated (larger than in any ancestral or potentially ancestral species) and has other unusual features. This might make it seem to represent a megadont species such as one of the robust australopithecines, but Grine rejects this possibility on anatomical grounds. Moreover, unlike the permanent posterior teeth, the deciduous molars increase in size through Middle Pleistocene *H. sapiens*.

Play it again, Sam - is it sex or species?

The interpretation of these Indonesian specimens is plagued with the same problems that were met in discussing the large Pliocene African samples such as the Hadar one - is the variation too much to represent a single species? From the time of their first description, robust specimens beginning with Sangiran 6 mandible clearly contrasted with specimens such as Sangiran 1 and were once placed in the genus "Meganthropus." F. Weidenreich saw this genus as a link between the human remains of Indonesia and China and their presumed giant "ancestor" *Gigantopithecus* (at the time he wrote this *Gigantopithecus* was only known from 3 teeth). It was subsequently joined by mandibles Sangiran 5 (a corpus fragment with worn molars that may be *Pongo*), S 8 (a broken specimen showing evidence of crocodile chewing), and S 9 (a robust specimen with a very narrow anterior toothrow and a "V" shape to its dental arcade). In spite of the problems with the provenience of many of the mandibles, they seem to come from a single early time range. G. Sighinolfi and colleagues examined the bone chemistry and mineralogy for a number of specimens attributed to the two taxa and concluded that most of the bone chemistry is the same. The main difference, they concluded, is in the accumulation of minerals that reflect the relative ages of the fossils - "Meganthropus" remains are almost invariably older, their bones more intensely mineralized.

In the decade following its discovery J. Robinson argued that "Meganthropus" was a robust australopithecine, which evoked a negative reply from G. H. R. von Koenigswald and began a debate that has continued to the present. Many of the Indonesian scholars and a few others such as J. Franzen, R. Orban-Segebarth and D. Tyler accepted the Robinson argument and came to believe that an australopithecine was present in Java, and even von Koenigswald changed his mind and came to support this contention in his later publications. However C. Lovejoy argued that teeth and mandibles alone cannot be used to distinguish australopithecines and *Homo* without associated cranial material, except at the extremes of the ranges, and a few authors such as F. Aziz and colleagues and Zhang Yinyun presented evidence against it. The most substantive basis for rejecting this claim comes from the comparative work of A. Kramer. In a series of phenetic analyses using multivariate approaches, and cladistic procedures searching for the relationship tree making the fewest assumptions, the mandibles were never linked to any of the australopithecine species or to *H. habilis*. Invariably, the closest relationship Kramer found was to other early *H. sapiens* and he concludes that there is no justification to the suggestion that there were australopithecines or australopithecine-like hominids in Java. This is further bore out by a consideration of the crania said to represent "Meganthropus", Sangiran 27 and 31. These are robust and archaic in appearance, but nothing at all like the australopithecine or australopithecine-like species. The earliest Indonesians contrast in having thick rather than thin cranial bone, greatly expanded cranial capacities, large supraorbital tori that are vertically thick and anteriorly projecting, pronounced angular tori, and dramatically expanded nuchal muscle attachments (and related occipital features such as broad nuchal tori). Their affiliations are with the early *H. sapiens* sample from Africa.

Indeed, the case for African affinities was also in the mandibular sample, although this could not be recognized until the Olduvai mandibles were published. The most robust of the Indonesian mandibles resembles African mandibles such as OH 22 in relative corpus thickness and especially the thickened basal margin. They are also similar in the development of internal tori across the inside of the symphysis. OH 22 is even relatively thicker in both symphysis and corpus, and has a better developed superior torus, but the resemblances clearly support what Kramer's more systematic comparisons show - the Indonesian anatomy, even at its most extreme, links the sample to other early *H. sapiens* and does not specifically or uniquely resemble australopithecines.

The implications of these robust specimens, however, are twofold. First, as mentioned above some of the variation is clearly *within* each sex (for instance Sangiran 4 and 31). The dimorphism in cranial robustness and other anatomical aspects is even greater. Dramatic sexual dimorphism in crania and faces is reflected in mandibular variation; differences as great as the Sangiran 1 and 6 comparison reveals are not unexpected. Marked dimorphism is also evident in the later Kabuh sample (see below). Second, comparison with other regions suggests that the pattern of robustness may be a unique regional feature of Indonesia rather than an evolutionary marker of "archaicness".

LATER MATERIAL

F. Sémah and colleagues report the excavation of several lithic artifacts from levels equal to the early Kabuh in age at Ngebung, a nearby site. These are the most convincing excavated lithics from the Early Pleistocene of Indonesia and their discovery lays to rest the possibility that the early Indonesians made no stone tools at all. Yet, lithic remains are rare on the island, a surprising fact given the stone tool making propensity of their African ancestors. A. Thorne and G. Pope have suggested a primary development of bamboo technology in the region, presumably replacing the need to make and transport the large number of stone tools that are found in other regions. This supple grass is easily worked with little more than a sharpened flake when it is fresh, and dries to a strong, resilient material. However likely, and I believe that this reconstruction is quite likely indeed, the fact is that bamboo technology relies on lithic technology - the production of sharp stone flakes that should be found somewhere. What is interesting about Ngebung is that the tools are rare, and thus far mainly cores and large flakes found far from the material sources and without manufacture debris. If nothing else they show that people curated their artifacts, carrying them far from the place where they were made. In the words of the authors, the technology was "limited by the scarcity and poor quality of raw materials".

Cranial Remains

The later portion of the Early Pleistocene crania from Java come from two sites, all in the Kabuh formation, and dated to earlier than the beginning of the Brunhes Normal, 200 kyr or less younger than the earlier crania.. These sites are near the villages of Sangiran and Trinil - the site where the first "*Pithecanthropus*" (later *H. erectus*, now *H. sapiens*) cranium was discovered (Trinil 2), as well as six femurs of less certain associations. The majority of the specimens come from the Sangiran site—seven fairly complete crania (Sangiran 2, 3,10,12, 17, and IX) and a number of less complete cranial fragments. Stratigraphically, Trinil is the oldest and Sangiran 10 the youngest.

Sangiran 17 is virtually complete Sangiran IX is almost so, while the other remains consist of more fragmentary skullcaps and occasional facial fragments. They fall into two size groups, larger and smaller, which almost certainly correspond to males and females as the groups also differ in robustness and the expression of muscle attachments. All exhibit:

- expanded cranial vaults (especially in length and breadth of the braincase and of frontal constriction),
- thickened cranial bone (wide layers of compact bone)
- a distinct angulation of the cranial sides at the temporal line,
- basal spongy bone development,
- thick projecting browridges separated from the forehead by a broad, weakly developed sulcus,

- broad and backward projecting nuchal torus separated from the occiput above it (occipital squama, or occipital plane) by a sulcus,
- greatly expanded nuchal muscle attachments,
- endocast features (petalial patterns and other asymmetries) that indicate left hemisphere dominance and right handedness.

The females (Trinil 2, Sangiran 2, 3, 10, and the long and narrow cranium IX) are smaller and thinner crania than the males and have much weaker muscle-attachment-related features (prominence of the temporal line, roughness and extent of the nuchal plane) and cranial buttresses (sagittal keel extending on to the frontal bone, angular torus, nuchal torus). Similar to the Africans, the males are 18% larger in cranial capacity. One specimen, cranium IX, also resembles African anatomy in the deep sulcus between the projecting supraorbitals and the forehead (this is partially the consequence of the very marked projection). The other females do not share this anatomy. In contrast to the Africans and the earlier Indonesians, browridge dimensions do not differ dramatically between the sexes. However there are, as usual, sex-related differences in the faces. Compared with Sangiran 17 the zygomatic bone associated with Sangiran 10 is quite small, and an isolated lower face, Sangiran 15b, has a shallow palate and short facial height (table 10.6). The differences are not dramatic as the Sangiran 10 zygomatic closely matches some of the earlier Pucangan (Sangiran 27) and African remains.

Table 10.5
Cranial Capacities for Early and Middle Pleistocene *H. sapiens* Samples[1]

	Female average	Male average
African	788 (n=2)	927 (n=3)
Indonesian Kabuh	875 (n=5)	1032 (n=2)
Chinese Zhoukoudian	965 (n=3)	1078 (n=4)

[1] Increasing cranial capacity is associated with younger dates; the African sample is oldest and the Chinese youngest

The males (Sangiran 12, 17, 19, and several others) are much larger and more robustly developed. Even relative to their larger size, three important sex-related features are the larger mastoids, the marked projection of the central portion of the nuchal torus, and a prominent downward pointing inion projection at its middle. Sangiran 17 (see figure 10.10) is the most complete adult early *H. sapiens* male cranium known. As I have reconstructed it, the face combines moderate height with marked flaring cheek development and large orbits that create a great facial breadth, and very pronounced facial prognathism. The cheeks, flaring outward and backward from their low positioned base on the face, are broadest at their base so that the outline of the face as seen from the front is pentagoid. A small buttress, the **zygomaxillary ridge**, extends across their surface along the suture between the zygomatic and the maxillary bones, and the upper part of the zygomatic where it forms the outer orbital border (the **orbital pillar**) is also thick and buttress-like. Prominent supraorbitals cross the top of the face like a bar of almost even thickness. Behind them, the frontal is quite flat and meets the back of the supraorbitals in a very shallow supratoral sulcus, contrasting with the strong angle of the deep sulcus found in the African crania, set off even more distinctly by the presence of a frontal boss. The broad sagittal keel is extends well onto the face of the frontal. Also unlike the Africans the frontal is more expanded in breadth behind the orbits and therefore the **postorbital constriction** is less (the effects of this on the size of the temporal fossa are unknown as its outer border, the zygomatic arch, is missing). Compared with the more fragmentary female facial remains, these faces indicate that there is more sexual dimorphism in the facial anatomy and dimensions than in the vault.

Indeed, other systematic differences distinguish the Kabuh Formation Indonesians from the generally earlier African remains. Cranial capacity is some 11% larger, and holding sex constant, the Indonesian specimens have much thicker vaults, thicker and more projecting browridges overhanging larger orbits, more prominent nuchal torus development, and stronger and more consistent expressions of the sagittal keel and the thickening and angulation of the vault along the temporal line (including the angular torus). The relative size of the nuchal muscle attachment area, however, is reduced and the lengths of the occipital and nuchal planes average close to equal. The reduction is dramatic compared with the Pucangan specimens, where the nuchal plane length is some 23% greater than the occipital plane length. Although the same sex cannot be compared, the Sangiran 17 male face is much more prognathic than the ER-3733 but at the same time its vertical height is markedly shorter, as is the even smaller Kabuh female Sangiran 15b. The comparable lower portions of these faces are also shorter than their earlier Indonesian counterparts, suggesting that facial reduction occurred after the earliest occupations. The dental sample is too small to determine whether there was associated posterior tooth size reduction, but there is some suggestion that no such reduction occurred. This comes from the observation that the Pucangan teeth are the same size as those of Late Pleistocene and Holocene Australians, who many consider to be among their descendants.

Table 10.6
Facial Dimensions[1] Compared

	Alveolar (lower facial) height	Nasal Breadth	Breadth across Lateral Incisor Roots	C-M^2 Length	Orbit Breadth	Orbit Height	Cheek Size (length along zygomatic-maxillary suture)	Central Supraorbital Thickness (vertical height)	Central Supraorbital Length (frontal squama to edge)
African									
ER 3733	32.0	36.8	23.0	49.5	44.2	36.2	35.8	9.7	23.2
ER 3883					42.0	36.4	42.8	14.2	21.1
ER 730								13.0	20.0
ER 1808								11.2	
OH 9					42.8			19.4	27.0
OH 12		26.0						10.0	15.3
Indonesians									
Sangiran 4	31.7	31.0	18.9	52.1					
27	33.5	26.5					39.0	14.6	
Trinil 2									21.4
Sangiran 2								11.9	22.4
18a									20,8
10								19.0	27.4
17	24.8	26.4		45.1	47.7	38.0	37.8	16.8	25.0
15b	21.0								
Chinese									
Gongwangling	23.0	31.0	19.2	39.2				17.9	

[1] See figure 10.14

Mandibles

The first ancient Indonesian human to be found was Dubois' discovery of a mandible fragment from Kedungbrubus, near Trinil. It has proven to be one of the most difficult specimens to interpret. Many years later, in his examination of the fragment, P. Tobias established that it belonged to a juvenile, with the premolar in the process of erupting. Its other characteristics are extreme robustness (relative thickness of the body) and the presence of two well-defined internal buttresses on the inside of the symphseal area. Sangiran mandible 21 is one of the most complete. It is of the same size and shape as Sangiran 9, especially similar in the straight but receding symphysis which is significantly deeper than the molar-supporting part of the corpus. However it differs from S9 it in having a rounded alveolar form, much wider at the front.

Postcranials

The valid understanding of the Trinil femur has continued to poise a problem because of its pathology, its seemingly modern anatomy even taking that pathology into consideration, and its significantly less fossilization as far as its internal crystallization is concerned. It was found a year after the cranium and at a different position in the large exposed area of the Trinil site. Increasing the suspicions about the provenience of this bone with the other Early Pleistocene remains is its association with several teeth of *Pongo*. Orangutans otherwise are not known from Indonesia until a much later faunal exchange with mainland Asia, where they are a diagnostic element in a new fauna reflecting the change from open woodlands to more humid forest conditions. G. Bartstra reports that Late Pleistocene sediments were present at Trinil, and that Dubois must have excavated through them without recognizing their distinction from the Kabuh levels below. Taking all of these considerations into account, it seems most likely that this bone is not associated with the early *H. sapiens* remains. The original naming of "*Pithecanthropus erectus*" was quite correct, but for the wrong reasons!

Early Pleistocene Remains from Eastern Asia

Human occupation of China is more than a million years old, and the earliest occupations known to the south are only slightly younger. The lithic technology that the earliest inhabitants used remained relatively stable for much of the Pleistocene, varying from what many have called a "Chopper-Chopping Tool" tradition (industries dominated by cores and simple flakes with little retouch) in tropical, subtropical and other forested regions to the more classic bifaces of the temperate zones to the north according to G. Pope. He suggests that bamboo, woods, and other forest resources provided the mainstay of hominid industries where the choppers are found for long periods, and that geography and ecology rather than chronology is the cause of archaeological variation. Some authors have hinted that the low frequency of bifaces and other symmetrically made tools is a reflection of human behavioral capabilities, but this is unlikely given the discovery and spread of the requisite technologies prior to the emergence of human populations from Africa, and the evidence suggesting other sophisticated aspects of human technology including the possibility raised by Jia Lanpo that most of the early Chinese archaeological sites have indications of fire.

CHINESE TEETH

East Asian dental remains first claimed to be of Early Pleistocene age have been reported from five regions:

- a lower first molar discovered in a drugstore in the Badong District, Hubei Province;
- three lower molars from Dragon bone cave in the Jianshi District, southwest Hubei Province that are associated with *Gigantopithecus* teeth;
- a mandible fragment with P_4-M_1 and an isolated I^2 from Wushan, Sichuan Province
- an upper first molar from a mountainous region in Luonan county, Shaanxi Province.
- a pair of upper central incisors from the surface of the extensive badlands at Yuanmou in Yunnan Province;

If correctly identified as hominid and accurately dated these may mark the earliest East Asian habitation as significantly older archaeological sites are unknown (the single exception, artifacts claimed to be 2 myr from Pakistan, are probably naturally flaked and not the result of human activities, according to workers such as R. Klein). However, the drugstore tooth will always be uncertain, and other dates appear to be later than first thought. The Jianshi remains are associated with early Middle Pleistocene fauna (although amino acid racemization dates for *Gigantopithecus* teeth from a similar cave in the very southern part of China suggests an age in excess of a million years). Varying opinions of the relationship of Yuanmou and other faunas and continued reassessments of the paleomagnetic data have converged on a latest Early Pleistocene age estimate,

Initial analysis of the Badong and Jianshi molars led to the conclusion that their closest affinities were to *Australopithecus africanus*, and they became widely known as the "Chinese australopithecines". However, casts of comparative specimens were unavailable at the time and workers now dispute that conclusion. The molars are quite large. In grinding area, they are well into the australopithecine range. Two of the lower molars, PA 502 and 503, are **antimeres** (from opposite sides of the jaw) with what appears to be an anomalous morphology. The other two differ from the normal australopithecine condition in that they are relatively elongated in contrast to the relative broadening found in the African samples. In his analysis Zhang Yinyun points out that the relative elongation is not found in australopithecine samples, or even in the elongated lower molars of the *H. habilis* and early African *H. sapiens* samples. It is, however, characteristic of the permanent and deciduous lower molars from Indonesia, and he suggests the two samples are validly linked on this basis. According to Zhang even the two molars with anomalous crown features resemble certain of the Indonesian remains.

The problems at Wushan stem from unclear provenience and improper identification. The upper lateral incisor from the site is quite small, has a curved face, and is deeply shoveled. Its provenience is unclear and its anatomy associates it with Late Pleistocene or more recent Chinese populations living further to the south. The mandible fragment is not human. It is probably one of the medium sized *Pongo* species.

The Luonan M^1, about the age of the Gongwangling cranium (see below), is considerably larger than teeth from its maxilla.

The Yuanmou incisors are surface finds from the Baozidongjing bed of the Baozidongjing locality in the Yuanmou basin, Yunnan. The two upper central incisors belong to a single individual and are somewhat anomalous in that they lack contact facets for the lateral (adjacent) incisors. Morphologically, their shoveling pattern combines a moderate expression of internal marginal ridges, straight occlusal crown shape, and an internal tubercle that only slightly bulges on the internal surface between the ridges but has an unusual upward projection extending toward the occlusal surface. These ridges are no more strongly expressed than on the isolated Indonesian upper incisors (several of these also have finger-like projections from the tubercle extending toward or to the occlusal surface). A moderate expression of marginal ridges is characteristic of many later South Chinese.

A tibia fragment reported from the site is not human.

GONGWANGLING CRANIUM

Thought to be even earlier than the isolated teeth, the Gongwangling cranium from near the village of Lantian, in east-central Shaanxi, south China, is in many respects similar to the Indonesian specimens. An Zhisheng dates cranium to some 1.15 myr. A forested environment with warm subtropical conditions characterized the region at that time and this, perhaps the earliest occupation of China, can hardly be regarded as a cold adaptation according to Qi Guoqin. The 780 cc cranial capacity Wu Rukang estimates for it is at the low end of the Indonesian range (only Perning is smaller), although the incomplete and distorted condition of the vault makes any estimate of its size problematic. Also like the Indonesian remains the forehead profile appears to be flat and there is a sagittal keel, the cranial bones are thick and browridges very well developed. On the face of things, Gongwangling is a female.

It has a low cranial height and a marked narrowing of the frontal behind the orbits. While the browridges are very thick and project markedly, they differ from those of the Indonesians in that they

- arch over the orbits,
- separate from the forehead by a deeper supratoral sulcus than most Indonesians,
- dip strongly downwards just over the nose
- form two separate bars over each orbit - they do not actually meet at the middle of the face.

The right side of the brow has been damaged and appears to have been pathological. R. Caspari believes that the bone was infected, perhaps as a consequence of some earlier trauma. A large portion of the left temporal bone is heavily buttressed and shows the beginning of what was probably a very broad temporal fossa. In sum, the vault shows a combination of small brain size, minimal frontal expansion, thickening of the vault bone and buttressing, and bony evidence of powerful chewing that aligns it with the **penecontemporary** Indonesian remains from the Pucangan Formation.

The reconstructed face is broad but neither tall nor robust, contrasting with the vault in a manner which is similar to Sangiran 17. Also like this specimen the cheeks begin very low on the maxilla, just above the toothrow, and between them and the nose lies a deep furrow or **canine fossa**. Otherwise this face contrasts markedly with those from Indonesia. The differences are undoubtedly influenced by the later (Kabuh) date for the better preserved Indonesian faces and the likelihood that Gongwangling is female, but in my opinion there is more to it than that. Nasal bones are strongly angled to each other, as they meet along the midline, and their juncture with the frontal is horizontally oriented and gently rounded (both of these are normal Asian features). The palate is broad and deep, with very widely spaced incisor sockets for the (missing) anterior teeth. At over 19 mm, the distance between the central incisor roots is even greater than Sangiran 4. The base of the cheek begins in an extremely anterior position, just behind the canine buttresses paralleling the sides of the nose - a very different location than in the Indonesian palates. Moreover, they appear to have been more forward facing and lack the posterior sweep found in Sangiran 17. The lower face is only moderately prognathic, as reconstructed, and the lower margin of the nose shows the remnants of a projecting nasal spine. Below this margin, the alveolar portion of the face is extremely flat.

REMAINS FROM VIETNAM

Two caves in Lang Son province, near the Chinese border, have yielded hominid teeth and *Gigantopithecus* remains in circumstances similar to the Jianshi recoveries. Some 10 teeth have been found in the Tham Khuyen and Tham Hai caves. Like the Jianshi specimens the molars in the sample are very large and some have well-developed cingula. It is quite likely that the populations represented are very similar to those found in similar circumstances to the north.

WHO GOES THERE ?

From the dated tool- and hominid-bearing sites, it seems evident that early *H. sapiens* spread throughout the Old World tropics and subtropics soon after the Acheulean industrial complex appeared in Africa. There are no other hominids from the eastern part of Eurasia, although persistent claims of australopithecine or australopithecine-like remains continue. Various Indonesian and Chinese scholars expected to find more archaic hominids and interpreted primate remains in this context, in some cases such as the attribution of "*Meganthropus*" crania to "*Paranthropus*" without even the slightest resemblance or basis in fact. Why the search for Asian australopithecines?

I believe there are three historic reasons. First is nationalistic, a condition that has also plagued the interpretation of the European fossil record, as we will discuss in the following chapters. Asian scholars had hoped to show the great antiquity of their ancestors through the demonstration that important steps in human evolution, perhaps the origins of the humans themselves, occurred locally. This prospect was promoted by the other two reasons.

Second, perhaps the most respected western scholar to work in the region, F. Weidenreich, had hypothesized toward the end of his career that the line of hominid development began with *Gigantopithecus* (at a time when this primate was only known from three molars), and progressively became dwarfed through "*Meganthropus*", and finally "*Sinanthropus*" which was directly ancestral to the modern condition. *Gigantopithecus*, according to this proposal, was the Asian australopithecine. Even as later, more complete, remains disproved this contention, the expectation that there were Asian australopithecines persisted.

Finally, certain early remains did seem to resemble the australopithecine condition, as in the size and robustness found in the early Indonesian mandibles and the size of the Jianshi teeth. Some individuals have widely publicized the discovery of australopithecine remains. This is, after all, the way that the Jianshi teeth were first announced. An almost toothless mandible fragment from Wushan has been described this way (it is actually a fossil ape - the missing P_3 was sectorial in shape). The misidentifications started decades ago, when G.H.R. von Koenigswald identified an ancient australopithecine-like hominid from South China based on worn, isolated teeth, which he named "Hemianthropus". These turned out to be worn postcanine teeth of a medium sized *Pongo* species. The resemblances of the other materials to *Australopithecus* species were real enough, but they were not *unique* resemblances. As Kramer and Zhang have shown, here are no synapomorphies that support the hypothesis of Asian australopithecines.

The Habitation of Western Eurasia

EARLY PLEISTOCENE EVIDENCE FROM WESTERN ASIA

There are two sites that have Early Pleistocene hominid remains, Ubeidiya in Israel and Dmanisi in Georgia. The former is a key region, as African dispersals most likely used the eastern Mediterranean. Migrating across the Straits of Gibraltar or across the central Mediterranean from Tunisia to Italy a possibility some have suggested, would require crossing open water, even at lowest sea levels. There is no evidence that the necessary technology existed before the Late Pleistocene (see Chapter 14). From western Asia, however, routes to both the east and the west are available. For instance, low water levels closed the Dardanelles a number of times during the glacial cycles. Ubeidiya lies just at this point of emergence. There, evidence links a series of early Acheulean/Developed Oldowan sites with reversed paleomagnetism readings and faunal correlations to Europe and Africa to an Early Pleistocene age that may be as old as 1.3-1.4 myr. The Ubeidiya hominids, several cranial fragments and two teeth, are not heavily fossilized compared with the rest of the fauna. The almost vertical strata make it difficult to be sure exactly where the specimens come from. One local archaeologist was heard to quip that a good kick by a cow could have sent these pieces across a half million years of strata or more. Chemical analysis shows that the human bones are younger than the Early Pleistocene faunal remains, so this may well have been the case.

The Dmanisi mandible is a Georgian find, from an uplands site, between the Black Sea and the Caspian Sea that is along a route from the Levant to central and eastern Asia. It's later Early Pleistocene age is suggested by the date of the volcanic tuff below it (1.8 myr or older, if it has been correctly dated), and the fauna associated with the mandible that is similar to that at Ubeidiya, according to E. Tchernov. The Georgian mandible preserves a complete corpus with a full, moderate-sized dentition. The individual died in their late teens, the third molar showing little wear. Like many other early *H. sapiens* mandibles from the later Early or Middle Pleistocene (for instance Ternifine), heavy wear on the anterior teeth contrasts with the molar wear. Dmanisi is perhaps most notable for being the only archaic mandible from the western part of Eurasia known *not* showing any specific Neandertal features (c.f. Chapter 13). It is most like the African mandibles from the later Early Pleistocene, for instance resembling the ER 15K mandible is many details. The mandibular body is thick and not particularly tall, with a curved symphseal surface having a **mandibular trigone** at its base, but completely lacking in projection (e.g. without a **mental eminence,** or chin). There are several **mental foramina**, a common feature in Pleistocene specimens from the Northern Hemisphere. The P_3 is especially diagnostic. It is an elongated tooth like the Olduvai Bed IV specimen OH 22, and has a dominant buccal cusp (but lacks an elongated Neandertal-like sloping outer surface). M_1, largest of the molars, has a wrinkled occlusal surface.

EUROPE

No hominid remains have yet been found in Early Pleistocene deposits to the west, in Europe, and as W. Roebroeks duscusses most European prehistorians now believe there is no significant habitation before some 500 kyr. There are several archaeological sites which seem to date from an earlier time, but none of the dates are convincing and in some cases it is unclear whether humans, as represented by evidence of their activities, were actually present. According to Klein, the oldest sites in the west where he believes firm dates can be linked to evidences of hominid activities with reasonable security are the Vallonet Cave and the Soleihac open air site. Both of these are from the Jaramillo Normal Subchron. Other European hominid sites dated only by the appearance of reversed paleomagnetism or Early Pleistocene fauna (Badger's Hole and Chilhac in France, Monte Poggliolo and Isernia in central Italy, Kärlich in west-central Germany, Stránská Skalá and Prezletice [with a broken animal molar misidentified as hominid] in the Czech Republic, and Šandalja lower cave in Croatia [with an several pebble tools and a broken animal incisor misidentified as hominid]) are for various reasons more problematic but not easily dismissed. What the early European sites have in common is the association of Oldowan-like tools (usually small collections of stones that appear to be choppers or utilized flakers selected out of a background of pebbles) with Early Pleistocene fauna. They lack handaxes or any other well-formed bifacial tools, and several (for instance Isernia) have been redated to more recent times. It is always possible that handaxes are absent because the sites are older than the Developed Oldowan, or that there is an absence of suitable raw material for controlled large flake production, or because of the failure of people to bring handaxes to these particular sites because they were not needed. It is also possible that the "tools" are not tools (as R. Dennell and others have suggested) and the "sites" are not sites, and that Europe was very sparsely or completely unoccupied until about a half million years ago.

Perhaps the most intriguing question to ask about the early Europeans is why their success seems to have been so late. In most other inhabited regions, successful adaptations and higher population densities were achieved much earlier than they were in Europe. The issue is not over the *earliest* habitation, which may well be as soon as in other regions, but the earliest *success*. As the late G. Isaac pointed out, this was not before the Middle Pleistocene and long after successful habitation of eastern Asia and Indonesia. One possible answer is indicated by A. Turner, who argues that the marked seasonality and generally cool and dry conditions that have characterized Europe for most of the Pleistocene make animals a seasonally key food resource. He suggests that it is the changing availability of large ungulates for scavenging that provides a firm resource base for the Middle Pleistocene Europeans. Accomplished scavenging depends on the presence of two elements in the local carnivore ecology -- the *presence* of appropriate carcass producers, and the *absence* of significant competition for carcasses of a useful size range. According to Turner, between some 1.5 and .5 myr, the predominant European carnivores were quite different from the African species (these were largely extant forms by this time). The European carnivores consisted largely of archaic cats with dentitions that maximized the amount of flesh that remained on their kills. This opened up broad opportunities for scavenging that brought a number of efficient scavenging species to Europe, including two gigantic hyena species. Ironically the inefficient cats made it difficult for a hominid scavenger to develop a stable adaptive pattern because of the competition. With the Middle Pleistocene replacement of these large archaic cats with the much more competent African flesh-eaters, the more efficient scavengers became extinct and the remaining scavengers are found in relatively smaller number, compared with the carcass-producing carnivores. The argument is that as competition for carcasses reduced, a more stable and productive niche for the hominids was possible.

Center and Edge

There is an interesting but not uncommon pattern to the geographic distribution of human variation toward the end of the Early Pleistocene, first noted by A. Thorne and explained by the "Center and Edge" hypothesis. It has long been recognized that differences between populations are inevitable when a species is widespread, especially when populations come to occupy different habitats. Evolutionists such as E, Mayr observe that the amount of polytypism decreases towards a species border. Thorne's proposal was about the pattern of these differences that developed in the earliest human inhabitants out of Africa. He noted that

- the fossil populations sampled at the peripheries of the human range at that time, places where many remains have been found such as Central Java, were far more homogeneous than samples from the center, eastern Africa where *H. sapiens* first was successful;
- early populations in various peripheral regions had quite different combinations of homogeneous features, often different character states of the same anatomy;

- some of the homogeneous features at the peripheries that differed from place to place could be linked to common characteristics found in populations from the same areas today.

The later point was first established by F. Weidenreich, and its implications are explored in Chapter 11.

A number of circumstances, and evolutionary mechanism mechanisms responding to them, promote marked variability at the center of a species' range, especially if this is where the species first appeared to be successful. It is quite likely that the center remains the region of optimal adaptation. A greater range of morphological variation will be tolerated within groups from that region because the problems of adaptation are most easily met. In addition, central populations have relatively higher population densities than peripheral populations and therefore often live closer together and are more often in contact where they can exchange genes and thereby increase the variation within them. Gene flow from other regions will be multidirectional at a species' geographic center. Moreover, differences between populations might be accentuated by competition between the more densely packed central ones. Combined, these would increase the heterogeneity of the region as a whole. Finally, at the center of the range of a colonizing species, the potential for loss of variability due to drift is minimized and selection is likely to be more relaxed for populations undergoing rapid expansion.

In the peripheral regions, or places that are ecologically marginal, events associated with the initial colonization and the subsequent period of local adaptation help to determine the combination of

- *differences between* populations in different regions,
- but at the same time *relative homogeneity within them.*

This is the primary basis for the observation that in peripheral regions some of the features that mark modern geographic variation have been found to appear in the initial immigrants. Colonizing populations were probably small, according to workers such as J. Birdsell who have attempted to model Pleistocene population movements. While augmenting the potential for the loss of variation because of genetic drift, this also increased the possibility of rapid adaptive change when new habitats were encountered. One effect was the same, because if the requirements of selection were strong, bottlenecks could occur and additional genetic variation would be reduced.

Therefore the morphological homogeneity that has been observed to characterize fossil human crania from peripheral sites with large sample sizes such as Sangiran (and later, Zhoukoudian and Ngandong) reflects a reduced number of genetic polymorphisms in nuclear (and mitochondrial) DNA because the characteristics of these gene pools were initially established by the partial isolation of numerous small populations with histories of drift and bottlenecking. The differences between the hominid samples from these peripheral sites reflect the fact that these histories were different. A. Templeton argues that these conditions are optimal for the rapid appearance of adaptive divergences. When populations are small, even if selection is intense additional differentiation of more neutral variants can be expected as well.

In the case of the Sangiran sample, it has been suggested that local isolation effects may have played a role in establishing the relative homogeneity as well. If there was such a role, I believe it was not of great importance for two reasons

1. the same process seems to have created similar homogeneity in other peripheral regions where, however, different features were established in high frequency, providing evidence for a different evolutionary history
2. the reflection of world-wide evolutionary trends in Indonesian hominid evolution, for instance brain size increase, suggests that no isolation was complete

An example of the homogeneity found *within* peripheral samples is in the forehead shape of the Indonesian sample. Virtually all of the specimens have a low, flat forehead with the sagittal keel on the parietal join extending onto it. There is only poor frontal boss expression and therefore a shallow supratoral sulcus (little hollowing) between the front of the forehead and the top of the supraorbitals. These tori are continuous and fairly straight across the face, and are usually well developed at the center over the nose. Not every specimen is identical and each of these features varies in the sample, but *most of* the *combination* of features characterizes all of the specimens. Most of these features appear in the African early *H. sapiens* remains as well, but the sample is much more variable in each of them and they are never found all together.

An example of the heterogeneity found *between* peripheral samples is in the face, The Sangiran faces have cheeks beginning well to the rear, their base over the anterior molars, and their sides angle backwards so that they do not face anteriorly. The Gongwangling face is quite different, the base of the cheeks being much more anterior, just behind the nose, and their angulation quite forward, producing extreme facial flatness. These are alternative character states that probably have no adaptive significance, although their anatomy was subsequently exapted into local adaptations. Thus flat Asian faces have been explained as cold adaptations and as adaptations to maximize the leverage of vertical muscle forces through the incisors, as they are most strongly expressed in living Eskimos. Yet, European Neandertal faces have been explained exactly the same way and these are as anatomically different as possible (see Chapter 13). The point is that both Eskimo and Neandertal anatomies are used in the adaptations suggested, but these are exaptations of preexisting morphology whose initial variation was established by the "center and edge" process and was not adaptive at all.

Summary

Early Pleistocene *H. sapiens* represents a segment of an evolving lineage. There are distinct trends in the period of the evolution documented in this Chapter, which spans the time from over 1.5 million years ago to about half that age, the beginning of the middle Pleistocene. However, its most important distinction is the fact that it was a successful colonizer of the more difficult African habitats and part of the world out of Africa. These were the first people to leave Africa. Their most marked evolutionary changes, both in the African populations and in other regions, accelerated as the period of colonization began.

Human populations spread through the tropics and subtropics of the Old World soon after the earliest Acheulean adaptations appear in Africa. Population increase and expansion into new habitats provides the best evidence of the new and more effective adaptations that emerged from the gathering, confrontational scavenging, and hunting abilities, and the cultural and technological developments associated with them, that seem to have characterized *H. sapiens* from its beginnings. The critical changes that accelerated the colonization process were social ones, as broad networks reflecting interactions and communication between populations provided the chance for populations to take advantage of new opportunities with fewer risks. The rapid spread of the Acheulean attests to these networks, just as the expanding human range reflects their consequences. What is important about the Acheulean, apart from the improvements in organization and technology it reflects, is the regular forms of its artifacts. Tools made according to a regular and predictable pattern can be a form of communication, as they can mark sexual division of labor, status, and even household identity - the fundamental bases of role differences and behavioral expectations. Yet, for all the adaptive and social changes that seem to have been part and parcel of the Acheulean, the similarities in adaptive patterns and skeletal morphology over the species' broadening range attests to a lack of ability to exploit varying habitats in specific and efficient ways.

While evidence of European habitation during the Early Pleistocene is restricted to often problematically dated (or interpreted) archaeological remains, hominid fossils are found in Western Asia, subtropical China, and Indonesia. These early hominids are characterized by small but increasing cranial capacities and posterior teeth and mandibles whose range of size and robustness, although reduced on the average, still extends far into the australopithecine range. Particularly in Indonesia where the sample is largest, sexual dimorphism in cranial features and mandibular robustness is dramatic enough to have been interpreted as taxonomic difference by some.

Subsequent trends in cranial evolution are best known from Asia, where the Indonesian sequence persists up to the Middle Pleistocene. The crania show evidence of continued expansion, especially in the frontal and posterior parietal areas of the brain if comparisons are made with the earlier Africans. Large as the Indonesian facial dimensions are, they reduce compared with the earlier Africans. The nuchal muscle attachment area is maximally developed in the earliest Indonesian specimens and subsequently decreases. These trends are expressed all across the inhabited world; for instance, cranial capacity expansion occurs in Africa as well, where Ternifine 4, the largest vault of the Early Pleistocene, is found just at its end. Yet, some evidence also suggests that regional population differences appeared, especially at the peripheries of the hominid range. A combination of regional peripheral homogeneity and certain marked differences between populations was established during the colonization process because of the different histories of selection and genetic drift in the colonizers.

The evolutionary trends evident in the Early Pleistocene hominids accelerate into the Middle Pleistocene. Directly and indirectly, adaptive expansions were the result of both cultural and morphological innovations which led to behavioral changes that in turn altered the nature and direction of selection acting on hominid populations. If early *H. sapiens* was evolving into a hunter/gatherer, the important point is that this was a *hominid* hunter/gatherer, adapting to the new pattern of resource exploitation both culturally and morphologically. The broadening of the fundamental niche greatly increased the ecological and geographic range of the species. The continuing development of culture as the major hominid adaptive mechanism, and the effects of this commitment, played a lead role in the evolution of human morphology.

ANATOMY OF A CONTROVERSY
100 Years of "*Pithecanthropus*" is Enough!

More than 50 years after E. Dubois discovered the first true "missing link" and named it "*Pithecanthropus erectus*", and 40 years after G. Schwalbe provided its comparative analysis, scientists such as W. LeGros Clark argued that a variety of similar hominid forms from other regions that had been found by then should all be lumped together with the Trinil remains, subsumed in the single species, "*Pithecanthropus erectus*". Slightly later F. Weidenreich, and a decade later E. Mayr (who was ultimately more influential), took the logic further and argued that only a single genus was necessary to describe the Pleistocene hominids, and proposed *Homo erectus* to replace "*Pithecanthropus erectus*", in order to clarify the evolutionary process by burying a taxonomic nomenclature that was obscuring it. Perhaps ironically, with the discoveries and theoretical advances of the decades since, the continued use of *H. erectus* now has become the major impediment to understanding the Pleistocene evolution of humans. There are good reason to consider the taxon invalid.

It has a distinct origin, in a cladogenic event some 2 myr if not even earlier. The subsequent lineage has shown itself to be biologically and culturally adapted to an increasingly broad range of ecologies, ultimately leading to its spread across the world more than a half million years after its appearance, coincident or just following the discovery of new adaptations and behaviors reflected in the Acheulean Industrial Complex. If we use *Homo habilis* to indicate the ancestral condition, *H. erectus*, the name often accepted for this lineage in the Early Pleistocene (but not used here, for reasons being discussed), differs in a number of ways. The vast majority of these distinctions also characterize the descendent species on this lineage, *H. sapiens*, so that the diagnosis of *H. erectus* relative to *H. habilis* largely characterizes *H. sapiens* as well. In other words, there is little difference between the features that distinguish the earlier part of the lineage from *H. habilis* and those that distinguish the later part of the lineage from *H. habilis*, and therefore little discrimination of taxonomic importance between the earlier and later parts of the lineage. Every one of the few features that are not shared between the earlier and later parts appear to be changes that respond to the evolutionary trends of:

1. increasing brain size,
2. improving cultural complexity,
3. the progressive substitution of technology for biology.

H. erectus, thus defined, is not at all a static species. It shows a number of evolutionary trends in the direction of *H. sapiens* and it is the consequences of these trends that form the main distinctions between the ancestral-descendent species.

Moreover like its descendent, *H. erectus* is a polytypic species, divided into several distinct geographic variants which show continuity in certain characteristics with the geographic varieties of the polytypic species *H. sapiens* through the sharing of unique combinations of morphological features. No region inhabited by both of these time successive species has a distinct or abrupt boundary between them. Quite different from the events at the origin of *H. erectus*, there is no evidence of an appearance of a new combination of features separating earlier and later populations in one area, let alone in every inhabited area as would have to be the case if *H. sapiens* had a single populational origin. Instead, the characteristics of *H. erectus* and *H. sapiens* are mixed in transitional samples that are found in the later Middle Pleistocene of every region where there are hominid remains.

Finally, no single definition has been found that distinguishes *H. sapiens* (defined traditionally as the descendent of *H. erectus*) in all regions. Criteria that apply to one area of the world are demonstrably invalid for other regions.

Evolutionary species, as described in Chapter 2, are similar to individuals in having real beginnings and ends, and have their own evolutionary tendencies. Neither *H. erectus* nor *H. sapiens* alone fit this description, but a lineage combining the two does. The meaning of these details is that there is no speciation involved in the emergence of *H. sapiens* from *H. erectus*. The absence of a branching event creating a distinct boundary at the "origin" of *H. sapiens*, together with the related patterns of polytypism in both "species", provide an explanation for the inability to develop a valid morphological definition of *H. sapiens*. No valid definition is possible because there is not a single region of origin from the preceding polytypic species. With neither clear distinctions nor a definition possible nor a distinct beginning for *H. sapiens* as narrowly defined, these reasons combine to require that the full *H. erectus* ⇨ *H. sapiens* lineage be regarded as a single evolutionary species - *H. sapiens*.

Attempts to sink *H. erectus* and merge it into *H. sapiens* meet with the by-now familiar Greek Chorus of "its the single species hypothesis again", and "absurd". However starting as long ago as the time I was born, paleoanthropologists began to propose exactly that (nothing but coincidence is meant or implied). The first was F. Weidenreich, who followed his "*Homo erectus*" proposition with an even more daring one, that all known fossil hominids be subsumed in *Homo sapiens* (when he suggested this in 1943, fragmentary australopithecines had been discovered but he did not consider them to be hominids). Others through the years have made similar suggestions, including , H. Hemmer, J-J. Hublin, J. Jelínek, R. Leakey, J. Robinson, and A. Thoma. Acting on my belief that it is correct I have adhered to this taxonomy throughout the text.

REFERENCES AND FURTHER READINGS

ACKERMAN, S. 1989 European prehistory gets even older. *Science* 246:28-30.

AIGNER, J.S., and W.S. LAUGHLIN 1973 The dating of the Lantian man and his significance for analyzing trends in human evolution. *American Journal of Physical Anthropology* 39:97-110.

AN ZHISHENG and HO CHUANKUN 1989 New magnetostratigraphic dates of Lantian *Homo erectus*. *Quaternary Research* 33:213-221.

ANDREWS, P. 1984 An alternative interpretation of the characters used to define *Homo erectus*. In P. Andrews and J.L. Franzen (eds): *The Early Evolution of Man, with Special Emphasis on Southeast Asia and Africa. Courier Forschungsinstitut Senckenberg* 69:167-175.

ARAMBOURG, C. 1955a A recent discovery in human paleontology: *Atlanthropus* of Ternifine (Algeria). *American Journal of Physical Anthropology* 13:191-202.

___. 1955b Le pariétal de L'*Atlanthropus mauritanicus*. *Comptes Rendus des Séances de l'Académie des Sciences*, Série D, 241:980-982.

ASFAW, B., Y. BEYENE, G. SUWA, R.C. WALTER, T.D. WHITE, G. WOLDEGABRIEL, and T. YEMANE 1992 The earliest Acheulean from Konso-Gardula. *Nature* 360:732-735.

AZIZ, F., J. DE VOS, and P.V. SONDAAR 1994 The *Homo* bearing deposits of Java and its ecological context. *Courier Forschungsinstitut Senckenberg* (in press).

BAKER, R.R. 1982 *Migration: Paths through Time and Space*. Hodder & Stoughton, London.

BARTSTRA, G. 1983 The fauna from Trinil, type locality of *Homo erectus*: a reinterpretation. *Geologie en Mijnbouw* 62:329-336.

BILSBOROUGH, A., and B.A. WOOD 1986 The nature, origin, and fate of *Homo erectus*. In B. Wood, L. Martin, and P. Andrews (eds): *Major Trends in Primate and Human Evolution*. Cambridge University Press, Cambridge. pp. 295-316.

BINFORD, L.R. 1982 The archaeology of place. *Journal of Anthropological Archaeology* 1(1):5-31.

___. 1987 Searching for camps and missing the evidence? Another look at the Lower Paleolithic. In O. Soffer (ed.): *The Pleistocene Old World. Regional Perspectives*. Plenum, New York. pp. 17-32.

BIRDSELL, J.B. 1958 On population structure in generalized hunting and collecting populations. *Evolution* 12:189-205.

___. 1967 Some predictions for the Pleistocene based on equilibrium systems among recent hunter-gatherers. In R.B. Lee and I. DeVore (eds): *Man the Hunter*. Aldine, Chicago. pp. 229-240.

BLACK, D., P. TEILHARD DE CHARDIN, C.C. YOUNG, and W.C. PEI 1933 Fossil man in China: The Choukoutien deposits with a synopsis of our present knowledge of the late Cenozoic in China. *Memoir of the Geological Survey of China*, Series A, Number 11.

BLUMENBERG, B. 1983 The evolution of the advanced hominid brain. *Current Anthropology* 24:589-623.

BONIFAY, E., and B. VANDERMEERSCH (editors) 1991 *Les premiers Européens*. CNRS, Paris.

BORDES, F. 1968 *The Old Stone Age*. McGraw-Hill, New York.

BOWER, B. 1992 Erectus unhinged. *Science News* 141:408-411.

CHAVAILLON, J., and Y. COPPENS 1975 Découverte d'Hominidé dans l'un des sites Acheuléens de Melka Kunturé (Ethiopie). *Bulletins et Mémoires de la Société d'Anthropologie de Paris* 2 (Série 13):125-128.

CLARK, J.D. 1994 The Acheulian Industrial Complex in Africa and elsewhere. In R.S. Corruccini and R.L. Ciochon (eds): *Integrative Paths to the Past. Paleoanthropological Advances in Honor of F. Clark Howell*. Prentice Hall, Englewood Cliffs. pp. 451-469.

CLARK, J.D., and H. KURASHINA 1979 Hominid occupation of the east-central highlands of Ethiopia in the Plio-Pleistocene. *Nature* 282:33-39.

CLARK, W.E. LeGROS 1937 The Status of *Pithecanthropus. Man* 37:60-62.

COPPENS, Y. 1966 An early hominid from Chad. *Current Anthropology* 7:584-585.

CROMPTON, R.H., and J.A.J. GOWLETT 1993 Allometry and multidimensional form in Acheulean bifaces from Kilombe, Kenya. *Journal of Human Evolution* 25(3):175-199.

DAVIDSON, I., and W. NOBLE 1993 Tools and language in human evolution. In K.R. Gibson and T. Ingold (eds): *Tools, Language, and Cognition in Human Evolution*. Cambridge University Press, Cambridge. pp. 363-388.

DAY, M.H. 1973 Locomotor features of the lower limb in hominids. *Proceedings of the Zoological Society of London* 33:29-51.

___. 1984 The postcranial remains of H*omo erectus* from Africa, Asia, and possibly Europe. In P. Andrews and J.L. Franzen (eds): *The Early Evolution of Man, with Special Emphasis on Southeast Asia and Africa. Courier Forschungsinstitut Senckenberg* 69:113-121.

DAY, M.H., and T. MOLLESON 1973 The Trinil femora. In M.H. Day (ed): *Human Evolution. Symposia of the Society for the Study of Human Biology* 11:127-154.

DENNELL, R.W. 1983 *European Economic Prehistory*. Academic Press, New York.

DENNELL, R., H. RENDELL, and E. HAILWOOD 1988 Late Pliocene artifacts from Northern Pakistan. *Current Anthropology* 29:495-498.

DE VOS, J 1985 Faunal stratigraphy and correlation of the Indonesian hominid sites. In E. Delson (ed): *Ancestors: The Hard Evidence*. Alan R. Liss, New York. pp. 221-220.

DE VOS, J., S, SARTONO, S. HARDJASAMITA, and P.Y. SONDAAR 1982 The fauna from Trinil, type locality of *Homo erectus*: a reinterpretation. *Geologie en Mijnbouw* 61:207-211.

DIBBLE, H.L. 1989 The implications of stone tool types for the presence of language during the Lower and Middle Paleolithic. In P. Mellars and C.B. Stringer (eds): *The Human Revolution: Behavioural and Biological Perspectives on the Origins of Modern Humans*. Edinburgh University Press, Edinburgh. pp. 415-432.

___. 1991 Local raw material exploitation and its effects on Lower and Middle Paleolithic assemblage variability. In A. Monet-White and S. Holen (eds): *Raw Material Economics among Prehistoric Hunter-Gatherers. University of Kansas Publications in Anthropology* 19:33-48.

DONALD, M. 1991 *Origins of the Modern Mind: Three Stages in the Origin of Culture and Cognition.* Harvard University Press, Cambridge.

DUBOIS, E. 1896 On *Pithecanthropus erectus*: A transitional form between man and the apes. *Scientific Transactions of the Royal Society of Dublin* 6:1-18.

___. 1937 Early Man in Java and *Pithecanthropus erectus*. In G.G. MacCurdy (ed): *Early Man: International Symposium.* Lippincott, Philadelphia.

FISHER, A. 1988 On the emergence of humanness. *Mosaic* 19(1):34-45.

FOLEY, R.A. 1991 The silence of the past. *Nature* 353:114-115.

FRANZEN, J.L. 1985a Asian australopithecines? In P.V. Tobias (ed): *Hominid Evolution: Past, Present, and Future. Proceedings of the Taung Diamond Jubilee International Symposium.* Alan R. Liss Inc., New York. pp. 255-263.

___. 1985b What is "*Pithecanthropus dubius* Koenigswald, 1950"? In E. Delson (ed): *Ancestors: The Hard Evidence.* Alan R. Liss, New York. pp. 221-226.

GAMBLE, C.S. 1994 Time for Boxgrove man. *Nature* 369:275-276.

GABUNIA, L., A. JUSTUS, and A. VEKUA 1989 Der menschliche unterkeifer. In: *Der altpaläolithische Fundplatz Dmanisi in Georgien (Kaukasus). Jahrbuch des Römisch-Germanischen Zentralmuseums Mainz* 36:109-111.

GERAADS, D., J-J. HUBLIN, J-J. JAEGER, H. TONG, S. SEN, and P. TOUBEAU 1986 The Pleistocene hominid site of Ternifine, Algeria: new results on the environment, age, and human industries. *Quaternary Research* 25:380-386.

GIBBONS, A. 1994 Rewriting - and redating - prehistory. *Science* 263:1087-1088.

GOODNIGHT, C.J. 1987 On the effect of founder events on epistatic variance. *Evolution* 41:80-91.

GOREN-INBAR, A. 1992 The Acheulean site of Gesher Benot Ya'aqov - an Asian or an African entity? In T. Akazawa, K. Aoki, and T. Kimura (eds): *The Evolution and Dispersal of Modern Humans in Asia.* Hokusen-sha, Tokyo. pp. 67-82.

GOULD, S.J. 1990 Men of the thirty-third division. *Natural History* (4/90):12-24.

GOWLETT, J.A.J. 1984 Mental abilities of early man: a look at some hard evidence. In R. Foley (ed): *Hominid Evolution and Community Ecology.* Academic Press, New York. pp. 167-192.

___. 1990 Technology, skill, and the psychosocial sector in the long term of human evolution. *Cambridge Archaeological Review* 9:82-103

GRINE, F.E. 1984 Comparisons of the deciduous dentitions of African and Asian hominids. In P. Andrews and J.L. Franzen (eds): *The Early Evolution of Man, with Special Emphasis on Southeast Asia and Africa. Courier Forschungsinstitut Senckenberg* 69:69-82.

GUGLIELMINO-MATESSI, C.R., P. GLUCKMAN, and L.L. CAVALLI-SFORZA 1979 Climate and the evolution of skull metrics in man. *American Journal of Physical Anthropology* 50:549-564.

HARRIS, J.W.K., and G. Ll. ISAAC 1976 The Karari Industry: Early Pleistocene archaeological evidence from the terrain east of Lake Turkana, Kenya. *Nature* 262:102-107.

HEMMER, H. 1969 A new view of the evolution of man. *Current Anthropology* 10(2-3):179-180.

HOLLOWAY, R.L. 1981 The Indonesian *Homo erectus* brain endocasts revisited. *American Journal of Physical Anthropology* 55(4):503-521.

HOTTON, F., S. LOURYAN, A. BOLLAERT, A. LEGUEBE, and J. DE VOS 1984 Etude radiologique du fémur n° 1 (*Homo erectus*) de Trinil (Indonésie). *Bulletin de la Société Royal Belge d'Anthropologie et de Préhistoire* 95:99-107.

HOWELL, F. C. 1961 More on Middle Pleistocene hominids. *Current Anthropology* 2:117-120.

___. 1977 The hominization process. In S. Tax and L. G. Freeman (eds): *Horizons in Anthropology*. Aldine, Chicago. pp. 59-74.

HOWELLS, W.W. 1980 *Homo erectus* -- who, when and where: a survey. *Yearbook of Physical Anthropology* 23:1-23.

HUBLIN, J-J. 1986 Some comments on the diagnostic features of *Homo erectus*. In V.V. Novotný and A. Mizerová (eds): *Fossil Man. New Facts, New Ideas. Papers in Honor of Jan Jelinek's Life Anniversary. Anthropos* (Brno) 23:175-187.

HUTTERER, K.L. 1985 The Pleistocene archaeology of Southeast Asia in regional context. *Modern Quaternary Research in Southeast Asia* 9:1-23.

HYLANDER, W.L. 1977 The adaptive significance of Eskimo craniofacial morphology. In . A.A. Dahlberg and T.M. Graber (eds): *Orofacial Growth and Development*. Mouton, The Hague. pp. 129-169.

HYODO, M., N. WATANABE, W. SUNATA, E.E. SUSANTO, and H. WAHYONO 1993 Magnetostratigraphy of hominid fossil bearing formations in Sangiran and Mojokerto, Java. *Anthropological Science* 101(2):157-186.

ISAAC, G.Ll. 1986 Foundation stones: early artifacts as indicators of activities and abilities. In G.N. Bailey and G.H. Curtis (eds): *Stone Age Prehistory*. University of Cambridge Press, Cambridge. pp. 221-242.

JACOB, T. 1973. Paleoanthropological discoveries in Indonesia with special reference to the finds of the last two decades. *Journal of Human Evolution* 2:473-486.

___. 1980 The *Pithecanthropus* of Indonesia: phenotype, genetics, and ecology. In L-K. Königsson (ed): *Current Argument on Early Man. Report from a Nobel Symposium*. Pergamon, Oxford. pp. 170-179.

JELINEK, A.J. 1977 The Lower Paleolithic: current evidence and interpretations. In B.J. Siegel, A.R. Beals, and S.A. Tyler (eds): *Annual Review of Anthropology*. Annual Reviews, Palo Alto. Volume 6:11-32.

JELÍNEK, J. 1978 *Homo erectus* or *Homo sapiens*? *Recent Advances in Primatology* 3:419-429.

___. 1981 Was *Homo erectus* already *Homo sapiens*? *Les Processus de l'Hominisation*. Centre National de la Recherche Scientifique, Paris, International Colloquium No. 599:91-95.

JIA LANPO 1985 China's earliest Paleolithic assemblages. In Wu Rukang and J.W. Olsen (eds): *Palaeoanthropology and Paleolithic Archaeology in the People's Republic of China*. Academic Press, New York. pp. 135-145.

JONES, P. 1981 Experimental implement manufacture and use: a case study from Olduvai Gorge, Tanzania. In J. Young, E. Jope, and K. Oakley (eds): *The Emergence of Man*. The Royal Society and the British Academy, London. pp. 189-195.

KEELEY, L.H. 1980 *Experimental Determination of Stone Tool Uses: a Microwear Analysis*. University of Chicago, Chicago.

___. 1982 Hafting and retooling: effects on the archaeological record. *American Antiquity* 47(4):789-809.

KENNEDY, G.E. 1991 On the autapomorphic traits of *Homo erectus*. *Journal of Human Evolution* 30(5): 30(5):375-412.

KLEINDIENST, M. R., and C. M. KELLER. 1976 Towards a functional analysis of handaxes and cleavers: the evidence from eastern Africa. *Man* 11:176-187.

VON KOENIGSWALD, G.H.R. 1942 The South-African Man-Apes and *Pithecanthropus*. *Carnegie Institute of Washington Publication* 530:205-222.

___. 1953 The Australopithecinae and Pithecanthropus. *Koninklijke Nederlandische Akademie van Wetenschappen te Amsterdam*, Series B, 56:403-413, 427-438; 57:85-91..

___. 1954 *Pithecanthropus, Meganthropus*, and the Australopithecinae. *Nature* 173:795-797.

___. 1956 *Meeting Prehistoric Man*. Thames and Hudson, London.

___. 1957 Remarks on *Gigantopithecus* and other hominid remains from Southern China. *Koninklijke Akademie Wetenschappen te Amsterdam*, Series B, 60:153-159.

___. 1973 *Australopithecus, Meganthropus*, and *Ramapithecus*. *Journal of Human Evolution* 2:487-492.

KRAMER, A. 1994 A critical analysis of claims for the existence of Southeast Asian australopithecines. *Journal of Human Evolution* 26(1):3-21

KRAMER, A., and L.W. KONIGSBERG 1993 The phyletic position of Sangiran 6 as determined by multivariate analysis. *Courier Forschungsinstitut Senckenberg* (in press).

KRUKOFF, S. 1967 Reconstitution de la largeur bi-pariétale totale d'un crâne à partir d'un os pariétal isolé. *Comptes Rendus de l'Académie des Sciences*, Série D, 264:1260-1262.

LARSEN, C.S. 1985 Dental modifications and tool use in the Western Great Basin. *American Journal of Physical Anthropology* 67:393-402.

LEAKEY, M.D. 1978 Olduvai Gorge 1911-75: a history of investigations. In W.W. Bishop (ed): *Geological Background to Fossil Man*. Scottish Academic Press, Edinburgh. pp. 151-155.

LEAKEY, R.E. 1989 Recent fossil finds from east Africa. In J.R. Durant (ed): *Human Origins*. Clarendon Press, Oxford. pp. 53-62.

LEINDERS, J.J.M., F. AZIZ, P.Y. SONDAAR, and J. DE VOS 1985 The age of the hominid-bearing deposits of Java: state of the art. *Geologie en Mijnbouw* 64:167-173.

LEOPOLD, A.C., and R. ARDREY 1974 Toxic substances in plants and the food habits of early man. *Science* 176:512-514.

LIU DONGSHEN and DING MENGLIN 1983 Discussions on the age of the "Yuanmou Man". *Acta Anthropologica Sinica* 2(1):40-48.

LOVEJOY, C.O. 1970 The taxonomic status of the *Meganthropus* mandibular fragments from the Djetis beds of Java. *Man* 5:228-236.

MAIER. W.O., and A.T. NKINI 1985 The phylogenetic position of Olduvai hominid 9, especially as determined from basicranial evidence. In E. Delson (ed): *Ancestors: the Hard Evidence*. Alan R. Liss, New York. pp. 249-254.

MANN, A. 1971 *Homo erectus*. In P. Dolhinow and V. M. Sanch (eds): *Background for Man*. Little Brown, Boston. pp. 166-177.

MATSU'URA, S. 1982 A chronological framing of the Sangiran hominids. *Bulletin of the National Science Museum*, Tokyo, Series D, 8:1-53.

MAYR, E. 1970 *Populations, Species and Evolution*. Belknap, Cambridge.

MEGGETT, M.J. 1962 *The Desert People: a Study of the Walbiri Aborigines of Central Australia*. University of Chicago Press, Chicago.

MOLNAR, S. 1972 Tooth wear and culture: A survey of tooth functions among some prehistoric populations. *Current Anthropology* 13:511-525.

O'BRIEN, E.M. 1981 The projectile capabilities of an Acheulean handaxe from Olorgesailie. *Current Anthropology* 22:76-79.

OLSEN, J.W. and R.L. CIOCHON 1990 A review of the evidence for postulated Middle Pleistocene occupations in Viet Nam. *Journal of Human Evolution* 19:761-788.

ORBAN-SEGEBARTH, R. and F. PROCUREUR 1983 Tooth size of *Meganthropus paleojavanicus*: an analysis of distances between some fossil hominids and a modern human population. *Journal of Human Evolution* 12:711-720.

POPE, G.G. 1985 Taxonomy, dating, and paleoenvironment: the paleoecology of early Far Eastern hominids. *Modern Quaternary Research in Southeast Asia* 9:65-80.

___. 1989 Bamboo and human evolution. *Natural History* 98(10):48-57.

___. 1993 Ancient Asia's cutting edge. *Natural History* 102(5):55-59.

POPE, G.G., and S.G. KEATES 1994 The evolution of human cognition and cultural capacity. In R.S. Corruccini and R.L. Ciochon (eds): *Integrative Paths to the Past. Paleoanthropological Advances in Honor of F. Clark Howell*. Prentice Hall, Englewood Cliffs. pp. 531-567.

QI GUOQIN 1990 The Pleistocene human environment of North China. *Acta Anthropologica Sinica* 9(1):340-349.

RADER, W.T., and C.E. PETERS 1993 Hypertrophy of the acetabulo-crystal buttress in *Homo sapiens*. *American Journal of Physical Anthropology* 92(2):149-153.

RIGHTMIRE, G.P. 1979 Cranial remains of *Homo erectus* from Beds II and IV, Olduvai Gorge, Tanzania. *American Journal of Physical Anthropology* 51:99-116.

___. 1984 Comparisons of *Homo erectus* from Africa and Southeast Asia. In P. Andrews and J.L. Franzen (eds): *The Early Evolution of Man, with Special Emphasis on Southeast Asia and Africa. Courier Forschungsinstitut Senckenberg* 69:83-98.

___. 1991 The dispersal of *Homo erectus* from Africa and the emergence of more modern humans. *Journal of Anthropological Research* 47(2):177-191.

ROBERTS, N. 1984 Pleistocene environments in time and space. In R. Foley (ed): *Hominid Evolution and Community Ecology*. Academic Press, London. pp. 25-54.

ROBINSON, J.T. 1953 *Meganthropus*, australopithecines and hominids. *American Journal of Physical Anthropology* 11:1-38.

___. 1955 Further remarks on the relationship between *Meganthropus* and the australopithecines. *American Journal of Physical Anthropology* 13:429-445.

___. 1967 Variation and the taxonomy of the early hominids. In T. Dobzhansky, M. Hecht, and W. Steere (eds): *Evolutionary Biology* 1:69-100.. Appleton-Century-Crofts, New York.

ROEBROEKS, W. 1994 Updating the earliest occupation of Europe. *Current Anthropology* 35(3):301-305.

ROSE, M.D. 1984 A hominine hip bone, KNM-ER 3228 from East Lake Turkana, Kenya. *American Journal of Physical Anthropology* 63:371-378.

SARTONO, S. 1972 Discovery of another hominid skull at Sangiran, Central Java. *Current Anthropology* 13:124-126.

___. 1975 Implications arising from *Pithecanthropus* VIII. In R.H. Tuttle (ed): *Paleoanthropology: Morphology and Paleoecology*. Mouton, The Hague. pp. 327-360.

___. 1982 Sagittal cresting in *Meganthropus paleojavanicus* von Koenigswald. *Modern Quaternary Research in Southeast Asia* 7:201-210.

___. 1986 New lights on human evolution in Southeast Asia. GEOSEA V Proceedings Volume 2, *Bulletin of the Geological Society of Malaysia* 20:269-288.

___. 1991 *Homo (Pithecanthropus) erectus*: Le débat sans fin. *L'Anthropologie* 95(1):123-136.

___. 1994 *Meganthropus paleojavanicus* von Koenigswald: its place in human evolution. *Courier Forschungs-institut Senckenberg* 171: (in press).

SCHICK, K.D., and D. ZHUAN 1993 Early Paleolithic of China and Easterm Asia. *Evolutionary Anthropology* 2(1):22-35.

SCHWALBE, G. 1923 Die Abstammung des Menschen und die ältesten Menschenformen. In G. Schwalbe and E. Fischer (eds): *Anthropologie*. Teubner, Leipzig. pp. 223-338.

SÉMAH, F., A-M. SÉMAH, and T. DJUBIANTONO 1990 *They Discovered Java*. Pusat Penelitian Arkeologi and Musee Nationale d'Histoire Naturelle, Jakarta.

SÉMAH, F., A-M. SÉMAH, T. DJUBIANTONO, and H.T. SIMANJUNTAK 1992 Did they also make stone tools? *Journal of Human Evolution* 23(5):439-446.

SHIPMAN, P. 1990 From a 'blinding glimpse of the obvious' comes a new theory about early humans. *Chronicle of Higher Education* (February 14):B1-B3.

___. 1994 New *H. erectus* dates creates a puzzle: who came first? *Journal of NIH Research* 6(5):42-48.

SHUTLER, R., and F. BRACHES 1988 The origin, dating, and migration routes of hominids in Pleistocene East and Southeast Asia. In K. Edward and Y. Chen (eds): *The Paleoenvironments of East Asia from the Mid-Tertiary*. Volume II. University of Hong Kong Centre for Asian Studies, Hong Kong.

SIGHINOLFI, G.P., S. SARTONO, and G. ARTIOLI 1993 Chemical and mineralogical studies on hominid remains from Sangiran, Central Java (Indonesia). *Journal of Human Evolution* 24(1):57-68.

SMITH, G.E. 1931 *The Search for Man's Ancestors*. Watts, London.

SWISHER, C.C., G.H. CURTIS, T. JACOB, A.G. GETTY, A. SUPRIJO, and WIDIASMORO 1994 Age of the earliest known hominids in Java, Indonesia. *Science* 263:1118-1121.

TCHERNOV, E. 1987 The age of the Ubeidiya Formation, an Early Pleistocene hominid site in the Jordan Valley, Israel. *Israel Journal of Earth Science* 36:3-30.

TEMPLETON, A.R. 1982 Genetic architectures of speciation. In C. Barigozzi (ed): *Mechanisms of Speciation*. A.R. Liss, New York. pp. 105-121.

THEUNISSEN, B. 1988 *Eugene Dubois and the Ape-Man from Java*. Reidel, Dordrecht..

THOMA, A. 1973 New evidence for the polycentric evolution of *Homo sapiens*. *Journal of Human Evolution* 2:529-536.

THORNE, A.G. 1981 The centre and the edge: the significance of Australasian hominids to African paleoanthropology. In R.E. Leakey and B.A. Ogot (eds): *Proceedings of the 8th Panafrican Congress of Prehistory and Quaternary Studies, Nairobi, September 1977*. TILLMIAP, Nairobi. pp. 180-181.

THORNE, A.G. and M.H. WOLPOFF 1981 Regional continuity in Australasian Pleistocene hominid evolution. *American Journal of Physical Anthropology* 55:337-349.

TOBIAS, P.V. 1966 A re-examination of the Kedung Brubis mandible. *Zoölogische Medeelingen* 41:307-320.

___. 1968 Middle and early Upper Pleistocene members of the genus *Homo* in Africa. In G. Kurth (ed): *Evolution and Hominisation*. Fischer, Stuttgart. pp. 179-194.

___. 1980 *Homo habilis* and *Homo erectus*: from the Oldowan men to the Acheulean practitioners. *Anthropologie* (Brno) 18:115-119.

TORRENCE, R. 1989 Tools as optimal solutions. In R. Torrence (ed): *Time, Energy, and Stone Tools*. Cambridge University Press, Cambridge. pp. 1-6.

TOTH, N., and K. SCHICK 1986 The first million years: the archaeology of protohuman culture. *Advances in Archaeological Method and Theory* 9:1-96.

TYLER, D.E. 1992 A taxonomy of Javan hominid mandibles. *Acta Anthropologica Sinica* 11(4):285-299.

TURNER, A. 1992 Large carnivores and earliest European hominids: changing determinants of resource availability during the Lower and Middle Pleistocene. *Journal of Human Evolution* 22(2):109-126.

UBELAKER, D.H., T.W. PHENICE, and W.M. BASS 1969 Artificial interproximal grooving of the teeth in American Indians. *American Journal of Physical Anthropology* 30:145-150.

WANG JIANGKE, CHEN SHUIXIA, LUO HONGHONG, and ZHONG YUEMING 1989 Amino acid racemization dating of fossils from Quaternary deposits of some caves in Guangxi. *Acta Anthropologica Sinica* 8:172-176.

WEIDENREICH, F. 1945 Giant Early Man from Java and South China. *Anthropological Papers of the American Museum of Natural History* 40:1 -134.

___. 1949 Interpretations of the fossil maternal. In W. W. Howells (ed): *Early Man in the Far East.* Wistar Institute, Philadelphia. pp. 149-157.

WIESSNER, P. 1983 Style and social information in Kalahari San projectile points. *American Antiquity* 49:253-276.

WOBST, M.H. 1977 Stylistic behavior and information exchange. In C.E. Cleland (ed): *For the Director: Research Essays in Honor of James B. Griffin.* Museum of Anthropology Anthropological papers 61, Ann Arbor. pp. 317-342.

WOLPOFF, M.H. 1971 Interstitial wear. *American Journal of Physical Anthropology* 34:205-228.

___. 1991 *Homo erectus* et les Origines de la Diversité Humaine. In J-J. Hublin and A-M. Tillier (eds): *Aux Origines d'Homo sapiens. Nouvelle Encyclopédie Diderot.* Presses Universitaires de France, Paris. pp. 97-155.

WOLPOFF, M.H., A.G. THORNE, J. JELÍNEK, AND ZHANG YINYUN 1993 The case for sinking *Homo erectus*: 100 years of *Pithecanthropus* is enough! *Courier Forschungsinstitut Senckenberg* 171:341-361.

WOO, T.L., and G.M. MORANT 1934 A biometric study of the "flatness" of the facial skeleton in man. *Biometrika* 26:196-250.

WOOD, B.A. 1984 The origin of *Homo erectus.* In P. Andrews and J.L. Franzen (eds): *The Early Evolution of Man, with Special Emphasis on Southeast Asia and Africa. Courier Forschungsinstitut Senckenberg* 69:99-111.

WU RUKANG 1966 The skull of Lantian man. *Current Anthropology* 7:83-86.

WU XINZHI and WANG LINGHONG 1985 Chronology in Chinese paleoanthropology. In Wu Rukang and J.W. Olsen (eds): *Palaeoanthropology and Paleolithic Archaeology in the People's Republic of China.* Academic Press, New York. pp. 29-51.

WYNN, T. 1993 Two developments in the mind of early *Homo. Journal of Anthropological Archaeology* 12:299-322.

YI, S. and G.A. CLARK 1983 Observations on the lower Paleolithic of northeast Asia. *Current Anthropology* 24:181-202.

ZHANG YINYUN 1984 The "*Australopithecus*" of West Hubei and some early Pleistocene hominids of Indonesia. *Acta Anthropologica Sinica* 3(2):85-92.

___. 1985 *Gigantopithecus* and "*Australopithecus*" in China. In Wu Rukang and J.W. Olsen (eds): *Palaeoanthropology and Paleolithic Archaeology in the People's Republic of China.* Academic Press, New York. pp. 69-78.

ZHOU GUOXING and HU CHENGCHIH 1979 Supplementary notes on the teeth of Yuanmou man with discussions on morphological evolution of mesial upper incisors in the hominoids. *Vertebrata PalAsiatica* 17:149-162.

ZHOU GUOXING, WANG BO, and ZHAI HONG 1991 New material of Yuanmou man. *Kaogu Yu Wenwu* 1991/1:56-61.

Figure 10.15
Stratigraphic Positions for Early Pleistocene *Homo sapiens*

Date (myr)	Africa	Indonesia	East Asia	Europe and Western Asia
			⇑	
0.7	Lainyamok (.70-.56)	⇑	Jianshi	
	OH 28 (.78-.70), ?Yayo?	*Ardjuna 9*	⇓	
	Ternifine (=Tighenif)	*Hanoman 13*		
0.8		⇓	Yuanmou	
		S10	⇓	
0.9	OH 12,*22* (.90-.78)	S2,3,12,17, Trinil		
1.0		S4, 13a	Gongwangling	
		S1,5,6,9,22 ?⇓?	Luonan	
1.1				⇑
1.2	Gomboré II (1.20-0.78)			*Dmanisi* [3]
1.3	OH 34±			⇓
1.4	OH 9, *Konso-Gardula*			
	OH 36, Omo P 996-17			
1.5	Gomboré Ib			
	ER 3883			
1.6	ER 1466, WT 15000	?Sangiran 27, 31[1]		
1.7	ER 730, 1808, 1821			
1.8	ER 3733	?Mojokerto [2]		
1.9	ER 2598			
	ER 3228			

[1]   This date depends on a problematic association of the specimens with the dated tuff. They could be more than a half million years younger

[2]   This date depends on a problematic association of the skull with the dated tuff. It could be more than three-quarters of a million years younger

[3]   Date is based on faunal correlations with Ubediya

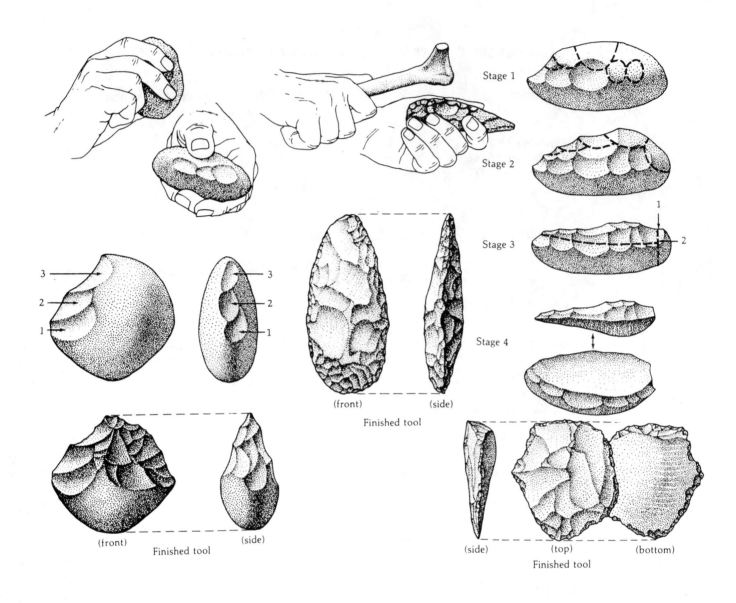

Stage 1

Stage 2

Stage 3

Stage 4

(front)   (side)

Finished tool

3
2
1

3
2
1

1
2

(front)   (side)

Finished tool

(side)   (top)   (bottom)

Finished tool

FIGURE 10.1 Acheulean tools.

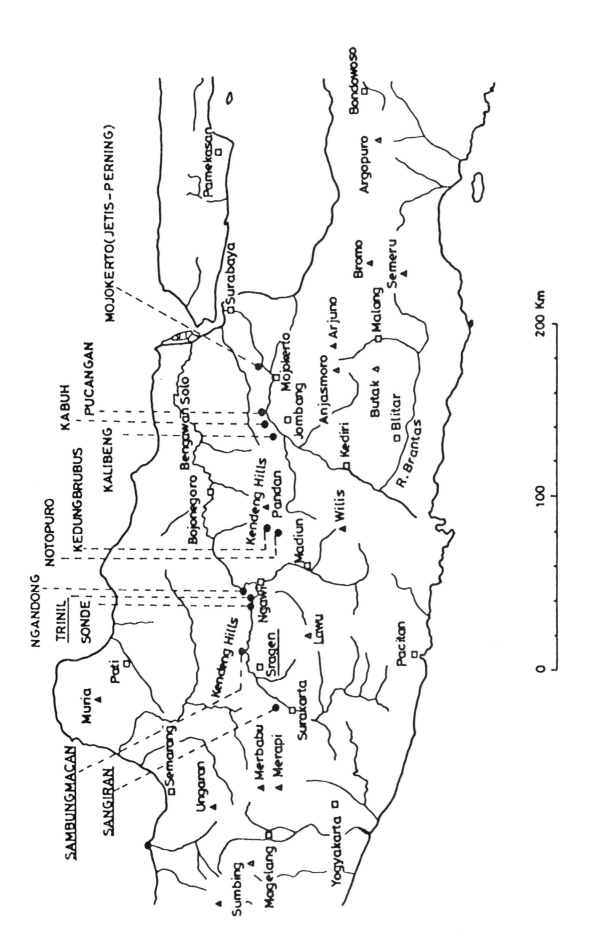

Map 10.2 Hominid and archaeological sites in Central Java, after Matsu'ura (1982).
FROM Matsu'ura, S. 1982 A chronological framing of the Sangiran hominids. Bulletin of the National
Science Museum, Tokyo, Series D, 8:1-53.

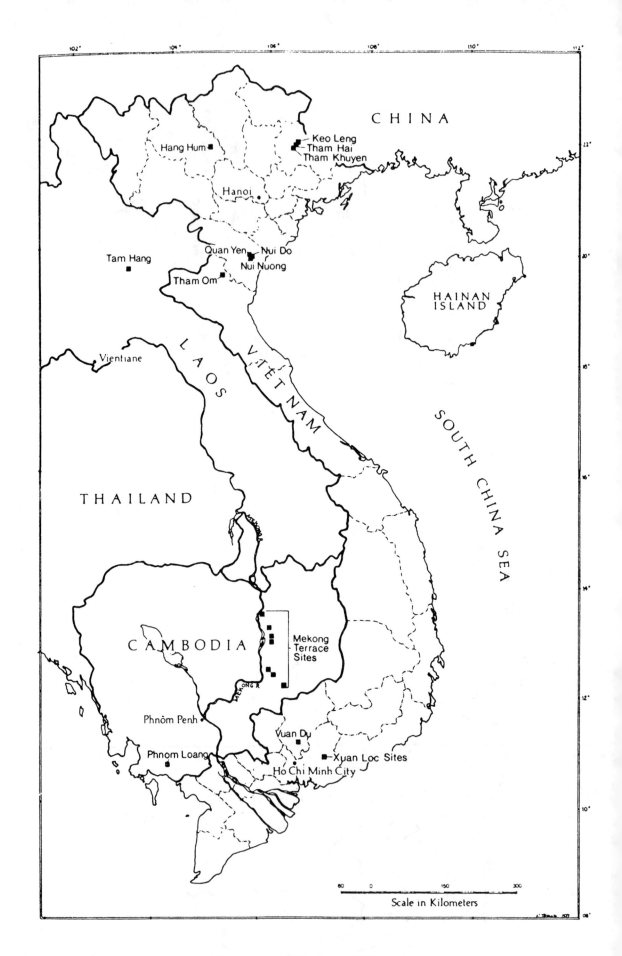

Map 10.3 Fossil human sites from Indochina, after Olsen and Ciochon (1990).
FROM Olsen, J.W. and R.L. Ciochon 1990 A review of the evidence for postulated Middle Pleistocene occupations in Viet Nam. *Journal of Human Evolution* 19:761-788.

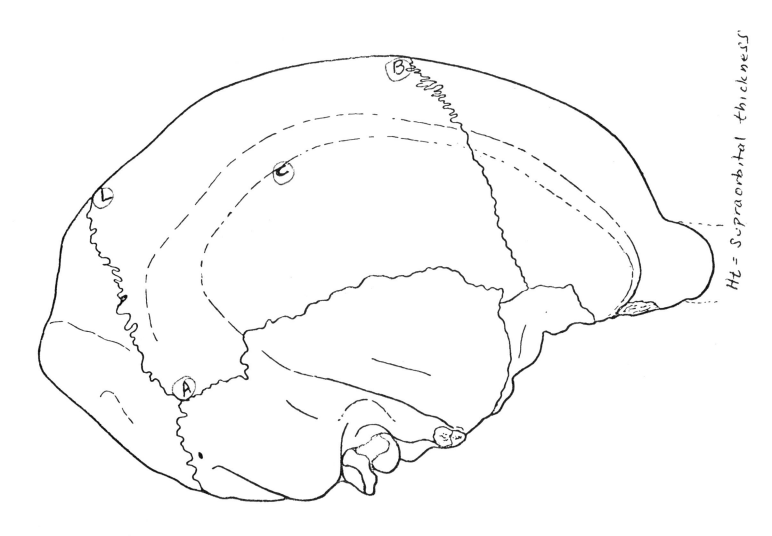

FIGURE 10.2 ZKT E-1, the earliest (ca. 578 kyr) of the Zhoukoudian crania, showing the positions of measuring points for parietal with thickness: B = bregma; C = bone center; L = lambda; A = asterion; Hi = height (or thickness) of the supraorbital torus (also see figure 9.11a). Adapted from Black (1930).

FROM Black, D. 1930 On an Adolescent skull of *Sinanthropus pekinensis* in comparison with an adult skull of the same species and with other hominid skulls, recent and fossil. *Palaeontologia Sinica*, Series D, Volume 7, Fascicle 2.

FIGURE 10.3 Olduvai hominid 9 cranium, after Rightmire (1990)
FROM Rightmire, G.P. 1990 *The Evolution of Homo erectus. Comparative Anatomical Studies of an Extinct Human Species.* Cambridge University Press, Cambridge, figures 11, 12, 14.

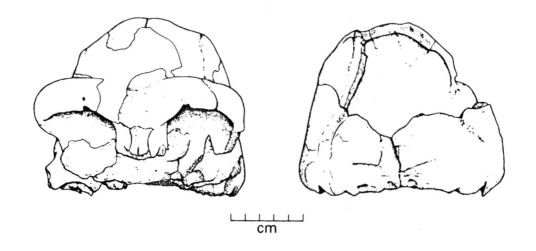

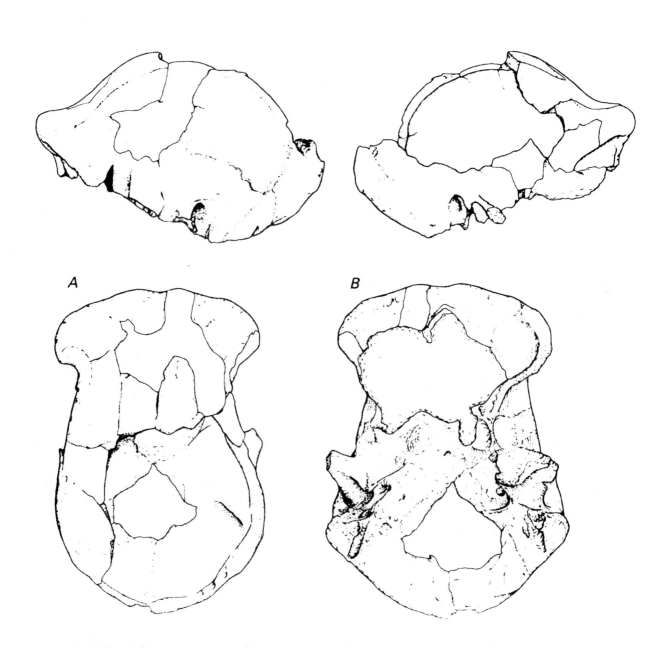

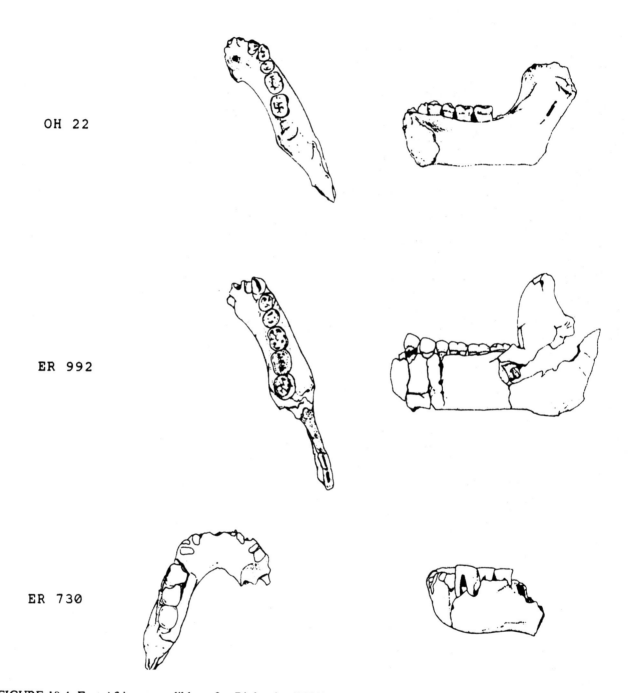

OH 22

ER 992

ER 730

FIGURE 10.4 East African mandibles, after Rightmire (1990).
FROM Rightmire, G.P. 1990 *The Evolution of Homo erectus. Comparative Anatomical Studies of an Extinct Human Species.* Cambridge University Press, Cambridge, figures 16, 23, 24, 25.

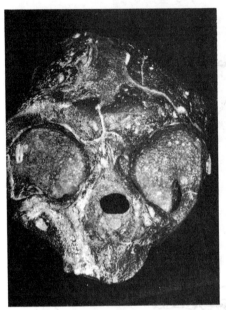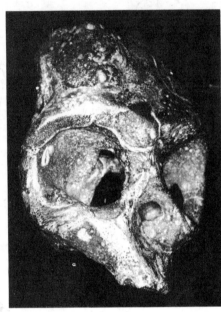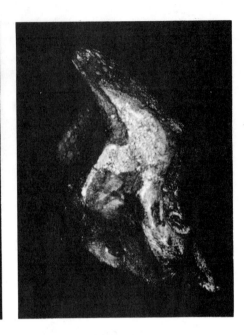

FIGURE 10.5 Chad face.

FIGURE 10.6 Specimens from Ternifine, after Rightmire (1990).
FROM Rightmire, G.P. 1990 *The Evolution of Homo erectus. Comparative Anatomical Studies of an Extinct Human Species.* Cambridge University Press, Cambridge, figures 29, 30.

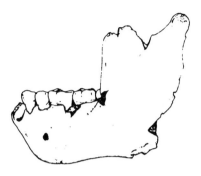

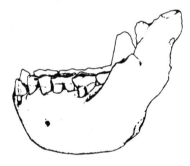
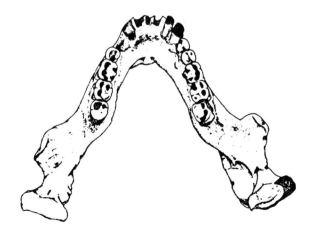
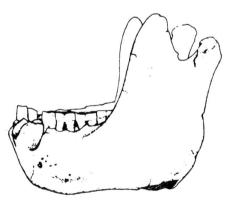

cm

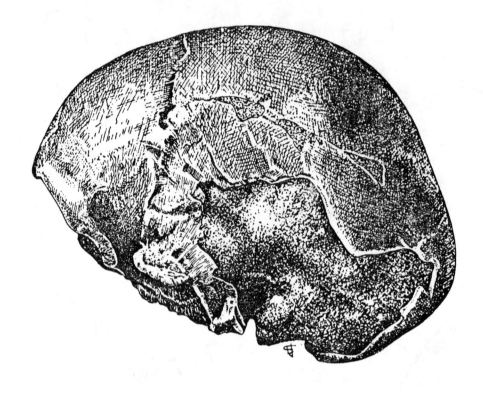

FIGURE 10.7 Mojokerto (Perning) child's cranium, after von Koenigswald (1956).
FROM von Koenigswald, G.H.R. 1956 *Meeting Prehistoric Man*. Thames and Hudson, London, figure 16

FIGURE 10.8 F. Weidenreich's reconstruction of the Sangiran 4 cranium, and its constituent pieces (not to the same scale). The two views of the posterior vault are lateral (left) and posterior; lateral, frontal, and a view from above the palatal piece are shown. The reconstruction shows the measuring points bregma (b), nasion (n), prosthion (p), and opistocranion (o), On the cranial portion the nuchal torus (t) and the sulcus (st) above it are clearly shown, as well as the sagittal keel (csg) and lambdoidal suture (sl). The open maxillary sinus (sm) and diastema (d) are indicated on the palatal piece.

FROM Weidenreich, F. 1943 The skull of *Sinanthropus pekinensis*: A comparative study of a
    primitive hominid skull. *Palaeontologia Sinica*, n.s. D, No. 10 (whole series No. 127), figures
    229, 230, 270.

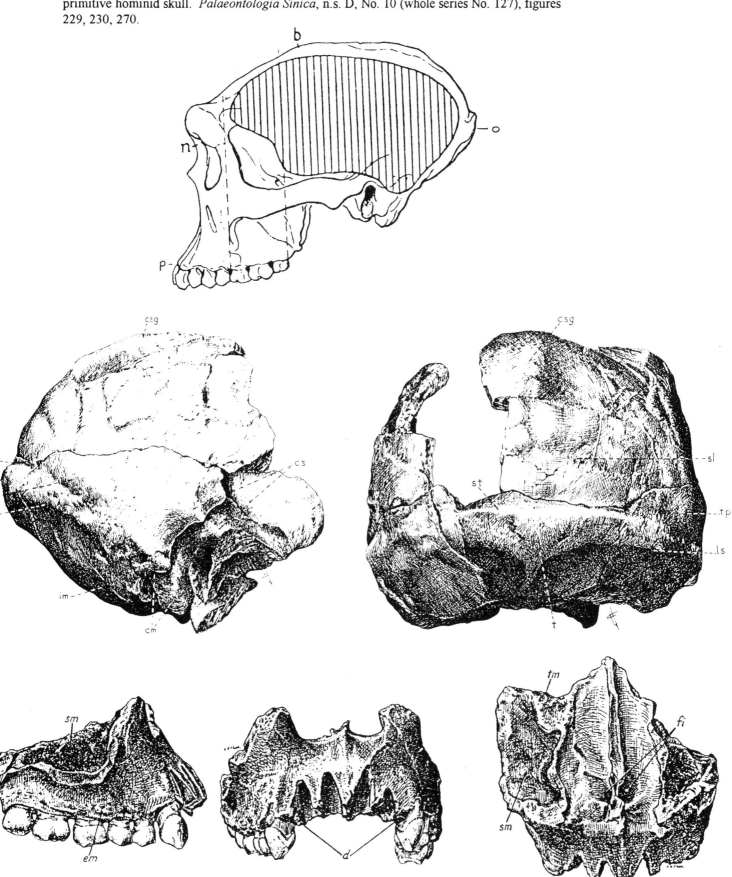

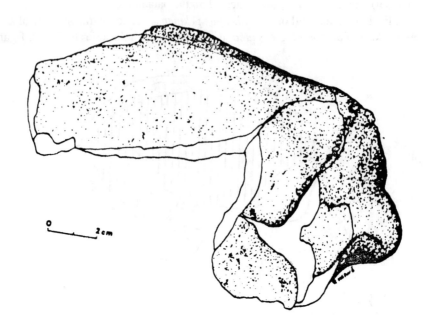

FIGURE 10.9 Sangiran 31 before reconstruction, after Sartono and Grimaud-Hervé (1983)
FROM Sartono, S., and D. Grimaud-Hervé 1983 Les pariétaux de l'hominidé Sangiran 31.
   L'Anthropologie 87:465-468, figure 1.

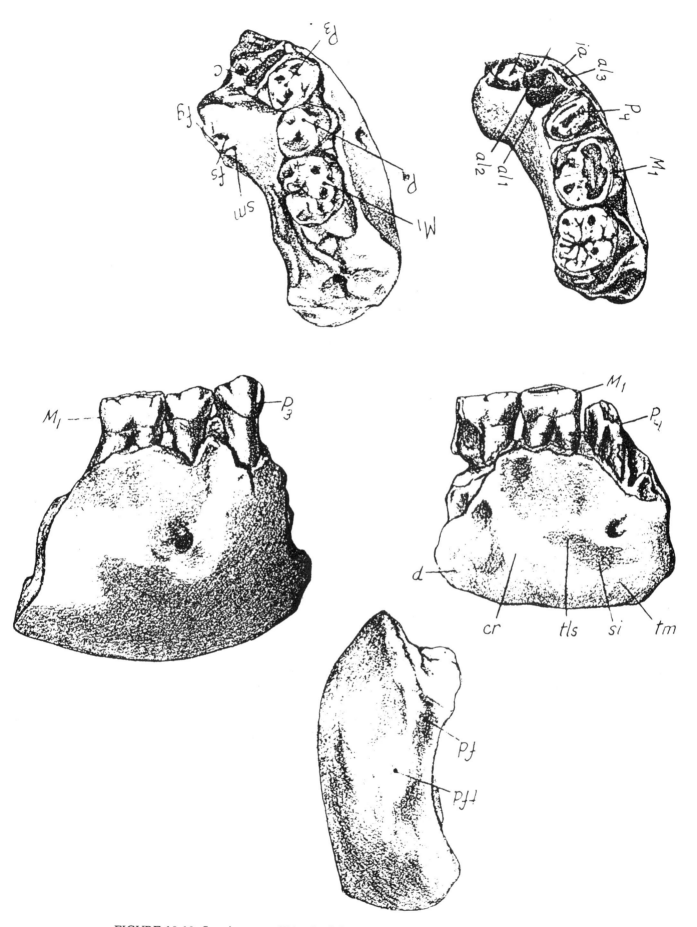

FIGURE 10.10 Sangiran mandibles 5 (right) and 6, after Weidenreich (1945). Shown re occlusal and lateral views, and the thick base of Sangiran 6.

FROM Weidenreich, F. 1945c Giant early man from Java and south China. *Anthropological Papers of the American Museum of Natural History* 40:1-134.

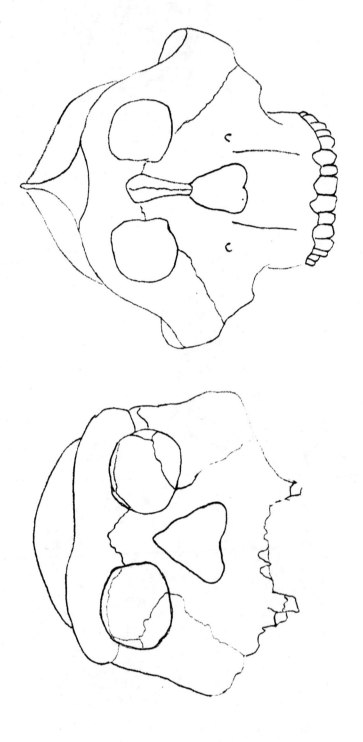

FIGURE 10.11 Sangiran 17 cranium compared with OH 5 (right), two massive faces constructed quite differently.

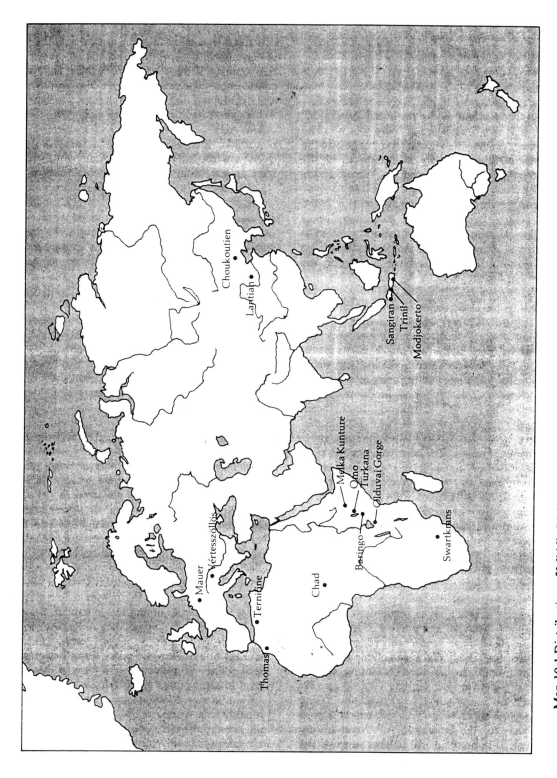

Map 10.1 Distribution of Middle Pleistocene humans.
From: First edition, Map 2

PART FOUR

THE EVOLUTION
OF MODERN PEOPLE

CHAPTER ELEVEN

Regional Evolution in the Middle Pleistocene

The division between the Early and Middle Pleistocene is generally agreed to conform to the last major reversal of the magnetic poles, resulting in the Brunhes normal polarity epoch that extends until present. Radiometrically, a date of about 780 kyr probably best marks the end of the Early Pleistocene (table 1.6). By that time, early *Homo sapiens* populations had expanded their ranges further, throughout the tropics and into semitropics of the Asia and the sometimes-islands to the southeast, and had come to inhabit habitats ranging from mountainous to arid. These populations underwent considerable further evolution in a variety of different habitats as they continued their geographic spread into temperate and eventually into cooler climates during the Middle Pleistocene, and finally came to occupy Europe in significant number. To some degree, genetic continuity, as reflected in the continued appearance of certain characteristics, appears to have been localized, at least over broad geographic areas. Yet a network of cultural and genetic communication throughout the species is indicated by the fact that similar technological and morphological changes characterize populations as much as 10,000 miles apart. Characteristics spread when they were advantageous, and one element that helped bring similar advantages across a wide geographic range was shared cultural and/or technological innovations. The evolutionary patterns are complex, and it is for good reason that G. Isaac once quipped that the Middle Pleistocene had best be regarded as "the muddle in the middle".

Because of this combination of localized continuity and species-wide changes, it is convenient to discuss the main evolutionary trends by geographic area. The discussion extends up to samples just prior to 250 kyr, a date without special climatic significance but the time just before clear evidences of modern anatomy are found throughout the human range and some authors believe "modern humans" first appeared as a distinct entity. The best sample spanning this period is from continental Asia, and for this reason it will be discussed first. The African sample spans it as well, and the European sample partially so, although human remains in significant number appear in Europe later than in the other major regions.

The discussions of the regions are followed by analysis of common trends and the behavioral and technological changes that oriented them. Reconstruction of some aspects of adaptation are suggested by the archaeological and morphological remains. The continued evolution of geographic distinctions is related to differences in adaptation allowed by an increasing adaptive sophistication.

The Sequence in China: Cranial Evolution

Beginning with Gongwangling, China not only has a very long hominid evolution sequence, but the large sample size from the Middle Pleistocene site of Zhoukoudian proved to be instrumental in developing a number of explanations about the pattern of human evolution, including the Multiregional Evolution hypothesis. There are enough specimens from the region to show:

- homogeneity at the periphery that is part of the Center and Edge model
- regional continuity in certain features linking the sample with modern Asians
- evidence of a gradual transition in the direction of modern forms, reflecting evolutionary trends that are common throughout the human range

Middle (as Early) Pleistocene human occupation sites from eastern Asia seem to reflect a climatic barrier. None are found further north than 48° and very few north of 40°, which authors such as F.C. Howell accept as "a closer approximation to the limit". At 39°, Zhoukoudian is near the northern edge of this range.

    The Zhoukoudian remains discovered before the Second World War were described and compared in a series of monographs by F. Weidenreich that remain without equal. Postwar discoveries are reviewed in the paleoanthropology volume edited by Wu Rukang and J.W. Olsen, and in papers by G. Pope that were particularly helpful in preparing this book.

Zhoukoudian (ZKT)

    The Zhoukoudian sample is a large and diverse accumulation. Specimens were discovered in excavations continuing to the present. This work has resulted in one of the largest hominid collections from a single site. Moreover, a series of papers and monographs on the prewar specimens by F. Weidenreich provides what are probably the most detailed descriptions and analyses of any fossil hominid collection. This is fortunate because all of the earlier material disappeared during World War II under circumstances that have never been clarified to anyone's satisfaction (this is discussed in books by Jia Lanpo and Huang Weiwen, and H. Shapiro).

    The Zhoukoudian site consists of a number of caves (termed localities) clustered in a range of low hills bordering the town of Zhoukoudian, located just 50 km to the southwest of Beijing. The site overlooks a broad plain, on an ecotone boundary between evergreen forest and lower, more open grasslands. Some 600-400 kyr ago, humans lived in the rock shelter portion of the large Locality 1 Cave (figure 11.1), at or near its opening. Of the more than 45 individuals recovered from the 40 m of excavated deposits in the Lower Cavern at Locality 1 (there is a Late Pleistocene/Holocene Upper Cave as well, discussed in Chapter 14), most come from levels 8-10. There are also several specimens from level 11 below, among the first to be recovered, and a few specimens with problematic dates come from the upper level 3. ZKT represents the most northern temperate extension of Middle Pleistocene *H. sapiens* before the last several hundred kyr; the climate for most of the period of occupation was not much different from today's, which is similar to that in the northern United States in seasonal extremes and temperature averages. During the span of the human occupation, the climate oscillated between colder and warmer several times. According to a review by Qi Guoquin there are two dry and cold periods represented (level 4 and 10-11), separated by a more temperate period. Level 3, holding the latest of the human remains, begins the development of a somewhat warmer climate.

Table 11.1
Numerical Dates from Zhoukoudian Locality 1

Level	Date	Basis
2[1]	420[2]	Uranium series on travertines, by Shen Guanjun and Jin Linhong
8-9[3]	418	ESR (Linear Uptake) by Huang Peihua and colleagues
10	442	Fission Track by Guo Shilun and colleagues
11[4]	578	ESR (Linear Uptake) by Huang Peihua and colleagues

[1] Cranium H3 and mandible H1 are from level 3, just below
[2] This actually means an date of >400 kyr, the maximum age of Uranium series accuracy according to H. Schwarcz
[3] Level of the Locus L material
[4] Locus E juvenile cranium level

The dates of this important hominid site (table 11.1) have long been debated. In 1991 alone, three successive issues of the IVPP Journal *Acta Anthropologica Sinica* (volume 10, numbers 2-4) published conflicting age estimates (the IVPP is the Institute for Vertebrate Paleontology and Paleoanthropology - the Chinese Academy of Sciences study group for vertebrate paleontology and paleoanthropology). Dating of the upper levels (1-3) is most problematic. Some other techniques have suggested a younger age, but these are contradicted by faunal analyses that suggest the hominids span only 100 kyr (work by J. Aigner) or 200 kyr (work by G. Pope). From the Uranium series date for level 2 to the level 11 ESR determination is a span of about 150 kyr, midway between these estimates. The dates are from different techniques and are not fully consistent with biostratigraphic, paleoecological, or sedimentological analyses reviewed by Liu. There is much more to be clarified about the age and span of this important site.

The archaeology and paleozoology of the Zhoukoudian hominids were interpreted to reflect the activities of big game hunters, bringing kills (mostly deer) back into the cave from both the forested areas and the open grasslands. Yet the deer are not the only animals in the cave. The numbers of the five main animal species found there are:

- hyena (>2000)
- thick-jawed deer (<2000)
- red deer (~1000)
- rhino (~1000)
- horse (<200)

According to M. Stiner, the association of large numbers of hyena, horse, and rhino bones is characteristic of hyena dens, and the question is how much of the faunal (and perhaps human) remains at ZKT is the consequences of hyena activity? Moreover, while humans may have occupied the cave from time to time, none of their artifacts can be clearly linked with hunting, in that they are not particularly associated with the animal remains according to a review by L. Binford and Chuankun Ho.

The evidence for at least some human occupation of the cave is found in their artifacts, the hackberry seeds that might be the remnants of intensive collecting, and the presence of fire. Cave activities suggested by artifacts include tool making (modification of wood and bone) and the preparation of vegetable foods. Upper layers (1-3) in the deposit contain dense concentrations of hackberry seeds, and these are also scattered within other layers. In addition, there are broken ostrich egg shells (which might also have served as containers) and some pointed bones and antlers with scratches that suggest their use for digging. There is evidence of fire in the cave, but whether it was used by the humans is a controversial and issue with an uncertain resolution. The cave deposits include at least four thick layers of ash. The latest of these is associated with an open-air occupation after the cave roof had collapsed. In this case, the ashes are concentrated in two spots, suggesting that the fire was confined to specific areas, but no stones surrounded it to form a hearth. In the other, deeper layers fossil human remains are found near the ash deposits. These layers also contain scorched stones and bones. However, because the ashes are spread widely across the cave floor it is unclear whether they are the remains of controlled fires in hearths (nothing like a hearth structure was reported) or perhaps the accidental burning of debris that accumulated on the floor of the cave and therefore not human-made at all. Neither human remains nor tools are especially concentrated in these ash layers, and the association of human remains, tools, and ash in this cave is too weak to be evidence that the humans either made or used fire.

Zhoukoudian Skulls

When the Zhoukoudian crania (figure 11.3) were first discovered the overwhelming majority of paleoanthropologists considered them to be quite similar to the Indonesian remains. Some 60 years later it seems clearer that the Indonesians are considerably earlier, perhaps twice the age, and comparisons with them are confused by the potential for both temporal and regional sources of variation. Nevertheless it is still evident that the Chinese specimens are closely related to the Indonesians - a relationship best expressed by the earliest Chinese cranium, from Gongwangling. The morphological features that tie these samples together include most of the basic aspects of cranial shape. Although there are differences in average cranial capacity (probably temporal in origin) and forehead shape (probably regional in origin), the Zhoukoudian and Indonesian specimens share the same long, low, thick vault morphology with the greatest cranial breadth at the base and greatest braincase breadth just above it and at the cranial rear. The cranial buttresses (browridge, nuchal torus, sagittal keel, spongy bone development over the mastoids) are equally well developed in both samples, and in both the vaults thicken and are gabled, distinctly angling between the sides and roof at the temporal lines. There are also certain anatomical similarities of the cranial base, such as the pronounced digastric sulcus and the deep and steep-faced mandibular fossae. These features suggest a similar development of the cranial strengthening system, as well as a general equivalence of brain shape.

Perhaps the most significant temporal difference is in brain size. The early Gongwangling cranium is within the Indonesian range, but the ZKT crania are generally bigger. Compared with the Kabuh-associated Indonesians (table 10.5) the ZKT males are 4% larger and the females 10% larger (there is less sexual dimorphism in brain size). The ZKT specimens are fully within the functionally normal range of modern human brain sizes. This is the earliest human sample for which this can be said.

Regional variation may be best expressed in the forehead and other facial distinctions (see table 11.2), although sexual dimorphism must also be taken into account since the reconstructed ZKT face is female and the best-preserved Sangiran face is male. There are a number of morphological features which, although differing in expression, characterize the sample of 6 fairly complete and several other more fragmentary crania from the Locality 1 Lower Cave. These, of course, are not absolute, nor are they universal. For instance Sangiran IX has a Zhoukoudian-like forehead profile with a distinct sulcus at the base of the forehead, and the frontal profile of the ZKT H3 vault is somewhat flatter than the others.

Table 11.2
General Differences between Kabuh Indonesian and Zhoukoudian Chinese Crania

	Usual Indonesian	**Usual Zhoukoudian**
Face	Prognathic	Orthognathic
Nasal profile	More projecting	Less, flat upper nasal bones
Cheek orientation	Lateral, anteroinferior	Flat, posteroinferior
Zygomatic process of maxilla	Base low	Base high
	Shelved (straight) lower margin	Maxillary notch
Supraorbital form over orbits	Horizontal bar	Arches over each orbit
Forehead shape	Flat	Rounded due to frontal boss
	No sulcus	Sulcus behind supraorbital
Frontal sinus	Expanded	Small or absent
Sagittal keel	Low and broad based	Tall and narrow based
Extrasutural bones within lambdoidal suture	absent	present at lambda (the meeting of lambdoidal and sagittal sutures)
Nuchal torus	More projecting, sulcus above	Less projecting, little or no sulcus
Occipital form seen from above	Broad and rounded	Narrower and elongated

The low vault and large nuchal torus of the ZKT folk result in a very angled occiput, like the Indonesian remains. In contrast to them, however, there is a distinct frontal boss. This feature creates a higher forehead and accentuates the sulcus between it and the top of the supraorbital torus. Another aspect of the expanding frontal is the increase in its breadth, especially just behind the orbits which reduces the postorbital constriction. Other contrasts include the less well developed cranial buttresses. For instance, thickness of the nuchal torus is only 70% the Kabuh value (torus heights are much more alike). Cranial thickness however are quite similar to the Indonesians.

The distinct system of cranial buttresses found in all the ZKT crania includes:

- basal spongy bone extending in front of the nuchal torus,
- a sagittal keel extending over both the frontal and between the parietals,
- a thickening along the parietal sides where they angle from more vertically oriented (cranial wells) to more horizontal (cranial roof),
- a continuous supraorbital torus
- a continuous nuchal torus

Weidenreich regarded these as forming a cranial strengthening system, seemingly enclosing the cranial vault with a system of supports. These reinforcements clearly cannot be related to strains caused by mastication since the much larger jawed australopithecines have very thin vault walls and none of these buttresses. An alternative source of strain may be related to activities that result in the great number of healed cranial injuries on these specimens (in contrast cranial injuries are virtually unknown in the australopithecine sample). Some of these are quite spectacular, yet the surrounding bone shows the knitting process that reflects healing. This demonstrates that the fractures were not postmortem. Is it possible that violence was so ubiquitous that it became a significant source of selection on human cranial vault anatomy? Several authors, beginning early in the century and most recently P. Brown have related cranial thickness to consistent acts of interpersonal violence, which would provide this unique human activity one of the longest antiquities. This certainly would indicate a considerable time depth to the violence sometimes thought to be the invention of Urban America, but before drawing conclusions from this vision of the short and nasty lives of our Paleolithic predecessors, let us not forget that the activities at Zhoukoudian pale before the behaviors humanity has unleashed upon itself just this century in Cambodia, in Soviet Russia of the 1930's, and in Nazi dominated Europe.

At first glance, the ZKT cranial sample appears surprisingly homogeneous - this is after all one of the samples that suggested the Center and Edge hypothesis discussed in Chapter 10. However, in spite of their similarities, the ZKT crania should not be thought of as a uniform sample. There is considerable variation at the site, as there is at all human fossil sites where there are more than a very few specimens. What confuses the assessment of the causes of variation at the site are the significant contributions of

1. sexual dimorphism
2. diachronic trends
3. allometry

Cranial variation partially reflects sexual dimorphism. The magnitude of dimorphism, however, is not really great; for instance, the 12% difference in size between male and female crania is less than most earlier samples. This decreased magnitude may explain why other sources of variatrion predominate, but I believe that if there were more associated faces, the pattern of sexual dimorphism would be more easily understood, and appear more distinct. This is because sex differences are more evident in faces than in crania, Further exacerbating the comparisons, in describing the sample Weidenreich noted that if the expression of muscle markings are used to suggest sexes for the crania, there are both large and small males and large and small females. He concluded that sexual dimorphism alone could not account for all the size variation and instead suggested the presence of a small and a large "type."

Table 11.3

Comparisons of ZKT Males at Different Levels

Level	Adult male crania	Mean Capacity	Lateral frontal thickness	Anterior parietal thickness	Posterior parietal thickness
3	H3	1140	8.5	6.4	6.5
7-8	I2, J4, L1, L3	1128	8.2	8.0	8.0
11	E1	915	9.0	10.5	9.0

Some of this variation is a consequence of the temporal spread at the site (table 11.3), for instance the E1 juvenile with a small, thick vault is distinctly earlier than the others, while H3 with a large thinner vault is later (both are male). When he originally studied the sample F. Weidenreich argued that there was no systematic difference between specimens from the top to the bottom of the cave, but in a more recent discussion Zhang Yinyun and others have claimed that systematic changes can be seen. The ZKT crania vary greatly in length and breadth, and cranial capacities range from an estimated 850 cc to 1,225 cc. A simple comparison of cranial capacity to the date reveals that brain size expands significantly over the 150 kyr that are sampled. In contrast cranial bone thickness and the development of some of the cranial buttresses such as the supraorbital torus, nuchal torus, and the sagittal keel all decrease over this period. This shows that these robust features are not a simple consequence of allometric size expansion alone, as some of the smallest expressions are in some of the largest specimens. Of the three potential causes of variation, only allometry can be eliminated as making a significant contribution.

Faces

Only 6 facial fragments were recovered from Zhoukoudian, although at the time of their discovery the three Locus L crania were associated with a large number of very fragmented facial bones. All of the crania Weidenreich examined were broken open at the base, and the faces were detached. Many of the facial remains were lost, which is why so few faces are known for the specimens. The question is whether this was the result of natural taphonomic process, perhaps the consequences of being buried in a cave, or whether humans treated human remains in special ways. Weidenreich thought that cannibalism may have played a significant role. One way to examine this question is to compare the proportion of facial remains in Middle Pleistocene humans with those of australopithecines, contrasting caves and open air sites. If cave preservation is the cause, the proportion of facial bones in the caves will be similar. If behavior is the cause, the proportions will differ between the australopithecines and the Middle Pleistocene humans. Table 11.4 shows this comparison. It reveals that in the australopithecines many facial bones are preserved relative to the number of frontal bones without faces. Unassociated facial bones are as much as twice as common as facial bones adhering to frontals. In contrast, the *Homo* sites show a small number of facial remains relative to the frontal bones without faces, and facial bones adhering to frontals are twice (or more) as common as isolated facial bones. While these results might reflect the consequences of a third unknown factor such as different predator or scavenging species at earlier and later times in Africa and Asia, the most likely explanation is that the difference is a matter of taxon and not taphonomy - human behavior is by far the more important cause of the differing bone proportions. It is quite likely that the humans were the agents who detached the faces and opened the cranial bases of the Zhoukoudian and Sangiran specimens.

Table 11.4
Facial Bone Preservation[1]

Australopithecus Sites	*Homo* sites	Cave	Frontal only (%)	Face only (%)	Frontal and face (%)
Sterkfontein		X	9	61	30
Swartkrans		X	4	57	39
	Zhoukoudian	X	70	10	20
	Sangiran		67	10	23

[1] percentage of specimens preserved with a frontal, face, or both

In one specimen, the L2 female, Weidenreich attempted to reconstruct the face using an associated maxillary fragment and some other pieces. C. Coon reconstructed a male, the L3 specimen, based on casts and left this at the Harvard Peabody Museum (he never published the reconstruction and it is not well known). Now that other Middle Pleistocene faces are known, it is apparent that these reconstructions were quite insightful. The reconstructed face of the female cranium combines a high cheek region and large orbits with a very reduced tooth-bearing portion of the maxilla. The nasal bones are broad and moderately curved, and (as in the later-discovered faces) the nose opening is broad. However, contrasting with Indonesian specimens, the lower face is not especially prognathic except just at the level of the alveolar margin, in the area holding large incisor roots with their vertically oriented crowns. The base of the small zygomatic is rather high above the palate, and there is a very distinct angle between the cheek and the external palate wall which establishes a notched lower contour of the cheek This feature, called the **malar notch** by G. Pope (also, alternatively, the **malar incisure** and **maxillary notch**), is characteristic of some Late Pleistocene and virtually all recent and living humans. In these latter characteristics, the maxilla used in the L2 reconstruction resembles two additional partial maxillas from the site.

The face Weidenreich reconstructed was the first known for these earlier Middle Pleistocene humans, and for much of the century came to characterize what was then regarded as *H. erectus*. However, we now recognize that the specimen is very late in the *H. sapiens* lineage, which began some 2 myr ago, and moreover is a female. Its gracility and small size have been misleading. Comparison of the L2 reconstruction with the earlier male face from Sangiran and the much earlier East African specimens provides a number of significant contrasts. On the average, other faces from the Middle Pleistocene have proven to be larger and more robust.

This face has played one other role in the understanding of human evolution. In his study of Neandertal faces (Chapter 13) Y. Rak used an archetype model to understand facial evolution, suggesting that various human facial variants evolved from a "generalized (i.e. unmodified) face" and came to be modified away from it in various ways. By "generalized face" Rak meant the facial morphology "shared ... by many primates, including modern humans and fossil species of the genus *Homo*", and he used the L2 reconstruction to exemplify it. Apart from all of the problems inherent in the archetype principle (these are discussed at some length in a historical context by A. Desmond), the fact is that other Middle and Early Pleistocene faces do not conform to this "generalized" morphology. For instance, in Rak's generalized face archetype the cheek regions below the orbits are transversely flattened, forward facing, with a surface that slopes slightly backwards from the orbit rim down (this is important in his thinking because Neandertal faces differ as much as one could imagine, a divergence from the archetype which Rak believes indicates a species difference). However, the male Sangiran 17 face has cheeks that slope down but markedly *forwards*, below the orbit rim. If one thought there *was* such a thing as a single "generalized" facial pattern for *Homo*, the Indonesian specimen is much more complete than any from Zhoukoudian and would be at least as good a candidate for identifying the "generalized" morphology. Further, if we were to use earlier dated specimens to establish what is "generalized", among the pre-dispersal faces ER 3733 resembles the ZKT reconstruction, but the cheeks of ER 3883 have an anterior-inferior orientation similar to Sangiran 17 and instead of being flat across from side to side they begin to angle backwards in a more medial position than any of the Asian faces discussed above. As is so often the case variation is the rule and no single pattern of plesiomorphic (or "generalized") facial anatomy can be identified within earlier *H. sapiens*.

Dental Remains

Considered in its entirety, there are four important aspects of the Zhoukoudian sample of over 150 teeth:

1. the regional differences in tooth size
2. the significance of anterior dental variation
3. the reflection of sex differences
4. the dental reduction seen in the Chinese sequence *and even within the Zhoukoudian sample*.

First, in their analysis of the Nariokotome youth (Chapter 9), B. Brown and A. Walker showed that except for the incisors there is very little difference between the dental remains from the Early Pleistocene African sample and the Zhoukoudian one. In isolation this would seem to suggest stasis in tooth size evolution (although see the discussion of anterior teeth, below), but in fact the picture is more complex. The dental sample from Indonesia is quite different from both of these samples in that the postcanine teeth are considerably larger - about midway between the *A. africanus* and ZKT averages. However, these differences cannot be interpreted as an evolutionary trend. While there is a significant average difference between the ZKT sample and the earlier Indonesian Putcangan hominids, the ranges of variation for individuals in each sample overlap. Moreover, throughout the Pleistocene the dentitions in the south of Asia were always larger than they were to the north. This difference has been exacerbated over time as the Australasian postcanine teeth have changed little (until the Holocene), while dental reduction in the north proceeded apace, even within the ZKT sample itself (see below).

The second developments are in the anterior dentition. These involve changes in incisor size, and the evidence these teeth provide about regional evolution. The ZKT incisors, like the earlier incisors from Indonesia and the Yuanmou teeth, are smaller than their early Pleistocene African counterparts. The difference is much greater in the maxillary first and mandibular second incisors. This is really the only significant difference between the dental samples. There is a change in the direction of evolution, however, as incisors differentially expand within the ZKT time range of the sample (see below), even as the postcanine teeth decrease in size.

The anterior teeth have also proven to be important in considerations of regional continuity. Particular attention is focused on the dental anatomy of the labial (inner) sides of the upper incisors, where ridges along the margins give the tooth surface the appearance of a coal shovel (the genesis of the term "shovel-shaped"). The feature can be found in all human populations but according to a review by J. Cadien it is highest in frequency in its most marked expression among Asians, especially those from the north. Weidenreich noted that this was also true in the past, and the observation has held long after his death as every fossil incisor from Asia is shovel shaped. However, some scientists have argued that this anatomy does not show a special link between ancient and modern Asians because several past human populations also commonly have shovel shaped incisors. Others contend shoveling is a plesiomorphic because it is found in the earliest *H. sapiens* specimens and therefore cannot be used to validly link populations. To resolve the issue, T. Crummett undertook a detailed analysis of the shovel shape form. She found that three independent anatomies on the labial surface define or contribute to the shovel:

1.   The development of elevated **marginal ridges** along the inner edges of the tooth.
2.   The expression of a **tubercle** (a bump or bulge of enamel) at the base of the tooth, also on its inner surface
3.   The shape of the surface of the tooth between the ridges, called **labial convexity**, in which a tooth may be anywhere from very straight mesial-distally, to extremely convex or curved.

Crummett showed that the ZKT upper incisors are morphologically similar to recent north Chinese, in their combination of pronounced marginal ridging and straight labial faces. They differ from the earlier teeth from further to the south in their more prominent marginal ridges (a difference also distinguishing northern and southern Asians today), and from the other fossil sample that commonly have shoveled incisors, European Neandertals, because of the dramatic labial convexity and strongly developed tubercles in these Europeans. If the early Pleistocene Africans define the ancestral condition, these Asians differ in their straighter crowns (they lack labial convexity) and more prominently developed marginal ridges.

In his discussion of the ZKT dental sample, F. Weidenreich argued that the size of most of the teeth clearly fits the interpretation of a large and a small form that corresponds to a distinct sex difference. Morphological variations between male and female dentitions, however, are mainly restricted to the canines. If his attributions are correct, the magnitude of sexual dimorphism in the ZKT dental sample is little different from that in most australopithecine dental samples. This similarity contrasts with the comparatively reduced dimorphism in the ZKT crania. The disparity could be a consequence of Weidenreich's use of size alone in dividing the postcanine teeth into female and male sets. However, it fits a overall pattern that seems ubiquitous through the Pleistocene. Within a range of variation not unlike that of living populations, body size dimorphism and many skeletal features that reflect it such as dental dimorphism do not significantly change, while the anatomical and metric dimorphism of cranial features continue to decrease significantly. As noted above, the assessment of dimorphism in the sample is undoubtedly influenced by the scarcity of facial remains. The potential for marked facial dimorphism is more evident in the mandibular sample, discussed below.

The ZKT teeth seem smaller than earlier samples from China (see Chapter 10). Moreover, within the ZKT postcanine teeth there is dental reduction, marked enough to be evident even over the 150 kyr time span represented by the human remains. Zhang Yinyun focused on the mandibular teeth as they are much better represented. He divided the dental sample into an earlier and later half, and small as the sample sizes are, each tooth from the canine on back showed reduction. Within each tooth group the later erupting teeth reduced the most, paralleling the pattern of dental reduction for Middle Pleistocene hominids as a whole. The incisors, in contrast, increased in size - the lateral tooth more so than the central one. Because the incisor sample is so small, this confuses the significance of the total pattern of incisor size changes. Decreasing size from the Early Pleistocene Africans to Zhoukoudian, and then the increase within the ZKT sample may just reflect sampling variation of teeth that are not significantly different.

ZKT Mandibles

There is a fairly large mandibular sample from ZKT, including materials discovered after World War II. These mandibles show a considerable amount of variation, more in fact than the crania. Weidenreich also considered this variation to be the result of sexual dimorphism, The two most complete mandibles, labeled Hl and Gl, have been interpreted as female and male. If this attribution is correct, it is interesting that the female mandible is too small to fit any of the complete crania, while the male mandible is too large! H1 comes from level 3, near the top of the lower cave, and A. Mann notes some anatomical differences with the other mandibles that may reflect this. However size is not one of them as several other mandibles are even smaller than H1. The existence of earlier small specimens shows that evolutionary change cannot account for the magnitude of ZKT mandibular differences.

The ZKT mandibles in general are characterized by large size and robustness, although both of these features are quite variable. The symphysis is broad and deep and well angled, although with no trace of a chin. Part of its size seems to be the result of the elongated anterior tooth roots. The vertical ramus is high, even in the smaller specimens, but not particularly broad. It begins at a position within the posterior tooth row, as in the Indonesian and African erectus mandibles. Locus B, findspot of some 25% of all material from the cave, is from level 4, very high in the sequence. It includes a series of juvenile mandibles whose eruption pattern (sequence and timing) shows the ZKT hominids to be fully within the human range. In this sample are several unworn or lightly worn P_3's. Their shape and the dominance of the buccal (outer) cusp is one of the main reasons why Weidenreich regarded the Zhoukoudian folk as very primitive. He considered them to be more ape-like than the small sample of South African australopithecines that had been found at that time because the australopithecine P_3's had equal sized cusps and other features than made them much less ape-like. Because australopithecine cranial and mandibular features were not very much like humans, he accepted only the later but more primitive ZKT specimens as true human ancestors.

Zhoukoudian Limbs

A number of postcranial remains are known from ZKT. The ZKT postcrania from the original excavations include seven femur fragments, two humerus fragments, a clavicle shaft, and a hand bone. Later excavations have recovered additional humerus and tibia shafts.

Basically, the limbs are characterized by adaptations that lend great strength to the bone. An example of these adaptations can be seen in the femurs, which show three modifications to increase bone strength and its ability to withstand compressive and bending forces: relative shaft thickness, anterior-posterior fattening of the shaft, and thick cortical bone of the shaft walls. These remains are very similar to some of the African specimens such as OH 28.

C. Ruff used a variety of techniques to estimate the body weight of the ZKT individuals represented by femurs. Specimen IV (M4) is the best preserved for this, and he suggests a weight of 56-58 kg for it. In fact all of these bones are of similar size and Ruff's total estimated range for the ZKT sample is 56-60 kg. Weidenreich estimated a length of about 41 cm for the M4 femur, probably a minimum according to Ruff and colleagues. At this length, and given the similar sizes of many of the Zhoukoudian limbs, the ZKT sample would seem to be substantially shorter than the earlier African one. The estimated difference in height is much greater than the estimated weight difference, reflecting the likelihood that the Zhoukoudian folk were adapted to the markedly cooler environment with stockier trunk shapes (and therefore greater weight at a given height).

Relations to the Earlier Specimens

Compared with the Gongwangling female cranium, Wu Rukang and Dong Xingren indicate several ways in which the ZKT samples differs - excepting vault size these are comparisons that are even more pronounced if they are restricted to only ZKT females. Generally the Zhoukoudian crania have

- larger cranial capacities (the ZKT female mean of 965 cc is much larger than the Gongwangling estimate
- less postorbital constriction
- thinner and less prominent supraorbital tori that do not extend as far to the sides
- larger frontal bossing and therefore a deeper supratoral sulcus
- thinner vault bones

There are few remains clearly dated to between this cranium and the other very earlier specimens discussed in Chapter 10, and the earliest individuals from the Zhoukoudian cave. The most complete of these is the 650 kyr mandible from Chenjiayao, near the village of Lantian. It is generally similar to the ZKT mandibles, and is the size (and anatomy) of a larger female. One interesting distinction is the congenital absence of the third molars. This is the earliest known case of missing third molars in *Homo*, a probable consequence of posterior tooth size reduction (the last erupting tooth of each type reduces most rapidly) that appears first in Asia because the orthognathic faces limit palate length. The environment, according to Qi Guoqin, was a cool-temperate one with open grasslands, making Chenjiayao the earliest of the temperate-adapted Asians.

LATER SPECIMENS FROM CHINA

ZKT Locality H and the Overlap of Archaic and Modern Morphologies

Several authors have suggested that towards the end of the Middle Pleistocene archaic and more modern morphologies overlapped in the Chinese fossil record. As is so often the case in paleoanthropology, a difference in species is suggested to some. The argument is based on specimens that seem to be the latest surviving examples of the archaic morphology. Others, like Wu Xinzhi, regard their variation as normal, a reflection of mosaic evolution, and show that evolution is not only mosaic at that time but continues to be mosaic through the later sample of Chinese hominids. A third possibility is that the dating that seems to show overlap is mistaken.

The level 3 cranium (H3) and mandible (H1) are important in this dispute. The mandible is one of the smaller in the sample, and the cranium is one of the larger in size, and certain structures differ from the earlier specimens. Part of the rear of the cranium was known to Weidenreich and the frontal and other connecting portions were discovered during the renewed excavations of the 1960's. According to Zhang Yinyun, writing with Qiu Zhonglang and colleagues who reconstructed and described the specimen, the more progressive features of H3 include:

- thinner supraorbital torus
- broad frontal bone
- thinner cranial bones
- higher and rounder upper border of the temporal squama
- decreased distance between internal inion (endinion) and external inion
- reduced nuchal torus projection
- broad occiput

Several of these features individually fall within the ZKT range, and indeed the fundamental similarities are with the other ZKT crania. Even still, taken as average changes and trends the evolutionary direction is toward modernity.

Level 3 was originally dated by Uranium series on fossil bone to approximately 230 kyr. The similarity of cranium H3 to the earlier ZKT specimens led to the suggestion that there was 200 kyr or more of stasis in regional morphology. Further confusing the situation there are other crania said to be of similar age, based in part on faunal links to the uppermost part of the ZKT lower cave sequence, but also because of numerical age estimates. The crania are from Tangshan and Hexian (discussed below), sites much further to the south. The age of Hexian was analyzed by Xu and You, who showed the site to be most similar to ZKT levels 3-4 (15 shared species) and 5 (13 shared species). A more direct dating of 270-150 kyr was based on Uranium series taken on teeth and bones and there are several confirming TL dates, although the chert used for these may not have been heated enough for these to be accurate. Faunal similarities were used to link Tangshan to the same approximate age.

However, faunal comparisons between north and south China have been traditionally problematic. Moreover, Uranium series cannot be accurately applied to bones and teeth. As noted above Shen Gaunjun and Jin Linhoing obtained stalagmite from above the H3 cranium position (this was easy to identify as part of the cranium was excavated by scientists from the IVPP after the second world war and loss of the ZKT fossils). They were able to show that the findspot in the cave, and therefore specimen, is much older, about 421 kyr (the probable range was 370-530 kyr, but the conservative interpretation is >400 kyr). The same Uranium series date and faunal evaluation problems plague the comparisons with Hexian and Tangshan specimens (see below). In fact as a group, although the three crania show considerable variation, they may be linked by faunal age assessment and archaic anatomy, and appear to be earlier than the more modern populations of the later Middle Pleistocene. Notable variability at this time is also evident in African and European samples.

Hexian and Tangshan: the other Archaic Specimens, from Subtropical China

Portions of several individuals were recovered from Longtandong (Dragon Pool) Cave, in Anhui Province near Hexian. There are several undescribed partial crania, and:

> PA 830: a baseless calvarium,
> PA 840: a frontal fragment with part of a supraorbital torus,
> PA 841: a parietal

There are also several mandibles and a number of isolated teeth. This is a subtropical site and apparently a place of occupation as faunal remains, especially deer, show cutmarks suggesting butchering. The Hexian hominid vault has a mixture of Zhoukoudian-like and Sangiran-like features that, if confirmed in other specimens, could reflect genic exchange along the eastern periphery.

The Hexian vault resembles the ZKT hominids in size (its cranial capacity of 1025 cc) and anatomical particulars including its forehead profile, rounding of the superior orbital border, an (albeit lower) sagittal keel extending from the frontal boss to the top of the head, and a deep and narrow mandibular fossa. Hexian is a broad vault with a markedly expanded frontal bone, especially in its breadth where expansion is expressed in its minimal postorbital constriction. It is most like the H3 cranium in many details, including

- flatter frontal bone and shallower supratoral sulcus,
- broad frontal bone, especially across the temporal fossae
- high arch of the temporal squama's upper edge,
- decreased distance between the internal and external inion.

At the same time, however, it also resembles some of the Indonesian remains. Like a few of the Indonesians Hexian has a weakly expressed supratoral sulcus behind the thick supraorbital torus of the frontal (unlike every ZKT cranium it lacks a district angle between the top of the supraorbitals and the forward face of the forehead). In contrast with the frontal there is a moderately incised supratoral sulcus on the occiput along with basal spongy bone and a marked angle between the sides and top of the parietals as seen from the rear. The nuchal part of the occiput is longer than the occipital squama above. It is quite different from the ZKT sample in the contour of the cranial rear, the distinct bulge at the center of the occiput, and the restriction of the nuchal torus to the protruding portion. The mixture of Zhoukoudian and Indonesian-like features accounts for why some Chinese scholars such as Dong Xingren describe it as ZKT-like and others like Haung Wanbo and colleagues liken it to later Indonesians such as the Ngandong sample.

A second cranium (PA 840/841) is comprised of supraorbital and parietal fragments of a more gracile individual. The torus is centrally thick, although diminishing laterally, and the supratoral sulcus is weakly developed as in the more complete cranium.

The dental remains and jaws from Hexian are quite large. Molar size is in the very upper portion of the ZKT size range. In fact, most of the Pleistocene postcanine teeth from South China are larger than those of similar age to the north (following the north-south gradient noted above). One of these teeth, an upper central incisors is said to be larger than any from ZKT, but it is actually a misclassified orangutan tooth. Matching the dental megadonty, the larger of the mandibles exceeds the ZKT range in corpus dimensions

The Tangshan skull, from the Huludong Cave in Tangshan hill, 26 km from Nanjing, is of similar age according to the analysis of associated fauna. With open cranial sutures the specimen may be an adolescent, and its moderately expressed supraorbital and nuchal tori could reflect age at death (they may also indicate that Tangshan is female). The supraorbitals are evenly thickened and horizontal (not especially arched over the orbits), extending smoothly over the center of the face and separated from the receding forehead by a deep sulcus. The occiput is not complete, but enough is present to show that the upper and lower parts of the bone are about equal in size. Cheeks, and the orbital profiles above them, are flat and forward-facing.

These specimens suggest there may have been a gradient in morphology running from the north to the south of East Asia. One place where such a gradient may be reflected is in the appearance of features that could be considered archaic in the East Asian context, but are continuously present and act as markers of regionality in Australasia. This possibility further confuses the interpretation of variation.

Crania from Yunxian

Hubei and Henan Provinces in central China have a number of hominid remains associated with fauna that mixes north and south Chinese elements. Beginning with the teeth from Badong and Jianshi Districts in Hubei described in Chapter 10, this region seems to be a focal point for megadont specimens. A large P_4 of Zhoukoudian age was found at the base of Xinghua Hill, Nanzho County, Henan. Just to the west seven teeth were recovered from the Bailongdong Cave, Hubei Province, and a scattered sample of teeth, as large or larger than those from Hexian, were reported from Longudong Cave from the Yunxian region, Hubei by Wu Rukang and Dong Xingren. "Longudong" is a common name for a cave site, as it means "Dragon Bone" and virtually any fossil findspot can have this name. Two crania subsequently found at Yunxian are the most complete of the archaic Chinese hominids.

The two crania are crushed and badly distorted. Yet both have faces and preserve more features together than any of the specimens described above. The less-well preserved specimen, EV 9001, has a prominent, well developed supraorbital torus (especially laterally). The face is relatively large, especially broad, and the nasal aperture is extremely wide. To its sides the maxillary bone is puffy and has a swollen appearance. There is a distinct malar notch bordered by a malar tubercle (this is a widely-spread modern human feature that first appears in East Asia, according to G. Pope). EV 9002 is a larger, more complete specimen with flatter and vertical face. It resembles the EV 9001 face in many details, including diagnostically important ones such as transverse facial flattening, horizontal lower cheek border, and c canine fossa. Like Weidenreich's ZKT L2 reconstruction, there is marked prognathism of the face below the nose. Part of the frontal squama is uncrushed, and a frontal boss is evident, contributing to the broad, shallow supratoral sulcus. Below it the supraorbitals arch over the orbits, and like Hexian the frontal is broad. The cranium also resembles Hexian in its shape as seen from above, emphasizing its expanded postorbital breadth and marked cranial breadth. At the root of the nose the nasal bones are flat and unprojecting, but below they angle outward and the nose was clearly more prominent than in many Pleistocene Chinese. The face is more massive than EV 9001 (in fact, more massive than any other Pleistocene Chinese fossil) but otherwise closely resembles that of EV 9001 except for the peg-shaped, reduced 3rd molar.

These specimens also seem to reflect the consequences of a geographic gradient, mixing characters of north and south Asian origin. Their uncertain age, mid-Middle Pleistocene on the basis of some associated fauna but terminal Middle Pleistocene on the basis of other associated species, makes attribution of the sources of variation difficult.

For instance, one or both specimens combine north Asian Middle Pleistocene features

- transverse middle and upper facial flattening,
- orthognathic profile (vertical facial orientation),
- high frontal inclination,
- canine fossa,
- pegged (small, single-cusped) M^3,
- high zygomatic process root with a malar notch

with south Asian characters such as

- general postcanine megadonty,
- a shallow and short mandibular fossa (particularly resembling Ngandong),
- moderate I^1 shoveling (according to T. Curmmett this is generally prevalent in South China)
- a shallow sulcus behind the browridges

Certain features are archaic, including a fairly marked occipital angle and a nuchal plane that is much larger than the occipital plane. Yet, the crania have very large vault sizes, large mastoid processes, and share an absence of either an angular torus or sagittal keel. These features are more progressive than those of any specimen mentioned above, leading scholars such as Wu Xinzhi to attribute a later age estimate to them. In their preliminary description Li Tianyuan and D. Etler conclude (p. 407):

> The new evidence of fossil hominid variability in east Asia afforded by the Yunxian crania indicates that Middle Pleistocene hominids were highly polytypic and regionally differentiated, perhaps even at the demic level. But the differential distribution of character states associated with *H. sapiens* in regionally disparate Middle Pleistocene human populations suggests that the events leading to the emergence of modern humans were not restricted to one area of the world alone.

The new evidence suggests one other thing. Before the crania were discovered the large teeth of this region seemed to be attributable to an early date, and were used to emphasize the course of dental reduction in China. Since then the dates have not become much better, but even in the unlikely event that the crania turn out to be as old as the Zhoukoudian remains it is evident that the megadontia is a regional feature in the Middle Pleistocene. Once again features that change over time and features that distinguish regions are confused.

Yiyuan

Numerous cranial fragments representing at least two individuals, portions of a femur and humerus, and seven teeth were found in a fissure opening into Qizi hill, in Shandong province which is in the southern part of northeast China. Once again the age of the site is only poorly resolved as the later part of the Middle Pleistocene. Lü Zun'e and colleagues suggest a number of affinities to the ZKT remains, in particular the continuously developed supraorbital torus (albeit thinner than most), bordered by a deep supratoral sulcus on the frontal bone (fragments of two different individuals show this), marked postorbital constriction, and the absence of significant frontal sinus development. The supraorbitals of the two individuals, however, resemble Ngandong in being thickest laterally and less well developed over the nose. The cranial bones are thick, and the pattern of thickness involving the bone of the outer cortex more than the internal spongy bone is an archaic feature. However some of the thickness measurements on the fragments are below the ZKT minimum. The maxillary teeth (5 of the 7) are unusually broad.

China and Regional Continuity

The Chinese fossil record has played a fundamental role in the development of ideas about regional continuity, and ultimately the Multiregional Evolution model that explained it. Weidenreich was the first to write about the continuity of anatomical features through Pleistocene human evolution in China. He took this to show that there was an evolutionary relationship between the ancient and modern inhabitants of Chin, *although he did not think that the Zhoukoudian folk were either **uniquely** or **solely** ancestral to living Chinese.* For instance, in the concluding section of his Zhoukoudian cranial monograph he wrote "there are clear evidences that *Sinanthropus* is a direct ancestor of *H. sapiens* with closer relations to certain Mongolian groups than to any other races".

He was subsequently misinterpreted and even misquoted on this point. C. Coon, in his hypothesis of parallel evolution of long lasting human races with different rates of evolutionary change, dedicates *The Origin of Races* to Weidenreich. W. Howells has been attributing a "Candelabra School" to Weidenreich in popular books since 1944 with *Mankind so Far,* and spanning a half century. According to this theory (which Howells quite correctly holds to be improbable), the races evolved out of contact and independently of each other. Yet nothing could be further from correctly describing Weidenreich's thinking. Weidenreich held races to be transient, not long-lasting, writing in his 1946 essay *The Human Races*

> So the problem of the origin of races arises. It is evident from the beginning that any search for stable archetypes, whether of Negroes, Mongolians, or any of the white racial groups, will be condemned to failure. All available facts indicate that crossing is not a late human acquisition which took place only when man reached his modern phase, but must have been practiced ever since man began to evolve. ... Only in the last phase [of human evolution] the modeling influences of environment and selection ... developed the racial differentiations as they appear today".

While certain lines of descent were reflected in the regional continuity of features, he was quite explicit in asserting that they did not reflect unique, isolated, or independent lineages, let alone long lasting races. Thus in discussing the Australasian fossil record,

> At least one line leads from *Pithecanthropus* and *Homo soloensis* to the Australian Aborigines of today. This does not mean, of course, that I believe all the Australians of today can be traced back to *Pithecanthropus* or that they are the sole descendant of the *Pithecanthropus -Homo soloensis* line.

The assertion of regional continuity has gained considerable ground in the face of an exploding fossil record. For instance, Wu Xinzhi, in examining the pattern of Middle Pleistocene evolution in China as it was known a half century later, divided features into more common, unique Asian ones and traits that progressively (but not at all evenly) changed through time. He gives the following as the main features showing regional continuity:

- anterior position and forward facing of the cheeks
- maxillary notch
- flat nasal profile with a low internasal keel and a weakly curved suture at the top of the nose (fronto-nasal/maxillary)
- sagittal keel that is narrow at its base and relatively tall
- extrasutural bones around lambda
- shovel shaping (Crummett describes the unique Asian pattern as combining straight crown shape and moderate to strongly developed marginal ridges)

Perhaps what is most important about the Early and Middle Pleistocene Chinese sequence is the fact that this peripheral region does show such distinct evidence of continuity in some anatomical features, while at the same time trends that are worldwide such as increased cranial capacity and decreasing cranial robustness characterize the sample, and certain modern characteristics that ultimately attain a worldwide distribution, from relative broadening of the crania vault to the maxillary notch, appear there first.

REMAINS FROM LAOS

The Tam Hang Cave in Northern Laos was the site of several pre-Second World War discoveries . Two molars and a temporal are associated with Early Pleistocene fauna, and slightly higher a child's cranial rear comes from a Middle Pleistocene level, according to J. Fromaget. The temporal was likened to the Zhoukoudian remains. The vault is quite similar to the Mojokerto child in shape, although the cranial bones are much thicker. Like the Javan, Tam Hang has a distinct flattening on the parietal rear and upper occiput, setting off the short vertical face at the back of the skull in a distinct **occipital bun**.

THE INDONESIANS

The Sambungmachen site is in central Java not far from Sangiran. The date of the skullcap and central tibia fragment found there is uncertain because it was discovered in an area where it is possible to confuse river terrace deposits with the underlying older deposits. It may be as old as Zhoukoudian but more likely is somewhat younger, perhaps even Late Pleistocene. The importance of the specimen is that it provides a morphological link between the earlier Kabuh remains from Sangiran and the large Late Pleistocene Ngandong specimens to be discussed in Chapter 12.

Sambungmachen (figure 11.4) is a male cranium, missing its face. Its temporal line is so strong that it forms a raised crest for its entire length, and there is a downward-pointing inion at the middle of the nuchal torus. Linking it to the earlier Indonesians are the

- broad depression over the browridge (especially over the nose)
- inward-canted parietal walls
- thickening at the rear of the temporal squama, where the thick crest over the ears and mastoids turns upwards,
- small mastoids,
- lack of significant backward projection for the nuchal torus.

Yet other characteristics foreshadow the features that are common at Ngandong, and authors such as D. Grimaud-Hervé clearly align it with the later sample. Compared with the earlier male Kabuh specimens, the Sambungmachan cranial capacity of 1100 cc is at the large end of the range. While the Sambungmachan male is somewhat smaller than the Ngandong males, it resembles them in

- the development of an **angular trigone** (a small backward-facing triangle whose tip is the temporal ridge) at the lateral corner of the supraorbital torus,
- lower positioned temporal lines,

- the reduction in the spongy bone at the sides and rear of the cranial base and the consequently higher position of the maximum cranial breadth,
- flattening of the parietal rear, along the midline,
- the flattening of the occipital plane of the occiput (and its vertical orientation),
- the doubled digastric sulci,
- the tall, vertical posterior border of the temporal squama (as described above)

Many of the local features showing regional continuity have considerable antiquity. This is especially visible in the flattened forehead, where there is an absence of the centrally located frontal boss, and broad sulcus in front of it, common at Zhoukoudian and also found in the later specimens from the Chinese sites of Maba and Dali (see Chapter 12).

The central shaft portion of a right tibia was found some years later, among animal bones taken for fluorine analysis. At midsection it appears to be a large bone, approaching the Kabwe specimen (table 11.11) and larger than its Zhoukoudian and Kabuh Indonesian counterparts. It is also considerably narrower than these. The cortex of the bone is extremely thick, the **medullary cavity** narrowed to only occupy some 30% of the internal diameters (it resembles Zhoukoudian in this). The thicker cortex provides more strength to resist twisting and bending, but to some extent this is negated by the transverse shaft narrowing (the earlier ZKT and Kabuh tibiae are broader).

AN INDIAN SKULL

Narmada is from Madhya Pradesh in central India. Recovered on the surface of a floodplain overlooking the Narmada river, the sediments adhering to the skull seem to link the specimen to fauna and artifacts from the Middle to early Late Pleistocene. At the moment there is no better date. The Narmada skull is about three-quarters of a largely faceless braincase, damaged as well as incomplete. According to K. Kennedy and colleagues it is probably female and certainly a younger adult. Kennedy and colleagues find Narmada broadly similar to many later Middle Pleistocene hominids, and contest the results of the previous, initial, study by M-A. de Lumley and A. Sonakia that likened it to earlier remains.

There a few features that are quite archaic, such as the dramatic development of spongy bone around the sides and rear of the cranial base (this is why, as table 11.5 shows, the maximum breadth of the cranial vault which includes this spongy bone is much greater than the maximum breadth of the braincase, taken higher on the skull, across the parietals). However, there are numerous progressive features that support Kennedy's view. These include the large cranial capacity (depending, of course, on where in the range of estimates the specimen actually lies), the markedly expanded cranial height, the expansion of the occipital plane bringing opistocranion well above the nuchal torus, and the broad frontal and occiput. The forehead is fairly high, a consequence of the marked cranial height; it is rounded, but there is no frontal boss, or bossing of the parietals. I believe that it greatest similarities lie with the later Middle Pleistocene or earlier Late Pleistocene Chinese remains (an assessment supported by F.C. Howell, who likens it to the Late Pleistocene Maba partial-cranium) . In these resemblances I would include

- the shape and configuration of the supraorbital tori and the curvature of the frontal squama, similar to Hexian (but not Zhoukoudian, except for H3),
- the round orbits, resembling the Upper Pleistocene Maba vault (Chapter 12).
- the form of the temporal squama, expression and position of the angular torus, occipital curvature, and details of the nuchal torus, similar to Zhoukoudian H3.

This suggests that a predominance of Asian features, first recognized in the Chinese specimens, may have extended all across the continent during the Middle Pleistocene. The possibility is further indicated by the analysis of the Zuttiyeh frontofacial fragment from the edge of Western Asia.

Table 11.5

Cranial Dimensions of the Most Complete Middle Pleistocene Hominids

	Cranial capacity	Cranial length	Cranial breadth	Braincase (parietal) breadth	Frontal breadth (min/max)[1]	Occipital breadth	Height from cranial base (basion)	Height from ear opening (auricular point)	Central supra-orbital torus height
Narmada	1155-1421	203	164	145	106/120	144	138	115	13
Bodo					114/		136		
Yunxian 2		<217	≈165		106/				18
Kabwe	1280	207	147	140	105/113	134	130	104	23
Petralona	1220	209	165	151	111/122	123	127	103	20
Dali	1200	210	152	153	105/109		120	104	19
ZKT L1	1225	200	150	138	/110	114		104	14
Arago 21	1166		145	145	104/108	114			12
ZKT H3	1140	207	158	145	98/118	127		96	11
Sambung-machan	1100	199	151	146	105/120	115		105	15
Ndutu	1100	146	141	120	/112				11
ZKT L3	1030	196	147	141	97/110	117		98	17
Hexian	1025	190	160	145	101/122	142		95	12
ZKT L2	1015	192	147	139	95/108	115		93	12
Sangiran 17	1004	207	161	146	101/119	116	115	96	17

[1]   Minimum frontal breadth is taken between the temporal notches (the medial borders of the temporal fossa, and maximum breadth is measured on the coronal suture

Western Asia

Ubeidya, as discussed in Chapter 10, is an important archaeological site that holds some of the earliest evidence for human populations outside of Africa and extends well into the Early Pleistocene, but the human remains are very fragmentary and unprovenienced. What unquestionably are the earliest of the Levant hominids come from deepest aspects of the Tabun Cave in Israel. This cave has the longest single sequence in western Asia. At its bottom, level G has reversed polarity, probably anchoring it in the Lower Pleistocene. Tabun Acheulean level E, considerably higher in the sequence and probably older than 150 kyr (possibly much older), preserved a molar and part of a thick walled femur shaft that, like all Early and Middle Pleistocene *H. sapiens* is broader transversely than its anteroposterior dimension. E. Trinkaus and has argued that this combination of thickness and shape reflects a high level of daily activity. Another two fragmentary femora were found in an Acheulean context at Gesher Benot Ya'acov, with an age of approximately a half-million years. They have the same shaft shape and thick walls, but according to D. Geraads and E. Tchernov both are unusually small. Femur 1 is the smallest of any pre-Late Pleistocene *H. sapiens* and femur 2, some 20% larger, still is smaller than most - it is about ZKT M1 size.

The best preserved of the Middle Pleistocene specimens from western Asia is the frontofacial fragment from Mugharet-el-Zuttiyeh, or the Galilee skull. It was excavated from near the bottom of the cave and is associated with a local Acheulean facies called the Acheulo-Yabrudian. Based on dates from other sites, especially the analysis of the Tabun cave, O. Bar-Yosef assesses the age as at least later Middle Pleistocene, suggesting that 350-250 kyr is the most probable range of estimates.

The small specimen, which is probably female, combines centrally thickened and laterally thinned supraorbitals that extend prominently and are separated from a distinctly bossed frontal by a broad sulcus. This contrasts with the thin and rather delicate zygomatics - a combination much like the Steinheim female cranium. (see below). Other archaic morphological features include a marked postorbital narrowing and a narrow maximum frontal breadth relative to the upper facial breadth. The many paleoanthropologists who have described or dealt substantively with it over the years since its discovery in 1925, including A. Hrdlička, J-J. Hublin, A. Keith, S. Sohn (with this author), E. Trinkaus, and B. Vandermeersch have achieved the most divergent possible range of interpretations of its relationships.

The most convincing similarities are with the Zhoukoudian folk, the full length of the Asian continent away (although quite possibly linked by East Asian-appearing specimens such as Narmada), and somewhat earlier. Most of the comparative information comes from ZKT L2 and L3, since few other specimens preserve parts comparable to Zuttiyeh. Like them the Zuttiyeh frontal bone is narrow and long; the squama is relatively uncurved, in spite of the narrow centrally located boss which also resembles the East Asians. Seen from above, the upper part of the face is flat from side to side. There is a suite of shared facial features. Zuttiyeh and the East Asians all exhibit a rounded superior orbital contour and supraorbital shape above it. Glabella is not prominent; in fact, from above the central supraorbital region is slightly depressed at the midline. Directly below it, the superior nasal region is level, both above and below the frontonasal suture where the nasal bones are transversely as flat as ZKT D1 and L1, and even flatter than H3, L2 (which is identical to Gongwangling), and L3. The Zuttiyeh nasals are also similar to the above in their lack of a sagittal keel, the level (e.g., lacking a depression) nasal root, and the vertical orientation of the preserved superior aspect of the nasal bones. The zygomatic is somewhat more laterally oriented than in L3, and is more similar to Weidenreich's L2 reconstruction in its anterolateral angulation (for instance as seen from above). The Zuttiyeh cheek is more gracile than the isolated L1 zygomatic, a male. However, Zuttiyeh is similar to it in the marked development of a tubercle along the lower third of the anterior face, above the tuberosity for the masseter attachment (which is missing on Zuttiyeh). On the whole, Zuttiyeh shares many features with the comparable portions of Gongwangling and Hexian as well. It would be wrong to simply conclude that Zuttiyeh is a displaced Zhoukoudianer, for there are differences as well as the similarities discussed here. Unlike the Zhoukoudian specimens and Hexian there is no frontal keel, the supraorbital tori are markedly reduced in their most lateral portions, and the frontal squama thickness is generally less. None the less, the relationship of these Asians is quite clear.

The significance of these morphological comparisons is linked to the distribution of the features in other samples that could, alternatively, be ancestral to Zuttiyeh. Such populations are found in Europe and Africa. Some workers have suggested that the flat face of Zuttiyeh and the Zhoukoudian remains is also shared by early *H. sapiens* from Africa. This is incorrect. In WT 15000, ER 3733 and 3883 there is variability in the orientation of the zygomatic, but in all three specimens the bulk of the zygomatic's face is oriented in a much more lateral direction than in Zuttiyeh. The description of these early Africans as "relatively flat faced" is not accurate. Most of the frontofacial features Zuttiyeh shares with the Zhoukoudian sample do not on the whole characterize Middle Pleistocene samples from other areas, although they are occasionally found in isolation For instance, with the possible exception of frontal narrowing, none of the metric distinctions of Zuttiyeh or its specific detailed morphological similarities to the Zhoukoudian remains characterize the Steinheim or Arago 21 females or the male vault from Petralona (these are discussed with other European specimens below).

With regard to the Middle Pleistocene African remains, none of the features linking Zuttiyeh and Zhoukoudian can be found in the female from Ndutu (also discussed below). A few similarities are shared with Kabwe and Bodo, but none with both. In all, while gene flow from Africa is a likely source of at least some variation in Levant populations, there is no basis for presuming a unique or even significant pattern of African ancestry for the western Asians.

The African Middle Pleistocene Sequence

With its much denser populations and regions of excellent site preservation, Africa is the best source of archaeological evidence left by Middle Pleistocene populations. In the earlier stages of the Acheulean, the distribution of sites is rather limited, but the situation changes by the end of the Middle Pleistocene. F.C. Howell and J.D. Clark suggest that the increase in the number of sites, their wider distribution, and the greater artifact densities at particular sites indicate an expansion of range and a higher population density.

This suggests an increasingly effective cultural adaptation. Later sites appear in new habitats, forest and semiarid areas that were formerly unoccupied. The effectiveness of the Acheulean scavenging and hunting adaptation had evolved to allow a wider range of resources to be utilized.

Open-air sites are numerous. Two of the larger excavated sites dating to this time period are Isimila in Tanzania and Olorgesailie (with a numerical date of 900-700 kyr) in Kenya. At Olorgesailie, there are numerous occupation levels on what was the shoreline of a lake. Several sophisticated analyses of the tremendous volume of materials were attempted, but more recent work suggests that much, perhaps most, of the stone tool and bone accumulations may result from taphonomic processes such as water sorting, and not from human activities.

Focusing on those sites that may better reflect the human use of space, numerous African sites provide traces of several different aspects of human adaptation. According to Clark, sites can be divided into three main types:

1. family or multifamily camps,
2. kill sites,
3. gathering sites.

The larger camp sites, covering areas of about 16 m^2 or more, may have supported as many as 50 people at a time, while many of the small sites were probably occupied by no more than a family group. Another aspect of adaptation is the appearance of special-purpose tool kits. The camp sites contain a wide variety of different tools. Tool concentrations at other sites seem to mark the place where an animal was butchered, a supposition in many cases verified by the study of cut marks on the animal bones. These tool kits usually comprise many sharpened flakes and a few large cutting implements. The third functional type of site characteristically has a large number of crude bifaces, often with a pick-like form, ranging from less than a half kg to well over 10 kg in size. These sites are found near forests or areas of heavy vegetation and circumstantial evidence suggests they are probably associated with gathering activities—digging, chopping and shredding, and perhaps some initial crushing of edible plants.

Evidence of how the tools were used come from several studies of their microwear. Overall the lithic technology was a primary one, used in turn to modify a wide range of materials. According to L. Keeley, edge wear and polish on many of the tools indicates their use on wood and other plant tissues, meat, bone, antler, and hide. Some of these were used in plant processing. Materials for stone tool, production were well-chosen; humans seems to have understood the flaking properties of various materials and usually chose the best for their tasks. They were able to manufacture the same range of tool types at varying sizes and using raw materials from many different sources.

The faunal remains indicate that humans regularly consumed meat from medium- and large-sized mammals, including giant baboons. This strongly suggests that hunting and confrontational scavenging was a cooperative and organized activity, dependent on networking between family groups or indicating seasonally larger populations. The main hunting weapons were likely clubs, modified thrown rocks, and in the later portions of the time span we find crudely sharpened wooden spears.

Another aspect of their increasing control over the environment is seen in the occasional association of humans with fire. At Swartkrans Member 3, C.K. Brain reports a spatial association of burnt bone (not from a winter grasslands fire but according to A. Sillen heated in a fire hot enough to be a campfire), bones with cutmarks, and digging sticks which I have argued earlier were probably being used by populations of *Homo*. This is the earliest convincing use of fire. While not well dated, it is clearly much earlier than the Zhoukoudian occurrences (if in fact the fires in this cave were human-made). The controlled use of fire is reflected in its persistent presence over long time periods, and its containment in **hearths** (circles of stones enclosing a camp fire that focus, contain, and sustain its heat). At the Cave of Hearths, one of the Makapansgat caves in South Africa, there is evidence of hearths in the Acheulean layers.

Finally, while the various African sites show functional specializations, there is a correspondence with the earliest European and Asian sites in the types of tools made, the manufacturing skill, and the activities they seem to represent. The lack of patterned regional differences may be a consequence of the relative simplicity of the technology, at least in so far as the lithic remains reflect it. In spite of the increased number of occupied habitats and the wide geographic range of human populations by the onset of the Middle Pleistocene, and the differing ecological conditions they encountered, the level of efficiency in exploiting the environment was not high enough to allow particular specializations. Yet, if the tool forms and their patterning reflect human mental abilities, and function as symbols in marking social status, relationships and roles, it is possible that this relative geographic uniformity holds more information for us. The lack of marked geographic patterning may reflect the expedient nature of the industries. Over and over again the same problems were solved the same ways with the same tool types, and (by this interpretation) the main source of non-functional variation is found in raw material availability. The question of to what extent tools reflect the social context they were made in is one of the most pressing in paleolithic archaeology.

EASTERN AFRICA

In this sample the ages of some specimens are tightly controlled; for instance, Bodo and the Masek Beds at Olduvai are clearly old. Others however can only be bracketed to a broad age-span, often much of the Middle Pleistocene, and their significance is necessarily reduced because of this problem.

Baringo

Two hominid mandibles and four postcrania (a metacarpal, two phalanges, and a virtually complete ulna) have been found in the Kapthurian formation west of Lake Baringo, Kenya. The site is in a normal polarity but otherwise can only very broadly be bracketed between tuffs dated at 660 and 240 kyr. It contains a fairly advanced Acheulean industry. The BK 67 mandible, the larger of the two, has a thinner body than the Olduvai and later Turkana specimens and its teeth are smaller. However, the ramus is very broad and high (suggesting that the face was large and that the individual is male). The symphysis is chinless but somewhat less backward sloping and unlike many of the earlier specimens it lacks all internal buttressing. BK 8518 was found a short distance away but is the same age. It is smaller but more robustly built (although not as much as OH 22), with a strong inferior transverse torus on the inside of the rounded symphysis. The ulna is shorter, more curved, and relatively thinner than OH 36 but with a larger elbow articulation than the earlier Olduvai 36 specimen (table 10.1). Its length corresponds to a height of about 172 cm. Thought to be associated with BK 67, we can use the body size estimate to examine tooth size relative to body size for BK 67. This relation is very reduced compared to the australopithecine condition, and even is smaller than WT 15K (perhaps not surprising, as the stripling youth is at least double and may be triple its age).

Bodo

The Ethiopian cranium, associated with Acheulean tools from the Middle Awash, is arguably the best dated of these specimens (J.D. Clark and colleagues report a 600 kyr estimate based on biostratigraphic and archaeological correlations to a nearby site with numerical dates). Unfortunately, because it has been the focus of political controversy and academic in-fighting (see Chapter 1), there have been no publications by the favored few who have been allowed to examine it. I was in one laboratory of a colleague who was given a cast of the reconstruction under the conditions that visitors could not measure it, take notes, or photographs, and I was never sure if it wasn't supposed to be kept on the shelf with its face toward the wall. The specimen was reconstructed by its discoverers, G. Conroy, C. Jolly, and D. Cramer, but afterwards fell into different hands. Found near the cranium was a second cranial fragment (BOD VP-1/1) and a distal humerus (BOD VP-1/2).

Bodo preserves a face and the anterior and top of the braincase. It is superficially similar to the more southern specimens such as Kabwe, discussed below, although the cranium is noticeably larger (table 11.5) and the face is broader and considerably more massive (table 11.6). The nose is extraordinarily broad (the broadest of any Pleistocene fossil), its lower margin guttered. Thick, robust cheeks angle backward from it. To the sides of the nose and below the orbits, the face of the maxilla enclosing the maxillary sinus has an inflated or "puffed out" appearance. A true deeply incised canine fossa is lacking, but just lateral to the nose there is a very shallow fossa. A long, sloping frontal begins above the thick browridge, and the temporal fossa appears to have been large. What remains of the cranial base shows it to be markedly flexed. The mandibular fossa has a flat, gradually sloped anterior face that is the usual consequence of an emphasis on anterior tooth loading.

Except for the dramatically thicker Kabwe supraorbital, the features associated with robustness are more pronounced than in the Kabwe cranium, although the face is about the same height. For instance the Bodo cheeks are much larger and somewhat less posteriorly angled. There is a weakly angled maxillary notch (the lower cheek borders are almost a straight line from the maxilla to the zygomatic arch), Bodo is the much broader face with a more projecting nose and a deeper nasal root (accentuated by the more prominent glabella). It is also a markedly taller cranial vault. Other progressive features include the division of the supraorbital torus into central and lateral elements, even though the torus is evenly developed in thickness.

Yet several traits clearly link the two. In both specimens there is a curious eversion in the supraorbital torus. The anterior surface of the torus at the middle of the cranium gradually becomes the superior surface laterally. Also similar are the

- flat to slightly convex anterior cheek surfaces,
- weakly angled maxillary notch,
- lateral orientation of the orbital pillars,
- alveolar prognathism,
- distinct frontal keel,
- eminence at bregma,
- angular torus,
- lengthened frontal bone.

T. White describes a series of cutmarks on the cranium. Some of these near the nasal root and at the base of the forehead, seem to indicate scalping. White believes the others also reflect defleshing.

Table 11.6
Facial Dimensions[1] of Middle Pleistocene African Crania

	Bodo	Kabwe	Ndutu
height of face from the top of the orbit to the **alveolar margin**	94	93	84
height of the midface from the bottom of the orbit to the alveolar margin	66	54	43
breadth of the upper face between outer orbital borders	125	122	101
breadth of the middle face between the bases of the zygomaxillary sutures	130	114	
breadth of the nose	43	31	28
central height (thickness) of the supraorbital torus	16	23	11

[1]   These are limited to dimensions that can be taken on all three specimens - Ndutu is by far the least complete of the three.

A second cranial piece was described by B. Asfaw. A thick left fragment of a parietal's lower rear corner, BOD-VP 1/1 has a very marked angular torus. The cranial bone thickening is mostly of the diploë and not the compact outer bone, a pattern found in later Middle Pleistocene hominids and unlike the dramatic compact bone thickening of the Sangiran and Zhoukoudian remains. Asfaw focused on the large overlap between the temporal squama and the lower parietal border. Y Rak, in his classic study of this region in *Australopithecus boisei*, suggests that this overlap functions in reducing masticatory strains above the temporal (from the mandibular fossa) by providing for some "give" between the bones. Asfaw reports the stria marking the region of overlap on the parietal show extensive overlap on other Middle Pleistocene specimens.

Contrasting with the crania, the humerus fragment is quite small, and apart from its thicker shaft walls it is quite similar to more recent and modern specimens. Variation in Middle Pleistocene African crania suggests the disparities between the robust crania and delicate humerus from Bodo probably reflects sexual dimorphism.

Olduvai

OH 23 is a large mandibular fragment from the Masek beds at the FLK site in Olduvai Gorge, approximately 600 kyr in age. It is a heavily built specimen with a few heavily worn postcanine teeth remaining (P_4-M_2). Its dimensions are quite similar to the very robust OH 22 (Chapter 10). Much later, perhaps half the age, is the OH 11 maxilla and craniofacial fragments, from the lower Ndutu beds. OH-11 is a small shallow palate with a smoothed nasal margin.

Lainyamok

Dated by faunal comparison to the earlier Middle Pleistocene, and bracketed by an overlying 380 kyr K/A date, a fragmentary femur and maxillary teeth were found at this Kenyan site. The three teeth, P^4-M^2, are moderate in size for a Middle Pleistocene hominid, even with the corrections to their dimensions that P. Shipman and colleagues had to make to compensate for their poor preservation and cracking. While larger than most Early and Middle Pleistocene African teeth, they are near the low end of the range at the megadont Arago site in France (see below). The femur is just a little broader than long at midshaft, where its dimensions are quite large - exceeded only by the "broomstick" ER 736 specimen (which has a similar midshaft shape) in the very tall Early Pleistocene sample. There is no reason to believe that the maxillary teeth and the femur are associated.

Ndutu

The Ndutu cranium from Tanzania, reconstructed by R. Clarke and described by P. Rightmire, is the female corresponding to the Bodo and Kabwe males. It is of similar age, somewhat younger than the Masek beds at Olduvai. Ndutu is a smaller skull (table 11.5) with cranial capacity between 1070 and 1120 cc according to R. Holloway, and a markedly smaller and more delicate face. There is more contrast with earlier specimens in the occiput than in the frontal region, which is marked by a projecting but thin supraorbital torus. This can be seen in spite of the fact that the supraorbital region is incorrectly set onto the frontal squama in the reconstruction. Compensating for these problems, its anatomy is more than reminiscent of ER 3733. However, what remains of the broken frontal suggests a more expanded breadth and a rather high angle for the forehead.

There is a sagittal keel on the parietal, somewhat over-accentuated by additional reconstruction problems on the right side. Rightmire finds the cranial rear particularly similar to Kabwe. The nuchal torus is weakly developed, except centrally; the occiput above it is high, and the occipital plane is vertical, bulging outward. At its top there is an extrasutural bone at the lambda position - the only archaic African specimen with this anatomy. The development of spongy bone at the cranial base is reduced, and the parietal walls are fairly vertical, as in the Kabwe cranium. There are parietal bosses, outward bulges at the center of the parietal, perhaps not as dramatic as the reconstruction suggests but clearly present. The face is notably smaller than the male faces in all dimensions. It shows little alveolar prognathism, lacks midfacial puffing, and the nose is moderately prominent.

Eliye Springs

The final East African specimen is Eliye Springs, a cranium recovered from a Lake Turkana beach that is *completely* undated. Described by G. Bräuer and R. Leakey, its anatomy suggests *but does not demonstrate* a later Middle Pleistocene age. ES 11693 is very eroded and much of the face has been destroyed. None the less, the cranial vault is clearly long, very broad at the base (much less so across the parietals) and low. It shows a number of features that, in association, seem to be regional for Middle Pleistocene hominids from eastern and southern Africa such as Bodo, Ndutu, and Kabwe. These are, first and foremost, the combination of a more archaic frontal (a low and moderately rounded frontal profile and a supratoral sulcus) with a more progressive cranial rear (rounded occipital contour lacking nuchal torus). Other similarities within this group include

- the extension of the frontal keel to the supraorbitals where it actually interrupts the supratoral sulcus,
- the flattening of this sulcus at the temporal lines,
- the length of the frontal from the lateral orbit to the coronal suture,
- the angled parietals with near vertical walls,
- the keeling of the inter-nasal suture,
- the depression of the nasal root.

Where Eliye Springs differs from the others is predominately in the complete lack of nuchal torus and the proportions of the face, which is quite broad but markedly shorter than the two males. Even still, the contour of the lower zygomatic border and the posterior orientation of the moderately puffy cheek with its very shallow canine fossa appears to be a common Middle Pleistocene African morphology.

Besides the facial proportions there are a few other features unique to this specimen. These include a small depression just above the nuchal lines at the midline (**suprainiac fossa**), and a flattened upper nasal area and infraorbital region.

Eliye Springs was discovered because of an unusually low lake level. If the water level in Lake Turkana continues to drop, it is possible that more like it will be recovered and their provenience established.

SOUTHERN AFRICA

Dates are also a problem for many of the specimens from southern Africa. It is widely presumed that Kabwe and Saldanha in the south are the same approximate age as Bodo and Ndutu to the north. Perhaps so, but the dating of the Middle Pleistocene sub-Saharan Africans could be optimistically described as tenuous!.

Kabwe (Broken Hill)

A cranium (E 686), maxilla (E 687), frontal bone (E 897), and a number of postcranial bones were discovered in a cave pocket exposed by lead mining near Broken Hill in Zambia. A chemical analysis comparing the hominid remains with animal bones from the pocket suggests that they may have been contemporaneous. The fauna is broadly similar to other Middle Pleistocene fauna. In addition, the artifacts found in the cave pocket, which were once thought to be First Intermediate (between the Early and Middle Stone Ages), are now considered to be an Acheulean-related industry. Thus both fauna and artifacts suggest a Middle Pleistocene age for this otherwise undated sample.

The Kabwe cranium, with its complete face, presents a contrast of ruggedness and gracility (see figure 11.5). The cranium is marked by a very large browridge, a low forehead, and well developed cresting near the center of the occiput. These features combine to give it the superficial appearance of a very archaic skull (W. Howells, a champion of the taxon, actually places it in "*Homo erectus*"), but in fact the specimen is considerably more modern-looking in its total morphology.

Its expanded capacity (almost 1,300 cc, see table 11.5) is one of the largest in the Middle Pleistocene African sample (the Bodo capacity, which is unknown, is probably larger). It is a long and relatively narrow cranium with little difference between the maximum cranial breadth and braincase breadth that reflects reduction in the basal spongy bone development. The long frontal is relatively flattened, with a strongly developed frontal keel extending over virtually the entire length of the squama and one of the most prominent sets of supraorbitals known. They are everted, with the anterior surface at the midline gradually twisting to become the superior surface laterally. The encroachment of the frontal over the supraorbitals results in a weakly developed supratoral sulcus. The E 897 frontal fragment has similar curvature and an equally well-developed temporal line, but is thinner. The sides of the E 686 vault are fairly vertical but show little bossing, and the parietal profile could be described as gabled. Toward the rear there is a weakly developed angular torus. The occipital squama is expanded and extends vertically above the enlarged nuchal torus, which is more crest-like than torus-like because it is so thin. With the reduction of the nuchal muscle attachment area, the proportions of this occiput are quite different than many earlier specimens, although the region (including mastoids) largely mirrors the Ndutu anatomy.

The face of this male is quite tall and narrow, especially compared with Bodo. It is not particularly prognathic and on the whole it is not thrust especially far forward - a special contrast with the European specimens to the north, described below. Reduction in the nuchal area is reflected in the gracility seen in structures that support facial muscle attachments. For instance, the zygomatic bones are thin and delicate, markedly reduced compared with most Middle Pleistocene males. They begin well above the alveolar margin and there is a slightly flexed malar incisure (in the Bodo face the much more massive cheeks come close to the toothrow and their lower border is even straighter, or more shelved). The zygomatics enclose a small temporal fossa. The upper jaw is tall but only moderately prognathic; the incisor portion at the front projects forward slightly more than the top of the nose. The front of the palate is deep, reflecting large incisor roots. Indeed, the incisors (and canines) are large relative to the Zhoukoudian teeth while the posterior teeth are about the same size (except for the reduced third molar). The virtually complete maxillary dentition is heavily worn. Many of the teeth have caries that produced very deep cavities, and some have completely rotted away. Thus chewing, if not breathing through the mouth, must have been very painful. P.-F. Puech and colleagues believe that this condition developed from more localized problems that resulted when this unfortunate individual failed to clean between his teeth. This oversight was surely idiosyncratic, as it is today, since much earlier folk were using toothpicks habitually enough to produce grooves on adjacent teeth (Weidenreich reported them for Zhoukoudian and D. Frayer and M. Russell review the topic because of the numerous grooves in Krapina Neandertal teeth, see Chapter 13).

The nose in the Kabwe face is large and has a sharp lower margin. Neither the nasal bones nor the lateral nasal margins are particularly projecting. To the sides of the nasal margins the cheeks are flat, not particularly puffy but also not incised with a canine fossa.

The E 687 maxilla discovered in the cave is frequently overlooked or classified differently from the cranium (JD Clark puts this in "early modern *Homo*" as opposed to "archaic *Homo*" for the skull). Although fragmentary, the palate appears quite similar to the palate of the cranium, despite certain smaller dimensions. Both specimens have long tooth rows, deep palates with steep walls in the molar region, and a very great distance between the molar rows. The greatest difference is in the snout. The space for the anterior teeth and the height of the lower face (from nasal margin to tooth row) are considerably less in this (possibly female) maxilla.

The Kabwe postcranial sample (including two innominates, femurs, a tibia, and some upper limb fragments) represents three or possibly more individuals. The bones are mostly large and robust but surprisingly modern in form and proportion. For instance, the E 793 femur shaft is elongated at its midshaft and the femur neck lengths of E 689 and 907 are greatly reduced compared with the Early Pleistocene specimens (particularly WT 15K). Of all the bones, only the E 691 tibia may possibly be associated with the male cranium (because of its close physical proximity in the cave). The body height suggested by this complete bone (its length is 41.5 cm) is about 176 cm. Other postcranials that less likely but still possibly could represent the same individual are the large male innominate (E 719) and the largest of the femurs (E 907). E 719 has a larger acetabulum than OH 28 and a thicker acetabulo-cristal buttress. The unusual thickening of the iliac blade, according to C. Stringer is unknown in any Late Pleistocene or recent specimens.

Other Remains

A cranium from Elandsfontein, on Saldanha Bay in the Orange Free State, South Africa, is very similar to the Kabwe cranium in most respects, although the face and cranial base were not preserved. The size and contours of the vault, the strong posterior angle of the browridge as seen from above, and the reduced nuchal torus combined with an expanded and bulging occipital plane align these crania with each other. In his analysis of the specimens, P. Rightmire finds the proportions and contours of the vault more similar to Ndutu (especially the more vertical or "filled out" cranial walls, in comparison with Kabwe), although the Tanzanian specimen is admittedly smaller.

Another sub-Saharan specimen is a small mandible with anomalous dental positions and wear, from the Cave of Hearths at Makapansgat in South Africa. Along with a radius fragment that is roughly contemporary, the mandible comes from Early Stone Age deposits equivalent to Kabwe in age. The posterior teeth are reduced in size, and the second molar is much smaller than the first. As in the much earlier Chenjiayao mandible, there is congenital absence of the last molar.

NORTH AFRICA

Earlier specimens

Dated later than the Tighenif specimens (Chapter 10), there is a group of mid-Middle Pleistocene remains from the Moroccan sites of Salé, the quarries at Thomas, and the Sidi Abderrahman Cave. J-J. Hublin argues that their age is approximately 400 kyr (ESR on a piece of associated bovid enamel at Salé is 389 or 455 kyr, depending on the uptake model). This would make them perhaps the same age or slightly older than the southern and eastern African crania described above. Salé is a very small (R. Holloway estimates about 880 cc cranial capacity, Hublin 925), thick, vault that lacks supraorbitals and face. It has a rounded frontal and a modern-appearing occipital contour that is affected by a pathological development of the nuchal region (figure 11.6). The cranium exhibits marked postorbital constriction, high prominent temporal lines, a sagittal keel extending on to the frontal bone, and its greatest cranial breadth is at the base. It further resembles other crania of early African specimens in its lack of a marked forehead slope (like Kabwe) and some parietal bulging (as in the Ndutu cranium). The occiput is extraordinarily broad (by modern standards). It is high and rounded with a shortened nuchal plane and very reduced nuchal torus. However, Hublin believes the region is pathological. The nuchal plane is usually divided into two parts by a transverse **inferior nuchal line**. Well behind it the **superior nuchal line** forms the lower border of the nuchal torus, if there is one, or if not it will form the prominent nuchal line dividing the nuchal plane from the occipital plane above. In Salé there is no inferior line, the superior line is in its position making the nuchal plane about half the length it probably would have been in a normal specimen. It is unclear how much this pathological development affects the shape of the occiput, but its modern rounded contour , at best, has an ambiguous significance. Unfortunately, the face and the anterior part of the frontal except for a small internal fragment are broken away. Nonetheless, the small size and gracility of the specimen suggest that it is female.

The frontal-facial fragment from the Thomas III quarry is generally similar to the two smaller, almost certainly female, crania discussed above. It seems to be rather small. Its moderately developed browridge projects well in front of a sloping forehead (the region is much like Ndutu in size and shape) which has an only poorly developed supratoral sulcus. The nasal angle is low. Vault shape as seen from above appears to have been globular, resembling Salé. There are a number of associated maxillary teeth. The lateral incisor and the first two molars are quite large, for instance falling above the Zhoukoudian sample range. Incisor expansion is especially significant as it also characterizes the European remains. The third molar is smaller than the second, as is the case in all known Middle Pleistocene palates. At the nearby Thomas I quarry, a mandible of another individual was recovered, with its third molar so reduced that it is even smaller than the first molar. While the Thomas mandible is considerably smaller than any of the Tighenif specimens, has larger posterior teeth.

Sidi Abderrahman (the 'Casablanca mandible') is a tall, massive mandibular body (there are actually two corpus fragments). It is the only obvious male specimen of the sample. It has large postcanine teeth and an anterior premolar with a very dominant outer cusp.

Mixed Morphology

African specimens from the middle part of the Middle Pleistocene, the approximate age of Zhoukoudian to slightly later, parallel the Chinese sequence in an interesting way - like the Asians there is a real mix of morphologies. Ndutu, Kabwe, Elandsfontein, Bodo, and Salé and Thomas Quarry crania show anatomical diversity that is reflected in a diversity of taxonomic opinion about them. Just reflecting on the opinions of the several authors who believe there are two (more or less) successive species in the genus *Homo* through the

Pleistocene, *H. erectus* and *H. sapiens*, as J.D. Clark put it, there is a "variable degree of mixing of *H. erectus* and modern characteristics." P. Rightmire regards only Thomas III as *H.* erectus of these crania while W. Howells places Kabwe and Elandsfontein in *H. erectus* (Bodo was not well known when he wrote this). In many ways the interpretations of one specimen alone, Ndutu, reflects these problems in a microcosm. In his first discussion of the cranium, R. Clarke regarded Ndutu as a new subspecies of *H. erectus*, largely based on the unexpected conclusion that the occipital contours and "thickened" nuchal torus were like the Zhoukoudian remains. But this is not correct. The occipital contour is quite unlike the Zhoukoudian condition and the nuchal torus even more different. Clarke has more recently come to agree with most others in classifying the specimen as *H. sapiens*.

Realistically, sexual dimorphism, incomplete preservation, and the difficulties of making systematic comparisons in a single place, whether with casts or the original specimens, are important elements in the perception of marked variation in these specimens. The Africans are, however, measurably more variable than the Zhoukoudian or Sangiran folk. Faces, are better represented in these sub-Saharan specimens than in most samples. They vary from the robust features of Bodo to the gracile structures of Kabwe and Ndutu. While some of the variation probably reflects sexual dimorphism both Bodo and Kabwe are male, and the contrast between them must be attributed to other factors. Time quite likely pays an important role as Bodo is evidently older. Other factors contributing to variation are the demographic and ecological influences on it. These are expected to differ for human populations at the center of the human range, discussed in Chapter 10 as part of the Center and Edge hypothesis.

ADAPTATION AND CHANGE IN AFRICA

Unlike the situation in Asia, the archaeological associations of the African specimens are well known. All are from sites with late versions of the Acheulean industrial complex. If *H. sapiens* evolved within the Acheulean, the origin of at least some of the changes (or continuations) in selection might be sought in the adaptations this lithic industry reflects.

The Acheulean complex supported what seem to have been unspecialized hunting societies at its onset, although according to African archaeologists such as J.D. Clark later developments included the appearance of regional and even local variants. These argue for the evolution of new adaptations and cultural specializations. The lithic technology itself is characterized by more trimming and retouch. Clark suggests that this might be the result of more persistent use of the same tool, which then needs to be resharpened as it becomes blunted. This, in turn, could mean that camping places were occupied for longer continuous periods, and implies more effective habitat utilization. In some areas, a new method for the preparation of flakes, called the "Levallois technique," appeared (see pp. xx-xx). By preparing the core before the flake was struck, much finer control over the final tool form resulted in more easily standardized tool forms and sharper cutting edges as only minimal retouch was required. This technology was critical in the subsequent development of the Middle Paleolithic from the Lower Paleolithic.

. Sets of roughly circular stones may have formed projectile weapons. When the stones in a set are tied together with strings of different length, the resulting bola, thrown with a twirling motion, can be used to trip or injure game. Evidence from other areas suggests that wooden spears with fire-hardened points were probably in use. These weapons had the important effect of increasing the distance between the hunters and their prey. Another innovation, perhaps continued from earlier times such as in Swartkrans Member 3, was the use of fire. As noted above this is reported from Cave of Hearths levels, including the hominid ones. Fire had an important effect on the continued posterior dental reduction because it means that many foods were cooked.

While there little direct evidence of the vegetal foods consumed, the continued development of hand axes and (later) even more pick-like forms used in digging attests to the importance of plant resources. The range of fauna that was hunted reflects an increasingly effective resource utilization.

As a whole, compared with the early Pleistocene Africans this sample shows the consequences of continued braincase expansion, reduction in the cranial superstructure, and posterior tooth reduction. The latter changes could probably best be subsumed under the concept of gracilization. There is a marked contrast between the more archaic frontals and the progressive occipital anatomy, basal spongy bone development is reduced markedly, and several of the crania are shorter and more rounded than their ancestors. Less certainly, there seems to be some evidence suggesting an increase in anterior tooth size (and use).

Perhaps changing attitudes about the African sample can best be exemplified through the history of the Kabwe fossils. The cranium, which seemed so robust and primitive when first reported more than 60 years ago, is now considered gracile, large-brained, and reduced when compared with earlier specimens. Taken to be a recent "African Neandertal" by some, and a late-surviving "*H. erectus*" by others, Kabwe is now viewed as a male in a progressive Middle Pleistocene population with marked sexual dimorphism.

The Evolutionary Sequence in Europe

The first substantial human occupation of Europe is very late compared with the long sequences in Asia and Africa. Most of the earliest specimens seem no more than penecontemporary with the earliest specimens from Zhoukoudian. Following the Boxgrove tibia (England), Mauer mandible (Germany), and a few isolated teeth from Italy (Fontana Ranuccio), there are a cluster of specimens dated to, or thought to date to within Oxygen Isotope Stages 11-9, a span of just under 150 kyr (table 1.6). This is a situation, and an age range, that is similar to the African specimens discussed above (figure 11.2). All of the earlier occupations occurred during periods of significant warming. Because of this it was assumed that these periods were interglacials rather than interstadials, and for most earlier specimens the Hoxnian (Stage 13) interglacial seemed implicated by faunal remains. This may be correct - *is* correct for some - but the general appreciation that there are milder periods interspersed within the earlier stadials in a glacial cycle, and the inconsistent and confused reflection of the numerous Pleistocene glaciations found in terrestrial deposits, makes dating the Middle Pleistocene sites of Europe by correlation to specific glaciations perhaps even more muddled than in other regions.

W. Roebroeks and colleagues argue that there was interglacial occupation of Europe through most of the Middle Pleistocene. The earliest sites are at least of stage 13 age, but most of the hominids are later. Their demonstration of early habitation is a real contrast to more traditional ideas that the higher latitudes were closed to archaic humans by their ecological circumstances. Particular difficulties are created by the seasonality of climate and resources, and the affects of the flickering climatic jumps and longer-term glacial cycles. These combine to create extreme periods of cold and warmth that have a marked effect on flora and fauna and create seasonal turnovers and fluctuations of key resources that are difficult to adjust to. Paleoanthropologists such as C. Gamble suggest that successful adaptation to higher latitudes, especially the temperate forests, required improved organization of technology, seasonal patterns of land use, and the intensification of regional alliances and support networks. With Roebroeks and colleagues demonstration that the environmental and habitat range of Middle Pleistocene Europeans was not much different from the more modern populations of the Late Pleistocene and Holocene, the implication is that these criteria for successful habitation had been met. The planning and organizational capacities of Middle Pleistocene populations were substantial. This, of course, does not make them completely modern in their capabilities - it is a larger step in that direction than had been expected. Occupation of the continent during the really cold parts of the stadials was not within their capabilities, and the great colonizations of the Late Pleistocene (for instance Australia and the Americas and the explosive expansion into the Pacific) required further, substantial biological and behavioral developments. These were unquestionably linked, the usual pattern in human evolution, as changes in organization and technology reflect continued evolution of cognitive abilities as well as increasingly complex traditions and other forms of culturally inherited information. The point is that improvements in the abilities to use difficult ecologies not sudden, but are spread through the Middle Pleistocene. The earliest occupations of Europe were interglacial, but the rich habitats of the cold steppes of Central and Eastern Europe were occupied well before the period's end.

The German site of Mauer is probably the earliest of the Middle Pleistocene sites, although the dating, insecure at best, places it only roughly between 700 and 500 kyr. One interpretation is that the mandible came from the base of the sands at the site, regarded as Cromerian interglacial in age (Oxygen Isotope stage 21) and even older than this range, but it is more probable that it is from a later warm period, perhaps as recent as stage 13. At best we can be sure of an earlier Middle Pleistocene age. When the

Mauer mandible was discovered in 1907, in a quarry near Heidelberg, it was recognized as being very large and robust (the sloping symphysis retains two internal tori) and was noted for its especially broad ramus and the fact that the second molar is larger than the first. Later comparisons revealed that it could be matched by the extreme variations in living humans. With the large Middle Pleistocene sample now available for comparisons Mauer is seen as a fairly gracile specimen with reduction in ramus height and the size of the posterior dentition. In contrast, the anterior teeth are large. It shows an early manifestation of two other features that are very common later in Europe: **taurodontism**, an enlargement of the pulp cavities of the molars, and dramatic buccal cusp dominance in the P_3.

Boxgrove, a central tibial fragment from West Sussex, is placed in Oxygen Isotope stage 13 by sedimentary analysis and biostratigraphy according to M. Roberts and colleagues. It is one of the largest specimens known (table 12. 2), the dimensions of the sizable shaft fragment suggesting a height of close to 1.9 m, virtually dwarfing the much later European Neandertals. The shaft walls are very thick and the medullary cavity small. Perhaps most significantly, the minimum shaft diameter, located about 2/3 of the way down the bone, is closer to the size of the shaft at its middle than is usual in fossil and recent humans. This minimum diameter position is a common place for the tibia to break (for instance in accidents where one foot becomes wedged and a person falls down), and its larger diameter and thick shaft walls combine to suggest that this was a very powerful and active person. If there was an "Incredible Hulk" contest for the ancient world, Boxgrove might well be declared the winner.

The remains from Bilzingsleben, near Weimar in eastern Germany, are also more securely dated, to about 400 kyr - the maximum age recognizable by Uranium series dating - or slightly older according to H. Schwarcz. The Bilzingsleben specimens are the most robust European cranial remains from this period, represented by bones from two adult specimens, and a molar. D. Mania, who discovered the remains, believes that most of them are from a single individual. Bilzingsleben I consists of:

- a virtually complete occiput,
- three pieces of frontal, including a central supraorbital fragment,
- two pieces of vault bone
- an upper molar

Bilzingsleben II is represented by two pieces, a left supraorbital torus fragment and part of a left parietal. In addition there are 5 mandibular teeth that cannot be ascribed to either, including a lower deciduous molar.

The Bilzingsleben 1 frontal is characterized by a tall supraorbital torus, a massive centrally located frontal sinus (and additional lateral ones), thick cranial bone, and a wide distance between the orbits. There is little curvature of the torus over the orbits, and the projection of the torus is considerable although the flat forehead is not separated from it by a marked sulcus. When compared with the much more complete cranium from Petralona, a later Middle Pleistocene European male (see below), the specimens are not very different although Petralona is generally the thicker of the two. The frontals share a high **nasion** position with a flat glabellar region above it. The central supraorbital region projects markedly anterior to the base of the low-angled frontal squama, and the anterior margins of the supraorbitals such as they are preserved in Bilzingsleben suggest that both specimens also share a low upper facial angle (as seen from above, the upper facial profile is not angled strongly backward). However, their occipital regions are quite different

Unlike virtually every other Middle Pleistocene European and African, Bilzingsleben I has a very archaic occiput. It is an angled bone with the far back of the skull clearly located on the broad, thick nuchal torus and not above it. Occipital breadth is by far the broadest of any middle Pleistocene European, while its height is the shortest. The occipital plane is wide but vertically short, merging evenly with the torus, which extends as a straight even bar across virtually the entire occipital rear. In describing it E. Vlček likens the specimen to OH 9, arguing for a significant link between the early European hominids and Early Pleistocene Africans. The Europeans, of course, came from somewhere, but I question whether a special link can be forged of anatomical features, in this case. Vlček believes, I think quite correctly, that the Bilzingsleben cranial shape was probably much like the Olduvai specimen. Yet, OH 9 has a much thicker and projecting central torus, and unlike Bilzingsleben I it has a long horizontal roof separated from the frontal squama by a deep sulcus. The occiputs are more similar, but an equally good case could be made linking Bilzingsleben with the Zhoukoudian occiputs. There is just not enough left of Bilzingsleben for this determination.

Table 11.7
Supraorbital Torus and Bone Thickness

	Steinheim	Arago	Petralona	Bilzingsleben	OH 9
Medial supraorbital					
height	17.8	19.6	23.5	18.2	25.2
projection from the internal frontal surface	19.5	23.0		25.0	31.5
Midorbit supraorbital					
height	16.2	12.8	19.0	17.1	18.4
projection from the internal frontal surface	20.7	29.0		30.9	32.0
Cranial thickness at					
bregma (on the frontal)	4.0	8.2	6.9	9.6	9.9
lambda (on the occipital)	8.5		12.6	10.9	
external occipital protuberance	11.1		24.0	17.0	18.5

The second adult has a large fragment of central-lateral frontal that is quite similar to Bilzingsleben I in its thick and even development, and its frontal profile. It also resembles many of the Atapuerca remains (see below) and clearly falls within their range of variation. The Bilzingsleben II supraorbital torus, like the structure on Bilzingsleben I, has been likened to more ancient human populations. However, the structure is no more thick and projecting than supraorbitals of other Europeans such as the larger Atapuerca specimens (e.g. AT 200). Both Bilzingsleben specimens and AT 200 lack a well excavated sulcus.

It is widely believed that there are no members of the taxon "*H. erectus*" in Europe, and I of course do not believe that the taxon is valid in any event, but if I *did* think that "*H. erectus*" was a valid taxon, I would have to agree with Vlček and Mania that Bilzingsleben I and II could be examples of it.

THE MIDDLE OF THE MUDDLE

Later European sites of the central portion of the Middle Pleistocene most likely cluster in the 400-250 kyr span. This vague statement may seem surprising since until recently, most of this sample was thought to be well dated. However, there are good reasons to question the application of the more ancient European glacial stages over all but very limited areas. Specimens once "securely" thought to be dated to the Hoxnian interglacial have been re-analyzed. Association with fauna indicating a Middle Pleistocene warm period was once invariably taken to mean Hoxnian, but in fact may relate to any of the Riss interstadials, and regional stratigraphies are not sensitive enough to discriminate which of these might be correct. I believe that the evidence, at the moment, best supports a stage 11-7 attribution for the remains discussed here.

Castel Di Guido, an Italian Acheulean site, has the potential of being the earliest of these although its dating remains uncertain. Estimates of 400-300 kyr derive from faunal and archaeological comparisons, but these are confused by the fact that the 6 specimens are surface finds. Four cranial pieces and two femoral fragments were found. A temporal and parietal of a single individual (combining CdG 5 and 6) are notable for their thickness. The temporal is small, with a robustly developed **supramastoid** region and a very thick squama. The mandibular fossa is deep and narrow in the anteroposterior direction, as it is in Atapuerca AT 124 and Steinheim (see below), but unlike a number of other European fossils. The parietal fragment is also very thick, in the European context only one specimen from Arago (Arago 47, see below) is thicker. Its thickness is attained by expansions of both cortical and internal spongy bone, unlike the earlier Asian hominids that mainly expand the outer cortex. It has an angular torus. The maxillary fragment is from the anterior of the bone. Apart from the enlarged maxillary sinus there is nothing particularly archaic about it. One of the femur shafts (CdG 2) is very flat. Its shape, specified by the indices of shaft form (anterior-posterior length divided by transverse breadth) is described by values for the indices that are at or below the range at the Zhoukoudian site, of similar age. This Chinese sample is the first place that flat femur shaft anatomy in earlier Middle Pleistocene humans was established. The other shaft, CdG 1, is very large and more rounded, the two dimensions at its middle are close to the same. The enlarged anteroposterior diameter is a consequence of the prominent, columnar *linea aspera*, a modern feature of the bone. Yet, it has thick cortical bone and a small medullary cavity, an archaic combination.

ATAPUERCA

By far the largest and most complete of the Middle Pleistocene samples to be discovered, the crania and other materials from this Spanish site are absolutely critical to the understanding of variability and evolution in Middle Pleistocene Europe. Even excessive taxonomizers such as C. Stringer have come to realize the implications of the fact that the Atapuerca specimens show marked variation. Variability in size and form is a normal populational characteristic in Middle Pleistocene Europe, and encompasses specimens at a single site that differ as much as individuals from different sites that were interpreted to be separate species. Still arguing for a different species *in* Middle Pleistocene Europe, he at least can no longer argue that there were two of them there.

The chamber of Sima de los Huesos (SH) at Atapuerca, near Burgos in northern Spain is the site of discovery of more than 24 individuals, based on dental evidence. Over 700 fragmentary-to-complete pieces have been found so far, and the site shows almost unlimited promise for future discoveries. According to J-L. Arsuaga and colleagues, in the latest of a long series of papers reviewing discoveries at the site, the sample "appears to document an early stage in Neanderthal evolution". A Uranium Series age for the site is greater than 300 kyr.

The most spectacular of the cranial remains are two adults (cranium 4 and 5) and a juvenile (cranium 6) discovered in 1992. Prior to these fairly complete specimens, over 110 fragmentary cranial pieces were already known, allowing the reconstruction of two partial cranial vaults and three additional occiputs. Cranium 4 seems male, based on its robust anatomy (especially at the cranial base and mastoid region) and large **endocranial** size of 1390 cc. Cranium 5 is a considerably smaller vault, about 1125 cc, and the 11 year old cranium 6 is about the same size. Cranium 5 has a smaller mastoid process size (known to distinguish sex at Atapuerca even before these crania were discovered), and occipital features that indicate it is female, and I believe this diagnosis is correct in spite of the large facial dimensions (see below). The crania are relatively high and broad, the greatest breadth at the cranial base (across the supramastoid crests) in the male but higher for cranium 5. Cranium 4 is as broad as Petralona, and the index of its height to length (65%) is almost exactly the same as the Greek specimen (67%).

Supraorbitals are strongly developed in all of the individuals, including the 11 year old, but considering the entire sample (fragments and complete specimens) there is considerable variation in thickness, projection, and the expression of the supratoral sulcus (for instance weak in the AT 200 fragment but strong in cranium 5). The tori are continuously arched over each orbit, they dip downwards near the center of the face and extend over the top of the nose - the glabella area is swollen. They are more evenly developed than the other Middle Pleistocene Europeans (table 13.2), the thicknesses measured at various places are closer to equal. This is an archaic feature, and another is the marked projection of the supraorbital; as measured from the inside of the skull behind to torus to the front edge of the torus, the projection for all the Atapuerca specimens reported so far is greater than the other Middle Pleistocene specimens. Below them the **interorbital** area is very wide and the nasal root is not depressed.

The cranium 5 nose does project outward from the face, but only from about its middle and below (an anatomy it shares with Yunxian). J. Arsuaga and colleagues remark on the strong middle facial prognathism. The face is vertically oriented, but in its entirety it is positioned unusually anterior to the cranial base. A similar anatomy can be seen in the juvenile cranium 6. The nasal area, indeed the entire midline of the face, is more anterior than the rest of these specimens, and the cheeks are laterally oriented accentuating the projecting nasal region. The maxilla to the sides on the nose is puffy and there is no canine fossa, although this feature varies in the sample and on the AT 404 facial fragment there is a well-developed fossa, much like Steinheim. The base of the cranium 5 cheeks is far posterior, emerging from the maxilla in the region of the second molar. The cranium 5 face is almost as broad as Petralona (nasal breadth is even broader) and just a little broader than Arago 21. Similarly, the height of the cheek is between them. Its lower border is high and arched, but there is much more of a maxillary notch than the other Europeans.

Frontals of the specimens are evenly rounded and not bossed. Cranium 5 has a low sagittal keel. Mastoids are large and well developed, projecting far below the cranial base. The occiputs are well rounded and to a greater or lesser extent the occipital plane bulges above and behind the nuchal torus so that the maximum length of the cranium is not located on the torus itself, but well above it. The adults have straight and laterally extensive but thin nuchal tori, with suprainiac fossae above. However, there is little or no lambdoidal flattening in any of the specimens and no expression of the typically Neandertal occipital bun (see Chapter 13).

The mandibular sample is large, although fragmentary. The pattern of fragmentation is interesting insofar as it resembles other large European cave sites such as the Late Pleistocene Krapina remains (see Chapter 13). Many of the Atapuerca pieces are broken in a manner that is so similar to the Krapina remains that individual specimens from one site specifically resemble specimens from the other. It has been suggested that trampling of isolated mandibles on the cave floor, probably by cave bears, might be responsible for these similar breakage patterns. Mandibular anatomy is also not dissimilar to the later Krapina remains, but in fact also resembles most of the Middle Pleistocene Europeans. In most cases the mandibles have a sloping, straight symphseal face with no development of a chin - they lack either a raised trigone or mental prominence on its front. A common and virtually unique European feature is found in the form of the opening for the mandibular nerve, on the inside of the ramus. The Atapuerca mandibles have what F. Smith named the "horizontal-oval" foramen form - this is quite descriptive as the shape of the foramen is oval and its orientation is horizontal. The other condition is to have the smooth rim of the foramen interrupted by a small groove that extends below it (see figure 14.#, mandibular foramen). The significance of this long lasting European feature will be discussed in Chapter 14.

Study of the dental remains by J. Bermúdez de Castro and others reveals no evidence of the marked anterior dental expansion that characterizes later Middle Pleistocene European populations (it is suggested that in terms of the evolutionary trends the 3rd premolar be considered part of the anterior sample). However, the beginnings of the trend can be found, as the ratio of anterior to posterior dimensions is greater than at earlier sites such as Zhoukoudian. On the whole the Atapuerca teeth are the same size or smaller than the earlier remains. The difference is less in the anterior teeth. It is a lesser amount of reduction, and not expansion, that accounts for their enlarged relative size.

Table 11.8
Some Distinguishing Features of Middle Pleistocene Dentitions[1]

	North African and Chinese	European
Upper incisors	flat crown shape	crown curved from side to side
Buccal cingulum	canines and postcanine teeth of both jaws	usually absent
P$_3$	vertical buccal face	sloping buccal face
P$_4$	square shape from additional cusps (molarization)	rectangular shape, usually 2 cusps
Lower premolar root number	2	usually 1
Lower molar cusp pattern	the anterior lingual cusp meets the posterior buccal cusp at the middle of the tooth	often the anterior buccal cusp meets the posterior lingual cusp at the middle of the tooth

[1]   From J. Bermúdez de Castro, M-A. DeLumley, and T. Crummett

Examination of the dental anatomy shows clear relations between these teeth and the somewhat later Neandertal samples. Compared with dental remains from other regions, the Atapuerca dentitions help establish a long temporal span for the presence of features that remain most common in Europe. These include the marked crown curvature of the upper incisors, and buccal cusp dominance and sloping buccal face in the P_3. Supporting the notion of continuity within Europe, according to Bermúdez de Castro the anatomy of the Atapuerca teeth also suggest a series of differences that distinguish them from North African and Chinese Middle Pleistocene dentitions in similar ways (table 11.8).

Bermúdez de Castro and colleagues also examined the question of sexual dimorphism in the dental remains by comparing dimorphism in the sample with the dimorphism in several human populations for which sex information is known. They were able to show that the magnitude of dimorphism was invariably greater in the fossil sample. The pattern of mandibular dimorphism differed as well, with less apparent overlap between males and females. This is similar to the pattern that F. Weidenreich posited for the Zhoukoudian remains.

Handedness was examined two different ways. Arsuaga and colleagues report that the frontal petalia (see Chapter 4) of several specimens is on the right side, suggesting right handedness because it reflects left hemisphere dominance. Dental studies by Bermúdez de Castro and colleagues used the direction of labial scratches across the anterior incisors. These are caused when stone tools are used to cut something held between the front teeth and the cutting is very close to the teeth, for instance a piece of meat or gristle. 23 teeth of at least 8 individuals were examined and the direction of the scratches showed all to be right handed. It is significant that buccal scratches were found on a deciduous canine. The possibility that pre-Neandertal (and Neandertal) children ate significant amounts of meat is further supported by a study of deciduous molar wear on the Gibraltar Neandertal child by C. Lalueza Fox and A. Pérez-Pérez. They microscopically examined the pattern and number of horizontal and vertical striations. The pattern as indicated by the horizontal to vertical striation ratio in this child of closely resembles that found in adults of high meat-intake populations such as Eskimos and Fuegians.

Table 11.9
Postcranial Remains from Atapuerca

Bone	Number in 1993
vertebrae	23
ribs	9
clavicles	7
scapulae	10
humeri	15
ulnae	5
radii	7
carpals	10
metacarpals	2
hand phalanges	76
sacrums	2
innominates	19
femora	30
tibiae	23
fibulae	19
patellae	6
tali	15
metatarsals	14
foot phalanges	44

Virtually all parts of the body are represented among the Atapuerca postcranial remains (table 11.9). These reveal the Atapuerca folk to be large and robust in comparison with earlier temperate northern hemisphere hominids. Body size can be compared using the sizes of arm (humerus) and leg (tibia) bones. Two of the three humeri (table 11.10) are the size of the Kabwe humerus, and all are substantially larger than the Zhoukoudian specimens.

Table 11.10
Humerus dimensions at the middle of the shaft

	Maximum diameter	Minimum diameter
Zhoukoudian J3	20.4	15.4
PA 64	21.7	16.1
Kabwe E 898	24.5	22.5
Atapuerca AT 25	24.5	18.8
AT 93	27.7	18.8
AT 217	25.0	21.0

Similarly, sizes of two tibial pieces are larger than the Sangiran and Zhoukoudian specimens (table 11.11), but in this case smaller than the Kabwe tibia thought to be associated with the cranium, and considerably smaller than Boxgrove. The size difference with the later is quite substantial, but there are too few specimens involved to know whether the difference is biologically significant (for instance whether it reflects sexual dimorphism, differences in climatic adaptation, an evolutionary trend for size reduction). The Atapuerca tibiae (like the earlier Boxgrove specimen) are considerably more elongated at midshaft than their earlier Middle Pleistocene counterparts and more similar to Sambungmachan.

Table 11.11
Tibia Size and Shape

	Midshaft anteroposterior diameter	Midshaft transverse diameter	Ratio
Sangiran 19B	27.7	23.3	119
Zhoukoudian PA 65	25.2	19.8	127
Sambungmachan	32.0	21.2	151
Kabwe E 691	34.1	24.5	139
Atapuerca AT 19	29.3	22.5	130
AT 85	27.6	20.0	138
Boxgrove	39.5	30.0	132

THE FEMALES: SWANSCOMBE, STEINHEIM, AND REILINGEN

Swanscombe and Steinheim were the first of the Middle Pleistocene European crania to be discovered. The Swanscombe skull fragments are the oldest known human remains from Britain. Originally a parietal and an occiput were found, in the mid-1930s, and described in a 1938 report by the Swanscombe committee. The other parietal was recovered after intensive search in 1955 and the complete cranial rear was subsequently analyzed by a number of authors. Steinheim was found in 1933 in a gravel pit near Stuttgart, Germany. A fairly accurate but incomplete description was given by H. Weinert, but his study was very brief. Weinert's study was against the will of F. Berckhemer, who excavated the skull and possessed it at the time - it was forced on him by Weinert's Berlin connections in the National

Socialist party. With this unsavory background, it never became a widely cited work, and the experience so embittered Berckhemer that he hid Steinheim under his bed for decades. Both specimens were thought to come from a Middle Pleistocene warm period, originally assumed to be the Hoxnian interglacial (stage 13, as all warm periods clearly before the Eemian once were). This is no longer clear. J. Cook and colleagues suggest Swanscombe derived from a cool period; they suggest stage 7, which seems confirmed by a TL date of 225 kyr. A date based on the epimerization of some non-marine mollusks correlated to the site is about 300 kyr. This is stage 8, and both stages are within the Riss complex of stadials. Steinheim could be as old as the Hoxnian, but it was originally thought to derive from a Riss interstadial and it remains possible that these two are penecontemporary.

The first interpretation of Swanscombe was that it was "virtually indistinguishable" from modern crania, although even then it was recognized as unusually low and broad. The occipital contour is evenly rounded, and there is no substantial development of a projecting nuchal torus. Consequently, the contour of the specimen, in side view, is modern appearing, though small.

Unfortunately, many of the features that might be useful in determining the relationships of the Swanscombe cranium are missing. However, there are hints of what these might have been like from the remaining vault bones. To begin with, although the first impression of the skull form is modern, the combination of features is not. The probability of finding a modern cranium with the Swanscombe dimensions is extremely small. The cranial height falls at the low end of the modern human range of variation, while the breadth of the occiput falls at the very high end. Only a very large modern skull would be expected to have the great occipital breadth, while only a very small one would have the cranial height.

Other archaic features lie at the rear and base of the cranium, where the development of spongy bone is marked and the nuchal muscle attachment area is large. Above it there is a suprainiac fossa. The position of the external occipital protuberance is well above the internal occipital protuberance like virtually every other Middle Pleistocene cranium. The internal protuberance is defined by the impressions of the occipital lobes of the brain but the external one is caused by the powerful nuchal ligament - its strength is indicated by how high above the internal protuberance that the external protuberance can be found.

The form of the missing portions of the Swanscombe cranium might be estimated with reasonable accuracy from Steinheim, a crushed and distorted specimen that preserves much of what Swanscombe lacks. The base of the cranium is broken open in a manner similar to the crania from Zhoukoudian. The whole left side has been twisted toward the midline, so that the single (fourth) premolar is almost at the middle of the cranium. Moreover, the back of the cranium is warped underneath and to the side, making the nuchal region appear more rounded than it actually was. Finally, the incisor-bearing portion of the upper jaw is broken away, which makes the face look much smaller and less prognathic than it probably appeared in life.

Table 11.12
Comparison of Some Middle Pleistocene Female Crania[1]

	Reilingen	Swanscombe	Steinheim	Salé
Length (measured without the frontal, from bregma to inion)	149	146	136	129
Parietal breadth	144	145	127[2]	130
Cranial height (basion-bregma)	(127)	125	105	110
Cranial capacity	≤1430[3]	1250	≈ 900	880

[1] The Atapuerca female capacity is 1125 cc.

[2] Although some compensation was attempted by symmetrically reconstructing the left side from the more complete right, this measurement is most likely to be affected by distortion.

[3] Estimate courtesy of R. Holloway.

As preserved, the dimensions and features are inaccurate, but more than sufficient to show that the braincase and face were small. Steinheim, in fact, is a *very* small cranium, much smaller than usually assumed. Dimensionally it is the same size or even smaller than Salé, whose capacity was determined at 880 cc, and under the circumstances a 900 cc estimate would be generous. The vault is quite gracile; muscle markings are weakly expressed, the nuchal plane is small for a Middle Pleistocene specimen, and the positions of the internal and external occipital protuberance are the same. The face is delicate in appearance. It is small for a Middle Pleistocene face, closest to the Tabun female (see Chapter 12), Zuttiyeh for the upper portion, and the Atapuerca fragment AT 404 in size. It is also approximately the size of Weidenreich's reconstructed Zhoukoudian female face and resembles it in the marked projection and substantial thickness of the browridges and the position of the forehead behind rather than above them. The browridges really contrast with the gracility of the face and cranial rear. They are vertically thicker and more anteriorly projecting than in most Neandertal males, a remarkably archaic feature for so small a face. But there are numerous specific contrasts. For instance, the browridge in Steinheim forms a much more dramatically double-arch contour, closely conforming to the shape of the orbits and dipping over the nose. Unlike the Chinese specimens it thins markedly toward the sides. Steinheim also exhibits more midfacial prognathism (forward projection of the nasal region and above). In spite of this the face is transversely flat, the flatness accomplished by bringing the outer parts of the cheeks anterior to match the midface, attained by lengthening the zygomatic arch. The prognathism, in other words, affects the entire face and not just the midline structures. Expanded maxillary sinuses help bring the entire face forward, but the midface is not expanded enough to describe as puffy or obscure the canine fossa, a morphology that is not unique as the AT 404 face has one as well.

Steinheim is more complete and reveals details of the cranium and face that Swanscombe cannot because it is only a cranial rear. It presents a combination of a more archaic front and less archaic rear that characterizes many of the African Middle Pleistocene crania.

When F.C. Howell reviewed the European Middle Pleistocene hominids in 1960 these were the only specimens known with cranial remains. At the time they were pivotal to the **Presapiens Hypothesis** as developed by H. Vallois (and later G. Heberer). The hypothesis, mainly applied to Europe, proposes that two separate lineages can be found in the Middle Pleistocene. One lineage (presapiens) evolved directly into modern *H. sapiens* populations and closely resembled these modern forms at an early date. The second lineage (preneandertal) evolved into the European Neandertal populations of the earlier Würm glaciation (see Chapter 13) and subsequently became extinct. In 1954 Vallois accepted only one Middle Pleistocene European fossil as representing presapiens, Swanscombe. According to Vallois, presapiens specimens are characterized by a thick, low-vaulted cranium with great occipital breadth, roughly square parietal borders, and lacking a prominent nuchal torus. The frontal is described as "upright and completely lacking any [supraorbital] torus." His description of the frontal is particularly curious since neither Swanscombe nor the only other European fossil he considered presapiens (Fontéchevade, a later French cranium just before the Würm) preserved the supraorbital region. Vallois regarded the other early European fossils known in 1954—Steinheim and the Mauer and Montmaurin mandibles—as preneandertal.

That the presapiens hypothesis received wide acceptance is probably more a reflection of the general belief that the Würm Neandertals were something apart from the mainstream of human evolution (a problem discussed in Chapter 13) than a result of convincing European fossil evidence for an early lineage division. In fact, scientists such as Breitinger, LeGros Clark, and Morant recognized the fundamental similarities of Swanscombe and Steinheim almost as soon as the two could be compared. Howell also emphasized their similarities and used them to underscore the ways in which Europe seemed distinct from the Middle Pleistocene remains from Africa and Asia. In the "origins of modern humans" sweepstakes, Howell weighed in with a European origin theory at that time, as he regarded the European specimens as generally more advanced.

In fact, where the two can be compared, compensating for distortion, Steinheim and Swanscombe are quite similar. Swanscombe is the larger (the estimated capacity is 1250 cc). Other shared features include:

- marked reduction of the nuchal torus and rounding of the occiput,
- narrow frontal (inferred from the angle of the parietals in Swanscombe).
- fairly vertical parietals of similar shape (long temporal border, short frontal border)
- thin vault bones
- an absence of significant lambdoidal flattening or bunning

The Steinheim mastoids are small and according to T. Stewart the anatomy of the surrounding region in Swanscombe is quite similar (there is no temporal) . He believes that the Neandertal-like occipitomastoid area suggests a similarly small mastoid process (an idea confirmed by the discovery of Biache, a later, very Swanscombe-like cranium discussed in Chapter 13).

The third female to be considered is Reilingen, an undated German specimen that can be linked to this group by its anatomy. Reilingen was dredged out of the Rhine river gravels, and later identified in a museum collection by A. Czarnetzki. The fauna it was found with is Middle Pleistocene, similar species to those found at Swanscombe, but the issue of whether it actually can be associated with that fauna can never be resolved. It is similar to Swanscombe, although somewhat larger (see table 11.12) and with a temporal bone. Like Swanscombe is has a suprainiac fossa. There are a number of specific similarities to later Neandertals, including the following:

- there is an occipital **chignon** (bun) with
  - lambdoidal flattening on the parietal and occiput creating its roof,
  - a flat surface (with the suprainiac fossa) above the weak nuchal torus at its rear
  - distinct lateral walls forming its sides
- the temporal line only reaches the lambdoidal suture at a very low position, the temporo-occipital juncture (**asterion**)
- the articular surface on the anterior wall of the mandibular fossa slopes gradually downward (it is not divided into vertical and horizontal surfaces)
- the maximum frontal breadth is greatly expanded compared with the other Middle Pleistocene females

Its mastoid process is one point of difference. While it is not immense by any means, the process is significantly larger (taller and broader) than that of Biache or the later Neandertal females. Never the less, in most regards it resembles Biache, and the question of whether it is an earlier example of the coalescence of Neandertal features, or a later specimen than the fauna (which is, after all, not directly associated) suggests, cannot be answered.

When they were the only Middle Pleistocene Europeans known, Swanscombe and Steinheim seemed to be an enigma. When these two were compared with earlier populations such as the Sangiran or Zhoukoudian ones, and even the later Neandertals, the vaults were recognized as unexpectedly gracile. The face of Steinheim seemed to confirm what the Weidenreich facial reconstruction of ZKT L II cranium showed when it was the only earlier Middle Pleistocene face known - the Neandertals were evolving bigger faces than their ancestors and therefore changing in a direction away from humanity. But then came the discoveries of numerous other Middle Pleistocene specimens with faces, beginning with far more robust Europeans such as Petralona and Asians such as Sangiran 17. Subsequent discoveries greatly increased this sample, as a reader of this chapter might appreciate. They established the criteria for sex determination, allowed the first-found Europeans to be identified as females, and required all comparisons to be made anew with females compared only with females, and males with males.

In my opinion insofar as the three European females differ from their Neandertal descendants they are more like other earlier Middle Pleistocene populations. Their variations, for instance, can be totally subsumed within the Atapuerca range. In no way are they more like modern European populations than either their contemporaries or their Neandertal progeny, and they cannot validly be used to establish an interpretation of a more modern appearing human line in Europe (as they have in the past). Most of their contrasts with phenacontemporary Europeans derives from the fact that they are women.

ARAGO

The Arago cave, in southeastern France, has at least twenty-three individuals recovered. A wide range of contradictory dates for the cave have been obtained by using various methods. The confused situation reviewed by Cook and colleagues more than a decade ago has not been improved. Of the human remains, eight are children. Some adult specimens are represented by single teeth, cranial fragments, and postcranial pieces, but Arago 2 and 13 are fairly complete mandibles, and Arago 21 is a virtually complete cranium, lacking only the temporal and occipital bones. In its reconstruction by M-A. de Lumley and colleagues the Swanscombe occiput was used to produce the appearance of a complete specimen. It also helps create the impression of female sex, as does a number of other features actually preserved on the specimen.

One of these is the small size of the vault. R. Holloway estimates a cranial capacity of 1166 cc, within the range of the Middle Pleistocene European females and, for that matter, within the normal range of living people. In studying the endocast he makes three points:

1. Broca's cap (see Chapter 4) and other speech areas are very well developed, within the modern human range and larger than many
2. Indications of the right parietal association area extensive "and of thoroughly human aspect"
3. Endocast shape is very similar to that of Swanscombe (he approves of the choice of occipital)

Holloway concludes that apart from the slightly more pointed frontal, the endocast is modern in its anatomy. He suggests from the asymmetry of the endocast that Arago 21 is right handed.

In general, Arago 21 is more like Steinheim dimensionally but more like Petralona anatomically. The frontal begins as much over as behind the browridge and does not narrow much behind it. This makes it appear more filled out than specimens such as Steinheim, but it does not have a frontal boss (this and other features are summarized in table 11.14). As a result of these two differences the Arago supratoral sulcus is less well excavated. The frontal is relatively broad just behind the orbits, the difference between this dimension (minimum frontal breadth) and maximum frontal breadth is not great. The parietal, discovered later than the frontofacial portion, expands outwards in the reconstruction, contributing to the "teardrop" cranial shape as seen from above. There is a marked parietal boss - this is common at Atapuerca where its expression is even more dramatic in Atapuerca 4 - and there is an angular torus. From the rear the cranial shape is gabled, with vertical sides and a gently up-sloping roof, again like anatomy found at Atapuerca but in this case resembling cranium 5. At the midline there is a low, broad sagittal keel.

The face is short and prognathic, with a puffy maxilla and straight lower cheek border that makes it appear as a small version of males such as Petralona and Apidima (see below). The browridges are fairly large and projecting, as seen from above they extend quite flatly across the face and angle backwards only toward their ends. Over the nose their thickness dimensions are between Steinheim and Petralona (table 11.7). Like Steinheim they thin toward the lateral edge, but the thinning begins more centrally and the Arago 21 thickness over the middle of the orbit is less than both. Below them, the nasal root is depressed (it is tucked under the overhanging supraorbital) and below it the nasal angle is quite low. This broad but fairly small face is dominated by expanded zygomatics, which shelve evenly onto the maxilla in a low position (as in Petralona). Maxillary puffiness obliterates the canine fossa, like some other Middle Pleistocene Europeans, and the alveolar region is markedly prognathic. Facial dimensions are almost invariably midway between Steinheim and Petralona, and in most cases much closer to Steinheim. In general, the most extensive similarities are with Atapuerca 5. The comparison of Arago to Petralona involves many of the same contrasts as the comparison of a female to male Neandertal, for instance Gibraltar to La Ferrassie. Arago has 85% the male facial height, just as Gibraltar has 85% the La Ferrassie facial height. The facial breadth comparisons are almost the same as well (93% compared with 92% for the two Neandertals). De Lumley suggests that Arago 21 is probably male. In my view, the facial comparisons and resemblance to the Atapuerca 5 female, cranial size, and dental variation (see below) support the female diagnosis. A second, much more incomplete partial maxilla (Arago 45) is quite similar.

Sex determination for the two well-preserved mandibles is less ambiguous. Differences in size and robustness are consistent with the idea that Arago 2 is female and Arago 13 is male. (The Arago 21 maxillary teeth lie between these in size.) The much larger male died as a teen with third molar just erupted, about 16 years old. The mandible has a very high, narrow ramus and rounded, sloping symphysis. The ramus of the much older (about 30) female mandible is lower but much broader (this is often unnoticed because an unconnected piece of anterior border and coronoid process is usually not shown with it). Its symphysis has one of the earliest discovered traces of a chin. At the base of the symphysis there is a moderate bulge in the form of a triangle, apex upwards. This is a **mental trigone** which, when more prominent, can be properly called a **mental eminence**. In its weakest expression, as in Arago 2, the trigone is clearly expressed but the eminence is only feebly developed.

The Arago teeth are remarkable for both their size and their variation. The largest mandibular dentition, Arago 13, has posterior teeth bigger than any known from the Middle Pleistocene! Several large molars of what appears to be a young specimen (Arago 1) are even bigger - dwarfing the type specimen of "*Paranthropus robustus*" (Kromdraai cranium TM 1517). In fact, the teeth of Arago 1 and 13 fall well within the late australopithecine size range, as well as in the range of morphological variation. However other dentitions are much smaller. The posterior teeth of the female mandible (Arago 2) are 65% the size of Arago 13's. When all of the Arago teeth are combined, which is a better estimate of the populational characteristics, the average posterior tooth size at Arago is reduced compared with earlier Middle Pleistocene samples. According to P-F. Puech the wear characteristics of the mandibular teeth are similar to high meat-intake populations such as Eskimos.

There are a number of fragmentary postcranial remains. A virtually complete innominate (Arago 44) can be compared with much earlier remains from Lake Turkana (ER 3228, Chapter 9) and Olduvai 28 (Chapter 10). While it is the largest of the three, details that reflect sex indicate that Arago 44 is female. The fundamental anatomy of these three innominates does not vary in any substantial way, they share a widely flared ilium and a strong buttress extending up it from the acetabulum. The Arago bone differing mainly in the greater breadth of the iliac blade. The blade expands behind the acetabulum, increasing the distance from the hip joint to the sacrum. This has the effect of making the pelvic inlet deeper, and therefore more circular in shape than the earlier pelves. If the female diagnosis is accurate, the large acetabulum suggest a body size not unexpected in populations with males as large as Boxgrove.

Other indications of size come from the femurs. Arago 48 is the size of the largest Kabwe femora and larger than any from Zhoukoudian. In a biomechanical analysis comparing several of the partial femora to a sample of robust Native American male specimens, C.O. Lovejoy reports that the Arago specimens are markedly stronger. The strength difference results from the bone's internal structure - the cortical bone is thick while the medullary cavity is small, a pattern also observed in the Zhoukoudian and other archaic human postcranial remains. Other Arago postcranial bones are adapted to powerful action as well. Lovejoy found the same relationship in making comparisons of several Arago fibulae with other specimens. In terms of their strength estimates, the four fibulae cluster in two groups (of two each). Moreover, the larger of these is more than 60% stronger than the smaller, almost certainly a reflection of sex differences in strength.

The marked variability at Arago, is in major part a consequence of sexual dimorphism. This is similar to the dimorphism at Atapuerca, a site that is also conspicuous for its variation. Variability, in fact, is the norm in these samples of more than a few individuals. This suggests how misleading the analysis of other sites with only single specimens might be, especially if sex determination is unclear. It helps emphasize the idea that it is samples and not individuals that should be compared.

THE GREEK MALES: PETRALONA AND APIDIMA

Petralona was discovered by some shepherds when they fell into a cavern near Thessalonika that is part of a complex cave system. Some reports state that they found a whole fossilized skeleton laid out on a limestone slab. However, other reports are contradictory, and the fate of the postcranial skeleton which was presumably found with the cranium is unknown. There probably wasn't any. Relating matrix on the cranium to strata in the cave, A. Latham and H. Schwarcz review a series of ESR and Uranium series dates (including their own), concluding that the minimum age for the skull is approximately 200 kyr, and no maximum age can be determined. In many respects, the Petralona cranium is a European version of the Bodo and Kabwe crania. The specimen is a male, combining an extremely large face with a low and robust braincase. There are great similarities between it and Kabwe, and yet also important differences.

The basic dimensions of the braincase are similar to those of Kabwe (table 11.5). Its main differences are in cranial breadths, which except for occipital breadth are substantially greater (it is the Kabwe occipital breadth that is the notably larger of the two). Petralona has a more robust appearance, mainly because of the different details of cheek development and the fact that it has more spongy bone at the cranial base than any other Middle Pleistocene European. The maximum cranial breadth is considerably greater than the braincase breadth. Some of this contrast is due to the extreme asymmetry of the Petralona cranium. As seen from the rear, the right cranial wall slopes outward, while the left wall is vertical and this side has less spongy bone. The asymmetric development affects the entire braincase; for instance, the right parietal is considerably more bulging than the left. The back border of the right temporal is flanged outward, possibly as the result of powerful horizontal fibers of the deeper part of posterior temporalis on this side.

The system of cranial buttresses is well developed in Petralona. The nasal and midorbital portions of the browridge are extremely thick, and (as in Steinheim) there is marked thinning to the sides. The browridge follows the superior orbital border (as in both Steinheim and Kabwe), rather than forming a straight bar at the base of the forehead. At its center, a slight furrow separates the two sides. There is a low sagittal keel involving only the central third of the parietals, and a low (unprojecting) but vertically thick nuchal torus extends across the back of the cranium.

The occiput is very broad; the estimated nuchal muscle attachment area is about the same as Kabwe. The occipital plane above it has a filled out appearance and is slightly longer than the nuchal plane. Petralona has a large extrasutural bone at the top of the occiput. Such bones usually form when the lambdoidal suture (between the occiput and the parietals) is under stress, as might result from powerful nuchal action drawing the occiput downward. These bones are not uncommon in Europe; for instance, the somewhat later Hungarian occiput from Vértesszöllös has one as well.

The tall Petralona face is undistorted and is one of the best preserved from the Middle Pleistocene. It is vertically set and lacks alveolar prognathism. The large rectangular orbits are widely separated and overlie robustly developed zygomatics, which are much deeper and better developed than those in Kabwe, more closely resembling the Bodo face in ruggedness. The lower border of the zygomatics angles gradually downward until it merges with the outer wall of the maxilla in a rather low position; the lack of a distinct maxillary notch on this border is called the "flying buttress." The region is similar to Arago 21 and clearly foreshadows the Neandertal condition. Also like the Arago female, and Neandertals, the cheeks begin in a fairly forward position but they angle strongly backward so that the fronts of the cheeks are at more than 45° to a plane from one side of the skull to the other. The maxillary sinuses are very large and are expanded outward, giving the face a puffy appearance, completely lacking a canine fossa (the region to the sides of the nose is convex). This morphology is associated with a forward projection of the entire face. However the puffiness is not as extreme as in the Neandertals and the maxillary face not as convex. Moreover there is not as much midfacial prognathism. The forward projection of this robust male face is not even as great as the Neandertal women. What remains of the nose is prominent in profile and broad. The internal nasal chamber is voluminous. I. Budil attempted a reconstruction of the supralaryngeal region below it (the region of the throat above the voice box) based on the anatomical features of the cranial base and the angulation of the styloid process (this process is the seat of a ligament that extends to the hyoid bone, at the top of the voice box, and its angle helps determine its position in the throat). His work suggests that Petralona had a low position for the vocal chords, and therefore had attained the paired attributes of crossed esophagus and trachea openings (enhancing the ability to choke) and a long space above the chords (enhancing the ability to produce a human range of vocalizations).

Table 11.13
Petralona and Kabwe

	Petralona	Kabwe
lateral supraorbital thinning	present	no thinning
supraorbital center seen from above	concave	convex, projecting
frontal squama	moderate sagittal boss	sagittal keel
nasal rim	at nasal floor/maxillary juncture	on maxilla, below and in front of nasal floor
nasal spine	more projecting	definite but less projecting
maxilla lateral to nose	convex (maxillary puffing)	flat
maxilla below nose	flat, vertical	prognathic
infraorbital foramen	low	high
Zygomatic bone face	flattened	angled
torus along palate roof	none	low, with two parallel ridges
mandibular fossa length	narrow, constricted	broad
zygomatic root, over mandibular fossa	narrow	wide
posterior temporal squama	flanged outward	flat
vertical dimension of nuchal torus	thick	thin
sulcus above nuchal torus	stronger	weaker
extrasutural bones	in lambdoidal suture	none

The very large dentition is set in a broad palate, marked by straight but diverging posterior tooth rows and a very straight line of anterior teeth, with the canine marking the corner. Both the size and proportions of the dentition and the form of the palate closely resemble Kabwe. In fact, Petralona and Kabwe seem generally similar, a point emphasized by several who have studied the crania. Yet, there are many specific differences between them (table 11.13). Many of these features also distinguish other Africans such as Bodo and other Europeans such as Arago 21. They also help differentiate Late Pleistocene Europeans and Africans.

The two Apidima crania were found quite near each other in a small coastal cave near Laconia.. Completely undated, their similarities to Petralona (especially Apidima 2) suggest the initial hypothesis that their ages are similar. Apidima 2 is a robust male, with massive cheeks that are posteriorly oriented and puffy enough to lack a canine fossa. Cranial dimensions are quite similar to Petralona, the Apidima length being slightly less while breadth and height are virtually identical. The cheeks are not as broad as Petralona, nor is the nose, and the face (and) nose not as tall, but on the whole there is a notable resemblance between these specimens. A. Coutselinis and colleagues describe several fractures on the cranial vault, most on the frontal bone. They attribute the individual's death to these, but the breaks may well have occurred after death.

DIMORPHISM AND OTHER RELATIONS

The pattern and magnitude of differences within this sample underlies much of the thinking about contemporary European lines. The idea of different contemporary human species in Europe is not limited to the older conjectures of Vallois, discussed above. Initial interpretations if the Vértesszöllös occipital by A. Thoma argued for early contemporary lineages. Paleoanthropologists such as J. Piveteau and M-A. de Lumley interpret the fossil record to show the presence of two European forms during the Riss glaciation (see Chapter 13). Their reasoning depends mainly on the shape of the parietal bone. The latest, and probably not the last, such attempt is that of Stringer, who wants to name the separate European species *H. heidelbergensis* - a name first applied to the Mauer mandible, and later dismissed when it was included in broader species such as "*H. erectus*".

I believe that all of this "evidence" is weak, or even nonexistent. By and large the data used to support theories of contemporary lineages within Europe are better explained by more mundane sources of variation, time, geography, and sexual dimorphism. Broad, geographic differences distinguishing Europeans from human populations in other regions seem to reflect racial variation within a polytypic species, and not differences between species. The variation seen within large samples such as Atapuerca should put an end to other theorizations for good.

The two most important sources of systematic variation within Europe are sexual dimorphism and evolutionary change. Apidima 2 and Petralona would make good males in a population containing females like Steinheim, Reilingen and Swanscombe, if that population had a magnitude of sexual dimorphism similar to that found at Atapuerca, and more than living people. Of course, they were not in the same population, but the point is that sexual dimorphism on a scale not unlike that found in earlier hominids could account for the variation in these crania. The pattern of features that differ fits a dimorphism model; the main contrasts are in:

- overall cranial size and capacity
- vault thickness
- superstructures and torusing (mastoid process, sagittal keel, nuchal torus)
- forehead curvature
- functionally related features of facial size and robustness

If the pattern of dimorphism is fully like the earlier African remains we can expect that dimorphism in body size is not as great. Neandertals from Europe (Chapter 13) retain a virtually identical pattern and magnitude of dimorphism, contrasting cranial and postcranial sex differences.

The other source of systematic variation is temporal. There are evolutionary trends that extend through the Middle Pleistocene Europeans (and beyond, through much of the Late Pleistocene). Some of the changes are European reflections of evolution that encompasses all human populations such as:

- significant cranial capacity expansion
- supraorbital reduction
- thinning of the cranial vault
- expansion of the occipital plane at the expense of the nuchal plane
- postcanine dental reduction

Others seem more unique to Europe. Many of these involve the face, and combine:

- mid-facial projection in front of the lateral parts of the face
- lateral facing outer orbital borders
- prognathism of the entire face
- maxillary puffing and the absence of a canine fossa
- verticality of the facial profile

Together, these are the sources of systematic anatomical variation.

Multiregional Evolution

The Multiregional model of human evolution describes the pattern of population variation and evolutionary change in a widespread, geographically diverse species that is internally subdivided. Based in the precept that the present is a valid model for interpreting the past, it attempts to frame how evolutionary change continued in the face of geographic dispersion without speciation - the pattern that seems to characterize the last 2 myr of human evolution. The key elements are

- the historic and adaptive processes that created and maintained the pattern of variation
- the dynamics of reproduction, communication, and population movements that link local populations and provide the network for advantageous changes - whether these are based on new gene combinations or new ideas - to diffuse throughout the species.

The species evolves as various localized advantageous changes spread widely and persist. The Multiregional model is an attempt to account for the combination of long-lasting diversity and species-wide evolution by examining the consequences of the species' internal structure - widespread diversification linked by gradations of continuously varying features that reflect gradients in selection, genic exchanges between adjacent populations, or both. The gradations persist when they balance the forces that create differences, for instance directional genic exchanges that often extend from the center to the edge of the species range, and local selection that is often most intense in more peripheral populations.

In a nutshell, the Multiregional Evolution model begins with the obvious - humans are a single widespread polytypic species, with multiple, constantly evolving, interlinked, populations whose dynamics can be partially explained by evolutionary processes that pertain to other widespread polytypic species in general. These processes can be understood both through clinal theory and the history and consequences of population placements relative to other populations - the center and edge mechanism described in Chapter 10. They have affected humans since *H. sapiens* became a single widespread polytypic species and therefore can explain patterns of morphological variation that we see in prehistory - patterns extending for a long time into the past, to the time when humans first successfully colonized regions outside of Africa. This is when evidence of regional continuities in different places first becomes apparent and convincing. As discussed in this chapter and before, there is no indication of speciations that would suggest different evolutionary processes.

The idea that humans evolved across the inhabited world, and that modern populations find their ancestry in many sources and not one, is not original to Multiregional Evolution or to its immediate predecessor, Weidenreich's Polycentric Evolution. But this does not as much give Multiregional Evolution historic depth as much as a historic headache because the doctrines developed in the last century involve the precept of the independent, simultaneous evolution of ancient races - the anathema of Multiregional Evolution (which is probably why its opponents often attribute this pre-Darwinian precept to it). The vision of independently evolving races is based on a pre-evolutionary theory called polygeny that was the opposition to the biblical origins theory, or monogeny. Like many older biological concepts, polygeny survived Darwinism and entered the twentieth century as part of the baggage from the nineteenth. In this century the separately evolving human lines were envisioned as independently originating in different ape taxa. Sir Arthur Keith subscribed to the idea in his *New Theory of Human Evolution*, after skirmishing with it for most of his career. As recently as 1936 the highly influential Harvard physical anthropologist E. Hooton wrote, in the race chapter of his influential textbook *Up from the Ape*

> during the Miocene period a family of giant generalized anthropoid apes, the Dryopithecus
> family, ... evolved both into the ancestors of existing and extinct forms of anthropoid apes
> and those of several varities of man. ... certain of the progressive Dryopithecus genera took
> to the ground in several parts of the anthropoid zone. Some of these became the ancestors
> of extinct human precursors, while others were the progenitors of the lines leading to
> present day races of man (pp. 372-373).

Hooton was the graduate advisor of W. Howells, and between these two Harvard anthropologists lie the responsibility of having trained almost all American paleoanthropologists, their graduate advisors, or the graduate advisors of their graduate advisors. Hooton's influence has been immense. Because of it, Multiregional Evolution addresses both the task of unraveling the complex evolutionary processes in a polytypic species, and unraveling itself from pre-Darwinian concepts that seem similar but actually are so very different.

GEOGRAPHIC DIFFERENCES

The two fundamental reasons why geographically disperse human populations differ are adaptation and history. In considering the affects of the Center and Edge process during regional colonizations (Chapter 10) some of the affects of history were outlined. In particular, more peripheral populations were found to be homogeneous for a number of features. Some of these were adaptive, important elements that helped populations meet the requirements of their environments. These appeared in high frequency in response to changes in the conditions that made them helpful, not always at the time of colonization. Others, however, were established during the history of genetic drift and bottlenecking at the time of the colonization process. These are homogeneous variants of anatomy that are equivalent alternatives. Established at high frequencies, especially in peripheral populations, some of these features disappeared but others persisted. Some cases of this persistence reflect an evolutionary momentum. Nonadaptive features initially at high frequencies may remain unaltered because no evolutionary forces change them. Others, however, become incorporated in local adaptations. These are examples of exaptation (see Chapter 2) because they were not initially established to promote the adaptation that was important later, and for this reason they can differ substantially between different populations meeting the same adaptive requirements.

Features such as these reflect past racial differences. The races themselves are transitory, but in many cases the features have not been. Whether established by adaptation or by other historic processes, the observation that characteristics of both types persisted for long periods of time, in some cases through the Late Pleistocene and some even to recent and living populations, is called **regional continuity**. The *explanation of regional continuity* in *Homo* is found in the Multiregional Evolution model that I developed with A. Thorne and Wu Xinzhi.

A DYNAMIC MODEL OF POLYTYPIC SPECIES EVOLUTION

How did populations retain geographic distinctions and yet evolve together? This is the apparent paradox that Multiregional Evolution addresses. If it is true that isolation is necessary for long term geographic differentiation, wouldn't that eliminate any common patterns of evolution unless they were fortuitous? If genic exchanges are required for common evolutionary directions, wouldn't they eliminate geographic distinctions? How could we possibly expect these two contradictory processes to be of just the right magnitude to allow both persisting regional distinctions and common evolutionary changes? And what, if anything, does this have to do with race?.

Part of the resolution of this paradox lies in the incorrect assumptions above. Isolation is not essential for maintaining geographic distinctions. Many of these differences are found in broad gradients, responding to selection that differs over a wide geographic range, for instance skin color that usually corresponds to the amount of solar radiation that skins are exposed to. This would be particularly characteristic of skeletal features that can reflect climatic adaptation such as relative limb lengths or nasal form. Their interpretation is complex because many, perhaps most, adaptive characteristics *function in several different adaptive* systems. Therefore the distribution of these features may respond to different evolutionary pressures. Relative limb length, for instance, is also important in different patterns of mobility. We discussed a good example of this with the skeletal variations occurring at the origin of *H. sapiens* (Chapter 9).

Another invalid assumption is that genic exchanges are necessary for there to be common directions to evolutionary changes in different populations. Exchanges may create these commonalties, of course, as advantageous alleles would spread widely because of the advantages they confer and result in the same evolutionary changes in different places. Human populations are particularly receptive to this process because communication systems could disseminate the very behaviors that make some of these alleles advantageous, such as new hunting technologies, improved organizational skills, or important changes in the communication systems themselves. Yet at the same time communication, the exchanges of ideas, information, and technology, could become an independent cause of common evolutionary directions. Disseminating ideas can create changes in selection, and populations with similar gene pools could respond in the same manner. As pointed out in Chapter 2, the similarities between human gene pools are more extensive than one might imagine. Geneticists such as R. Lewontin have long argued that the vast majority of human genetic variation is within populations and not between them, and it is commonly quipped that any two fruit flies have more genetic differences than the most extreme two people. There is ample opportunity for similar selection to cause similar changes. These two processes are not independent. When ideas and artifacts spread, genes frequently spread as well.

However, a more important resolution to the paradox lies in the affects these contradictory elements have on each other. They are both part of a single process - clinal variation. Gradually varying distributions of a feature can develop when the source of selection it responds to varies gradually, such as skin color corresponding to differences in solar radiation as noted above. Clines will also form when there are contradictory evolutionary forces affecting a feature; for instance, genic exchanges and selection. Populations are usually more numerous and denser toward the center of a species range, sparser and less common toward the edge. Population movements are usually from denser to sparser regions, and advantageous new alleles or allele combinations are more likely to first appear in the center as there are bigger gene pools there, these then spreading outward because of the advantages the confer. Toward the peripheries, however, there may be opposing forces. Selection may oppose novel incoming alleles or allele combinations because

- conditions affecting selection are different at the periphery
- novel genetic material disturbs local adaptive valleys on the genetic landscape comprised of stable coadapted genetic combinations (see Chapter 2),
- the changes interfere with local kin-recognition systems (see below).

Genic exchange acting on a feature in one direction and selection in the other will create a cline, even if the source of selection is not distributed along a gradient.

These opposing forces will invariably form a balance. Similarly, genic exchanges and genetic drift can oppose each other. Especially when the genic exchanges come from gene flow (individual or population movements), many alleles introduced into more peripheral populations by successful immigrants are unimportant, minimally advantageous or neutral to selection in a peripheral environment. Disadvantageous alleles, of course, would disappear. Because peripheral or ecologically marginal populations are more subject to drift there is a second possibility for balances to form. This is because drift often leads to the loss of rare or infrequent alleles. The balance creating a cline is between the source and loss ends of an allele's distribution. As evolutionists such as B. Charlesworth have pointed out, these balances control how much genetic differentiation appears between populations. In discussing the mechanisms that cause geographic variation he asserts

the extent of genetic differentiation between two or more local populations is determined by the balance between gene flow and natural selection or random genetic drift (p. 476).

Thus there are two sources of clines:

- geographic gradients of selection
- opposing evolutionary forces

Long lasting genetic differentiation created by clinal balances is commonly thought to be the main cause of human racial variation (see papers by A. Brues, J. Birdsell, F. Livingstone). It is the central contention of Multiregional Evolution that these shifting balances extend far into the past, for the entire history of *H. sapiens*. While the populations changed and the details of the balances varied with the ongoing process of evolution, local continuities for certain features lasted for long periods of time. *These account for the observations of regional continuity, and at the same time create the potential for a historical as well as a clinal dimension to modern population variation.*

The most important characteristic of these clines is in how they relate the conflicting causes of variation. When there are clines, the *balance of forces* define the *steepness of the gradient*. Just as a see-saw can balance children or cheeseburgers, clinal balances are independent of the absolute magnitude of the forces and depend only on their relative sizes. The comparison of magnitudes creates the slope of the gradient - whether a feature varies a lot or a little from one place to another. But once there is a cline it means that one of the forces cannot overwhelm or swamp out the other - they will always form a gradient.

Why should some clinal patterns be long lasting? Why long-term continuity in some features, especially at the peripheries? Three factors come into play. The first of these is the homogeneity that is

- more common in subdivided species (**Wahlund effect**),
- more prevalent in small populations because of genetic drift (marginal population are smaller than more central ones),
- more often found in the colonizing populations (and their descendants) of colonizing species

Homogeneous features, once established, will not change unless they become disadvantageous.

The other two factors are long lasting adaptations and exaptations. They differ mainly over the role of history, as exaptations rely on the anatomy already present and can only be readily identified when there is the potential for equivalent adaptations. For example, western European and eastern Asian populations probably came to differ in the elements contributing to maxillary incisor shoveling quite by accident; that is, a consequent of the colonization process or of small peripheral population effect. According to T. Crummett, in Europe crown curvature became a more important element than marginal ridges, while in Asia the marginal ridges were more prominent and the crowns straighter. When both came under selection to increase incisor strength in a limited space due to decreasing jaw size, European crowns became more curved and Asian crowns more heavily ridged. The contrasting exaptations are important markers of regional continuity in the two areas.

Regional continuity vs *evidence for* regional continuity

In developing the Multiregional model I realized that long-lasting adaptations may appear because the need for them never changes. For instance, the Bergman/Allen rule predicts that cold adapted humans need relatively short limbs to retain body heat. A succession of unrelated populations over a long period of time may retain relatively short limbs in a cold climate because of this adaptation alone. A succession of related populations may also retain short relative limb length both because of the requirements of adaptation and the influences of history. One cannot be distinguished from the other, and therefore clearly adaptive features may *reflect* an evolutionary continuity *but they cannot be used to prove it*. None the less, continuities in adaptive characteristics are an expected product of the evolutionary process and may well be the most common form of regional continuity.

Exaptations are quite different in this regard, since by their very nature they are dependent on history as well as the adaptive process. The adaptations influenced by already existing morphology have the potential of equivalence - the same requirements met in different ways. Long-term equivalent exaptations are sure markers of regional continuity.

The other place to seek evidence for regional continuity is in nonadaptive features. These are very unlikely to persist if the history or a region is marked by population replacements. Several good examples of these are discussed in Chapter 13, in regard to the question of whether European Neandertal populations were completely replaced.

One other point. Regional continuity can probably never be established by examining single traits, or features one-at-a-time, as P. Habgood has argued. There is simply too much normal variation for this to work - its that partitioning of genetic variation again, there is much more variation within populations than between them. Habgood shows that as far as the *demonstration* of regional continuity is concerned, complexes involving combinations of several features must be examined to focus through the blurred picture that normal variation creates. This is not an aspect of the process but of its identification.

Kin recognition

Kin identification is local source of selection for unique features that has the potential to produce long-term continuity, but only when there have not been significant population replacements. Cues for recognizing potential mates are very important in maintaining reproductive boundaries between species, and mate recognition is of particular importance among sibling species, or when an adaptive radiation brings closely related species into competition. Reproductive boundaries are an important element in maintaining a species cohesion and establishing its unique evolutionary pattern. However, kin recognition within an internally subdivided species plays a somewhat different role because potential mates are not just a matter of mates who are fertile, but involves more complex social issues.

An understanding of the roles of recognition in internally subdivided species has never been intensively examined. Certain mechanisms of mate recognition, balancing learned behavior and genetic predisposition to recognize key resemblances, have evolved to meet this problem in polytypic species where migrations and mate exchanges provide special opportunities for interactions with unrelated individuals. The complex nature of one recognition role derives from the fact that choosing mates based on simple similarity would maximize matings with sibs, or other very close kin. Yet ignoring any similarities could result in mate choice outside the species. How a balance is reached is suggested by P. Bateson's study of Japanese quail. These birds show a clear preference for first cousins, remaining in their proximity significantly more often than in proximity to birds with other degrees of relationship (including sibs) and to unrelated birds. In fact, the quails spent the *least* time in the proximity of their sibs. Time spent in proximity is directly related to mate choice in this species. Bateson posits that they are poised to prefer mates who are slightly different from the individuals they are familiar with in early life.

In humans and other social species, there are more complex problems of interactions between related or potentially related individuals. Recognition comes to play a double role in humans, where systems of kinship and alliance are of significant importance, not only in mate choice but other interactions where genic level selection plays a part. M. Flynn suggests that recognizing related individuals might be of particular consequence in peripheral populations, during periods when there were influxes of new people. Identification of related people is an important aspect of inclusive fitness theory, discussed in Chapter 2. Many workers have suggested an explanation involving genic level selection for some aspects of human social evolution, as well as for the evolution of human language because it requires shared syntactic laws for speaking and understanding. These considerations stem from the fact that related individuals are much more likely to share genetic variations, and one function of society is to help related individuals help each other. Recognition, in the quails, is based on their plumage. In humans recognition of related individuals is largely based on features of the face. It is almost certainly not a coincidence that the face is where many of the externally visible features showing regional continuity are found, as facial characteristics play am important role in helping to recognize those related by systems of kinship or alliance.

The role played by features that promote recognition is therefore potentially important. Supporting this idea is the fact that at the neuroanatomical level the mechanisms of facial recognition are quite complex and distinct. Information is extracted from faces in specific parts of the brain, mostly in the right hemisphere (the non-dominant hemisphere for right handed people). There are three important regions that correspond to the way in which facial recognition proceeds. At the base of the visual cortex at the back of the head, one area processes the visual input and keys onto the unique features of the face. The second region, at the tip of the temporal lobe and well in front of the first, stores information about individuals. Names are stored separately from other biographical information which is why it is possible, if not common, to recognize individuals and associate them with particular times or places but not remember their names (the scourge of college professors!). A third area, positioned between these, is a secondary association area that links the recognition and information storage regions. It is here that the question of "familiar or not?" is settled. The neuroanatomy of this facial recognition system is unique to humans, and seems to be the consequence of the kind of neural reorganization posited by R.L. Holloway. As in so many other reorganized neural pathways, the earlier limbic links between the recognition are storage regions remain, providing an emotional association for each recognition process. Clearly this is a neural processing system with unique importance in human evolution.

GENETIC SUPPORT

Is there support from genetic analyses for the precept that long-term geographic differences were maintained within the widespread human species because of clinal balances between genic exchanges, drift, and selection? The answer here is a resounding "yes". Most geneticists focus either on genetic variation within populations or between species. Only a few have analyzed problems of evolution *in-between these*, within species such as ours, with a wide geographic range and internal subdivisions. The Multiregional Evolutionary precept of humanity as an evolving subdivided species, with its demes occupying distinct adaptive valleys (see Chapter 2), was developed from evolutionary studies of Th. Dobzhansky, R. Lande, A. Templeton, and perhaps most importantly S. Wright who innovated the important concepts of isolation by distance and the shifting balance theory. This theory holds that geographic demes within a species occupy distinct adaptive valleys, and that a species thus subdivided has the maximum potential for adaptive evolution because of the way its genetic variation is partitioned. Wright's view implies that a widespread species subdivided into local demes with some genic exchange can evolve rapidly in the face of ecological changes, even develop genetic revolutions, without speciation.

While subdivision into local demes with some genic exchange is a good description of humanity today, the question is whether it characterized out species in the past as the Multiregional model asserts? Or, to the contrary, does modern human genetic variation all derive from a single recent source. The key issue is whether genic exchanges can account for this pattern in which both differences and similarities persist for long periods. There is considerable genetic evidence that reflects the presence and consequence of ancient subdivisions, and supports the Multiregional model.

- A. Templeton analyzed mtDNA and showed that the pattern of dispersion of different genetic lineages failed to reveal (1) a single recent source or (2) an 'Out-of-Africa' population expansion. His analysis *did* show that the world wide distribution of genetic lineages could only be attributed to early genetic divergence between regions and subsequent genetic contacts between populations with magnitudes mitigated only by the distances between the populations (isolation by distance). The genetic contacts continued for the entire time period marked by the evolution of human mtDNA variations from their last common ancestor.

- In their analysis of the genetic structure of ancient human populations, using characteristics of extant mtDNA, H. Harpending and colleagues (see Chapter 14) conclude "our results show that human populations are derived from separate ancestral populations that were relatively isolated from each other before 50,000 years ago".

- Xiong Weijun and colleagues examined the distribution of several very rare alleles in the nuclear DNA. These were found in two individuals, one of Japanese and the other of Euro-Venezuelan origin. Assuming they were derived from a single mutant ancestor, their complexity indicates a time of origin of at least a half million years, but their persistence since then at a very low frequency shows that there was no population bottleneck (i.e. an 'origin' event) over that period.

- Li Wenhisung and L. Sadler compared nucleotide and protein diversity in human and Drosophila DNA. The levels of protein diversity are quite similar, but nucleotide diversity is much lower in humans. They attribute this difference to a small but stable population size through most of human prehistory, rather than a bottleneck. This is because humans and chimpanzees share many common alleles for the major histocompatability complex genes. If there had been a severe bottleneck (a replacement by individuals from a single source) long after the hominid-chimpanzee split, most of these shared polymorphisms would have been lost.

- L. Excoffier examined the distribution of mtDNA variations and showed that the more ancient variations were so widely spread that there must have been restricted genic exchanges from an early time.

- Studies of genetic variation on the Y chromosome (the male-transmitted counterpart to mtDNA) show the greatest variability to lie in several populations, none African. No single source of origin for variations on this chromosome could be isolated, and the distribution of variation suggests long term contacts between populations.

- Harpending and colleagues studies the probability distributions of pairwise mtDNA comparisons within populations for evidence of past population structure and size expansions (this is discussed further in Chapter 14). They conclude: "our results show that human populations are derived from separate ancestral populations that were relatively isolated from each other before 50,000 years ago".

Geneticists like M. Stoneking have argued that the date of mitochondrial Eve is critical for the multiregional model. This date is, in fact, critical for the "Eve theory" (see Chapter 12) but as Templeton points out it is irrelevant for the Multiregional model. Only if human groups were isolated after Eve's time would her age be of importance. The hypothesis that human populations were connected by low levels of genic exchanges means that any age could be compatible because her mtDNA type could potentially spread throughout the world at any time.

A PATTERN

Multiregional Evolution is a model of how evolution works in a widespread polytypic species. It stems from the basic observation that some of the features that distinguish major human groups such as Asians, Australians, and Europeans evolved over a long period of time close to or at the places these people are found today. The model was developed for our own species because more is known about its prehistory than any other. It is predictive (and thereby has the potential of being disproved) over the issue of pattern. For instance, if it could be shown that human evolution preceded as a series of sweeping population replacements by successively better adapted forms, each with their own separate origin (something like what the late P. Teilhard de Chardin proposed), Multiregional Evolution would be clearly disproved, wrong. But unlike theories such as the "Eve theory" or the "Single Species hypothesis" it is not a focused theory about or interpretation of particular evolutionary events (modern human origins or australopithecine species in these cases). Multiregional Evolution is based on the precept that the present is the best basis for modeling the past, and posits that populations in polytypic species remain differentiated for the same reason that they evolve without speciation - because of the matrix of genic exchanges (and in the human case information exchanges) they establish. Human evolution, as A. Thorne wrote, happened everywhere because every area was always part of the whole.

The prediction of this model that has proven to be most contended is over the issue of modern human origins. Multiregional Evolution predicts that modern humans do not have a single point or place of origin. Instead, they appeared because of the coalescence of rapidly spreading adaptive traits that originated at different times and in different places, each conferring advantage on those who had them. Modernization, in other words, was an ongoing process in widespread populations, and not a single dramatic event in a single population. I have used the analogy of modern humans as the pattern of interfering waves that are created when stones are thrown into a pond, landing at different times and in different places). The implications of this expectation for modern human origins is explored in the next chapter.

Archaeological Changes

The Acheulean was anything but a static industry marking a time of little or no change in human cultural evolution. Changes in the Acheulean involved three main factors:

- ·a marked improvement in skill, which almost surely resulted from a more accurate preconception of tool form, and an expanded ability to translate the preconception accurately into a better-made product through a series of rules (hand-and-eye coordination)
- an increase in the number of different distinguishable tools, and the appearance of fire use and eventually of fire-hardened spears. Specific tool types became better defined, and more work seems to have been involved in their manufacture.
- the appearance of pre-formed flakes using Levallois-like techniques (see Chapter 12); for instance, the "Victoria West" technology found at late Acheulean sites such as those in the Kapthurin Formation near Lake Baringo, Kenya. Here, the flake that is to become the biface is fully shaped before it is detached from the core.

Several new flaking techniques supplemented the earlier "stone-on-stone" process that characterized the Oldowan and earlier Acheulean assemblages. The most important of these, according to R. Klein, was the discovery that softer objects such as wood or antler could be used to strike off flakes. An indirect percussion technique may also have come into use. This involves using wood, bone, or antler as an intermediary between the hammerstone and the object being flaked. These new techniques resulted in much greater control over the size and form of the flake being struck, and consequently over the form of the completed tool. Handaxes and cleavers from this time appear aesthetically pleasing because of their regular form, symmetry, and straight edges. An importance for aesthetics is also suggested by evidence of red coloring material, seemingly collected by hominids, at Olduvai upper Bed II, much later at Terra Armata and elsewhere.

The main distinguishing characteristics of the later industries are found in the refinement of preexisting tools, although some new types of tools were also developed. It appears that people had a clearer mental image of the tool to be made before manufacture began, and the degree of standardization for the various tool types was greatly increased compared with the earlier industries. Forms such as the oval and the triangle were accurately reproduced with a great number of standardized variations. These developments largely depended on the evolution of both the ability to preconceive form and skill in producing that form. There are no "hand axe genes" in the human genotype; it was the structural aspects of the neural models underlying tool-making behavior that were inherited, and thereby subject to evolutionary change. The observable industries are important because they reflect the degree of motor skill and the complexity of the rule systems underlying the imposition of increasingly arbitrary form on the environment.

Continued changes in the many different hand axe sizes and forms supports the suggestion that they were made for a variety of purposes. In addition, there are sharp-edged cleavers (a chopping and cutting tool the size of a hand axe) and, somewhat later backed blades (one side is blunted for handling). Tools for working wood, such as burins, have been found, and there are numerous flakes made into scrapers and notched "denticulate" tools. Worked bone is rare and wood is virtually nonexistent (it is much less likely to be preserved than stone), but a sharpened wooden spear was recovered from the English site of Clacton. There is no convincing evidence of hafting stone onto wood, creating composite tools.

Tool kits varied from place to place, and the combination of refinement and standardization of older tool types and the development of new tool types greatly increased the adaptability of human populations. This is clearly reflected in their expanding range. The archaeological record became increasingly complex through the Middle Pleistocene because of the development of new technologies and tools and the appearance of extensive geographic variation.

Finally, later Acheulean sites yield the first good evidence of art and body decoration. There are lumps or red ochre that have been rubbed smooth at Terra Amata (France) and Beçov (Hungary), incised parallel lines on several bones at Bilzingsleben (Germany), a pebble carved in the form of a human figurine from Berekhat Ram (Israel), and engraved ivory at Tata (also Hungary).

A Pattern to Evolution

Middle Pleistocene hominids everywhere are characterized by significant brain size expansion, and most Middle Pleistocene hominids have brain sizes that lie within the normal range of modern variation. There are changes in cranial proportions, expansion of the frontal positioning the forehead over the browridge and expansion of the upper occiput even as the size of the attachment area for the nuchal muscles and the development of the supportive spongy bone at the cranial base decrease. Dental changes include decreases in posterior tooth size (especially for the later-erupting premolar and molars), and in some regions increased anterior tooth size.

Consequences of these trends are seen in the cranium, face, and mandible. Braincase breadth approaches (and finally exceeds) cranial breadth as the brain expands and the spongy bone development reduces (figure 11.7). This changes the orientation of the temporalis muscle. Still pulling predominantly upwards and backwards, a smaller inner-directed component (mandible-wider-than-cranial-base) becomes outer-directed (cranium -wider-than-mandible). As the braincase finally became broader than the face. its appearance changed as well.

BRAINCASE

The differential expansion of the frontal bone can best be seen in the development of frontal rounding and boss development in some populations, and increased frontal height in others. Frontals in general become broader at their rear (maximum frontal breadth), and eventually just behind the orbits as well (minimum frontal breadth). Brain size increase also affects the occipital plane. Among other things, this portion of the bone encloses the posterior parietal association areas of the brain, where cross-modal transfer takes place. Evidence suggests a continued process of neurological changes, and endocasts of specimens in the later Middle Pleistocene have all of the markers of modern human abilities that might be expected on endocasts, including well developed language areas. Judging from areas that proportionally increase the greatest, the likelihood is that the main expanding elements are in the two corresponding regions of the brain, the frontal lobes and the posterior parietal region, and that expansion involves

- more connections between the sensory and motor association areas and some frontal areas (affecting monitoring, ordering, and sorting)
- development of an increasingly complex network of direct connections in the posterior parietal association area.
- increase in the visual processing area

The importance of the simple increase in brain size should not be overlooked. Larger size means more neurons and more pathways between them. These are a necessary requirement for the ontogenetic development of complex neural models such as those underlying human language and cultural behavior, as discussed in Chapter 4.

THE POSTERIOR DENTITION

Reduction is the trend for the cheek teeth. In some regions the process is gradual, in others there are certain times of accelerating change, but the direction is always the same. Reduction is greater in the later erupting teeth of each class, and more in the molars than in the premolars. In both jaws the P4 decreases more than P3, and M3 decreases more than M2, which in turn decreases more than M1

Selection seems to maximize grinding area in the young, even while reducing the occlusal area in adults. The importance of maximum grinding area in the young is suggested by the fact that the deciduous (milk) teeth expand in size over this time span (and in fact well into the Upper Pleistocene). This may correspond to earlier weaning, which might help promote shortened birth spacing (one means of allowing population expansion). Its potential effect on the period of infant dependence is less clear.

INCREASING ANTERIOR TOOTH USE

A general trend to increase anterior tooth sizes, especially breadths can be demonstrated in some regions, particularly Europe and possibly Africa (the dental samples are smaller here). All three anterior teeth expand, but the greatest change is in I^2, which at the extreme in Late Pleistocene Europe is equal to I1 in breadth. With larger maxillary teeth erupting into a limited space, the dimensions of shovel shaping become enhanced as alternative ways to strengthen the incisors. There is a changing pattern of anterior tooth use, and it does not seem to be directly associated with chewing food. Instead, it may result from using the mouth to grip and hold objects. Even today, jaw muscles can exert more force than the hands, and the nuchal muscles provide a powerful force for pulling an object held in the mouth. One documented use of the anterior teeth is related to what appears to be new patterns of food preparation associated with animal protein - gripping meat while cutting off pieces, preshredding foods for the young, and so on. This is reflected in labial scratches across the anterior tooth faces. Greater use of the anterior teeth as part of the tool kit seems to accompany the elaboration of more traditional tools and an improved ability to exploit the habitat—more intensive means of environmental manipulation.

FACIAL CHANGES

The important facial changes involve continued increases of facial breadths and the appearance of expanded, puffy maxillas in many regions. Three factors contribute to facial breadth increases:

1. expansion of the frontal bone, which pushes the position of the temporal fossa outward and requires broader faces in spite of the fossa's decreasing size
2. continued emphasis on grinding during mastication, selecting for increased lateral forces from the masseter muscle which are best accomplished by broadening the cheeks
3. increasing anterior tooth size, broadening the nasal opening - and broad noses as well as large, widely spaced orbits characterize most Middle Pleistocene samples.

It is possible that large orbits reflect expanded eye size, and serve to maximize the number of rods and cones. This could be related to selection for more visual information processing capacity, one of the changes reflected in the continued expansion of the brain's posterior, discussed above.

Vertical loading of the anterior teeth is functionally related to the size of the browridge when the forehead slope deviates markedly from the facial slope, creating an angle between them. The height of the forehead changes in some Middle Pleistocene populations and forehead shape changes in others. These affect supraorbital torus evolution in different ways, and the evolutionary process is even more complex because of the importance of this region, as the top part of the face, in kin recognition. There is no simple description for the changes in the torus. Different parts of it decrease in some geographic regions and increase in others. By the beginning of the Late Pleistocene, or soon thereafter, the structure begins to reduce, and is lost in some populations.

The maxillary puffing that becomes so common can be related to anterior tooth use as well. Holding an object between the anterior teeth and pulling or twisting it with the nuchal and posterior temporalis muscles creates forces that pull the tooth crowns outward. One consequence is that the roots, and the lower portion of the face holding them, expand where anterior tooth use gains importance. While this serves to anchor the front teeth better and reinforce their roots, it also means that when pulling an object gripped between the teeth the whole front part of the lower face (the teeth, their roots, and the bone holding them) is pulled outward, creating tensile strain in the facial bones. This strain is concentrated in the bone just to the sides of the nose, where the canine roots help transmit it to the midfacial region. At the same time, forces in a quite different direction are generated by the simultaneous downward pull of the masseter muscle on the lower border of the zygomatic arch. These create a combination of bending and tension in the face, and the changing form of the midface is the response. There was an addition of bone in the area where the strain is greatest, along the sides of the nose. The bone added surrounds an expanded maxillary sinus, and the total affect is to create a flat sheet of bone between the anterior teeth and the masseter attachment - the sites of application for two oppositely directed forces. The canine fossa is minimized or disappears.

MANDIBULAR CHANGES

With reduced use of the postcanine teeth, the mandibular structures supporting the posterior teeth also reduce. The main effect of these changes is to dramatically decrease the breadth of the corpus; corpus height changes less (the amount of tooth use it is also related to body size) and the external dimensions (mandible length, breadth) barely change at all. On the average, breadth at the symphysis and internal buttressing also reduce substantially.

T. White developed a biomechanical explanation for the appearance of the mental eminence during the latest Middle Pleistocene.. He notes that in small-brained hominids the temporalis muscle (see figure 4.14) has an inward orientation from the mandible because it attaches on a small braincase. As the muscle fires its main line of action is upward and backward, but there is an inward orientation as well. When the breadth of the braincase is less than the breadth of the cranial base, it is also less than the breadth of the mandible, accounting for this inward component of the muscle. This inward orientation acts to pull the sides of the mandible together when the muscle is used, creating the need for an internal buttress where the sides meet. Over time, as the temporalis decreased in size and the cranial walls became wider, these buttresses were poorly expressed, or just absent. However, as the breadth of the braincase became greater than the breadth of the cranial base and therefore greater than the breadth of the mandible, the fibers of the temporalis muscle angle outward from the mandible as they extend toward their cranial attachment. This causes the inward component to become an outward component, and temporalis muscles draw the sides of the mandible apart. Buttressing is necessary on the external surface of the symphysis rather than on the internal one (a wishbone-breaking effect), and a mental eminence, or true chin, appears.

Summary

Once humans became a successful colonizing species, a distinct pattern of evolutionary change developed that has continued throughout the Pleistocene. Middle Pleistocene populations are characterized by the seemingly contradictory observations of continued differentiation and longtime establishment of regional features, and common direction and pattern of evolutionary change. Both of these persist through the Late Pleistocene, although population explosions and more gradual expansions have obscured the pattern to some extent. The Middle Pleistocene is anything but the muddle in the middle it was once described as, but instead may reveal the best evidence for the pattern that describes most of the colonizing phase of human evolution.

Populations in all regions show increases in brain size (especially in the frontal lobes and posterior parietal area), and decreases in posterior tooth functions and size as the masticatory pattern shifts and the anterior teeth are increasing incorporated into the tool kit. Many aspects of the skeleton became more gracile. Toward the end of the Middle Pleistocene, virtually everywhere there are cases of seemingly mixed morphology, with modern and archaic features juxtaposed. Some of these are a consequence of dating problems, but other cases reflect the application of typological expectations to normal variation. Regional features characterize skeletal remains from different areas, often found in the earliest inhabitants, and these persist throughout the Middle Pleistocene. Many, although not all, are facial and would reflect easily visible similarities and differences. The seemingly contradictory observations of regionalization and species-wide evolutionary changes is explained by the Multiregional Evolution model.

ANATOMY OF A CONTROVERSY
Human Species in Europe

L.S.B. Leakey suggested that the fragmentary remains from Kanjera in Tanzania represented a Middle Pleistocene presapiens contemporary with (what he regarded as) "pithecanthropines" (these remains have been redated to the Late Pleistocene, see Chapter 14). The date of 29 kyr once accepted for Kabwe seemed to establish dramatically different humans in southern Africa. L. Briggs proposed that the Ternifine mandibles represented two different hominid types. D. Collins attempted to demonstrate contemporary hominid lineages associated with what he interpreted as different culture traditions. Yet historically, it is Europe that has been the virtually singular focus of modern human origins theories and interpretations of multiple lineages. Only with the "Out of Africa", or "Eve" theory did the focus fundamentally shift away from the continent, and even still, in the minds of many, Europe continues to play a critical role in understanding modern human origins.

Questions continue to be raised about a European contribution to modern population origins. These invariably revolve around the "Neandertal Issue" -- the debate over whether most, some, or no Neandertals were on the direct line of modern human ancestry. So powerful has been the notion that Europe was the center of human evolution, it was taken as a given that if some or all of the Neandertals were not ancestral to moderns, another *European* lineage was. Hence, Vallois' "Preneandertal" and "Presapiens" theories. Europe continues to loom so strongly in the minds of some paleoanthropologists that they imagine the replacement of Neandertals in Europe by more modern populations proves the theory of replacement everywhere. Eurocentrism is not as common today as it has been in the past, and the fact is that Europe does play a significant role in human evolution - one role of many. The question we still grapple with is what that role is.

Apart from the old-fashioned "stages of human evolution" approach which minimizes the evolutionary importance of regional differentiation, most workers have recognized a unique combination of features in the Middle and early Late Pleistocene European sample and have envisioned one or more distinct, and in some cases separate, evolutionary lines in Europe. At the extremes, there are two different positions that both assume distinct European regional variation.

In his very influential paper of 1960, F.C. Howell suggested the interpretation that there was a European lineage in the Middle Pleistocene, *more advanced* than the "pithecanthropines" of Asia. Swanscombe and Steinheim were ancestral to modern humans according to this model, and only the late "classic" Neandertals evolved off in a different direction and became extinct. Because Howell regarded the earlier Neandertals such as those from Krapina and Saccopastore as modern human ancestors, *broadly speaking Neandertals were ancestral to modern Europeans in this interpretation.*

As a diametrically opposite alternative to modern human origins in the Middle Pleistocene European sample, C. Stringer believes the Europeans were separate evolutionary species throughout most of the Pleistocene, whose evolution terminated in the extinct Neandertals. More than 30 years after Howell, he contended that *Homo heidelbergensis* divided from *H. sapiens*, perhaps as early as the time of the first significant populating of the continent, or certainly soon thereafter. The argument that this regional variation is at the species level is based on his contention that the culmination of that lineage, Neandertals, became extinct without contributing to the modern European gene pool. The idea that Neandertals are a separate species is not a new one, and the extension of its base into the Middle Pleistocene is not an unreasonable expectation of this precept. However, the broad biological implications of a unique European lineage include predictions that there will be evidence of reproductive isolation and the presence of a singular, unique, pattern of evolutionary change. The idea that Neandertals could be the last members of this evolutionary species, when their every contact with contemporary "modern" populations reveals evidence of interbreeding, is contradictory.

As far as the second implication is concerned, identifying unique regional features for a long period of time is not enough for species diagnosis, according to the evolutionary species definition. There must also be unique evolutionary tendencies, and no evidence of genic exchange that would make its history of descent shared by members of other species. Therefore, the Stringer theory requires evidence that:

- Neandertals *did not* (implying they *could not*) interbreed with the populations that are theorized to replace them
- there were significant differences in evolutionary *direction* in the European sample, as *H. heidelbergensis* is viewed over time.

If the evolutionary tendencies in this alleged evolutionary species is the same as the trends in contemporary *H. sapiens,* and if there is evidence of mixture between these two species, we can conclude that the identification of two contemporary evolutionary species is incorrect. We will examine these two question in the discussion of *H. heidelbergensis* below.

The Howell and Stringer views agree on the observation that there was a distinct European morphotype with a long ancestry through the Middle and most of the Later Pleistocene, but differ on the question of its contribution to modern Europeans. The differences are manifest in how the Middle Pleistocene Europeans are interpreted. According to Howell's interpretation they are the Middle Pleistocene ancestors of modern humans. According to Stringer's view these are the founders of a distinct hominid species that evolved in parallel to the rest of humanity for most of the remaining Pleistocene, and then became extinct some 35 kyr ago.

Historic interpretations of the European materials began with the first discovered crania, Steinheim and Swanscombe. Both of these happen to be females in populations now recognized to have marked sexual dimorphism and because female crania are more gracile than males, their discovery first contributed to the precept that the Europeans were "more modern" than their contemporaries. It is productive to review the cranial sample as it is now known, since both females and males are represented. With recognition of the import of the variation at Atapuerca and realization that the archaic features of the Bilzingsleben crania can be explained by their early date, the interpretation of different species *within* Europe can be discarded. The question now is over the relation of the Middle Pleistocene Europeans to other populations.

I analyzed 16 features on the 4 best preserved European crania (Arago 21, Atapuerca 5, Petralona, Steinheim) and on the 3 best Chinese specimens spanning the same time range (Dali, Yunxian 2, Zhoukoudian LII). Three main sources of variation and/or similarity can be considered: time, sex, and region. The specimens of both groups span enough time for temporal variation to be a possible source of similarity (the early specimens from both regions could be most similar to each other, etc.). Males and females are represented in both samples. Moreover, the 16 features are observations that are independent of size and unambiguously preserved on all 7 specimens.

I did a cladistic analysis, using the ER 3733 specimen to determine which features are apomorphic (these unique traits are the important ones for determining relationships). The analysis showed two clusters that were clearly based on region, and not sex or time:

1. **European**: Petralona, Arago 21, and Atapuerca 5 closest, Steinheim slightly more distant (it shares more features with the Asians than the other European crania do)
2. **East Asian**: ZKT 11 and Dali closest, Yunxian 2 more distant (it shares more features with the Europeans than the other crania do).

The two clusters sharing the largest number of shared characters support the contention that distinct regionality contributes significantly to the pattern of Middle Pleistocene variation. Furthermore, the clusters are somewhat more distinct than even this analysis shows. This is because many of the shared features that do no contribute to the clusters are also actually regionally different. For instance, Chinese paleoanthropologists who have studied the European specimens point out that while both groups have a sagittal keel, the Chinese form is invariably narrower and taller than the broad, low European anatomy. There are also differences in the form and expression of the angular torus.

The analysis shows one more thing; that is, a European (Steinheim) is distinguishable from the rest because of its Asian features and an Asian (Yunxian) distinct from the others because it shows European features (so much so that the two best analyses differ only on the position of Yunxian - one puts it with the other Asians and the other positions it as the most distant branch of the Europeans). By each revealing evidence of what could be understood as admixture between the regions, Steinheim and Yunxian 2 supports the interpretation that there was no species distinction between populations at the two ends of Eurasia in the Middle Pleistocene. They indicate that so-called *H. heidelbergensis* in Europe and *H. sapiens* in Asia are not each unique lines of descent, but rather appear to be the two ends of a continent-wide network of genic exchanges.

As a whole the sample testifies to two propositions:

1. that these Europeans had a unique combination of regional features
2. that there is evidence of contact between them and, at the least, their Asian contemporaries.

If there was speciation for the Europeans, it came later in time than the Middle Pleistocene.

This question is further examined in Chapter 13, but a preview will be useful to complete this discussion. One of the French crania from Biache (dated between 196 and 159 kyr) is of some considerable interest in the European narrative. This is because it is one of the earliest specimen to show a preponderance of Neandertal features, including:

- lambdoidal flattening extending onto the occiput,
- semi-circular cranial contour in *norma lateralis*
- small mastoids and an expanded **juxtamastoid process**,
- broad *semispinalis capitis* insertion
- weakly expressed nuchal torus, extending horizontally across most of the occiput
- a very broad elliptical suprainiac fossa
- transversely rounded upper incisor crowns with marked lateral ridges

The Biache 1 female lived after the Europeans discussed in this chapter, but shares a number of distinct features with the earlier Swanscombe female (a "Swanscombe with ears", according to one pundit), therefore providing a link between the earlier and later Europeans. What does the comparison of earlier and later Europeans tell us about the direction of evolutionary change in Europe?

The argument for local evolution of the Neandertals broadly from earlier European populations is widely accepted and incontrovertible. The progressive "neandertalization" of the Europeans continues through much of the Late Pleistocene. This implies that in the pre-modern European deme there was continued regional differentiation. However, besides "neandertalization" this deme shows a number of other evolutionary trends including:

- significant cranial capacity expansion
- supraorbital reduction
- thinning of the cranial vault
- expansion of the occipital plane at the expense of the nuchal plane
- postcanine dental reduction
- appearance of a true mental eminence
- diminution of sexual dimorphism

These are the evolutionary trends that characterize human populations throughout the Middle and early Late Pleistocene in every region where they have been found. Their unequivocal presence in Europe would reflect a hereto forth unheard of number of evolutionary homoplaises developing in the Europeans, if the Europeans were genetically isolated from other human populations, as the interpretation of a different European species implies. However, because the Europeans share these evolutionary tendencies with other human populations, the interpretation of genetic isolation is unlikely to be correct. As D. Etler put it, "*H. heidelbergensis*" is a taxon whose time has probably come and gone, twice". Of course, we can expect that this conclusion will lead to renewed refrains of the Greek Chorus - "its the single species hypothesis again", and "absurd"!

REFERENCES AND FURTHER READINGS

AGUIRRE, E. 1991/2 Atapuerca: land change, caves, and humans over the Middle Pleistocene. *Journal of Human Ecology* 2(3) and 3(1):227-270.

AGUIRRE, E., J-L. ARSUAGA, J-L., J-M. BERMÚDEZ DE CASTRO, J-M. CARRETERO, A. GRACIA, I. MARTINEZ, P.J. PEREZ, and A. ROSAS 1991 Les hominides fossiles d'Ibeas, mise a jour de l'inventaire. *L'Anthropologie* 95(2/3):473-500.

AIGNER, J.S. 1981 *Archaeological Remains in Pleistocene China.* Beck, München.

___. 1988 Dating the earliest Chinese Pleistocene localities: the newly proposed O^{18} correspondences. In P. Whyte, J.S. Aigner, N.G. Jablonski, G. Taylor, D. Walker, and P. Wang (eds): *The Palaeoenvironment of East Asia from the Mid-Tertiary*, Volume II. Centre for Asian Studies, Hong Kong. pp. 1032-1061.

ARSUAGA, J-L., J-M. CARRETERO, A. GRACIA, and I. MARTINEZ 1990 Taphonomical analysis of the human sample from the Sima de los Huesos Middle Pleistocene site (Atapuerca/Ibeas, Spain). *Human Evolution* 5(6):505-513.

ARSUAGA, J-L., I. MARTINEZ, A. GRACIA, J-M. CARRETERO, and E. CARBONELL 1993 Three new human skulls from the Sima de los Huesos Middle Pleistocene site in Sierra de Atapuerca, Spain. *Nature* 362:534-537.

ASCENZI, A., A.M. MARCHETTE, and M. MICHELI 1986 Comparison entre l'homme de Tautavel, les Anténéandertaliens d'Italie, et l'homme de Saccopastore. *L'Anthropologie* 90:515-537.

BAR-YOSEF, O. 1992 The role of western Asia in modern human origins. *Philosophical Transactions of the Royal Society,* Series B, 337:193-200.

BATESON, P. 1982 Preferences for cousins in Japanese quail. *Nature* 295:236-237.

BEALS, K.L., C.L. SMITH, and S.M. DODD 1984 Brain size, cranial morphology, climate, and time machines. *Current Anthropology* 25:301-330.

BEDNARIK, R.G. 1992 Palaeoart and archaeological myths. *Cambridge Archaeological Journal* 2:27-57.

BERMÚDEZ DE CASTRO, J-M. 1988 Dental diseases and Harris lines in the fossil human remains from Atapuerca-Ibeas (Spain). *Journal of Paleopathology* 1:131-146.

BERMÚDEZ DE CASTRO, J-M., T.G. BROMAGE, and Y.F. JALVO 1988 Buccal striations on fossil human anterior teeth: evidence of handedness in the Middle and early Upper Pleistocene. *Journal of Human Evolution* 17(4):403-412.

BERMÚDEZ DE CASTRO, J-M., A.I. DURANT, and S.L. IPIÑA 1993 Sexual dimorphism in the human dental sample from the SH site (Sierra de Atapuerca, Spain): a statistical approach. *Journal of Human Evolution* 24(1):43-56.

BETTINGER, R.L. 1987 Archaeological approaches to hunter-gatherers. In B.J. Siegel, A.R. Beals, and S.A. Tyler (eds): *Annual Review of Anthropology.* Annual Reviews, Palo Alto. Volume 16:121-142.

BILSBOROUGH, A. 1976 Patterns of evolution in Middle Pleistocene hominids. *Journal of Human Evolution* 5:423-440.

BINFORD, L.R. 1987 Were there elephant hunters at Torralba? In M.H. Nitecki and D.V. Nitecki (eds): *Evolution of Human Hunting*. Plenum, New York. pp. 47-105.

BINFORD, L.R., and N.M. STONE 1986 Zhoukoudian: a closer look. *Current Anthropology* 27(5):453-475 (and 28(1):102-105, 28(3):358-262).

BIRDSELL, J.B. 1957 Some population problems involving Pleistocene man. *Cold Spring Harbor Symposia on Quantitative Biology* 22:47-69.

___. 1972 The problem of the evolution of human races: classification or clines? *Social Biology* 19:136-162.

BLACK, D. 1936 Evidences of the use of fire by *Sinanthropus*. *Bulletin of the Geological Society of China* 11:107-108.

BLACK, D., P. TEILHARD DE CHARDIN, C.C. YOUNG, and W. PEI 1933 Fossil man in China. *Memoirs of the Geological Survey of China*, Series A 11:1-166.

BOWEN, D.Q., S. HUGHES, G.A. SYKES, and G.H. MILLER 1989 Land-sea correlations in the Pleistocene based on isoleucine epimerization in non-marine mollusks. *Nature* 340:49-51.

BRACE, C.L. 1981 Tales of the phylogenetic woods: The evolution and significance of evolutionary trees. *American Journal of Physical Anthropology* 56:411-429.

BRÄUER, G. 1990 The occurrence of some controversial *Homo erectus* cranial features in the Zhoukoudian and East African hominids. *Acta Anthropologica Sinica* 9(4):350-358.

BREITINGER, E. 1955 Das Schädelfragment von Swanscombe und des "Praesapiensproblem". *Mitteilungen der Anthropologischer Gesellschaft im Wein* 84/85:1-45.

___. 1957 On the phyletic evolution of *Homo sapiens*. In W.W. Howells (ed): *Ideas on Human Evolution*.: Harvard University Press, Cambridge. pp. 436-459 (also *Anthropologischer Anzeiger* 21:62-83)

BRIDGLAND, D.R., P.L. GIBBARD, P. HARDING, R.A. KEMP, and G. SOUTHGATE 1985 New information and results from recent excavations at Barnfield Pit, Swanscombe. *Quaternary Newsletter* 46:25-39.

BRIGGS, L.C. 1968 Hominid evolution in Northwest Africa and the question of the North African "Neanderthaloids". *American Journal of Physical Anthropology* 29:377-386.

BROWN, P. 1993 Cranial vault thickness in Asian *Homo erectus* and modern *Homo sapiens*. *Courier Forschungsinstitut Senckenberg* 171.

BRUES, A. 1972 Models of clines and races. *American Journal of Physical Anthropology* 37:389-399.

BUDIL, I. 1994 Functional reconstruction of the supralaryngeal vocal tract of fossil human. *Human Evolution* 9(1):35-52.

BYE, B.A., F.H. BROWN, T.E. CERLING, and I. McDOUGALL 1987 Increased age estimate for the lower Paleolithic hominid site at Olorgesailie, Kenya. *Nature* 329:237-23.

CADIEN, J.D. 1972 Dental variation in man. In S.L. Washburn and P. Dolhinow (eds): *Perspectives on Human Evolution*, Volume 2. Holt, Rinehart, and Winston, New York. pp. 199-222.

CANN, R.L. 1988 DNA and human origins. In B.J. Siegel, A.R. Beals, and S.A. Tyler (eds) *Annual Review of Anthropology*. Annual Reviews, Palo Alto. Volume 17:127-143.

CHARLESWORTH, B. 1983 Models of the evolution of some genetic systems. *Proceedings of the Royal Society of London*, Series B, 219:265-279.

CHASE, P. 1991 Symbols and Paleolithic artifacts: style, standardization, and the imposition of arbitrary form. *Journal of Anthropological Archaeology* 10:193-214.

CHEN TIEMEI, YUAN SIXUN, GAO SHIJUN, and HU YANQUI 1987 Uranium series dating of fossil bones from Hexian Chaoxian fossil human sites. *Acta Anthropologica Sinica* 6(3):249-254.

CHEN TIEMEI and ZHANG YINYUN 1991 Paleolithic chronology and possible coexistence of *Homo erectus* and *Homo sapiens* in China. *World Archaeology* 23:147-154.

CHIA LANPO 1975 *The Cave Home of Peking Man*. Foreign Languages Press, Peking.

CLARK, G.A. 1989 Alternative models of Pleistocene biocultural evolution: a response to Foley. *Antiquity* 63(238):153-159.

CLARK, J.D. 1980 Early human occupation of African savanna environments. In D.R. Harris (ed): *Human Ecology in Savanna Environments*. London: Academic Press. pp. 41-71.

___. 1989 The origins and spread of modern humans: a broad perspective on the African evidence. In P. Mellars and C.B. Stringer (eds): *The Human Revolution: Behavioural and Biological Perspectives on the Origins of Modern Humans*. Edinburgh University Press, Edinburgh. pp. 565-588.

CLARK, J.D., and J.W.K. HARRIS 1985 Fire and its roles in early hominid lifeways. *The African Archaeological Review* 3:3-28.

CLARK, J.D., J. DE HEINZELIN, K.D. SCHICK, W.K. HART, T.D. WHITE, G. WOLDEGABRIEL, R.C. WALTER, G. SUWA, B. ASFAW, E. VRBA, and Y.H.-SELASSIE 1994 African *Homo erectus*: old radiometric ages and young Oldowan assemblages in the Middle Awash Valley, Ethiopia. *Science* 264:1907-1910.

CLARKE, R.J. 1990 The Ndutu cranium and the origin of *Homo sapiens. Journal of Human Evolution* 19(6-7)699-736.

COLLINS, D. 1969 Culture traditions and environment of early man. *Current Anthropology* 10:267-316.

CONKEY, M. 1980 The identification of prehistoric hunter/gatherer aggregation sites: the case of Altimira. *Current Anthropology* 21:6-9-630.

COOK, J., C.B. STRINGER, A.P. CURRANT, H.P. SCHWARCZ, and A.G. WINTLE 1982 A review of the chronology of the European Middle Pleistocene hominid record. *Yearbook of Physical Anthropology* 25:19-65.

COUTSELINIS, A., C. DRITSAS, and Th. PITSIOS 1991 Expertise médico-légale du crâne Pléistocène LA01/S2 (Apidima II), Apidima, Laconie, Grèce. *L'Anthropologie* 95(2/3):401-408.

CRONIN, J.E., N.T. BOAZ, C.B. STRINGER, and Y. RAK 1981 Tempo and mode in hominid evolution. *Nature* 292:113-122.

CRUMMETT, T. 1994 The three dimensions of shovel-shaping. *Proceedings of the Ninth International Symposium on Dental Anthropology.* Angelo Pontecorboli Editore, Florence.

CZARNETZKI, A. 1982 Steinheim skull - a morphological comparison with Tautavel man. In H. de Lumley (ed): *L'Homo erectus et la Place de l'Homme de Tautavel parmi les Hominidés Fossiles.* 1ᵉʳ Congrès International de Paléontologie Humaine, Nice, Prétirage. Volume 2:875-893. Louis-Jean, Nice.

DAEGLING, D.J. 1993 Functional morphology of the human chin. *Evolutionary Anthropology* 1(5):170-177.

DAY, M.H. 1982 The *Homo erectus* pelvis: punctuation or gradualism? In H. de Lumley (ed): *L'Homo erectus et la Place de l'Homme de Tautavel parmi les Hominidés Fossiles.* 1ᵉʳ Congrès International de Paléontologie Humaine, Nice, Prétirage. Volume 2: 411-421. Louis-Jean, Nice.

___. 1986 *Homo erectus*: an old species with new problems. *Bulletin de la Société royale belge d'Anthropologie et de Préhistoire* 97:33-44.

DE BONIS, 1986 *Homo erectus* et la transition vers *Homo sapiens* en Europe. In M. Sakka (ed): *Définition et Origines de L'Homme.* Centre National de la Recherche Scientifique, Paris. pp. 253-261.

DE BONIS, L., and J. MELENTIS 1982 L'homme de Petralona: comparaisons avec l'homme de Tautavel. In H. de Lumley (ed): *L'Homo erectus et la Place de l'Homme de Tautavel parmi les Hominidés Fossiles.* 1ᵉʳ Congrès International de Paléontologie Humaine, Nice, Prétirage. Volume 2:847-874. Louis-Jean, Nice.

DEINO, A., and R. POTTS, 1990 Single crystal 40Ar/39 Ar dating of the Olorgesailie Formation, southern Kenya rift. *Journal of Geophysical Research* 95, number B6: 8453-8470 (reprinted in E. Delson, I. Tattersall, and J.V. Van Couvering (eds.) *Paleoanthropology Annuals* 1:117-137).

DELSON, E. 1991 Combien d'espèces du genre *Homo* existe-t-il en Europe? In E. Bonifay and B. Vandermeersch (eds): *Les Premiers Européens.* Editions du Comité Travaux Historiques Scientifiques, Paris. p 283.

DE LUMLEY, H. 1969 A paleolithic camp at Nice. *Scientific American* 220(5):42-49.

DE LUMLEY, H., and M.A. DE LUMLEY 1974 Pre-Neanderthal human remains from Arago cave in Southwestern France. *Yearbook of Physical Anthropology* 17:162-168.

DESMOND, A. 1982 *Archetypes and Ancestors.* University of Chicago Press, Chicago.

DOBZHANSKY, Th. 1944 On species and races of living and fossil man. *American Journal of Physical Anthropology* 2(3):251-265.

___. 1962 *Mankind Evolving: the Evolution of the Human Species.* Yale University Press, New Haven.

___. 1963 The possibility that *Homo sapiens* evolved independently 5 times is vanishingly small. *Scientific American* 208(2):169-172.

DODO, Y. 1986 A study of the facial flatness in several cranial series from East Asia and North America. *Journal of the Anthropological Society of Nippon* 94(1):81-93.

DRENNAN, M.R. 1956 Note on the morphological status of the Swanscombe and Fontéchevade skulls. *American Journal of Physical Anthropology* 14:73-83.

ENDLER, J.A. 1977 *Geographic Variation, Speciation, and Clines.* Princeton University Press, Princeton.

ETLER, D.A. 1990 A case study of the "*erectus*" - "*sapiens*" transition in Asia: Hominid remains from Hexian and Chaoxian Counties, Anhui Province, China. *Kroeber Anthropological Society Papers* 71-72:1-19.

EXCOFFIER, L. 1990 Evolution of human mitochondrial DNA: evidence for a departure from a pure neutral model of populations at equilibrium. *Journal of Molecular Biology* 30:125-139.

FALK, D. 1993 Meningeal arterial patterns in great apes: implications for hominid vascular evolution. *American Journal of Physical Anthropology* 92(1): 81-97.

FEREMBACH, D. 1979 L'émergence du genre *Homo* et de l'espèce *Homo sapiens*. Les faits. Les incertitudes. *Biométrie Humaine* 14:11-18.

___. 1986 Proposition de Phylogenèse et de Taxonomie du Genre *Homo*. In V.V. Novotný and A. Mizerová (eds): *Fossil Man. New Facts, New Ideas. Papers in Honor of Jan Jelinek's Life Anniversary. Anthropos* (Brno) 23:127-138.

FOLEY, R. 1987 Hominid species and stone-tool assemblages: how are they related? *Antiquity* 61:380-392.

FRAYER, D.W., M.H. WOLPOFF, A.G. THORNE, F.H. SMITH, and G.G. POPE. 1994 Reply to "resolving the archaic-to-modern transition" by G. Krantz. *American Anthropologist* 96(1):152-155.

FROMAGET, J. 1940 Les récentes découvertes anthropologiques dans les formations préhistoriques de la Chaine Annamitique. In F.N. Chasen and M.W.F Tweedie (eds): *Proceedings of the Third Congress of Prehistorians of the Far East*. Government Printing Office, Singapore. pp. 51-59.

GAMBLE, C.S. 1987 Man the shoveler: Alternative models for Middle Pleistocene colonization and occupation in Northern Latitudes. In O. Soffer (ed): *The Pleistocene Old World: Regional Perspectives*. Plenum, New York. pp. 81-98.

___. 1994 Time for Boxgrove man. *Nature* 369:275-276.

GILL, G.W., S.S. HUGHES, S.M. BENNETT, and B.M. GILBERT 1988 Racial identification from the midfacial skeleton with special reference to American Indians and whites. *Journal of Forensic Sciences* 33(1):92-99.

GOREN-INBAR, N. 1986 A figurine from the Acheulean site of Berekhat Ram. *Mitakufat Haeven* 19:7-12.

GOWLETT, J.A.J. 1987 New dates for the Acheulean age. *Nature* 329:200.

GRIMAUD-HERVÉ, D. 1986 The parietal bone of Indonesian *Homo erectus*. *Human Evolution* 1(2):167-182.

GUO SHILUN et al. 1991 Fission track dating of the 4th layer of the Peking man site. *Acta Anthropologica Sinica* 10(1):73-77.

HABGOOD, P.J. 1989 The origin of anatomically modern humans in Australasia. In P. Mellars and C.B. Stringer (eds): *The Human Revolution: Behavioural and Biological Perspectives on the Origins of Modern Humans*. Edinburgh University Press, Edinburgh. pp. 245-273.

HOLLOWAY, R.L. 1982 *Homo erectus* brain endocasts: volumetric and morphological observations with some comments on cerebral asymmetries. In H. de Lumley (ed): L'*Homo erectus et la Place de l'Homme de Tautavel parmi les Hominidés Fossiles.* 1er Congrès International de Paléontologie Humaine, Nice, Prétirage. Volume 1:355-369. Louis-Jean, Nice.

HOOTON, E.A. 1931 *Up From the Ape.* MacMillan, New York.

___. 1949 Human Evolution: A Review of *A New Theory of Evolution* by Sir Arthur Keith. *Antiquity* 23(91):126-128.

HOWELL, F.C. 1960 European and Northwest African Middle Pleistocene hominids. *Current Anthropology* 1:195-232.

___. 1981 Some views of *Homo erectus* with special reference to its occurrence in Europe. In B.A. Sigmon and J.S. Cybulski (eds): *Homo erectus. Papers in Honor of Davidson Black.* (combined bibliography at end of volume). University of Toronto Press, Toronto. pp. 153-157.

___. 1986 Variabilité chez *Homo erectus*, et problème de la présence de l'espèie en Europe. *L'Anthropologie* 90:447-481.

HOWELLS, W.W. 1942 Fossil man and the origin of races. *American Anthropologist* 44:182-193.

HRDLIČKA, A. 1926 The Rhodesian man. *American Journal of Physical Anthropology* 9:173-204.

HUANG PEIHUA, JIN SIZHAO, LIANG RENYOU, LU ZONGJIA, ZHENG LIZHEN, YUAN ZHENXIN, FANG ZHAOMENG, and CAI BINGXI 1991 Study of ESR dating for burying age of the first skull of Peking man and chronological scale of the cave deposit in Zhoukoudian site. *Acta Anthropologica Sinica* 10(2):107-115.

HUBLIN, J-J. 1985 Human fossils from the north African middle Pleistocene and the origin of *Homo sapiens.* In E. Delson (ed): *Ancestors: The Hard Evidence.* Alan R. Liss, New York. pp. 283-288.

___. 1988 Les plus anciens représentants de la lignée prénéandertalienne. *L'Homme de Néandertal*, Volume 3, *L'Anatomie.* Université de Liège, Liège. pp. 81-94.

___. 1989 Les caractères dérivés d'*Homo erectus*: Relation avec l'augmentation de la masse squelettique. In G. Giacobini (ed): *Hominidae: Proceedings of the 2nd International Congress of Human Paleontology.* Jaca Books, Turin. pp. 199-204.

___. 1990 Les peuplements paléolithiques de l'Europe: Un point de vue paléobiogéographique. In: *Paléolithique moyen récent et Paléolithique supérieur ancien en Europe.* Colloque international de Nemours. *Mémoires du Musée de Préhistoire d'Ile-de-France* 3:29-37.

ISAAC, G. Ll. 1975 Sorting out the muddle in the middle: an anthropologists post-conference appraisal. In K.W. Butzer and G.Ll. Isaac (eds.): *After the Australopithecines.* Mouton, The Hague. pp. 875-887.

JACOB, T. 1972 The problem of headhunting and brain-eating among Pleistocene men in Indonesia. *Archaeology and Physical Anthropology in Oceania* 7:81-91.

___. 1976 Early populations in the Indonesian region. In R.L. Kirk and A.G. Thorne (eds): *The Origins of the Australians.* Australian Institute of Aboriginal Studies, Canberra. pp. 81-93.

JAEGER, J-J. 1981 Les hommes fossiles du Pléistocène moyen du Maghreb dans leur cadre géologique, chronologique, et paleoécologique. In B.A. Sigmon and J.S. Cybulski (eds): *Homo erectus. Papers in Honor of Davidson Black.* (combined bibliography at end of volume). University of Toronto Press, Toronto. pp. 159-187.

JELÍNEK, J. 1978 Comparison of Mid-Pleistocene evolutionary process in Europe and in South-East Asia. *Proceedings of the 1978 Liblice Symposium on Natural Selection*, Praha. pp. 251-267.

___. 1980a Variability and geography. Contribution to our knowledge of European and north African Middle Pleistocene hominids. *Anthropologie* (Brno) 18:109-114.

___. 1980b European *Homo erectus* and the origin of *Homo sapiens*. In L.K. Königsson (ed): *Current Argument on Early Man*. Pergammon, Oxford. pp. 137-144.

___. 1982a The east and southeast Asian way of regional evolution. *Anthropologie* (Brno) 20:195-212.

___. 1982b The position of anteneanderthals among the hominids. In H. de Lumley (ed): *L'Homo erectus et la Place de l'Homme de Tautavel parmi les Hominidés Fossiles*. 1ᵉʳ Congrès International de Paléontologie Humaine, Nice, Prétirage. Volume 2:937-948. Louis-Jean, Nice.

JIA LANPO 1989 On problems of the Beijing-man site: a critique of new interpretations. *Current Anthropology* 30:200-205

JIA LANPO and HUANG WEIWEN 1990 *The Story of Peking Man. From Archaeology to Mystery*. Oxford University Press, Oxford.

KEITH, A. 1919 The differentiation of mankind into racial types. *Annual Reports of the Smithsonian Institution* 1919:443-453.

___. 1949 *A New Theory of Human Evolution*. Philosophical Library, New York

KEELEY, L.H. 1977 The functions of Paleolithic flint and tools. *Scientific American* 237(5):108-126.

KENNEDY, K.A.R., A. SONAKIA, J. CHIMENT, and K.K. VERMA. 1991 Is the Narmada hominid an Indian *Homo erectus*? *American Journal of Physical Anthropology* 86(4):475-496.

KLEIN, R.G. 1973 Geological antiquity of Rhodesian man. *Nature* 244:311-312.

KNAUFT, B.M. 1991 Violence and sociality in human evolution. *Current Anthropology* 32(4):391-428.

VON KOENIGSWALD, G.H.R. 1949 The Pleistocene In: *General Geology of Indonesia and Adjacent Archipelagos*. Government Printing Office, The Hague.

VON KOENIGSWALD, G.H.R., and F. WEIDENREICH. 1939. The relationship between *Pithecanthropus* and *Sinanthropus*. *Nature* 144:926:929.

KOERTVELYESSY, T. 1972 Relationships between the frontal sinus and climatic conditions: a skeletal approach to cold adaptation. *American Journal of Physical Anthropology* 37:161-172.

KOLATA, G. 1986 Anthropologists suggest cannibalism is a myth. *Science* 232:1497-1500.

KRANTZ, G.S. 1994 Resolving the archaic-to-modern transition. *American Anthropologist* 96(1):147-151.

KRETZOI, M., and V.T. DOBOSI (editors) 1990 *Vértesszöllös: Site, Man, and Culture*. Akadémiai Kiadó, Budapest.

LATHAM, A.G., and H.P. SCHWARCZ 1992 The Petralona hominid site: Uranium series re-analysis of 'Layer 10' calcite and associated paleomagnetic analysis. *Archaeometry* 34(1):135-140.

LEIGH, S.R. 1992 Cranial capacity evolution in *Homo erectus* and early *Homo sapiens*. *American Journal of Physical Anthropology* 87(1):1-14.

LEVINTON, J.S. 1982 Estimating stasis: can a null hypothesis be too null? *Paleobiology* 8:307.

LEWONTIN, R.C. 1984 *Human Diversity*. W.H. Freeman, San Francisco.

LI WENHISUNG and L. SADLER 1991 Low nucleotide diversity in man. *Genetics* 129513-523.

LI TIANYUAN and D.A. ETLER 1992 New Middle Pleistocene hominid crania from Yunxian in China. *Nature* 357:404-407.

LIN SHENGLONG 1989 Physical environment since Pliocene and the evolution of fossil man in China. *Acta Anthropologica Sinica* 8(3):209-215.

LIU DONGSHENG and DING MENGLIN 1984 A tentative chronological correlation of early human fossil horizons in China with the Loess-Deep Sea records. *Acta Anthropologica Sinica* 3(2):93-101.

LIU ZECHUN 1985 Sequence of sediments at Locality 1 in Zhoukoudian and correlation with loess stratigraphy in northern China and with the chronology of deep-sea cores. *Quaternary Research* 23:139-153.

LIVINGSTONE, F.B. 1961 Comment on "Middle Pleistocene Hominids" by F.C. Howell. *Current Anthropology* 2:117-118.

___. 1962 On the non-existence of human races. *Current Anthropology* 3:279-281.

LOVEJOY, C.O. 1982 Diaphyseal biomechanics of the locomotor skeleton of Tautavel man with comments on the evolution of skeletal changes in late Pleistocene man. In H. de Lumley (ed): *L'Homo erectus et la Place de l'Homme de Tautavel parmi les Hominidés Fossiles*. 1er Congrès International de Paléontologie Humaine, Nice, Prétirage. Volume 1:447-470. Louis-Jean, Nice.

MACINTOSH, N.W.G., AND S.L. LARNACH 1972 The persistence of *Homo erectus* traits in Australian aboriginal crania. *Archaeology and Physical Anthropology in Oceania* 7:1-7.

MANIA, D. 1990 *Auf den Spuren des Urmenschen: Die Funde aus der Steinrinne von Bilzingsleben*. Deutscher Verlag der Wissenschaften, Berlin.

MANIA, D., AND U. MANIA 1988 Deliberate engravings on bone artifacts of *Homo erectus*. *Rock Art Research* 5(2):91-132.

MANIA, D., and E. VLČEK 1981 *Homo erectus* in middle Europe: the discovery from Bilzingsleben. In B.A. Sigmon and J.S. Cybulski (eds): *Homo erectus. Papers in Honor of Davidson Black*. (combined bibliography at end of volume). University of Toronto Press, Toronto. pp. 133-151.

___. *Homo erectus* from Bilzingsleben (DDR) - his culture and his environment. *Anthropologie* (Brno) 25:1-45.

MANN, A. 1981 The significance of the *Sinanthropus* casts, and some paleodemographic notes. In B.A. Sigmon and J.S. Cybulski. (eds): *Homo erectus. Papers in Honor of Davidson Black*. (combined bibliography at end of volume). University of Toronto Press, Toronto. pp. 41-62.

___. 1982 Behavior and demography of *Homo erectus*. In H. de Lumley (ed): *L'Homo erectus et la Place de l'Homme de Tautavel parmi les Hominidés Fossiles*. 1er Congrès International de Paléontologie Humaine, Nice, Prétirage. Volume 2:997-1014. Louis-Jean, Nice.

MARSHACK, A. 1981 Paleolithic ochre and the early uses of color and symbol. *Current Anthropology* 23(2):188-201.

MORANT, G.M. 1938 The form of the Swanscombe skull. *Journal of the Royal Anthropological Institute* 68:67-97.

MURRIL, R.I. 1975 A comparison of the Rhodesian and Petralona upper jaws in relation to other Pleistocene hominids. *Zeitschrift für Morphologie und Anthropologie* 66:176-187.

OAKLEY, K.P. 1955 Fire as a paleolithic tool and weapon. *Proceedings of the Prehistoric Society* 21:36-48.

OVEY, C.D. (editor) 1964 *The Swanscombe Skull. Occasional Papers of the Royal Anthropological Institute* 20.

PATTERSON, H.E.H. 1992 The recognition concept of species. In: M. Ereshefsky (ed): *The Units of Evolution: Essays on the Nature of Species*. MIT Press, Cambridge. pp. 139-158.

POPE, G.G. 1988 Recent advances in Far Eastern Paleoanthropology. In B.J. Siegel, A.R. Beals, and S.A. Tyler (eds): *Annual Review of Anthropology*. Annual Reviews, Palo Alto. Volume 17:43-77.

___. 1992 Craniofacial evidence for the origin of modern humans in China. *Yearbook of Physical Anthropology* 35:243-298.

POPE, G.G., and J.E. CRONIN 1984 The Asian hominidae. *Journal of Human Evolution* 13:377-396.

PROTSCH, R. 1981 The Kohl-Larsen Eyasi and Garusi hominid finds in Tanzania and their relation to *Homo erectus*. In B.A. Sigmon and J.S. Cybulski. (eds): *Homo erectus. Papers in Honor of Davidson Black*. (combined bibliography at end of volume). University of Toronto Press, Toronto. pp. 217-226.

PROVINE, W.B. 1985 The R.A Fisher-Sewall Wright controversy and its influence on modern evolutionary biology. *Oxford Surveys in Evolutionary Biology* 2:197-219.

PUECH, P-F., H. Albertini, and N.T.W. Mills 1980 Dental destruction in Broken-Hill man. *Journal of Human Evolution* 91(1):33-39.

RIGHTMIRE, G.P. 1980 Middle Pleistocene hominids from Olduvai Gorge, northern Tanzania. *American Journal of Physical Anthropology* 53:225-241.

___. 1981 Patterns in the evolution of *Homo erectus*. *Paleobiology* 7:241-246.

___. 1986a Body size and encephalization in *Homo erectus*. In V.V. Novotný and A. Mizerová (eds): *Fossil Man. New Facts, New Ideas. Papers in Honor of Jan Jelínek's Life Anniversary. Anthropos* (Brno) 23:139-150.

___. 1986b Stasis in *Homo erectus* defended. *Paleobiology* 12(3):324-325.

___. 1988 *Homo erectus* and later Middle Pleistocene humans. In B.J. Siegel, A.R. Beals, and S.A. Tyler (eds): *Annual Review of Anthropology*. Annual Reviews, Palo Alto. Volume 17:239-259.

65

ROEBROEKS, W., N. CONRAD, and T. VAN KOLFSCHOTEN 1992 Dense forests, cold steppes, and the Paleolithic settlement of northern Europe. *Current Anthropology* 33(5):551-586

ROPER, M.K. 1969 A survey of the evidence of intrahuman killing in the Pleistocene. *Current Anthropology* 10:427-459.

ROSAS, A. 1987 Two new mandibular fragments from Atapuerca/Ibeas (SH site). A reassessment of the affinities of the Ibeas mandibles sample. *Journal of Human Evolution* 16(5):417-427.

SABAN, R. 1982 Les emprientes endocraniennes des veines mén ingées moyennes et les étapes de l'evolution humaine. *Annales de Paléontologie* 68:171-220.

SARICH, V.M. 1971 Human variation in an evolutionary perspective. In P. Dolhinow and V. Sarich (eds): *Background for Man*. Little Brown, Boston. pp. 182-191.

SAUER, N.J. 1992 Forensic anthropology and the concept of race: if races don't exist, why are forensic anthropologists so good at identifying them? *Society for Science in Medicine* 34(2):107-111.

SCHICK, K.D. 1994 The Movius line reconsidered: perspectives on the earlier Paleolithic of Eastern Asia. In R.S. Corruccini and R.L. Ciochon (eds): *Integrative Paths to the Past. Paleoanthropological Advances in Honor of F. Clark Howell*. Prentice Hall, Englewood Cliffs. pp. 569-596.

SHAPIRO, H. L. 1974 *Peking Man*. Simon and Schuster, New York .

SHEN GUANJUN 1986 U-series dating of deposits from the Prince cave, northern Italy. *Archaeometry* 28(2):179-184.

SHEN GUANJUN AND JIN LINHONG 1991a U-series age of Yanhui cave, the site of Tongzi man. *Acta Anthropologica Sinica* 10(1):65-72.

___ 1991b Restudy of the upper age limit of Beijing man site. *Acta Anthropologica Sinica* 10(4):273-277.

SHREEVE, J. 1994 Infants, cannibals, and the pit of bones. *Discover* 15(1):39-41.

SHIPMAN, P. 1993 On the origin of races. *New Scientist* (16 January) 34-37.

SIGMON, B.A. 1982 Comparative morphology of the locomotor skeleton of *Homo erectus* and the other fossil hominids, with special reference to the Tautavel innominate and femora. In H. de Lumley (ed): *L'Homo erectus et la Place de l'Homme de Tautavel parmi les Hominidés Fossiles*. 1er Congrès International de Paléontologie Humaine, Nice, Prétirage. Volume 1:422-446. Louis-Jean, Nice.

SOGNNAES, R.F. 1956 Histological evidence of developmental lesions in teeth originating from paleolithic prehistoric and ancient man. *American Journal of Pathology* 32:547-576.

SOHN S. and M.H. WOLPOFF 1993 The Zuttiyeh face: a view from the east. *American Journal of Physical Anthropology* 91:325-348.

STEWART, T.D. 1950 The problem of the earliest claimed representatives of *Homo sapiens*. *Cold Spring Harbor Symposia on Quantitative Biology* 15:97-107.

___. 1964 A neglected primitive feature of the Swanscombe skull. In C.E. Ovey (ed): *The Swanscombe Skull Occasional Papers of the Royal Anthropological Institute*, No. 20. pp. 151-160.

STINER, M.C. 1992 The place of hominids among predators: interspecific comparisons of food procurement and transport. In J. Hudson (ed): *From Bones to Behavior. Proceedings of the Eighth Annual Visiting Scholars Conference 1991.* Southern Illinois University Press, Carbondale.

STONEKING, M. 1994 In defense of "Eve: - a response to Templeton's critique. *American Anthropologist* 96(1):131-141.

STRINGER, C.B. 1978 Some problems in Middle and Upper Pleistocene hominid relationships. In D. Chivers and K. Joysey (eds): *Recent Advances in Primatology.* Academic Press, London. 3:395-418.

___. 1983 Some further notes on the morphology and dating of the Petralona hominid. *Journal of Human Evolution* 12:731-742.

___. 1985 Middle Pleistocene hominid variability and the origin of Late Pleistocene humans. In E. Delson (ed): *Ancestors: The Hard Evidence.* Alan R. Liss, New York. pp. 289-295.

___. 1986 An archaic character in the Broken Hill innominate E. 719. *American Journal of Physical Anthropology* 71(1):115-120.

___. 1992 Replacement, continuity, and the origin of *Homo sapiens.* In G. Bräuer and F.H. Smith (eds): *Continuity or Replacement? Controversies in Homo sapiens Evolution.* Balkema, Rotterdam. pp. 9-24.

___. 1993 Secrets of the pit of the bones. *Nature* 362:501-502.

STRINGER, C.B., F.C. HOWELL, and J. MELENTIS 1979 The significance of the fossil hominid skull from Petralona, Greece. *Journal of Archaeological Science* 6:235-253.

SVOBODA, J. 1987 Lithic industries of the Arago, Vértesszöllös, and Bilzingsleben hominids: comparison and evolutionary interpretation. *Current Anthropology* 28(2):219-227.

SZPIR, M. 1992 Accustomed to your face. *American Scientist* 80(6):537-539.

TEILHARD DE CHARDIN, P. 1956 *The Appearance of Man.* Harper and Row, New York.

TEMPLETON, A.R. 1994 "Eve: hypothesis compatability versus hypothesis testing. *American Anthropologist* 96(1):141-147.

THOMA, A. 1981 The position of the Vértesszöllös find in relation to *Homo erectus.* In B.A. Sigmon and J.S. Cybulski (eds): *Homo erectus. Papers in Honor of Davidson Black.* (combined bibliography at end of volume). University of Toronto Press, Toronto. pp. 105-114.

THORNE, A.G., and M.H. WOLPOFF 1992 The multiregional evolution of humans. *Scientific American* 266(4):76-83.

TURNER, C.G. 1993 Cannibalism in Chaco Canyon: the charnel pit excavation in 1926 at Small House Ruin by Frank H.H. Roberts, Jr. *American Journal of Physical Anthropology* 91(4):421-439.

VALLOIS, H.V. 1962 The origin of *Homo sapiens.* In W.W. Howells (ed): *Ideas on Human Evolution.* Harvard University Press, Cambridge. pp. 473-499.

VAN VALEN, L.M. 1986 Speciation and our own species. *Nature* 322:412.

VILLA, P. 1991 Middle Pleistocene prehistory in Southwestern Europe: the state of our knowledge and ignorance. *Journal of Anthropological Research* 47(2):193-217.

VLČEK, E. 1986 Les Antenéandertaliens en Europe Centrale et leur comparaison avec l'Homme de Tautavel. *L'Anthropologie* 90:503-513.

___. 1989 *Homo erectus* in Europa. *Ethnographische-Archäologische Zeitschrift* 30:287-305.

WEIDENREICH, F. 1937a The Forerunner of *Sinanthropus pekinensis*. *Bulletin of the Geological Society of China* 17:137-144.

___. 1937b New discoveries of *Sinanthropus pekinensis* and their bearing on the *Sinanthropus* and *Pithecanthropus* problems. *Bulletin of the Geological Society of China* 16:439-470.

___. 1938a *Pithecanthropus* and *Sinanthropus*. *Nature* 141:376-379.

___. 1938b The face of the Peking woman. *Natural History* 41:338-360.

___. 1939 Six lectures on *Sinanthropus pekinensis* and related problems. *Bulletin of the Geological Society of China* 19:1-110

___. 1940. Man or Ape? *Natural History* 45:32—37.

___. 1941 The site and the technique of excavation at Choukoutien, China. *Transactions of the New York Academy of Sciences*, Series II, 4:23-31.

___. 1946 *Apes, Giants, and Man*. University of Chicago, Chicago.

___. 1947 Are human races in the taxonomic sense "races" or "species"? *American Journal of Physical Anthropology* 5(3):369-371.

___. 1949 Interpretations of the fossil material. In W.W. Howells (ed): *Early Man in the Far-East*. Wistar Press, Philadelphia. pp. 149-157.

WEINER, J.S. and CAMPELL, B.G. 1964 The taxonomic status of the Swanscombe skull. In . C.D. Ovey (ed): *The Swanscombe Skull*. Royal Anthropological Institute, London. pp. 175-209.

WHITE, T.D. 1985 *Acheulean man in Ethiopia's Middle Awash Valley: the Implications of Cut Marks on the Bodo Cranium*. Nederlands Museum voor Anthropologie en Praehisorie, Amsterdam.

___. 1986 Cut marks on the Bodo cranium: a case of prehistoric defleshing. *American Journal of Physical Anthropology* 69:503-509.

___. 1992 *Prehistoric Cannibalism at Mancos 5MTUMR-2346*. Princeton University Press, Princeton.

WOLPOFF, M.H. 1980 Cranial remains of Middle Pleistocene European hominids. *Journal of Human Evolution* 9:339-358.

___. 1982 The Arago dental sample in the context of hominid dental evolution. In H. de Lumley (ed): *L'Homo erectus et la Place de l'Homme de Tautavel parmi les Hominidés Fossiles*. 1er Congrès International de Paléontologie Humaine, Nice, Prétirage. Volume 1:389-410. Louis-Jean, Nice.

___. 1984 Evolution in *Homo erectus*: the question of stasis. *Paleobiology* 10(4):389-406.

___. 1986a Stasis in the interpretation of evolution in *Homo erectus*: a reply to Rightmire. *Paleobiology* 12(3):325-328.

___. 1986b More on Zhoukoudian. *Current Anthropology* 27(1):45-46.

WOLPOFF, M.H., WU XINZHI, and A.G. THORNE 1984 Modern *Homo sapiens* origins: a general theory of hominid evolution involving the fossil evidence from east Asia. In F.H. Smith and F. Spencer (ed): *The Origins of Modern Humans: A World Survey of the Fossil Evidence.* Alan R. Liss, New York. pp. 411-483.

WOOD, B.A. 1991 Review of *The Evolution of Homo erectus* by G.P. Rightmire. *Journal of Human Evolution* 21(6):491-496.

WU RUKANG 1960 The unbalanced development of the physical features of *Sinanthropus pekinensis* and its interpretation. *Vertebrata PalAsiatica* 4:17-20.

___. 1964 Mandible of *Sinanthropus lantianensis. Current Anthropology* 5:98-101.

___. 1966 The skull of Lantian man. *Current Anthropology* 7:83-86.

___. 1983 Hominid fossils in China and their bearing on human evolution. *Canadian Journal of Anthropology* 3:207-214.

___. 1985 New Chinese *Homo erectus* and recent work at Zhoukoudian. In E. Delson (ed): *Ancestors: The Hard Evidence.* Alan R. Liss, New York. pp. 245-248.

WU RUKANG (ed) 1985 *Multi-Disciplinary Study of the Peking Man Site at Zhoukoudian.* Science Press, Beijing.

WU RUKANG and DONG XINGREN 1985 *Homo erectus* in China. In Wu Rukang and J.W. Olsen (eds): *Palaeoanthropology and Paleolithic Archaeology in the People's Republic of China.* Academic Press, New York. pp. 79-89.

WU RUKANG and LIN SHENGLONG 1983 Peking man. *Scientific American* 248(6):86-94.

WU RUKANG and WU XINZHI 1982 Comparison of Tautavel man with *Homo erectus* and early *Homo sapiens* in China. In H. de Lumley (ed): *L'Homo erectus et la Place de l'Homme de Tautavel parmi les Hominidés Fossiles.* 1er Congrès International de Paléontologie Humaine, Nice, Prétirage. Volume 2:605-616. Louis-Jean, Nice.

WU XINZHI 1990 The evolution of humankind in China. *Acta Anthropologica Sinica* 9(4):312-321.

WYNN, T. 1979 The intelligence of later Acheulean hominids. *Man* 14:371-391.

___. 1993 The evolution of tools and symbolic behavior. In A. Locke and C. Peters (eds): *The Evolution of Human Symbolic Behaviour.* Oxford University Press, New York.

XIONG WEIJUN., WENHSIUNG LI, I. POSNER, T. YAMAMURA, A. YAMAMOTO, A.M. GOTTO JR., and L CHAN 1991 No severe bottleneck during human evolution: evidence from two apolipoprotein C-II deficiency alleles. *American Journal of Human Genetics* 48:383-389.

XU QINQI and OUYANG LIAN 1982 Climatic changes during Peking Man's time. *Acta Anthropologica Sinica* 1(1):79-90.

XU QINQI and YOU YUZHU 1984 Hexian fauna: correlation with deep-sea sediments. *Acta Anthropologica Sinica* 3:62-67.

YI, S. and G.A. CLARK 1983 Observations on the lower Paleolithic of northeast Asia. *Current Anthropology* 24:181-202.

YUAN SIXUN, CHEN TIRMEI, and GAO SHIJUN 1986 Uranium series chronological sequence of some Paleolithic sites in South China. *Acta Anthropologica Sinica* 5(2):179-190.

ZHANG YINYUN 1991 An examination of temporal variation in the hominid dental sample from Zhoukoudian Locality 1. *Acta Anthropologica Sinica* 10(5):85-95.

Figure 11.2
Stratigraphic Positions for Middle Pleistocene *Homo sapiens*

Date (myr)	Africa	Indonesia	Asia	Europe and Western Asia
0.1	Klasies LBS, Jebel Irhoud 4 (127-87) Mumba (132-109) Laetoli 18	⇑	Xujiayao (125-100) Maba (140-119)	Krapina (129-100), Saccopastore (129-122) Pech de l'Azé >103), Tabun C Bourgeois-Delaunay (151)
	Florisbad	Ngandong Ngwa(?) ⇓	Xindong (169-145) Jinniushan (187±) Chaohu (200-167)	[Montmaurin, Lazeret, Fontéchevade (stage 6)] Biache (196-159)
0.2	Rabat (=Kébibat) Eyasi Wadi Dagadlé		Dingcun[a] (210-160), Changyang (216-179), Dali[a] (230-180), Tongzi (240-206)	Ehringsdorf (≈200) Vértesszöllős (211-160) Tabun E, Petralona (>200) ⇓
			Narmada Yunxian ⇓	Pontnewydd (251-195)
0.3	OH 11 (Ndutu Bed) ⇑		Yiyuan ⇓	Swanscombe Atapuerca, Zuttiyeh ⇓
	Kabwe, Ndutu, Elandsfontein ⇓		Hexian Tangshan ⇓	
0.4	Salé, Thomas Quarry, *Sidi Abderrahman*		ZKT H3 ↑ ZKT D1, L1-3	Bilzingsleben ↓
	Cave of Hearths			Fontana Ranuccio
0.5		⇑ Sambungmachan ⇓		Boxgrove Gesher Benot Ya'aqov
			ZKT E1	
0.6	Bodo *OH 23* (Masek)			
	Baringo (.66-.24)		*Chenjiayao*[a]	*Mauer*↕
0.7	Lainyamok (.70-.56)			

[1] Dates or date ranges given are based on numerical techniques

[a] Radiometric date confirmed by Oxygen Isotope Stage date estimates from Loess sequence position by Liu and Ding (1984)

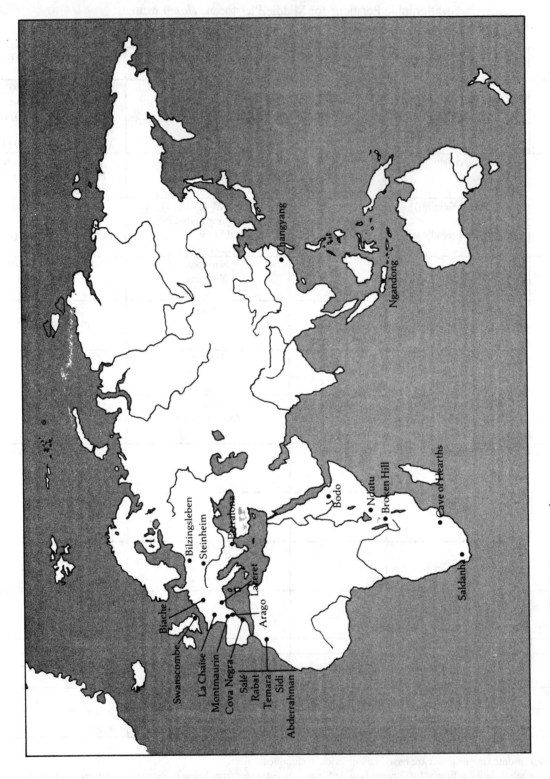

Map 11.1 Distribution of Middle Pleistocene humans.
From: First edition, Map 3

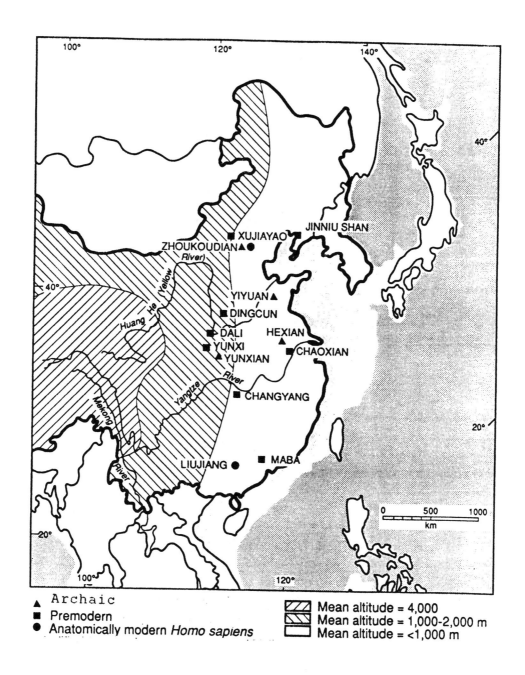

Map 11.2 Hominid and archaeological sites in China, after Pope (1992).
FROM Pope, G.G. 1992 Craniofacial evidence for the origin of modern humans in China. *Yearbook of Physical Anthropology* 35:243-298, figure 1.

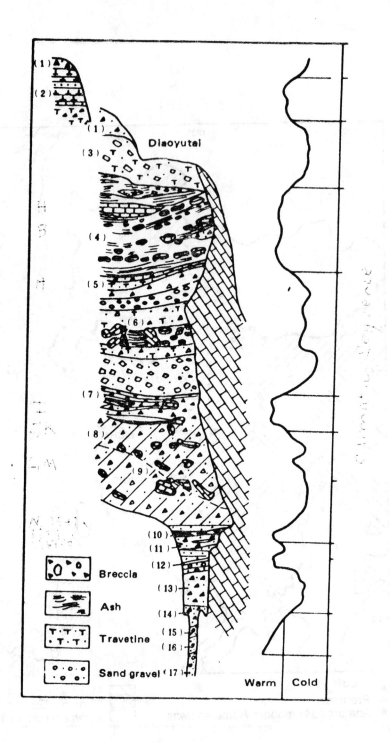

FIGURE 11.1 Stratigraphy of the Locality 1 cave at Zhoukoudian, adapted from Liu Zechun (1985)
FROM Liu Zechun 1985 Sequence of sediments at Locality 1 in Zhoukoudian and correlation with loess
stratigraphy in northern China and with the chronology of deep-sea cores. *Quaternary Research* 23:139-
153.

FIGURE 11.3 Zhoukoudian crania from locus L, after Weidenreich (1943).
FROM: Weidenreich, F. 1943 The skull of *Sinanthropus pekinensis*: A comparative study of a primitive hominid skull. *Palaeontologia Sinica*, n.s. D, No. 10 (whole series No. 127), figures 55, 57, 58, 67, 69, 70, 79, 81, 82.

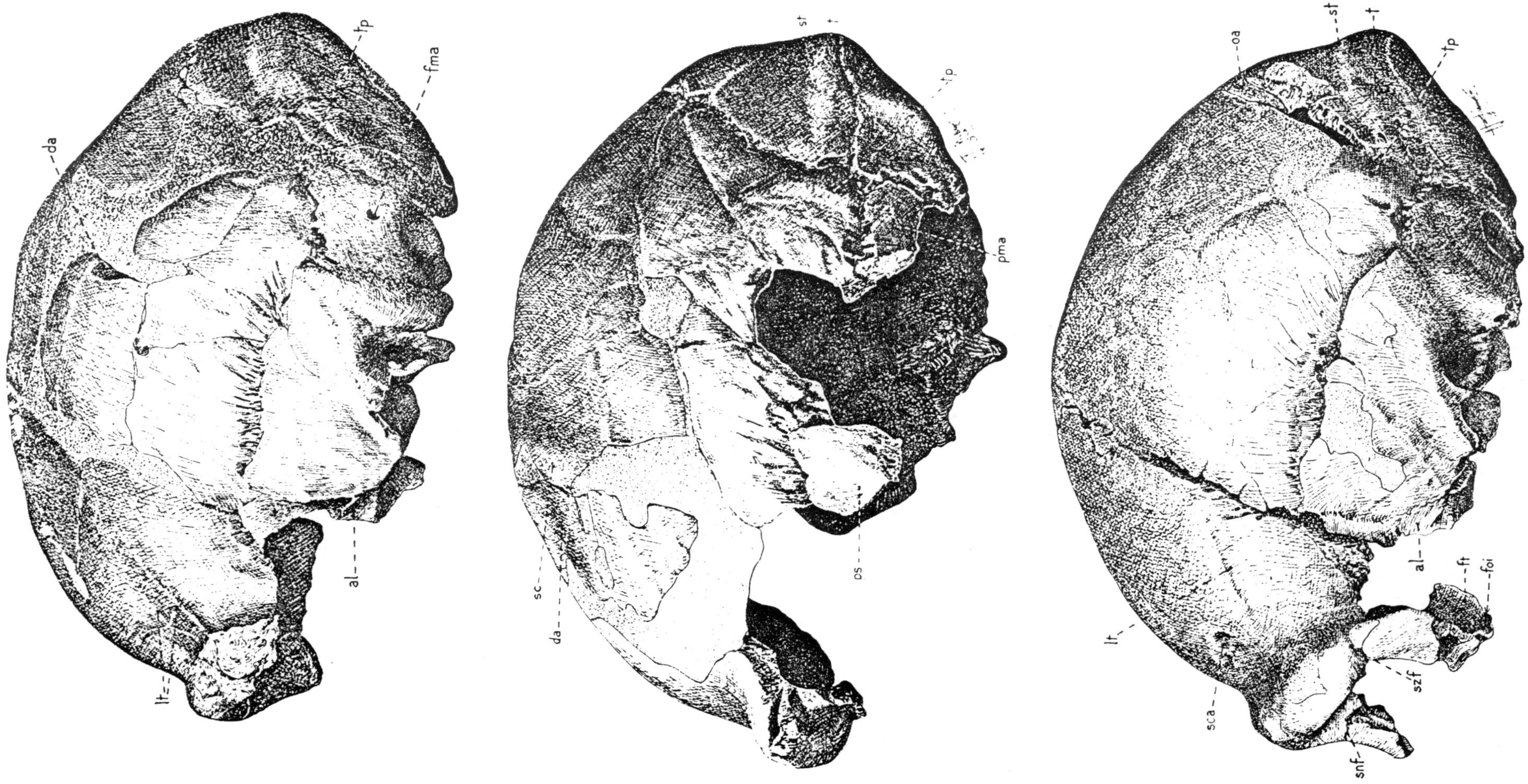

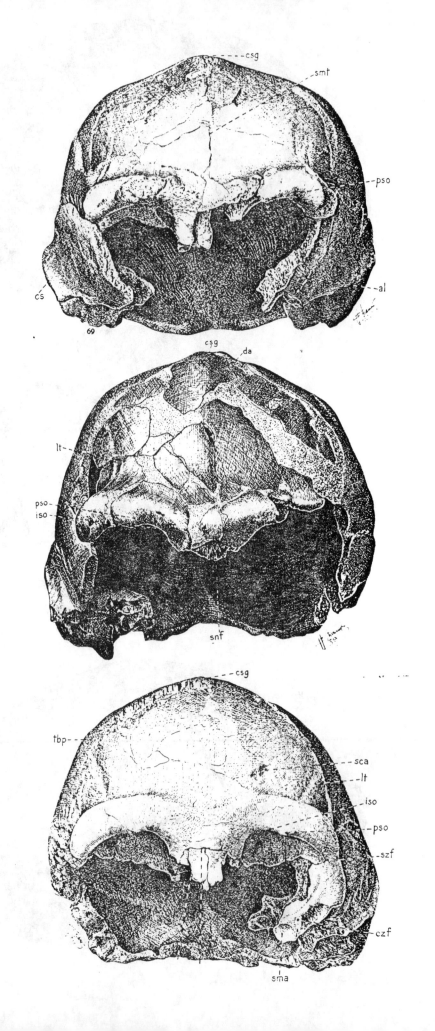

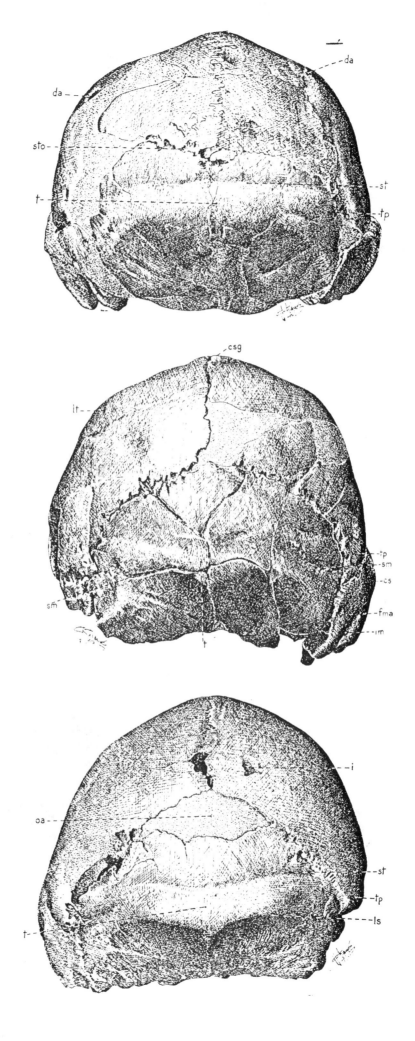

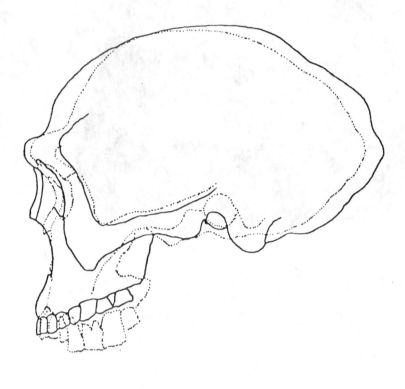

······ ER 3733
—— Choukoutien 11

FIGURE 11.4 Weidenreich's reconstruction of ZKT 11 compared with ER 3733, a comparison of two female crania in lateral view.

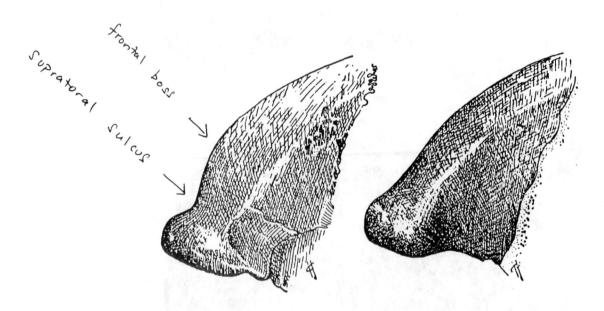

frontal boss

supratoral sulcus

FIGURE 11.5 A comparison of Zhoukoudian (left) and Sangiran frontal profiles, contrasting the frontal boss and supratoral sulcus of the Chinese specimen with the more flattened forehead of the Indonesian. After von Koenigswald (1956).
FROM von Koenigswald, G.H.R. 1956 *Meeting Prehistoric Man*. Thames and Hudson, London, figure 7.

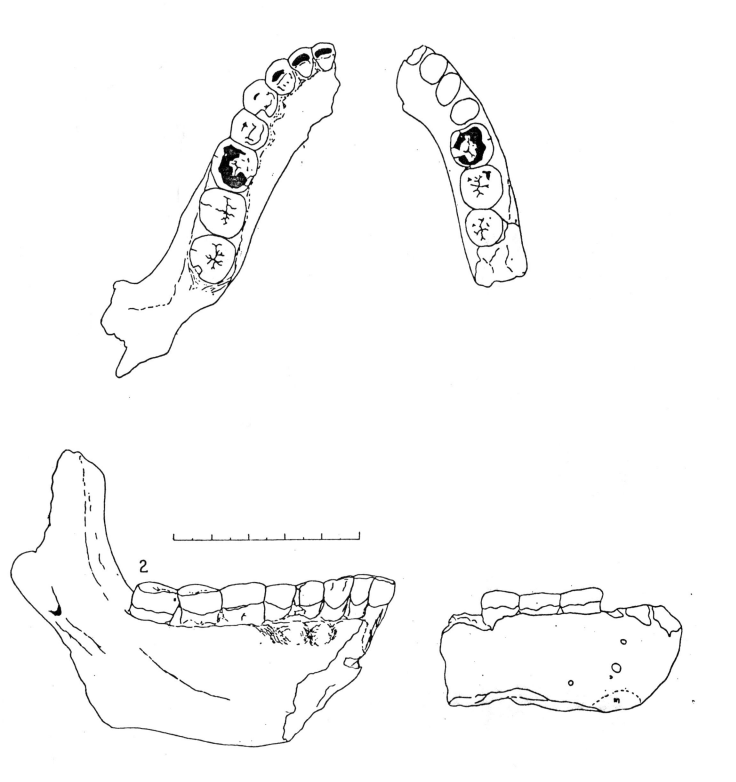

FIGURE 11.6 Zhoukoudian male (G1, left) and female (A2) mandibles, after Weidenreich (1936).
FROM Weidenreich, F. 1936 The mandibles of *Sinanthropus pekinensis*: a comparative study.
Palaeontologia Sinica, Series D., Volume 7, Fascicle 3.

FIGURE 11.7 Lateral view of Chenjiayao and some Zhoukoudian mandibles. The Locus H specimen is the youngest of these.

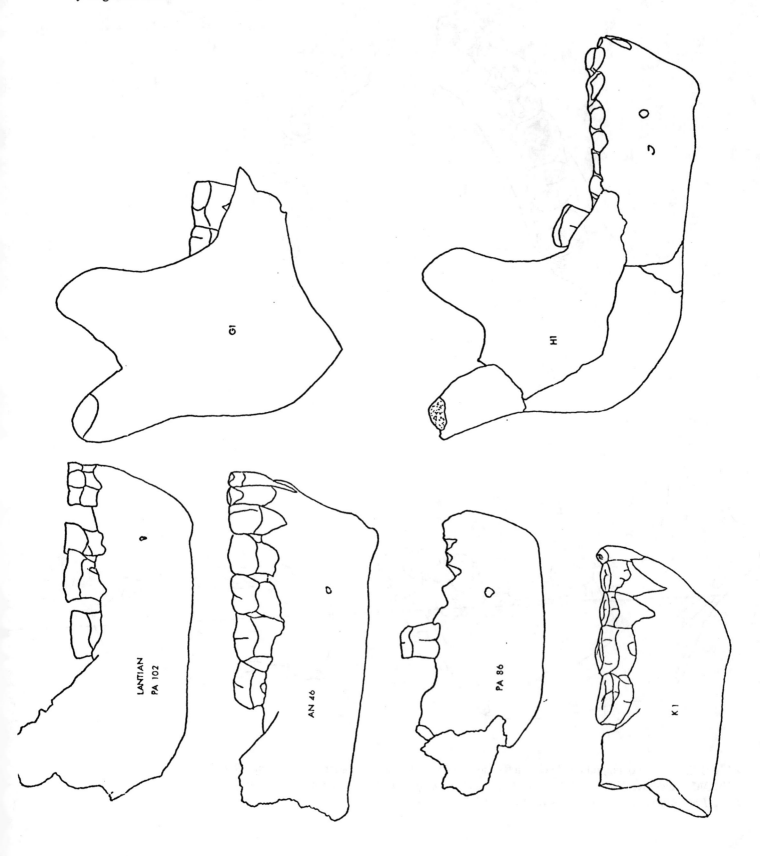

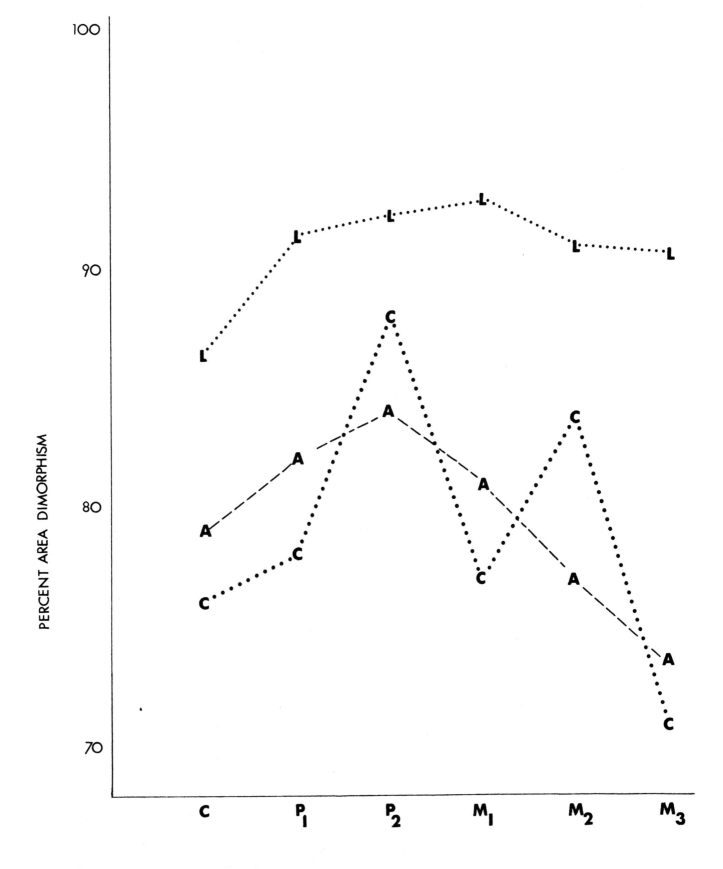

FIGURE 11.8 Average sexual dimorphism in Zhoukoudian compared with dimorphism in *Australopithecus africanus* (A) and a modern population (Libben, an Ohio Amerind site). The small Zhoukoudian sample seems to approximate the australopithecine condition, but sex determination for many isolated teeth is not always certain.

rear ⟵⟶ front

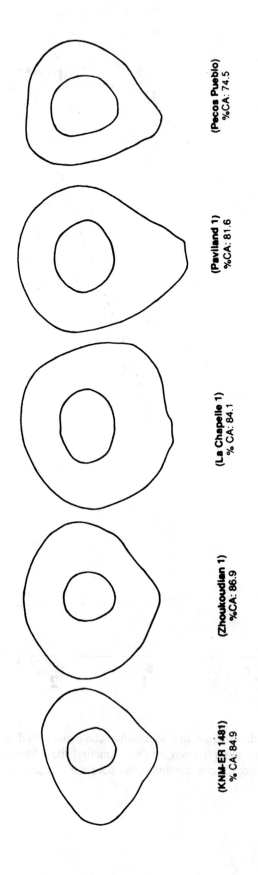

(KNM-ER 1481)   (Zhoukoudian 1)   (La Chapelle 1)   (Paviland 1)   (Pecos Pueblo)
% CA: 84.9   %CA: 86.9   % CA: 84.1   %CA: 81.6   %CA: 74.5

FIGURE 11.9 Midshaft cross-sections of femora showing the internal cortical bone distribution (and its percentage of the total cross-sectional area), after Ruff and colleagues (1993). The specimens shown are ER 1481 (probably *H. habilis*), Zhoukoudian, La Chapelle (a Neandertal), and a recent European (Paviland) and Amerind (Pecos Pueblo). Only the recent two have a strongly developed pilaster on the rear surface.
FROM Ruff, C.B., E. Trinkaus, A. Walker, and C.S. Larsen 1993 Postcranial robusticity in Homo. I: Temporal trends and mechanical interpretation. American Journal of Physical Anthropology 91(1):21-53.

FIGURE 11.10 Reconstruction of the Hanoman 1 cranium, after Widianto and colleagues (1994).
FROM Widianto, H., A-M. Sémah, T. Djubiantono, and F. Sémah 1994 A tentative reconstruction of the cranial human remains of Hanoman 1 from Bukuran, Sangiran (Central Java). In J.L. Franzen (ed): *100 years of Pithecanthropus: The Homo erectus problem. CourierForschungsinstitut Senckenberg* 171:47-59.

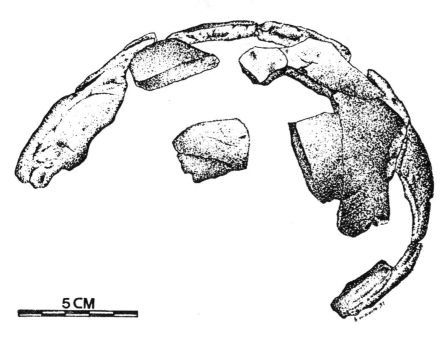

5 CM

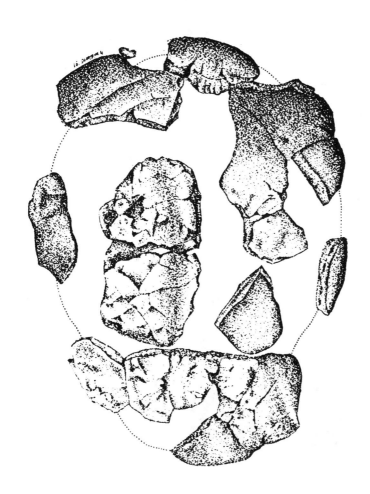

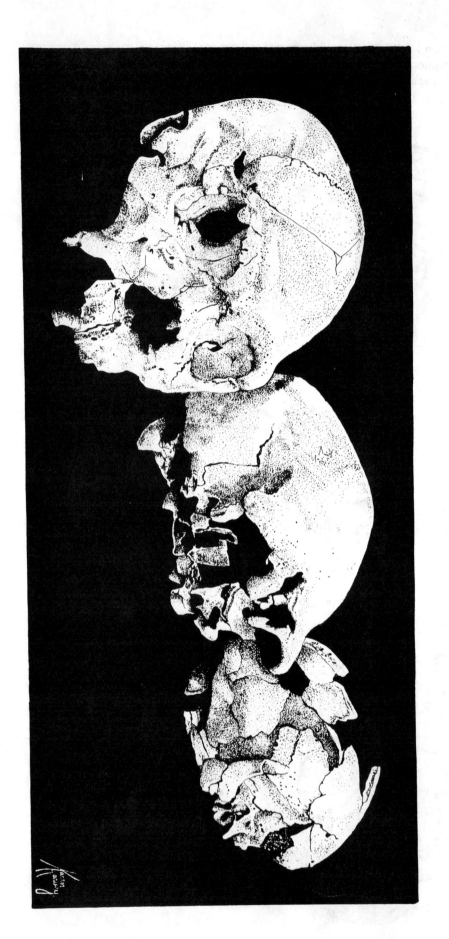

FIGURE 11.13 Atapuerca cranium 5 (left), 4 (center) and 6. Drawing by K. Harvey.

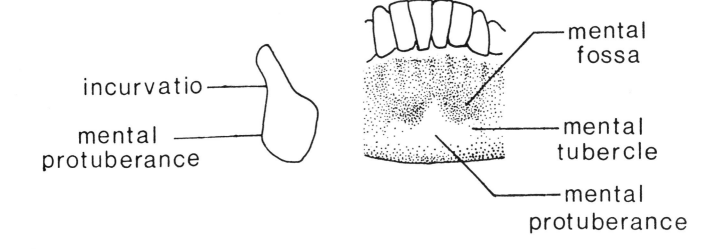

incurvatio

mental
protuberance

mental
fossa

mental
tubercle

mental
protuberance

Figure 11.4

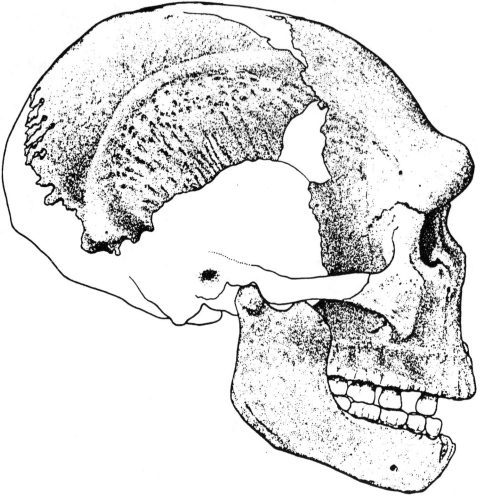

Figure 11.15

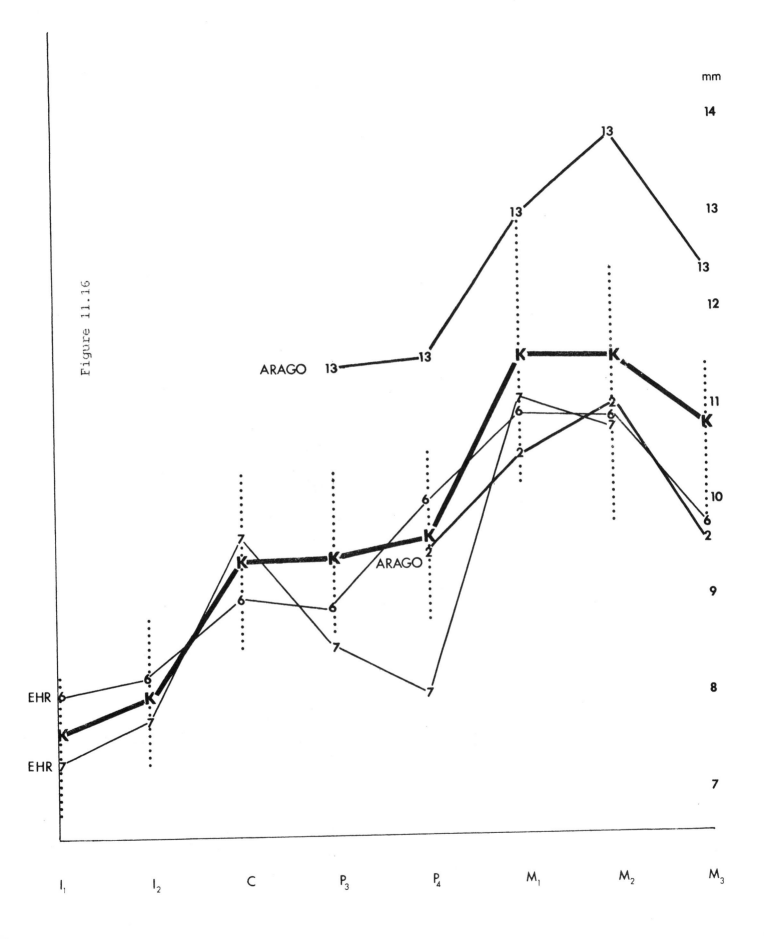

Figure 11.16

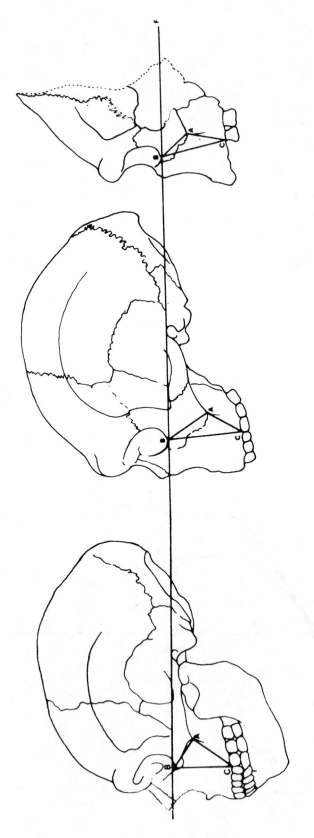

Figure 11.17

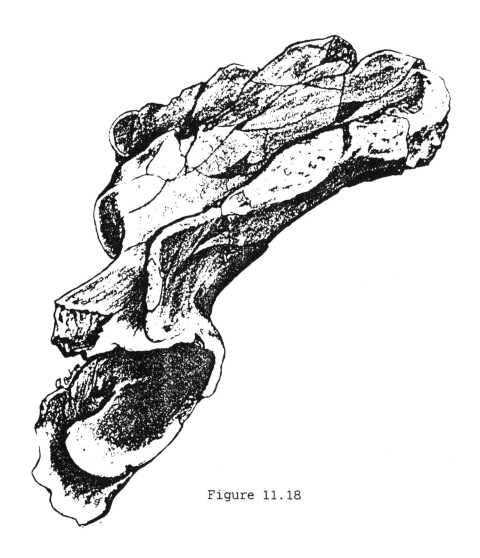

Figure 11.18

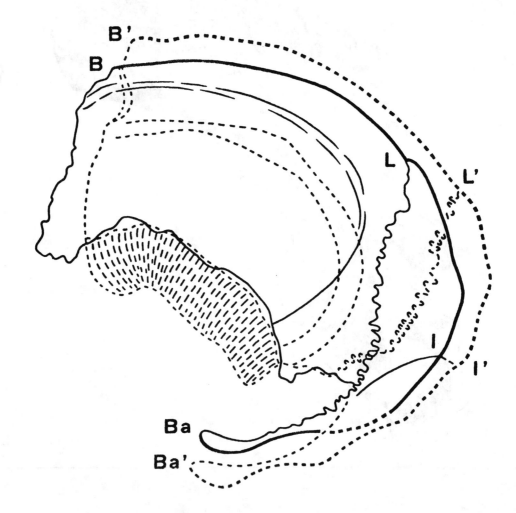

Figure 11.20

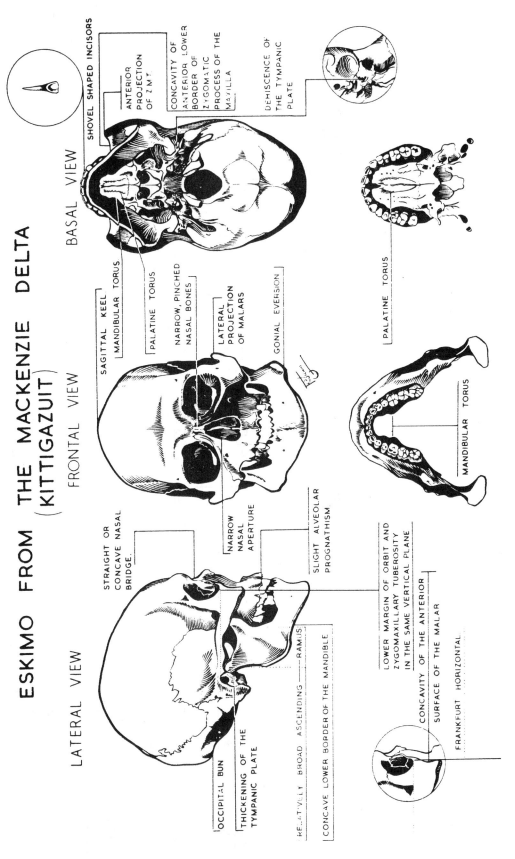

ESKIMO FROM THE MACKENZIE DELTA
(KITTIGAZUIT)

LATERAL VIEW

FRONTAL VIEW

BASAL VIEW

SHOVEL SHAPED INCISORS

ANTERIOR PROJECTION OF Z.M.T.

CONCAVITY OF ANTERIOR LOWER BORDER OF ZYGOMATIC PROCESS OF THE MAXILLA

DEHISCENCE OF THE TYMPANIC PLATE

SAGITTAL KEEL

MANDIBULAR TORUS

PALATINE TORUS

NARROW, PINCHED NASAL BONES

LATERAL PROJECTION OF MALARS

GONIAL EVERSION

PALATINE TORUS

MANDIBULAR TORUS

STRAIGHT OR CONCAVE NASAL BRIDGE.

NARROW NASAL APERTURE

SLIGHT ALVEOLAR PROGNATHISM

LOWER MARGIN OF ORBIT AND ZYGOMAXILLARY TUBEROSITY IN THE SAME VERTICAL PLANE

CONCAVITY OF THE ANTERIOR SURFACE OF THE MALAR

FRANKFURT HORIZONTAL

OCCIPITAL BUN

THICKENING OF THE TYMPANIC PLATE

RELATIVELY BROAD ASCENDING RAMUS

CONCAVE LOWER BORDER OF THE MANDIBLE

Figure 11.22

Table 11.14

Comparisons of Instructive Anatomy for Complete Middle Pleistocene Specimens

Specimen	alveolar profile	maxillary notch	high zygomatic base	puffy midface	Cheek orientation	fronto-nasal and fronto-maxillary suture	nasal angle	frontal boss	bregmatic eminence	Tall sagittal keel	prominent glabella	arched supra-orbitals	vertical parietal walls	angular torus	flexed occipital angle	nuchal torus
Petralona	flat	no	no	yes	angled	curved	higher	no	no	no	no	no	yes	no	no	strong
Bilzingsleben						curved				no	yes	no	no	yes	yes	strong
Arago 21	prognathic	no	no	yes	angled	curved	higher	no	no	low, weak	no	no	yes	yes	no[2]	weak[2]
Steinheim	prognathic	no	no	no	flat	straight	higher	yes	no	no	yes	no	no	no	no	weak
Atapuerca 5	flat	yes	yes	yes	angled	curved	higher	no	no	no	no	yes	yes	no	no	strong
ZKT 11	prognathic	yes	yes	no	flat	straight	lower	yes	yes	yes	yes	yes	no	yes	yes	strong
Dali	flat	yes	yes	no	flat	straight	lower	yes	yes	yes	yes	yes	no	yes	no	strong
Yunxian 2	prognathic	yes	yes	no	flat	straight	higher	no	no	yes	yes	no	no	no	yes	strong

[1] Features with character states varying in the sample, with a minimum of two specimens for each state

[2] Uses Swanscombe morphology

[3] From author's observations, Li and Etler (1992), Pope (1992), and Arsuaga and colleagues (1993)

CHAPTER TWELVE

The Origins of Modern Humans

The last 250 kyr is the period in which modern humans appeared. Whether by modern we mean people who are skeletally similar to the recent and living, or we mean people who behave in recognizably modern ways, there is broad agreement that by 40-50 kyr they can be found in a number of places. Many paleoanthropologists believe that their first appearance is considerably earlier. The period when modern humans are first identified straddles the beginning of the Late Pleistocene, the span comprised of the last glaciation and short interglacial before it (beginning with Oxygen Isotope stage 5e about 128 kyr).

"Modern human" has proven to be an illusive and slippery term to define. M. Wobst puts the problem well. There is a kind of cone of modernity, the base in the present or recent past encompassing everyone, and the more ancient time slices producing smaller and smaller samples of things that are modern. At the point of origin there is nothing modern at all. Such a cone makes it appear as if modernity has a single origin, it must appear first somewhere, but this is a result of looking from the present to the past and not taking the evolutionary perspective of a populational approach to the issue of how the past produced the present. Deeper than the issue of how to define modernity, is understanding the evolutionary process that produced it. Perhaps one of the most important questions that has emerged from paleoanthropological debates during the last quarter of this century is whether modern humans can even be said to have a particular or specific origin - indeed, whether they can be accurately diagnosed as a distinct entity at all.

The idea that all modern humans descend from a single unique African source is the basis for the "Eve" theory, the most extreme of the last decade's "Out of Africa" hypotheses of modern human origins. According to this theory Eve's descendants totally replaced other peoples until only their progeny were left. Other, less extreme hypotheses interpret the fossil record to show that *a population of modern humans* evolved in Africa and gradually and less dramatically spread, mixing with the peoples they encountered until few of the original population's features were left. Both of these, opposite ends of a range of theories, are based on the idea of a *single populational origin* for modern humans.

The other explanation of modern human origins is that the various *features of modern humans* had separate roots in different regions, and these spread by gene flow and population movements until they prevailed. This is part of the Multiregional Evolution interpretation (discussed in Chapter 11) I developed with A. Thorne of the Australian National University and Wu Xinzhi of the Institute for Vertebrate Paleontology and Paleoanthropology in China. We based our thinking on our different experiences with the human fossil record, trying to use the evolutionary processes seen in the present to explain F. Weidenreich's and our own observations of regional continuity from past to present populations in different regions. Multiregional Evolution posits that there was no single origin for modern people.

This chapter covers a 200 kyr period beginning some 250 kyr ago. Analysis of hominid evolution at this time is complex for two reasons. First, the samples are large. More recent populations are bound to be better represented by fossils. Moreover, the practice of burial became widespread during this period, increasing the number of remains. An additional contributing factor is the marked populational increases that occurred over this period. The number of Middle Pleistocene humans alive at any one time are may have been quite small. Guesstimates are considerably less than a million - 125,000 was proposed by H. Harpending and colleagues, and 500,000 suggested by K. Weiss. Genetic data suggest that major population size expansions may have begun in several regions by some 80 kyr. Second, clear elements of continuity with recent and living people are found in the larger and more complete samples of various areas. It becomes increasingly difficult to distinguish common or grade features (and their evolution) from those which are area-specific.

The available samples allow four geographic areas to be considered: East Asia, Africa, and West Asia will be discussed in this order, which also corresponds to the order of increasing sample size. Following this is a review of the fourth area, Europe, and the "Neandertal problem" in Chapter 13. The issues raised by the evolutionary sequence in Europe are complex and the data set very large, so this region has a chapter to itself.

This period is not just a time of origins. Colonization continues into increasingly difficult habitats. During this interval humans successfully expanded into very cold and arid environments. It is also the time of the last innovation to visibly spread across the entire inhabited world. Prepared core technology is probably the final cultural element to enjoy a really worldwide distribution before the steel axe and the Bible.

PREPARED CORES AND THEIR IMPLICATIONS

Two significant developments in tool-making technology occurred which laid the foundation for the subsequent evolution of all human populations. An early discovery, already mentioned, was that stone can be shaped by softer materials, such as bone or wood, as well as by stone itself. The use of softer striking materials allowed finer work to be done, producing straighter and sharper edges.

The second development was truly insightful and revolutionary. This was the invention of the prepared core, or "Levallois" technique (figure 12.1). Prior to this, stone was shaped by striking flakes with another stone or with bone, antler or wood. The implement was shaped as flakes were struck off. In earlier Acheulean industries there is great variation in the skill exhibited in the finished tools; as the required abilities improved, throughout the Acheulean the evolution of skill and foresight is shown by the increasing standardization of tool types. Basic forms were preconceived, and were not just the consequences of the reduction processes, and greater and greater effort was made to flake implements into a desired shape. Continued retouch work on some flakes shows that they too were fashioned into specific forms. With increasing knowledge of raw material, skill, and the ability to preconceive form and translate the mental image accurately into performance, the raw material itself began to impose more limitations on the final product. As far as we can tell, these behavioral changes were related to the evolution of certain parts of the brain. And it was not until these changes occurred that a complex manufacturing technique such as the Levallois could arise.

What makes the Levallois technique revolutionary is that it introduced a second step into the manufacture of tools, further removing the shape and initial preparation of the raw material from the form of the finished product. The technique is used to prepare flake tools by pre-shaping the core they are struck from. It consists of flaking a core to a contour that is something like a turtle shell so that when a single flake is struck from it, it will immediately have the desired appearance. This flake is the finished tool and usually needs no additional retouch on its extremely sharp edges, at least until there is use wear. It was not simply a more skillful way of fashioning stone, because Levallois required a certain degree of neurological complexity and the ability to formulate (or learn) and follow a complex set of rules. When tools are made by direct or indirect percussion, there is an immediate feedback as the stone is being worked, since each step makes it look more like the desired form. The Levallois technique does not have this feedback potential because the core does not look like the Levallois flake that will be struck from it.

The prepared-core technique appeared in Africa, Europe, and Asia within the middle-to-later stages of the Acheulean industrial complex in the Middle Pleistocene. The technique was first used to further refine the manufacture of tool types already present, but by the end of the Middle Pleistocene, its potential to produce a whole new range of tool types had begun to be exploited. The neurological evolution that allowed the discovery of this technique came as a result of selection occurring during the time span of the Acheulean complex. Once present, the technique opened up a new adaptive potential that was soon realized, although increasingly in different ways from region to region.

The archaeological changes are recognized in the designation of a class of Paleolithic industries, the Middle Paleolithic, first identified at this time. Middle Paleolithic industries are predominated by prepared core flake technologies and numerous flake tools, and the occasional area where bone tools proliferate (for instance one in Zaire, another in Crimea). Middle Paleolithic industries are distributed throughout the inhabited world. Ideas spread widely , suggesting contacts and population movements. Yet at the same time there are significant regional differences. Variants include industries made on flakes not struck from prepared cores, significant use of bone tools, and the use, even predominance, of tools made on elongated blades. Some of these are widespread and long lasting, but others are quite short lived. These evolving technologies allowed a fine control over the final form of a tool regardless of the material used. Once they were established, a proliferation of tool types was inevitable, and eventually industries based on many special-purpose tools appeared. Hand axes and choppers, the "boy scout knives" of their time, were often replaced by these special-purpose tools, and stone tools for working bone and wood proliferated. The comparison and contrast of worldwide similarities and regional (even local) differentiation is similar to the anatomical observations that underlie the Multiregional Evolution model discussed in Chapter 11.

Some of the most important of the worldwide anatomical changes can be directly linked to Middle Paleolithic technology. These include reductions in skeletal traits that reflect body strength, and changes found in the anterior teeth and the parts of the face that support their roots. Incisors and canines reduce in all the Late Pleistocene populations, although at different rates and magnitudes. In some cases, such as the European Neandertals, the reduction caps a long Middle Pleistocene trend for anterior tooth size expansion. The change in selection for them, in all likelihood, was initiated by technological developments within Middle Paleolithic industries. The appearance of efficient special-purpose tools made of stone, wood, and bone reduced the need for using the incisors as part of the tool kit, both directly as tools and more indirectly as a vise while using other tools. The change in behavior (i.e., the development of special-purpose tools) preceded the change in morphology (incisor reduction).

The beginning of size reduction in the anterior teeth also helps explain certain other ways in which modern populations differ from their early Late Pleistocene predecessors. In particular, the changes in anterior tooth use affect cranial form because of the functional bases of the nuchal and supraorbital tori, and through the alterations in a number of cranial muscle attachments. These, of course, are not the only and may not even be the most important ways in which populations at the beginning and end of the Late Pleistocene differ, but they are a significant aspect.

Specimens from Eastern Asia

INDONESIA

Indonesia is an excellent place to begin the discussion of cranial evolution since the largest single collection of later Middle Pleistocene crania comes from the island of Java. Fifteen specimens (two tibias and thirteen vaults or vault fragments) were recovered from the High Terrace of the Solo River near Ngandong, and an additional female was discovered at nearby Ngawi. This sample (often called the Solo remains) was discovered in the 1930s (except for a few recently recovered fragments and the Ngawi specimen) and its dating has been a persistent problem. The specimens were initially placed in the Late Pleistocene because of associated fauna also found in High Terrace deposits. To obtain numerical dates J. Bartstra and colleagues located the original findspot of the crania. Animal bones from the lowest levels of the High Terrace were dated by Uranium/Thorium to 101±10 kyr, seemingly verifying the late Pleistocene age. However, High Terrace dates from a nearby river site are 165 kyr, and similar deposits in Central Java (Notoporo sands and gravels) can only be said to be younger than a fission track date of 250 kyr. A recent Potassium/Argon date from a tuff near the site approximates 500 kyr, although the relation of the dated tuff to the High Terrace is unclear. F.C. Howell accepts a 115-85 kyr date for this sample, and I believe this is a reasonable assessment.

The Ngandong crania (figure 12.2) were recovered over a distance of several hundred feet along the river. Considering them together as a sample may be justified, but they do not necessarily represent a single biological population. All of the crania (including Ngawi) lack faces, and the cranial base is preserved in four (currently Ngawi and Ngandong crania 6 and 11 - it was also preserved in cranium 1, as illustrated by W. Oppenoorth, but evidently broken and lost during cleaning). It is possible that the other cranial bases and faces were broken away at the time of death, to remove the brains, although the crania have never been systematically examined for the cutmarks that might remain from such activities. As discussed in Chapter 11, taphonomy is probably not the explanation of the condition of these specimens. In any event, our knowledge is limited to details of the cranial vault.

The specimens were studied intensively by F. Weidenreich. His untimely death during the preparation of a monograph describing them resulted in its publication, after his death, in the state of completion he left it. However he also made detailed comparisons of the specimens as part of his Zhoukoudian crania monograph and a subsequent dissertation on the specimens was written by A. Santa

Luca. Of the thirteen crania or cranial fragments, nine are adult or at least fully grown and one is clearly a young juvenile or child (in this assessment I differ from Weidenreich). I believe that adult crania 5, 9, 10, and 11 are male and that Ngawi and Ngandong specimens 1, 4, 6, and 8 are female. The young specimen, cranium 2, is probably male. Sex determination is based on cranial size, projection and size of the nuchal torus, and the development of a prominence, an **external occipital protuberance**, at the middle of this torus in the males. These features show no overlap between males and females. Other characteristics that do overlap but show an average difference between the sexes include vault thickness and development of the lines and crests marking muscle attachments. While Weidenreich regarded the degree of sexual dimorphism as less than at Zhoukoudian, I believe that the opposite is the case and that in general the Ngandong crania are the same or even more variable.

Table 12.1
East Asian Brain Sizes

	Female average	Male average
Indonesian Kabuh	875 (n=5)	1032 (n=2)
Chinese Zhoukoudian	965 (n=3)	1078 (n=4)
Indonesian Ngandong[1]	1093 (n=2)	1177 (n=4)

[1]   Ngawi, is smaller than any of these females. While her capacity is as yet unknown, it would lower the female average and thereby accentuate the dimorphism.

The crania are larger than the Sangiran or Choukoutien specimens; according to R. Holloway average cranial capacity (table 12.1) increases from the Kabuh to the Ngandong Indonesians by 12 percent to a middle sex average of 1,135 cc. The increase is about the same for males and females and sexual dimorphism is virtually identical based on these measures (it would be larger if a capacity were known for Ngawi). Holloway's findings from his studies of these specimens include a strong Broca's area and a normal lateralization pattern reflected in right frontal and left occipital petalias. In general Holloway concludes they are a homogeneous sample with more in common with ZKT and Kabuh endocasts than with Neandertals. Moreover, they are not simply expanded versions of the earlier Indonesians, and some of the differential changes do not continue earlier trends. For instance, in early and Middle Pleistocene remains the cranial breadth increased much more than braincase breadth as the basal spongy bone expanded. Examination of the Solo remains reveals a very different pattern: braincase breadth continues its increase while the total cranial breadth is much the same. Thus these breadths approach each other in magnitude (Chapter 11 describes similar trends in Africa and Europe). The maximum braincase breadth position is higher and more anteriorly placed, and the cranial contour is rounded as seen from the rear. The other marked expansions are in cranial height and in the breadth of the frontal bone where it borders the temporal fossa. Thus these crania are taller and show less frontal narrowing and much less difference between cranial and braincase breadth. Additional details that differ include the loss of the elongated depressions extending parallel to the sagittal keels, lambdoidal flattening of the cranial rear, square parietal shape, and weaker and lower positioned temporal lines.

Two other changes reveal differential expansion of certain parts of the brain. Continuing an earlier trend both frontal and occipital areas seem more filled out. Expansion of the frontal lobes brings the forehead above the supraorbitals from its earlier position more behind them, and there is no demarcation between the top of the supraorbital and the frontal squama in these specimens. A distinct regional feature is the backward extension of the torus at the outer corner of the orbit, along the temporal line. This forms **a lateral frontal trigone**, a knob-like backward-facing triangle that can be found in many Late Pleistocene Australian crania. It is also found on Ngawi, and to a lesser extent on Sambungmachan. Posterior parietal expansion is seen in the marked bulging of the occipital plane above the nuchal torus.

A consequence of the changing forehead morphology is expressed in the browridge. With a forehead that is better positioned to help resist stress, browridge thickness reduces. In the Solo sample the main reduction is in the central portion of the torus (this is quite opposite the European reduction pattern). The browridge more closely approximates the contours of the orbits, and a depression over the nose results in its distinct separation into right and left sides.

Another aspect of changing selection is seen in the occiput. While the upper portion of the bone expands, the attachment area for the nuchal muscles decreases by some 30 percent compared (by sex) with the Sangiran remains. In most earlier hominids this attachment area makes up the major part of the bone, but in the Solo sample the proportions are reversed and the occipital plane dominates. At the same time, however, there is an expansion in the size of the nuchal torus. This structure is more prominent than in most earlier Indonesian crania, especially in its backward projection.

The Solo remains (including Ngawi) have some unique features that may reflect small population size on an isolated island *cul de sac*. Besides the frontal trigone, there is a fissure on the base of the temporal bone that extends along the roof of the mandibular fossa instead of on its back side between the fossa and the ear opening, and the foramen ovale on the cranial base, to the sides of the palate rear, is doubled instead of its normal single expression. These were probably established by genetic drift because they are not adaptive variations.

Table 12.2
Dimensions of Complete or Almost Complete Tibiae

	Box-grove	Solo 12	13	Kabwe 691	Shanidar 1	2	Amud	Tabun	Qafzeh 3	Skhul 4	5
maximum length			372	415	355	337	(384)	314	364	430	412
midshaft circumference	105	104	82	93	93	97	101	74		96	100
index		90	82	71	76	71	63	75		79	72
minimum circumference	97	94	80	81		87	86	70	77	85	90
relative minimum circumference (%)			21	20		26	22	22	21	20	22
distal end length			41	37	39	37	37	32		42	
distal end breadth			41	51	54	54		43	43	51	
relative breadth (%)			11	12	15	16		14	12	12	

The general impression of the Solo sample suggests very powerful and muscular people. This is expressed in the bony evidences of muscle attachments, as well as in the form and thickness of the bones themselves. While they may not have been as powerful as earlier humans, the development of the nuchal region (although reduced) suggests that large faces were probably still an important part of hominid adaptation. However, the steep-sided, narrow mandibular fossae indicate that really pronounced anterior tooth use may not have been an important element in this adaptation. This cannot be confirmed until dental and facial remains are found. In any event, the evolutionary trend was toward reduction, but direct evidence indicates that there was still selection for maintaining strengthened crania. As an example of such selection, four of the crania (all from Ngandong) show healed scars where the scalp was penetrated during life. While hunting or other accidents may account for these wounds, most researchers believe they are the consequences of interpersonal violence.

The two tibiae also reflect the size and power of these people. The Ngandong folk are quite large (table 12.2). The better preserved tibia has a length that corresponds to a body height of 167 cm and the larger could be as tall as 188 cm if it has similar proportions (about the size estimated for Boxgrove). Solo 13 is a fairly slender bone, with relatively small shaft diameters, and very small relative articular surface size (and squared shape). It is as modern as any of the penecontemporary fossils including the so-called "modern human" ones from Western Asia.

There are a number of regional similarities that point to a specific relation between this sample and the earlier Indonesians, a contention supported by the intermediate anatomy of Sambungmachen (see Chapter 11). In general:

- the frontal bone is flat, without any development of a frontal boss, and merges onto the top of the supraorbital torus
- the supraorbital torus is close to horizontal in orientation
- there is a distinct frontal keel extending over virtually the entire squama
- there is a **prebregmatic eminence**, a cross-like elevation at the meeting of the sagittal and coronal sutures
- the top of the vault is evenly curved along the sagittal suture.

These similarities and others indicate relationship - almost certainly descent. But *descent* is not *identity* and in my view cannot be taken to mean that the Ngandong remains are "*Homo erectus*", as some paleoanthropologists who believe this is a valid species have suggested (mainly W. Howells and his students such as P. Rightmire and A. Santa Luca). This is a classic case of confusing regional features with traits that could be taken to indicate evolutionary grade (whether or not grade is given a formal taxonomic characterization).

The problem can be seen both in the Ngandong remains themselves (the expanded brain size and proportional increases in frontal breadth and occipital plane length, coupled with supraorbital reduction) and in the relationship these specimens have with certain Late Pleistocene Australians. The earliest Australians arrived by sea before 60 kyr. We must conclude that these first inhabitants are clearly modern as judged by their behavior - the beginning of continued crossings of the formidable water barrier isolating Australia - because of the technological and organizational skills that are implied. Yet, their skeletons show the persistence of the Javan complex of features, albeit along with further braincase expansions and other modernizations. Although no fossil remains are clearly dated earlier than about half this age, there are several dozen well preserved late Pleistocene/early Holocene fossils that demonstrate

- the continued regionality of the combination of Australasian skeletal features described above
- the Javan source area for the majority of Australia's first colonists
- the fact that the combination of features which distinguishes modern Australoids from other living human populations is precisely that which distinguished their regional predecessors from their contemporaries in East Asia, Africa and Europe

Besides the vault and facial characteristics discussed above and in Chapter 11, features linking the ancient Indonesians with Australians include elements of the mandibles. A. Kramer isolated seven traits that both characterize the fragmentary Early Pleistocene Indonesian mandibles and uniquely resemble modern Australians, but specifically differ from Africans (an alternative ancestral source for modern Australians, according to the "Out of Africa" theory).

Perhaps of greatest interest are the similarities the Ngandong remains show to an uncertainly dated specimen from Late Pleistocene deposits in the region of the Willandra Lakes. WLH 50, a male, is the size and mostly the shape of an average Ngandong male, perhaps differing mostly in its further occipital plane expansion and the division of his supraorbital into lateral and central (**supracilliary**) elements. The cranial vault has numerous detailed anatomical similarities to the Ngandong remains. In one analysis, D. Frayer and colleagues compared WLH 50 with Ngandong and Ngaloba (Laetoli 18), the most archaic-appearing of the African fossils of equal age, and an alternative ancestor for WLH 50 according to the "Out of Africa" theory. The "Out of Africa" theory requires that WLH 50 must be in the same group as the African "Eves," since they are its ancestors. However, the Multiregional Evolution prediction is that the earlier and later Australasians will be more closely linked. The analysis found 12 features which linked WLH 50 with the Ngandong sample and not to the African, *but not one feature* that uniquely linked WLH 50 and Ngaloba and not also Ngandong. It is very unlikely that so detailed a series of resemblances could be due to chance.

WLH 50, of course, is a modern human. The basis for this assertion is *where* he died (as the descendant of cross-oceanic colonizers) and *who he closely resembles* (several of the Holocene Australian specimens). His numerous similarities to the Ngandong crania suggests that they are directly ancestral to the modern humans of this region in the same sense that any of the regional Pleistocene predecessors of modern populations are. Ngandong has a similar relationship to later Australians that, for instance, the Klasies remains have to Pleistocene South Africans or Skhul and Qafzeh remains have to later Levantines. In both cases the Pleistocene anatomy is more robust and archaic than ever found in living descendants, but the likenesses mark a closeness of relationship.

CHINA

Isolated teeth seemingly associated with later Middle Pleistocene and earlier Late Pleistocene faunas are known from several East Asian countries, but the vast majority of diagnosable remains come from China. The Chinese fossil record from this period includes a number of specimens, several virtually complete crania and much of a postcranial skeleton. A considerable time span is represented, and suggestions of a broad geographic range for the regional anatomical complex is suggested by the resemblances of Narmada (India) and Zuttiyeh (Israel) to the East Asian remains.

Isotope Stage 7

The specimens from Oxygen Isotope stage 7 are the Dali cranium from Shaanxi Province and several teeth from Tongzi in Guizhou Province.

Dali was found in river gravels, and sustained some damage on its lower face that has never been reconstructed. The maxilla was pushed upwards, making the lower face appear shorter than it actually was. Dali is a robust male cranium, somewhat under 30 years of age according to Wu Xinzhi and Wu Maolin. It is a large, thick vault with a small braincase (just above the Zhoukoudian male mean of 1078 cc, at 1120 cc Dali is smaller than the Ngandong male average), and very large supraorbital tori that arch over the upper orbits. The fairly low forehead begins behind the ridges (there is a sulcus between them), with a distinct frontal boss whose midline is interrupted by a narrow sagittal keel. The braincase expansion is reflected in the elevated position of its greatest breadth to above the cranial base, the fact that the enlarged minimum frontal breadth is almost as great as the maximum, the expanded occipital squama relative to the nuchal plane, and the well-developed parietal bosses. Several features resemble Ngandong hominids, such as the angular torus, temporal-frontal articulation in the temple region (the usual articulation is parietal-sphenoid), thick vault bones, and the depressed area where the browridges meet over the nose. Yet the form of the supraorbitals is quite different, as is the parietal bossing, the large extrasutural bone at the cranial rear (lambda), and the weakly developed nuchal torus that only extends across the middle third of the occiput.

The Dali face is broad, transversely flat, vertical (according to G. Pope, even taking the breakage into account), and generally resembles the distinguishing aspects of the Zhoukoudian faces (table 11.2), including the elevated lower cheek border and the presence of a maxillary notch. In fact the angle formed of lines connecting the nasal bones to the sides of the face is as large (145°) as the Eskimo mean (the larger the angle, the flatter the face). The orbital pillars face forward, and nasal bones are narrow, flat, and oriented nearly vertically, with a constricted internasal crest. Their suture with the frontal bone forms a gently curved, almost horizontal line. To the sides of the nose there is moderate swelling of the maxilla along the nasal border. In aggregate these are East Asian features that extend right through recent and modern populations of the region.

The 6 human teeth from Tongzi include a central incisor that is shoveled in the normal East Asian pattern. It has moderately strong marginal ridges, a lingual tubercle, and a straight buccal face. The other teeth are undiagnostic.

Isotope Stage 6

Isotope stage 6 remains include the cranium and much of a postcranial skeleton from Jinniushan in Liaoning Province, a maxilla and occiput from Chaohu (also variously known as Chaoxian and Yanshan) in Anhui Province, the Changyang maxilla from Hubei, a child's parietal (with an extrasutural bone at lambda) and teeth from Dingcun (Shanxi), and teeth from Xindong (Hebei)

Jinniushan combines a cranium and a postcranial skeleton with four vertebrae, some ribs, an innominate, ulna, patella, and 30 hand and foot bones of a young woman. The were found in a consolidated fissure-filling in an isolated karst prominence. The age of the remains was assessed as 187 kyr (165-195) by Chan Tiemei and colleagues, based on ESR from associated mammal teeth assuming the EU model. The cranial vault is large (her 1260 cc exceeds all earlier East Asian females), and has

- unusually thin vault bones
- a gabled cranial contour
- a broad frontal bone
- central supraorbital thinning
- a gracilized posterior region with marked nuchal plane reduction.

These combine to make Jinniushan the earliest specimen with this mixture of modern features. A number of paleoanthropologists including Chan and colleagues, G. Pope, and the specimens describer Lü Zun'e, regard the case for an early appearance of modernity in Jinniushan as good as the cases made for African (Klasies) and West Asian (Qafzeh) samples of almost half the age (discussed below).

Chan Tiemei and colleagues assert: "the morphology of the skull suggests a strong local component of evolution, consonant with the 'multiregional continuity' model of the evolution of *H. sapiens*." Thus, Jinniushan is not just progressive - it retains a number of distinct Asian features in the face and forehead that closely resemble the Zhoukoudian female and to some extent Yunxian. These include:

- arched supraorbitals with a sulcus separating them from the frontal squama,
- a tall narrow keel on the frontal bone
- flat and vertical facial orientation,
- marked facial breadth,
- the top of the nasal bones makes a horizontal juncture with the frontal
- a high position for the maxillary notch
- incisor shoveling, marginal ridges combined with a straight incisor blade and a tubercle with ringer-like projections extending above it
- M^3 reduction

The Jinniushan skull is larger, a little shorter and narrower, but taller, than Dali (see Chapter 11). An important difference is in the dramatically thinner cranial bones, contributing to why two crania of similar external dimensions have dissimilar cranial capacities. However, the main contours of the two are surprisingly similar, as are many of the vault details such as the long sagittal keel, elevated position of the maximum cranial breadth, and angled occiput with a rounded profile. Jinniushan's face is the same height, moderate swelling borders the nose in a similar manner, there is rounding of the lower lateral corner of the orbits, and the cheeks are equally flat and prominent but smaller and more delicately built. However, the Junniushan orbits are lower and broader, the nose is narrower and has a higher nasal angle, and to its sides the maxilla is less inflated. Marked differences occur in the smaller mastoid process, and thinner supraorbital tori, especially over the middle of the orbit. The crania are similar enough to suggest that most of the important variants reflect sexual dimorphism, but time and geography may play roles as well.

The postcranial remains are among the few from the Chinese Pleistocene. The innominate is large relative to the height of the individual (165 cm estimated from the ulna length), with a relatively enlarged acetabulum, and it has a moderately elongated pubis. The ulna is gracile, with a relatively small articular surface, weak muscle markings, and shaft that is thin relative to the length of the bone. Yet, according to

Lü its shaft walls are very thick and the medullary cavity takes up only the central third of the bone. These internal characteristics imply much more strength than the muscle markings suggest.

Chouhu is a more fragmentary, possibly male, specimen that was found in a consolidated fissure-fill on Yanshan hill, consisting of a separate maxilla and occiput. The maxillary dentition is notable for the relatively heavy, flat, wear on the lateral incisors (the centrals are missing). Zhang Yinyun attributed this to the use of the teeth for biting off hard, tough foods and other non-masticatory purposes. The occipital anatomy is quite unlike earlier specimens such as Hexian and Zhoukoudian H3. The bone is broader but less angled at the clearly defined torus, and the occipital plane is more rounded. A distinct line marks the upper surface of the torus but there is no supratoral sulcus. Instead, there is a shallow suprainiac fossa just above the downward dip at the torus center.

Table 12.3
Cranial Dimensions for Specimens with Faces[a]

	Dali	Jinniushan	Jebel Irhoud 1	Laetoli 18	Tabun	Skhul 5	Qafzeh 9[1]	Qafzeh 6	Shanidar 1	Amud 1
capacity	1200	1260	1305	1367	1271	1518	1531	1569	1600	1740
cranial length	210	196	196	205	183	193	198	196	208	215
breadth	152	148	152	140	144	145	140	145	158	157
height	118	123				128			135	
minimum frontal breadth	105	114	107	104	102	104	105	110	110	115
central parietal thickness	11.2	6.5	10.0	14.0	7.5	5.5	6.0	8.0	8.0	7.0
facial height	74	74	71	72	79	73		73	88	89
breadth	144	148	156			145		145	145	154
zygomatic bone height[4]	53	49	55			48	47	56	51	54
orbit height	34	32	37		37		36	36	36	38
breadth	45	52	45		37	46	44	47	47	44
index	76	62	82		100		82	77	77	86
nose breadth		31	35	28	36		33	32	31	
Supraorbital height: medial		14.5	14.1	22.0	17.3	15.1	17.0	19.0	18.0	14.7
central	19	11.4	11.6	14.0	12.3	9.2	5.0	16.5	15.7	13.0
lateral		13.8	13.7	14.0	12.2	10.2	7.8	13.8	10.2	9.8
Ulna length		260			242	282	275		273	
upper notch breadth		22			22	27	24		27	
index (%)[2]		8.5			9.0	9.6	8.6		9.9	
body height[3]		165			156	182	172		169	174

[a] Definitions of the measurements are shown in figure 12.3
[1] Subadult
[2] Other ulnas include Shanidar 5 (length=249, index=10.2), Shanidar 4 (length=255, index=10.3) Qafzeh 7 (length=271, index=8.5), Kebara (length=274, index=10.2), and Skhul 4 (length=293, index=9.4)
[3] See Table 12.9
[4] Taken along the zygomaxillary suture.

Changyang, a cave discovery from a region considerably to the south, is similar to Chouhu and Junniushan, but also has features more common in South Asia. Forward-positioned cheeks and flat middle face are suggested by the preserved anatomy. The nose reveals an interesting combination of features, including narrow lower breadth and a sharp, upward-curving lower nasal border lacking a projecting nasal spine (this contrasts with the distinct Jinniushan spine). Below it, the maxilla is moderately prognathic and convex in sagittal view. The size of the canine socket and the development of a bony buttress around it suggest that the tooth was probably quite large. Changyang is smaller than Chouhu, both dentally and in its decreased lower face height. It is quite possible that this difference reflects sexual dimorphism.

Zhang Yinyun analyzed the dentitions of these specimens as a group (including the slightly older Tongzi teeth which he believes were mistakenly put in a more primitive evolutionary grade). He finds, in general, that the dental anatomy of the teeth closely resemble earlier dentitions. Tooth size for most teeth also resemble the earlier specimens, but the incisors are reduced. When they were first described, the Xujiayao teeth (see below) were said to represent a 'Neandertaloid' type of *H. sapiens*, coexisting with more modern specimens. However Zhang discounts the interpretation that two different human types were coexisting.

Isotope Stage 5e

The final sample may be as late as Isotope stage 5e. These are the remains from Maba (Guangdong Province) and Xujiayao (Shanxi).

Table 12.4
Mosaic Expression of Archaic Features in Chinese Fossils

	Dali	Xujiayao	Maba	Chaohu	Jinniushan
Thick vault bones	X	X	-	-	-
Pronounced postorbital constriction	-	?	X	?	-
Sagittal keeling on frontal	X	?	weak	?	X
Glabella projection	concave	?	concave	?	straight
Sharp occipital angle	X	-	?	-	X
Protruding occiput	-	-	-	-	X
Concavity below nuchal torus	X	X	?	-	X
Extrasutural bone at lambda	X	X	?	-	-
Angular torus	X	-	-	?	X

The Maba skullcap, a cave find from south China, is a braincase missing only the occiput, and the upper portion of the face. While it is larger than any of the Choukoutien crania, there are many points of resemblance to those earlier inhabitants of north China. The upper face is very flat, the cheek is anterior-facing, and (like Dali) the nasal bones seem narrow compared with the broad area between the orbits. The nasal suture with the frontal is flattened, on the same horizontal plane as the adjoining suture between maxillary and frontal bones. The fairly thick browridges are arched over the orbits and are separated from it be a supratoral sulcus. Internally a small frontal sinus is restricted to the area between the orbits. The forehead has an enlarged frontal boss, which bulges centrally very much like the Choukoutien foreheads. A weak sagittal keel begins at its center. Maba has vault bone thinning comparable to Jinniushan, smaller central and lateral supraorbital heights, and a somewhat higher nasal angle. The latter is a resemblance to the European Neandertals, as are the round orbits, medial supraorbital thickening, and posterior-lateral slant to the upper part of the face. W. Howells regarded it as a Neandertal specimen, while G. Pope calls it the most Neandertal-like of the Pleistocene Asians. By themselves these resemblances may well be simply individual variations without particular implication, but later specimens suggest that Maba may be the earliest to reflect consequences of developing Late Pleistocene genic exchanges across the North Asian tier. However I do not believe it is a Neandertal and agree with Zhang's assessment based on the dentitions.

With some 10 individuals represented, the Xujiayao site holds the second-largest Pleistocene sample from a single location in East Asia. There are some 15 cranial fragments, a juvenile maxilla, and isolated teeth, found scattered within a small area at a juncture between a stream and a larger river. The vault pieces are quite thick, in some cases thicker than Zhoukoudian, but other aspects of the bones are progressive. Two partial occiputs are much less angled than the earlier specimens, with rounded posteriors, weak nuchal tori, and extrasutural bones at lambda according to Wu Xinzhi. The parietals suggest low but curved vaults with prominent temporal lines but lacking angular tori or sagittal keel. The maxilla holds a shovel-shaped incisor and is less prognathic than its Zhoukoudian or Jinniushan counterparts.

There are two main points to be made about this diverse sample from China. First, they share numerous regional features, as enumerated above. The most common of these are the

- extrasutural bone at lambda,
- narrow sagittal keel on the frontal,
- anteriorly positioned frontal boss,
- flat face with anteriorly oriented orbital pillars,
- shape of the nasal root
- horizontal, level, frontomaxillary and nasofrontal sutures
- vertical face lacking significant alveolar prognathism
- rounded orbital margin at the lateral lower corner
- shovel-shaping of the maxillary incisors based on moderate to strong marginal ridges and straight buccal surface form

Not every individual has every feature, of course, but they are in high frequency and commonly occur in combination. Most of these features are found in the earlier specimens.

Second, as a group these crania are intermediate between the earlier archaic Chinese remains and the recent/modern East Asians (table 12.4). They have larger vaults that have low foreheads but are higher and more curved along their tops. Frontal expansion is indicated by the expanded frontal boss and greater postorbital breadth. There is also more curvature at the cranial rear, especially of the occipital plane, as the distinctive angle between the nuchal and occipital planes is variably lost and the size of the occipital plane predominates. Cranial reinforcement structures are reduced in expression, including the keeling and the various tori. The nuchal torus is only moderately or even poorly developed, and always absent laterally. The vault sides are gabled and instead of a parietal keel along the edge there are often well-developed parietal bosses. The mastoids are moderate to small and the mandibular fossae broad and shallow. Tori and keels decrease in expression, although all specimens retain browridges, set off from the forehead by a supratoral sulcus and enclosing variably expressed frontal sinuses. On the whole the browridges are reduced, with the most marked change over the center of the orbits. The faces are vertical and transversely broad and flat, with a moderate nasal angle and a broad, flattened nasal root. The cheek base is in a high position and a malar notch is invariably present.

African Populations

Through the later Middle and earlier Upper Pleistocene, the fossil and archaeological record is quite complete in Africa and the emerging picture of hominid evolution has become fairly well understood. This picture belies C. Coon's assertion that the origins of modern Africans are unknown. Previously in this century when fewer African fossils were known, and the important ones incorrectly dated, Africa was often regarded as the "dark continent." Earlier this century paleoanthropologists generally attempted to fit the African fossil record into a European framework. However this all changed as it became evident that it was Europe that lay at the periphery of early human habitation. During the Upper Pleistocene, Africa supported a human population many times larger than the European one. With its diversity of habitats and optimum conditions, Africa lies at the center of the evolutionary picture, and some believe it to be the single place where modern humans emerged.

Despite (or cynics might say "because of") the wealth of data, the relation of Middle Pleistocene to recent and modern populations, and the question of modern human origins, remain unresolved. Indeed, just as the Multiregional model predicts, there is more morphological diversity among the Africans, at the center of the human range, than among Europeans or East Asians at the periphery (this point is buttressed by a Wu Xinzhi and G. Bräuer study of regional variation in 17 features). What is clear is that the new discoveries, and the redating of older ones, show that major technological innovations and efficient habitat-specific adaptations appear as early in Africa as anywhere else, if not earlier. Much the same can be said of the modernizations found in the evolving Africans.

According to J.D. Clark, the later Middle Pleistocene marks a time of important changes in African stone tool industries. All across Africa the Middle Paleolithic, called the Middle Stone Age (MSA), developed out of local Acheulean - large bifacial cutting and chopping tools dropped out of assemblages while the Mousterian-like (e.g. based on Levallois - see Chapter 11) small flake component predominated. Clark attributes the change to the development of hafting, attaching stone (or other) cutting edges to wood. Bone artifacts and some articles of personal adornment, such as ostrich egg shell beads, appear in the MSA and at one locality excavated A. Brooks and colleagues, along the Semiliki river near where it flows into Lake Albert in Zaire, barbed bone points and grindstones dated to about 82 kyr have been discovered. If the dates, based on the ESR analysis of animal teeth and TL taken on sand, are verified and actually relate to the artifacts, these grindstones and bone points are much earlier than once thought (for instance, barbed bone points first appear in Europe at less than 40 kyr). However, these materials will probably remain controversial as long as they are unique. Numerical dates position the beginning of the MSA to over 180 kyr, according to a review by P. Allsworth-Jones.

The African MSA may be earlier than the other Middle Paleolithic variations, and it certainly is equally or more complex. Some of its distinct qualities include

1. grindstones for the preparation of plant foods,
2. use of marine resources such as shellfish and seashells transported over 100 km or more,
3. use of bone including barbed bone points,
4. the **hafting** of the spear and projectile points (attaching them to wood shafts).

There are marked regional differences within Africa: early variants from the southernmost part feature long blades and woodworking tools such as burins, central African sites combine Levallois-based tools and more traditional Acheulean bifaces, North Africa is more dominated by Levallois-based technologies. The above-mentioned distinctions are regional - none spread throughout the entire MSA range.

Later Middle Pleistocene MSA sites are not numerous but have been found throughout the African continent while Late Pleistocene sites are even more common. However dating generally remains a problem, especially in the critical period when modern features and behaviors seem to be emerging. Only one of the important hominid sites said to be close to 100 kyr or older has valid numerical dates, and with the absence of reliable dates, the link between modernizations of anatomy and of behavior proves difficult to draw. Yet, this sample is absolutely critical for understanding two things

1. the origin of living African populations
2. the question of whether all living humans can uniquely trace their ancestry to an African population of this time

LATE MIDDLE PLEISTOCENE REMAINS

Human remains from the latest Middle Pleistocene literally span the continent, from Morocco in the north, to South Africa. The earlier sites are from Tanzania and Djibouti. Somewhat later are specimens from Morocco and South Africa.

Perhaps the most controversial of the earlier sites is Eyasi, near Lake Tanganyika in Tanzania. M. Mehlman's interpretation of the site places it in excess of 130 kyr, and the Acheulean artifacts found on the surface suggests an earlier age; F. Masao, for instance, suggests an age on the order of 200 kyr. Fragments of three fossil crania were discovered by the Kohl-Larsen expeditions (in 1935 and 1938, see Chapter 6), and a complete cranium was reconstructed by H. Weinert. He taxonomized it into a new genus and species (*Africanthropus njarasensis*) that was widely and justifiably ignored. From his study of the published pictures (he obviously could not return to Germany), F. Weidenreich questioned the reconstruction's accuracy and the conclusions Weinert drew from it. (Weinert thought the skull was similar to "*Homo erectus*".) I have examined Weinert's reconstruction and can only comment that it is even worse than Weidenreich imagined.

Fortunately, the occiputs of both Eyasi 1 and 2 are fairly complete, and some information may be gained from them. Both are broad and have a reduced nuchal torus (more so in Eyasi 1). The difference in torus development is reminiscent of the difference between Omo 1 and 2 (see below). L. Wells likens the Eyassi 2 torus to that of Kabwe.

Only a small portion of the right supraorbital region of Eyasi 1 remains. There is no separation between the frontal bone and the browridge, and the torus is projecting but not particularly thick. (The impression of a large torus actually comes from the reconstructed portion.) Weidenreich described this browridge as "the thickened end of an otherwise continuous frontal slope," a description which holds equally well for the Omo crania, Ngaloba, and probably for the Kanjera material as well (Chapter 14) if the thickening of this "thickened end" is reduced.

From southwest Djibouti, the Wadi Dagadlé maxilla is 250 kyr or less, on the basis of some preliminary TL dates. The isolated lower face is prognathic and megadont, resembling the Kébibat specimen (see below).

The Kébibat teenager is from the Mifsud-Giudice quarry, near Rabat. Faunal analysis places it in the late North African Middle Pleistocene, and this is verified by a TL date of >200 kyr from a layer above. The cranium of a young man (13-14 years old) was probably complete when he was fossilized. However, his remains were blasted to pieces during a mining operation. What remains is part of a mandible, maxillary pieces, an almost complete dentition, and a large number of cranial fragments (few bigger than a quarter). The mandible has a vertical symphysis and a distinct mental trigone but no prominent bulge (and therefore is chinless), and it has multiple mental foramena. Taking age into account, the moderately thickened vault bones appear to combine archaic and progressive features. Impressions of the internal blood vessels that supplied the brain and proportions of the occipital lobes are reminiscent of earlier hominids, while the high occiput with reduced nuchal torus more closely resembles more modern remains (although this could easily be a consequence of the youth's age). There is an elliptical suprainiac fossa. Kébibat is megadont, although the teeth are somewhat reduced compared with the earlier Middle Pleistocene Africans. The main reduction is in the mandibular molars. The premolars of the mandible and the maxillary posterior teeth more closely resemble those of earlier Africans. The incisors and canines (as measured by transverse breadth) are as large or larger.

The most recent of these Middle Pleistocene specimens is the partial cranium from Florisbad, South Africa. Like Kabwe, its importance was first misunderstood because of recent dates mistakenly attributed to it. Various radiocarbon dates from the peat layer in which the fossil was discovered resulted in a date range of from 35 to 47 kyr, which means that it is beyond the range of radiocarbon dating. Uranium series estimates show it to be older than 100 kyr. The specimen consists of the sides and part of the front of the face of an adult woman. Most of the back and cranial base are missing. The frontal and the face are the most diagnostic of the preserved features.

The frontal is broad, low and evenly curved, with a wide sagittal keel, and a shallow sulcus well above the tall supraorbitals (taller than Kabwe over the nasal root, as R. Singer points out, but much less projecting). The supraorbitals can be described as a thickening at the forward edge of the sloping frontal bone, whose thickness is marked. They notably thin toward their outer ends, and are depressed just over the nose. The face, as reconstructed by R. Clarke, is short but very broad, and quite archaic in its expanded maxillary sinuses and consequently puffy cheeks. The orbits are set far apart and the nasal bones are broad and have little angulation. Judging from the size of the tooth sockets and the preserved third molar, the dentition was moderate in size. In his comparisons, Clarke emphasizes its similarities to the Ngaloba specimen (although the face in this Tanzanian is more delicately built and lacks the puffiness to the sides of the nose).

Florisbad has long been considered a "phylogenetic link" between the earlier Middle Pleistocene complex of features and living African populations (although not by P. Rightmire, who is probably more familiar with the African sequence than any other paleoanthropologist - he believes that no definite links can be drawn between the Middle Pleistocene Africans and modern populations). Florisbad is not a modem cranium, nor is it simply an "African Neandertal", as M. Drennan once described it. Combined with the other archaic penecontemporary remains, I believe that it does provides such a phylogenetic link, and with other specimens that have faces such as Ngaloba and Jebel Irhoud 1 it confirms the existence of a widespread African variant with its own evolutionary tendencies. The distinctness of this African variant would seem to extend back at least into the later Middle Pleistocene.

UPPER PLEISTOCENE EAST AFRICA

East Africa is where the earliest Upper Pleistocene remains are said to be found. Two sites, Omo and Ngaloba, have yielded important specimens whose dates, unfortunately, have remained uncertain.

The Omo specimens

Three fragmentary crania and postcranial remains are said to come from the Kibish formation at Omo (Ethiopia), the same broad area north of Lake Turkana that has yielded many australopithecine fossils. Numerical dating of the specimens has been beset with problems. The Omo 1 cranium and partial skeleton was found *in situ* at site KHS, at a disconformity between Beds d and e of Member I, associated with several Levallois flakes and other undiagnostic artifacts. Cranium 2 and the Omo 3 frontal fragment are surface finds. Omo 2 may have eroded out of a level equivalent to Omo 1, but the PHS site where it was found is 2.5 km away and across the Omo river. Omo 3 may correlate with overlying Member III, but it is also a surface find, from a locality that has not been described in detail. The only date was published in 1969 - a 130 kyr Uranium/Thorium determination on shell from Bed f of Member I. Shell is a notoriously inaccurate source of materials for this dating technique, and the specimens dated are from a source well below Omo I (and probably not referable to Omo 2 and 3 in any known way). A faunal date of 60,000 kyr has been suggested as well, and conventional radiocarbon from Member III indicates an age of <30 kyr. The site cannot be relocated, which is why newer techniques have not been tried, and it would not be out of line to regard the Omo remains as unassociated and undated with any resolution greater than " Late Pleistocene".

The two fairly complete crania (Omo 1 and 2) are widely assumed to be from the same approximate level (although this may be incorrect - they are not directly associated). Their particular importance lies in both the features they share and the variation that occurs between them.

Both crania are large (over 1,400 cc). Their similarities include a broad nuchal attachment area, an expanded occiput above this area, fairly thick cranial bone, and a sagittal keel. These are fairly archaic features. Other aspects of these specimens are more modern, such as their size, vault curvature, low nuchal torus position (internal and external occipital protuberances are in the same position in each) and very reduced supraorbital region . Although in both the cranial base retains a fair amount of spongy bone, and is the site of greatest cranial breadth in Omo 2, the parietal walls are vertical and maximum braincase breadth is high in both individuals. Omo 1 and 2 are also similar to each other in supraorbital and forehead form. The frontal is long, broad, and downward sloping. As it approaches the orbits it thickens, so that the supraorbital torus is actually a slight bulge on the end of an otherwise smooth bone. However, Omo 3 has a thick supraorbital over the nose. There is no separation of this region from the frontal in any specimen, no supratoral sulcus.

They are, of course, not the same. There are contrasts between Omo 1 and 2 in proportions and morphology. Omo 2 is somewhat more archaic in appearance, with a lower vault and a much broader and more angled occiput - resembling Kabwe although more filled out. It would be wrong, however, to assume it is the more archaic in all features. For instance, reduction of the supraorbital over the outer portions of the orbits is marked in both specimens but more marked in Omo 2. Omo 1 has a thinner frontal but thicker parietals and occipital. Omo 1 generally does appear more modern in its higher vault, reduced nuchal torus, and higher, more rounded occiput. It has been reconstructed and the plaster modeling of the face makes it appear even more modern yet. The reader should be cautioned that the reconstruction is very deceiving and there is absolutely no basis for so modern-appearing a facial reconstruction in the very fragmentary nature of the few preserved unconnected facial bones. An associated mandible has a definite chin, and an isolated canine would be judged small against the anterior teeth of contemporary Europeans. Over 50 pieces of postcranial material belonging to Omo 1 are said to be robust but not outside the range of living people, according to analysis by M. Day and colleagues. They conclude that the skeletal features are closest to a Sudanese sample used in the comparisons, most likely because the environmental conditions at Omo were similar to modern Sudan. However of the long bones only the clavicle length is known and humerus length can be estimated. These bones are slender, even compared with Skhul/Qafzeh specimens, and the joint surfaces are relatively small. Body height is about 172 cm. Limb proportions cannot be determined.

The most interesting aspect of the variation at Omo is that while one cranium appears more "modern" than the other, there is no biological reason to question that they represent individual variants of similar populations. In a multivariate analysis that did *not* include measurements reflecting unique features of the skulls, C. Stringer divided the crania, and his sample, into "archaic" and "modern" and nevertheless found that the archaic specimen most similar to Omo 1 is Omo 2. Variation characterizes these African sites, whether the earlier Kabwe remains or the specimens from Eyassi, Klasies or Jebel Irhoud (see below) are considered. Moreover, there are similarities with the Middle Pleistocene African sample in both the morphology and the pattern of variation. The frontal shows both the best evidence of anatomical similarity between the specimens and continuity for both in the African sequence. The continuity is found in

- the broad sagittal keel,
- the long, broad, and fairly flat shape of the bone
- the anatomy of the supraorbitals (a thickening at the end of the frontal)

Several authors have noted the resemblances of Omo 1 to certain West Asian specimens such as Skhul 5. Such comparisons are phenetic and must ignore the frontal anatomy described above (which is quite different at the two sites) but apart from vague proportions there is another point of similarity. Skhul, too, is a site marked by variation and the equivalent to Omo 1 and 2 can be seen in the comparison of Skhul 5 and 9. In fact, as discussed below there is much to be said for the contention of broad similarities between human remains from northern Africa and around the Mediterranean. It is quite possible that the main thing these sites share is elevated patterns of genic exchanges, indicating that Africa and the regions near it were anything but isolated at the beginning of the Late Pleistocene. Placing Omo directly in a pattern of circum-Mediterranean genic exchanges however, is difficult because by in large the regional features in these crania are shared with populations to the south, such as those represented by Florisbad and Ngaloba. Moreover, any pattern of associations requires that the crania could be more clearly related to each other, and to a date. At the moment I would concur with P. Rightmire's more cautious assessment "it may be too soon to identify the Omo skeletons as related unequivocally to recent humans."

Ngaloba (Laetoli 18)

The most complete of the MSA-associated specimens is from the Ngaloba Beds of the Tanzanian site of Laetoli. A cranium with a virtually complete face was recovered, bracketed in age to between 129 and 108 kyr by Uranium series dates. The Ngaloba cranial features are moderately robust but the cranial bone is extraordinarily thick (thicker than Florisbad). In general shape the cranial vault closely resembles Omo 2, although the Ngaloba frontal is smaller and flatter, the sagittal keel is more weakly expressed, and the supraorbitals are less projecting (they both lack a supratoral sulcus). Omo 2 has much more supraorbital torus development centrally, but more reduction laterally. The Ngaloba supraorbital torus is evenly thickened over the orbits and extends prominently in front of the low forehead. While the frontal angle is low (the frontal is similar to Kabwe according to several multivariate analyses), the cranium as a whole is fairly high because the frontal bone is very long compared with earlier Africans. The parietals are bossed and their greatest breadth, about midway up the bone, creates a rounded profile in rear view. The face and occipital region contrast with the more archaic frontal. For instance the nuchal torus is only minimally developed (in contrast it is vertically thickened at the midline in both Omo crania) and the occiput bulges markedly above it much as in Eyassi 1. The face is lightly constructed, short (shorter than Qafzeh 6 or 9 or Skhul 5), and has a distinct canine fossa (differing thereby from the puffy Florisbad midface). It has accentuated alveolar prognathism.

The Ngaloba cranium may be earlier than the Omo specimens, and it is tempting to suggest an evolutionary sequence in which it represents an intermediate between Omo and Broken Hill (this would work particularly well for the frontal and occipital anatomy). However, the Omo dates are uncertain, and Ngaloba is only a single specimen of uncertain sex. Rather than seek evidence of evolutionary sequence, it is more reasonable to treat Laetolil as approximating the same broad spatial and temporal sample as Omo and examine the apparent variability that results.

The combination of features has proved to be confusing. Ngaloba has been regarded as fully modern by E. Delson and J.D. Clark, and almost modern by G. Bräuer and C. Stringer. It cannot be modern, in the literal sense that no recent or living African closely resembles it. However as Rightmire asserts, "it provides firmer evidence than the Omo assemblage for a modern presence in East Africa". This is why it was used in the comparison with the penecontemporary Ngandong and later WLH 50, discussed above.

SOUTH AFRICAN REMAINS

Klasies

The best dated sample of South African human remains from the early Upper Pleistocene is from the Klasies River Mouth Cave (see Chapter 14 for a discussion of the Border Cave remains, which some workers believe are equally old). There are a number of cranial fragments, frontal and zygomatic pieces, maxillary and mandibular remains, and postcranials (a vertebrae, parts of an ulna and clavicle) spread through several layers and associated with a Middle Stone Age industry. Most of the specimens come from a 90 kyr level, but two maxillary fragments are older, by perhaps as much as 30 kyr. Fragmentation happens without human activities, but T. White identified cutmarks on the frontal and suggests that there may have been cannibalism contributing to the condition of the specimens.

Because of their fragmentation the specimens have proven difficult to analyze; yet, the fact that they are accurately dated makes them pivotal in discussions of modern human origins in Africa. Indeed, some paleoanthropologists have claimed that these fragments prove an *early and unique* African origin for all modern humans because of their modernity. Does this assertion hold up to close scrutiny? The frontal and zygomatic fragments are described as gracile and modern, especially the KRM 16425 frontal which lacks significant supracillary arch development, although as F. Smith points out it might be a juvenile. Whether or not it is, the breadth between the orbits is much greater than Holocene and several of the Late Pleistocene Africans, and the bulging region just over the nose is actually quite similar to Florisbad. The KRM 16651 zygomatic is even more archaic, taller than every Middle and early Late Pleistocene African zygomatic except for Bodo's. This is especially significant given the trend for facial reduction and gracilization in these Africans. Beginning with Kabwe, the African fossil sequence is characterized by specimens with small, lightly built cheek bones, and the Klasies specimen is quite different. Moreover, F. Smith points out that the cross-section of the orbital pillar (the zygomatic's frontal process) is thick and triangular, not thin and flattened as is invariably found in virtually all recent and living people.

Some of the specimens are small and gracile (a usual consequence of being small) - especially the AA43 and ZZ44 maxillae and KRM 14695 and 16424 mandibles. Others are much larger and more robust, and it is quite possible that the magnitude of sexual dimorphism was unusually great. Cross-cutting the size differences, both the largest and smallest mandibles completely lack chins. In fact of the four symphyses preserved, these two (KRM 13400 and 14695) lack even a mental trigone and a third (KRM 21776) has only a weakly developed trigone (similar Neandertals are called "chinless"). The most complete mandible, KRM 41815, has a chin. It is an old individual from a nearby cave (Cave 1b), related to the main site sequence by archaeological comparisons.

Based on the sizes of the few postcranial remains body sizes, not unexpectedly given the tooth and mandible sizes, seem quite short. Small body size is of interest because of the recent inhabitants of the

Cape and the question of their ancestry. When the Dutch settled the Southern Cape, they identified several native groups:

- San: "Bushmen" hunter/gatherers, and "Strandlopers" who gathered marine resources
- Khoikhoi: "Hottentot" pastoralists (they herded sheep and cattle)

The distinctions were as much economic as biological, and together they are referred to as Khoisan. These were among the smallest African peoples, second only to Pygmies, and the understanding of Khoisan origins is tied to theories about all sub-Saharan populational origins (see Chapter 14), and also to racial politics in formerly-apartheid South Africa. One major dispute is whether these small peoples evolved locally or are the sole remnants of a once Africa-wide hunting/gathering population. The issue raised by Klasies is about the evidence for local antiquity. According to P. Rightmire and H. Deacon, the Klasies postcranials are no larger than recent San. The proximal ulna is small and slender, with relatively large joints (E. Trinkaus regards it as archaic in the anatomy of the elbow joint and discriminant analysis associates it with archaic and not modern samples, according to T. Holliday and colleagues). It is about the average length for a San male. The first metatarsal is from an even smaller individual. Its length is 56 mm, compared to a 66 mm length for the Omo 1 bone. In fact, in an evolutionary context Klasies is the earliest really small African population, which goes a long way towards explaining its gracility.

Deacon suggests that the Klasies remains may be ancestral to modern San. He supports this contention with the argument that the archaeology suggests isolation for MSA populations from the Southern Cape, possibly as the San evolved their unique features. As A. Morris puts it, "the actual physical evidence for the linking of the Klasies specimens with any extant regional morphology is actually extremely thin". There is no special anatomical basis for this suggestion except for the small body size (and in fact Deacon thinks that size reduction happened much later, in the Holocene). However, there is a real absence of evidence on this issue as no later human remains are known from the Southern Cape until the latest Pleistocene. Small size could be a significant link, and if it was true that these earliest Late Pleistocene folk had a significant contribution to modern San it would explain why L. Vigilant and colleagues have observed that their mitochondrial variations seem so distinct from other African populations.

Sea Harvest (Saldanha Bay)

A few human fragments (a terminal finger bone and a P^4) were found in what appears to have been a hyena den at this coastal site, dated to between 128 and 75 kyr (Oxygen Isotope stage 5) by analysis of associated animal remains. The tooth is quite large, compared with MSA associated dental remains (see below), and the phalanx is relatively slender and elongated. No direct comparisons with Klasies are possible, but these remains, from what F. Grine and R. Klein believe to be a single individual, certainly appear to have been substantially larger

Dental remains

Across southern Africa a variety of sites, mostly caves, have yielded dental remains from the Middle Stone Age. Cave sites are often problematic. For instance, human remains and MSA artifacts were associated in Equus cave, but it has been suggested that the artifacts were washed in from a nearby site and a radiocarbon dates shows the human remains to be Holocene. Whether or not they are ancient as claimed, F. Grine asserts that they resemble teeth from Klasies. Other similar isolated teeth known from MSA context, from Die Kelders Cave and Witkrans, are somewhat smaller (although still at the top of or outside of the Klasies range). They show the same "modernity" features as the Klasies teeth (table 12.5) - exceptionally small size compared with earlier specimens. In writing on these various samples, F. Grine and M. McCrossin concur that they show links with modern South Africans and help establish continuity across the past 100 kyr (however P. Rightmire and A. Morris do not support this contention). Grine makes two claims:

1. modern dental reduction has already been accomplished in Southern Africa by the MSA,
2. there are specific anatomical links between the teeth he studies (Equus and Die Kelders Caves) and today's non-San inhabitants

McCrossin, in studying Witkrans concludes that the late Pleistocene populations of sub-Saharan Africa formed a distinct group that differed noticeably from their circum-Mediterranean contemporaries. This parallels the conclusions of studies by T. Simmons and F. Smith discussed below.

The other very similar MSA association is from the well dated Tanzanian site of Mumba Rock Shelter. The Mumba MSA teeth are quite small, under the San means according to G. Bräuer and M. Mehlman, who are content to describe them no more specifically than as "modern".

Table 12.5
Mandibular Molar[1] Size Variation

	M_1 length	M_1 breadth	M_2 length	M_2 breadth
South Africa				
Cave of Hearths	13.0	11.1	12.0	10.3
Klasies				
16424	9.6		9.1	8.7
13400	12.8	11.1	12.3	10.7
149696	12.0	11.2		
Witkrans				
UCMP 85497	13.1	12.1		
UCMP 12344			11.6	
Die Kelders 6242	12.2	12.2		
Equus Cave H5 (1b)	13.5	11.1		
East Africa				
Mumba XII			11.2	9.2
North Africa				
Rabat	13.0	11.0		
Sidi Abderrahman	13.0	11.6	14.4	11.4
Jebel Irhoud 3	14.8	12.4		
Haua Fteah			11.9	11.4
Témara	12.7	11.9	11.8	12.0

[1] Its not that these teeth are the hear-all and end-all of all dental evolution, its just that most of the sites I want to compare here preserve them.

NORTH AFRICAN SPECIMENS

North African remains from the earlier Upper Pleistocene are from Morocco, Libya, and Ethiopia. The earliest of these are two crania, a juvenile humerus, and a juvenile mandible from Jebel Irhoud, Morocco, the others are mandibles from Haua Fteah (Libya) and Dire Dawa (Ethiopia). All of these are associated with a variant of the Mousterian, or MSA.

Irhoud Crania

The Jebel Irhoud cave, a Moroccan site, provides the only evidence of North African Mousterian-associated crania. The most complete cranium, JI 1, was accidentally discovered during mining operations in the cave, and according to F.C. Howell a partial cranium (JI 2) and child's mandible (JI 3), and numerous Mousterian artifacts, were also discovered "without fully documented provenience" other than "having occurred 'low' in the infilling sequence". An edentuous mandible fragment (JI 5) was found in the faunal collection. Only the juvenile humerus shaft (JI 4) was excavated under controlled conditions, from level 18. It may be the same individual as the 7 year old JI 3. The site's date is based on ESR taken on horse teeth from level 17. The dates are 127-87 kyr using the early uptake model and a less acceptable 190-105 kyr assuming linear uptake. This would date the bottom of the site (the humerus and possibly the mandible) to Oxygen Isotope stage 5d-5c - the age of Ngaloba, Klasies, and in Europe the Neandertals from Krapina. The relation of the crania to these dates is unclear, but given the excavational history they are quite likely to be younger.

The humerus is generally archaic, with thick shaft walls and a small medullary canal, a flattened shape, and an unusual amount of muscularity if it really is the same specimen as the mandible and therefore the same young age. These features are found in young Neandertals, but might also be characteristic of other archaic children - there is no way to know. The crania have much more specific information for ascertaining relationships.

The two Jebel Irhoud crania are broadly similar in size; in general, their similarities and differences parallel those of the Omo crania in that the vault of one specimen is more archaic than the other. They have numerous features that to a varying degree are found in sub-Saharan Africa, and yet others, especially in the forehead and occipital region, are unusual in an African setting. The vaults are fairly high and very broad, the maximum breadth - like the Omo crania - not as far to the rear as in Neandertals. The browridges are continuous and prominent (but not especially large), and the bulging forehead begins above and behind them, separated from the top of the supraorbitals by a supratoral sulcus that is stronger in JI 2. The supraorbitals themselves are continuous but reduced laterally. The occiputs are well rounded and the position of the prominent nuchal line is low. With the cranial base reduction, the parietals are more evenly curved as seen from the rear, and particularly in JI 1 their contour is Neandertal-like (particularly similar to Spy 2), almost circular in this view because the maximum breadth of the cranium lies at about the middle of the vault rather than at its base. There is a well developed parietal boss. especially in JI 1. The differences between the crania could be due to sex; if so, not much dimorphism is expressed. Cranium 2 has thinner cranial bones and a more rounded forehead (it has an unfused **metopic suture** - a sagittal suture that in this case extends for the entire frontal squama's length - Krapina 20, a penecontemporary Neandertal, has a similar anatomy). The JI 2 vault also has slightly stronger temporal lines, a more angled occiput with stronger lambdoidal flattening and a lower opistocranion (position of maximum length), a larger nuchal area, somewhat more prominent mastoids that are thicker and more blunted at the tip, and more robust spongy bone development at the cranial base where the position of maximum cranial breadth lies. These features suggest it might be male. Cranium 1 is usually regarded as female because of its delicate cheeks and weak muscle markings. Yet, it has the more archaic braincase. The differences are not great, and realistically it is difficult to develop a good case that the two are of different sex.

The face of Jebel Irhoud 1 is complete except for the teeth. It is fairly tall and quite broad, almost equaling the Broken Hill face in breadth. However, like the penecontemporary Florisbad and Ngaloba faces, it is much more delicately built. The zygomatics are very thin, although there is a robust masseter attachment. At their base, they form a sharp angle with the face, and there is a shallow canine fossa. The nose is very broad and is guttered, with a smooth, indistinct lower margin. The orbits are large, and rounded in appearance. There is less of the midfacial prognathism of the Middle Pleistocene European or earlier African specimens. Instead, there is considerable alveolar prognathism; the incisor-bearing portion of the face projects beyond the rest of the face. In these features, the face closely resembles Ngaloba and contrasts with most Neandertals. One element of difference is in the frontal and supraorbitals. The forehead rounding and supratoral sulcus, as described above, are quite different and JI has a weak sagittal keel. Another distinction is the form of the supraorbital, as (unlike JI 2) it is thinnest in the position over the middle of the orbit and thickens about equally over the nose and laterally.

It is easy to see continuity with earlier samples. A Middle Pleistocene population such as that represented by Bodo, Kabwe, and Ndutu could develop into one with the Jebel Irhoud features through supraorbital and facial reduction (especially in the maxillary area), frontal expansion, and some expansion of the upper portion of the occipital bone. However, to do so would require a set of cranial changes somewhat different from those taking place to the south, quite possibly influenced by genic exchanges from other areas. One such other area might be the Levant, where older specimens such as Zuttiyeh are said to show special resemblances to JI 1.

F. Smith argues that the pattern of supraorbital reduction across sub-Saharan Africa is quite different than the circum-Mediterranean pattern. To the south his data show that reduction is evenly distributed across the torus, while in the populations surrounding the Mediterranean the mid-orbital and lateral elements reduce while over the nose there may actually be expansion of supraorbital height. Mid-orbital reduction is often greatest, as over evolutionary time the torus divides into a supercillary arch and lateral portions. Jebel Irhoud follows the circum-Mediterranean supraorbital pattern, according to Smith, although differently in the two crania - more central reduction in JI 1, more expansion over the nose in JI 2. The crania show other non-African but clearly circum-Mediterranean features, such as occipital bunning, that "is most likely to be the result of genetic influence from Europe, where bunning occurs earlier ... patterns of human gene flow are complex and multidirectional during the Late Pleistocene".

If they are the recipient of Neandertal genes, are the Jebel Irhoud crania Neandertals? There are too many distinctions from the European norm for this to be the case. There were Neandertal-like populations in western Asia early enough to influence the Jebel Irhoud morphology, but as discussed below it is unclear whether even they can be called Neandertal.

Singa

The Singa skull from eastern Sudan, a faceless cranium, has been enigmatic since its discovery in 1924. C. Stringer and colleagues have suggested the possibility of an Acheulean association, other proposed dates range from early Late Pleistocene to a 17 kyr estimate based the radiocarbon analysis of a crocodile tooth from a site (said to be similar) 15 km away. It has been called a "Neandertaloid", a Neandertal-modern "hybrid", a "Proto-Bushman", and pathological. It is the last of these that has stood the test of time, and makes the best sense of the contradictory features of the specimen.

Actually, there are some resemblances to Jebel Irhoud 1, particularly in the frontal region and supraorbitals. The cranial posteriors, however, contrast. The temporal and occipital regions are greatly shortened in Singa, and the basal spongy bone development is much less. Singa's occipital contour is rounded rather than flattened and the mastoids are much smaller. Internal and external occipital protuberances are in similar positions (they are well separated in Jebel Irhoud). Singa also differs in a long depression surrounding and paralleling the sagittal suture for virtually its entire span. Some of the features of the cranial rear are probably a consequence of Singa's pathological status according to Stringer and colleagues. Other areas involved include the marked bone thickening at the well developed parietal bosses. Because the source of the pathology remains unclear, it is not possible to determine which aspects of the cranium are pathological, and which are normal. Between this problem and its uncertain age, Singa is likely to remain enigmatic.

Mandibles and Teeth

One incontrovertible characteristic of the North African dentitions is that they are large compared with their sub-Saharan counterparts. There are other differences, including the "+" cusp pattern (Chapter 3) in the Irhoud 3 first lower molar - a European (e.g. Neandertal) and manifestly not a sub-Saharan resemblance. The Jebel Irhoud mandible, belonging to a child of slightly more than seven years, has a definite mental eminence with a distinct mental trigone and tubercle, and a concave surface below the incisors. Despite this modern-appearing anatomy on the external symphysis, the internal surface resembles much more archaic specimens in its thickness and doubled tori, and fairly horizontal surface behind the incisors. Its anterior teeth are quite small but like all of the dentitions from this region the molars are large.

The 46-40 kyr Haua Fteah mandibles are associated with the Levallois-Mousterian, found on the margins of a large hearth. They consist of only the posterior portions of two diminutive individuals. In both mandibles, the ramus is rather short and squat; its anterior edge begins at the position of the third molar. The latter feature is significant because it reflects a lack of marked midfacial prognathism. When this prognathism is expressed in its extreme, the maxillary teeth are so far forward that as the mandibular teeth shift forward to meet them a **retromolar gap** is opened between the last molar and the ramus (articulating with the cranium), which might be thought of as remaining in a stable position. Thus these mandibles "fit" the morphological expectations of the Jebel Irhoud 1 face with its distinct canine fossa and lack of midfacial prognathism. A similar specimen may be the jaw from Dire Dawa, Ethiopia, dated to 77-61 kyr by obsidian hydration analysis. Another small individual, this one is badly eroded and all the teeth are broken away.

AN AFRICAN VARIETY

There are a number of features that appear to link Middle and early Late Pleistocene sub-Saharan African populations. Even more conservative researchers such as P. Rightmire admit to an evolutionary continuity between Middle and Upper Pleistocene specimens. Features generally characteristic of this variant include a long, broad, flattened frontal (with variable supraorbital development), an anterior position for the highest point on the cranium, and nearly vertical parietal walls above a broad, massive cranial base. There are other more specific similarities discussed above. According to Rightmire, evolution of this braincase form over the Middle and early Late Pleistocene was largely a matter of cranial capacity expansion, "filling out" various areas, which gradually resulted in a steeper occiput and a broader frontal bone, and one could add, consequent changes in supraorbital anatomy.

Yet, what about subsequent populational continuity? As J. Jelínek points out, in the North African fossil record the earlier Late Pleistocene is very well represented. The latest crania show clear continuity with recent and modern African populations, in his view. He is not alone in this contention, and the significant question is whether the pattern of relationships visible in North Africa applies throughout the continent. For instance, does J-J. Hublin's conclusion about the North African sample holds equally well in African south of the Sahara?

> the fossil evidence would support the regular, even if accelerated, incrementation
> of modern features in the late Middle Pleistocene and early Upper Pleistocene
> rather than the quick and clear cut emergence of an Adamic 'anatomically
> modern man'.

Most of the earlier Late Pleistocene sub-Saharan crania are linked by a series of anatomical similarities, especially of the frontal bones. There is a good case to be made for a special resemblance between Florisbad, Omo 2, and Ngaloba. Yet, some paleoanthropologists have long emphasized the absence of clear regional features marking the emergence of modern populations in Africa, questioning whether the earlier populations can be clearly linked with recent and modern ones. This does not mean that Africans have no ancestors; the relations of archaeological sequences across this time span shows significant *in situ* populational continuity without recourse to the biological issues, and a metric study by F. Thackeray shows gradual and continuous evolution of mandibles from Southern Africa spanning the entire Late Pleistocene. This is an assessment of features and not of the biological continuity that they may or may not reflect. Scientists echoing these sentiments include P. Rightmire, F. Smith and P. Habgood (who however did identify one regional characteristic). Even still, others such as F. Thackeray and G. Bräuer interpret the sub-Saharan record of Late Pleistocene evolution to show continuity, and as mentioned above some even find evidence of an early San-Negroid differentiation.

On the whole the case for continuity is more persuasive, in my view, but it is hampered by the virtual absence of convincing dates for the critical linking specimens. It is ironic that in sub-Saharan Africa, where 'Out of Africa' theories claim modern humans originated, the question of continuity between early Late Pleistocene populations and the recent and modern inhabitants is most controversial.

Western Asia

The western part of the Asian continent is, in the words of O. Bar-Yosef, the intersection of Pleistocene migration routes spanning Africa, Europe, and Asia. Significant contributions from each are found in the human remains from this area, and this has led to a real confusion of regional (e.g. Pleistocene racial) and evolutionary (e.g. archaic vs modern) features in the samples. The confusion is exacerbated by the dramatic changes in the dates attributed to large, important human samples. In fact, prior date estimates have been the major problem barring the interpretation of this region. At one time, most or all of the Near Eastern archaic sapiens specimens were thought to come from the latest portion of this time span (35-45 kyr) because of radiocarbon dates that were not dates at all, but were minimum determinations because the sites were beyond the technique's range of accuracy. Radiocarbon determinations such as 40 kyr actually mean >40 kyr. Ironically, before radiocarbon was applied it was believed that the bulk of the (then known) human remains from Western Asia were dated to before the Würm glaciation, a belief whose time has come (again).

Table 12.6
Stratigraphic Context for the Levant Hominids
According to O. Bar-Yosef, and used with his permission

Industry (Bar-Yosef)	common Tabun tool forms	Hominid specimens	Date (kyr)[2]
Late Mousterian	Long, narrow flakes Short, broad based **Levallois points** from unidirectional or radially prepared cores	Amud cranium Kebara Tabun B (possible cranium position)[1]	47-55 TL, 41.5? 60/64 ESR, 60 TL 86/103 ESR
Middle Mousterian	Ovate radially prepared **Levallois flakes** Low frequencies of triangular points	Qafzeh hominids Skhul B Tabun C mandible (stated cranium position)[1]	96/115 ESR, 92 TL, 96 US 65/92 and 93/108 ESR[4] 119 TL, 40 and 80 US 102/119 ESR, 101.6 US, 110 TL (weighted average)
Early Mousterian	Long unidirectional flakes with triangular or parallel sides	Tabun D	122/166 ESR, 110 US, 250 TL (average)[a]
Acheulean		Zuttiyeh Tabun E[3]	250-350 154-182/188-213 ESR 296-350 TL[b], 164 US

[1]   The female cranium was reported to probably come from layer C, although it could have been from B. The problem is that the deposits slump, away from the cave walls, but the site was excavated in artificial horizontal layers. The slumping means that a specimen high up in the lower layer (C) near the cave wall could be at the same horizontal level as one from the bottom of the (slumped) higher layer (B) away from the wall. The uncertainty is because the excavator was not present when workers recovered the cranium. If the cranium is from B, as Bar-Yosef believes, it would fit his precept that all of the so-called "Neandertals" were late in the sequence, and therefore came from somewhere else.

[2]   The techniques are Electron spin resonance (ESR), Thermoluminescence (TL), and Uranium series (US): ESR dates are given in the form EU/LU

[3]   An early date for Tabun layer E is supported by the observation that layer G has reversed magnetic polarity

[4]   These dates are for two teeth whose proveniences are unknown, except that they come from the human burial layer (B). Grün gives 46±5-93±6 kyr for the level.

[a]   There is a problem at this level, however, and the spread of dates is quite wide, overlapping with the layer below

[b]   W. Farrand argues that in the Levant, ESR dates based on early uptake (EU) are most consistent with other date estimates, and that the TL technique greatly overestimates the ages at Tabun. These data support his observations.

MOUNT CARMEL CAVES

Tabun and Skhul are nearby caves in a small wadi (gully) near the Israeli coast, the Wadi-el-Mughara of Mount Carmel. Discoveries of human burials in the caves between 1929 and 1934 provided the first large sample of fairly complete Paleolithic humans. When they were first described, the individuals were thought to all date to the same time, and the sample was treated as a single population in the substantive monograph compiled by T. McCown and A. Keith. Later, however, they became known for just the opposite - a demonstration that Neandertal and modern populations either coexisted or alternated in Western Asia.

The female cranium and associated postcranial skeleton from the Tabun cave is one of the most important of these specimens because of its completeness (it was a burial) and the resemblances some say it shows to European Neandertals. However, on the basis of their original, systematic study McCown and Keith did not regard the Tabun woman as a European Neandertal but as one end of the range of variation in a single Mount Carmel population, and laid the groundwork for more than a half-century of shifting interpretations. Their treatment of the specimen is reflected in discussions of virtually all her skeletal elements. For instance, in analyzing the Tabun woman's femur they asserted:

> No matter what part or aspect we consider, the Palestinian femur is not of the Neanderthal type of Europe. It does show occasional leanings towards this type, but in nearly all its features it must by judged neanthropic . . . These conclusions are reinforced when we consider . . . the patella and its relation to the knee-joint. . . . The Tabun woman in this, as in other features of the leg and thigh is evidently akin to the Skhul type.

The woman was recorded as recovered from Tabun level C. However there was some potential for confusion as the levels in the cave were not evenly laid down, and because of the position of the skeleton, D. Garrod, the excavator, thought that it might have been interred from the level above, Tabun B. In fact Garrod was not present when workmen found and excavated the skeleton. Even worse, in subsequent excavations of the cave A. Jelinek noted the possibility that the skeleton came from Tabun D! If the reader is confused by where the Tabun woman comes from, seasoned researchers stumble on this problem as well; in one book by C. Stringer and C. Gamble she is from Tabun B on one page, and Tabun C 17 pages later!

Once again poor provenience may play a spoiler's role in interpreting an important specimen. This is because of a theory developed by B. Vandermeersch and O. Bar-Yosef about the origin of (what they call) the Levantine "Neandertals". [If I sound hesitant about taxonomizing the Levant sample, it is because I do not believe they can be placed in discrete categories. This is discussed below]. Vandermeersch and Bar-Yosef argue that the Levant specimens described as "Neandertals" (including Tabun *if* it is from level B) have later dates than the other Levantines (Skhul and Qafzeh - regarded by many as modern humans) because the "Neandertals" are not native to the region. They propose that these are the descendants of European Neandertal immigrants, fleeing the deteriorating conditions of glaciating Europe at the onset of the last Ice Age. As a scenario this is quite possible. Continued accumulating evidence, reviewed in Chapter 1, shows that the climate of the last interglacial and Würm glaciation was considerably more variable than once thought, and that the onset of glacial conditions was quite rapid. The Würm glaciation, like the others, began with the sudden commencement of conditions favoring the expansion of ice sheets, and existing glaciers were able to thicken because they were frozen to their beds. Through this time, however, the shorter-term cycle of climatic flickers continued, with rapid temperate oscillations tending toward warmer conditions within each brief (7-12 kyr) cycle. The warming conditions and the geothermal heat trapped in the ice sheet's bed by the insulating ice sheet itself led to rapid breaking of the frozen bond and the glacial ice collapsed and spread quickly. For ice sheets near the ocean this resulted in the massive iceberg discharges that have been found at the terminations of these short cycles; inland, the ice virtually lunged for some distance across the northern continents. The decreased ocean salinity that results from the large number of icebergs and the lowered air temperatures began the flicker cycle anew and the now spread out but thinned ice sheets built-up in thickness again and the growth-lunge process began anew. The important aspect of these events is that they cause dramatic changes within individual lifespans, certainly within two human generations. If these changes had been gradual, *in situ* adaptation might have been a likely and reasonable response for the human populations. However with knowledge of better conditions just one or two generations ago, and in some cases rumors or direct observations of nearby ice sheets, it is much more likely that populations would be tempted to move and try to recapture what must soon have become an idealized caricature of the "good old days". Movement to more temperate regions would be facilitated by widespread social networks, a point made by C. Gamble in his discussions of human colonizations. He refers to these Middle Paleolithic populations as 'pioneers', and with the movements imposed on them by the changing climatic conditions they surely would have welcomed Conestoga Wagons! It was F.C. Howell who first posited that under these conditions the European populations would be expected to shift toward the European Mediterranean regions. As M. Fogarty and F. Smith point out, movements to the southeast were possible as well because the Daradanelles were closed many times during the lower sea levels that existed for much of the glacial period. Immigration to western Asia and further east, especially for central European populations, must have been common.

In fact, the idea of European intrusions into the Levant as an explanation for some elements of European anatomy is not unreasonable, and need not depend on a late date for Tabun as this region may well have been an intermittent part of the European range much earlier than the last glaciation cycle. Even if we were sure of the specimen's placement in the Tabun Cave, the date would remain problematic in any event. As table 12.6 shows, the three dating techniques used there do not agree. ESR (especially early uptake model) and Uranium series dates are quite similar, but the TL determinations for the same level are much older. Moreover, even if the Tabun woman came from level B, the ESR dates place it in the Qafzeh time range and not equal to the much younger Kebara and Amud specimens. It seems likely that she overlaps in time with Levantine remains that are not generally regarded as "Neandertal" - an important point in judging the validity of McCown and Keith's more than half-century old interpretation.

The Tabun woman has the smallest skull known from the Middle Paleolithic populations of the Levant. Her 1271 cc brain size (table 12.3) is barely larger than the size estimated for the Swanscombe female, but in fact quite a bit bigger than the Middle Pleistocene European female *averages* from either Europe or Africa. At 156 cm (table 12.9) she was a little woman, not much taller than the heights that could be estimated for the Klasies specimens. Unlike the South Africans, however, her diminutive size did not affect frontal bone gracility. Her forehead is marked by thick (especially centrally), projecting supraorbitals that are arched and follow the contours of the orbits. They are quite flat transversely and are separated from the rounded frontal boss by a deep sulcus. In contrast, her cranial rear is smooth and rounded and her occiput is high, lacking an occipital bun and with an only weakly developed nuchal torus and spongy bone at the cranial base. The Tabun face is tall. For instance, while the cranium is shorter and narrower than African specimens such as Ngaloba or Jebel Irhoud 1, its face is larger. The nose is narrow and not especially prominent, but the entire face projects anteriorly, reflecting midfacial prognathism (much of the maxilla is broken away, making it impossible to determine how expanded the maxillary sinus was.) The mandible reflects this condition through a forward shift of the tooth row, leaving a retromolar gap. The symphysis lacks any external trigone. The dentition contrasts small posterior teeth and very large anteriors, and the lateral maxillary incisors are almost as large as the central ones.

McCown and Keith recognized Tabun as a site with considerable variation because of the anatomy of Tabun 2, a second mandible discovered in Tabun C. McCown initially regarded the mandibles as different morphological types, and it was only in the development of the Mount Carmel monograph that their similarities (except for the sex-related distinctions) and population affinity were emphasized. Tabun 2, a male, has a prominent mental eminence and shows other characteristics that according to some much more closely align it with the Qafzeh sample than with the Levantine "Neandertals". Perhaps its greatest importance is its provenience, from the same level that the Tabun woman may have come.

Unfortunately, dating problems have plagued the nearby Skhul Cave as well, beginning with the initial interpretation as Riss/ Würm, followed by a mid-Würm date, and then more recently a pre-Würm estimate once again. The most recent dates, however, are based only on two teeth said to come from the burial level, B, and they are quite different in age. The early uptake ESR determinations are 65 and 93 kyr, not far from the Uranium series dates of 40 and 80 kyr for the same two but very different from the 119 kyr TL determination. Some have suggested that these show two hominid levels of different times, others point to the fact that no other evidence supports this, and others yet such as this author wonder if it all doesn't just show that two animal teeth in the Natural History Museum of London cannot be used to date this far away site. It might be as young as the later Levant "Neandertals" such as Kebara and Amud, it may be as old as Qafzeh, it could even be, as originally supposed, the same age as the Tabun woman - regardless of whether she comes from level B or C.

Cranial and postcranial fragments representing at least fourteen individuals were found at Skhul. The sample is the largest from the Levant, and along with the sample from the nearby site of Qafzeh, it is claimed to be the least archaic. However, Skhul is in no way identical to living populations and like the other Levant remains, the specimens are characterized by a mixture of modern and archaic features. Its marked variability continued to amaze McCown and Keith throughout their description of the material.

The best preserved crania are males (Skhul 4, 5, and 9, see figure 12.4). This lends to the impression that the sample is characterized by large cranial size (the average capacity for the three is over 1550 cc). The vaults are long, moderately tall (although not as tall as the west Asian "Neandertal" males), and often very broad, with robust muscle attachments and well developed crests and tori. Other archaic features are related to the anterior dentition and its use, and in fact there is little difference between the sizes and proportions of teeth from this sample and the teeth of European Neandertals, according to research by D. Frayer, even though the anterior teeth are the smallest in the Levant sequence. Facial breadths are also similar to these penecontemporary Europeans, but facial heights are somewhat less. Midfacial prognathism is less extensive than in even the southern-most Europeans and the Jebel Irhoud specimens, and Skhul 4 has a weakly expressed canine fossa. The other faces are too damaged in the nasal region for this determination, and the various facial reconstructions have been questioned (and in some cases redone). Even more unlike the Europeans, the faces are transversely flat, especially the middle and upper portions where the nasal area barely projects in front of the outsides of the orbits. Again, this projection is generally less than in Jebel Irhoud. Following from the facial differences, the retromolar gap is reduced or absent. Chins are weak to moderate.

Related to the above, the nuchal area of the cranium is extensive and the maximum extent of muscle attachment rises high above the cranial base. Other cranial features, however, are somewhat less archaic. For instance the maximum breadth lies high on the parietals and there is generally a gabled rather than circular contour to the rear outline. Supraorbitals are continuously developed and thickest over the nose, with somewhat less but evenly expressed thickness over the mid-orbit and laterally - not really much different from the Neandertals (European and West Asian) in their thickness and projection in front of the forehead. However, in a few Skhul supraorbitals there is a tendency for the torus to be divided into lateral and medial elements by a distinct groove. Some of the occipital variation also reflects divergences from the archaic condition with occipital contours that are high and rounded and a complete absence of bunning.

Table 12.7
Supraorbital Torus Dimensions

	Medial		Central		Lateral	
	projection	height	projection	height	projection	height
Skhul 2	14.3	16.2	16.5	13.0		10.5
4		19.0		11.2		11.5
5		15.1		9.8		10.2
7				11.5		10.5
9	17.5	15.0	22.5	12.5	24.0	11.5
Tabun	16.5	17.3	19.0	12.5	23.5	12.2
Amud		14.9	23.0	13.0	24.0	9.8

Variation in these three males is of interest. Skhul 5 is often used to characterize the sample, although more was preserved of the Skhul 4 face (and it is larger and otherwise more Neandertal-like). A recent reconstruction of Skhul 4 emphasizes its marked midfacial prognathism and high nasal angle, and Skhul 9 is the lowest cranium of the three, with the most receding forehead (McCown and Keith described it as reflecting a predominance of 'Neandertal' features). In fact, McCown and Keith describe paleoanthropic (e.g. "Neandertal") extremes for features from each of these Skhul specimens (see table 12.8); for instance the nasal process of Skhul 4, the orbit shape of Skhul 9, relative radius dimensions of Skhul 5. F.C. Howell recognized the Skhul range of variation as overlapping with that of the early

European Neandertals. B. Arensburg comments on the range of morphological variation, for instance arguing that the contrasts between Skhul 5 and 9 are so great that they make a separation between "Neandertals" and modern humans at the site impossible. A series of analyses by R. Corruccini concluded that the multivariate variation at Skhul ranges between "Neandertal" and "modern" cranial form, and J. Kidder and colleagues reach a similar conclusion regarding Skhul 4 and 5 from their multivariate studies.

The female specimens are less well preserved. Skhul 2 has a well defined chin, probably the best expressed in the sample, but a pronounced, continuously developed supraorbital torus as well that would make it impossible to categorize her as an "anatomically modern human" woman by any definition. Skhul 7, an as yet unreconstructed female specimen, has the highest number of "Neandertal" characteristics listed by McCown and Keith. This is not to argue that females from the site are more archaic, but rather that the males have been miscategorized as "anatomically modern".

One of the most "Neandertal"-like features of the entire sample is the supraorbital development. Researchers from Weidenreich to Vandermeersch have focused on the importance of this continuous, well developed structure and although it is often asserted that the Skhul tori do not attain the size of "Neandertals" this is not the case. The range of Skhul supraorbital dimensions (table 12.7) generally encompass the dimensions of Tabun and Amud, the Levant specimens regarded by many as "Neandertals" (but see below). When they do not it is because Amud structures are *smaller* than any of the Skhul remains.

The Skhul postcrania provide important information regarding size, proportions, and dimorphism. Skhul 7 is only 154 cm tall, while Skhul 4 and 5 average 180 cm. which is markedly taller than the 172 cm. Omo 1 male. This gives a rather large height dimorphism figure, 86%, but the sample sizes are quite small. The average **midsex** (that is, the mean of the male average and the female average) height for the sample is 167 cm. Limb proportions differ markedly. For instance, Skhul 5 has low brachial (forearm=radius/humerus) and crural (leg=tibia/femur) indexes. They reveal short distal limbs that if taken to reflect climate would mean that Skhul 5 was part of an immigrant population from the north. This hardly fits the Vandermeersch/Bar-Yosef idea of European Neandertal immigration to the Levant, however, as the brachial index is even lower than that of Tabun - the Levant "Neandertal" who is supposed to be the immigrant according to this theory. Even more confusing is the fact that the distal limbs of Skhul 4, a male of almost the same height, are quite long and approximate many tall sub-Saharan Africans of today. If we examine the limb lengths relative to trunk size a different picture emerges, especially if comparisons are made with cold adapted populations. Relative to the size of the vertebrae, the Skhul 4 and 5 postcranials (upper and lower limb) are longer than those of the European Neandertals. In fact, they are longer than the Neandertals from Shanidar Cave in Iraq (see below). Thus limb proportions and limb-to-trunk ratios could suggest different histories of climatic adaptation. Are these highly variable Skhul specimens the descendants of European and African populations that met and mixed in the Levant, lost all cranial reflections of their origin, elongated their limbs, but retained the limb proportions of their differently adapted ancestors? Or, is it possible that there are non-climatic explanations of limb proportions? This issue will be discussed further below.

The Skhul postcrania are characterized by the loss of many features related to muscular strength. Shaft proportions and measures of the articular surfaces are small relative to limb length. Moreover, there is a marked change in shaft form; for instance, the femurs generally lack midshaft flattening and internal thickening of the cortical bone. The innominates are quite variable. They are fragmentary, but the preserved potions combine robustly developed crests and tuberosities and unusual variation in the shape of the front part of the pelvis. In the few complete pelves of *Australopithecus* the pubis was found to be unusually long. The fossil record for this structure is minimal because it is so easily broken, and these pubes are the earliest ones known for *Homo*. Marked pubic length characterizes the Skhul 9 male pubis, but the Tabun female and Skhul 4 male pubes are shorter and there is no reason to posit unusual obstetric (for the Tabun woman) or locomotor variation for them.

An archaeological analysis by A. Ronen suggests the possibility that the skeletal material may not all be (more or less) synchronic, as is commonly assumed. Two groups of different ages are possible: Skhul 3 and 6-10 the earlier and 1, 4, and 5 later. While some paleoanthropologists suggest this could account for part of the variation, the discussion above shows that archaic features are not concentrated in either of these sub-samples. It is possible, however, that the more "modern" features of Skhul 4 and 5 could reflect a more recent age (Skhul 1 is a young child). However, similar "modern" variation is encountered even earlier at Qafzeh (see below), where there is no evidence of markedly different burial times.

Morphological analysis, carefully applied in a comparative context by workers familiar with both the Mount Carmel specimens and the comparative samples, alternatively has put the Skhul remains in the "Neandertaloid" camp and has portrayed them as "anatomically modern *Homo sapiens*". While it is possible that some of these scientists were simply in serious error, an alternative and more reasonable explanation of this diversity is that the question of what is and what is not "anatomically modern *Homo sapiens*" cannot be resolved morphologically.

THE HYBRIDIZATION ISSUE

As discussed above and in Chapter 11, variation beyond the "expectations" of many paleoanthropologists was encountered in the late Middle and early Late Pleistocene fossil records of China, Europe, and Africa. In these cases the initial reaction to it was to provide a taxonomic explanation, which ultimately did not hold up. The Mount Carmel caves rubbed the noses of the paleoanthropological profession in variation, this time historically earlier than the other cases. Variation here, however, was not immediately taxonomized, it was placed in an evolutionary context where the issue raised was whether the variability came from sampling a population in the process of evolution, or was the result of hybridization between races. The sequence of interpretations was quite different from the other regions, and ironically it was only later that taxonomy was brought forward as the answer.

When they set upon their systematic analysis of the human remains from Mount Carmel, published in monographal form in 1939, McCown and Keith believed that the specimens from the two almost-adjacent caves, Skhul and Tabun, were of the same geological age. Their examination and comparison of the large sample convinced them

> As our investigations proceeded we encountered so many characters which linked
> Skhul to the Tabun type that we were ultimately obliged to presume that we had
> before us the remains of a single people.

McCown and Keith clearly thought of Tabun as one of the extremes in the variation they reported (table 12.8), but it was often the case that *one of the Skhul specimens is also to be found at that extreme*. That Tabun fit in the expected range of variation was also supported by their demonstration of common unique features shared by Tabun and Skhul:

- Marked space enclosed within the curvature of the ribs
- Expanded 4th segment of the sternum
- Absence of a central pit in the glenoid fossa
- High cubital angle of humerus
- Anatomical configuration of first metacarpal
- Subtrochanteric cross section of the femur

Had there been no Tabun woman recovered, the Mount Carmel remains would still have a regularly expressed Neandertal-like extreme for most of the features showing variation at the site. Of course there *was* a Tabun women, and her subsequent "archaeological/geological redating" by F.C. Howell (see below) played an important role in transforming this explanation (and others) into a taxonomic one, as paleoanthropologists overlooked the variation within Skhul alone. This was made easier than one might have expected because after their study the collection was divided evenly between institutions on three continents, the Harvard Peabody Museum, the Natural History Museum of London, and the Rockefeller Institute of Jerusalem, and no paleoanthropologist has seen them all together since.

Table 12.8
The Extremes of Variation at Mount Carmel
as reported by McCown and Keith[1]

Feature	Specimen(s)[2] at the Extremes	
	Paleoanthropic (i.e. Neandertal-like)	Neanthropic (i.e. modern human-like)
Cranial Characteristics		
nasal index	T 1	Sk 5
nasal process of maxilla	Sk 4,	Sk 5
nasal roof notched	T 1, Sk 9	Sk 2, 5
narrow nasal bones	T 1	Sk 5
orbit height	Sk 9	Sk 5
mastoid process	T 1, Sk 7	Sk 4, 5
nuchal area breadth	Sk 6	T 1, Sk 5,9
Mandibular Characteristics		
mental eminence	T 1	Sk 2, 4
Postcranial Characteristics		
thorax barrel-shaped	T 1	Sk 4
Intercostal muscle expansion	Sk 5	T1
thickened rib cross section	T 1, Sk 5	Sk 4, 7
medial ridge of ribs	Sk 5	Sk 4
elongated pubis	Sk 9	Sk 4
scapular coracoid morphology	T1	Sk 5
clavicle morphology	T1	Sk 5
Width of the forearm	T1, Sk 7	Sk 5
relative radius length	Sk 5	Sk 4, T1
curved radius shaft	T 1, Sk 7	Sk 4, 5
relative size of distal radius end	T1	Sk 7
curved ulna shaft	T1, Sk 7	Sk 4
form of coronoid process	Sk 2, T1	Sk 5
uncinate process of the hamate	T1	Sk 5
apical tuberosity of triquetrum	Sk 4	T1
general carpal morphology	T 1	Sk 5
relative femur shaft robustness	Sk 5	Sk 4
femur shaft curvature index	Sk 6	T 1
lesser trochanter expression	T 1	Sk 4, 5
linea aspera and pilaster expression	T 1, Sk 7	Sk 4
midshaft rounding	T1, Sk 7	Sk 5
horizontality of tibial condyles	T 1	Sk 4
fibular shaft rounding	T 1	Sk 4
morphology of the foot	T 1	Sk 4

[1]   This table does not attempt to review all of the varying features of the Mount Carmel sample. Data presented only reflect characteristics in which the Mount Carmel specimens (including Tabun) vary along an axis that McCown and Keith describe in terms of similarity to European Neandertals and early modern humans of Europe. Given here are the extremes they report, when such an axis can be defined.   Not listed are features in which the whole sample approximates the paleoanthropic or the neanthropic conditions, although both exist in abundance. In fact, the table can be misleading in that by emphasizing the features that vary *within* the Levant sample, the unique features *shared* by the specimens within it are necessarily ignored. Yet, it is these that McCown and Keith emphasized in their analysis and the conclusions they drew from it.   Data are also not presented for variables which McCown and Keith found to overlap between paleoanthropic and neanthropic European samples.

[2]   **Sk** refers to Skhul specimens, **T** to Tabun.

While McCown and Keith clearly considered the Mount Carmel sample to represent a single biological population, they regarded the range of variation to be unusually great - there was nothing else quite like it in the fossil record of the time - and felt obligated to explain its magnitude. It figures prominently in their explanation that they regarded the variation as reflecting two distinct extremes that were linked by intermediate features. The extremes were the paleoanthropic (European Neandertal-like), and neanthropic (early modern European-like, often exemplified by Cro Magnon). They provide two definitions of the intermediate features: transitions that fell between these extremes, and intermediates that formed a series linking the extremes.

Their interpretation of the pattern of variation was based on the fact that they could not identify clear antecedents or contemporaries for either extreme. Ironically, the date of the Mount Carmel caves was then thought to be some 100 kyr, earlier than the Western European Neandertals just as it is now, but for most of the period between their writings and today, the specimens were thought to be half that age or less. Because they could distinguish later Neandertals and moderns in Europe, McCown and Keith explained the Mount Carmel variation as the result of a population in the process of evolutionary divergence, in their words "in the throes of evolutionary change". The Mount Carmel population, in their view, was not an ancestor of the moderns, but of the Neandertals, and their modern-appearing features were plesiomorphic, reflecting the ancestral condition for both branches before the Neandertal specializations.

Many more recent studies have borne these precepts out, for instance R. Corruccini's multivariate analysis of the Skhul crania or the S. Ben-Itzhak and colleagues study of shaft thickness and strength in humeri. Yet, McCown and Keith might have found others of the current assessments surprising. Many today have come to regard Tabun as a Neandertal and the Skhul hominids as modern humans, or as is commonly said (though rarely defined) "anatomically modern *Homo sapiens*."

The initial reaction, however, was not to deny the pattern of variation McCown and Keith reported, but to explain it differently. Some paleoanthropologists, for instance F. Weidenreich and W. LeGros Clark, also interpreted it as transitional, but as evidence of a Neandertaloid evolution into moderns. Others turned to a hybridization explanation.

When C. Coon published *The Races of Europe* in 1939 the completed Mount Carmel monograph was not yet available. Never the less, he reviewed what was known of the Mount Carmel remains from the preliminary publications and concluded that the characteristics of the sample were a consequence of hybridization between "Neandertals" and a more modern group. He may have been the first paleoanthropologist to support the hybridization explanation that McCown and Keith rejected. This was soon followed by a substantive discussion by the population geneticist Th. Dobzhansky, who also rejected the interpretation that the Mount Carmel population was in the throes of evolutionary change, and provided the firmest basis for a hybridization explanation. From the genetic point of view, Dobzhansky addressed the possible causes of a range of variation which included "individuals ranging from a typical Neanderthalian to a *Homo sapiens* with some characteristics of the former".

> Since this difference was doubtless a resultant of numerous interacting genes, the interpretation of McCown and Keith is excluded. Indeed, two types differing in a system of genes cannot crystallize out of a mixed population without the interbreeding of these types being prevented by a spatial separation. The Mount Carmel population arose, therefore, as the result of hybridization of a Neandertaloid and a modern type, these types having been formed earlier in different geographical regions.

Dobzhansky did not think it likely that the Mount Carmel sample was an unusual one, and thereby drew an important phylogenetic conclusion from it, addressing the relations of the "Neandertals" to other populations:

> hybridization of the Neanderthalian and the modern forms must have been a frequent occurrence, at least in Palestine ... Therefore the data of McCown and Keith prove something very different from what these authors themselves thought they demonstrated,

namely that the Neanderthal and the modern types were not isolated reproductively, and, hence, were races of the same species rather than distinct species.

I find the details of the McCown and Keith monograph insightful and correct, and Dobzhansky's explanation of them incontrovertible. Yet, his hybridization explanation has been largely discounted in subsequent publications. One important reason for this is the widespread acceptance of the precept of a Levantine evolutionary sequence spanning *from* Neandertal *to* modern human populations, as first proposed by F.C. Howell some 20 years after the monograph was published. Howell argued that Tabun was substantially earlier than Skhul, providing an alternative explanation for the variation at Mount Carmel by allocating its sources to phylogenetic differences expressed over time. He coined the description of the Skhul remains as "proto-Cro Magnon". According to this view the Levantine hominids were indeed in the throes of evolutionary change, but could be separated in time to show the progression clearly. Howell thereby connected the Levant "Neandertals" to ancestral Neandertals (the "generalized" populations of central Europe) and the Skhul remains to (their presumed) more modern Western European descendants, in particular those from Cro Magnon. For most of the three decades following his seminal paper, it is this interpretation that has been the most widely accepted.

One consequence of the transitional interpretation affects the phylogenetic position of the Skhul sample. With the Tabun female earlier and regarded as more "Neandertal" like, Skhul came to be regarded as modern - first "Proto-Cro Magnon" and later just "anatomically modern *Homo sapiens*". The change from a "Neandertaloid" to an "anatomically modern" interpretation of the Skhul hominids was *not* the consequence of a reanalysis or new specimens. Besides, it was generally forgotten that the problem of variability in the Mount Carmel hominids is not simply the outcome of combining the Skhul and Tabun samples (the variation at Skhul itself is problematic in that it extends into the "Neandertal" range), and that variation is a problem not limited to the Skhul cave. Remembering the variation at Tabun, the argument that Tabun was the earlier of the two sites, and in particular that Tabun layer C is earlier than the Skhul hominid-bearing strata, does not resolve the issue of explaining (what first appeared to be) contemporary variation by showing it was actually not contemporary

An earlier Tabun date *did* seem to resolve the evolutionary issue, providing a sequence of populations that showed progression from a Neandertal to a modern form, although this was unacceptable to some paleoanthropologists. For instance, A. Thoma argued that too many differences separated Skhul from modern *Homo sapiens* for it to be ancestral in the time allotted, according to the mutation model he proposed (each different trait was supposed to be the result of an independent mutation). Others asserted that there was insufficient time for a Tabun-like "Neandertal" to evolve into Skhul. These, however, can no longer be regarded as relevant problems because the most likely interpretation of the evidence is as it was originally - the two are penecontemporary. If one cannot be ancestral to the other, we are back to the original issues.

One interpretation is that there are genetically isolated, distinct and diagnosable human species in the Levant sample. As S. Gould puts it:

> if Neanderthals and modern humans lived in the Levant and maintained their integrity
> without interbreeding for 60,000 years before the great replacement in western Europe,
> then the two are separate species by the primary criterion of reproductive isolation

Thus in a triumph of typology, what began as separate poles in a continuous range of variation ultimately became the idea that in the Levant there were distinctly different "Neandertal" and "proto Cro Magnon" populations, and that they remained separate and distinct for a long period of time. The difficult and confusing aspects of variation were submerged as the names of the extremes attained reality. As Gould himself realizes, "we must never doubt the power of names, as Rumpelstiltskin learned to his sorrow". Yet, this interpretation comes face to face with an archaeological problem - the behavioral similarities linking all of the Levantine Mousterian sites are extraordinary. Moreover, it is very difficult to discount the original evidence that was brought forward to support the other interpretation, hybridization. For hybridization to be a valid explanation, the mixing populations must be races within a single species.

QAFZEH

The other large early Israeli site is the cave of Qafzeh, where a series of burials were recovered from several Mousterian levels (table 1.2). Various numerical date estimates suggest an age of 95-90 kyr. This is older than most estimates for Skhul. At least fifteen individuals have been reported. The specimens are robust in many respects, but of all the Levantine samples, Qafzeh is generally thought of as the least Neandertal-like. Crania are high and generally well rounded, with reductions in tori (for instance all supraorbitals are divided into central and lateral elements) and other reflections of muscularity, and the postcranial remains are gracile compared with earlier specimens. This fits the "Neandertal refugee" model as Qafzeh dates to a time that presumably is before the cold-fleeing population influx. Be that as it may, as documented in B. Vandermeersch's monographal treatment Qafzeh is every bit as variable as Skhul.

Part of the problem in assessing the position of the Qafzeh material is the "type specimen" usually chosen to represent the site - Qafzeh 9. It is a 172 cm. tall young man, of late adolescent age. The bulk of the cranial superstructures, the crests and tori, would not be expected on a male of this age, and the central portion of his supraorbital region is missing, but the fact is that his forehead is high, his occiput rounded, and his brow region divided into a supercillary arch and weak lateral toral structure in an anatomy that would be considered modern anywhere in Europe and Western Asia today. The other complete male cranium, Qafzeh 6, is an older adult with a very Skhul 5-like form (but much of the cranial bone is isolated and floating in plaster so that the actual cranial form is unclear). His supraorbitals are thick, prominent and projecting, with no tendency to thin over the center of the orbit. Qafzeh 6 has a broad nose and preserves nasal bones. Their angle to the face is low and it is clear that the nose was not prominent. The face is short and broad, and like Qafzeh 9 there is a canine fossa and a marked maxillary notch. An incomplete female cranium, Qafzeh 5, is an anatomical contrast to the others. Her forehead and cranial rear are flattened, the surfaces meeting at the top of the skull to form a distinct angle. The supraorbitals are weakly developed, really a thickening at the end of the sloping frontal. Qafzeh 3 is a 160 cm. tall woman. Her supraorbitals are continuous (although division into orbital and lateral elements can be seen), thick, and projecting in front of the high and rounded forehead. Cranial bone is thick and the occipital is very broad. The position of the external occipital protuberance is far removed from the internal one, and in general Vandermeersch describes her cranial rear as archaic. I find the specimen far too archaic to be considered an anatomical modern.

The Qafzeh people were about the same height as the Skhul folk, the males slightly smaller and the females slightly larger but no more so than accidents of sampling would explain. Midsex average heights for the two samples are 167 cm for Qafzeh and 166 cm for Skhul. They were slender, but often with thicker limb shafts than those from Skhul. Other differences include a shorter pubic ramus (Qafzeh 9 compared with Skhul 4 or 9). The Qafzeh sample tends to have larger anterior teeth with generally more wear relative to the posteriors. The mandibles generally do not retain the gap between the last molar and the ramus, and there is moderate to prominent chin development. In general, W. Howells supposition that there are more Neandertal or Neandertal-like traits in the Skhul sample than there are in Qafzeh would appear to be correct.

Some resemblances of the Qafzeh folk are with African populations to the south, others more like Asians such as Jinniushan. None of these similarities are unique, they do not show a distinct pattern of ancestry from earlier populations in one region or another, but perhaps more than any other Pleistocene population except Skhul, they reveal the true extent of the web of population interconnections. Ironically the one population they are not particularly similar to is the Upper Paleolithic Europeans, the putative descendants assigned to them by the appellation "proto-Cro-Magnons" that is often used to describe them. The most African-like features are the narrow skull and subnasal prognathism of Qafzeh 9, and the forehead supraorbital anatomy of Qafzeh 5. The idea that the Levant is a mixing grounds for different populations is certainly bore out by these remains. Yet, the resemblances are more with recent Africans than with the earlier Late Pleistocene remains discussed above, except in the sense of the general circum-Mediterranean features shared by Jebel Irhoud, Qafzeh 6, Skhul 5, and to a lesser extent the others. There are no special resemblances with any of the specimens promoted as "early moderns" from sub-Saharan Africa: Omo crania, Klasies, or even Border Cave (see Chapter 14).

Table 12.9
Body Sizes for Archaic West Asians

Specimen	Limb length (cm)	Stature estimate (cm)[1]
Shanidar 6	**femur=38.8**	**149**
	tibia=30.0	
Skhul 7	**radius=21.4**	**154**
	ulna=23.9	158
Tabun	humerus=28.7	153
	radius=22.7	161
	ulna=24.2	160
	femur=41.7	**156**
	tibia=31.4	151
Qafzeh 3	**tibia=36.4**	**160**
Shanidar 4	humerus=30.5	160
	radius=23.0	163
	ulna=25.5	165
	femur=42.5	**160**
Shanidar 2	**tibia=33.7**	**163**
Shanidar 3	**humerus=31.5**	**164**
Shanidar 5	ulna=24.9	163
	femur=45.0	**166**
Shanidar 1	radius=24.9	170
	ulna=27.3	172
	femur=46.2	169
	tibia=35.5	168
Qafzeh 7	**ulna=27.1**	**170**
Qafzeh 9	humerus=33.0	171
	radius=25.3	170
	ulna=27.5	173
	femur=47.6	**172**
Skhul 6	**femur=47.7**	**172**
Kebara	humerus=32.4	168
	radius=25.8	**173**
	ulna=27.4	173
Amud	**femur=48.2**	**174**
	tibia=386	175
Skhul 4	humerus=33.7	174
	radius=27.6	178
	ulna=29.4	177
	femur=49.4	**177**
	tibia=43.4	181
Qafzeh 8	humerus=37.6	184
	tibia=43.4	**181**
Skhul 5	humerus=37.8	185
	radius=26.8	175
	ulna=28.2	175
	femur=51.8	**182**
	tibia=41.2	176

[1] Based on European regressions, boldfaced figures (whenever possible from femur or tibia) are the estimates representing each specimen in the text and summary statistics

In fact, P. Smith points to a number of significant differences between even the most modern-appearing of the Klasies mandibles (KRM 41815) and the much more modern appearing mandibles from Qafzeh. If Qafzeh represents an early outflowing of modern people from Africa, a supposition that is far from clearly correct, their ancestors or collaterals remain unidentified. In fact it would be simpler, and more in concert with the facts, to assume that this anatomy first appeared in the Levant earlier and spread southward.

THE LATER "NEANDERTALS"

Kebara:

The Kebara specimen is the upper part of a male postcranial skeleton (from neck to pelvis with fragmented femur), as well as a mandible, hyoid bone, and a single upper 3rd molar, recovered during excavations of the Mousterian levels at the cave. Excepting the undescribed Jinniushan woman and the as yet unexcavated Bari Neandertal (see Chapter 13) Kebara has the only complete pelvis known between the australopithecines and the numerous modern human burials of the later Late Pleistocene. A full monographal treatment of the skeleton is published in a volume edited by O. Bar-Yosef and B. Vandermeersch. It is dated to some 60 kyr by the TL technique.

Kebara was about 173 cm tall, according to B. Vandermeersch. C. Ruff estimates a 76 kg weight, which is considerably less than the weight estimates for European Neandertals of similar height. For instance, the weight estimate for La Ferrassie, a European Neandertal male of almost exactly the same height, is 86 kg (table 13.9). This and other evidence combines to suggest that Kebara is slenderer and more lightly built than the cold-adapted Europeans. S. Churchill contends that the trunk was shallow, not rounded, and that the lower rib cage was not expanded so that the pelvic brim form probably does not correspond to trunk shape. (However like the Europeans the rib-bearing and lumbar portions of the trunk are relatively elongated.) Also reflecting a weight difference, joint sizes are small compared with bone lengths. For instance, table 13.10 shows that the relative radius head size is 8.4% of the bone length while in four European Neandertals it ranges from 9.1% to 10.4% (and is even relatively larger in the West Asian specimens from Tabun and Shanidar 4). The Kebara humerus and ulna have small articular surfaces as well.

Perhaps the most important aspect of this burial is the discovery of its hyoid bone, the only one known from the fossil record. Because the hyoid is only connected to the rest of the skeleton by muscles and ligaments, its shape is influenced by the strength and orientations of these connections. Therefore, with this bone and the cervical vertebrae and mandible it was possible to reconstruct the important elements of the vocal tract. According to B. Arensburg and colleagues this remarkably human-appearing bone was part of vocal apparatus that was fully human, with a deep throat and other details reflecting the ability to produce the full range of sounds used in human speech.

All 24 vertebrae of the back are known for this specimen. Neck length appears slightly shorter (relative to the rest of the back) than is normally true in living people, and the lower neck vertebrae have more horizontal spines than is usual (see the discussion of the Shanidar postcranials, below) but generally these vertebrae are unremarkable when compared with today's. The comparisons are quite different, though, when made with earlier remains. Kebara is the one of the earliest Late Pleistocene specimens associating vertebrae with other postcranial elements, and the first to do so following the very early *H. sapiens* youth WT 15K. It is the first to provide evidence of the vertebral body size expansion that characterizes Late Pleistocene humans. Earlier hominids have small vertebral bodies, with surface areas, especially at the lower end of the vertebral column and sacrum, as little as half modern size relative to body weight. The question is why there should be an expansion of vertebral body size without any obvious change in locomotion or evidence of a significant change in activity levels or patterns. B. Latimer suggests that the change responds to the increasing requirements of the intervertebral disk that comes with an elevated life span. As discussed in Chapter 6 and 7, australopithecines and early *Homo* had a maximum lifespan of some 35 years. Several studies have shown that Late Pleistocene hominids (Neandertals and their successors in this region and Europe) lived maximally about 10 years longer. This is not unlike pre-Columbian Amerind samples and native populations prior to their exposure to the European-Urban evolved infectious diseases; these populations had a few individuals living older than 45, and although their sample sizes are much larger, their basic demography appears to have been quite similar to Late Pleistocene populations. The additional 10 years, an almost 30% increase, is quite important because of the vertebral disks. Latimer points out that humans and all other bipedal hominids place extreme twisting stress on the disks between their vertebrae. This is because as they walk or run, leg swings and arm swings are 180° out of phase. The effect of twisting on these disks are unknown in any other vertebrate, and human disks begin to deteriorate and **herniate** by 35-40 years of age. Australopithecines and their early *H. sapiens* successors rarely or never reached this age, but as humans began to live longer Latimer posits that selection began to play a role in adapting the disks to better resist the lifelong torsion. This adaptation was accomplished by an increase in size, requiring that the vertebral bodies increase in size as well.

The Kebara pelvic inlet is more rounded than the earlier specimens, the anterior-posterior dimension more closely approximating the transverse one. This shape extends through the pelvic aperture, and the pelvic outlet is also more rounded. One would assume that these differences also characterize female pelves. If so, C. Ruff suggests they mean the second rotation of birthing (Chapter 4) had come to characterize the Kebara folk, and that their babies were born with their heads facing the sacrum rather than the hip. The significance of this change is in its indication that head size at birth had taken on a greater importance than shoulder breadth in affecting constraints on the size and form of the pelvic aperture. Large heads cannot pass through a narrow, elliptical aperture and since the pelvis couldn't widen further, expanded anterior-posterior diameter was the response. This change occurred earlier than Kebara and reflects the significant brain size expansion of the Middle and Late Pleistocene, if female pelvic form can be accurately predicted from a male.

The size of the Kebara male inlet, of course, provides no information about head size relative to pelvic aperture size at birth (K. Rosenberg reports that in living people the head size averages greater than the inlet size), but there are some hints that suggest head size at birth may not have been much different than in some living populations. In fact one line of evidence could mean that Neandertal infant head size was smaller. R. Tague argues that if the modern pattern of sexual dimorphism applies, Kebara women would have had an even more constricted pelvic *outlet* than moderns. However, since modern births are extremely difficult, Rosenberg argues it is unlikely that Neandertal births were even more difficult. Therefore, either Neandertal head size was smaller at birth, or more likely the pattern of sexual dimorphism differs from moderns, as L. Hager has long maintained.

Rosenberg reports that the Kebara inlet breadth is not unexpected for a human male of his size (as estimated from acetabulum size, or from C. Ruff's weight estimate of 76 kg). Inlet breadth is related to the length of the pubis, this bone after all is the front wall of the inlet, and the pubis length is elongated in two of the four Levantine men with preserved pubes - Kebara and Skhul 9. However the elongated pubis of Kebara does not reflect a correspondingly large birth canal size in females as once thought, a point demonstrated above, and also by the fact that the only female pubis, that from Tabun, is not elongated relative to her size. Why, then, is the long pubis retained in some of the males?

A solution to this question was suggested by Y. Rak, during his study of the Kebara pelvis. He compared how the position of the pelvic inlet set within the frame of the pelvis in Kebara, with the inlet position in a series of moderns. Rak noted that as seen from above, Kebara differed in appearing as though the inlet was shifted forward within this frame. As one might imagine the differences caused by this shift, the inlet's rear, the sacrum, is more anterior and therefore this weight-bearing portion is closer to the biacetabular line. In life the pelvis is tilted forward in most postures, positioning the weight bearing surface at the top of the sacrum (this supports the trunk) directly above the acetabulum where weight is transmitted to the lower limbs. The Kebara difference is that less tilt is required. The front of the inlet is more anterior as well, because of the forward shift, which explains why the pubes are longer in this and certain other archaic specimens. Kebara, the only archaic pelvis for which both pelvis inlet breadth *and* pubis length are known, has the inlet size expected for his body size, but a somewhat longer pubis. Other features characterizing this pelvis (and some others including some of those attributed to European Neandertals - but note that important specimens from this time period in East Asia such as the Jinniushan pelvis have not yet been described) are a consequence of the changed orientations required by this differing inlet position. The iliac blades are broader and the acetabula face more to the sides, evidently the ancestral adaptation. This is a useful model for understanding how the Kebara pelvis differs from modern ones. It is not an *evolutionary* model, however, because it is the modern pelvic form that evolved from the Kebara one, with a *backward* shift of the pelvic inlet within the frame of the pelvis, and the concomitant required changes in pelvis form.

E. Trinkaus suggests that Kebara descended from cold adapted populations because his limbs are short. Stringer and Gamble argue that body proportions show Kebara to have a "clearly cold-adapted body shape". But, is Kebara really like cold-adapted populations in its postcranial remains? The Kebara trunk is relatively large (the clavicular/humeral index, and pelvic breadth/stature index shown in table 9.1, are both high). Yet as noted above the shape of the Kebara rib cage is unlike the cold-adapted Europeans. The Kebara brachial index of 80 is well above the European Neandertal mean of 74, and even above the average for the Skhul and Qafzeh samples (76), showing that the lower arm is long relative to the upper (definitely *not* a cold adaptation). In fact, if any Levantine could be said to descend from a cold adapted population on these criteria, it would be Skhul 5, with a brachial index of 71.

Amud

The Amud Cave, near Lake Tiberias in Israel, is the site of discovery for a fragmentary but largely complete male and 4 additional specimens, and is likely to yield more as excavations continue. Of the more fragmentary material, Amud 2 is a piece of an adult upper jaw, and Amud 3 consists of cranial and facial fragments from a child about four years old. Amud 4, a portion of an infant's temporal bone, comes from the earliest layer, and Amud 7 is a more recently discovered 10 month old infant burial from a stratigraphically lower position that has preliminary TL dates of 47-55 kyr according to Y. Rak. The Amud 1 male is close to this antiquity, approximately the same age as the later of the Shanidar remains. Represented by a complete cranium and fragmentary postcranial skeleton, the burial can be skeletally sexed as a male, 174 cm tall, who died in his mid-20's. A complete monograph describing and comparing him was edited by H. Suzuki and F. Takai. Amud 1 has the largest cranial capacity of any of the Levant specimens (1740 cc) and analysis of the associated skeleton suggests that he is probably also one of the tallest individuals (about 174 cm.).

Amud 1 differs from Middle and earlier Late Pleistocene hominids in a number of features, as detailed in H. Suzuki's description of the cranium and the analysis of the postcranial skeleton by B. Endo and T. Kimura. It also differs markedly from penecontemporary European Neandertals. The skull is higher and more strongly curved. The occipital is markedly higher and there is no bunning or lambdoidal flattening at the cranial rear. The attachment area for the nuchal muscles is low (the external and internal occipital protuberances are at the same position), and there is a thin, weakly developed nuchal torus. The mandibular fossa is deep and the mastoids large, dwarfing the juxtamastoid eminence. Also unlike the Europeans, the upper edge of the temporal bone, where it overlaps with the parietal, is rounded. The browridges are reduced in vertical dimensions and projection, their central and lateral sizes falling near or even below the Skhul range (table 12.7), and tend to separate into central and lateral elements. They enclose a broad frontal sinus (in the Europeans but not Amud this sinus extends upwards, above the torus and into the face of the frontal bone). The reconstructed face is flatter (less peaked along the midline) and has a markedly reduced magnitude of midfacial prognathism, and this with the lower face unconnected (it floats in plaster) and positioned too far forward in the reconstruction. However, there is a retromolar space in the mandible and the chin is only moderately developed. Orbits are large and rounded, and also like European Neandertals the face is quite tall (table 12.3) and the transverse contour of the vault is rounded.

Comparison with Jebel Irhoud 1 is of special interest, as this specimen is regarded as an archaic form of modern human by some paleoanthropologists, and simply an early modern human by others. Amud has a larger vault but smaller and less projecting supraorbitals that are better divided into medial and lateral sections. The Amud forehead begins in a position that is more over these supraorbitals than behind them (the Irhoud condition), the frontal bone is much broader, the face is more angled at the midline and vertically oriented (these are European-like as compared with the African-like Irhoud features), but while equally broad (and with the same orbit and cheek sizes) it is much taller. Like Jebel Irhoud 2 there is a metopic suture for the full length of the frontal bone, but it is fused in Amud. There certainly are differences between Amud and Jebel Irhoud 1 (and 2), but I believe it would be difficult to assess which of these are "more modern". This is probably the wrong question to ask.

The dentition is quite small and the anterior teeth are markedly reduced compared with earlier specimens, whether European or Levantine (c.f. Skhul and Qafzeh). In his description of the dentition H. Sakura finds the closest relations to the Tabun female. Unlike most of the European Neandertals (but similar to the Skhul dentitions) these specimens show reduction in overall incisor size and relative reduction of the fourth premolar compared with the third. The palate is shortened and the Amud teeth are reduced compared with virtually all Neandertal samples except the latest ones such as those from the French site of Hortus (see Chapter 13). Never the less, relative incisor size and the lateral maxillary incisor breadths which are the same as those of the centrals are features specifically resembling the European Neandertal condition.

Amud is taller than the all of the Shanidar specimens, and other males such as Qafzeh 7 and 9 and Skhul 6, but not as tall as Qafzeh 8 or Skhul 4 and 5 (table 12.9). Amud, and to a large extent Tabun, lacks many of the European (and later Shanidar sample) Neandertal features. Its limbs are not as robust - joint surfaces and shaft thickness are relatively smaller. With a crural index of 80, it can no more be said to reflect cold adaptation than Skhul 5, who has the same crural index. Endo and Kimura systematically compared the features of the fragmentary Amud skeleton to European Neandertals and Skhul 4. They found Amud intermediate, but, in their words, slightly closer to Skhul in the comparisons. Examining their data shows that the preponderance of closest postcranial resemblances are between the two Levantines, when only unique similarities are examined. To wit:

- **24** characters link Amud with Skhul 4 *but do not appear in European Neandertals*
- 14 characters link Amud with European Neandertals *but do not appear in Skhul 4*
- 8 characters link Skhul 4 with European Neandertals *but do not appear in Amud*

Table 12.10
West Asian Body Size and Proportions

	"Neandertal"[1]	Skhul/Qafzeh	North Africans (Afalou/Taforalt)	ER 15000
Female height	153 (149-156)	157 (154-160)	163	
Male height	167 (160-174)	176 (170-182)	173	188
Brachial Index	78	77	78	80
Crural Index	77	83	84	88
Height dimorphism	92%	89%	94%	

[1] Includes Amud, Tabun, and the Shanidar specimens

THE ISSUE OF CIRCUM-MEDITERRANEAN GENIC EXCHANGES

These Levantine populations, like their African penecontemporaries, represent the end point of an evolutionary process with immediate predecessors that are only poorly known. If we viewed history, adaptation, and genic exchanges as three important factors influencing their similarities and differences, it remains difficult at the moment to isolate the effect of similarities and differences in ancestry. While the crania, mandibles, and teeth evidence the same tendencies that were discussed for Africa, many of the specific details of change differ between these regions. Similarities involve the expansion of cranial capacity and the differential expansion of frontal and occipital areas, shrinking of the basal structures associated with strengthening, and reduction and gracilization of the face. On the other hand, no Levantine hominids show the browridge reduction expressed in several of the sub-Saharan Africans, and similarly anterior tooth size reduction there is greater than in the Levant (a response to technology differences?). Lack of substantial reduction in the anterior teeth may be causally related to the maintenance of larger Levantine supraorbitals, as well as to the greater expression of expanded maxillary sinuses and the related morphological complex of midfacial prognathism with its consequent anterior positioning of the mandibular teeth relative to the mental foramen and ramus.

Superficially, the North Africans more closely resemble penecontemporary Levantines, especially in cranial and upper facial form, and there is much to be said for the contention of several researchers that North African and sub-Saharan sequences require separate consideration. Workers such as J-J. Hublin and W. Howells point to the similarities between specimens such as Jebel Irhoud 1 and Skhul 5, and as discussed below they are more broadly shared. However, there are detailed specific differences between the Levantine and North African faces as well, including alveolar prognathism, the reduction of midfacial prognathism and appearance of canine fossae, and anterior dental reduction in North Africa. What is most interesting are the elements of both that resemble Europeans. The identification of these has lead to the development of two different circum-Mediterranean genic exchange models.

The first of these was raised by T. Simmons and colleagues. They argue that the specific form of occipital bunning in the North African sample appeared first and uniquely in Europe, and therefore reflects the existence of genic exchanges around the Mediterranean. It is ironic that only the earlier non-Neandertals of the Levant are bunned in a similar manner - the "Neandertals" generally lack this feature. Most of Simmons and colleagues work is with the frontal bone. Their analyses show striking similarities between the Irhoud crania and specimens from Qafzeh, and the relationships between these and European Neandertals such as Gibraltar that suggest that "modern humans in the circum-Mediterranean region are derived from this web of interconnecting lineages".

A second model was proposed by Y. Rak. His model is a biogeographic one, relying on the isolation by distance concept to account for the continuous variation of earlier Late Pleistocene human populations around the Mediterranean, with (what he regards as) speciation between its European (e.g. Neandertal) and North African (e.g. modern human) extremes. Rak suggests that the central position of the Levantine populations in this pattern accounts for their marked variability. He mainly differs from Simmons and colleagues in assessing a species-level difference at the extremes (as the archaic hominid walks) of the Mediterranean world. This assessment derives from his contentions that facial anatomy is uniquely derived at the African end and pelvic anatomy is uniquely derived at the European one. For reasons discussed above I do not believe that either anatomical interpretation is the case and am more inclined to agree with the Simmons and colleagues interpretation of this web of interconnected lineages.

ARE THERE LEVANTINE NEANDERTALS?

The woman from Tabun, it will be remembered, was not initially described as a Neandertal, but as representing the "Neandertal" end of a continuous range of variation at Mount Carmel. Long after this interpretation, and after the typologists triumphed in creating a reality for this appellation, Levantine "Neandertals" came to exist and B. Vandermeersch proposed an explanation of *why* the Neandertals entered the Levant. He began with the precept, ultimately proved to be correct, that the Qafzeh folk were earlier than the "Neandertals" in this region. The emigrations of Neandertals out of Europe - certainly indicated by the circum-Mediterranean genic exchange models described above - were related to the onset of glacial conditions as the Würm began. Neandertal characteristics in the Levant, by this model, are actually European characteristics, expressed in a region that Bar-Yosef once described as a cross-roads for intercontinental migrations. But if these contentions are correct, are some of the Levantines "Neandertals" and others not (the Neandertal *versus* moderns interpretation), or is it as McCown and Keith described when they had the full Skhul sample before them? Was the Late Pleistocene Levant populated by peoples with a mixed morphology spanning the range between Neandertal (e.g. European) and non-Neandertal (e.g. Asian and African) poles?

The specimens ascribed to "Neandertal" and "non-Neandertal" samples are not without their systematic differences. For instance, even though the Levantine "Neandertals" are virtually the same height as the Skhul/Qafzeh sample - the midsex height means are 165 and 166 cm - relative distal limbs differ (table 12.10). The "non-Neandertals" have brachial and crural indices of 77 and 83, virtually the same as a sample of recent North Africans from Afalou. The Neandertal brachial index is even higher than these, 79, but the crural index at 78 differs and is lower (although it is the same as Skhul 5 and not as low as in the European Neandertals). J. Bytnar and colleagues claim there are some dental and mandibular shape differences, and the development of the mental eminence distinguishes these samples although their ranges largely overlap. Furthermore, Y. Rak and colleagues believe that specimens even as young as the 10 month old Amud 7 infant can be identified as "Neandertal". Yet, in his analysis of the Amud skull, H. Suzuki notes the marked similarity of Amud with certain Skhul specimens, and finds Skhul 4 more similar to Amud than Skhul 4 is to Skhul 5. B. Arensburg argues that a combination of modern and archaic anatomical features in the highly variable Levant hominids makes use of "Neandertal" undesirable - a point clearly supported by the multivariate analyses of R. Corruccini and J. Kidder and colleagues, and by the absence of substantial strength or use-pattern differences in the internal structure of humeri reported by S. Ben-Itzhak and colleagues..

    To examine the pattern of variation for all the relevant features, not just those that diagnose the two "Neandertals" in the Levant sample, A. Kramer and colleagues undertook a phylogenetic analysis of the full set of earlier Late Pleistocene Levant crania, to see whether the two "Neandertals" shared a set of uniquely derived traits that clustered them together as a linked anatomical entity. They did not share such a set. Instead, the several most probable analyses showed that Tabun and Amud were never solely associated with each other (figure 12.5). This result reinforces the idea that Levantine "Neandertals" are not a diagnosable entity. There are, no doubt, plenty of European genes in the Levant sample, but no Europeans.

Figure 12.5
Phylogenetic Analysis of Levant Crania[1]

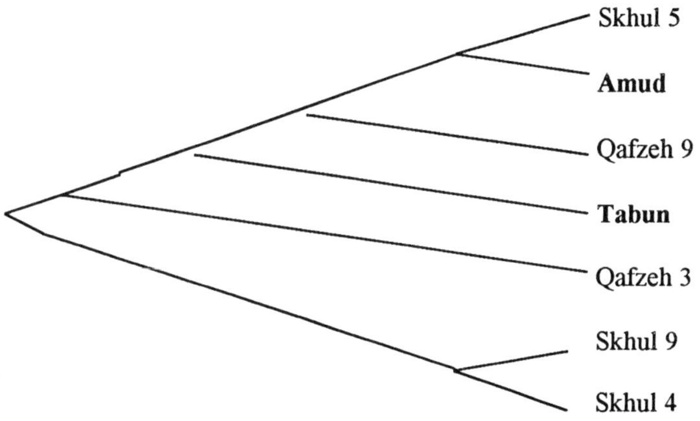

[1] From Kramer and colleagues

Zuttiyeh and Levantine Relationships

    Another way of looking at the relationships of the various Levant specimens is in terms of whether there is common inheritance. The Zuttiyeh specimen (see Chapter 11) is a useful vehicle for examining this question, as it is the oldest of the Levant crania. Table 12.11 shows that the unique features that link Zuttiyeh to the Zhoukoudian sample are equally shared by both "Neandertal" and "non-Neandertal" crania. The influence of Zuttiyeh on both of these samples must reflect a close relation with each other.

    The two complete Levant "Neandertals" do not have the same east Asian features; Tabun retains many more than does Amud (because of an earlier date?). This supports the hybridization explanation, but has two other implications as well. First, it shows that the influence of European features can be found before the last glaciation began. There may well have been European refugees fleeing increasingly difficult conditions who came to the Levant (the past, once again, presaging the present), but the network of populational contacts extended to a much earlier time. Second, numerous east Asian characteristics are also found in Skhul and Qafzeh specimens, again in some more than in others, where they are characterized as "modern". They are not really "modern" but rather "non-Neandertal" - two categories that are often confused. What is most interesting is that the source of the features regarded as modern is as much Asian as African. Africa, by these data, cannot be considered the sole source of "modernizing features".

Table 12.11
Levant distribution of features shared by Zuttiyeh and the Zhoukoudian crania

	Tabun	Amud	Qafzeh 3	5	6	9	Skhul 4	5	9
Frontal curvature	O	X	-	-	X	-	O	O	O
Narrow frontal boss	X	O	O	X	O	O	O	O	-
Short Temporal fossa	-	O	-	-	X	X	O	O	-
Supratoral sulcus: size and morphology	X	O	O	X	X	O	O	X	X
Depression at glabella	X	O	X	-	O	-	X	O	-
Shallow **nasal root**	X	O	X	-	O	-	X	O	-
Nasal bones transversely flat	-	O	O	-	O	-	-	-	-
Tubercle on zygomatic anterior face	-	X	-	-	X	X	O	O	-
Anterolateral orientation of zygomatic	-	O	-	-	X	X	O	O	X
Vertically oriented superior nasal bones	-	O	X	-	O	-	-	-	-

X: present
O: absent
-: part not preserved

Differing Adaptations?

Some of the systematic differences said to exist between the samples would seem to reflect variation in functions and behaviors. Yet the paradox raised by interpretations of "Neandertals" and "modern humans" in the Levant is that their behavioral adaptations do not seem to differ significantly. As Bar-Yosef puts it in describing the region, "The Mousterian struggle for survival lasted over 100,000 years. The amount of typological and technological variability among the lithic industries and the nature of the sites is rather limited". The problems raised by a lack of a behavioral basis for the anatomical variations are two:

1. What, if not behavior, accounts for the differences between samples, said to be so contrasting by some workers like Y. Rak that they are distinct human species, when their behaviors are the same?
2. How does modern human form relate to modern human behavior, especially if the latter is not the cause of the former? As Bar-Yosef and Vandermeersch put it in the subtitle of their *Scientific American* article, "*Homo sapiens* preceded Neanderthals on Mount Carmel and followed a similar pattern of life for 60,000 years. Biology thus cannot explain the cultural revolution that then ensued."

This paradox has been an especially irritating one, as it strikes to the heart of the presumption that differences in form follow from differences in function. There have been three attempts to resolve it by showing that behavioral differences were actually there. One of these involves a reinterpretation of the archaeology at Qafzeh and Kebara and the other two focus on differences in subsistence activities.

B. Shea analyzed the Mousterian tools at Qafzeh and Kebara with special focus on the wear they show due to their uses for varying activities. He found use wear to be virtually identical, coincidentally noting that at both caves very few of the artifacts *showed* actual use wear - he argued that woodworking tools predominated and most were used for a very brief time and then discarded. Shea did find that while both sites had hafted implements including projectile points (he takes this to reflect "the ability to predict the likelihood of recurring tasks"), the frequency of points in the assemblage was higher at Kebara.

Subsistence activities were inferred from studies by D. Lieberman and E. Trinkaus. Lieberman examined the dental cementum (see Chapter 4) in the teeth of gazelle, one of the prey species found at a number of Levantine Mousterian sites, for evidence of which season they were killed in. He gave the 6 of the 7 seasons he identified a numerical value and then calculated the mean and variation of the individual gazelle teeth studied at each site. Focusing on the hominid-bearing levels, Qafzeh had an average death season of 5.2 (5 is spring in Lieberman's season-numbering system) with little variation, and Kebara averaged 4 (the one season value he had not assigned) with about twice as much variation. From this study of one of the prey species, Lieberman argues that the Qafzeh "moderns" occupied their cave only during the spring and therefore circulated between different areas in different seasons, like virtually all hunter/gatherers, taking advantage of different resources when they came available. The Kebara "Neandertals", on the other hand, are said to have occupied their site all year long. The evidence for this is from levels 7-10 where the variation is much higher and about half the gazelle were fall/winter kills and the other half spring/summer (the "Neandertal" burial, however, is from well below, level 12). Lieberman contends that the level 7-10 hominids, who he assumes were also "Neandertals", were more sedentary and seasonally stable, finding resources by radiating outward to different areas from a single habitation. He argues that the radiating subsistence pattern requires more energetic output as resources become more depleted, and therefore is associated with higher levels of body strength. This interpretation, however, is flawed by several problems, including oversimplifications, errors in data presentation and the demonstrable tendency for larger samples to show a wider seasonal spread (the Kebara samples are quite small). Moreover, the interpretation is contradicted by the other analysis of hominid activities.

Trinkaus, in his analysis, cites data showing higher frequencies of mice found in the hominid levels at Qafzeh than at Kebara. He suggests longer-term Qafzeh occupations (presumably more garbage created a better microhabitat for the diminutive rodents). For him, evidence of reduced body strength is associated with this greater sedentism. The evidence for reduced activity levels is anatomical rather than archaeological. Trinkaus argues that living foragers have a higher angulation between the neck and the shaft of the femur than do less active populations, and shows that the neck-shaft angles at Qafzeh and Skhul (except for Skhul 4) are higher than those of Amud and Tabun - even for the children from these sites, which is part of the basis for his claim that the Skhul/Qafzeh folks are less mobile and therefore more modern. Yet, evidence Trinkaus has presented elsewhere seems contradictory. For instance, the long lower legs at Skhul and Qafzeh, relative to the shorter ones of the Levant "Neandertals", are probably activity related instead of climate related, because Skhul/Qafzeh and the Levant "Neandertals" have the same elongated lower arms and this more likely reflects the climatic adaptation. Longer legs would support the interpretation that Skhul/Qafzeh folk are more mobile - a better fit to the archaeological data but not the rodent remains. The difference in femur neck-shaft angles may well reflect the relatively broader "Neandertal" pelves.

Now what do these differing patterns infer? Here's the rub - as long as they are associated with hominids widely regarded as "Neandertal" and "anatomically modern" (e.g. Skhul and Qafzeh), it is automatically assumed that the moderns are somehow better adapted and the attempts to show this are innovative. For instance, R. Milo and D. Quiatt (see Chapter 13) contend that since more points mean the "Neandertals" were hunting more, "early moderns were expending significantly less overall effort on subsistence". In the Lieberman study, the multi-seasonal "Neandertal" occupations with their radiating subsistence patterns are likened to the pre-agricultural Levantine Natufians and are said to expend higher levels of energy while collecting (but presumably also hunting much more, according to Shea). However, Lieberman contends that despite several tens of thousands of years of trying, unlike the Natufians they failed in this adaptation because "they compensated by working harder". These authors and Trinkaus agree that the "Neandertals" worked harder, but do not concur on interpretations of the mobility patterns that lead to the harder work. Perhaps this is not surprising, as seasonality *versus* sedentism, or concentric *versus* radiating subsistence patterns, are not distinct adaptations but extremes of a range of adaptation that any group might utilize under different conditions, according to R. Kelley. Moreover, let us not forget that no hominid can be directly associated with the different archaeological or paleozoological indicators of adaptive difference. And even if they could be, the comparisons that lead Trinkaus to regard the Skhul/Qafzeh sample as more modern are at best confused. Skhul/Qafzeh are unlike all Late Pleistocene hunter/gatherers, not just the "Neandertals" but unlike the "modern" Europeans that followed them as well. They are so much more modern that their neck-shaft angles are similar only to agriculturists and urban peoples, an unlikely interpretation for these 90 kyr or older populations.

It seems as if part, perhaps most, of the solution to these seemingly paradoxical relationships (or the absence of expected relationships) is found in a fourth possibility - examination of the presumption that the biological differences between the samples themselves are distinct and diagnosable. This interpretation has been overstated, in my view. McCown and Keith's assessment of the contrasting anatomies as extreme ends of a continuous range remains the most accurate appraisal, which means that none of the Levantine folk, strictly speaking, were Neandertals. The same cannot be said of their penecontemporaries to the northeast.

FURTHER EAST

Shanidar

The Shanidar Cave, in the Zagros mountains of Iraq, is a higher (765 m above sea level, and located well above a valley floor) and more northerly archaic hominid sample. There are some nine individuals from level D, two children and seven adults, and every specimen includes postcranial remains. Some of the Shanidar hominids were killed by rockfalls. In one case, the bodies were recovered and buried in one spot, with a man (Shanidar 4) positioned above two women (6 and 8), who were placed above a baby (9). The grave may have been covered with flowers (but the evidence here is unclear as the pollen which is the basis for this interpretation may have been inadvertently carried to the site by the Kurdish excavators). If the flowers were intentionally placed in the grave during the burial, some implications beyond the symbolic one are medicinal - the plants represented by pollen could have been used to treat traumas and inflammatory injuries. Other specimens thought to be buried include 1, 3, and the infant 7.

Although the specimens are spread through several strata in the cave they cluster into two groups (table 12.12). The earlier group consists of individuals 2, 4, 6-9. While their age has been estimated at about 60 kyr, E. Trinkaus believes that the date for these older specimens could easily be double that. According to R. Solecki's interpretation of the complex burial, 4, 6, 8, and 9 may have been closely related. The later group—specimens 1, 3, and 5—has been directly dated by radiocarbon to an age of 46 kyr. - an early radiocarbon date that is widely cited but actually means the specimens are older than 35-30 kyr or so. This part of the sample is probably best thought of as penecontemporary with Amud.

Table 12.12
The Shanidar Hominid Sample

Specimen	Sex	Age at Death[1]	Height (cm)
late group			
1	M	35-40	169
3	M	41±7	164
5	M	40±7	166
early group			
2	M	20-30	163
4	M	36±7	160
6	F	24±7	149
7		2/3	
8	F	20-30	
9		0.5-1	

[1] From Trinkaus

The Earlier Shanidar Group

Within the earlier group, Shanidar 2 is the best preserved. According to work by T.D. Stewart and E. Trinkaus (who published a comprehensive monograph on the site), the fairly complete postcranial skeleton and crushed cranium belong to a rather short young man. His 163 cm height is close to that of the other male from this level, Shanidar 4's 160 cm. Comparing them with the much smaller Shanidar 6

(149 cm) woman gives an estimated 92% sexual dimorphism and a diminutive midsex height average of 155 cm. If accurate, this would make the earlier Shanidar sample some 10 cm shorter than the Levantine "Neandertals".

The Shanidar 2 cranium appears to have been very large, although it is too fragmentary for an accurate brain size estimate. The vault is characterized by an angled occiput with what Trinkaus described as a prominent occipital torus, a robustly developed basal area, and large mastoids. Like the Levantine "Neandertals" there is no occipital bunning, but also no suprainiac fossa. The better-preserved facial area indicates a large face with a continuous browridge of moderate thickness and a somewhat inflated maxillary sinus which creates a maxillary anatomy similar to Kabwe - a concave surface to the sides on the nose that is not deeply incised enough to be a canine fossa. The even more fragmentary Shanidar 4 cranium appears generally similar where comparable. The faces are robust and relatively flat across. The browridge is also comparable, centrally thick with little thinning toward the sides. The frontal is low and relatively short.

Shanidar 2, 4, and 6 have fairly complete dentitions. While the samples are small, the average canine size and posterior tooth size appear to be reduced compared with the Middle Pleistocene European sample. The Shanidar 2 dentition is only lightly worn, but Shanidar 4 has heavy wear that is strongly differential - the incisors are much more reduced by wear than the posterior teeth. The mandibles of specimens 2 and 4 are fairly stout and the ramus of Shanidar 2 is low compared with those of Riss and earlier Europeans. The most significant aspect of the two mandibles is the forward shift of the tooth row relative to the ramus and body. This feature, associated with the forward shift of the maxillary teeth, is an indirect result of midfacial prognathism. As a consequence, the ramus begins just behind the last molar, and the mental foramen (the opening allowing the nerve, artery, and vein supplying the lower face to pass from inside the mandible) is positioned under the first molar. In specimens without this forward shift of the teeth, the mental foramen is positioned under the premolars. Shanidar 4 differs slightly, lacking the gap between the last molar and the ramus. The facial and mandibular anatomy of these specimens reflect a low to moderate expression of midfacial prognathism.

In discussing these crania and mandibles, Trinkaus describes the cranial and facial anatomy as "non-Neandertal" and asserts that the specimens lack all derived Neandertal traits. In this respect they are similar to the Levantine 'Neandertals".

The Later Group

Shanidar 1, 3, and 5 are from the upper portion of level D. All three are probably male. The sex of Shanidar 1 and 3 can be determined from features of the pelvis, and Shanidar 5 can be diagnosed from his cranial size and robustness . Bones of the Shanidar 1 lower limb suggest a stature of 169 cm. With the height estimates of Shanidar 3 (164 cm) and 5 (166 cm), these three males average some 5 cm taller than the males in the earlier group.

When the Shanidar 1 burial was discovered, the uppermost portion of the right humerus was found to be atrophied, and the lower portion as well as all of the remaining bones of the right forearm were missing. The right arm was not functional and, and possibly as a result it was amputated at or above the elbow during life. This amputation and the fact that Shanidar 1 survived it and lived to a fairly old age (for a Middle Paleolithic human) provide some insight into several aspects of life in the Shanidar cave. The amputation indicates that some form of preventive medicine was practiced (the ephedrine-producing plant represented by pollen found in the Shanidar 4 burial could be used to treat shock). That Shanidar 1 survived the trauma implies a period of intensive care following it. He probably was an important contributing member in his society, and his physical condition suggests that these contributions were not in hunting! Indeed, Shanidar 1's disorders were not limited to the right arm. The left ankle was abnormally developed in a way that suggests an injury to the lower leg early in life. The right ankle was arthritic, possibly from bearing most of the body weight. The marks of other injuries were found on the cranium. The most severe of these flattened the lateral border of the left orbit. One compensation for these life experiences is the unusual size and robustness of the left arm. Another is found in the evidence that Shanidar 1 supplemented his working left hand with his mouth. As T. Stewart noted, the wear on his front teeth reflects their distinctive use for purposes other than chewing. Several other specimens also show evidences of trauma during life, from the scalp wound on the Shanidar 5 vault to rib wounds on Shanidar 3.

The Shanidar 1 cranium is very large compared with earlier and most penecontemporary males. The cranial capacity is 1,600 cc, and the braincase is broader and higher than in the Middle Pleistocene European males. Brain size expansion (frontal and posterior parietal areas of the endocast are larger) and reduction in the basal spongy bone contribute to the more filled-out appearance of the skull. The frontal bone is unusually long, especially in relation to the parietals and in site of the frontal boss it is flattened along its length. There is virtually no postorbital narrowing. The maximum cranial height is in a posterior position, and behind it the vault steeply descends to the bulging occiput, just above the low, weakly developed nuchal torus. According to Trinkaus there is no suprainiac fossa. The combination of long and relatively flat frontal, posterior position of greatest cranial height, and strongly arched parietals also characterizes Shanidar 5. Trinkaus suggests both of these crania may have been artificially deformed by flattening the forehead when they were very young (the affects are more marked on Shanidar 5).

The Shanidar 1 face is large, but compared with the earlier Shanidar males it is gracile in the development of the zygomatics and other features reflecting the strength of muscle attachments. Because the face is strongly angled, from the nose on back, the zygomatic bones face as much laterally as forward and are flat (when the midface is flat across, rather than angled, the zygomatics have a distinct bend between the forward-facing part under the orbits and the side-facing portion meeting the temporal bone and enclosing the temporal fossa). The nose is narrow but prominent, although its angle to the face was not particularly high. Expanded maxillary sinuses result in convex surfaces to the sides of the nose, and corresponding to this development of midfacial prognathism there is a gap between the last mandibular molar and the front of the mandibular ramus. The mandible has an incipient mental eminence.

Many of these features closely resemble the Amud male. Shanidar is about 5 cm shorter and has a somewhat smaller cranial capacity (although quite high by any standards). There are a few other details in which the Shanidar male differs:

- thicker supraorbital over the nose,
- lack of clear supraorbital division into central and lateral elements
- better expressed supratoral sulcus (the front of the forehead is a little more posterior),
- rounder frontal profile,
- narrower face,
- shallower mandibular fossa
- larger juxtamastoid process,
- marked lambdoidal flattening

These features link the later Shanidar remains to the European Neandertals by showing Shanidar 1 to be more similar to the European Neandertals than Amud is. Even still, Shanidar 1 and Amud have a remarkable resemblance of general form, and of many details.

E. Trinkaus has reconstructed the Shanidar 5 cranium and face. The specimen combines a number of features which result in a more archaic appearance than is usual in the Upper Pleistocene hominids. Aspects of the vault attributable to deformation are described above. Besides these, however, the frontal is separated from the thick browridges by a shallow groove. The supraorbitals follow the orbital contour, attaining their maximum thickness in the central region. Below them is the largest of all Neandertal noses (Shanidar 1 is one of the narrowest); the nasal bones show a very high angle in lateral profile, and follow an "S"-shaped curve so that they begin to angle downward at their most anterior point. The top of the nose projects far forward; for instance, it is very anterior to the outer orbital pillars which results in an angled face (and flat zygomatic bone as noted for Shanidar 1). The nose is bordered by expanded maxillary sinuses, creating a puffy midface. The robustly developed zygomatics merge evenly onto the maxilla, as in the western European Neandertals. Trinkaus observes that the central incisors show the same occlusal rounding as in Shanidar 1. The few preserved postcanine teeth are large.

Trinkaus notes that many of the similarities linking these two faces also contrast them with the earlier Shanidar sample while aligning them with the more western Neandertals of Europe. Remembering the comparisons of Shanidar 1 with Amud, this link seems to have been forged in Western Asia during the last glaciation; or, perhaps more accurately, we can say that the rate of genic exchanges was elevated during this time.

Postcranial remains

The several skeletons buried in the Shanidar cave afford a detailed glimpse of postcranial anatomy. Most of what we know about this sample comes from functional analyses published by E. Trinkaus and his students. They describe the postcranial remains as robust (meaning relatively thick, with prominent muscle attachments), with several features linking them with the European Neandertals such as

- long spines on the cervical vertebrae (these relate to powerful neck muscles, particularly those important when the front teeth are used as tools)
- relatively long clavicles
- upper limb muscularity (shown from the scapula to the terminal phalanges)
- bulky femur and tibia shafts with large joint surfaces and thick shaft walls
- broad toe bones

While nothing about these features suggests differences in locomotion or manipulation abilities from more recent people, they reveal some variations in their habitual patterning and certainly show the consequences of markedly greater body strength.

Afghanistan and North

There are several sites in western and central Asia (using the Ural/Caucasus boundary to define where Europe ends and Asia begins), further east than Shanidar, that seem to mark the eastern-most extent of the range of archaic European morphology. Beginning furthest to the south Darra-i-Kur is a right temporal from the Mousterian levels at this Afghan cave - radiocarbon dated to 30 kyr (meaning <30 kyr). L. Angel regards it as a transitional specimen, anatomically more similar to moderns than to Neandertals. In this region of the world, it surely can be said that archaeology is no guide to anatomy.

Just to the north, southeast of Tashkent, 10 worn teeth and a distal humerus were found in the Sel'Ungur cave, below travertines dated to 126 kyr (F.C. Howell believes these were deposited in stages 6/7). According to Y. Islamov, the teeth are undiagnostic and the humerus has very thick cortical bone with a correspondingly reduced medullary cavity.

Westward, Teshik-Tash is a small cave southwest of Tashkent in the rugged mountains of Uzbekistan, some 1500 meters above sea level. A young (8-9 year old) Neandertal boy was buried in a shallow grave that was covered by seemingly purposefully arranged goat skulls (mountain goat is the predominant faunal element). The Mousterian found throughout the 5 levels at the site is quite similar to some of the European Mousterian variants. C. Gamble believes this site is quite important in understanding the development of specialized hunting. His argument is that the cave reveals evidence of hunting specialization because there are only rare carnivore bones and the goat remains show no evidence of animal gnawing. These facts indicate that the site was not a carnivore den, and that the faunal remains are the consequence of Neandertal activities. Specialized hunting may therefore have been important in the expansions into rugged mountainous areas, according to Gamble. Far to the west, the Neandertals at the Würm III Spanish site of Zaffaraya (see Chapter 13) may be adapted to a semi-mountainous area in a similar way. Sites such as these show that there was nothing in Neandertal biology or cognitive abilities to preclude specialized hunting adaptations.

Comparing children is always difficult because ages are often quite disparate, but Teshik Tash has many elements of the anatomy of a European Neandertal already fairly well expressed (for some features even more so than the 13 year old Le Mousterier male from France). For instance, the occiput is bunned and the supraorbital development already continuous and significant, especially for an individual that had not yet reached puberty. This is not the result of misunderstanding the specimen's age at death. The dental age is consistent for all the incompletely developed teeth, as long as it is assumed that the relative development of the third molar suggests a mid-teen (ca. 15 year) eruption like most other Middle

Paleolithic (and earlier) humans. The postcranial skeleton is also consistent with this age, showing none of the evidences of adolescence. As F. Weidenreich pointed out, it is difficult to find a modern European of similar age with so high a skull relative to its length. The face is not as puffy as the Neandertal children (for instance Roc de Marsal or La Quina 18), the left side of the maxilla has a concave surface and a shallow fossa is present. Weidenreich likens it to certain of the Skhul crania (especially Skhul 5) and N. Minugh-Purvis, who compared it with Neandertal and other children of similar age, concluded Teshik Tash resembles European Neandertals most closely in the vault but lacks some of the usual midfacial features of Neandertals. She interprets the specimen as reflecting genetic exchanges between western and eastern Asia.

A Single Place of Origin for Modern Humans?

The main difference between the Multiregional interpretation of modern human origins I have developed here and the several single origins theories (including some that are variations of Multiregional Evolution such as F. Smith's and L. Aiello's) revolves on the issue of whether modern human *features*

- arose at different times and various places, spreading independently because of their advantages, or
- arose in a single population and spread with its success replacing (as in the Eve theory) or hybridizing with (as in the Multiregional variants) natives they encountered

Much of the issue reflects the problems with the definition of modern human. The question is whether modern humans appeared as a single discernible morphology, as one would expect if they had a single population origin. C. Stringer and M. Day have proposed several definitions of modern human based on skeletal features that could be identified on human fossils. P. Brown showed that these do not classify a significant number of recent and living Australians as modern, and I demonstrated the same problem for Late Pleistocene and Holocene fossils. This problem, of course, is not with the Australians who are each and every bit as modern as the authors of the definition, but with their definition of modernity. The question is whether there can ever be one. J. Kidder and colleagues approached the inquiry using multivariate statistics. From the Eurasian evidence alone they concluded that a diagnosis of modern human is not possible. The question, in the end, is not whether modern humans are significantly different from their forebears, but whether the differences can be characterized the same way everywhere or if they are distinct to some degree from one place to another. It seems quite difficult to support the former from studies of recent and living human anatomy.

Biology is not the only source of evidence. M. Stiner argues that on the basis of the archaeological record there is more than one place where modern human behaviors emerge relatively early. In the arena of food procurement, modern behavioral capacities are not likely to be manifest in the addition or loss of a basic foraging component such as scavenging or hunting, but rather involve how the various components are integrated in adaptive strategies. And procurement is only part of the problem, as successful strategies also involve transport, dismemberment, processing and cooperative behaviors ranging from the hunt itself to the necessary requisite of infant care. To provide an example, she contends that the most significant changes leading to modernity in food procurement strategies in South-Central Europe occurred late in the Middle Paleolithic and involve:

- incorporation of scavenging into the social matrix for hunting, pooling the products of both at the same residential places
- spatial and temporal overlap of hunting and scavenging activities
- increased focus on hunting prime adult mammals, in an intermediate body size range
- the beginnings of the use of stone-lined hearths to intensify or contain heat

Clearly the behavioral transition to modernity was multistaged and not the sweep of a single set of "advanced behaviors". Moreover, in different regions the changes came in differing combinations and sequences. For instance, hearths are found at the Levantine Neandertal site of Kebara, but only rarely in the European Mousterian. C. Stringer and C. Gamble regard hearths as a clear sign of modernity, but they are consistently found in the Châtelperronian, a European lithic industry associated *only* with Neandertals. These paleoanthropologists, who believe in a singular origin for modern humans and their behaviors, liken the advent of modern behaviors to the flicking on of a light switch, rather than the slow turning of a rheostat (leading A. Marks to quip that the switch must have short-circuited in various places), but the whole analogy is much too simplified and Eurocentric to be useful.

Some linguists believe that another source of information is found in language evolution. Linguists such as V. Shevoroshkin have proposed that all languages can be traced back to a common recent mother tongue, presumably marking the beginnings of language and supporting the idea of a single origin for moderns. Languages can be classified according to similarities, and for closely related languages these reflect common development from a particular (although unlike genes, hardly a unique) source - for instance the Romance languages of Europe are descendants of Latin. However, languages can merge together (this blurs the whole concept of ancestry), information exchanges insure elements of one can spread widely (making distantly related languages appear to be more closely related), and rates of changes are neither universal nor constant. The fact is that linguists lack a reliable method to determine distant relationships between languages. Tree-divergence methodology, the commonly used analytical technique for tracing language evolution, is an inappropriate tool. It ignores mergers, the effects of language elements spreading, and the fact that many languages are related along gradients rather than being entities distinct from each other. The tree divergence methodology will always make languages *appear to* derive from a common source (the trunk) *whether or not* they actually did so. Even if there was an ancient divergence from a single source, it could never be demonstrated.

Finally there is a problem of causality. It now seems clear that modernizations in anatomy and behavior are largely independent of each other. With the problem of defining modernity so complex, the descriptions of what constitutes modernity differing from one region to another, and the appearances of modern characteristics and behaviors at different times and places, the interpretation that these somehow reflect a single recent origin for modern humanity is demonstrably incorrect.

Summary

This chapter examines issues surrounding the origin or origins of modern humans. The anatomical changes leading to the recent (for instance terminal Late Pleistocene) pattern of human variation extend well into the Middle Pleistocene, and the evolutionary process is reflected in the fossil records of Indonesia, East Asia, Africa, and western Asia (especially its fringe, the Levant). Fossil records in each are examined over a period of approximately 250-50 kyr. Each area has its own pattern of emerging modernity, even as the common changes of cranial capacity expansion, dental reduction, increasing gracility, and the differentiation of living groups within the major races (such as the San and Negroids) are reflected in the fossil record. All is not differentiation, however, as there are several good cases of genic exchanges reflected in fossil anatomy, such as the evidence for circum-Mediterranean gene flow. Many elements of modern behaviors appear during this period; for instance prepared core and flake technologies, hafting, the use of bone (including sophisticated weaponry such as barbed bone points), grindstones, and a proliferation of woodworking tools, but only a few of these achieve universal or near universal distribution. Like the skeletal elements of modernity, most are local and some quite short lived. The organizational aspects of modernity can be found from place to place, especially toward the end of this period, but like the skeletal elements never together.

As for the origin of modern humans then, it seems as though some taxonomic categories such as "anatomically modern *H. sapiens*" simply cannot be brought to bear with accuracy. As applied to Middle Paleolithic or Middle Stone Age peoples they are unreliable and do not reflect real *anatomical* or *behavioral* entities. The accurately dated skeletal remains said to be "anatomically modern" (Klasies,

Qafzeh, Skhul) are categorized on the basis of anatomy, but for Klasies the modernity is based on a limited number of carefully selected characteristics found on only several specimens, and for Qafzeh and Skhul the "modern" features are variable and the populations appear archaic in comparison with the latest Pleistocene and Holocene humans. They cannot be considered "anatomically modern" by any meaningful definition that doesn't also include most or all penecontemporary peoples generally described as archaic. Moreover there is the issue of Ngandong, a sample which stands to the recent and living Australians in the same relationship that Klasies has to recent and living South Africans (possibly specifically to San) and Qafzeh and Skhul have to recent and living Levantines. Ngandong cannot be excluded from the discussion of modernity. None of these examples evince modern behaviors - the behavioral revolution of the later Late Pleistocene is seemingly independent of the anatomical process. Three facts emerge:

1. there is no single place of origin for a related package of features called "modern anatomy" *or* "modern behavior"
2. elements of "modern" anatomy appear long before significant evidence of modern behaviors
3. modernity means different things in different places

Modernity, I conclude, did not have a single origin and in fact probably should not be anatomically defined at all. Modern humans are a state of mind.

ANATOMY OF A CONTROVERSY
Out of Africa - Out of Luck?

The idea that modern humans have a single recent origin is older than Darwin's writings. Of course predating evolution this was the monogenic, or biblical, interpretation but after Darwin's writings it was incorporated into evolution theory as a branching model. In a 1905 essay on the origin of humanity, J. Kollmann argued that the human races were derived from African Pygmies, thereby proposing the first "Out of Africa" theory. Kollmann had published in some detail on the Pygmies and argued that *Homo primigenius* (Neandertal) was more divergent than any of the races derived from the Africans and therefore had a different origin. Thus from the beginning "Out of Africa" was tied to the Neandertal issue. The next year, G. Schwalbe reviewed the current competing origins theories and emphasized the *human* nature of the fossils from Trinil and the Neandertal remains. He addressed Kollmann's assertion and argued that the Pygmies were too recent and too specialized to be a common ancestor for the human races. Whether a stages or a branching interpretation of modern human origins was proposed, Schwalbe contended that fossil hominids were either the direct precursors of modern humanity or their closest relatives.

The bush *versus* ladder debate continued through this century, although a specific "Out of Africa" theory never came back into focus until its last quarter. When Howells summarized the competing modern human origins theories 70 years after Schwalbe the same fundamental question remained - did modern humans derive (in his words) "from more archaic hominids, already present in the same regions" or "from a single origin"? He realized that "the two hypotheses are irreconcilable". Although clearly favoring the single origin model, Howells concluded "present evidence does not disprove either". At the time he felt that the time and place of origins could not be settled, although just a year earlier (and too late to be referenced in Howells' paper), R. Protsch published the genesis of the current "Out of Africa" models, ironically in the same journal.

Protsch developed the model that is fundamental to all current "Out of Africa" theories. If all modern humans are uniquely descended from Africans we can expect three predictions to hold up:

1. The earliest modern humans should be found in Africa.
2. Only in Africa should there be transitional fossils leading to modern humans.
3. The earliest modern humans outside of Africa should share unique, presumably African, features that reflect their common origin.

Protsch examined evidence for the first of these and argued hat the earliest modern humans were African. In his scheme only the Border Cave infant was directly dated (e.g. as opposed to dates determined from fauna or flora thought to be of the same age as the hominid) to an age as old as Neandertals, but this was enough. Because he regarded Border Cave as representing a more modern population, Protsch concluded that Africans evolved first and all living races descended from them.

P. Beaumont and colleagues developed additional details on an African origins theory also based on Border Cave, arguing that the spread of modern humans could be linked to their development of modern technology. Beaumont and colleagues, whose main thrust was not the dating question, accepted early date estimates for other specimens as well and based their contentions on the earlyness and modernity of Border Cave (like Protsch), but also Omo Kibbish and Klasies River Mouth Cave.

G. Bräuer derived his African origins theory from Protsch's work, adding to the list of ancient "moderns" from south of the Sahara. In his first presentations of the idea, Laetoli 18, Omo, and Florisbad were presented as the transitional group, borderline between archaic and modern anatomy (over the years the composition of this group has changed). Bräuer envisions the origin of modern humans as a process with two elements: a single source, and the hybridization and replacement of archaic populations with the expanding moderns. He gathered support for all three predictions of the theory, not only finding evidence of moderns and near-moderns (i.e. transitional specimens) in Africa but claiming that African features can be found in the earliest moderns elsewhere. Thus in 1989 he asserted that

> The ancestors of the inhabitants of Europe and Western Asia of some 30,000
> years B.P. consisted of modern Africans with some admixture of Neandertals.

Least there be any confusion on this issue, let the reader be assured that there is absolutely no evidence that could support such a proposition. Over the years Bräuer has shifted his emphasis from the hybridization aspect (he initially published on a Late Pleistocene European frontal bone from Hahnöfersand which he interpreted to be a Neandertal/modern hybrid) to a primarily replacement process. He has also shifted the tone of his rhetoric and has become accusatory, if not incinerary, loosing focus on the scientific issues and more and more addressing what he perceives as motivations and hidden agendas in the works of others.

The strongest "Out of Africa" statement comes from the "Eve" theory. All of human genetic variation does not attain the magnitude that can often be found in a single race of frogs. The explanation of why modern humans are so similar to each other in their nuclear and mitochondrial is an important part of understanding origins. The "Eve" Theory explains this similarity by a common recent ancestry, and bases this contention on an interpretation of the evolution of mtDNA. If all of today's mtDNA originated in a single African individual who lived some 200,000 years ago, as the "Eve" theorists contend, what happened to the mtDNA of all the other women who lived then? "Eve" theorists claim that Eve's descendants replaced all other populations without mixing with them, therefore extinguishing their mtDNA lines. As M. Stoneking and R. Cann, two of the original "Eve" theorists, once put it "the rather staggering implication is that the dispersing African population replaced the non-African resident populations without any interbreeding". Since the replacement was without mixture, we must have inherited all of our nuclear DNA lines from the "Eve" population as well, according to the theory, and that means that Eve was literally, as well as figuratively, a common mother. It also means that "Eve" founded a new species, since a worldwide replacement of human populations without mixture would be impossible unless mixture was impossible.

In their development of the "Eve" theory C. Stringer and P. Andrews take a strongly 'Out of Africa" position. They describe the theory as proposing

> Africa as the probable continent of origin of *Homo sapiens* [meaning modern *Homo
> sapiens*], with an origins for the species during the early part of the Late Pleistocene,
> followed by an initiation of African regional differentiation, subsequent radiation from
> Africa, and final establishment of modern regional characteristics outside of Africa.

The main elements here are the African origin, African regional divergence, and subsequent later spread and replacement, as other regional features are founded later. Their order is important because of the clear prediction that the earliest moderns in other regions should have some shared African features if the theory is true.

The best support for this theory came not from paleoanthropology, however, but from the studies of mtDNA cited above. These seemed to point to an African origin for all of the mtDNA lineages because the highest genetic variation and the deepest (most ancient) genetic roots were African, according to the early analyses. The "last hired, first fired" principle seems to apply here, though. D. Maddison and A. Templeton demonstrated that the data had been improperly analyzed (he showed that the computer program used to analyze the data was applied inappropriately). The algorithm used to indicate which roots are most ancient is too slow to work with large data sets, and it was concluded that the place of origin (the region with the last common ancestor of all existing human mtDNA variants) cannot be determined from mtDNA data. A second algorithm, based on the repetitive joining of most similar pairs (nearest neighbor-joining) can link all of the observations, but suffers from a similar problem. Since there is only one output, there is no way to examine its probability. Further argument for an African origin of mtDNA was based on the contention that Africans have the highest level of genetic diversity (presumably meaning that populations had evolved there the longest). But this assertion has never been demonstrated statistically, and in any event requires the (invalid) assumption that the evolutionary processes were random and involved no genic exchanges. In fact, Templeton determined that there is no statistical significance to the difference in diversities of African and Asian mtDNA. Finally, H. Harpending and colleagues studied probability distribution of pairwise mtDNA differences within populations for evidence of past population expansions (this is further discussed in Chapter 14). They found evidence of several significant expansions, but none fitting the expectations of a recent 'Out-of-Africa' model of modern human origins.

> "If there was indeed a single large expansion from Africa about 100,000 years ago,
> we should see the signature of it in the mtDNA differences, but instead we see
> indications of multiple later expansions associated with modern technology instead
> of modern morphology."

The argument that mtDNA reveals an African origin for modern humans has not stood up to scientific scrutiny.

Several archaeologists have provided worldwide summaries of archaeological change in support of the "out of Africa" view. J.D. Clark argues that the first modern humans can be associated with ecologically specialized tool kits that were first appearing some 200 kyr ago. These tool kits are of the Middle Stone Age (MSA), but what hominids are actually found with this industry? Several teeth from the Mumba Cave in Tanzania are undiagnostic, and are considerably younger than 200 kyr. In fact, all of the MSA-associated specimens with verifiable dates (Florisbad, Ngaloba, Klasies) greatly postdate the time when Clark theorizes they first appeared. The Klasies specimens are half the age of the archaeological changes. In the aggregate these African MSA "modern", or "near modern", are not particularly earlier than specimens similarly described from Indonesia and both East and West Asia. We do not know who made the earlier MSA, but the tendency of earlier MSA specimens such as Ngaloba and Florisbad to be more archaic is notable. Moreover, Clark admits that "the fact that the technology and behavior of the first modern humans in Africa do not appear to be all that different from those of the Neanderthals, poses a major problem" to his theorizations.

Moreover, there is a seemingly insurmountable problem that archaeological analysis has raised. The claims of African-like features in the Qafzeh remains leads a few paleoanthropologists, such as L. Aiello, to support the claim that the proof the earliest moderns evolved in Africa is that they are first found at its doorstep with African features, in the Levant (R. Klein would add, at a time when generally African fauna was in the region). However this would mean that the Levantine Middle Paleolithic should have its roots in Middle Paleolithic industries of North Africa, and a systematic examination of this question by A, Marks indicates that this is not the case. He finds no relationship between the Levantine Middle Paleolithic and that of Egypt and the Sudan, concluding that "each area saw considerable local continuity in both technological and typological development".

Klein's "Out of Africa" model is considerably later and has nothing directly to do with the "Eve" theory. Klein argues that only in Africa can the appearance of modern behavior be linked to modern form. He believes the underlying cause for all of the important Late Pleistocene developments - the major transformation in human behavior that he proposes occurred some 40 kyr ago - "reflects the last in a long series of biologically based advances in human mental and cognitive abilities". Fossil and genetic evidence, he continues, "suggest that the critical neural change occurred in Africa". A similar model presented by P. Allsworth-Jones is more narrowly confined to explaining the African evidence. He argues that modernity of the fossils from Klasies and Border Cave show that the transition happened in Africa first. The variable mix of modern and archaic features, especially at Klasies, is explained as the natural consequences of finding a transitional population, but so certain is he of their modernity that the main issue he raises is whether the hominids from these sites are modern but whether they are more similar to Negroes or to San. Like Klein, in fact citing Klein, he attributes the success of the moderns to "neurological change leading to syntactic language".

The archaeological models, in the end, do not rely on convincing archaeological data but assume biological causation. They thereby suffer from their reliance on a confused and contradictory literature written about the fossil hominids, although even given this it is surprising to find Klein repeating D. Pilbeam's much older assertion that with the appearance of modern humans evolutionary changes substantially cease. This has been long discarded because of the publications on Late Pleistocene and recent evolutionary changes, some of which were stimulated by Pilbeam's very assertion.

The substantial elements of "Out of Africa" are really not modified by the archaeological deliberations. The theory is weakest over the problem of transitional specimens, as there is no lack of appropriate predecessors for modern humans virtually everywhere there are hominid samples to be found - including among the Neandertals (see Chapter 13). Each region has periods of significant variation and both general and regionally specific modern attributes are found in lower frequency at a time prior to the first appearance of moderns.

The question of whether the earliest moderns are found in Africa is beset by two issues - the very problematic dating of the two allegedly early sites with more complete specimens, and a lack of agreement on what "modern human" means in an anatomical sense. The cranial and most mandibular materials from Border Cave remain unprovenienced and their age may never be more definitely determined than older than 30 kyr. We have gone little beyond Protsch in dating these specimens. Yet as F. Smith notes, they remain important in our thinking because we tend to interpret the very much more fragmentary Klasies specimens in their context, taking certain traces that might reflect modernity there to actually indicate it because they are found at Border Cave as well. Perhaps the situation at Omo-Kibbish is best described by Allsworth-Jones, an "Out of Africa" supporter: "it is unfortunate that the situation at Omo leaves quite a lot to be desired in terms of the contextual associations of the three hominid specimens found there". In fact they were found at different locations and may not even be penecontemporary, they cannot be clearly related to the single date that was determined for the site (well below what is said to be the Omo 1 findspot), and the dating technique used was recognized as being unacceptable, even by the scientists who applied it in 1967. To regard these specimens as "dated" in any sense is to make a travesty of the serious attempts underway to determine dates for the human fossil record (for instance, see the A. Aitken, C. Stringer, and P. Mellars volume).

Klasies is quite a different case, as here the provenience and dating are not at issue. What is at issue is how to define modern. Stringer and Day proposed an anatomical definition that could be used on fossil remains - a combination of features that were given specific metric or morphological descriptions, like high foreheads, rounded crania, reduced or absent browridges. Their attempt did not begin with the precept of what modern *is*, but rather what it *is not*. They tried to show that European Neandertals were not modern, but in doing so provided a definition that also excluded substantial numbers of recent and living Australians. The definition, of course, was withdrawn but now two problems remain. Not only do we lack a operational definition for diagnosing modernity in the fossil record, but we can now question whether such a definition is even possible. According to the "Eve" theory it must be as all moderns have a common recent ancestry. But in addressing modernity, Multiregional Evolution suggests that the definition of what is meant to be a stage within our long-lasting polytypic species may not be possible at all - given the precept that we must proceed from the acknowledgment that all recent and living people are modern.

Certainly however we define modern it must be a populational distinction. It is misleading and incorrect to use a single aspect of modernity to characterize a sample as modern (this seems to be the preferred approach to the Klasies sample), or to argue that the first appearance of a modern feature marks the origin of modern humanity (this would assume that there was a single origin for modern humanity - the very issue that at the moment is most contentious). Where would we start? Perhaps with the chin of SK 74, the flexed cranial base of WT 17400, the malar notch of ZKT 11? The question arises over Klasies because in spite of its fragmentary nature we can go beyond individual pieces of isolated anatomy and address the issue of its sample characteristics. Many of the Klasies specimens are quite small, one of the mandibles has the smallest molar teeth I have ever recorded and the arm and foot bone suggest that Klasies may be the earliest pygmy-sized African population (remember Kollmann). Diminutive body size contributes to the impression of modernity as smallness usually creates skeletal gracility. Yet even given this, the sample as a whole is surprisingly archaic. For instance, facial size is indicated by the size of an isolated zygomatic bone and some dimensions of the frontal that lack browridges. These elements are as large or larger than most Middle Pleistocene Africans. Other anatomical details are archaic, such as the columnar anatomy of the outer orbital border, or the fact that two of the four mandibular symphyses lack chins and a third has only a weak mental trigone. Even the frontal is problematic, as F. Smith suggests it may be juvenile. Klasies cannot be considered a modern *sample* on either anatomical or behavioral grounds.

Adding to the difficulties for the "Out of Africa" theory, early moderns are found out of Africa at the same age as or earlier than Klasies, and not just in Western Asia where they are (probably incorrectly) perceived as a branch of the Africans. For instance the 187 kyr Jinniushan has the earliest modern combination of vault expansion and cranial bone thinning. Moreover, controversy over the dating of the Late Pleistocene Australian cranium WLH 50 (see Chapter 14) has obscured the true meaning of this critical specimen. Its marked and detailed similarities to the Indonesians from Ngandong imply that this sample may be modern human as well. The focus on West Asians and the MSA Africans as the earliest moderns reflects the fact that they have some modern *European* features, but ignores the early appearance of modern features that characterize other regions.

Finally, even if Border Cave and Klasies were unquestionably the earliest modern remains, a further challenge is which of their African features can be found in the earliest moderns on other continents. The most convincingly African of the features shared by hominids at these sites is the supraorbital reduction, indeed the absence of even supercillary arches in the Klasies specimen. Early modern humans from neither Europe (Mladeč) nor Australasia (WLH 50) fit this expectation. These fossils, and other early moderns such as Chinese remains, lack most other unique features of recent or living Africans as well. Discriminant functions and other race identification techniques fail to classify any of them as African.

R. Caspari and I wrote:

> We believe that the widespread characterization of non-European Middle Paleolithic/Middle Stone age skeletal remains [e.g. Klasies, Qafzeh, etc.] as 'morphologically modern' reflects the fact that they are not Neandertals (members of a European clade) rather than whether they are archaic or modern in grade, Attributes of archaic and modern samples vary appreciably in different regions, and therefore while Late Pleistocene temporal changes occur and are important, we believe these can only be understood in a regional context. Besides, there is much to be said for the idea that human populations are modern when they behave in recognizably modern ways, no matter what they look like.

REFERENCES AND FURTHER READINGS

AIELLO, L.C. 1993 The fossil evidence for modern human origins in Africa: a revised view. *American Anthropologist* 95(1):73-96.

___. 1994 Reply to "resolving the archaic-to-modern transition" by G.S. Krantz. *American Anthropologist* 96(1):151-152.

ALLSWORTH-JONES, P. 1993 The archaeology of archaic and early modern *Homo sapiens*: an African perspective. *Cambridge Archaeological Journal* 3(1):21-39.

ARENSBURG, B. 1989 New skeletal evidence concerning the anatomy of Middle Paleolithic populations in the Middle East: the Kebara skeleton. In P. Mellars and C.B. Stringer (eds): *The Human Revolution: Behavioural and Biological Perspectives on the Origins of Modern Humans.* Edinburgh University Press, Edinburgh. pp. 165-171.

ARENSBURG, B., L.A. SCHEPARTZ, A-M. TILLIER, B. VANDERMEERSCH, and Y. RAK 1990 A reappraisal of the anatomical basis for speech in Middle Paleolithic hominids. *American Journal of Physical Anthropology* 83(2):137-146.

BARINAGA, M. 1992 "African Eve" backers beat a retreat. *Science* 255:686-687.

BARTSTRA, G.J., S. SOEGONDHO, AND A. VAN DER WIJK 1988 Ngandong man: age and artifacts. *Journal of Human Evolution* 17(3):325-337.

BAR-YOSEF, O. 1989 Upper Pleistocene cultural stratigraphy in southwest Asia. In E. Trinkaus (ed): *The Emergence of Modern Humans. Biocultural Adaptations in the Later Pleistocene.* Cambridge University Press, Cambridge. pp. 154-180, and combined references for the volume on pp. 232-276.

___. 1990 Mousterian adaptations - a global view. *Quaternaria Nova* 1:575-591.

___. 1992 Middle Paleolithic human adaptations in the Mediterranean Levant. In T. Akazawa, K. Aoki, and T. Kimura (eds): *The Evolution and Dispersal of Modern Humans in Asia.* Hokusen-sha, Tokyo. pp. 189-215.

___. 1994 The contributions of Southwest Asia to the study of the origin of modern humans. In M.H. Nitecki and D.V. Nitecki (eds): *Origins of Anatomically Modern Humans.* Plenum Press, New York. pp. 23-66.

BAR-YOSEF, O., and D. PILBEAM 1993 Dating hominid remains. *Nature* 366:415.

BAR-YOSEF, O., and B. VANDERMEERSCH (editors) 1991 *Le Squelette Moustérien De Kébara 2.* Centre National de la Recherche Scientifique, Paris.

BAR-YOSEF, O., and B. VANDERMEERSCH 1993 Modern humans in the Levant. *Scientific American* (April):94-100.

BAR-YOSEF, O., B. VANDERMEERSCH, B. ARENSBURG, A. BELFER-COHEN, P. GOLDBERG, H. LAVILLE, L. MEIGNEN, Y. RAK, J.D. SPETH, E. TCHERNOV, A-M. TILLIER, and S. WEINER 1992 The Excavations in Kebara Cave, Mt. Carmel. *Current Anthropology* 33(5):497-550.

BEAUMONT, P.B., H. DE VILLIERS, and J.C. VOGEL 1978 Modern man in sub-Saharan Africa prior to 49,000 years B.P.: A review and evaluation with particular reference to Border Cave. *South African Journal of Science* 74:409-419.

BELFER-COHEN, A. 1988 The evolution of symbolic expression through the Upper Pleistocene in the Levant as compared to Western Europe. In M. Otte (ed): *L'Homme de Néandertal*. Volume 5:25-29. *Etudes et Recherches Archéologiques de l'Université Liège, Liège.*

BELFER-COHEN, A., and E. HOVERS 1992 In the eye of the beholder: Mousterian and Natufian burials in the Levant. *Current Anthropology* 33:463-473.

BEN-ITZHAK, S., P. SMITH, and R.A. BLOOM 1988 Radiographic study of the humerus in Neandertals and *Homo sapiens sapiens*. *American Journal of Physical Anthropology* 77(2):231-242.

BINFORD, L.R., and J. SABLOFF 1982 Paradigms, systematics, and archaeology. *Journal of Anthropological Research* 38:137-153.

BINFORD, S.R. 1968 Early Upper Pleistocene adaptations in the Levant. *American Anthropologist* 70:707-717.

BIRDSELL, J.B. 1953 Some environmental and cultural factors influencing the structuring of Australian Aboriginal populations. *American Naturalist* 87:169-207.

BRÄUER, G. 1984 The "Afro-European *sapiens* hypothesis" and hominid evolution in East Asia during the late middle and upper Pleistocene. In P. Andrews and J.L. Franzen (eds): *The Early Evolution of Man, with Special Emphasis on Southeast Asia and Africa*. *Courier Forschungsinstitut Senckenberg* 69:145-165.

___. 1992 Africa's place in the evolution of *Homo sapiens*. In G. Bräuer and F.H. Smith (eds): *Continuity or Replacement? Controversies in Homo sapiens Evolution*. Balkema, Rotterdam. pp. 83-98.

BRÄUER, G., F. ZIPFEL, and H.J. DEACON 1992 Comment on the new maxillary finds from Klasies River, South Africa. *Journal of Human Evolution* 23(5):419-422.

BROOKS, A.S. 1988 Middle Paleolithic/Middle Stone Age. In I. Tattersall, E. Delson, and J. van Couvering (eds): *Encyclopedia of Human Evolution and Prehistory*. Garland Press, New York. pp. 341-349.

BRIDGES, P.S. 1991 Degenerative joint disease in hunter-gatherers and agriculturists from the southeastern United States. *American Journal of Physical Anthropology* 85(4):379-391.

BROWN, P. 1990 Osteological definitions of "anatomically modern" *Homo sapiens*: a test using modern and terminal Pleistocene *Homo sapiens*. In L. Freedman (ed): *Is Our Future Limited by Our Past?* Proceedings of the Third Conference of the Australasian Society of Human Biology. Centre for Human Biology, University of Western Australia, Nedlands. pp. 51-74.

BRUES, A. 1959 The spearman and the archer: an essay on selection in body build. *American Anthropologist* 61:457-469.

CANN, R.L. 1987 In search of Eve. *The Sciences* 27:30-37.

___. 1992 A mitochondrial perspective on replacement or continuity in human evolution. In G. Bräuer and F.H. Smith (eds): *Continuity or Replacement? Controversies in Homo sapiens Evolution*. Balkema, Rotterdam. pp. 65-73.

CAVALLI-SFORZA, L.L., A. PIAZZA, P. MENOZZI, and J. MOUNTAIN 1988 Reconstruction of human evolution: bringing together genetic, archaeological, and linguistic data. *Proceedings of the National Academy of Sciences USA* 85:6002-6006.

CHASE, P.G. 1987 Middle Paleolithic symbolism. *Journal of Anthropological Archaeology* 6:263-296.

CHASE, P.G., and H.L. DIBBLE 1990 On the emergence of modern humans. *Current Anthropology* 31(1):58-59, 64-66.

CHEN TIEMEI, YANG QUAN, and WU EN 1994 Antiquity of *Homo sapiens* in China. *Nature* 368:55-56.

CLARK, G.A. 1992 Continuity or replacement? Putting modern human origins in an evolutionary context. In H. Dibble and P. Mellars (eds): *The Middle Paleolithic: Adaptation, behavior, and Variability.* University of Pennsylvania Museum, Philadelphia. pp. 183-205.

CLARK, G.A., AND J.M. LINDLY 1989 Modern human origins in the Levant and Western Asia. *American Anthropologist* 91:962-985.

CLARK, J.D. 1992 African and Asian perspectives on the origins of modern humans. *Philosophical Transactions of the Royal Society,* Series B, 337:201-215.

CLARKE, R.J. 1985 A new reconstruction of the Florisbad cranium, with notes on the site. In E. Delson. (ed): *Ancestors: The Hard Evidence.* Alan R. Liss, New York. pp. 301-305.

COLLIER, S. 1989 The influence of economic behavior and environment upon robusticity of the post-cranial skeleton: a comparison of Australian Aborigines and other populations. *Archaeology and Physical Anthropology in Oceania* 24:17-30.

CONDEMI, S. 1988 A review and analysis of the Riss-Würm Saccopastore skulls: can they provide evidence in regard to the origin of Near Eastern Neandertals. In: *L'Homme de Néandertal.* Volume 3, *L'Anatomie.* Université de Liège, Liège. pp. 81-94.

COON, C.S. 1939 *The Races of Europe.* MacMillan, New York.

CORRUCCINI, R.S. 1992 Metrical reconsideration of the Skhul IV and IX and Border Cave 1 crania in the context of modern human origins. *American Journal of Physical Anthropology* 87(4):433-445.

CRUBÉZY, E. and E. TRINKAUS 1992 Shanidar 1: a case of hyperostotic disease (DISH) in the Middel Paleolithic. *American Journal of Physical Anthropology* 89(4):411-420.

DAY, M.H. 1972 The Omo human skeletal remains. In F. Bordes (ed): *The Origin of Homo sapiens. Proceedings of the Paris INQUA Symposium.* UNESCO, Paris. pp. 31-36.

DAY, M.H., and C.B. STRINGER 1982 A reconsideration of the Omo Kibish remains and the erectus-sapiens transition. In H. de Lumley (ed): *L'Homo erectus et la Place de l'Homme de Tautavel parmi les Hominidés Fossiles.* 1er Congrès International de Paléontologie Humaine, Nice, Prétirage. Volume 2:814-846. Louis-Jean, Nice.

___. 1991 Les restes crâniens d'Omo-Kibish et leur classification à l'intérieur de genre *Homo.* *L'Anthropologie* 95(2/3):573-594.

DEACON, H.J. 1992 Southern Africa and modern human origins. *Philosophical Transactions of the Royal Society,* Series B, 337:177-183.

DEACON, H.J., and R. SHUURMAN 1993 The origins of modern people: the evidence from Klasies River. In G. Bräuer and F.H. Smith (eds): *Continuity or Replacement? Controversies in Homo sapiens Evolution.* Balkema, Rotterdam. pp. 121-129.

DELSON, E. 1988 One source not many. *Nature* 332:206.

DIBBLE, H.L., and N. ROLLAND 1993 On assemblage variability in the Middle Paleolithic of Western Europe. In H.L. Dibble and P. Mellars (eds): *The Middle Paleolithic: Adaptation, Behavior, and Variability.* University of Pennsylvania Museum Monograph 72, University Museum Symposium Series IV:1-28.

DOBZHANSKY, TH. 1944 On species and races of living and fossil man. *American Journal of Physical Anthropology* 2(3):251-265.

DUBOIS, E. 1936 Racial identity of *Homo soloensis* Oppenoorth (including *Homo mojokertensis* von Koenigswald) and *Sinanthropus pekinensis* Davidson Black. Koninklijke Akademie Wetenschappen te Amsterdam, Series B, 39:1180-1185.

ECKHARDT, R.B. 1987 Evolution east of Eden. *Nature* 326:749.

ETLER, D.A., and LI TIANYUAN 1994 New archaic human fossil discoveries and their bearing on hominid species definition during the Middle Pleistocene. In R.S. Corruccini and R.L. Ciochon (eds): *Integrative Paths to the Past. Paleoanthropological Advances in Honor of F. Clark Howell.* Prentice Hall, Englewood Cliffs. pp. 639-675.

FEREMBACH, D. 1972 L'ancestre de l'homme du Paleolithique superieur etait-il neandertalien? In F. Bordes (ed): *The Origin of Homo sapiens.* Proceedings of the Paris INQUA Symposium. Unesco, Paris. pp. 73-80.

FOGARTY, M.E., AND F.H. SMITH 1987 Late Pleistocene climatic reconstruction in North Africa and the emergence of modern Europeans. *Human Evolution* 2(4):311-319.

FRAYER, D.W., M.H. WOLPOFF, F.H. SMITH, A.G. THORNE, and G.G. POPE 1993 The fossil evidence for modern human origins. *American Anthropologist* 95(1):14-50.

GALLOWAY, A. 1938 The nature and status of the Florisbad skull as revealed by its non-metrical features. *American Journal of Physical Anthropology* 23:1-16.

GILES, E., and S.H. AMBROSE 1986 Are we all out of Africa? *Nature* 322:21-22.

GILL, G.W., and B.M. GILBERT 1990 Race identification from the midfacial skeleton: American Blacks and Whites. In G.W. Gill and S. Rhine (eds): *Skeletal Attribution of Race: Methods for Forensic Anthropology.* Anthropological papers of the Maxwell Museum of Anthropology, Number 4:47-53.

GIOVANNI, D-B. 1993 Migrations, genetic variability, and DNA polymorphisms. *Current Anthropology* 34(5):765-775.

GOULD, S.J. 1976 Ladders, bushes, and human evolution. *Natural History* 85(4):24-31.

___. 1989 Grimm's greatest tale. *Natural History* 2/89:20-28.

GOWLETT, J.A.J. 1987 The coming of modern man. *Antiquity* 61:210-219.

GRIBBIN, J. and J. CHERFAS 1982 *The Monkey Puzzle: Reshaping the Evolutionary Tree*. Bodley Head, London.

GRINE, F.E., and R.G. KLEIN 1985 Pleistocene and Holocene human remains from Equus Cave, South Africa. *Anthropology* (State University of New York at Stony Brook) 8:55-98.

GRINE, F.E., R.G. KLEIN, and T.P. VOLMAN 1991 Dating, archaeology, and human fossils from the Middle Stone Age levels of Die Kelders, South Africa. *Journal of Human Evolution* 21(5):363-396.

GRÜN, R., C.B. STRINGER, and H.P. SCHWARCZ 1991 ESR dating of teeth from Garrod's Tabun cave collection. *Journal of Human Evolution* 20(3):231-248.

GRÜN, R., N.J. SHACKLETON, and H.J. DEACON 1990 Electron-spin-resonance dating of tooth enamel from Klasies River Mouth Cave. *Current Anthropology* 31(4):427-432.

HABGOOD, P.J. 1989 An examination of regional features on Middle and early Late Pleistocene sub-Saharan African hominids. *South African Archaeological Bulletin* 44:17-22.

___. 1992 The origin of anatomically modern humans in east Asia. In G. Bräuer and F.H. Smith (eds): *Continuity or Replacement? Controversies in Homo sapiens Evolution*. Balkema, Rotterdam. pp. 273-288.

HAGER, L.D. 1991 Bony pelvis of archaic *Homo sapiens*. *Encyclopedia of Human Biology* 1:1511-1527. New York: Academic Press.

HEDGES, S.B., S. KUMAR, K. TAMURS, and M. STONEKING 1992 Human origins and analysis of mitochondrial DNA sequences. *Science* 255:737-739.

HOLLOWAY, R.L. 1980 Indonesian "Solo" (Ngandong) endocranial reconstructions: preliminary observations and comparisons with Neandertal and *Homo erectus* groups. *American Journal of Physical Anthropology* 53(2):285-295.

HOWELL, F.C. 1958 Upper Pleistocene men of the Southwest Asian Mousterian. In G.H.R. von Koenigswald (ed): *Hundert Jahre Neanderthaler*. Kemink en Zoon, Utrecht . pp. 185-198.

___. 1959 Upper Pleistocene stratigraphy and early man in the Levant. *Proceedings of the American Philosophical Society* 103:1-65.

___. 1994 A chronostratigraphic and taxonomic framework of the origins of modern humans. In M.H. Nitecki and D.V. Nitecki (eds): *Origins of Anatomically Modern Humans*. Plenum Press, New York. pp. 253-319

HOWELLS, W.W. 1976 Explaining modern man: evolutionists *versus* migrationists. *Journal of Human Evolution* 5:477-496.

___. 1989 *Skull Shapes and the Map: Craniometric Analyses in the Dispersion of Modern Homo*. *Papers of the Peabody Museum of Archaeology and Ethnology* 79:1-189.

HUBLIN, J-J. 1987 Qui fut l'Ancêtre de l'*Homo sapiens*? *Pour la Science* 113:26-35.

___. 1992 Recent human evolution in northwestern Africa. *Philosophical Transactions of the Royal Society*, Series B, 337:185-191.

ITZKOFF, S.W. 1985 *Triumph of the Intelligent: The Creation of Homo sapiens sapiens*. Paideia, New York.

JACOB, T. 1981 Solo man and Peking man. In B.A. Sigmon and J.S. Cybulski (eds): *Homo erectus. Papers in Honor of Davidson Black*. (combined bibliography at end of volume). University of Toronto Press, Toronto. pp. 87-104.

JAMES, S.R. 1989 Hominid use of fire in the Lower and Middle Pleistocene: a review of the evidence. *Current Anthropology* 30:1-26.

JELINEK, A. 1982 The Tabun cave and Paleolithic man in the Levant. *Science* 216:1369-1375.

___. 1992 Problems in the chronology of the Middle Paleolithic and the first appearance of early modern *Homo sapiens* in Southwest Asia. In T. Akazawa, K. Aoki, and T. Kimura (eds): *The Evolution and Dispersal of Modern Humans in Asia*. Hokusen-sha, Tokyo. pp. 253-275.

JELÍNEK, J. 1985 The European, Near East, and North African finds after Australopithecus and the principal consequences for the picture of human evolution. In P.V. Tobias (ed): *Hominid Evolution: Past, Present, and Future.. Proceedings of the Taung Diamond Jubilee International Symposium*. Alan R. Liss, New York. pp. 341-354.

KEITH, A. and T.D. MCCOWN 1937 Mount Carmel man: his bearing on the ancestry of modern races. In G.G. MacCurdy (ed): *Early Man*. Lippincott, Philadelphia. pp. 41-52.

KELLEY, R.L. 1992 Hunter-gatherer mobility strategies. In B.J. Siegel, A.R. Beals, and S.A. Tyler (eds): *Annual Review of Anthropology*. Annual Reviews, Palo Alto. Volume 21:43-66.

KENNEDY, G.E. 1992 The evolution of *Homo sapiens* as indicated by features of the postcranium. In G. Bräuer and F.H. Smith (eds): *Continuity or Replacement? Controversies in Homo sapiens Evolution*. Balkema, Rotterdam. pp. 209-218.

KIDDER, J.H., R.L. JANTZ, and F.H. SMITH 1992 Defining modern humans: a multivariate approach. In G. Bräuer and F.H. Smith (eds): *Continuity or Replacement? Controversies in Homo sapiens Evolution*. Balkema, Rotterdam. pp. 157-177.

KLEIN, R.G. 1977 The ecology of early man in southern Africa. *Science* 197:115-126.

___. 1989 Biological and behavioral perspectives on modern human origins in southern Africa. In P. Mellars and C.B. Stringer (eds): *The Human Revolution: Behavioural and Biological Perspectives on the Origins of Modern Humans*. Edinburgh University Press, Edinburgh. pp. 529-546.

___. 1992 The archaeology of modern human origins. *Evolutionary Anthropology* 1(1):5-14.

___. 1994 Southern African before the Iron Age. In R.S. Corruccini and R.L. Ciochon (eds): *Integrative Paths to the Past. Paleoanthropological Advances in Honor of F. Clark Howell*. Prentice Hall, Englewood Cliffs. pp. 471-519.

KNÜSEL, C.J. 1992 The throwing hypothesis and hominid origins. *Human Evolution* 7(1):1-7.

VON KOENIGSWALD, G.H.R. 1958 Der Solo-Mensch von Java: ein tropischer Neanderthaler. In G.H.R. von Koenigswald (ed): *Hundert Jahre Neanderthaler*. Böhlau, Köln. pp. 21-26.

KOLLMANN, J. 1905 Neue Gedanken über das alte Problem von der Abstammung des Menschen. *Globus* 87(7):141-148.

KOLOSSOV, YU. G., V.M. KHARITONOV, and V.P. YAKIMOV 1975 Palaeoanthropic specimens from the site of Zaskalnaya VI in the Crimea. In R.H. Tuttle (ed): *Paleoanthropology. Morphology and Paleoecology.* Mouton, The Hague. pp. 419-428.

KRAMER, A. 1991 Modern human origins in Australasia: replacement or evolution? *American Journal of Physical Anthropology* 86(4):455-473.

KRAMER, A., T.L. CRUMMETT, and M.H. WOLPOFF 1994 Morphological diversity in the Upper Pleistocene hominids of the Levant: two species? *L'Anthropologie* (in press).

LEAKEY, L.S.B. 1972 *Homo sapiens* in the Middle Pleistocene and the evidence of *Homo sapiens* evolution. In F. Bordes (ed): *The Origin of Homo sapiens.* Proceedings of the Paris INQUA Symposium. UNESCO, Paris. pp. 25-30.

LEAKEY, R.E., K.W. BUTZER, and M.H. DAY 1969 Early *Homo sapiens* remains from the Omo River region of South-west Ethiopia. *Nature* 222:1132-1138.

LEROI-GOURHAN, A. 1975 The flowers found with Shanidar IV, a Neanderthal burial in Iraq. *Science* 190:562-564.

LEWIN, R. 1987 Africa: Cradle of Modern Humans. *Science* 237:1292-1295.

___. 1990 Molecular clocks run out of time. *New Scientist* (2/10/90):38-41.

___. 1993 *The Origin of Modern Humans.* W.H. Freeman, New York.

LIEBERMAN, D.E. 1993 The rise and fall of seasonal mobility among hunter-gatherers. The case of the southern Levant. *Current Anthropology* 34(5):599-631.

LIEBERMAN, D.E., and J.J. SHEA 1994 Behavioral differences between archaic and modern humans in the Levantine Mousterian. *American Anthropologist* 96(2):300-332.

LIEBERMAN, P. 1993 On the Kebara KMH 2 hyoid and Neanderthal speech. *Current Anthropology* 34(2):172-175.

LIETAVA, J. 1988 A differential diagnostics of the right shoulder girdle deformity in the Shanidar I Neanderthal. *Anthropologie* (Brno) 26(3):183-196.

___. 1992 Medicinal plants in a Middle Paleolithic grave Shanidar IV? *Journal of Ethnopharmacology* 34:263-266.

LIN SHENGLONG 1987 Trends of distribution of early man in China. *Acta Anthropologica Sinica* 6(3):190-195.

LINDLY, J.M., and G.A. CLARK 1990a On the emergence of modern humans. *Current Anthropology* 31(1):59-63, 64-66.

___. 1990b Symbolism and modern human origins. *Current Anthropology* 31(3):233-261.

LÜ ZUN'E 1994 Mosaic evolution of Jinniushan archaic *Homo sapiens*. In G. Krantz and Ho Chuankun (eds): *Human Variation in the Pacific Region.* Proceedings of the Circum-Pacific Prehistory Conference , Seattle. In Press.

MADDISON, D.R. 1991 African origin of human mitochondrial DNA reexamined. *Systematic Zoology* 40:355-363.

MANSON, J.H., and R.W. WRANGHAM 1991 Intergroup aggression in chimpanzees and humans. *Current Anthropology* 32(4):369-390.

MARKS, A.E. 1992 Upper Pleistocene archaeology and the origins of modern man: a view from the Levant and adjacent areas. In T. Akazawa, K. Aoki, and T. Kimura (eds): *The Evolution and Dispersal of Modern Humans in Asia.* Hokusen-sha, Tokyo. pp. 229-251.

___. 1994 A Levantine perspective. *Cambridge Archaeological Journal* 4(1):104-106, 117-119.

MASAO, F.T. 1992 The Middle Stone Age with reference to Tanzania. In G. Bräuer and F.H. Smith (eds): *Continuity or Replacement? Controversies in Homo sapiens Evolution.* Balkema, Rotterdam. pp. 99-109.

McCOWN, T.D. 1934 The oldest complete skeletons of man. *Bulletin of the American School of Prehistoric Research* 10:12-19.[1]

___. 1950 The genus Paleoanthropus and the problem of superspecific differentiation among the hominidae. *Cold Spring Harbor Symposia on Quantitative Biology* 15:87-94.

McCROSSIN, M.L. 1993 Human molars from later Pleistocene deposits of Witkrrans cave, Gaap escarpment, Kalahari margin. *Human Evolution* 7(3):1-10.

McDERMOTT, F., R. GRÜN, C.B. STRINGER, and C.J. HAWKESWORTH 1993 Mass-spectrometric U-series dates for Israeli Neanderthal/early modern hominid sites. *Nature* 363:252-255.

McDERMOTT, F., C.J. HAWKESWORTH, R. GRÜN, and C.B. STRINGER 1993 Dating hominid remains. *Nature* 366:415.

MEHLMAN, M.J. 1984 Archaic *Homo sapiens* at Lake Eyassi, Tanzania: recent misinterpretations. *Journal of Human Evolution* 13:487-501.

___. 1986 Provenience, age, and associations of archaic *Homo sapiens* crania from Lake Eyasi, Tanzania. *Journal of Archaeological Science* 14:133-162.

MORANT, G.M. 1928 Studies of Paleolithic man III. The Rhodesian skull and its relationships to Neanderthal and modern types. *Annals of Eugenics* 3:227-336.

O'CONNELL, J.F., K. HAWKES, and N. BLURTON-JONES 1988 Hadza hunting, butchering, and bone transport and their archaeological implications. *Journal of Anthropological Research* 44:113-161.

___. 1992 Patterns in the distribution, site structure, and assemblage composition of Hadza kill-butchering sites. *Journal of Archaeological Science* 19:319-345.

OPPENOORTH, W.F.F. 1937 The place of *Homo soloensis* among fossil man. In G.G. MacCurdy (ed): *Early Man.* Lippincott, Philadelphia.

PILBEAM, D.R. 1972 *The Ascent of Man.* MacMillan, New York.

POPE, G.G. 1991 Evolution of the zygomaxillary region in the genus *Homo*, and its relevance to the origin of modern humans. *Journal of Human Evolution* 21(3):189-213.

___. 1992 Replacement versus regional continuity models: the paleobehavioral and fossil evidence from East Asia. In T. Akazawa, K. Aoki, and T. Kimura (eds): *The Evolution and Dispersal of Modern Humans in Asia.* Hokusen-sha, Tokyo. pp. 3-14.

PROTSCH, R. 1975 The absolute dating of Upper Pleistocene sub-Saharan fossil hominids and their place in human evolution. *Journal of Human Evolution* 4:297-322.

RAK, Y. 1990 On the difference between two pelvises of Mousterian context from the Qafzeh and Kebara caves, Israel. *American Journal of Physical Anthropology* 81(3):323-332.

___. 1993 Morphological variation in *Homo neanderthalensis* and *Homo sapiens* in the Levant: a biogeographic model. In W.H. Kimbel and L.B. Martin (eds): *Species, Species Concepts, and Primate Evolution.* Plenum, New York.

RENSBERGER, B. 1980 The emergence of *Homo sapiens. Mosaic* 11(6):2-12.

___. 1981 Facing the past. *Science 81* (October):40-51.

RIGHTMIRE, G. P. 1976 Relationships of middle and upper Pleistocene hominids from sub-Saharan Africa. *Nature* 260:238-240.

___. 1978. Florisbad and human population succession in southern Africa. *American Journal of Physical Anthropology* 48:475-486.

___. 1981 Later Pleistocene hominids of eastern and southern Africa. *Anthropologie* (Brno) 19:15-26.

___. 1984 *Homo sapiens* in sub-Saharan Africa. In F.H. Smith and F. Spencer (ed): *The Origins of Modern Humans: A World Survey of the Fossil Evidence.* Alan R. Liss, New York. pp. 295-325.

___. 1989 Middle Stone Age humans from eastern and southern Africa. In P. Mellars and C.B. Stringer (eds): *The Human Revolution: Behavioural and Biological Perspectives on the Origins of Modern Humans.* Edinburgh University Press, Edinburgh. pp. 109-122.

RONEN, A. 1976 The Skhul burials: an archaeological review. In B. Vandermeersch (ed): *Les Sépultures Néandertaliennes.* Centre National de la Recherche Scientifique, Paris.

ROSENBERG, K.R. 1988 The functional significance of Neandertal pubic length. *Current Anthropology* 29(4):595-617; 30(4):486-488.

RUFF, C.B., W.W. SCOTT, and A. Y-C. LIU 1991 Articular and diaphyseal remodeling of the proximal femur with changes in body mass in adults. *American Journal of Physical Anthropology* 86(3):397-413.

SABAN, R. 1977 The place of Rabat man (Kébibat, Morocco) in human evolution. *Current Anthropology* 18:518-524.

SCHWALBE, G. 1906 *Studien zur Vorgeschichte des Menschen.* I: Zur Frage der Abstammung des Menschen. Schweizerbartsche Verlagsbuchhandlung, Stuttgart. pp. 10-80.

SCHWARCZ, H.P., W.M. BUHAY, R. GRÜN, H. VALLADAS, E. TCHERNOV, O. BAR-YOSEF, and B. VANDERMEERSCH 1989 ESR dating of the Neanderthal site, Kebara Cave, Israel. *Journal of Archaeological Science* 16(6):653-659.

SHEA, J.J. 1989 A functional study of the lithic industries associated with hominid fossils in the Kebara and Qafzeh caves, Israel. In P. Mellars and C.B. Stringer (eds): *The Human Revolution: Behavioural and*

Biological Perspectives on the Origins of Modern Humans. Edinburgh University Press, Edinburgh.. pp. 611-625.

SHEVOROSHKIN, V. 1990 The mother tongue. *The Sciences* May/June:20-27.

SHREEVE, J. 1991 Moshe the Neanderthal and our family tree. *Smithsonian* 22(9):114-127.

SIMMONS, T. 1994 Archaic and modern *Homo sapiens* in the contact zones: evolutionary schematics and model predictions. In M.H. Nitecki and D.V. Nitecki (eds): *Origins of Anatomically Modern Humans.* Plenum Press, New York. pp. 201-225.

SIMMONS, T., and F.H. SMITH 1991 Human population relationships in the Late Pleistocene. *Current Anthropology* 32(5):623-627.

SIMMONS, T., A.B. FALSETTI, and F.H. SMITH 1991 Frontal bone morphometrics of southwest Asian Pleistocene hominids. *Journal of Human Evolution* 20(3):249-269.

SMITH, F.H. 1992 Models and realities in modern human origins: the African fossil evidence. *Philosophical Transactions of the Royal Society of London*, Series B, 337:243-250.

___. 1994 Samples, species, and speculations in the study of modern human origins. In M.H. Nitecki and D.V. Nitecki (eds): *Origins of Anatomically Modern Humans.* Plenum Press, New York. pp. 227-249.

SMITH, F.H., A.B. FALSETTI, and S.M. DONNELLY 1989 Modern human origins. *Yearbook of Physical Anthropology* 32:35-68.

SMITH, P., R.A. BLOOM and J. BERKOWITZ 1984 Diachronic variation in humeral cortical thickness of Near Eastern populations. *Journal of Human Evolution* 13:603-611.

SINGER, R. 1958 The Rhodesian, Florisbad, and Saldanha skulls. In G.H.R. von Koenigswald (ed): *Hundert Jahre Neanderthaler.* Kemink en Zoon, Utrecht. pp. 52-62.

SMITH, P. 1977 Regional variation in tooth size and pathology in fossil hominids. *American Journal of Physical Anthropology* 47:458-466.

___. 1982 Dental reduction: selection or drift. In B. Kurtén (ed): *Teeth, Form, Function and Evolution.* Columbia University Press, New York. pp. 366-379.

SOLECKI, R.S. 1971 *Shanidar, the First Flower People.* Knopf, New York.

___. 1975 Shanidar IV, a Neanderthal flower burial in Northern Iraq. *Science* 190:880-881.

STEÇŚLICKA, W. 1947 The systematic position of Ngandong-Man. *Annales Universitatis Mariae Curie-Sklodowska* (Lublin) Sectio C, 2:37-109.

STEWART, T.D. 1960 Form of the pubic bone in Neanderthal Man. *Science* 131:1437-8.

___. 1977. The Neanderthal skeletal remains from Shanidar Cave, Iraq: a summary of findings to date. *Proceedings of the American Philosophical Society* 121:121-165.

STINER, M.C. 1993 Modern human origins - faunal perspectives. In B.J. Siegel, A.R. Beals, and S.A. Tyler (eds): *Annual Review of Anthropology.* Annual Reviews, Palo Alto. Volume 22:55-82.

STRINGER, C.B. 1979. A re-evaluation of the fossil human calvaria from Singa, Sudan. *Bulletin of the British Museum of Natural History* (Geology) 32(1):77-83.

___. 1988 The dates of Eden. *Nature* 331:565-566.

___. 1989 Documenting the origin of modern humans. In E. Trinkaus (ed): *The Emergence of Modern Humans. Biocultural Adaptations in the Later Pleistocene.* Cambridge University Press, Cambridge. pp. 67-96, and combined references for the volume on pp. 232-276.

___. 1990a The Asian connection. *New Scientist* (November 17):33-37.

___. 1990b The emergence of modern humans. *Scientific American* 263(6):98-104.

___. 1993 New views on modern human origins. In D.T. Rasmussen (ed): *The Origin and Evolution of Humans and Humanness.* Jones and Bartless, Boston. pp. 75-94.

___. 1994 Out of Africa - a personal history. In M.H. Nitecki and D.V. Nitecki (eds): *Origins of Anatomically Modern Humans.* Plenum Press, New York. pp. 149-172.

STRINGER, C.B., and P. ANDREWS 1988 Genetic and fossil evidence for the origin of modern humans. *Science* 239:1263-1268.

STRINGER, C.B., L. CORNISH, and P. STUART-MACADAM 1985 Preparation and further study of the Singa skull from Sudan. *Bulletin of the British Museum of Natural History* (Geology) 38(5):347-358

STRINGER, C.B., R. GRÜN, H.P. SCHWARCZ, and P. GOLDBERG 1989 ESR dates for the hominid burial site of Es Skhul in Israel. *Nature* 338:756-758.

STRINGER, C.B. and E. TRINKAUS 1981 The Shanidar Neanderthal crania. In C.B. Stringer (ed): *Aspects of Human Evolution.* Taylor and Francis, London. pp. 129-165.

TAGUE, R.G. 1992 Sexual dimorphism in the human bony pelvis, with a consideration of the Neandertal pelvis from Kebara cave, Israel. *American Journal of Physical Anthropology* 88(1):1-21.

TATTERSALL, I. 1992a Biological and cultural innovation in human evolution. *Evolutionary Anthropology* 1(3):112.

___. 1992b Human origins and the origins of humanity. *Human Evolution* 7(2):17-24.

TCHERNOV, E. 1992 Biochronology, paleoecology, and dispersal events of hominids in the Southern Levant. In T. Akazawa, K. Aoki, and T. Kimura (eds): *The Evolution and Dispersal of Modern Humans in Asia.* Hokusen-sha, Tokyo. pp. 149-188.

TEMPLETON, A.R. 1992 Human origins and analysis of mitochondrial DNA sequences. *Science* 255:737.

TOBIAS, P. V. 1968. Middle and early Upper Pleistocene members of the genus *Homo* in Africa. In G. Kurth (ed): *Evolution and Hominidization,* 2nd edition. Fischer, Stuttgart. pp. 176-194.

TILLIER, A-M. 1986 Quelques aspects de l'ontogénèse du squelette cranien des Néanderthaliens. In V.V. Novotný and A. Mizerová. (eds): *Fossil Man. New Facts, New Ideas. Papers in Honor of Jan Jelínek's Life Anniversary. Anthropos* (Brno) 23:207-216.

___. 1992 The origins of modern humans in Southwest Asia: ontogenetic aspects. In T. Akazawa, K. Aoki, and T. Kimura (eds): *The Evolution and Dispersal of Modern Humans in Asia.* Hokusen-sha, Tokyo. pp. 15-28.

TILLIER, A-M., B. ARENSBURG, B. VANDERMEERSCH, and Y. RAK 1991 L'apport de Kébara à la palethnologie funéraire des Néandertaliens du Proche-Orient. In O. Bar-Yosef and B. Vandermeersch (eds): *Le squelette Moustérien de Kébara 2. Cahiers de Paléoanthropologie.* Centre National de la Recherche Scientifique, Paris. pp. 89-96.

TRINKAUS, E. 1976 The morphology of European and Southwest Asian Neandertal pubic bones. *American Journal of Physical Anthropology* 44:95-104.

___. 1982a Artificial cranial deformation in the Shanidar 1 and 5 Neanderthals. *Current Anthropology* 23:198-199.

___. 1982b Evolutionary continuity among archaic *Homo sapiens.* In A. Ronen (ed): *The Transition From Lower to Middle Paleolithic and the Origin of Modern Man.* British Archaeological Reports, Oxford. International Series 151:301-314.

___. 1984 Western Asia. In F.H. Smith and F. Spencer (ed): *The Origins of Modern Humans: A World Survey of the Fossil Evidence.* Alan R. Liss, New York. pp. 251-293.

___. 1992 Morphological contrasts between the Near Eastern Qafzeh-Skhul and late archaic human samples: grounds for a behavioral difference? In T. Akazawa, K. Aoki, and T. Kimura (eds): *The Evolution and Dispersal of Modern Humans in Asia.* Hokusen-sha, Tokyo. pp. 277-294.

___. 1993a Femoral neck-shaft angles of the Qafzeh-Skhul early modern humans, and activity levels among immature Near Eastern Middle Paleolithic hominids. *Journal of Human Evolution* 25(5):393-416.

___. 1993b Comment on "The rise and fall of seasonal mobility among hunter-gatherers" by D.E. Lieberman. *Current Anthropology* 34(5):620-622.

TRINKAUS, E., and D.D. THOMPSON 1987 Femoral diaphyseal histomorphometric age determinations for the Shanidar 3, 4, 5, and 6 Neandertals and Neandertal longevity. *American Journal of Physical Anthropology* 72(1):123-129.

TRINKAUS, E. and M.R. ZIMMERMAN 1982 Trauma among the Shanidar Neandertals. *American Journal of Physical Anthropology* 57:61-76.

ULLRICH, H. 1986 Manipulations on human corpses, mortuary practice, and burial rites during Paleolithic times. *Anthropos* (Brno) 23:227-236.

VALLOIS, H.V., and B. VANDERMEERSCH 1975 The Mousterian skull of Qafzeh (Homo VI). An anthropological study. *Journal of Human Evolution* 4:445-456.

VANDERMEERSCH, B. 1981 Les premiers *Homo sapiens* au Proche-Orient. In D. Ferembach (ed): *Les Processus de l'hominisation.* Colloques Internationaux du Centre National de la Recherche Sciéntifique, Paris. No. 599:97-100.

___. 1989 The evolution of modern humans: recent evidence from Southwest Asia. In P. Mellars and C.B. Stringer (eds): *The Human Revolution: Behavioural and Biological Perspectives on the Origins of Modern Humans.* Edinburgh University Press, Edinburgh. pp. 155-164.

___. 1992 The Near Eastern hominids and the origins of modern humans in Eurasia. In T. Akazawa, K. Aoki, and T. Kimura (eds): *The Evolution and Dispersal of Modern Humans in Asia*. Hokusen-sha, Tokyo. pp. 29-38.

VIGILANT, L., R. PENNINGTON, H. HARPENDING, T.D. KOCHER, and A.C. WILSON 1989 Mitochondrial DNA sequences in single hairs from a southern African population. *Proceedings of the National Academy of Sciences USA* 86:9350-9354.

WEIDENREICH, F. 1937 The relation of *Sinanthropus pekinensis* to *Pithecanthropus, Javanthropus*, and Rhodesian man. *Journal of the Royal Anthropological Institute* 67:51-66.

WEISS, K.M. 1984 On the number of members of the genus *Homo* who have ever lived, and some evolutionary implications. *Human Biology* 56(4):637-649.

WEISS, K.M., and T. MARUYAMA 1976 Archaeology, population genetics and studies of human racial ancestry. *American Journal of Physical Anthropology* 44:31-50.

WELLS, L.H. 1957 The place of the Broken Hill skull among human types. In J.D. Clark (ed): *Third Pan-African Congress on Prehistory*. Chatto and Windus, London. pp. 172-174.

WHITE, T.D. 1987 Cannibals at Klasies? *Sagittarius* 2(2):6-9.

WOLPOFF, M.H. 1986 Describing anatomically modern *Homo sapiens*: a distinction without a definable difference. In V.V. Novotný and A. Mizerová. (eds): *Fossil Man. New Facts, New Ideas. Papers in Honor of Jan Jelínek's Life Anniversary. Anthropos* (Brno) 23:41-53.

___. 1992 Theories of modern human origins. In G. Bräuer and F.H. Smith (eds): *Continuity or Replacement? Controversies in Homo sapiens Evolution*. Balkema, Rotterdam. pp. 25-63.

WOLPOFF, M.H., and R. CASPARI 1990 On Middle Paleolithic/Middle Stone Age hominid taxonomy. *Current Anthropology* 31(4):394-395.

WOLPOFF, M.H., J.N. SPUHLER, F.H. SMITH, J. RADOVČIC´, G. POPE, D.W. FRAYER, R. ECKHARDT, and G. CLARK 1988 Modern human origins. *Science* 241:772-773.

WOLPOFF, M.H., A.G. THORNE, F.H. SMITH, D.W. FRAYER, and G.G. POPE 1994 Multiregional Evolution: a world-wide source for modern human populations. In M.H. Nitecki and D.V. Nitecki (eds): *Origins of Anatomically Modern Humans*. Plenum Press, New York. pp. 175-199.

WU RUKANG 1986 Chinese human fossils and the origin of Mongoloid racial group. In V.V. Novotný and A. Mizerová. (eds): *Fossil Man. New Facts, New Ideas. Papers in Honor of Jan Jelínek's Life Anniversary. Anthropos* (Brno) 23:151-155.

WU XINZHI 1988 Comparative study of early *Homo sapiens* from China and Europe. *Acta Anthropologica Sinica* 7(4):287-293.

WU XINZHI and G. BRÄUER 1993 Morphological comparison of archaic *Homo sapiens* crania from China and Africa. *Zeitschrift für Morphologie und Anthropologie* 79(3):241-251.

WU XINZHI and WU MAOLIN 1985 Early *Homo sapiens* in China. In Wu Rukang and J.W. Olsen (eds): *Palaeoanthropology and Paleolithic Archaeology in the People's Republic of China*. Academic Press, New York. pp. 91-106.

ZHANG YINYUN 1986 The dental remains of early *Homo sapiens* found in China. *Acta Anthropologica Sinica* 5(2):103-113.

___ 1989 Tooth wear in early *Homo sapiens* from Chaohu and the hypothesis of use of anterior teeth as tools. *Acta Anthropologica Sinica* 8(4):314-319.

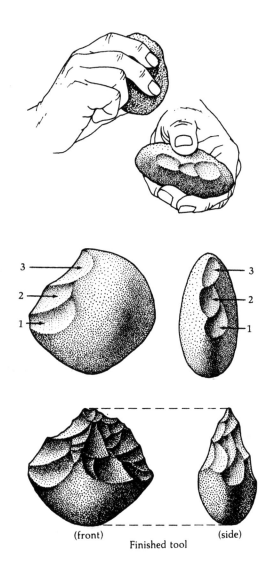

(front)   (side)

Finished tool

FIGURE 12.1. The three Lower and Middle Paleolithic stone tool making techniques. **FROM** First edition, figure 10.9.

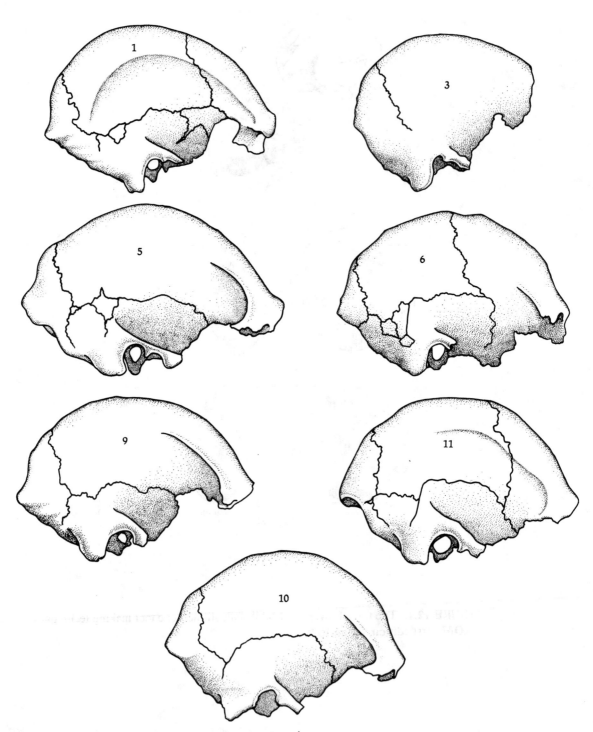

FIGURE 12.2 The seven best preserved Ngandong crania.
FROM First edition, figure 10.1

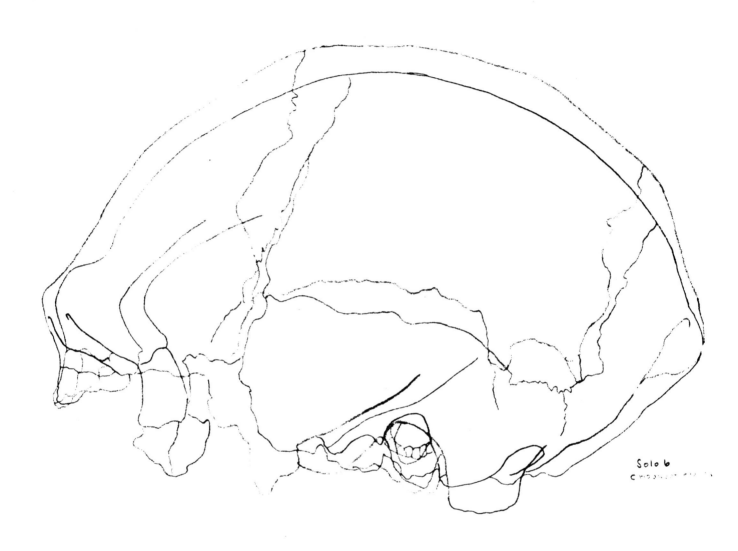

FIGURE 12.3 Comparison of Ngandong 6 and Zhoukoudian L3.

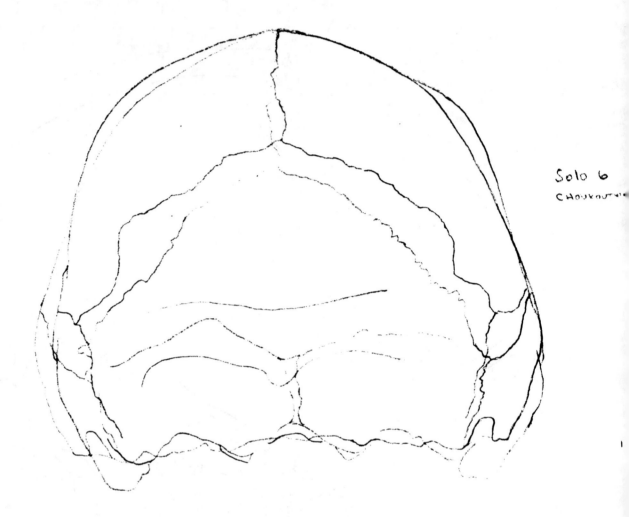

Solo 6
CHOUKOUTIEN

FIGURE 12.4 Dali (below) and Jinniushan faces, after Pope (1992). This comparison contrasts a male and female, but the contrast is accentuated by the later date of Jinniushan.

FROM Pope, G.G. 1992 Craniofacial evidence for the origin of modern humans in China. *Yearbook of Physical Anthropology* 35:243-298, figure 2.

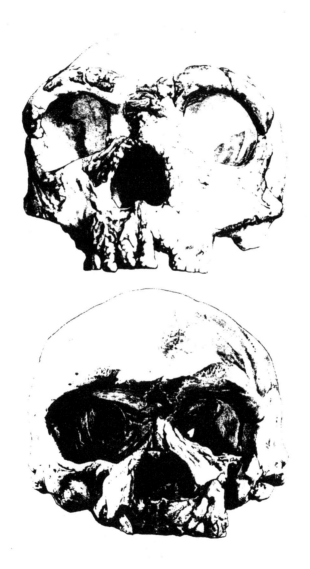

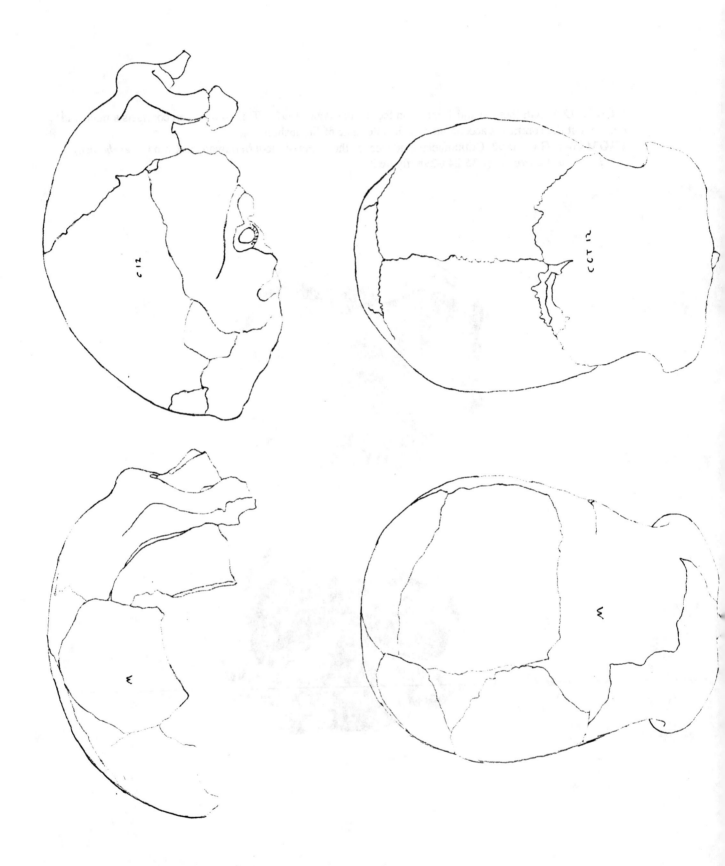

FIGURE 12.5 Comparison of the Maba vault (left) and ZKT 12. Maba is larger and more filled out. Some regard it as the most Neandertal-like of the Chinese Late Pleistocene specimens.

FIGURE 12.6 Description of dimensions shown in table 12.3, using a drawing of the Tabun female from McCown and Keith (1939) in frontal, superior, and lateral views.
FROM McCown, T.D. and A. Keith 1939 *The Stone Age of Mount Carmel: The Fossil Human Remains from the Levalloiso-Mousterian.* Vol. II. Oxford at the Clarendon Press, figures 181, 187, 189.

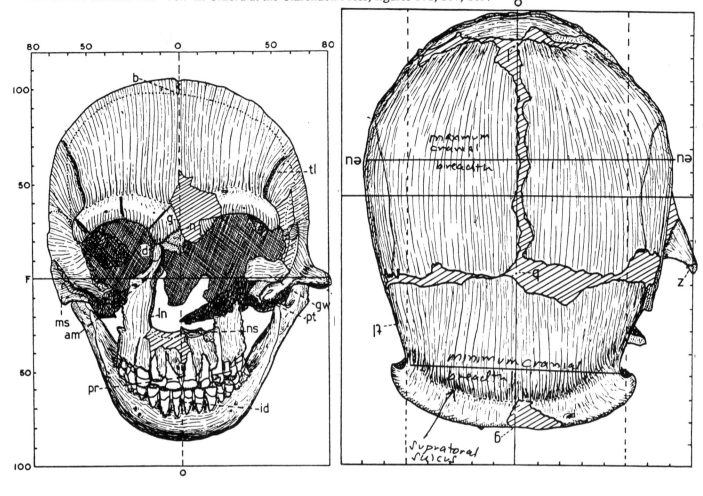

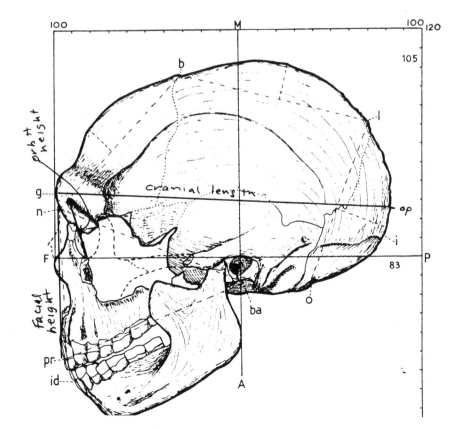

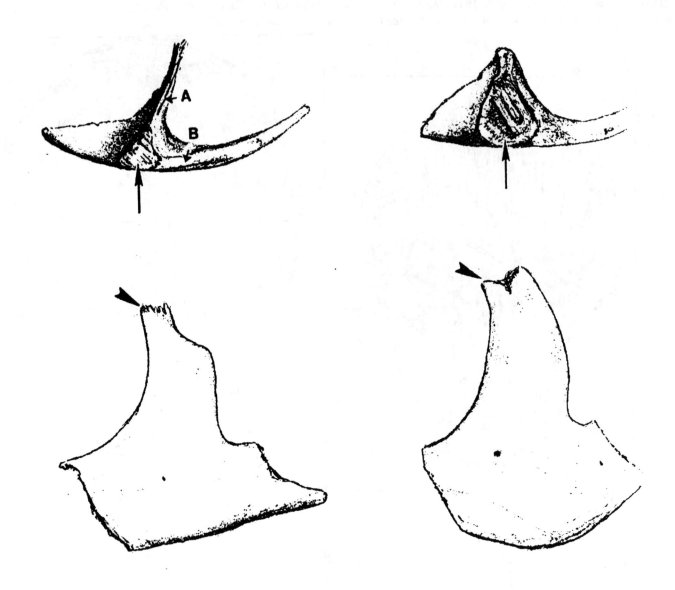

FIGURE 12.7 Klasies zygomatic (KRM 16651, right) compared with a modern African, after Smith (1992).
The comparison shows the archaic thickness of the orbital pillar and the expansive, triangular articulation
with the frontal (arrow). Height of the cheek portion of the bone's body is greater than every Middle and Late
Pleistocene African except Bodo.
FROM Smith, F.H. 1992 Models and realities in modern human origins: the African fossil evidence.
      Philosophical Transactions of the Royal Society of London, Series B, 337:243-250, figure 1.

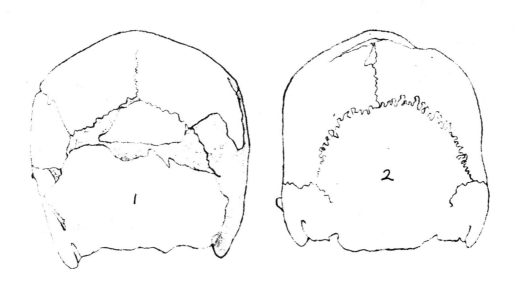

FIGURE 12.8 Posterior view of Omo 1 and 2.

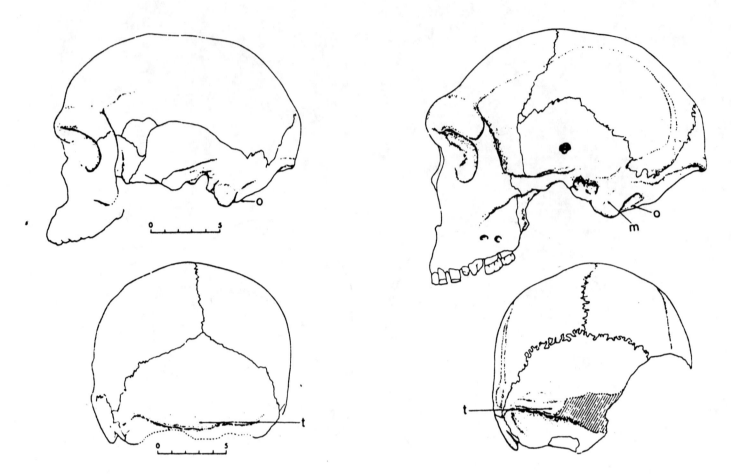

FIGURE 12.9 Comparison of Jebel Irhoud 1 (left) and the earlier Kabwe vault, after Santa Luca (1978). The figure shows the nuchal torus position (t), the mastoid process (m), and the juxtamastoid eminence (o) in both. **FROM** Santa Luca, A.P. 1978 A re-examination of presumed Neandertal-like fossils. Journal of Human Evolution 7:619-636, figures 9-12.

FIGURE 12.10 Comparison of facial features and projection, and details of the cranial rear, in the females from Tabun (left) and Gibraltar, after McCown and Keith (1939).

FROM McCown, T.D. and A. Keith 1939 *The Stone Age of Mount Carmel: The Fossil Human Remains from the Levalloiso-Mousterian.* Vol. II. Oxford at the Clarendon Press, figure 190.

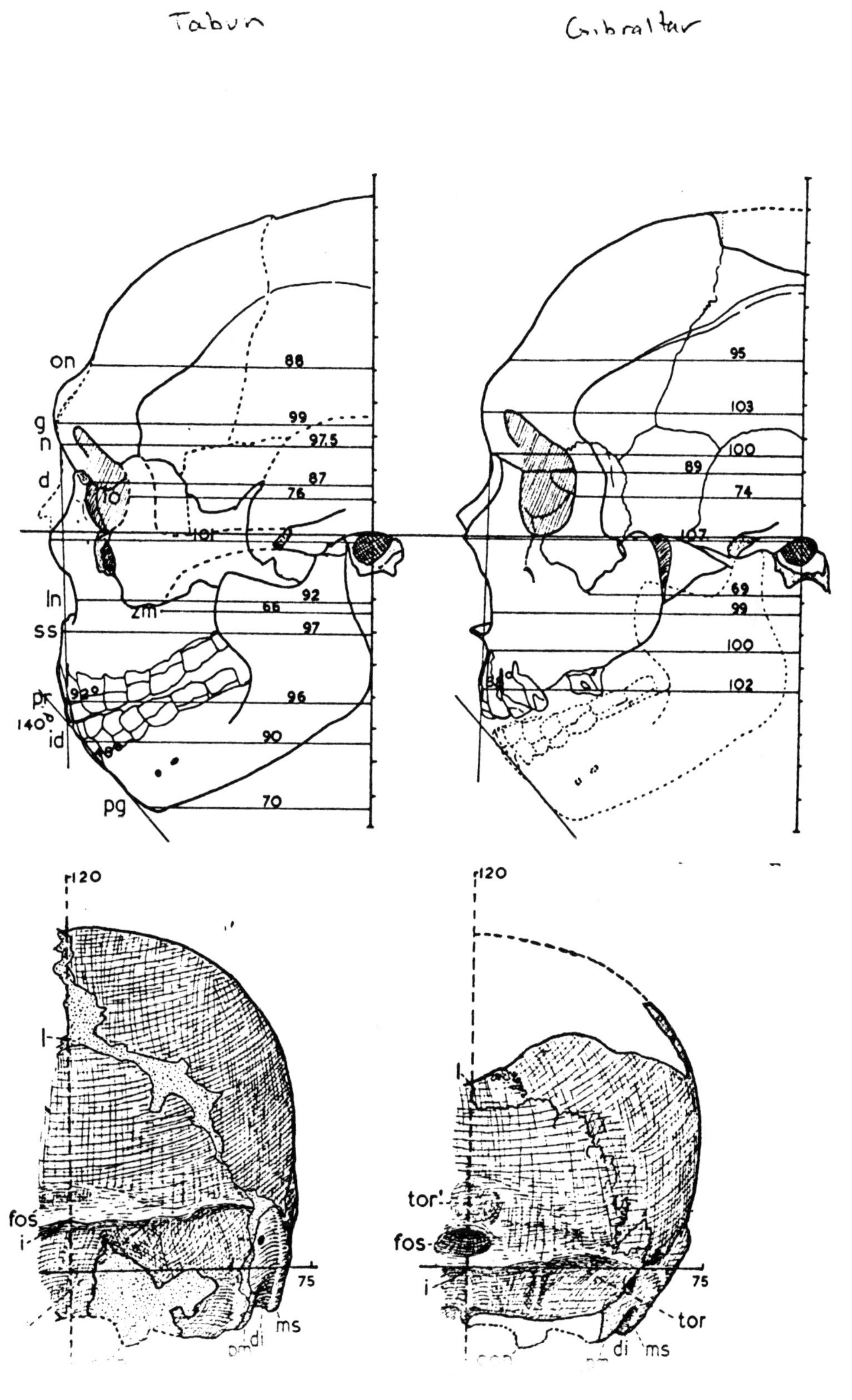

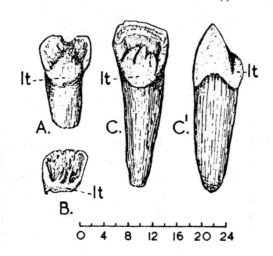

I^1

A - di^1 Tabun Series IV
B - di^1 Krapina
c I^1 Tabun Series III

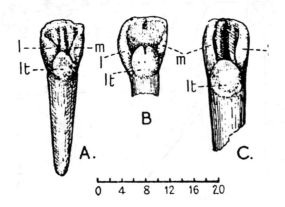

I^2

A - Tabun Series I
B - Krapina
C - Tabun Series III

FIGURE 12.11 Isolated Tabun maxillary incisors compared with Krapina teeth, after McCown and Keith (1939).
FROM McCown, T.D. and A. Keith 1939 *The Stone Age of Mount Carmel: The Fossil Human Remains from the Levalloiso-Mousterian*. Vol. II. Oxford at the Clarendon Press, figures 121,122.

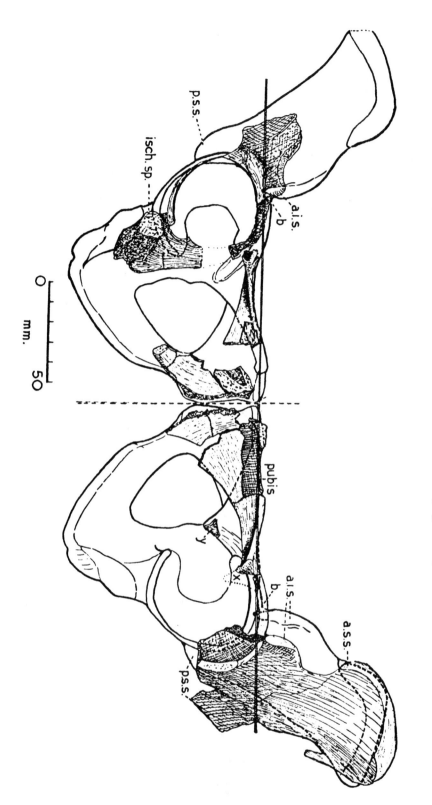

FIGURE 12.12 Reconstruction of the Tabun female pelvis, as seen from the front, modified after McCown and Keith (1939).

FROM McCown, T.D. and A. Keith 1939 *The Stone Age of Mount Carmel: The Fossil Human Remains from the Levalloiso-Mousterian.* Vol. II. Oxford at the Clarendon Press, figures 39, 40.

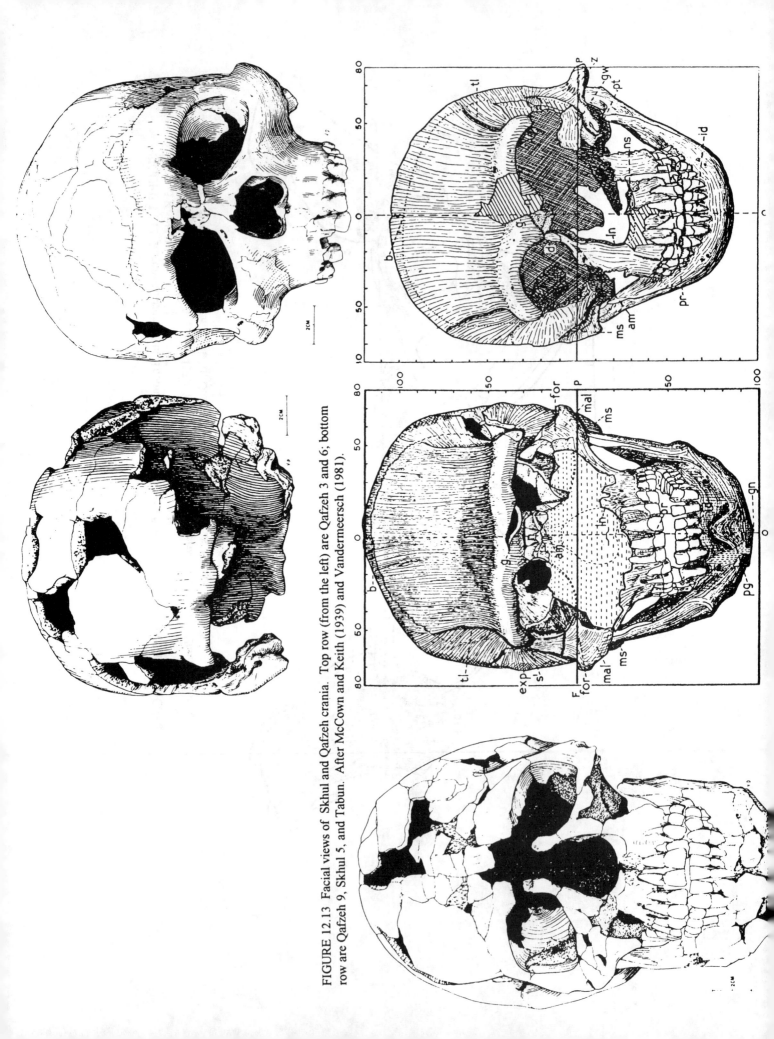

FIGURE 12.13 Facial views of Skhul and Qafzeh crania. Top row (from the left) are Qafzeh 3 and 6; bottom row are Qafzeh 9, Skhul 5, and Tabun. After McCown and Keith (1939) and Vandermeersch (1981).

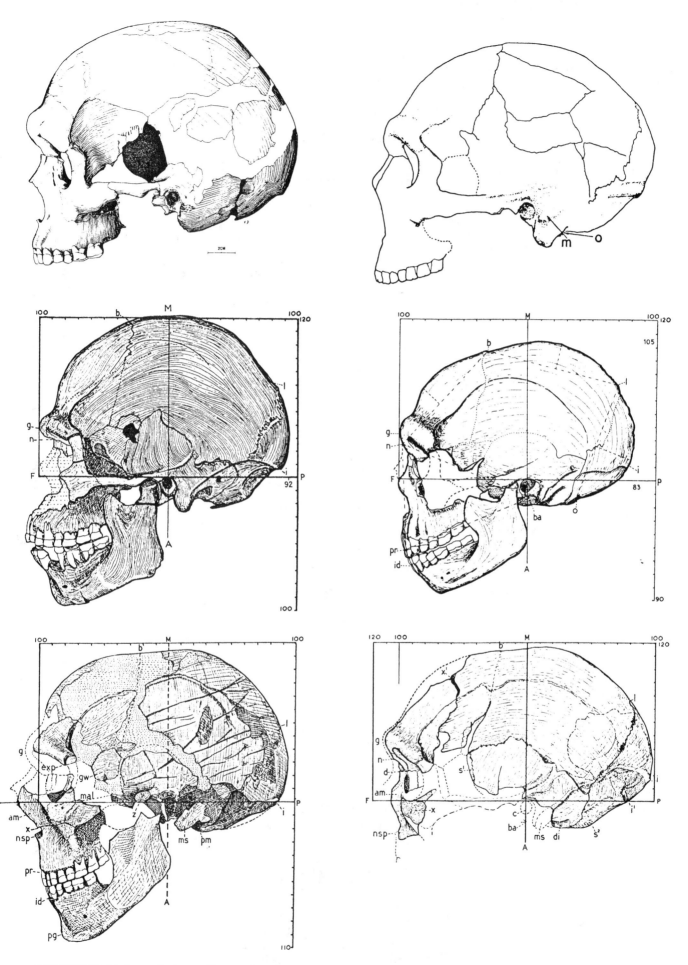

FIGURE 12.14 Lateral views of Levant crania. Top row (from left) are Qafzeh 6 and Amud, middle row are Skhul 5 and Tabun, bottom row are Skhul 4 and 9. . After McCown and Keith (1939), Santa Luca (1978), and Vandermeersch (1981).

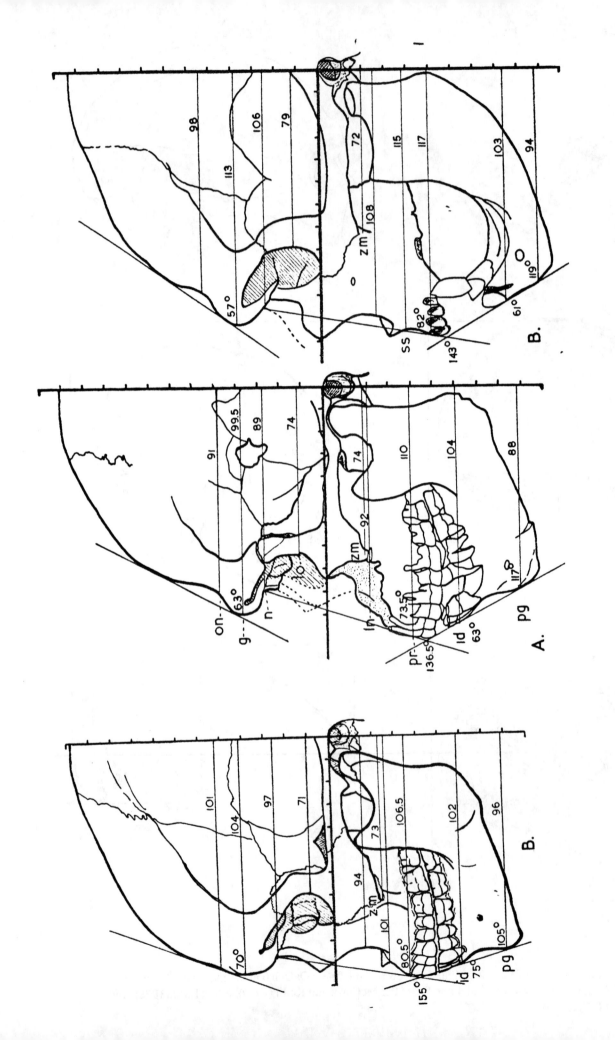

FIGURE 12.15 Comparison of facial profiles and projections in an Australian (left), Skhul 5, and La Chapelle Neandertal (right), after McCown and Keith (1939).

FROM McCown, T.D. and A. Keith 1939 *The Stone Age of Mount Carmel: The Fossil Human Remains from the Levalloiso-Mousterian*. Vol. II. Oxford at the Clarendon Press, figures 172, 173.

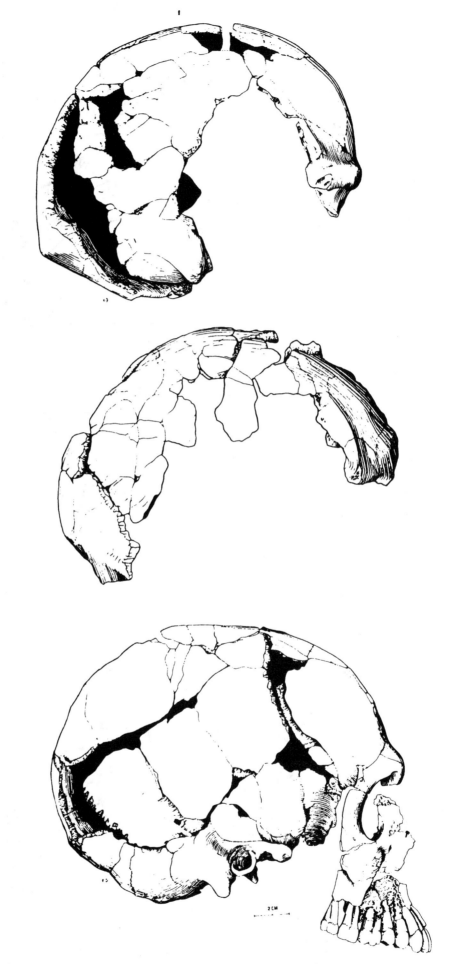

FIGURE 12.16 Lateral views of Qafzch crania (from the top) 3, 5, and 9. . After Vandermeersch (1981).
FROM Vandermeersch, B. 1981 Les hommes fossiles de Qafzch (Israël). Centre National de la Recherche
Sciéntifique, Paris, figures 10, 30, 34.

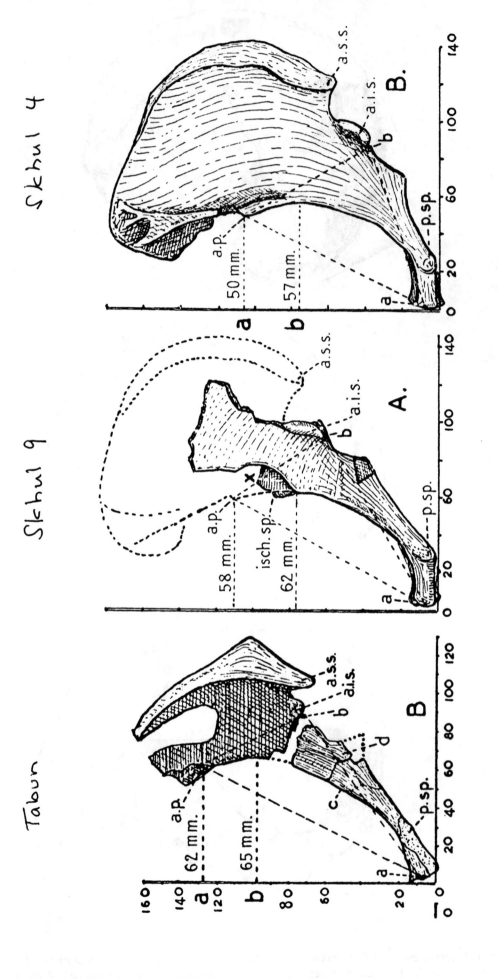

FIGURE 12.17 Comparison of Levant pubes, as seen from above, after McCown and Keith (1939).
FROM McCown, T.D. and A. Keith 1939 *The Stone Age of Mount Carmel: The Fossil Human Remains from the Levalloiso-Mousterian.* Vol. II. Oxford at the Clarendon Press, figures 58, 60.

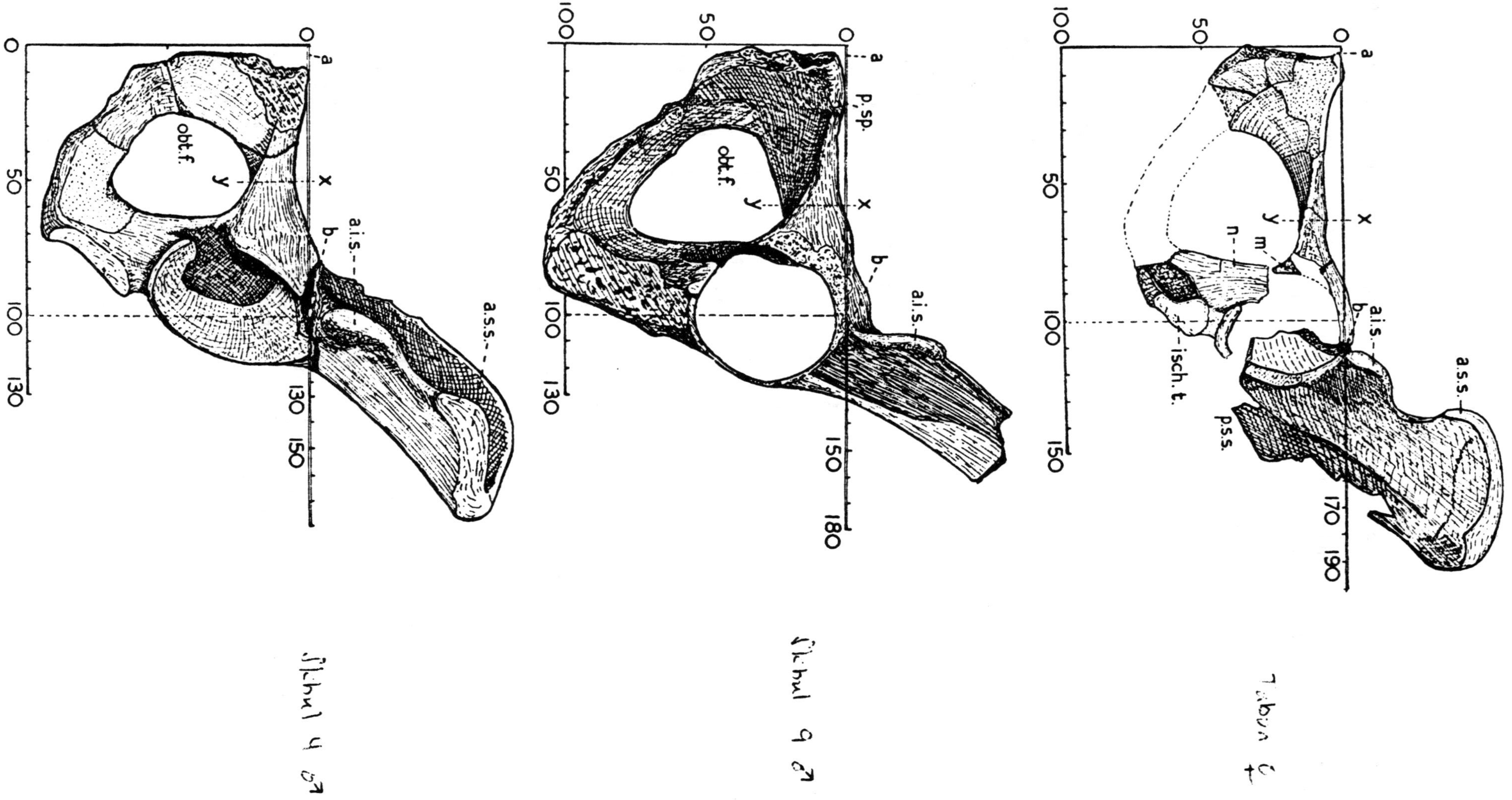

FIGURE 12.18 Comparison of Levant innominates, as seen from the front, after McCown and Keith (1939). FROM McCown, T.D. and A. Keith 1939 *The Stone Age of Mount Carmel: The Fossil Human Remains from the Levalloiso-Mousterian.* Vol. II. Oxford at the Clarendon Press, figures 37, 50.

FIGURE 12.19 Comparison of Neandertal and Skhul femora, as seen from the front, after McCown and Keith (1939).
FROM McCown, T.D. and A. Keith 1939 *The Stone Age of Mount Carmel: The Fossil Human Remains from the Levalloiso-Mousterian.* Vol. II. Oxford at the Clarendon Press, figure 28..

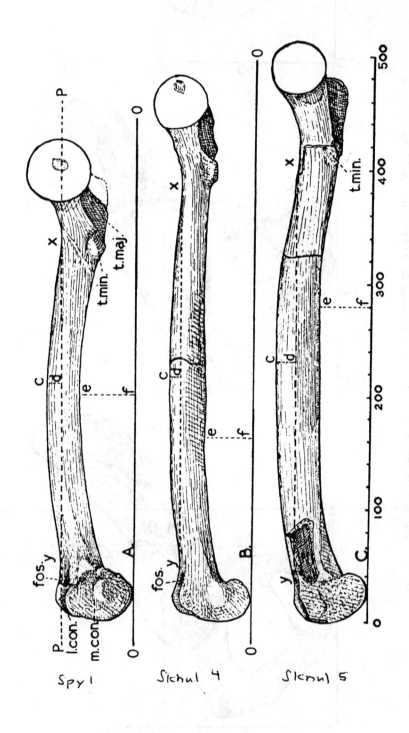

FIGURE 12.20 Comparison of Neandertal and Skhul femora in posterior view, after McCown and Keith (1939). The figure shows the linea aspera and other details of the posterior surface.
FROM McCown, T.D. and A. Keith 1939 *The Stone Age of Mount Carmel: The Fossil Human Remains from the Levalloiso-Mousterian.* Vol. II. Oxford at the Clarendon Press, figure 32.

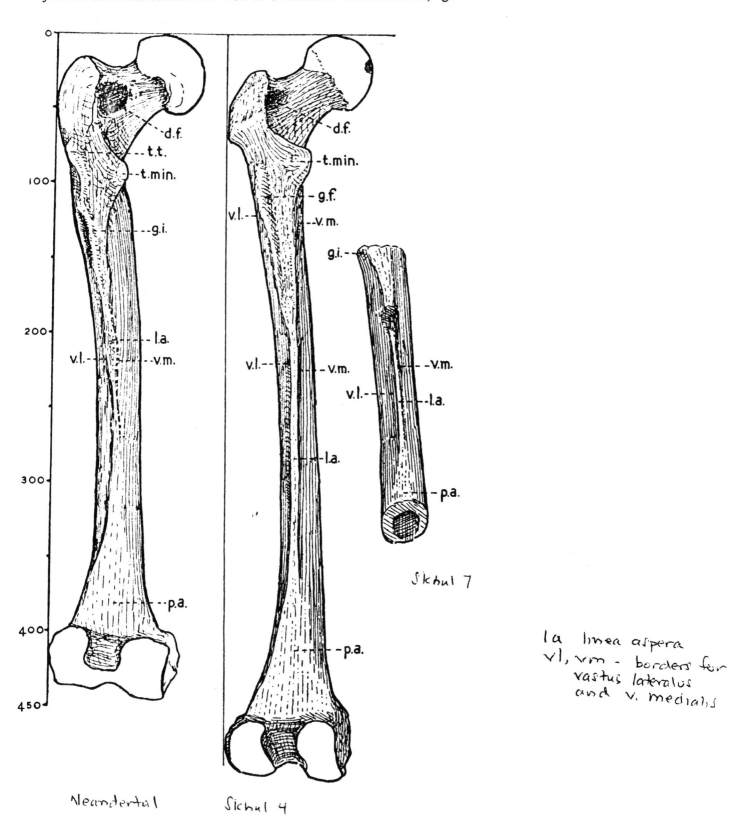

Neandertal   Skhul 4   Skhul 7

la linea aspera
vl, vm - borders for
  vastus lateralus
  and v. medialis

FIGURE 12.21 Comparison of the Tabun (above) and Skhul 4 feet, in views from above and from the side, after McCown and Keith (1939).

FROM McCown, T.D. and A. Keith 1939 *The Stone Age of Mount Carmel: The Fossil Human Remains from the Levalloiso-Mousterian.* Vol. II. Oxford at the Clarendon Press, figures 1,2.

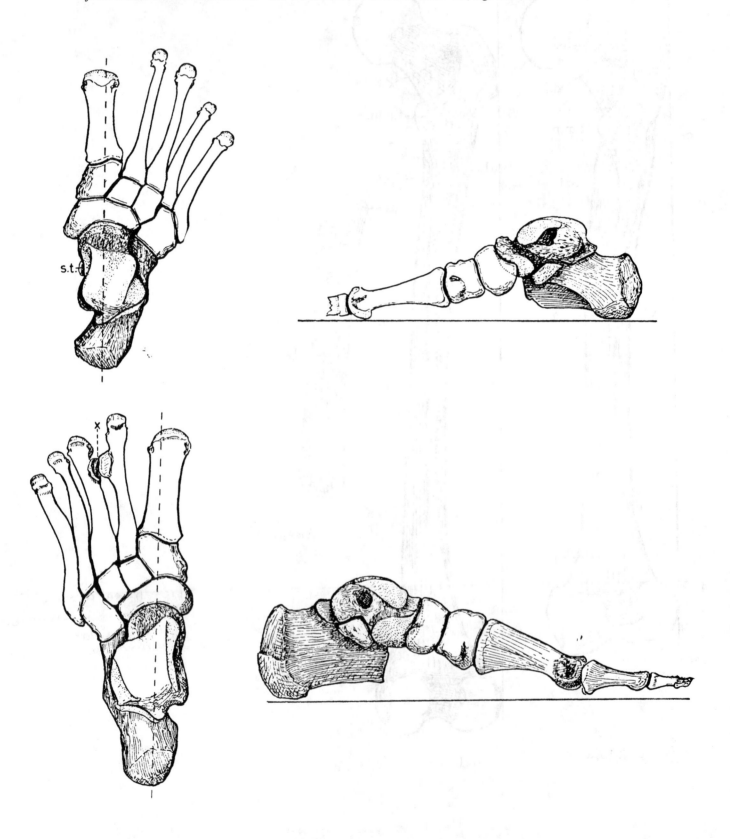

FIGURE 12.22 Comparison of Levant and a Neandertal forearm, after McCown and Keith (1939).
FROM McCown, T.D. and A. Keith 1939 *The Stone Age of Mount Carmel: The Fossil Human Remains from the Levalloiso-Mousterian.* Vol. II. Oxford at the Clarendon Press, figure 110.

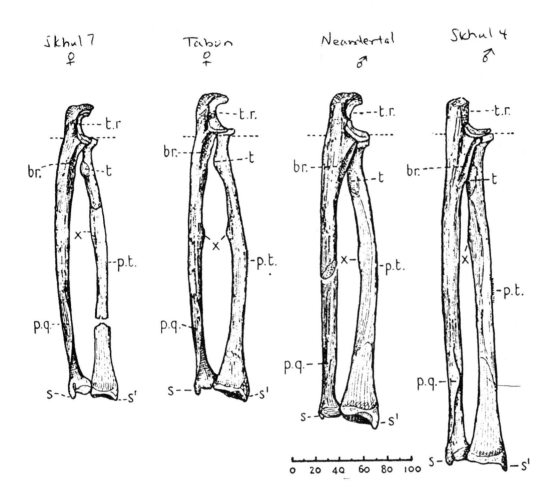

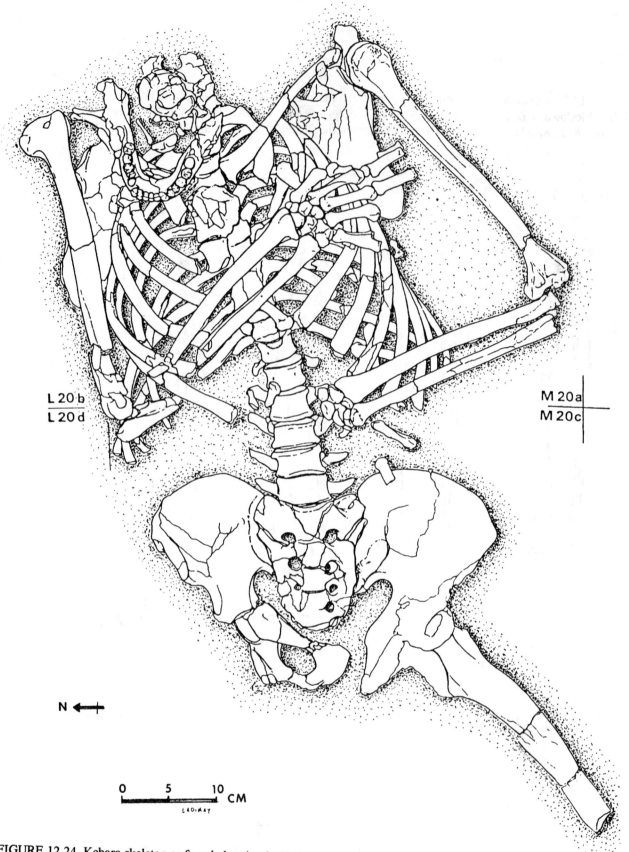

L 20 b
L 20 d

M 20a
M 20c

N ←

0   5   10 CM
LADIRAY

FIGURE 12.24 Kebara skeleton as found, drawing by D. Ladiray.
FROM Tillier, A-M., B. Arensburg, B. Vandermeersch, and Y. Rak 1991 L'apport de Kébara à la
Palethnologie Funéraire des Néanderthaliens de Proche-Orient. In O. Bar-Yosef and B. Vandermeersch
(eds): *Le Squelette Moustérien De Kébara 2.* Centre National de la Recherche Scientifique, Paris. pp.
89-95, figure 2.

FIGURE 12.25 The Kebara innominate, after Rak (1991).
FROM Rak, Y. 1991 The pelvis. In O. Bar-Yosef and B. Vandermeersch (eds): *Le squelette Moustérien de Kébara 2*. Cahiers de Paléoanthropologie, Centre National de la Recherche Scientifique, Paris. pp. 147-156, figure 2.

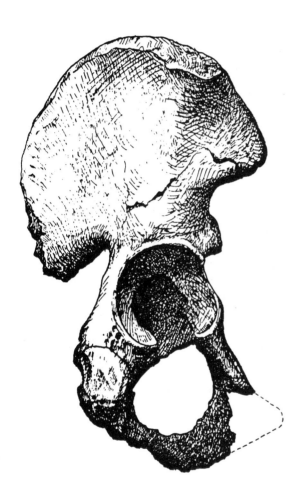
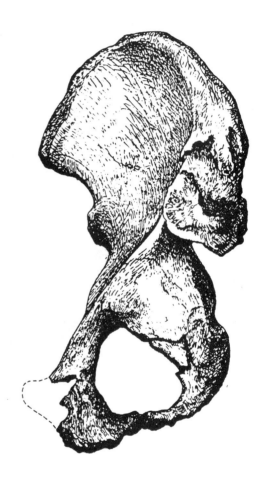

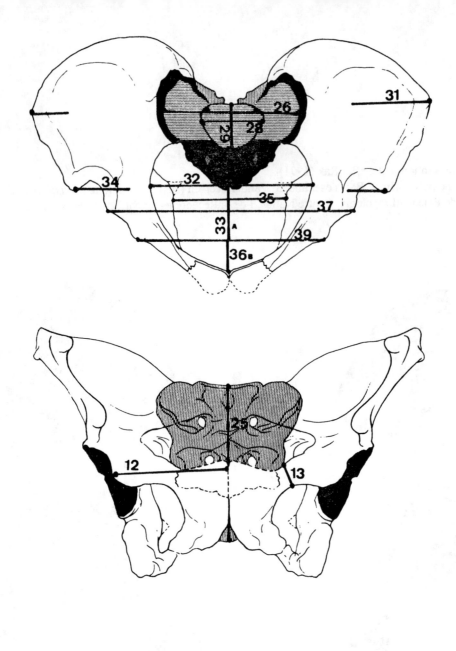

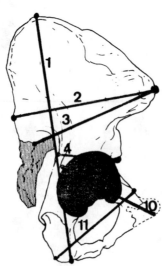

FIGURE 12.26 The reconstructed Kebara pelvis, after Rak (1991).

FROM Rak, Y. 1991 The pelvis. In O. Bar-Yosef and B. Vandermeersch (eds): *Le squelette Moustérien de Kébara 2.* Cahiers de Paléoanthropologie, Centre National de la Recherche Scientifique, Paris. pp. 147-156, figure 4

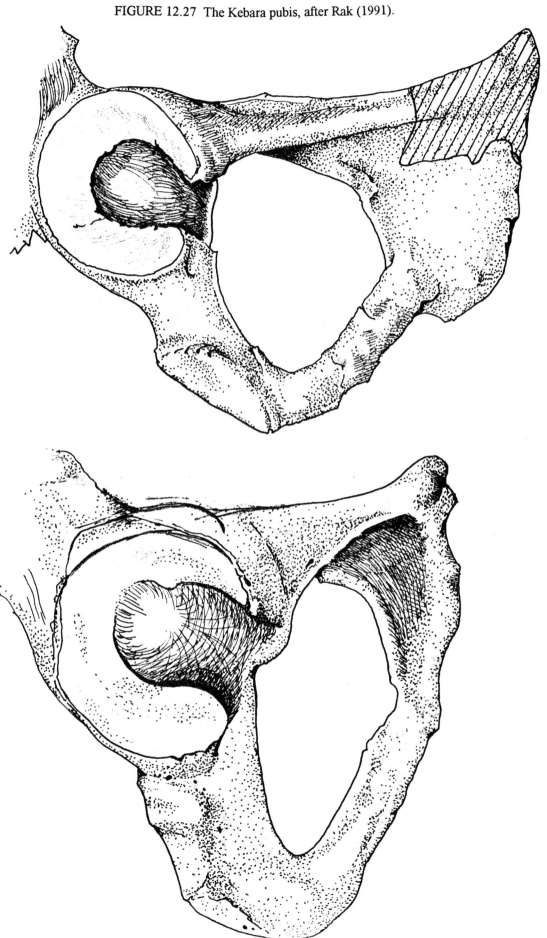

FIGURE 12.27 The Kebara pubis, after Rak (1991).

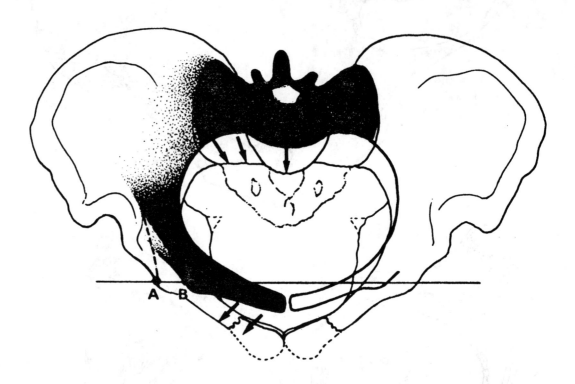

FIGURE 12.28 The Kebara pelvis superimposed on a similar sized recent one, as seen from above, after Rak (1991). The figure illustrates Rak's contention that the Kebara pelvic aperture is in a more anterior position within a similar frame.

FROM Rak, Y. 1991 The pelvis. In O. Bar-Yosef and B. Vandermeersch (eds): *Le squelette Moustérien de Kébara 2*. Cahiers de Paléoanthropologie, Centre National de la Recherche Scientifique, Paris. pp. 147-156, figure 15.

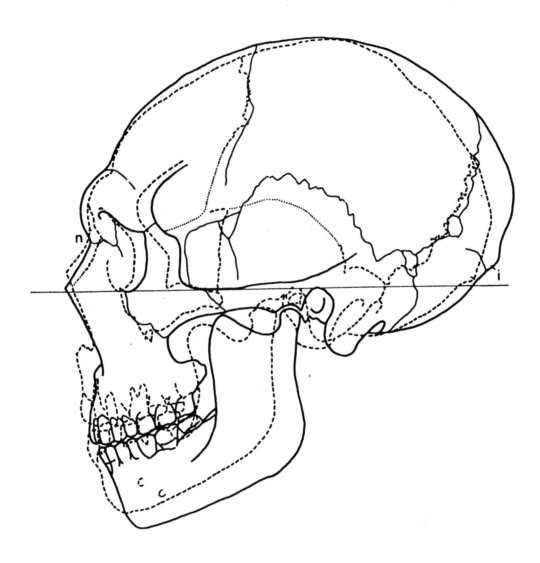

FIGURE 12.31 The Amud skull compared with Shanidar 1, after Suzuki (1970).
FROM Suzuki, H. 1970 The skull of the Amud man. In H. Suzuki and F. Takai (eds): *The Amud Man and his Cave Site*. University of Tokyo, Tokyo. pp. 123-206, figure VIII-23.

FIGURE 12.32 The Amud skull compared with Skhul 4, after Suzuki (1970).
FROM Suzuki, H. 1970 The skull of the Amud man. In H. Suzuki and F. Takai (eds): *The Amud Man and his Cave Site*. University of Tokyo, Tokyo. pp. 123-206, figure VIII-24.

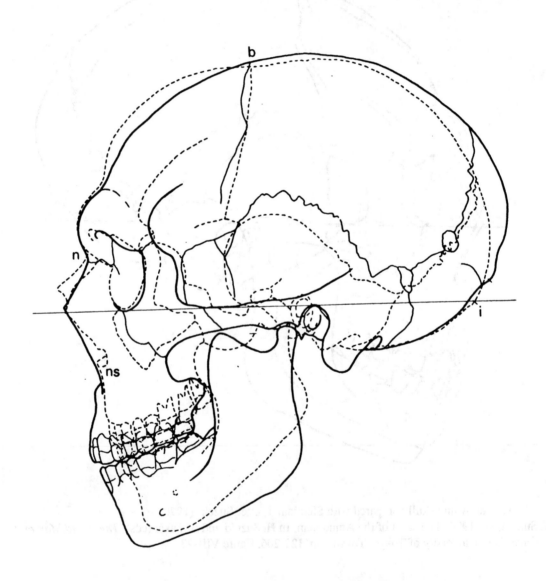

FIGURE 12.33 Comparison of Levantine "Neandertal" and Skhul/Qafzeh tooth size, showing the mean values and the standard deviation range for mandibular tooth breadths.

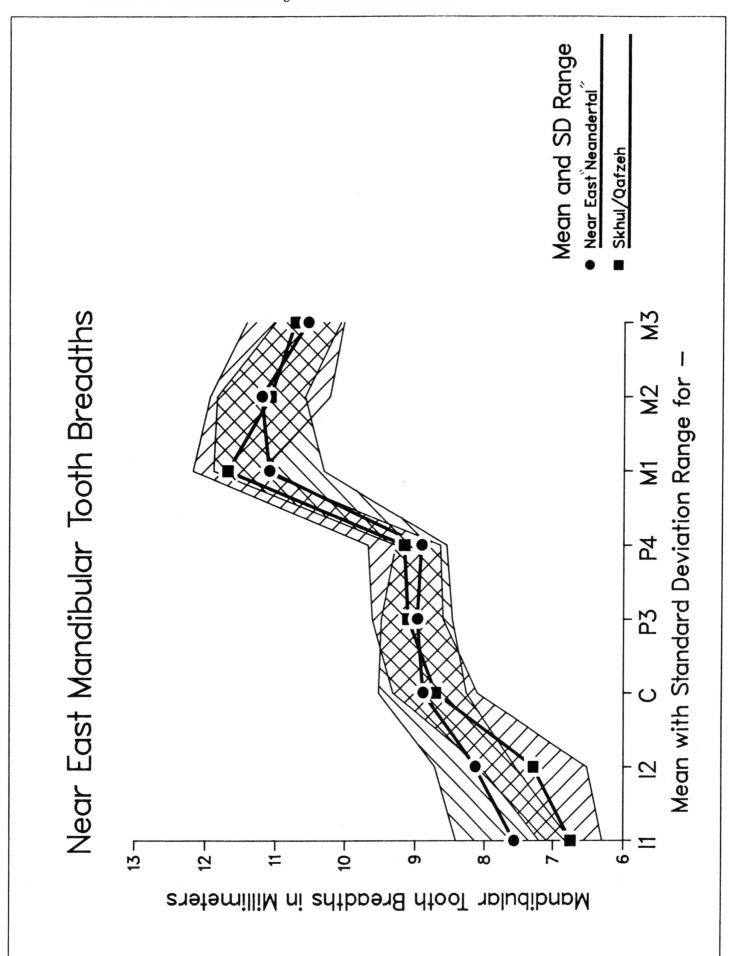

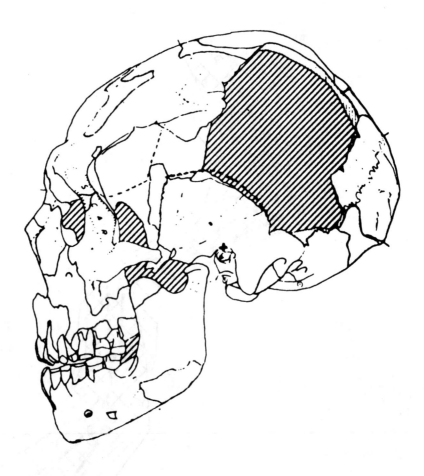

FIGURE 12.34   Shanidar 1, after Stewart (1958).

FROM Stewart, T.D. 1958 The restored Shanidar I skull. Annual Report of the Smithsonian Institution for
  1958, pp. 473-480.

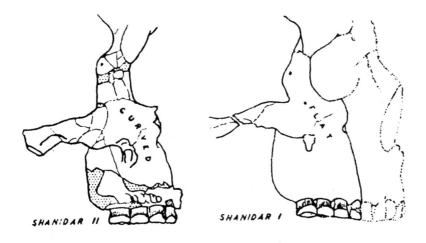

FIGURE 12.35   Shanidar 1 and 2 faces compared, after Stewart (1961).

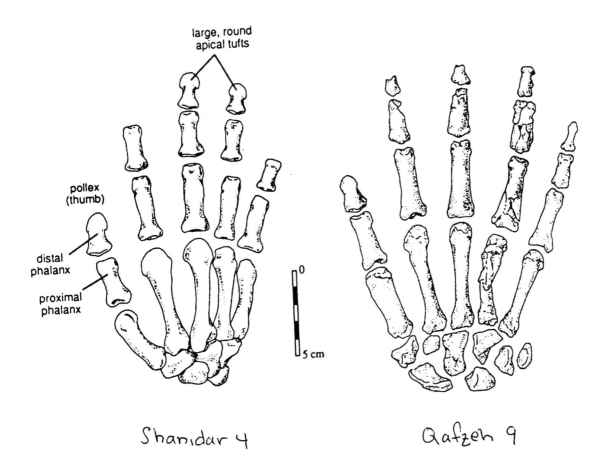

FIGURE 12.36 Shanidar and Qafzeh hands compared, after Klein (1990).
FROM Klein, R.G. 1990 The Human Career. Human Biological and Cultural origins. University of
    Chicago Press, Chicago, figure 6.13.

CHAPTER THIRTEEN

The European Neandertals

Europe and a good part of western Asia, for most of the last quarter million years, has been home to an enigmatic and troublesome race called Neandertal (Neanderthal is the older German spelling and really should only be used by those who regard these folk as a distinct species, as species names are carved in stone and cannot change even when common spelling does). Neandertals were first discovered, or in some cases recognized, in the middle of the last century: the Engis child from Belgium (1829), Forbes Quarry from Gibraltar (1848, but not recognized as particularly special until 1865), and of course the Neandertal skeleton from the Feldhofer cave (1856). The 'Neandertal question" - the place of the Neandertals in human evolution - is paleoanthropology's oldest problem, since the first archaic fossils to be discovered were Neandertals. Why have Neandertals been such a problem? Simply put, it is because they rubbed the question of a savage and primitive European ancestry right in the face of the European scientific world and as luck had it, their practice of living in caves and burying their dead quickly gave those scientists a lot to talk about, once paleoanthropologists realized where and how to look. The early history of discoveries and interpretations is detailed in books by J. Radovčić, C. Stringer and C. Gamble, E. Trinkaus and P. Shipman, and H. Wendt.

The problem of how to interpret the Neandertals has a long history in the development of scientific thought. More than a century ago, through his writings Darwin urged natural scientists to undertake a very ambitious project - to connect all living species in a phylogenetic tree based on common descent. The first such tree specifically addressing humans was constructed by E. Haeckel, Darwin's Prussian disciple (also see Chapters 3 and 6). He used anatomical similarities as the basis of this tree, and the kind of similarities he recognized between human races were quite similar to the similarities he recognized between primate species. The phylogeny he created postulated hypothetical ancestors between ape and man - *Pithecanthropus alalus* speechless ape-man. The fate of the Neandertals was already sealed before their fossils were placed on the human family tree, the position for them taken up by "*Homo stupidus*". Haeckel put his phylogeny in a geographic context, producing in 1870 a tree with its base in the lost continent of Paradise, and branches spreading across the world. The first single origin theory was not *Out of Africa*, but *Out of Paradise*. Some races were more evolved than others, with the Europeans the final end products.

With the discovery of a human fossil record, the relation of the pre-diluvial relics to modern humans was pushed to relevance. The bones from the Neander Valley, near Dusseldorf, were clearly unusual. They were originally attributed to a "barbarian race of European natives" but the most popular prevailing view soon came to be that the ape-like features showed that Neandertal Man could not be a human ancestor. This was formalized by William King, Professor of Anatomy from Galway, Ireland, who was the first to apply a formal terminology to express his contention that the Neandertal remains should be classified as a distinct species - *Homo neanderthalensis*. This is why the name is written in formal taxonomies as *Homo neanderthalensis* King. Yet at the same time, Darwin's "Bulldog", T. Huxley, attributed the Neandertal findings to an extreme variety of modern man. Thus, at the very time of its first discovery, the classic sides of the Neandertal debate were already joined.

In the German speaking world the equivalent species name was "*Homo primigenius*" and this became widely used in central Europe. G. Schwalbe, the German anatomist and evolutionist, took the opportunity provided by the Trinil skull cap discovery in 1891 to review what was known of human evolution. In 1906 he proposed two different schemes which encapsulate perfectly the Bush vs Ladder dichotomy that S. Gould published some 80 years later. Schwalbe could not decide between these two very different models, and his dilemma is reflected in today's disputes.

Soon thereafter H. Klaatsch, a Berlin anatomist, became involved in the debate. He reconstructed an idealized model of the Neandertal, based on the original faceless skullcap, a mandible from the Belgian site of Spy, and an isolated upper jaw fragment from the Croatian site of Krapina, proclaiming "whenever a well preserved Neandertal skull is discovered, it is sure to look like my reconstruction". Klaatsch thereby originated the "common knowledge" that Neandertals were homogeneous - even before there were significant comparisons to be made. Klaatsch created another of the long-lasting Neandertal myths with his contention that Neandertals and modern people were contemporaries in Europe. He "found" them together at the Krapina site, where he imagined there was a great battle for possession of the rockshelter. In France the discoveries at Le Moustier (a Neandertal youth and an infant) and Combe Capelle (a "modern" specimen) were claimed to be contemporaries as well.

With the discoveries of several complete French Neandertal burials, the French paleontologist M. Boule epitomized these ideas in his contention that the Neandertals were "a homogeneous type, which differ greatly from all living types". He accepted them as a distinct species, lying somewhere between chimpanzees and Europeans, but as a separate side branch in the sense of Schwalbe's bush. Yet, Boule's view was more complex than generally appreciated. He wrote:

> Whereas the Neandertal man of Europe occupies the position of a type apart, ... which seems according to all the evidence to have vanished without issue, the little we know about this type in Asia shows it as included within a regular evolutionary sequence.

As views of human evolution came to incorporate the synthetic theory, developed in the early 1940's, a half century ago, the species status for Neandertals slowly was dropped. T. Dobzhansky, a Russian émigré geneticist, applied evolutionary criteria to the question in 1944. He re-analyzed the Mount Carmel remains from Israel. As discussed in Chapter 12, the resemblance of people in this collection to both Neandertals and moderns, to differing degrees, had been interpreted by T. McCown and A. Keith as the results of the population being "in the throes of evolutionary change". Dobzhansky took issue with this interpretation, arguing it is much more probable that the variation was the result of intermixture between Neandertals and less specialized populations. For Dobzhansky, and many later workers (for instance E. Mayr, in his famous 1950 re-evaluation of human taxonomy) this proof of mixing showed that there was a single species at Mount Carmel, and Neandertals became a *Homo sapiens* subspecies (*Homo sapiens neanderthalensis*). Later, a further retreat from taxonomy was forced by the continued confusion of temporal subspecies with geographic subspecies, and Neandertals became, for many, the European version of archaic *Homo sapiens*. These views prevailed until the middle of the last decade, when the Eve theory was developed.

As European ancestors, their position rose and fell, not because of the advance of scientific discoveries as much as because of the spirit of the times. The first discoveries fit well into the developing evolutionary ideas in Darwin's time. They were the expected savages of the past that fit the needs of T. Huxley 's model of biological and LH. Morgan's model of social evolution. But fulfilling a worry expressed by P. Broca, a great French anthropologist of the time ("I would rather be a perfected ape than a degenerated Adam"), other discoveries just past the turn of the century culminating in Piltdown seemed to suggested that modern humans were as ancient or even earlier. There was a concerted effort, especially in western Europe, to remove Neandertals from their place in the human family tree. This was quite successful and with the exception of a small continuous intellectual thread from scientists of central and eastern Europe, the Neandertals were widely regarded as extinct cousins by paleoanthropologists, even as evolutionists had come to treat them as a vanished human race. The paleoanthropological influence was by far the predominant one in US training, reflecting the power of the intellectual tradition stemming from E. Hooton to W. Howells and ultimately F.C. Howell. It is ironic that the few central and eastern European paleoanthropologists who immigrated in the earlier part of the century (A. Hrdlička, F. Weidenreich for instance) worked in museums where they had no direct intellectual influence as the teachers of generations of students.

Perhaps a real key to understanding the popularity that extinction arguments maintained (and perhaps still maintain) in Western Europe is, as C. Stringer and C. Gamble themselves note, the way in which the Neandertal extinction became a metaphor for all colonialist invasions. For instance, as the Quennells put it in a popular book from the middle of *this* century:

His large head, with the thick frontal bones, must have been very good for butting a
brother Neanderthal, but it was no use against the stone wall of advancing civilization,
and like the Tasmanian and Bushman, the Red Indian and Australian of nowadays, he
fades out of the picture and his place is taken by a cleverer people.

The lives (and loves) of extinct Neandertals were more than objects of fascination (as authors such as J.
Auel know so well), the founding of modern Europe in a wave of invasion and extinction fit neatly within
the social fabric.

The reason there is a debate today is largely because of what Trinkaus and Shipman call the
"Renaissance of Neandertals". New discoveries and the reinterpretation of older ones continued to force
Neandertals back into the fold of humanity. Somehow as the intellectual trends of the second part of this
century developed, the Neandertals changed for some from the Quennells' Stone Age bone heads into the
flower children of Shanidar. The development of the Synthetic Theory of Evolution and the injection of
population genetics into evolutionary and finally paleoanthropological thinking had much to do with these
changes. Once again there were real intellectual controversies over scientific issues to be taken into
account, but also a social fabric.

The debate persists, and what I write here will no doubt quite justifiably be considered part of it.
Trinkaus and Shipman put it well.

Despite a major change from the 19th century emphasis on progress and betterment to
the 20th century emphasis on isolating ourselves from all but our most remote near-
human ancestors, the themes in Neandertal studies have remained relatively constant.

The Late Middle Pleistocene Europeans

First the issue of where the European Neandertals are from. The answer is unequivocally Europe! The
Neandertals themselves first appear as a diagnosable population within Europe by the beginning of the
Late Pleistocene (variously at the beginning of the Eemian, or the Riss-Würm Interglacial, or Oxygen
Isotope Stage 5e). Their predecessors, as discussed in Chapter 11, share enough similarities to leave the
issue of ancestry unchallenged. Regional continuity in Europe is particularly well established, so much so
that some have considered the Middle Pleistocene Europeans a distinct species. Perhaps the earliest
archaic Europeans who could justifiably be interpreted as showing a coalescence of Neandertal features
come from Oxygen Isotope Stage 7, a time of fluctuating climate within what was once simply regarded as
the penultimate glaciation, the Riss. These include the remains from the Pontnewydd cave (Wales), the
Vértesszöllös specimens (Hungary), and the material from the German site of Ehringsdorf, near Weimar.

The Welsh remains are quite fragmentary, pieces of the jaws could represent a single 8 year old child
and an isolated adult or near-adult molar. Features that could be used to support the claim that these
specimens resemble the Neandertals include the very dominant buccal cusp of the P_3 and the
taurodontism of the postcanine teeth. C. Stringer (for instance in *In Search of the Neanderthals*, written
with C. Gamble), focuses on the importance of taurodontism in establishing this relationship. He writes
that the Pontnewydd teeth "can only be linked to the later Neandertals by the common trait of molar
taurodontism". I concur with the idea that this and other European specimens from before the Würm
resemble Neandertals, probably for the very simple reason that they either *are* Neandertals or they *are
directly ancestral to them*. The problem with this assessment, or perhaps the caution that needs to appear
on the package enclosing this widely held contention, is that once identified there is a curious tendency to
regard features that can be used to diagnose whether particular specimens are Neandertals as evidence that
Neandertals became extinct without descendants - certainly an opinion held prominently by the above-
mentioned Stringer and Gamble!. The problem here was perhaps best analyzed by F. Weidenreich in his
essay on Neandertals and the ancestors of *Homo sapiens*, discussing (somewhat sarcastically) the use of
taurodontism to identify Neandertals.

Adloff and Keith found that the molar teeth of European Neandertal Man are characterized by a particular spaciousness of the pulp cavity which, according to them, was thought missing in anthropoids, as well as *Homo sapiens*. The authors, therefore, considered taurodontism an expression of specialization characteristic of Neandertal Man. Since the peculiarity would not appear in modern Man, they concluded that their bearers, that is the Neandertalians, must have been extinguished without leaving any descendants. But already at the time when this feature was claimed as an example of specialization, it was known that both presuppositions were erroneous. Typical taurodontism occurs in orang-utan and chimpanzee and, on the other hand, is not rare among certain races of modern mankind, as for instance, Eskimos and Bushmen. Thus the possibility at least remains ... that the European Neandertalian inherited it from an orang-like ancestor and transmitted it to the Eskimo. But in no case could it be concluded from these facts that the Neandertal man had disappeared from the surface of the earth without descendants.

No single feature can diagnose a Neandertal, any more than forensic scientists attempting to identify human dead can tell which race an individual comes from with a single features. However distinct human racial variations may appear, the fact that most genetic variation is within populations and not between them creates the necessity of using multiple features to establish probable geographic or regional identity. This problem is no less true in the past, and specifically with regard to the question of when Neandertals appear in Europe. It is quite possible that there is no dramatic event or specific time marking when this occurred. Both Uranium series and Thermoluminescence dates place the Pontnewydd hominids in Oxygen Isotope Stage 7, if the provenience and faunal associations are accurate.

The Hungarian site of Vértesszöllös is rather less securely dated; an early Thorium/Uranium date and a study of the microfauna places it in the same time range as Zhoukoudian but Uranium series dates suggest a much younger age (225 and even 185 kyr). Discovery of a non-conformity in the site makes the relation of the fragmentary hominids to either the microfauna or the stalagmites dated by the Uranium techniques a problematic one. The poorly fossilized remains of two individuals have been found. One is a child of about 7 years, represented by the fragments of a milk canine and molar and a permanent molar. An analysis of these teeth shows that they are similar to teeth from Zhoukoudian, but somewhat larger. The second individual is an adult, represented by most of an occiput. The bone is thick and has a well-developed nuchal torus across its back, in a fairly high position. The great breadth of the bone leads to a very large nuchal muscle attachment area. The upper part of the occiput is flattened, between this region and torus is a short vertical surface marking the bone's rear. On this face is a shallow suprainiac fossa, asymmetrically developed with the left side larger. A distinct sulcus separates the nuchal torus from the nuchal plane below, and the whole region across which the torus is well developed projects backwards and is delineated by its angled vertical sides. In all, the anatomical configuration resembles a Neandertal-like occipital bun, although unlike the later Europeans part of the posterior projection is attained by cranial thickening. The size of the occiput suggests a cranial capacity of over 1,300 cc. When A. Thoma described the specimen he could not decide whether it represented (what he called) *H. erectus* or was a "pre-*sapiens*" or even an "early *sapiens*". He called it *Homo erectus/sapiens*. I have emphasized the more archaic features and its resemblance to other earlier Middle Pleistocene hominids, while C. Stringer, focusing on its differences, regards it as the latest of the pre-Neandertals in his European species "*Homo heidelbergensis*" and W. Stecślicka allocates it to the Neandertals. The fact is that the bone may be too incomplete and eroded to be certain of its affiliations. According to H. Ullrich we may be more certain of the individual's fate, as he believes there are human-made cut marks at the neck muscle attachments.

A Uranium series date of 205 kyr, and 200 kyr from an ESR determination made on calcite place the specimens from the Fischer and Kämpfe quarries at Ehringsdorf near or at the end of Stage 7. The hominid sample includes a faceless cranial vault and partial endocast (H), adult and adolescent mandibles (F and G), four parietals (A through D), and a femur shaft (E). Associated with mandible G are a number of teeth and additional postcranial remains. The Ehringsdorf H vault was reconstructed more than 3 times since its discovery in 1925; an early attempt by F. Weidenreich, followed by O. Kleinschmidt and finally E. Vlček. Each one of these reconstructions takes on a somewhat different character, but whether one chooses the most Neandertal-like or the least Neandertal-like attempt (Weidenreich's), Ehringsdorf H is different in a number of respects from the Würm Neandertals of Western Europe. The frontal begins behind the only moderately developed browridge, and a distinct, centrally located frontal boss is retained. The details of the forehead are reminiscent of Steinheim (although with a greatly reduced supraorbital) and Arago 21. Another archaic feature is the very prominent mastoid process, also notable at Atapuerca. Additional similarities to Atapuerca include the expanded occipital plane (**opistocranion**, the rear-most point of the vault, is high above the center of the nuchal torus) and the placement of the position of the highest point on the vault which is behind **bregma** (the meeting of the sagittal and coronal sutures at the back of the frontal bone). As viewed from the rear, the reconstructed outline of the braincase is circular. The greatest breadth is about midway up the parietals, and the basal breadth is greatly reduced. However, this aspect of cranial shape is variable at Ehringsdorf; for instance, varying in rear view from the rounded form of the H skull (and parietal B) to more vertically sided parietals C and D with a distinct angle at the temporal line position separating the parietal side from the roof (this closely resembles Atapuerca cranium 5) There is also considerable variation in cranial bone thickness, the thin cranial vault with moderate supraorbitals suggesting that Ehringsdorf H may be female.

Yet, there are certain more progressive features which generally or specifically (as in the case of the rounded posterior cranial contour) resemble Neandertals. The brain size (estimated at 1450 cc) is large relative to the earlier specimens, especially if the diagnosis of female sex is correct. The back of the cranium protrudes to form an occipital bun in the Kleinschmidt reconstruction (although it is more evenly rounded and less protruding in Vlček's reconstruction, resembling Atapuerca 5). There is a thin but distinct nuchal torus, and above it like several other early Europeans there is a paired suprainiac fossa (all have the fossa, but only some have it paired).

The two mandibles (F and G) belonged to an old adult and a 10-11 year old juvenile. They share the combination of large (particularly broad) anterior teeth and reduced or modern-sized posterior teeth. The F mandible has so much anterior tooth wear that the incisors are worn down to nubs. In specimens of this age, lifelong mesial migration of the teeth positions them forward, overshadowing the symphysis. The forward angle of the teeth in the jaw creates a little mesial movement every time there is force on the teeth - adjacent teeth wear against each other (**interproximal wear**) and the teeth slowly move toward the front of the mouth (**mesial drift**). In both mandibles, the third molar (unerupted in the juvenile) is considerably smaller than the other two. In the old adult, there is a **retromolar** gap as the forward border of the vertical ramus begins distinctly behind the third molar. The toothrow appears shifted forward in F, positioning the large mental foramen under the first molar (in earlier specimens it is variably under the premolars). This could be a result of its advanced age, as described above the teeth move mesially during life, but it is an anatomy that characterizes many other European specimens from this time and later. While a mental trigone is distinct in both Ehringsdorf mandibles, a combination of prognathism and the forward angle of the incisors overhangs it and makes the mandibles appear receding and chinless. Excepting the small mental trigone of Arago 2 these features are generally different from the earlier French mandibles. Many of the above-mentioned characteristics are shared by some or all of the Atapuerca mandibles, and as a set they closely resemble the European Würm Neandertals.

Of the postcranial remains, the Ehringsdorf E femur is best known. Male, by the sexing criteria at Krapina (table 13.4), it is similar to Arago 48 in size and anatomy, a large, robust bone with a very thick cortex.

In fact, scientists such as F. Smith unequivocally regard these specimens as Neandertals. Some workers find "progressive tendencies" in them, others "archaic tendencies", but all of them are almost certainly viewing normal variation and succumb to the understandable temptation of overinterpreting details of single specimens. Smith has suggested that the situation at this site, excavated under uncontrolled conditions at the beginning of the century, may be more complex than it appears, citing the Mousterian industry of the lower Travertine and the absence of distinct pre-Late Pleistocene fauna. Yet, as they say, a rose by any other name ... Ehringsdorf may be the earliest unquestionable Neandertal site.

More abundant remains are found in Oxygen Isotope Stage 6, a 198-129 kyr period marking the end, and coldest, portion of the penultimate glaciation. A number of hominid sites have been reported, in western Europe. These mark the earliest occupation of a temperate area during the coldest portions of a glaciation. To date, these have yielded a good number of cranial fragments, teeth, and mandibles, as well as a few postcranial remains. The large number of European finds, however, should not be taken as an indication of an unusual population density humans in glaciated Europe, but rather of an unusual population density for the archaeologists and others seeking early human remains. In fact, it is quite likely that Europe was largely depopulated at this time, a possibly that would not be reflected in the predictable occupations in the limited number of south-facing caves. Human fragments are known from several countries, for instance the small piece of cranial bone from Casal de'Pazzi in Italy, but the most complete remains are from France. The French sites more or less precisely dated to a span within the period are Biache-Saint-Vaast and the La Chaise cave of Bourgeois-Delaunay. Whether these are Neandertals or not, an issue largely obscured by their incompleteness, they are very Neandertal-like

The most complete of the fragmentary specimens are from Biache-Saint-Vaast. There are two partial crania from this site, the maxilla and cranial rear of a female and parts of the face and vault of a male specimen. The female vault is small (capacity estimated at about 1200 cc) and fairly low; the nuchal muscle attachment area is weakly developed and the small nuchal crest only covers the middle portion of the occiput. Her posterior teeth are 95% the area of Arago 21's, but otherwise the two females cannot be compared since different portions of the cranium are preserved. Biache is quite young, the third molar just coming into occlusion and other tooth wear indications suggest an age of about 15 years at her death. She is very similar to Swanscombe; even the same parts are preserved and A. Thorne likes to refer to it as a Swanscombe with ears. Biache also includes the back of the temporals, a palate with posterior teeth and a very diagnostic incisor. An important difference from Swanscombe is the lambdoidal flattening, a flat area at the back of the skull in the region where the occiput and parietals meet. This helps set the rest of the posterior vault off in an even more Neandertal-like bun than Vértesszöllös has, because the bulging rear is not a result of unusual thickening (this vault is very thin, in fact), but rather reflects the shape of the brain. The bun is not the only Neandertal-like feature. Other similarities include

- suprainiac fossa
- very small mastoids that do not project below the cranial base
- circular cranial contour as seen from the rear
- thin cranial vault
- a lateral maxillary incisor with large marginal ridges, a tubercle, and strongly developed labial crown convexity - a pattern that T. Crummett shows is uniquely characteristic of Neandertals

The rounded contour is reflected in the fact that the greatest cranial breadth is located part way up the parietals. This is a consequence of two evolutionary trends which characterize all of the adult Rissian Europeans.

1. reduction in spongy bone development at the cranial base, which decreases basal breadth
2. continued expansion of the parietal association areas of the brain, which increases the breadth across the parietals

As a result, the shape of the vault as seen from the rear is circular, with the maximum diameter about one-third the distance from the base to the top. B. Vandermeersch, in describing this specimen, regards it as a Neandertal with its diagnostic features perhaps less pronounced. I would only take issue with the "less pronounced" part.

A partial fragmentary cranium and mandible (hominid 17), and other fragments and teeth from the Bourgeois-Delaunay cavern at La Chaise are only slightly younger, dated to older than 151 kyr by a Uranium-Thorium determination on an overlaying cave travertine. BD 17 has been vaguely likened to "pre-Neandertals" like Swanscombe by workers such as A. Thoma (in his view, however, more closely resembling specimens such as Swanscombe means "more modern"). However, in agreement with workers such as Vandermeersch my assessment is that it is quite Neandertal-like or even more archaic (for instance as in the thick cranial vault bones, prominent, laterally expansive nuchal torus, and large molar teeth). It is similar to Krapina D (see below), but for the wider separation between the internal and external occipital protuberances. Certainly the occipital configuration, temporal features such as the dwarfing of the (actually well-developed) mastoid process by the paramastoid process, and mandibular features such as the retromolar space closely resemble the Neandertals. The mandible is large and chinless.

A number of specimens are more poorly linked to this time period, toward the end of the penultimate glaciation. Specimens from the Suard cave at La Chaise are so uncertainly provenienced that they can only be said to come from Oxygen Isotope Stages 6 or 7. The Montmaurin mandible and vertebrae, Orgnac III, Lazeret, Vergranne, and Fontéchevade, from France, can be no more precisely dated than to somewhere within Stage 6.

Crania are represented at Suard by fragments including a large portion of a vault (Suard 1), an occiput (Suard 2), and additional fragments and teeth. A child's mandible with additional teeth (Suard 13) was also found at the site. Suard 1 includes the frontal (without the anterior forehead) and parietals of a small head - the capacity estimated at 1065 cc. The specimen is long, low, and thick-boned. The estimated maximum cranial breadth is very great, located about midway up the parietals which reflects a rounded cranial contour which is similar to Biache. Parietal shape is elongated, a feature shared with a number of pre-Würm specimens and once thought to be of phylogenetic significance (see below). Suard 1 preserves an unusual feature in its metopic suture, extending down the middle of the frontal from its rear to most forward preserved point. The Suard occiput (La Chaise 2) is also similar to the Biache female. Viewed from the side, the contour is fairly circular with only a short vertical face enclosing a broad suprainiac fossa above the weakly developed nuchal torus. The position of the torus is low; the occipital plane above it is expanded, while the nuchal plane below is shortened. The impressions left by the brain on the inside of the occiput are markedly asymmetric; the larger left side indicates right-handedness.

There are a number of deciduous teeth among the Suard remains, and several other specimens that contribute to a substantial pre-Würm milk tooth sample. One example is the very large deciduous upper milk canine from Vergranne. The environment suggested by the cave fauna is cool-steppe - this is one of the few pre-Würm Europeans with this association. The crown is worn at a steep angle along its labial face so that the entire top edge is sharpened and blade-like. In general the European deciduous teeth are larger than their earlier Middle Pleistocene counterparts (figure 13.1). This is quite different from the general reduction experienced by the permanent canines and postcanine teeth. Of the several suggestions as to why the difference, most evidence points toward earlier weaning, causing significant occlusal wear to commence at an earlier age. The larger crown size allows the teeth to last longer.

The best preserved European mandible reported from this time span is Montmaurin, from France. It resembles the Mauer mandible in its corpus robustness but it has a narrower ascending ramus and is smaller, about the right size to fit Steinheim. It also differs from Mauer in anatomical details including symphysis morphology, outward angulation of the condyles, and other features, and could easily fit in the Arago sample.

The crushed innominate from the Italian cave of Prince is problematically dated to 220 kyr (direct Uranium-Thorium) or 160-110 kyr (Uranium series on its level). It is generally slightly smaller than Arago 44, but its pelvic inlet is expanded in the anterior-posterior direction. The tendency for larger inlets is the result of bigger head size at birth. It has a large but shallow acetabulum relative to other dimensions, and a dominant anterior inferior iliac spine. M-A. deLumley emphasizes its Neandertal resemblances, while B. Sigmon finds it similar to Arago 44. Perhaps it can be considered transitional, but truly it is difficult to make much of this poorly preserved specimen.

The Lazaret cave, near Nice, has yielded remains of three hominids from the later part of the Riss. Two are represented by single teeth, and the third by a parietal. The associated industry is described as "evolved" Acheulean. The two teeth are a milk molar and a small, worn lower canine. The parietal, belonging to a juvenile about nine years old, has been studied in some detail. Although some of its features such as the thin vault may be due to youth, the shape of the bone is elongated (like the Suard parietals), and along the top the sagittal suture does not have as much curvature as occurs in modern crania. The youth apparently died as the result of a bone infection.

The two cranial fragments from Fontéchevade have been interpreted as "more modern" than later Neandertal specimens. The main feature thought to show that these specimens represent a "presapiens" (as opposed to a "preneandertal") ancestral population is their supposed lack of browridges. Fontéchevade 1 is a frontal fragment from what might be a juvenile individual consisting of the portion just over the nose and some surrounding bone from behind it. It has two characteristics which are said to distinguish it from earlier specimens and also from some of the later European Neandertals—thin cranial bone and the virtual absence of any bulging corresponding to the central portion of a browridge. However, interpretation of the fragment is confused by the possibility that it is a juvenile, since these features could reflect no more than a young age at death (thicker cranial bone and a torus might possibly have developed later in life).

Fontéchevade 2 consists of the skullcap of an older individual with parietals and most of the frontal, missing only the supraorbital-bearing portion. Its interpretation is even more contentious because the entire face and browridge region are broken away. The French paleontologist H. Vallois argues that no browridge was present before the specimens was broken because of the form of the remaining frontal and the position of its sinus. However, others have disputed the interpretation of frontal form and a close examination of the remaining bone reveals what appears to be a shallow sulcus and the back of the top of a (otherwise missing) supraorbital on the right lateral side. While cranial capacity is moderate (about 1,350 cc), the vault is not much unlike crania contemporary with it. The maximum parietal breadth of the cranium is very large and its position is located midway up the vault as seen from the rear. Its position at the far posterior of the cranium results in a cranial contour, as seen from the top, which is also very similar to that of the Würm Neandertals (as well as its contemporaries). If anything, instead of being "more modern" than the later European Neandertals, Fontéchevade 2 is similar to them or more archaic.

These specimens form the basis for one of the older divergence theories about Neandertal origins. As reviewed by H. Vallois this is the **Preneandertal Hypothesis**, which posits that Neandertals diverged from a line leading to modern Europeans just before the last glaciation, or perhaps toward the end of the penultimate one. He distinguishes this from the **Presapiens Hypothesis** (Chapter 11) which posits that this split was much earlier (the supporters of *Homo heidelbergensis* are the modern inheritors of this idea).

When Fontéchevade 2 was virtually the only decent specimen known of this sample from the penultimate glaciation of Western Europe, Vallois argued that the anatomy of the missing forehead was probably smooth and rounded. Even though only the very back of the sinus remained on the bone, there was, he believed, no room for an expanded frontal sinus that would be found in a projecting browridge. Therefore the supraorbital torus must have been absent, he reasoned. However, Vallois had also shown that otherwise the cranial contours and dimensions closely resembled the Neandertals, and A. Sergi formalized this relationship with a series of comparisons that discredited the preneandertal hypothesis. Another blow was delivered by E. Trinkaus, who argued that Fontéchevade 1 was as likely a juvenile as not, thereby giving its non-projecting supraorbital an ontogenetic rather than a phylogenetic explanation. But like a Medusa this idea keeps springing up in different forms and has proved hard to kill. Subsequently M-A. deLumley proposed that two different human groups could be identified on the late Riss sample, primarily based on her analysis of the parietal shape (at least this was not based on the anatomy of missing portions). She identified an elongated form as represented by Suard 1 and Lazeret that presumably led to Neandertals, and a more squared form based on Cova Negra (a Spanish parietal thought then to be of equivalent age but subsequently redated to the Würm) and Fontéchevade that led to the modern Europeans. The pre-modern line presumably had an ancestry extending back to Swanscombe and Arago. Actually, Sergi's research applies to this contention equally well, and it was thoroughly discredited by B. Vandermeersch who provided ample grounds for rejecting any special or unique presapiens lines in Middle or early Late Pleistocene Europe.

It seems to me that once again non-Neandertal has been confused with modern. In particular, any and every features of these pre-Würm specimens what could be claimed as different from Neandertals has been used to establish the presence of a more modern lineage in Europe, thereby "solving' the problem of where modern Europeans came from. But in fact these variations are virtually inevitably found to lie within the Neandertal range and whatever the fate of the European Neandertals and however the question of their contribution to the ancestry of post--Neandertal Europeans is resolved, it is evident that the resolution will not be based on parallel evolving European lineages.

The European Riss/Würm

Europe provides the best sample that can be dated to Oxygen Isotope Stage 5e, the short period of interglacial climate that lies between the Riss and Würm glaciations. This was a time when conditions were warmer than today, and contrasts with the cooling of the subsequent stage 5 periods that culminated in the last set of glacial advances, the Würm in Europe. The European hominid evidence spanning this period is regionally distinct and is clearly foreshadowed by the specimens discussed above. In spite of uncertainties resulting from insecure provenience for some of the remains, a large sample can probably be dated to this period or one of the following stage 5 divisions.

The greatest single dating problem is the fact that the effects of the Würm climatic oscillations differ from one part of Europe and western Asia to another, and the perceived onset of the glaciation may not be the same everywhere. Some local geologists divide the glaciation into an early and late stage (this is more common in eastern Europe), others recognize 3 or 4 distinct advances (or in some cases even more). Ultimately, accurate interregional dating must be based on something beyond association with a glacial stage. This is not always possible.

WESTERN EUROPE

The Western European sample includes two crania from the Italian gravel pit of Saccopastore, dated by faunal comparisons, and a French mandible from Malarnaud. At 14 years of age Malarnaud was virtually adult and not likely to grow more; the fact that both ramus and corpus are extraordinarily small suggests the mandible is a female.

The Saccopastore specimens are thought to be female (number 1) and a less complete male (number 2). Recently described by S. Condemi, these specimens are clearly Neandertal in character and yet provide a link between these Europeans and their predecessors. Condemmi emphasizes the similarities of facial structure with Arago (especially the zygomatics), even as Stringer and Gamble describe Saccopastore 2 as "a scaled down Petralona" - these may not be contradictory assessments. In fact Saccopastore 1, the only compete European Neandertal cranium not requiring reconstruction, has a flexed basicranium and a distinct suprainiac fossa, and lacks lambdoidal flattening and an occipital bun. Moreover, the angle at the top of the nose is rather low, only toward the middle of the nasal bones does the structure become projecting.

The middle face is prognathic. C. Coon once described Neandertal faces by imagining them to be made of rubber with a form that appears to be the result of taking a Middle Pleistocene face by the tip of the nose and pulling it forward. The angle of the cheeks to a transverse plane is marked, as this imaginary pulling of the nose brings along the structures to its sides. The middle face projection is so great that there is a horizontal surface between the bottom of the orbit and the nasal margin (this is the result of a dramatically expanded maxillary sinus, often called maxillary puffing). Another consequence of the increased facial projection is a lengthening of the cranial base (measured from the top of the nose to the back of the cranium). The Saccopastore 1 face fits this description quite closely.

Saccopastore 2 is the larger and visibly more robust of the pair. With cranial capacities of 1245 and 1300 cc, however, the male is not much larger than the female and both are smaller than most of their Würm counterparts. According to S. Sergi, other (I would say possibly related) differences from the more northerly Neandertal males include

- a lesser magnitude of middle face projection,
- shorter temporal fossae,
- better development of the canine fossa (the zygomaxillary hollowing),

These could reflect an earlier date for Saccopastore, or the consequences of a south-north cline in cold adapted features related to the nose, or of course both as the earlier date places the crania in a warmer time period.

Finally, there is a largely complete Neandertal skeleton from Altamura cave, near Bari in Italy. According to V. Pesce Delfino and E. Vacca the face is heavily encrusted (figure 13.2), but enough can be seen to suggest that the specimen is a male Neandertal with a strongly projecting midfacial region lacking a canine fossa, a straight lower cheek border, rounded orbits, a broad and prominent nose, and a thick supraorbital torus (divided over the nose) set off from the frontal by a broad supratoral sulcus. Like some of the earlier remains, Bari has a sagittal keel and a squared-off anterior palate. The cranium does not appear to be especially large, and the postorbital constriction is pronounced. Much of the postcranial skeleton was preserved. Male sex is also indicated by pelvic features. The femora have large heads and a weak pilaster, although the *linea aspera* is pronounced (it resembles the Krapina Neandertals [see below] in these features). Height, estimated from femur length, is some 160-165 cm, about the same as La Chapelle (table 13.1).

CENTRAL AND EASTERN EUROPE

Using the Rhine and the German high plains as the eastern border of western Europe, the Riss/ Würm sample from regions farther to the east and south is much larger than its western counterpart. Apart from the pieces from the Slovakian site of Gánovce and small deciduous and permanent molars from Taubach in Germany, it is dominated by the very large sample from Krapina in Croatia.

Gánovce is a natural endocast, with a few adhering cranial bone pieces. It is long, low and broad with a clearly delineated occipital bun, and a maximum breadth in the mid-parietal region. The cranial capacity is 1320 cc. Found with it are natural molds of a fragmentary left radius and fibula. The specimens are indistinguishable from other Neandertal remains.

KRAPINA

Excavated between 1899 and 1905 the Krapina rockshelter in Croatia has yielded one of the largest fossil hominid samples known from a single site. Based on the dentitions about eighty individuals are represented. All of the Krapina remains have been cataloged in a publication by J. Radovčić and colleagues. The material was originally described in a series of papers and a rather complete (century. His excavation techniques were far in advance of contemporary practices. For instance, Gorjanović used the fluorine method of relative dating to show that the hominid and Pleistocene faunal remains at Krapina were contemporary some fifty years before the same technique was used in England to discredit the antiquity of the Piltdown material. The deposits in the cave were ultimately divided into 9 stratigraphic units (a basal level and 1-8) and he carefully wrote the level number on many of the human and animal bones recovered - this at a time when excavation finesse in Western Europe was characterized by the recovery of the Spy skeletons in Belgium - two head-to-head burials that were excavated without recording notes or leaving a stratigraphic column at the site and whose bones were irrevocably mixed up on the way to the laboratory. Although Krapina hominids were scattered through the time span of the site, extending from interglacial conditions to a colder, probably glacial period in level 5 and above, most were recovered from a single layer within Isotope Stage 5e called the "*Homo* zone". According to H. Schwarcz, preliminary ESR analysis indicates that the age of level 8, Krapina's topmost level, is 100 kyr. These data suggest that the base of Krapina, and the "*Homo* zone", may be at the end of the previous glacial advances (the fauna is temperate, not glacial, in character), some 129 kyr ago, and that the site may span less than 30 kyr in Oxygen Isotope Stage 5e and 5d, and possibly a small part of 5c.

The quarrying excavations left some 23% of the human bones with fresh breaks, according to M. Russell. However many of the breaks are much older, originating at the time that the specimens were fossilized. For example, the frontal of the Krapina C skull was broken off of the vault before fossilization and was eventually interred in a different area of the cave. This is why its coloration is quite different from the remainder of the specimen. The causes of the earlier fragmentation are unclear, but comparison with other cave sites such as Atapuerca suggests that trampling of decayed corpses by cave bears may have been an important element. The fragmentary nature of the specimens made them difficult to interpret, and in spite of the size of this immense collection, historically the focus of analysis shifted to the fewer but much more complete Neandertal burials found immediately afterwards in Western Europe. Thus, an early opportunity to appreciate Neandertal variability was lost.

Krapina Teeth

Because of its large size, the Krapina dental sample is particularly informative. There are 191 isolated teeth and 90 additional teeth in or associated with jaws, representing between 75 and 82 individuals. This extensive sample allows analysis of tooth size, variation, morphology and wear characteristics.

Taken as a whole, the Krapina teeth are larger than their Riss/Würm counterparts elsewhere. Only earlier hominids have larger posterior teeth, and no Pleistocene hominid sample has anterior teeth which average as large as those from Krapina. In the maxilla the expansion affects the lateral incisors more than the central ones; in 5 out of 13 cases the lateral incisor is broader than the central one, a condition virtually unknown outside of the Neandertals. The major factor contributing to the anterior tooth size expansion is the development of strong lingual tubercles. With the marked labial convexity of the crowns and moderate marginal ridge development, these comprise a unique pattern of European incisor shoveling, as described by T. Crummett. She views this anatomy as a mechanism for strengthening the teeth and increasing their occlusal area without changes that would make them take up more room in the toothrow. This anatomy distinguishes them from the Pleistocene Chinese and the plesiomorphic African condition. Crummett suggests that various populations evolved from the earlier African condition through emphasis on differing aspects of the shoveling complex. There seems to be a trade-off as when ridges are strongest the convexity is weakest. This suggests selection for increased size without taking up more room has acted to establish differing frequencies of these traits in various regions.

The large incisors are also marked by large incisor roots, no doubt an important reflection of the way these teeth were used. More direct evidence of anterior tooth use can be found in the pattern of wear. In some of the more complete specimens, incisor wear exceeds the wear on the surrounding teeth. Several of the unworn Krapina incisors were used to get accurate counts of the perikymata (see Chapter 4). The data A. Mann's group developed shows the Krapina Neandertals to have much higher perikymata numbers than a research team lead by C. Dean reported for at least one of their western European counterparts. High, regionally influenced, variability in perikymata numbers is one reason why they are no longer thought to reflect development times. However, the regionality itself may be important.

Krapina teeth are no more variable than the dentitions of recent skeletal populations, although the large samples serve to highlight just how much variation this means. While it is likely that their normal individual variation accounts for many of the dental differences at Krapina, comparison of size in complete adult mandibles suggests that sexual dimorphism may also be a contributing factor. As in the Zhoukoudian sample, the mandibles show more dimorphism than the teeth or crania. In fact, several normal anatomical markers of dimorphism are largely absent in this collection, and the small size of canines in massive mandibles such as Krapina H indicates that by themselves no teeth can be reliably used for sex determination.

Several different facets of these dental remains each provide insight into the people's lifeways. The individual ages indicate that an overabundance of young people died in the cave (or an underabundance of older adults). Many of the teeth show hypoplasia, a developmental deformity associated with periods of sickness and/or starvation during the time of tooth development. Interrupted enamel development was recorded in 13 of 18 individuals in a study by S. Molnar and I. Molnar (in contrast, T. White's examination of hypoplasia in the Swartkrans australopithecine teeth revealed a frequency of only 17%). A study of enamel thickness on the unworn molar crowns by S. Molnar and colleagues shows that on the average the enamel surfaces are the same thickness as in a large sample of living people, but because the Krapina teeth are larger their *relative* enamel thickness is less (actually, they are so different that the ranges barely overlap). The authors suggest that the average difference in thickness might reflect periods of interrupted enamel development during periods of illness early in life when the enamel is developing. It is possible that within the "*Homo* zone" where most of the human remains were found, the cave was used as a shelter for the sick (most of whom would be children) while the remainder of the tribe inhabited open-air sites as they followed game. This would account for the relative scarcity of adult remains at the cave, since many of the adults would have died elsewhere. A seasonal or occasional use of the cave is also suggested by what appears to be their burial customs, described below. However, in another analysis C. Larsen and colleagues found that the enamel defects indicated a high but not remarkable level of health-related problems

Several of the dentitions show unusual anomalies. A number of individuals share what might best be termed "a P_4 problem". Some mandibles are missing one or both of these teeth, in others it is rotated and in a strange position in the jaw. Is this a genetic anomaly shared because the individuals are related? Because of a shared cultural practice? The explanation is unclear. One common feature of many dentitions that does reflect the result of a shared behavior is the presence of toothpick grooves in many specimens. These are hollows between adjacent teeth, usually just at the gumline, that D. Frayer and M.

Russell believe to be the result of using fairly rigid toothpicks to clean the spaces between the teeth. Similar toothpick wear has been reported at earlier sites such as Zhoukoudian.

Crowding is not unusual in these dentitions. In one case there is a maloccluded, partially erupted M_3, in another the premolars are poorly aligned, and a third specimen has severe incisor crowding. These specimens provide support for the idea that changing patterns of food preparation, and perhaps diet, play an important role in posterior dental reduction. Cooking and other aspects of food preparation are more likely the key causes of this change as it is worldwide (albeit not synchronic) and it is unlikely that any single dietary shift happened everywhere. Workers such a T. Campbell and J. Wallace have argued that most masticatory variation in hunter/gatherers results from differences in food preparation and not diet. Reductions in the amount of chewing and the magnitude of force it involves would immediately affect the mandible, as bone growth is much more responsive to individual behaviors than the sizes of much earlier developing teeth. Children who, perhaps because of better food preparation, chewed less would experience less jaw growth and when their teeth finally erupted they would be crowded for lack of sufficient space. Eventually tooth crowding creates infections and other dental problems that lead to selection to reduce tooth size. Individuals with naturally smaller teeth experience fewer of these problems. In this process, Krapina is clearly at a transitional juncture in this Pleistocene-long process, a population for which the genome is still producing teeth that in many cases are too large to fit in the jaws that develop along (what was then) a normal trajectory. Crowding in the anterior dentition would be exacerbated in this sample, because of the size increases discussed above. The affects are ameliorated only by the fact that most of these expansions are in breadth, and in anatomical features such as shoveling which have a specific morphology that strengthens the teeth without causing them to take up any additional room in the toothrow.

Krapina Mandibles and Crania

Of the sixteen or more mandibles or mandibular fragments, only a few are adult and only mandible J is complete. In spite of only being about 20 at the time of death, this massive jaw shows the results of arthritis in the temporomandibular join, a well developed case of periodontal disease, and some other dental pathologies. All of the adults represented were prognathic, with the ramus beginning behind the last molar. The symphyses are straight and angled posteriorly, and only the adolescent mandible D shows evidence of a mental eminence. Variation in the adult corpus size is marked, and it is likely that small specimens, such as G, are female, while H and J are male. The sample of upper jaws is smaller than the mandibular sample, and unfortunately no maxilla can be associated with a cranium. The faces do not appear to have been large, and one small fragment of middle face shows that there was no canine fossa.

Analysis of the cranial sample presents many problems because of the extreme fragmentation of the bones. There are a large number of largely unidentified cranial fragments. The best preserved specimen is the C skull, cranium 3 (table 13.2) which lacks most of the base and posterior region and the lower face. Although widely regarded as a female, its browridges are among the thickest at the site. The widely separated orbits angle considerably toward the rear, resulting in a pronounced "beaking" at the facial midline as seen from above, also reflected in the backward angulation of the zygomatics. This "beaking" is accentuated by the high nasal angle, the nasal prominence however beginning midway down the nose from its root as it does in Atapuerca cranium 5 and Saccopastore 1. The suture between the nasal bones does not continue as a straight line up to the root as it does in virtually all humans (and other primates). Just short of the top of the nasals it deflects to the left side, reaching the **nasofrontal suture** well to the side instead of at the top of the small upward-facing triangle that the suture forms. This **nonmetric trait** is a rare human anomaly, occasionally occurring in small groups of relatives. According to F. and M. Smith, it occurs on all three Krapina specimens preserving the region. These are from the *Homo* zone and it is possible that they are related. This suggests the interpretation that a single tribe might have used the cave, perhaps seasonally, for decades or for generations. The Krapina cranium 3 face is delicate and lightly built compared with earlier specimens, what remains of the middle face reflects maxillary puffing. The frontal, discovered among the fragments and reconstructed by the author, shows a moderate bulge in an otherwise receding forehead. Along the face of the frontal, about midway up the center of the bone there are a series of thin scratches extending from side to side. These seem to be the result of using a knife to help remove the scalp. Archaic features include a low cranial height, thick vault bones, and marked spongy bone development at the cranial base where, unlike many later Neandertals (and some earlier specimens), the greatest cranial breadth is retained. The mastoids are small, a feature sometimes found in the Würm Neandertals. Many of these features seem to have been common in earlier European females (Arago 21 and Ehringsdorf H, for example). The combination of facial beaking and a high nasal angle (prominent nose) is characteristically European.

Table 13.2
Krapina Numbers and Letters

Krapina Number	Krapina Letter	Level
Cranium	Cranium	
1	A	8
2	B	3
3	C	4
4	D_1 (frontoparietal)	4
5	D	4
6	E	3
Maxilla	Maxilla	
1	A	
2	B	7
3	C	5
4	D (and mandible D)	4
5	E	4
6	F (and mandible H)	4
Mandible	Mandible	
7	A	
8	B	
9	C	7
10	E	5
11	F	
12	G	6
13	J	4
14	K	5

The less complete crania and cranial fragments, where comparable, provide a series of contrasts and consistencies. For instance, the E skull or cranium 6 is smaller and more delicately built than cranium 3 but has an even higher nasal angle and in life probably had a more prominent nose. The browridges are smaller than the cranium 3 torus, and unlike them they are clearly divided from the low frontal by a groove. The third fairly complete specimen, the D skull or cranium 5, consists of a large and very robust cranial rear (occipital, parietals, and temporal). This is not to be confused with a "D cranium" incorrectly associating a frontal (cranium 4) with the parietoccipital that was reconstructed and published by C. Brace. Cranium 5 is low and very broad, supporting large mastoids and a prominent nuchal torus with a suprainiac fossa above it. Its maximum cranial breadth is at the cranial base, as in cranium 3. The back of the skull is bunned, combining moderate lambdoidal flattening and a projecting cranial rear. Similar in many ways to cranium 10, another incomplete cranial rear, the two are almost certainly a males.

There are a large number of additional, less complete crania, each with its own piece of the puzzle. For instance Cranium 20, the top of a head, has a metopic suture like Suard 1. The juvenile cranium 2 preserves much the same areas as Biache and is similar to it in size and in the presence of flattening at the rear of the cranium. Other younger juveniles show that many of the features common in Neandertals are found at a very young age.

Table 13.3
Supraorbital Reduction

	Thickness			Projection		
	Medial	Central	Lateral	Medial	Central	Lateral
Bilzingsleben	18.0	17.0		25.0	31.0	
Petralona	23.0	19.0	11.5			
Steinheim	18.0	16.0	9.2	19.5	21.0	24.5
Arago	20.0	13.0	12.0	23.0	29.0	26.0
Atapuerca 121	16.0	16.0	14.0		31.0	35.0
Atapuerca 200	16.5			26.0		
Atapuerca Cranium 4		12.0	11.5			
Atapuerca Cranium 5		14.1	14.6			
Krapina adult mean	17.5	11.0	12.5	20.0	24.0	24.0
Krapina range	16-22	7-14	10-17	17-23	23-26	23-27
Vindija 202		9.5	11.3		19.0	19.5
260		8.5	11.0		21.0	22.5
261		8.3	10.5		23.0	24.5
262		8.6	10.0		16.0	22.0
284		8.0	10.4		16.0	22.0
305	20.5	10.4		19.0	18.5	
St. Césaire	18.0	8.5	9.2			

The numerous more fragmentary pieces are important to an assessment of the variability at Krapina. Temporal fragments, for instance, reveal variation in the mastoid process that ranges from mastoids that are even smaller than in cranium 3 to large projecting mastoid structures that extend well below the occipitomastoid crest in a decidedly *un*-Neandertal like manner. Frontal fragments vary in preservation from fairly complete, such as crania 4 and 23, to very fragmentary pieces. They give evidence of an average reduction in browridge thickness compared with earlier Europeans such as the Atapuerca remains, Petralona and Steinheim (table 13.3). The sample shows considerable variation in frontal size and morphology; some specimens have vertically tall tori with little projection, others are thin but project markedly, and of course there are all the combinations between. The variability at the site, perhaps its most important aspect, spotlights the difficulties in dealing with more singular remains. Even relatively complete specimens such as Ehringsdorf can be easily accommodated within the Krapina range, as F. Smith points out, making it virtually impossible to address issues of evolutionary change without the advantages of being able to compare fairly large sample sizes such as Krapina and Atapuerca. However variability cries out for explanation and in this case the usual potential sources, sex and idiosyncrasy, are joined by a third. The dental remains show a inordinate number of subadult individuals. Variation due to age is difficult to assess from fragmentary bones of this age because small pieces cannot often be classified as female or young male, gracile adult or teenage.

In sum, the several best-preserved Krapina crania show some degree of variation, and the isolated fragments suggest that the actual cranial variation at the site was far greater than these few specimens indicate. F. Smith argues that in their total morphological pattern the specimens are unquestionably Neandertal, with:

- low and broad vaults
- broad, shallow temporal fossae with a low anterior articular face
- prominent continuous supraorbitals with large frontal sinuses restricted to them
- receding foreheads with frontal bossing
- columnar outer orbital margins in a lateral orientation
- a broad upper nasal region lacking any depression at the nasal root
- a concave, angled nasal profile

However, they do show certain consistent differences from their later, western European counterparts. Some of these differences are surely due to their date. For instance, Like the Saccopastore specimens, comparing by sex these crania are smaller than most of the Würm Neandertals. Appreciation of the differences has been hindered by the fragmentary nature of the site and the fact that the two most nearly complete specimens (crania 3 and 6) are probably female (in Western Europe Neandertal women were buried much less frequently then men, making sex bias an important element skewing comparisons).

Krapina Postcrania

An enormous number of fragmentary postcranial remains were recovered from Krapina. There are 130 specimens catalogued from the lower trunk and limbs alone, which could represent as many as ninety different individuals according to E. Trinkaus (but probably far fewer, see below). Data from these remains provide evidence for a moderate-sized robustly built physique. They differ from most modern humans in a number of ways. Excepting some details of the pelvis, all of these are related to their robust body build and strength. As authors such as F. Smith and E. Trinkaus have noted, there is nothing about these remains to suggest different locomotor patterns or functions than can be found today.

Krapina provides the earliest fairly complete postcranial set for Late Pleistocene humans. In fact, it is one of the largest postcranial sample known from before 30 kyr. The Krapina folk resemble their more archaic predecessors in a number of postcranial features. These include the following traits that diverge from the modern condition:

- thickening of the shaft walls in all the long bones
- elongation of the front of the pelvis and the associated thinning of the upper portion of the pubis
- anterior position of the pillar-like buttress running up the ilium
- curved ribs enclosing a rounded trunk form
- lateral orientation of the glenoid (scapular-humeral) joint

There are three adaptive complexes represented here, reflecting muscular strength, pelvic adaptations, and chest shape. The first of these is related to bone strength - cortical bone thickening is marked, but somewhat reduced compared with earlier samples. There are other strength-related variations that show reduction; for instance, the flattening at the middle of the femur shafts is lessened. The second was already discussed in regard to the West Asian specimens. The lengthening of the front of the pelvic inlet responds to three factors:

1. an anteriorly positioned pelvic inlet with the sacrum close to the biacetabular line - with the long pubes this flares the ilia outwards and rotates them backwards which makes the position of the iliac pillar (resisting adductor force) appear more anterior on them.

2. a pelvic inlet that is large relative to body height (but not relative to body weight
   - these are relatively heavy individuals).
3. the affects of a trunk shape (reflected in rib and clavicle curvature) that was
   more rounded, or "barrel-shaped," than in most living people.

The third complex, rounded or "barrel-shaped trunk, reflects a cold adaptation that maximizes body mass in the core (where body heat is produced) and gives it the most heat-retentive shape. It also influences pelvis shape, as noted above, and changes the scapula orientation to make the shoulder joint appear more lateral-facing. An accompanying adaptation not discernible at Krapina (because there are no associated limbs) is to minimize the extremities (where body heat is lost)

The Krapina folk were large, but the question is exactly how they compare with their European predecessors. Table 13.4 shows this for two proximal femora. These are useful to compare because there is enough of each left to show they are both adults, and their sizes (especially compared with more complete specimens such as La Ferrassie 1 and 2) indicate that one is male and the other female. Compared by sex, there is no difference in shaft size, and no reason to suggest a significant difference in body size.

Table 13.4
Femur Dimensions

	Head Diameter	Anterior-Posterior Length below the lesser trochanter	Medial-Lateral Breadth below the lesser trochanter
Arago 38	40		
Arago 48		28.8	35.3
Castel di Guido		21.0	29.8
Ehringsdorf E		29.8	35.3
Krapina 213 (male)	53	30.9	36.6
214 (female)	44	26.2	30.7

However not all postcranial comparisons give the same results. Comparison of the Arago 44 female innominate with Krapina females 209 and 211 shows the Krapina innominates to be generally smaller. Krapina humeri are definitely smaller than their Atapuerca counterparts, but the three that can be compared may all be females. In all, we cannot disprove the hypothesis that body size at Krapina differs significantly from earlier Europeans, but if it does differ the direction is toward smaller size at Krapina.

The Burial Issue

Cannibalism was the original interpretation given to the fragmentary Krapina remains. Gorjanović-Kramberger first made the suggestion and it has survived as a highly regarded scenario for the site. Yet, contradicting this interpretation is evidence suggesting that natural processes created the bone breakage, and that many specimens were buried. In his review of Gorjanović-Kramberger's field notes, Radovčić calls attention to the large patch of darkened humus at the back of the "Homo zone" that Gorjanović noted. He suggests that the high organic contact of this area marks the site of hominid burials. The possibility of burials at Krapina is indicated by the very unusual distribution of preserved bones. Virtually every element of the skeleton is conserved, including large numbers of delicate bones that are virtually never found because they break and deteriorate so easily; for instance the 16 patellae, or the paper-thin ethmoid bone from the inner orbital wall. Trinkaus compared the pattern of bone preservation, which parts of bones and which bones remain, with buried and non-buried Neandertal samples and with other known burials. On the whole, Krapina is very similar to the 16 reported Neandertal burials and more recent burials. He suggests that slightly under 15 burials would account for most of the bones at the site.

M. Russell attempted a different approach to the burial question. She examined the pattern of cutmarks. Many authors have regarded these cutmarks as a reflection of defleshing prior to eating; that is, cannibalism. However the bones lacked some of the diagnostic reflections of butchery, such as evidence of smashing for marrow extraction (bone marrow is a highly desired source of fat). Russell inventoried the position and details of all the cutmarks in the collection and used these data to examine two potential causal hypotheses:

1. butchery (the corpses were cut up and butchered like any other meat-bearing species)
2. secondary burial (the corpses were disarticulated after the bones were cleaned of most or all of their flesh

She argued that secondary burial was a better explanation of the data for 3 reasons

1. the pattern of cutmarks (where they were found and at what densities) matched other skeletal collections of recent populations who practiced disarticulation after defleshing
2. the pattern was different from a collection of butchered Reindeer bones from another Neandertal site, Combe Grenal (in meat processing the cutmarks are in different places and there are fewer marks on the bone as the butchers avoid scratching the bone so as not to dull their implements)
3. The sharpness of many of the cutmarks indicated that there were made directly on the bone (disarticulation without flesh) and not through flesh as would be the case if they reflected meat removal.

Russell describes the secondary burial process, which she posits for Krapina, as practiced in living groups as follows (p. 389):

> Corpses were allowed to decompose underground for varying amounts of time. When enough deaths had occurred within a social group to make a secondary burial ceremony desirable, the accumulated remains were disinterred and any remaining soft tissue carefully removed from the bones with stone knives.

The corpses would then be disarticulated at their joints, bundled together, and reburied.

Her work reveals one of the earliest instances of hominid burials, and certainly the earliest secondary burials. The significance is twofold. Burial of any sort is a clear reflection of a belief system. There is no reason to think that interment reflects only friendly feelings for the deceased or the desire to remove a large moldering objet from the living area - either of these would have lead to intentional burials much earlier in human evolution. Second, the import of secondary burial is the evidence it provides for advanced planning and long term organization of activities - abilities often denied to Neandertals because of how their archaeological traces are interpreted (this is particularly well-discussed in a series of interviews published by J. Fischman).

However, Russell's studies have not been without criticism. Champions of the cannibalism hypothesis have argued that the Krapina cutmark pattern is also similar to animal butchery patterns at other Neandertal sites, and that in some cases high numbers of cutmarks can be seen as well. These observations may indicate different styles or traditions for butchering animals - they certainly do not help clarify the secondary burial issue.

In sum, there is very convincing evidence for some burials at Krapina, based on the distribution of bones that were preserved. A good case can be made that some of these were secondary burials, but the case if far from airtight and the possibility of cannibalism cannot be excluded.

The Mystery of Level 8

The topmost layer at Krapina is level 8, so close to the roof of the cave that specimens could not have been buried into it from some higher, later deposit. Dated to 100 kyr the industry is Mousterian according to J. Simek, and given the above one would expect that the specimens in it are Neandertal. This, however, is not completely clear. Implications of the several specimens found in this level are discussed in Chapter 14.

Krapina's Place in European Evolution

Well publicized at the time of its discovery, the detailed knowledge of this site awaited an analysis that could effectively utilize the fragmented specimens. Although many paleoanthropologists have studied this invaluable collection (several beginning their professional careers there) knowledge of the Krapina hominids largely comes from the efforts of F. Smith. The importance of Krapina results from the size of the sample and the fact that nearly all body parts are represented. While an excellent description of the material was available early in the development of European paleoanthropology, it was never given the full consideration it deserved. Perhaps this was the result of the typological thinking prevalent earlier in this century. J. Radovčić , however, argues that the main impediment was the eclipse of this large but fragmentary sample by the spectacular discovery of several very complete specimens from France, La Chapelle and La Ferrassie. One or two individuals (especially the C skull and the J mandible) came to represent a sample whose most important feature was its size and variation. However, workers were aware of the variability. In fact, there was an attempt to show that both modern-type people and Neandertals were present. It was thought that the former population exterminated the Neandertals and butchered them, thereby accounting for the fragmentary condition of the bones. Such an interpretation cannot be supported. The "modern type" is actually represented by the remains of younger individuals and bone fragmentation is the common condition at most sites.

Krapina presents a gracilized development from earlier European morphology. Its most unusual aspect is the magnitude of anterior tooth size expansion. The size of the sample provides insight into the extent of genetic variation present at one location in pre-Würm Europe. This genetic variation provided the basis for subsequent evolutionary change.

The European Würm Neandertals

The complex of deteriorating climate changes leading to the Würm glaciation begins with Oxygen Isotope stage 5d, some 122 kyr ago. At that time the sea core record of ocean ice shows that a series of increasingly severe climatic oscillations began. The onset of glacial conditions on the continent may not reflect these changes initially because the less severe nature of the earlier fluctuations may have allowed local conditions to predominate at first. By some accounts the glaciation proper began by stage 5b (93 kyr), and by others stage 4 (74 kyr). Further into the glacial cycle, however, glacial or glacial-related conditions prevailed everywhere. The continental ice sheets that developed shifted **periglacial** tundra conditions southward and eastward. Even as conditions were moderated by the ocean in at the western edge of the continent, they worsened considerably to the north where the Low Countries were turned into polar deserts, and eastward where the open plains became simply uninhabitable.

The rapid oscillations included some small ameliorations just after 40 kyr (continental evidence for these is interpreted as the Middle Würm interstadial), and an even more severe onset of cold begins with Isotope stage 2, at 32 kyr. This reaches its maximum at some 27 kyr, which is the latest date for Neandertal occurrences either culturally or as distinguishable anatomical entities, and an even more severe maximum at 18 kyr..

The European Würm Neandertals are known from over 70 sites, according to R. Klein. Most of the more complete remains are from the Western European burials, a smaller number of relatively complete specimens come from the circum-Mediterranean world. For the more fragmentary remains, however, the geographic distribution is more broadly across Europe and extends into central Asia where sites such as Denisova and Oklandnikov in the Altai Mountains of south-central Siberia have Mousterian industries and isolated teeth with Neandertal characteristics, according to C. Turner. Neandertals are probably the single most intensively studied group of fossil humans, with numerous general works reviewing their morphology, adaptation, ecology, and behavior. Monographal treatments are available for most of the complete specimens (table 13.5). While some paleoanthropologists have focused on explaining their anatomy in an adaptive context, the main point of many of these studies has generally been to call attention to and explain what appears to be a number of "unusual" features, with special reference to the question of whether or not the latest European Neandertal populations were ancestral to the "modern" European populations that succeeded them.

Table 13.5
Monographs or Very Long Papers Written on Complete Adult European Neandertals

Specimens	Author(s)	Date
Spy	J. Fraipont and M. Lohest	1887
Neandertal	G. Schwalbe	1901
La Chapelle	M. Boule	1913
La Quina	G. Henri-Martin	1923
Le Moustier	H. Weinert	1925
Saccopastore 1	S. Sergi, S. Condemmi	1948a, 1991
Saccopastore 2	S. Sergi, S. Condemmi	1948b, 1991
La Ferrassie	J-L. Heim	1976, 1982a,b
Mt. Circeo	M. Piperno and G. Scichilone (editors)	1991

Neandertals were clearly temperate and cold climate adapted Eurasians, but they did not live in all habitats. They preferred hilly or semi-mountainous areas, the source of virtually all skeletal remains associated with the Mousterian. Stringer and Gamble point out that their use of the open plains of eastern Europe, and higher mountainous areas, first began in the middle of the Late Pleistocene, perhaps 60 kyr. Moreover, as they put it, "Neanderthals in the northern parts of the continent tended to abandon and re-occupy regions more frequently than their southern counterparts, as climate affected the abundance and predictability of animal resources".

The majority of the sample was excavated some time ago under less-than-perfect conditions, and thus the exact stratigraphic position of some of the important finds is unknown. Recent reviews of the older sites and the careful excavation techniques used with more recent discoveries allow many specimens to be placed within the context of the main European Würm advances, but beyond the question of accurate excavations and dates, the question is complex because theoretical considerations have come to play an important role in viewing the temporal contexts of these earlier-discovered sites for which numerical dates cannot be obtained. The problem is whether the different **facies** (varieties) of the Mousterian represent an evolutionary sequence, ethnic differences, or varying functions (or of course any combination of these). According to some researchers the Mousterian facies are simply functional responses to environmental differences. If, however, differing traditions create the variation it would imply the possibility that biological variation within the Neandertals can be linked to the facies (the issue of culture=biology again). There is one facies of the Mousterian that emphasizes hand axes, called Mousterian of Acheulean tradition (although there is no special link known with the earlier Acheulean folk). A single juvenile male from the French site of Le Moustier is the only specimen known to be associated with this facies, and the arguments rage on as to whether this teenager is biologically different from other Neandertals because of its implications for resolving the question of why there are Mousterian varieties. Only with the possibility that the different Mousterian facies represent a developmental sequence can the cultural context be used to date associated Neandertals. The issue revolves about the accuracy of the electron capture dating techniques, as all but the most recent Neandertal sites are beyond the accurate range of radiocarbon. Thus, in their Thermoluminescence dating of Le Moustier at 40 kyr, H. Valladas raised the possibility that the Mousterian of Acheulean tradition was later than the other Mousterian facies, a possibility seized by the archaeologist P. Mellars who used it to suggest that most other Neandertals are much older, but subsequently argued against by N. Ashton and J. Cook, and which will continue unabated until direct dates can be ascertained for important specimens excavated earlier this century.

CRANIAL FORM

Considering the sample as a whole and for the moment ignoring the geographic, temporal, and sex differences within it, there are a number of average differences that distinguish these Europeans from their ancestors. Yet virtually every feature of the Würm Neandertal sample is found, at lower frequency, before the Würm. Compared with this earlier sample, the Würm Neandertal cranial capacity is distinctly larger, and the crania tend to be longer and relatively narrower. Changes in the Neandertal crania leading to the increased capacity are as much morphological as metric. Neandertal skulls look more filled out, with prominent frontal, parietal, and occipital plane bossing. The parietal bosses are quite posterior, giving Neandertal crania a "teardrop" shape when they are viewed from above.

Many aspects of Neandertal cranial anatomy are anything but robust. Vault bones, for instance, are quite thin and the cheeks are small and delicately built. Spongy bone development at the cranial base is markedly decreased. Combined with the parietal expansion and posterior bossing this results in the consistent pattern of braincase breadth exceeding basal breadth. The position of maximum breadth is far to the rear of the cranium, about midway up the parietals. Thus even more often than in their predecessors, as seen from the rear, Neandertal crania take on a circular appearance.

Brain Size

Würm Neandertal brain size averages almost 12% larger than their Middle Pleistocene European predecessors (table 13.6). The sexual dimorphism is a little greater than these earliest Europeans, about the same as the Zhoukoudian sample. Neandertal brains are often described as unusually large, or larger than modern humans, and there have been numerous explanations for why human brain size subsequently decreased. However, this was not the case. The sample has more males than females and an average not taking that into account could appear unusually big. However, the middle sex average is 1431 cc, a figure that lies between the average capacities of two different English samples (1386 cc and 1480 cc) and is close to the mean for many other European populations. Given the several studies that link cranial capacity to climate, suggesting that larger capacities are associated with cooler environments, a comparison with Eskimo mean capacities may be more relevant. Populational averages for several Eskimo groups exceed 1550 cc, more than 100 cc larger and for people who are probably not substantially heavier. These issues are discussed at length by P. Tobias, and C. Beals and colleagues, but I believe the possibility that Neandertal brain sizes are *smaller* than expected for similarly sized and adapted modern human populations could be productively entertained.

Table 13.6
European Brain Sizes

	Female average	Male average
Middle Pleistocene	1134 (n=6)	1305 (n=2)
Würm Neandertal	1286 (n=4)	1575 (n=7)

R. Holloway speculates along similar lines, suggesting that critical elements in Neandertal brain size include body mass, temperature, and metabolism. There are, he asserts, no demonstrable differences between the anatomical features revealed on Neandertal endocasts, and those of living humans (this is a theme found in the works of virtually all paleoneurologists who have made the comparisons). He did find evidence that Neandertal brains were slightly larger in the anterior part of the occipito-parietal zones. If this reflects a larger primary visual striate cortex, it would parallel the markedly higher visual striate cortex he has found in Australian Aborigines, who consistently have higher test scores for visuospatial abilities than Europeans. The relatively lager size of this area may be related to occipital bunning.

Changes at the Cranial Rear

Changes in the occiput are significant. Neandertals generally have only a short, weakly developed nuchal torus. The position of the torus is lower than in earlier Europeans. Thus the length of the nuchal muscle attachment area decreases, while the height of the occiput above it increases. Even though the occiputs are as broad, or even broader, than earlier specimens, the effect is to further reduce the attachment area for these muscles. However, the changes are more complex than simply larger or smaller. Neandertals emphasize the nuchal muscles that extend across the entire rear of the head - muscles important in stabilizing the head or in pulling it back (as in anterior tooth loading). The actions of these muscles create a broad pull across the occiput (the evenness and reduced magnitude accounts for the weak nuchal torus expression). This torus dips downward at the midline and according to R. Caspari, during ontogeny as its anatomy develops there is bone resorption just above the torus which creates the suprainiac fossa, a common feature in the earlier Europeans (as this morphological combination coalesces) and a ubiquitous characteristic of Neandertals.

Another change in the occiput is the flattening of the area above the back of the skull, called "bunning," As seen in many of the specimens, this flattening accentuates the short vertical face above the nuchal torus and extends back onto the parietals. The sides of the bun are flattened as well. Bunning elongates the back of the skull. The short vertical face is also important in suprainiac fossa formation, according to Caspari, as a taller face would be able to resist the tension created by the downward nuchal muscle pull without a fossa (or a broad torus) forming. The earliest appearance of the full bunning morphology is in Biache; the subsequent change is one of frequency. To some extent, the more horizontal orientation of the nuchal plane is a compensation for its decreased area. While the total area of nuchal muscle attachment decreases, and the lever arm for the musculature is shorter, the more horizontal plane maintains a larger muscle cross-section than its size suggests.

Other characteristic features of the posterior region, including the decrease in spongy bone and moderate (but variable) size of the mastoids, are probably consequences of reduced muscularity. The small mastoids may also result from the more anterior placement of the foramen magnum. In the evolution of Neandertal midfacial prognathism the throat moves anteriorly along with the face, preserving the anatomical relationships that are important in swallowing, breathing, and speech. The sides of the cranial base do not shift, however, which is why a line drawn between the ear openings is in front of the foramen magnum in earlier Europeans, but behind it in Neandertals. The posterior position of the mastoid process, relative to the axis of rotation for the head, improves the leverage of the **sternocleidomastoid muscles** which turn the head and stabilizes it when the front teeth are used. With better leverage the muscles produce less force on the mastoid process, and its size is moderate or small.

However one element in the mastoid region is large. Internal to the mastoids and separated from them by a broad digastric sulcus is a large juxtamastoid process.. This prominence (sometimes divided into a paramastoid process laterally and an occipitomastoid crest medially by the groove for the occipital artery) can be larger than the mastoid process and appear to dwarf it in side view. According to J. McKee and B. Helman the muscle usually attaching there is the digastric; it often has muscle fiber attachments in the digastric sulcus and a tendon attachment on the paramastoid process.
E. Trinkaus proposes that the marked development of the structure indicates strong muscular forces produced by the digastric muscles. One function of these is to **retract** the mandible (pull is backwards), and he therefore suggests that the anatomy is part of the adaptation to anterior tooth loading. McKee and Helman note that the variability in these structures is marked (as is the variability in muscle attachments on them), and conclude that the region may not be a reliable taxonomic indicator.

Supraorbital Torus

To some degree the Neandertals are known for their browridges, characterized (or caricatured) by them as being robust. Browridge development is predictable for Neandertals from M. Russell's model (Chapter 9), as these people combine facial stresses from anterior tooth use, and an angle between the receding forehead and vertically oriented face. While adult browridge size in this sample is remarkably variable, average characteristics combine reduced projection and decreased thickening compared with earlier Europeans. For instance, few male Neandertals have browridges as thick and projecting as the Steinheim female. In all cases the torus is continuous over the orbits. It arches over the eye sockets rather than forming a straight bar, and generally appears much less prominent than in the earlier Europeans because the frontal begins more above than behind it. Moreover, the frontal is characteristically bulging, providing a distinct raised forehead, albeit positioned at a receding angle. There are no cases of sagittal keeling on the frontal. Even a single site such as Krapina holds virtually the entire known Neandertal range of browridge sizes and anatomies, but at the same time there are average trends over the Neandertal time span that are discussed below.

THE FACES

Neandertal faces have much in common with the earlier Middle Pleistocene Europeans, but there are some important contrasts as well. Many of the unique or more dramatic features of Neandertal facial morphology center about the nose. A fully fleshed Neandertal nose must have been a phenomenal sight. Almost every specimen is characterized by a nasal aperture of very large dimensions. The few remaining nasal bones, those not destroyed by the Neandertal habit of breaking open the midface to remove the brain, indicate that north of the circum-Mediterranean area the nasal profile was highly angled so that the fleshy nose was extremely prominent. (Few fleshy reconstructions accurately show this.) Accentuating the appearance that these noses had in life is the fact that Neandertal crania are broader than Neandertal faces (this relation is virtually unknown in earlier specimens with smaller brain sizes). Everything from the wide cranial rear forward must have created the appearance of a pyramid, with the nose its apex.

Directly to the sides of the nose, the maxillary sinuses are expanded outward, giving the midface a puffy appearance and a flat or even convex surface (this region has a vertically oriented canine fossa along the sides of the nose in many other human populations). To the sides of this region, the zygomatics angle strongly backward. Thus, between the nasal margins and the zygomatic arch, the orbital margins and the alveolar margin, the cheeks so defined lie in a flat, backwards angled plane. Combined with the great cranial breadth, the total effect of these features is a strongly projecting midfacial profile to the sides of a larger projecting nose, which could only have accentuated its appearance in life.

The prominence of the nose and maxillary sinus expansion are part of the Würm Neandertal adaptive complex expressed in the prognathism of the total face. From the top of the nose to the tooth row, the entire face projected strongly in front of the cranium, although its sagittal profile was fairly vertical. There are two opposite trends: degree of alveolar projection just below the nose is reduced compared with most earlier Europeans (but see Petralona), while above the projection is markedly greater. This facial projection, the strong posterior angulation of the cheeks, and the high nasal profile results in an exaggerated combination of facial features still found in many Europeans.

The magnitude of facial projection varies both by sex and by geography. Projection of the middle and upper face is greater in the northern males than in the southern ones, and greater in both than in the females. The southern males and females also differ from the northerners in their reduced backward extension of the skull and lesser degree of occipital bunning, although not in cranial height or browridge projection.

Several theories have been developed to explain the facial anatomy by modeling the functions of faces constructed like Neandertals. E. Trinkaus regards the Neandertal complex as the result of maintaining large, functionally important anterior teeth (and their supporting roots and alveolar bone) while the masticatory muscles and their zygomatic support system retreat to a more posterior position as part of the general trend for facial reduction. In this model the midface is "left" in a projecting position.

Two models are based on the biomechanical function of the flattened cheek region described above. W. Hylander, F. Smith, and others including this author have focused on the requirements of resisting the stresses caused by masticatory force, a function related to the importance of the expanded Neandertal anterior dentitions (there is a subtle difference with Trinkaus here, as he regards the large midface and expanded anterior dentitions as retentions of the ancestral morphology). Y. Rak and B. Demes relate specific midfacial structures to this function. Rak argues that the almost sagittal angle of the cheek (this is a bit of an idealized exaggeration) is created by the need to resist masticatory forces in the sagittal plane that cause a rotation within the facial structure, the front of the face moving up and the rear (for instance, the bask of the palate) moving down. In Rak's thinking these are mainly upward forces in the midface caused by vertical loads on the anterior teeth (for instance holding something tightly between the incisors). Rak envisions the vertically and almost sagittally oriented cheek as best positioned to resist this. Demes focuses on the forces created in each cheek by the combination of upward force on the incisors and downward force created by the masseter muscles. She argues that a flat sheet of bone filling in the space between will be the best adaptation to these forces as it would deform least and minimize local areas where deformation could concentrate (especially at angled surfaces). The reader might remember that this is very similar to Rak's explanation of australopithecine facial anatomy, and in fact these two explanations are not contradictory.

The last of these adaptive models, really the brainchild of C. Coon, is cold adaptation. It does not particularly contradict the biomechanical models discussed above, and it seems most probable that a full understanding of Neandertal facial anatomy is complex, and involves both several adaptations and the influence of evolutionary history.

COLD ADAPTATION

One of the primary functions of the nose is to warm and moisten the inspired air. The size and shape of the nose are related to the efficiency of this function. Nasal breadth is also affected by the breadth between the canines. The breadth across the canines is large in the Neandertals because the canine and incisor teeth are large; in fact, large anterior teeth probably help account for the expanded nasal breadths in all of the Middle Pleistocene samples. Thus, before the emergence of cold-adapted Neandertals, there was a background of broad nasal openings. Selection to improve the efficiency of the nose in warming and moistening air exapted this anatomy, expanding the height of the nasal aperture and the projection of the nasal bones to increase the functional capacity of the nose by providing for more internal volume in the nasal cavity, where the warming and moistening occur. The large size of the Neandertal nose is an exaptation to a cold and dry environment—conditions characteristic of steppe and northern tundra that prevailed over their range during much of the last glaciation.

Nose size is not the only cold adaptation of Neandertal facial morphology. As Coon points out, in living people the nasal passages lie close to the arteries that supply blood to the brain. Breathing in cold air would act to cool the blood in these arteries, and this could be disadvantageous because the brain is sensitive to temperature changes. Neandertals descended from European populations which, as we have seen, already had expanded maxillary sinuses and midfacial prognathism. Selection to maintain arterial blood temperature acted on this already present complex in the cold-adapting Neandertals. Further increases in midfacial prognathism added to the distance between the nasal passages and the arteries supplying the brain, which reduced cooling of these arteries by inspired cold air. Facial projection is greater in the northern sample than in the southern one, as one might expect if it corresponds to a cold adaptation. A third adaptation can be seen in the blood supply to the face. The foramena that bring blood vessels to the facial tissues are larger and more numerous in the European Neandertals.

There are some other indications of cold adaptation in the European Neandertals. Trunk shape, limb proportions, and even to some extent relative joint sizes are similar in all cold adapted peoples. C. Ruff shows that pelvic width is maximized in most cold adapted populations, reflecting the broad trunk that follows from Bergman's rule. Limbs are shortened compared with tropical or subtropical folk, as described below.

ANTERIOR TOOTH USE

The largest anterior tooth sizes were achieved in Europe before the Würm. In the evolution of pre-Würm Europeans, the anterior teeth were found to expand while the posteriors reduced. As part of this expansion the internal tubercles were maximized on all the maxillary anteriors, and marginal ridges increased in prominence while the crowns became more curved in the maxillary incisors, all reflections of packing increased dental tissue into a limited space according to T. Crummett. During the Würm reduction characterizes much of this dental morphology. The latest Neandertals have anterior teeth dramatically smaller than the pre-Würm Europeans (table 13.7). This represents a change in the direction of selection.

The cause of reduction was first proposed by the Croatian paleoanthropologist D. Gorjanović-Kramberger. Working at the turn of the century on the Krapina hominids and their culture, he realized that the subsequent reduction of jaws and teeth must have come from the replacement of their functions by tools. Direct evidence that Neandertals used their teeth as tools subsequently came much later, from the Shanidar cave discovery (Chapter 12) of an individual with an amputated arm. Studying Shanidar 1, T. Stewart realized that his front teeth were worn heavily and obliquely in a way that showed he used his mouth to replace the missing hand, and it was soon realized that this "peculiar" wear was not restricted to Neandertals with amputated arms. C. Brace suggested that the Neandertals quite regularly used their anterior teeth for purposes other than chewing, and while debated over the years (for instance see the J. Wallace paper and commentary following), other evidence such as the scratchmarks found on the outer surfaces of incisors discussed in Chapter 11 help confirm this interpretation. We have come to regard this as a complex that evolved through the entire Pleistocene. What is interesting about the Neandertals is that this behavior must have been changing during the time of the European Mousterian. They present the first evidence of reduction in anterior tooth use.

Table 13.7
Maxillary Anterior Tooth Breadths in earliest and Latest Neandertals

	I^1 breadth	I^2 breadth	C breadth
Krapina Average	8.9	8.9	10.3
(range)	(8.1-9.7)	(7.8-9.9)	(9.5-11.4)
Much later Neandertals:			
Hortus Average	7.9	7.9	9.3
Vindija 290	8.3		
289		8.4	
287			10.6
St. Césaire	7.9	8.0	9.7

As noted above, some aspects of Neandertal craniofacial morphology are related to the various functions of their large anterior teeth. Their size, structural reinforcements such as the marginal ridges and internal tubercles, equality of maxillary central and lateral incisor dimensions, and their relatively heavy wear, attest to an important role for them. This anatomical complex has a significant effect on their facial anatomy. The large incisor roots help maintain the large lower face and keep the front of the palate broad, accounting in part for the large Neandertal nasal breadth. The strain in the maxillary bone (especially to the sides of the nose) from consistent loading of the front teeth helps account for the expanded maxillary sinus.

Eskimos are another cold adapted population that are well known for their high levels of anterior tooth use. Yet, Neandertal craniofacial anatomy appears quite different from that of Eskimos, and the question is why. The two are populations that share powerful anterior tooth use and cold adaptation, and a purely adaptive explanation of anatomy predicts that they should be quite alike - certainly more similar than they actually are. M. Spencer and B. Demes examined the question of whether there are any Neandertal and Eskimo resemblances, with regard to how their crania and faces have adapted to intense anterior tooth use. Rather than to directly compare Neandertals with Eskimos, a misleading procedure because of other sources of difference, they compared Neandertals to 4 chronologically older Afroeuropean crania, and Inuit Eskimos to other Amerinds, to look for parallel differences in the biomechanics of anterior tooth use. The corresponding similarities they noted in these paired comparisons include one very important relationship. In considering the efficiency of anterior biting the problem is similar to any see-saw. The load arm (bite force lever) should be short relative to the force arm (muscle force lever). They calculated these lever arms around the mandibular fossa, which is the fulcrum of the system and found that the ratio of muscle arm to load arm increased in both cases (this similarity is also found in the narrower comparison of Neandertal males with earlier European males). Their work shows that Neandertals and Eskimos share improved leverage for anterior biting, compared with the ancestral condition. They conclude both are well designed for efficient use of the incisors. There are additional contrasts between the masticatory mechanics of the samples. The authors attribute these to dietary differences, but in fact a more reasonable explanation is found in the regional differences between the populations they evolved from.

POSTCANINE TEETH

Posterior teeth reduce as well, although the magnitude of change is not as dramatic. Postcanine tooth size reduction preceded throughout the Pleistocene and in all regions of the world (albeit at different rates and according to different patterns). No special explanation is necessary to account for the reduction in Neandertals, but it has been suggested that cooking might have played an influential role. Cooked foods often require less chewing, reducing jaw growth and creating a source of selection for smaller teeth to fit in them. One speculation is that the cooking process itself may have begin as a way to defrost frozen meat. The increasing number of hearths found at Mousterian cave sites in regions with long winter freezes supports this suggestion.

EVOLUTION OF DECIDUOUS TOOTH SIZE

One final aspect of the Neandertal dental changes bears on the life histories of these populations and earlier ones. The European deciduous teeth, as mentioned above, increase in size into the Late Pleistocene (figure 13.1). This increase reverses only in the latest Neandertal, populations such as the Hortus sample, with substantially smaller deciduous teeth. If the continued increase was a consequence of marked tooth wear due to abrasives in the diet and late weaning, its reversal probably reflects changed in these conditions; in particular, less tooth wear reflecting earlier weaning. I believe that this trend can be explained by the hypothesis that the Neandertals came under selection to maintain or increase population size by earlier weaning and shorter birth spacing. Shortened birth spacing is the only effective alternative to lowered mortality rates for maintaining or expanding population size in the face of increasing difficulties. With the deteriorating climate of the Würm stadials, those populations that remained in Europe were under increased selection to maximize their fertility in response to their progressively more difficult problems of survivorship. O. Soffer suggests that improvement in "female specific technological advances in the preparation of soft weaning foods" may have been a critical cause underlying this change. If so, and there just is no evidence one way or the other, female-specific food preparation technology may have had a second consequence. As women applied an improved technology to the **premastication** and other treatments of their own foods, it could account for the much more rapid gracilization changes in women's facial skeletons, as compared to men, that D. Frayer notes when comparing Neandertal samples by sex to the Europeans who followed them.

GROWTH AND DEVELOPMENT

Neandertal children have been alternatively described by different authors as

- born with unusually large brain sizes,
- accelerated in their fetal growth rates,
- elongated in their gestation length,
- accelerated in childhood growth and development.

There is a large sample of European Neandertal children (table 13.8) and it would be safe to say that their study suggests that none of these contentions are correct. Research by A-M. Tillier and N. Minugh-Purvis fails to distinguish any aspect of Neandertal growth and developmental rates from the normal modern human range. While Neandertal brain size at birth is unknown, R. Tague's analysis of the Kebara pelvis diameter (Chapter 12) suggests that unusually large newborn head size is improbable. Instead, A-M.

Tillier's age-specific comparisons of Neandertal children's brain sizes with those of modern European children fail to reveal any significant differences.

Table 13.8
Ages of Immature European Neandertal Crania

	Age at Death
La Ferrassie 5	fetus
La Ferrassie 4b	term fetus
Hortus 1	neonate
Krapina 17	2
La Ferrassie 8	2
Subalyuk 2	2-3
Pech de l'Azé	3
Roc de Marsal	3
Engis 2	4-5
Devil's Tower	4-5
Carigüela 2	4-8
Chateauneuf	6
La Quina 18	6-7
La Fate	±8
Teshik Tash	8-9
La Ferrassie 3	±10
Le Moustier	13

OTHER ASPECTS OF LIFE CYCLE

My research at Krapina indicated a third molar eruption of 15 years at the site, and subsequent analysis of earlier human and australopithecine specimens suggested that this has been the norm for most of human evolution. This would imply the modern eruption delay for this tooth that characterizes most populations (erupting on the average at 18 years or later) is a recent evolutionary development. At the time of last molar eruption the cranial sutures are beginning to fuse in earlier human populations, but Neandertal cranial suture fusion is later, suggesting a longer period of brain growth. With tooth eruption times known, it is possible to estimate ages at death for many specimens, based on their tooth wear. Neandertals erupted their teeth rapidly, but within the modern human range of population means except for the last molar. As noted in the Krapina discussion above, all archaic populations retained the ancient condition of third molars erupting quickly (3-4 years) after the second. The eruption times provide the basis for estimating the Krapina paleodemography, revealing an underabundance of adults in the cave sample.

Neandertals, like earlier populations, had tooth size and structure characteristics designed to last an average lifespan. This is about a decade longer than the australopithecine lifespan, with dental destruction and loss virtually complete by the middle 40's instead of the middle 30's . Dental aging reveals that heavily worn dentitions such as those of the La Ferrassie adults regularly characterized individuals in their mid-30's. Conformations of these dental age estimates comes from a variety of independent techniques such as bone histology. E. Trinkaus used all aging techniques to estimate the mortality pattern of the entire Neandertal sample. Using a battery of standard demographic approaches (and estimating numbers for some of the invariably missing infants) Trinkaus determined a mortality distribution for all the Neandertals and compared it with some recent and living hunter/gatherers. One of his collations is reproduced, in modified form, in table 13.9, where the comparisons are with a recent (Libben) and living (Ache) New World hunter/gatherer sample. If these are taken to reflect part of a normal range for mortality profiles, the Neandertals differ mainly in having somewhat higher child and adolescent mortality and a concomitantly lower number of adults left to survive to old age (where they would appear as old adults in the distribution, a category that Trinkaus defines as >40). This means a shorter average lifespan for the Neandertals, and suggests that the potential for grandparenting remains infrequent (although not the virtual impossibility of earlier hominid populations). Small numbers of older adults places more emphasis on anything that improves fertility when expanding populations are important.

Table 13.9
Mortality Distribution for Neandertals[1]

	Neandertal	Libben (skeletal)	Ache (living)
Neonate	20[a]	18	21
Child	16	13	19[2]
Juvenile	13	9	11
Adolescent	13	14[3]	14[3]
Young adult	31	32	16
Old adult	7	14	19

[a] Partially estimated
[1] Data are in percentages
[2] C.O. Lovejoy and colleagues have argued that elevated child mortality in living hunter/gatherer populations results from their exposure to European infectious diseases that evolved in urban contexts
[3] Includes somewhat older individuals than the Neandertal category because of earlier Neandertal M3 eruption. Because the categories are not fully comparable, mortality rate for Neandertal adolescents is actually higher if age rather than developmental stage is meant

Whatever else, these mortality distributions appear quite different from the mortality pattern of game acquired by human hunting. M. Stiner's research suggests that Late Pleistocene humans predominately obtained meat by confrontational scavenging (indicated by old adult dominated prey remnants) or cooperative ambush hunting (indicated by prime adult dominated prey remnants). Neither pattern describes the mortality distribution of the Neandertals themselves, which indicates that if cannibalism was as ubiquitous as some paleoanthropologists believe (for instance T. White), it may not have been primarily nutritional.

MANDIBLES

Neandertal mandibles are notably variable in size and anatomy. Several that represent older individuals give important life history clues. For instance, the C. Lalueza and colleagues microwear study of the older adult Spanish specimen from Bañolas attributes most of the wear to mastication of a hard and abrasive diet, and (for the anterior teeth) to manipulative activities. While the examination of the Devil's Tower (Gibraltar) child suggested a high level of meat intake because the teeth were likened to Eskimo tooth wear, this analysis revealed the greatest similarities with modern hunter/gatherer groups with a more prominently vegetarian diet. It is possible that the dietary difference is age related, given the biochemical manifestations of high levels of Neandertal meat intake.
Two important evolutionary trends are apparent in Würm Neandertal mandible sample:

- retraction of the forward position of the tooth row with respect to the ramus
- appearance of a true chin, or mental trigone and eminence.

Since both of these features first appear in pre-Würm Europeans, the Würm morphology represents a shift in frequencies rather than the sudden appearance of new features.

The anterior positioning of the tooth row is one of the consequences of midfacial prognathism, since the more forward placed maxillary dentition must be met by the mandibular dentition. This morphology is common in most Würm Neandertals, but the prognathism condition decreases over the Neandertal span. As the cranial joint for the mandible remains the in the same position (as noted above the foramen magnum position tracks the facial changes but the lateral cranial base features do not), the two consequences of this change are

1. the reduction and loss of the retromolar space (by the time of the latest specimens some mandibles such as La Quina 9 lack it completely)
2. the posterior position of the mental foramen (it is found under M_1 in many later specimens rather than under one of the premolars).

It is as if the ramus and foramen remained stationary as the teeth shifted forward with the face - a not-unreasonable description. Let me caution to add, however, that like all Neandertal features these are neither ubiquitous among the Neandertals nor unique to them. As E. Trinkaus points out, the frequencies for posterior mental foramen position vary and a posterior position can be found in most populations. Like any other race, Neandertals can only be diagnosed by combinations of many features, and each individual has a different combination.

The appearance of a chin corresponds to a different, independent evolutionary trend—the expansion of the braincase and resulting change from a lateral to a medial component to the angulation of the temporalis muscle. Chins are common in most later Neandertals.

POSTCRANIAL REMAINS

Neandertal postcrania are characterized by a number of features once thought to be distinctive or unusual but now known to be characteristic of even more ancient hominid postcranial remains. Moreover, adequate understanding of this material has been plagued by early reconstructions of the La Chapelle skeleton. These remains are from an old male who suffered from severe arthritis, which deformed many of his skeletal elements. Along with other misconceptions, this led to a 1913 reconstruction of Neandertal posture as bent-kneed, with head thrust forward and a divergent big toe, which "may have played the part of a prehensile organ," according to M. Boule, the reconstructor. While it is true that a seminal analysis by W. Straus and A. Cave has shown this to be incorrect, the image of "Alley-Oop" is still with us.

To begin with, how large were the European Neandertals? They are often described as "short and stocky," although this description often results from a backward perspective, comparing them with living people rather than with their contemporaries and ancestors (and even then, the fact is that the average height of French Neandertals is about the same as the pre-World War I French). Based on the known postcranial remains, the average height for eight Neandertal male specimens is about 165 cm, while the five female specimens average 156 cm. The middle-sex average (average of male and female means) of 160 cm suggests little change from earlier Europeans (although all are much smaller than the much earlier Boxgrove specimen), and there no difference at all from the Western Asian sample (see Chapter 12). Trunk shape, relative limb shaft and joint sizes, and other indicators of muscularity (see below) clearly show they were stocky. To estimate how much they weighed, I have used the minimum ratio of stature to weight for a European population published by S. Molnar. This must be modified because C. Ruff and colleagues argue that Neandertals are about 20% heavier than modern humans of the same height. Combining them gives average male weight of 84 kg and 80 kg for females - the middle sex average is 82 kg. The heaviest Neandertal known, by this determination, is some 86 kg - to my dismay considerably lighter than me.

To some extent, as Coon, Trinkaus, and others have argued, body proportions within this sample suggest a cold adaptation through trunk thickening and limb shortening, although it is unlikely that climate alone fully accounts for the distribution of limb proportions or relative limb lengths, or body sizes. The best evidence of the importance of climate for these variations is the fact that at least some systematically differ from the specimens in Western Asia (see table 12.9). Several lines of evidence indicate that the Europeans have a larger, more rounded trunk relative to other bones that reflect body size. For instance, clavicles are long relative to body height, indicating that these Europeans have broad shoulders. The clavicles have a pronounced "S" shape; with the greater rib curvature, and shoulder morphology, this indicates a more rounded or barrel-like trunk form. This shape is one of the adaptive responses to the cold and features like expanded clavicle length relative to trunk height only characterize the European (presumably cold adapted) Neandertals, and not the so-called Western Asian ones. A deep, rounded trunk maximizes heat retention in the body core.

Table 13.10
Neandertal Body Size*

Specimen	Limb length	Stature estimate (cm)[1]	Weight estimate (kg)[2]
La Naulette	ulna=21.5	**149**	**76**
La Ferrassie 2	humerus=28.6	153	
	radius=20.5	151	
	ulna=22.5	153	
	femur=41.1	**155**	**79**
	tibia=31.1	151	
Spy 1	radius=21.5	**156**	**80**
Krapina 189	radius=22.0(est)	**158**	**81**
La Quina 5	humerus=32.0	**164**	**84**
Spy 2	femur=43.0	**161**	**83**
	tibia=33.4	163	
La Chapelle	humerus=31.3	164	
	radius=22.7	162	
	femur=43.5	**162**	**83**
Regourdou	humerus=31.0	163	**84**
	radius=23.3	164	
Neandertal	humerus=31.2	164	
	radius=23.9	166	
	femur=44.2	**164**	**84**
Kiik Koba	tibia=34.5	**165**	**85**
St. Césaire	ulna=25.5(est)	**165**	**85**
Lezetxiki	humerus=32.4	**167**	**86**
La Ferrassie	humerus=34.0	172	
	radius=24.5	169	
	ulna=27.5	173	
	femur=46.0	**169**	**86**

* Only the most complete limbs are shown. Figures in boldface are the values for each specimen used in summary statistics, whenever possible these are based on lower limb lengths

[1] Based on Northern Europeans

[2] According to Molnar the minimum European stature/weight ratio is 2.34, for Turkestanis, and the ratio for Finns is 2.44. In this estimate the Turkestani value is used, further modified because C. Ruff and colleagues suggest Neandertal weights are about 20% greater than the weights of modern humans of the same height

[3] Based on the stature estimate from both radius and ulna

Another feature characteristic of the Europeans is relative limb proportions. In both upper and lower limbs, the bones farther from the trunk are short relative to those closer: radius compared to humerus, and tibia compared to femur. Their proportions are similar to other cold-adapted populations, for instance

Lapps and Eskimos (tables 14.5 and 14.6). The arm (but not leg) proportions differ in the West Asian specimens (table 12.9). Shortening the limb lengths farthest from the body also helps retain heat, since heat loss is greatest away from the trunk. All of the Neandertal limbs were short relative to body weight; or, as I prefer to think of it, the trunk is heavy relative to its height. The massive trunk is, in part, a consequence of the rounded trunk form discussed above and the lengthened rib and lower back vertebrae, and can also be seen in the surface area of the vertebrae, whose bodies are large (in surface area or volume) relative to their height. There is a price to pay for this adaptation, though. Short lower limbs may be well adapted to the hilly or mountainous regions where Neandertals are found, but they would make long distance walking more energetically costly. Curiously, limb shortening did not affect the size of European Neandertal hands and feet.

Climate, as noted above, is not the sole cause of differences in Neandertal trunk size and limb proportions and anatomy. Other important factors include

- the ability of populations to buffer against the affects of climate through clothing, or in behavioral adaptations
- dietary resources, especially during the growth period
- the pattern of mobility

Many of the differences are linked to the higher level of activities that were normal in Neandertal populations. Neandertal limb morphology shows that they were quite strong, in that their muscles regularly produced high levels of force. Joint motion studies of bone after bone show that in most cases forces were applied over the full range of joint positions, and not just in one particular spot as we would expect if a special activity had resulted in the osteological evidences of power. Elevated levels of strength have anatomical consequences, and these are not limited to the European populations, but can also be found in the Western Asian specimens, as discussed in the last Chapter. In general the muscle attachments that are clearly reflected in limb anatomy are very robustly developed. Another result of strength adaptation combined with limb shortening in this sample can be seen in shaft bowing , shaft curvature in the anterior-posterior plane. Shaft bowing is a direct response to forces acting on the shaft— in this case, a combination of marked muscularity and elevated body weight relative to the shortened limbs. The bone tends to reform in a way that minimizes the amount of bending forces in it. Bowing, like many other anatomical features of these folk, is a response to *both* climatic and strength-related adaptations.

A similar example visible in Neandertal anatomy is in sizes of articular surfaces relative to bone length. Articular surface sizes respond to muscle use because more force through a joint is invariably met by an expansion of the contact area so that the joint pressure (force/area) will not increase. Joint surfaces are large in Neandertals, compared with other populations, but relatively larger in the cold adapted populations because of their shorter limbs. One example of this is seen in table 13.11. Here the diameters of the joints at both ends of the radius and the circumference at its middle are compared with radius lengths. While the samples overlap, the European Neandertals tend to have thinner shafts but larger articular surfaces at both ends. These relations hold for all of the limb bones.

Strength adaptations can be much more readily seen in the internal distribution of bone, where workers such as L. Lanyon and C. Rubin argue behavior-related changes are most likely to occur during life. Studies of Neandertal humeri by B. Senut, E. Trinkaus and colleagues, and S. Ben-Itzhak and colleagues, using computerized tomography, reveal very thick cortical bone and a diminished medullary cavity. This is similar to the internal structure of other archaic limbs and reflects the consequences of dramatically elevated activities that could only be guessed at from the external anatomy. There was marked asymmetry found between the strength of the right and left bones, a clear reflection of hand preference. The Ben-Itzhak study showed the asymmetry to be much more marked in men, while Trinkaus and colleagues note marked asymmetry in both sexes (but the issue is confused by the presence of injuries in some specimens - the strength difference may have developed as reactions to arm immobilization - see Chapter 4). In any event Neandertal men have unusually strong right arms.

Table 13.11
Radius Proportions[1]

	maximum length	head diameter (proximal joint)	ratio (%)	midshaft circumference	ratio (%)	wrist surface breadth (distal joint)	ratio (%)
La Ferrassie 2	205			38	18.5	29.6	14.4
Spy 1	215			41	19.1		
Krapina 189	220	21.7	9.9				
Regourdou	233	21.1	9.1	40	17.2	37.2	16.0
Neandertal	239	23.5	9.8	42	17.6	33.8	14.1
La Ferrassie 1	245	25.4	10.4	41	16.7		
Tabun	227	19.7	8.7	33	14.5	29.6	13.0
Shanidar 4	230	21.9	9.5	43	18.6	34.5	15.0
Kebara	258	21.8	8.4	48	18.6	32.9	12.8

[1] Measurements in millimeters

OTHER SKELETAL FEATURES

Neandertal bodies are perhaps the best understood of all ancient human populations. Their combination of similarities and differences has presented an interpretive challenge for more than a century. With interpretations constrained by the overwhelming evidence that Neandertals functioned in the same fundamental way as other subarctic hunter/gatherers and responded to the same biological constraints, analysis of the Neandertals has joined the studies of australopithecine locomotion in legitimizing the importance of biomechanics as an indispensable interpretive tool. There is much to be understood about Neandertals beyond the obvious expositions of their anatomical reactions to high levels of muscular strength and activity.

Early studies of Neandertal feet suggested that they were unusual in many respects. However, this conclusion did not hold up because it was the result of comparisons with modern Western Europeans, who normally wear shoes. More recent studies have shown that Neandertal-like feet are characteristic of most preindustrial modern populations; thus the supposed Neandertal distinctions turn out to be more an artifact of not wearing shoes than of a particular Neandertal adaptation.

Tibial strength in a number of specimens was examined in a study by C. Lovejoy and E. Trinkaus. Using the three Neandertal tibias naturally broken at midshaft (La Chapelle and the West Asian specimens Amud and Shanidar 6) they analyzed the internal bone distribution and calculated strength characteristics. These three specimens were dramatically stronger in their ability to resist twisting and bending than the norm in a recent American Indian population of similar body height. They were, however, much closer to the strength characteristics of the remains from a Cleveland Steel-worker who died during the last century. Neandertals were very strong, but likening them to the Pleistocene incarnation of the Incredible Hulk is probably an over exaggeration.

Relatively complete pelves and more fragmentary innominates indicate a series of features which are similar to the anatomy of the more complete Kebara specimen (discussed in Chapter 12). Except for the influences of climate, details of the pelves and their explanation do not differ from the Kebara specimen discussed in Chapter 12, and include differences that respond to three main elements:

1. position of the pelvic inlet (from work by Y. Rak)
2. pelvic inlet size in short, heavy populations (from work by K. Rosenberg)
3. requirements of supporting a barrel-shaped trunk (from work by F. Smith), but with a broader base because of the Europeans' increased chest capacity.

La Ferrassie 1, the most complete specimen, has an elongated pubis but not one that is excessively lengthened for a male of his size. The one thing this anatomy does *not* reflect is unusual Neandertal neonate or infant head size (as once thought). A-M. Tillier has shown that the heads of newborn and young Neandertals are not unusually large.

Neandertal pelvic anatomy combines skeletal robustness, an anterior position for the pelvic inlet, and an inlet whose size scales to body weight and not body height as does the rest of the pelvis. Presumably the scaling of the inlet responds to birth canal requirements, but as K. Rosenberg points out the situation is confused by the fact that the best preserved specimens are males. L. Hager argues that pregnancy is a significant source of selection on female pelvis shape, as women spend a significant portion of their adult lives carrying a growing fetus, which can be quite large in populations that are heavy relative to their height. Unfortunately none of the European Neandertal female pelves are complete enough to ascertain the relevant details of their birth-related anatomy. The general robustness of European Neandertal pelves, for instance as indicated by a thick, prominent iliac pillar, a large acetabulum relative to other dimensions, and a dominant anterior inferior iliac spine, were found to characterize earlier European innominates from Krapina, Arago, and Prince.

J. Musgrave demonstrates that while Neandertal hands were "squat and powerful," and muscularity of the index finger was marked, the thumb was not short, as previously believed. Trinkaus points to several features of Neandertal hands that indicate an especially powerful grip. For instance, muscles that oppose the thumb against the other fingers leave exceptionally prominent markings, Roughened areas and projections on the wrists bones show that the carpal tunnel was quite large. This is the passageway for the tendons than close the fingers, and by implication they were very big.

European Neandertal trunks, as noted above, are barrel-shaped in that they are unusually deep (anterior-posterior), but they are also relatively broad at the base of the rib cage. Clavicles are long relative to the humerus and in general the chest capacity appear elevated in these folk. This is similar to other cold-adapted Europeans such as Aleuts. Two particularly interesting things have come from attempts to understand their shoulder anatomy. The first of these is the anatomy of the scapula's lateral border, the long edge under the glenoid fossa. On this lateral border there is a groove (or grooves) for the teres minor muscle, one of the two muscles that cause lateral rotation of the humerus (most of the muscles cause medially directed rotation, by far the more powerful action). In Neandertals this lateral groove is commonly either dorsal (back-sided) or there are two grooves, one of which is dorsal. S. Churchill and E. Trinkaus believe that the dorsal groove variation responds to the generally marked shoulder muscle development, but if true we would expect to see it much more commonly in right scapulae. F. Smith suggests that it relates to the orientation of the scapula itself, a difference created by their altered (i.e. barrel-shaped) chest shape.

The second has to do with the form of the glenoid joint. It has always been recognized that this joint seemed unusually narrow and shallow in the Neandertals. A study by Churchill and Trinkaus shows that the depth and height could be explained by the size and anatomy of the humerus (for instance, it's relatively large head size), and that the main critical difference was the breadth of the joint. Narrow and shallow joints also characterize earlier humans, even australopithecines, so the question they focused on is why this joint became broader in more recent humans. They argue that the broader joints reflect more habitual arm movement from back to front, and suggest that this change corresponds to much more dramatic movements at the extreme ends of forward and backward motions. Pitching a baseball comes to mind.

As noted above, the Ben-Itzhak and colleagues study shows really dramatic asymmetry in the internal strength characteristics of Neandertal humeri. Combined with the Churchill and Trinkaus study these suggest that powerful arm like clubbing and thrusting spears left their mark on Neandertal skeletal anatomy, but that throwing was not as important an activity.

VARIABILITY IN THE NEANDERTALS

Following the above discussion of Neandertal characteristics, it is especially important to emphasize the variability in the European sample and attempt to understand its causes and evolutionary importance. The European Neandertals are anything but the "homogeneous and invariant" sample that they are often considered to be. Perhaps more than for any other group of fossil hominids, the interpretation of the European Neandertals has been plagued by the "type" concept and the idea that the sample has little variability. In the words of Coon, "They are in fact so homogeneous that a strong selective agency must have been pruning off deviant individuals." Nothing could be further from being correct.

The Influence of Typology

As a result of the completeness of the skeleton, and its lengthy and prestigious publication by M. Boule in 1913, the "old man of La Chapelle" came to represent the total Neandertal sample. The fact that a decade or more ago J-L. Heim's similarly detailed publications appeared on the equally complete and likely more "typical" skeletal remains from La Ferrassie (discovered at about the same time) has not significantly detracted from this perception. However, the history of this problem is not simple, since early in the century other Neandertals have been described in some detail (table 13.5). As early as 1930, a review of all the then-known Neandertals by A. Hrdlička suitably emphasized their variability.

The choice, whether or not purposeful, of La Chapelle as the "typical" Würm Neandertal was particularly unfortunate for two reasons. First, the Würm sample is extremely variable and thus no single specimen could adequately represent it. Second, within the range of Würm Neandertal variation, many features of the La Chapelle skeleton lie at the extreme. In no other specimen are the distinctive Neandertal characteristics so pronounced.

The often unrecognized point is that other Würm Neandertals differ from La Chapelle, and in some cases the contrast is considerable. Šala and Gibraltar, for instance, have much smaller browridges. La Ferrassie lacks lambdoidal flattening, or "bunning." So does Le Moustier, and the fact that the younger Teshik Tash is bunned shows this cannot be age-related variation. In the Feldhofer Cave skullcap the forehead is considerably lower than in La Chapelle. In Spy 2, it is higher. The usual rounded cranial contour, as seen from the rear, finds its exception in the parallel sided Spy 2, and in fact many details of this specimen are similar to the earliest post-Neandertal Europeans. In the mandibles, the contour of the symphysis varies from completely chinless in La Chapelle, Regourdou, and Le Moustier to a definite chin development in La Ferrassie, Mt. Circeo 2, Zaffaraya. and La Quina 9.

Although much of this variation is temporal, some of it follows no particular pattern over time, as in the contrasts between the two Spy crania. Nor do the archaic or modern variants all appear on the same specimens. For instance, Le Moustier combines lack of bunning and a chinless mandible, while La Chapelle, which is "hyperneanderthal" in most features, has one of the highest foreheads. Mixed into the Neandertal range of variation is a set of less common but clearly present features which, when in higher frequency, characterize the post Neandertal Europeans.

Sexual Dimorphism

One major factor contributing to systematic variation in the Neandertals is sexual dimorphism. A measure of the amount of dimorphism can be ascertained by comparing the reconstructed heights of specimens with sexable postcrania. Average female height is 95 percent of the male average, well within the population range for living humans (some 90-96%).

E. Trinkaus and J-L. Heim admit that Neandertal postcranial dimorphism is within the modern human range, but point out that they are unusual in that external muscle markings and other evidences of robustness such as relative joint sizes and shaft thickness do not distinguish the sexes at all. This can be seen in the comparison of the largely complete La Ferrassie male and female postcranial skeletons. While there is a 14 cm difference in reconstructed body heights (as calculated from femur length), there is a virtually total lack of corresponding sex difference in skeletal features that result from strength and the level of muscular activity. In fact, the female femur shaft is relatively thicker and shows more anteroposterior flattening than the male, although the relative head size of the femur and relative head and shaft size of the humerus are smaller. There just is no consistent pattern. However, studies of internal bone mass distribution (see above) reveal a much more marked pattern of sex differences. The right arm of Neandertal males stands out for being unusually strong - much stronger than either Neandertal females or most modern humans.

In the context of this postcranial dimorphism, the pattern of sex differences in the crania stands in marked contrast. As in modern humans, sex differences are greater in vault length and height than in the various vault breadth measures. However, average dimorphism in the Neandertals is three times as great.

Dimorphism in Neandertal facial heights is even greater. However, while some females, such as Gibraltar, have markedly reduced browridges, the large size of this structure in the Spy female suggests that this may not be a consistent sex difference. Large browridges were a persistent feature of earlier European females, showing that the pattern as well as the magnitude differs from the modern condition. The disparity between cranial and postcranial dimorphism exists throughout the Pleistocene.

The Latest European Neandertals

The evolutionary process within the Neandertal sample is reflected in both archaeological and anatomical changes. Large samples of fairly well dated late Neandertal remains have been recovered from European sites, both Mousterian and early Upper Paleolithic. The material is often fragmentary, but generally informative. These latest Neandertals continue the trends found within the European Neandertal Würm sample, and while morphologically the specimens more closely resemble Neandertals than anything else, they have the highest frequencies of post-Neandertal European characteristics.

Mousterian culture persists for a long time as well. If the early Aurignacian dates suggested for sites in Northern Spain, Bulgaria, and elsewhere are correct the overlap of Middle and Upper Paleolithic cultures could be for as long as 15 kyr. For instance at the top of the Mousterian sequence in the La Quina cave in France, artifacts and a few hominid teeth date to about 35 kyr. The Mousterian is particularly tenacious in the peripheral areas of Western Europe (from the viewpoint of human populations that could not cross water) like Portugal, or south Spain where the Zafarraya cave shows persistence of the Mousterian several thousand years after the onset of Oxygen Isotope Stage 2 which marks the beginning of the really cold Würm oscillations.

HORTUS

The cave, really a fissure, at l'Hortus in southern France yielded about fifty hominid fragments dated to the latest portions of Würm 2. While jaws and teeth are best represented, cranial fragments and postcranial remains have also been found. M. Stiner and S. Kuhn have suggested that the accumulation may be the remains of a hyena den.

The sample is notable for its fragmentary condition, rarity of children, and marked evidence of dental reduction within the Neandertals. Dental reduction in the l'Hortus sample occurs in all the teeth, but especially characterizes the anteriors. These are smaller than the other late Neandertals (table 13.7). Yet, the fact that the incisors were still used for gripping is indicated by oblique and horizontal knife scratches across two labial faces. To some extent, unlike the other spiciness in this late Neandertal sample with small anterior teeth, these may reflect small body size. Hortus 4 (about fourteen years old) is the best preserved of the jaws retaining teeth. The specimen combines a poorly developed mental eminence with an anterior position for the ramus relative to the teeth. Two femoral fragments and part of a radius are the same size or smaller than the La Ferrassie 2 female. These may be females or juveniles, but we cannot discount the possibility that a small population is sampled here. In describing, l'Hortus M-A. de Lumley concludes that these late specimens are not evolving in a more modern direction. With the above proviso I place a rather stronger emphasis on the evidence for anterior dental reduction, since I believe this change is a key to understanding many of the facial and cranial distinctions of modern populations in Europe.

VINDIJA (Mousterian)

The Vindija cave is only some 15 miles from the Croatian site of Krapina. A large number of fragmentary hominid remains have been recovered from the very latest Mousterian layers (G_3), positioned on top of a deep Mousterian sequence and overlain by an Aurignacian level (G_1). The G_1 and later Vindija hominids are discussed in separately below.

The G_3 Neandertals are stratigraphically dated to the end of Würm 2, penecontemporary with the l'Hortus Neandertals. They are quite clearly more recent than those from Krapina, a site with which

Vindija is often compared to show evidence for evolutionary change in the Neandertals of South Central Europe. In these comparisons, Vindija unquestionably differs in ways that are almost invariably in the direction of modern Europeans. The most pronounced of the cranial differences include:

- reduced middle face prognathism and less projecting upper face
- thinner and less projecting supraorbitals (table 13.3 - the thinning is most marked over the middle of the orbit, where it presages a division of the torus into supercillary and lateral portions, the most common European anatomy).
- narrower nasal aperture, more prominent nasal spine, and a smaller facial height below it (this is shown in two specimens, the larger cannot be aged but the smaller is unequivocally adult)
- reduced breadth for the anterior teeth
- the absence of occipital bunning
- thinner cranial bone

The mandibles vary in size; most have a distinct (although not prominent) mental eminence, and on the average the symphysis is markedly more vertical. The number of specimens with multiple mental foramena are fewer, and the foramen sizes are smaller. While the ramus usually begins behind the last molar, the retromolar space is much less than at nearby but much earlier Krapina, and in one Vindija specimen the space is closed and the ramus overlaps the last molar. Generally, the mandibles are less Neandertal-like than the Hortus mandibles.

Some have attributed the progressive features in these specimens to small body size, or a preponderance of subadults. However, the comparisons showing these trends were limited to adult specimens only, and a substantive review of body size by Trinkaus and Smith shows that the sample is not significantly smaller than the other Neandertals.

KŮLNA

Kůlna cave, in the Moravian Karst region, yielded a partial right maxilla and parietal from near the top of the Mousterian sequence. The climate was glacial, matching the two radiocarbon dates of 45 and 38 kyr (realistically, meaning <32 kyr, but it must be earlier than the interstadial), and like Vindija it is stratigraphically late in Würm 2.. The Kůlna maxilla is a Neandertal, on the basis of the fact that the root socket for the lateral incisor is as large as the central incisor root socket. Tooth wear indicates that it is a young adult. Although the lower face is tall, the nasal aperture is narrow, and both F. Smith and B. Vandermeersch believe that a shallow canine fossa was present (the region is incomplete on the fragment and the observation is problematic). J. Jelínek regards the parietal as Neandertal-like in shape, and believes it may represent the same individual as the maxilla.

ŠIPKA

Although Šipka is only a small part of a jaw, it is diagnostic. This anterior symphysis of a 9 year old is a late Neandertal, also from the hills of the Moravian Karst region. Discovered in 1890 and associated with a Mousterian industry, it appears to derive from the middle Würm interstadial and therefore is later than Kůlna and penecontemporary with Saint Césaire. The symphysis has a receding chin but with remnants of a weakly developed mental eminence and a mental trigone according to J. Jelínek. Incisor size is very small, at or near the minimum for the Neandertal range. Like the l'Hortus and Vindija Mousterian remains, it seems to reflect the trend of pronounced anterior dental reduction.

ZAFARRAYA - THE LAST NEANDERTAL?

The early Aurignacian of the Iberian peninsula only appeared in the far north of Spain and it was not until the later part of the earlier Upper Paleolithic that the more modern industries and technologies penetrated throughout this peripheral region. In Portugal, L. Straus and colleagues report Mousterian sites dated to as recently as 32-29 kyr, and a molar said to be Neandertal is from the Mousterian sequence at the Columbeira cave where the date at the bottom of the sequence is 29 kyr. According to J-J. Hublin at the top the Mousterian levels in the Zafarraya cave of Alcaicin, southern Spain, have been radiocarbon dated to 29 kyr, squarely in Würm 3. Excavations during the 1980's have yielded a partial femur and mandible, which according to M. García Sanchez are both Neandertals. More recently excavations directed by Hublin recovered additional remains, including a upper incisor that is curved and has marginal ridges, and partial innominate with a pubis. High in the mountains and far to the south these Mousterians, specialized mountain goat hunters according to Hublin, may be the last Neandertals.

The mandible has a number of features aligning it with the late Neandertals. It is a small specimen (about the size of the Hortus remains) showing a vertical symphysis with a mental trigone and a moderate mental eminence, a mental foramen position under P_4, and a gap between the front of the ascending ramus and the back of the third molar. The anterior teeth appear to be small.

The femur is attributed to a male. It is of moderate male size, about that of La Chapelle. Like many of the Neandertals its midshaft cross section is close to circular, the length and breadth dimensions are about equal and there is no strong pilaster development along the femur's posterior surface. However, the femur neck is quite unlike Neandertals. It is absolutely and relatively thin (anterior-posterior dimension), while most Neandertal femur necks are much thicker. Femur neck thinning is the normal anatomy in the post-Neandertal Europeans.

TRENDS

In 1951 F.C. Howell published a seminal analysis of Neandertal evolution in which he attempted to find evolutionary trends within the Neandertal sample. Because the direction of the changes he observed were away from the modern human condition, he developed a hypothesis based on isolation and adaptation to account for European Neandertal divergence. With the samples and dates available today it is apparent that the distinct evolutionary trends within the European Neandertal sample are quite different than he thought, invariably *in the direction* of the post-Neandertal Europeans. Of course, some individual specimens can juxtapose the temporal variations of the *sample*, reflecting the fact that individuals at any time can be expected to vary normally, but when the sample is considered as a whole, the European evolutionary trends that can now be recognized *within the Neandertals* include:

- reduction in the cranial superstructures (mid-orbit and lateral supraorbital, and nuchal tori) and cranial bone thickness
- expansion of the supercillary aspect of the supraorbital torus
- anterior dental reduction
- reduction in the prognathism of the middle face
- nasal breadth reduction
- appearance of a true mental eminence with a mental trigone
- increased elongation of the femur shaft and development of the *linea aspera*

NEANDERTALS OF THE UPPER PALEOLITHIC

In much of Europe the Middle Paleolithic gave way to the Upper Paleolithic during the period of climatic ameliorations beginning after 40 kyr known as the Middle Würm interstadial. These improved conditions are when human populations reënter Europe and it has long been assumed that the end of Neandertals came with the arrival of modern Europeans with new technologies and behaviors called the Upper Paleolithic. This seductive picture of peripheralization and replacement, however, is confused by the evidence that Neandertals are directly associated with the early Upper Paleolithic at some sites (see below), and the fact that no other human populations can be clearly connected to the three earliest Upper Paleolithic industries - Szeletian, Châtelperronian, and Aurignacian (see Chapter 14). It is further belied by the evidence that the these three earliest Upper Paleolithic industries may have developed locally in Europe from Middle Paleolithic predecessors. Because of its association with Neandertals it has become convenient to think of the Châtelperronian as a hybrid industry (an idea first proposed by F. Bordes in

1972, before an associated Neandertal was recognized), perhaps reflecting populations of enculturated Neandertals who were able to learn some things from their immigrant neighbors, but even this makes assumptions that are, at the moment, unwarranted..

Never mind that the physical remains of these expected immigrant neighbors have yet to be found, the real problem with this interpretation is that in areas where the Châtelperronian and Aurignacian overlap or interdigitate at sites, as in Cantabrian Spain, they have high numbers of Middle Paleolithic tools. Archaeologists such as L. Straus argue it is unlikely that one of these Upper Paleolithic industries is derived or hybridized from the other. The continued modeling of cultural interactions after the colonial experience is invalidated by the likelihood that Middle and Upper Paleolithic cultures may have overlapped in Europe by as much as 15 kyr.

So much for the cultures, but what of the human populations? There are only a few themes that have extended through my career (unlike some I am proud to admit that accumulating data and new theoretical perspectives lead me to modify my interpretations of the past). One of them was first expressed when writing with D. Brose I argued that understanding human evolution requires us to disassociate culture and biology. Looking at (and listening to) the contortions required of Neandertal interpretations when culture and biology are thought to be linked during this period has only reinforced the importance of this theme in my thinking.

Saint Césaire (Châtelperronian)

The cranium, mandible, dentition, and postcranial skeleton of this 36 kyr old specimen combine to unequivocally demonstrate that it is a Neandertal - almost certainly a male based on estimated body size (table 13.10) and the size of the vault bones that are preserved. None the less, in some ways it varies systematically from the earlier Mousterian-associated specimens. For instance, there is central and lateral supraorbital thinning, the thickness of the torus is smaller than the Vindija mean and for its lateral expression even below the range (table 13.3). There is marked midfacial retraction (reduction of prognathism), especially as compared with specimens such as La Chapelle and La Ferrassie. Other differences include

- reduced anterior tooth size (table 13.7)
- smaller, lower appearing orbits,
- smaller cheeks,
- markedly narrowed nose, and
- a flattened rear surface of the mastoid process.

There are several unusual aspects to its postcranial skeleton, such as what appear to be unusually short arms. Perhaps its most interesting condition is the midshaft femur shape. Unlike other Neandertals the form of the femur shaft is elongated front-to-back (Neandertal femurs are generally rounded at the midshaft, or expanded transversely in a pattern similar to earlier hominids).

While Saint Césaire has been described as a "typical Neandertal", it can be no more typical than any other specimen in a population; typical, after all, is a concept of typology and not of evolutionary biology. In fact, for many features it is not even similar to the Neandertal norm. One thing that is quite unlike most other Neandertals is the association of the specimen with a Châtelperronian level, and not even the earliest one in the cave. Even authors such as C. Stringer, J-J. Hublin, and B. Vandermeersch, who champion the idea of Neandertal extinction, regard the Châtelperronian as an Upper Paleolithic industry, with a normal complex of Upper Paleolithic attributes including everything from personal ornamentation to blade technology, stone hearths, and huts. The potential of attributing these behavioral attributes to Neandertals was disturbing enough for one participant at the 1987 Cambridge conference on *The Human Revolution* to quip "it must have been a pet".

Perhaps the most interesting aspect of this late Neandertal is *where* it was found. As the champions of extinction put it, these Upper Paleolithic Neandertals were hardly pushed into a "backward or isolated area" to perish "with a whimper, not a bang" (as Stringer proclaimed in another publication), but were "situated in a [desirable] region densely occupied during the Middle and Upper Paleolithic".

Arcy-Sur-Cure (Châtelperronian)

In describing the isolated teeth from the Châtelperronian levels of the Grotte du Renne at Arcy-sur-Cure in France, A. Leroi-Gourhan first proposed that there was a retention of archaic morphology, describing the teeth as having "preserved in part paleoanthropine characteristics" (for instance the taurodontism of the molars). D. Brose and I subsequently emphasized the Neandertal-like size and anatomy of the anterior teeth. With the discovery at Saint Césaire it now seems likely that the reason these teeth seemed to resemble Neandertals is that they *are* Neandertals.

Bacho Kiro (Bachokiran, so-called "Pre-Aurignacian")

A piece of child's mandible from level 11 in the Bulgarian cave of Bacho Kiro is associated with an industry that is unconvincingly regarded as Aurignacian and therefore more properly called "Bachokiran", or "Pre-Aurignacian". A radiocarbon date of <43 kyr would be very early for an Upper Paleolithic industry, let along a true Aurignacian. While this industry is not Aurignacian, it may well be an Upper Paleolithic variant of some sort or another, at least as far as the blade technology is concerned (although blades are found in Middle Paleolithic variants from the Levant to Southern Africa). The date is a problem, as it is beyond the valid range of the radiocarbon technique, and a second problem lies in the completely uninformative nature of the very fragmentary specimen. The 7 year old's mandibular corpus (BK 1124) with dm_1 and a canine socket is the only specimen from this level. The molar size certainly fits in the Neandertal range, for instance it is has exactly the same dimensions as the Taubach tooth, but it is too worn to observe surface morphology. This could well be a Neandertal specimen. If it is the best case that can be advanced to support the idea that the earliest Aurignacian is not associated with Neandertals, but instead can be linked to modern Europeans, and that these together are intrusive in Europe, on both archaeological and biological grounds the case is very weak indeed.

Vindija (Aurignacian)

Level G_1, the earliest Aurignacian at Vindija, was deposited in a warm period. The presence of a split-based bone point, found *in situ* according to J. Radovčić, has been used to identify the industry as Aurignacian, but the lithics contain a mixture of Middle and Upper Paleolithic elements (as do all earlier Aurignacians). It seems as though the further east the sample is taken, the closer the relation that the Aurignacian seems to have with the Middle Paleolithic. Just above it, level F_d has additional diagnostic Aurignacian artifacts, and shows absolutely no evidence of any mixture with the underlying Mousterian levels. These archaeological remains are similar to the earliest Upper Paleolithic in the region, at a time not unlike the first appearance of the Aurignacian in Germany and France. There are a small number of fragmentary human remains scattered through these two levels.

Simply put, the cranial fragments from the earliest Aurignacian in G_1 are not significantly different from the Mousterian-associated Neandertals below. For instance, the partial mandible Vi 207 is the same size as the earlier specimens and has a distinct retromolar space. The Vi 307 zygomatic has the thick columnar frontal process (lateral orbit border) characteristic on Neandertals and other archaic humans (but not post-Neandertal Europeans). In this archaic anatomy the articulation of the zygomatic with the frontal on the outer orbital bar is thick and triangle-shaped in cross section. In fact with its multiple accessory foramena the specimen is anatomically and metrically quite similar to Krapina zygomatics. Certain features on the internal surface of the Vi 208 parietal also are most common in the Neandertals. As a sample, perhaps these are not sufficiently unique features to be diagnostic (it is possible that no fragmentary remains *could* be diagnostic for what is no more than a regional or racial difference within our species), but they are suggestive. At the least they show the absence of significant morphologic or metric distinction between the Middle and the earliest Upper Paleolithic humans at Vindija.

Pieces from the F_d level are also fragmentary. Vi 204/302 is a large portion of two posterior parietals that, according to F. Smith and colleagues, is somewhat more gabled in profile as seen from the rear than the usual Neandertal condition (but see Spy 2). One key to the identity of the Vindija F_d Aurignacians may be found in the anatomy of their upper incisors. As mentioned in the Krapina discussion, T.

Crummett's description of three dimensions for incisor shovel-shape morphology resulted in the identification of a unique Neandertal pattern in which moderate marginal ridge development is associated with a large tubercle and marked labial convexity. In fact one of the most extreme manifestations of this form is found in the Saint Césaire teeth and it is possible that this feature does not particularly change through the Neandertal span, a point that fits Crummett's explanation of the anatomy since she believes it is one of several ways to maximize crown size in a limited alveolar space and therefore should not reduce until there is significant anterior dental reduction - even moreso than the late Neandertals and earlier post-Neandertal Upper Paleolithic populations (which D. Frayer has shown have Neandertal-sized anterior teeth). There are two upper incisors from Vindija Aurignacian levels. Vi 290, an I^1 from level G_1, has heavy marginal ridges, a large tubercle with finger-like projections extending up the labial surface and is very markedly curved. Its crown dimensions approach the Krapina mean values. Vi 289, an I^2 from F_d, is extremely curved with very strong marginal ridge expression - virtually at the maximum end of the Neandertal range (a position shared with St. Césaire). In fact, these two teeth are strongly and diagnostically Neandertal-like in their shoveling anatomy.

Does this mean that Neandertals made the Aurignacian at Vindija, and perhaps elsewhere in central Europe where it appears early? Could be! But the association is so unexpected that it will undoubtedly take more complete diagnostic crania for this possibility to become fully convincing. Even then, there will be those who continue to believe the best explanation is that the Neandertals were kept as pets.

Changing Lifeways

The Middle Paleolithic, according to M. Stiner, was a period of dramatic changes in human lifeways. In Europe and Western Asia, the organization of the Mousterian adaptations was "internally complex and geographically diverse". Her work, and that of others, shows that complex and intricately organized behavioral repertoires are not necessarily modern ones.

One important aspect of Neandertal adaptation that has emerged from biochemical analyses of their bones is a relatively high level of protein intake. Studies of amino acid residues by G. Ball and colleagues, and carbon/nitrogen ratio analysis by H. Bocherens and colleagues strongly suggest that many Neandertals consumed a significant amount of protein. Much of the interesting behavioral change reflected in the archaeology revolves about how this protein was obtained.

As early as Krapina there is evidence of a complex set of behaviors for acquiring meat. P. Miracle's analysis of the age distribution and pattern of cutmarks on the Merck's Rhinoceros remains from that site reveals a young-juvenile dominated collection, lacking virtually any evidence of carnivore gnawing. He argues that these animals were small enough to have been completely consumed by large cats or scavengers such as cave hyenas, and therefore were probably acquired by human hunting. Young juveniles are not easily parted from their mothers, and focus on hunting them requires "tactics [that] imply at least a coordinated, situational response by groups of Neandertals". The equal numbers of individuals represented by heads and skeletons indicate that whole carcasses were brought back to the rock shelter, and evidence of burning was concentrated on the ends of meat-bearing bones, which Miracle interprets to mean they were roasted while they still held the meat.

Some insight into the ability of Neandertals to change their adaptations, and the process of behavioral evolution within the Mousterian, can be gained from a series of studies by M. Stiner and S. Kuhn. They focused on a series of sites on or near the west-central Italian coast, dated to 110-35 kyr, examining the relationship between subsistence and technology. The industries found in the earlier sites (110-55 kyr) are classic Mousterian, often based on Levallois cores flaked in a centripetal manner to produce one or two tools (in the centripetal technique flakes are struck concentricity around a flat rounded pebble, spiraling toward the center, until the core has a proper shape for removal of the utilized flake. The advantage of the technique is that it maximizes tool size and the number of sharp edges on each tool - an important aspect when the source material consists of small pebbles. A platform core reduction technique (see below) is also used, but much more rarely. The most archaic of the subsistence adaptations is characterized by the scavenging of ungulates, mainly deer. Most of the animal remains are from old individuals, and there is a strong bias for head parts to be transported to the shelters. The heads were fragmented, and studies indicated that intact heads were broken open (presumably to extract the brains) while still fresh. These activities took place largely in the spring. Stiner and Kuhn suggest that this season, when temperate mammals have the least amount of body fat (it is the peak period of animal deaths by starvation), may have been a time of crisis for protein-dependent Neandertals, as fat and/or carbohydrates are needed to digest protein (also, shellfish are notoriously poor in fats). The carbohydrate and protein contents of brains and the sheaths that surround them are maintained even during periods of starvation. Scavenging the heads of dead and possibly frozen ungulates for fat and carbohydrate resources was an effective spring adaptation to these circumstances. Stiner and Kuhn do not believe that Neandertals were uniquely scavengers, or that they even mainly obtained protein this way. In the modern context what they find most unusual about this adaptation is the fact that it is so clearly separated from hunting, both seasonally and spatially. For animal protein modern human hunter/gatherers rely on a mixed strategy of hunting, and both active and passive scavenging and the products of all three strategies are typically pooled at a single residence.

The later set of sites, dated after 55 kyr, indicate a significant adaptive shift, and provide evidence of hunting activities. This is indicated by three aspects of the fauna that show a marked change

1. The ratio of the number of bones to the minimum number of individuals they could represent increases - this ratio reflects how complete the animal utilization and transport was by examining how many bones from each carcass were brought back to the residence.
2. The ratio of the number of bones from heads to the number of bones from limbs decreases - this ratio, focusing mainly on large bones, clearly reflects the way that meat was obtained as hunting results in a ratio similar to the anatomical ratio, or weighed in the direction of more limbs (lower ratio).
3. The ratio of prime aged to old aged adults increases. Mostly the number of prime aged adults responds to the success of ambush hunting - many other hunting strategies and scavenging take a preponderance of the oldest (and youngest) individuals.

A shift to significant hunting is indicated by the evidence for much more complete carcass utilization, a move away from the strong emphasis on heads, and the successful taking of prime aged adults. Many meat-bearing bones were returned to the residential sites, and were processed for meat and marrow.

Accompanying this are changes in technology. Core reduction much more often uses a platform-oriented procedure that maximizes the number of flakes than can be struck. A striking platform is prepared at the end of an elongated core (or in some cases at both ends) and flakes are removed parallel to the long axis. These, however, are rarely blades (flakes twice as long as they are wide) because they often do not extend along the entire core length, and the cores themselves are usually small rounded pebbles. One would think that the greater emphasis on platform cores would reflect shifts in raw materials, as the technique is most conveniently practiced on larger elongated pebbles, and is most advantageous when suitable raw materials are scarce. Stiner and Kuhn, however, show that these elements do not account for the variation. The main factors, they argue, are related to the life histories of the tools themselves. The centripetal cores produced large flakes that were frequently resharpened because they were often reused. These artifacts were more often transported and clearly were curated in a manner that some archaeologists claim Neandertals were incapable of. Yet, this mobile, transported industry was the earlier of the two, and the one associated with scavenging. The later shift of emphasis to platform-produced flakes reflects less intensive reuse of tools (they were easier to come by - more were made from each core), and reduced mobility as indicated by fewer transported or exotic artifacts.

Stiner and Kuhn argue that what links the subsistence and lithic changes is a differing pattern of land use and mobility, dictated by how the Neandertals searched for resources. Scavenging, they suggest, implies frequent movements and wide-ranging search patterns because of its unpredictability and the dispersed nature of its targets. This brought an advantage to centripetal core reduction as larger flakes that were resharpened and modified over a longer period of time could be produced. The tools were curated, and were most useful in a mobile adaptation where the need for them is not predictable. The subsequent hunting adaptation was planned and organized, and clearly focused on more concentrated food sources. Far richer resources were returned from the successful foray; indeed, there was little discarding even of the less economical body parts. This strategy allowed for more restricted ranging for food and longer occupation times, advantages that replaced the premium on large modifiable tools with one on efficient use of lithic resources. Thus, the shift to increase use of platform flaking which produced such an abundance of (albeit smaller) flakes that resharpening was no longer at a premium (and the fact is that resharpened edges are never as sharp as the original flake edge). Bigger tools were only made when it was important for them to be curated. This, in some respects, is similar to a hunting hypothesis put forward by S. Binford, who argued that the transition from the Middle to the Upper Paleolithic in the Levant involved a shift to the specialized hunting of medium to large migratory herd animals. She credited this change to the appearance of novel cognitive and anatomical features with the modern humans she believed could be associated with the Upper Paleolithic; for instance, foresight, advanced planing, and complex communication skills, a technology allowing killing at a distance, and long legs for efficient long distance walking. It is now clear that this association of culture and biology cannot be made. Whatever cognitive and anatomical requirements this adaptive shift required, they clearly were there in the later Mousterian Neandertals.

As B. Hayden characterizes them, the European Mousterians were sparse and highly mobile. O. Soffer points out that in Europe and across the North Asian tier their skeletal remains certainly seem to have been restricted to the hillier and mountainous regions where high population densities are generally hard to attain. More open plains or steppe sites are less usual and lack associated diagnostic human remains. Geographic variation is reflected in the fact that in the richest areas Neandertal populations were much denser and perhaps less mobile, and there is evidence of burial, ritual, regional exchange, and limited art. However, other variations are temporal. In at least some areas such as west-central Italy there is a significant adaptive shift of the sort often (incorrectly) said to characterize the Middle to Upper Paleolithic transition. This is found in the increased hunting success, the reliance on more than scavenged ungulate brains for late winter and early spring fat, and the use of a platform-based technology for core reduction (in Africa a similar procedure was used to manufacture the microliths of the Late Stone Age, while in the European Upper Paleolithic platform reduction of longer cores, striking flakes that transversed their entire length, was the basis of the blade tool industries). There and elsewhere continued habitat expansion involved three main types of adaptation:

1. an open-area cold adaptation, which allowed populations to utilize arctic areas without dependence on caves;
2. a high-altitude adaptation, which led to the crossing of western Asia's northern mountain barriers;
3. the first effective adaptation to tropical rain forests.

The critical factors allowing this expansion of the fundamental niche were tied to both social and technological adaptations that developed throughout the Mousterian span. Social networks and alliance systems were, according to C. Gamble, an absolute necessity for these changes as they provide a broad source of knowledge about new habitats and backups that make their initial utilization less risky. Technological developments include

- a proliferation of both stone and in some Mousterian facies also bone tools (these are important in entering new habitats as bone is a much more predictable resource than stone suitable for toolmaking),
- the invention of composite tools (for instance hafted stone points) that are more efficient and promote killing at a distance,
- the development of structures adequate for an open-area habitation in frigid regions,
- the further evolution of efficient hunting and food gathering and preparation techniques.

TRAUMA

Neandertal skeletons show the consequences of trauma, just as those who came before them. However, with the much more complete skeletal representation afforded by Neandertal burial customs it is possible to gather statistics on the frequency and distribution of traumatic injuries. In a paper read before the American association of physical anthropologists T. Berger and E. Trinkaus examined the pattern of 25 injuries that showed some evidence of healing, on 17 Neandertals. They found a high number of head, neck, and upper limb injuries but virtually none on the pelvis or lower limb. They attribute the later to a very low survivorship after lower body injuries and argue that any loss in mobility was probably fatal. On the other hand incapacitating injuries of the upper body were often survived. A. Mann reports of two serious head wounds at Krapina that show signs of healing. One of these, he suggests, was severe enough to cause unconsciousness for weeks. These individuals were clearly attended during the healing process.

COULD NEANDERTALS THINK?

The way Neandertal thought processes have been treated in some of the paleoanthropological literature has come to remind me of a story told by Bob Newhart about the experiment showing that fish can think. As he tells it, a great scientist set out to prove that fish can think. He began by feeding his fish, spreading food at the top of their tank, at exactly 5 pm. The fish came to the surface to feed at 5:15, but by then the food was gone, waterlogged and sunk to the bottom. The next day he put the food out at 5:15, but the fish came up to feed at 5:30 and missed it again. The next day he fed them at 5:30, but they came up at 5:45 and again missed their meal. The next day they died of starvation. This proves that fish can indeed think, declared the scientist, but not fast enough!

Several different aspects of Neandertal thought processes have been examined. These can be divided into reflections of their cognitive and symbolic abilities.

Neandertal Cognition

Based on analyses of Neandertal behavior as reflected in the archaeological record, some paleoanthropologists have argued that they could not anticipate future patterned animal movements (E. Trinkaus), or anticipate future needs for tools (P. Chase and H. Dibble), and indeed may have lacked future tenses and were unable to construct clauses about the future (R. Whallon, who also believes Neandertals lacked the ability to make alliances, which is part of the reason why they did not develop ethnic distinctions in his view, and may not even have been capable of forming extended families). L. Binford and a number of scientists seemingly influenced by his thinking regard the Neandertals as generally *lacking culture* as we know it, or for that matter as we have posited it for Pliocene hominids (perhaps at its most extreme this is evident in the J. Fischman interview).

The fundamental bases for these interpretations is found in the reconstruction of Neandertal cognitive abilities based on the archaeological remnants of their behaviors. Cognition may be examined through behaviors visible

- in the patterning of subsistence activities,
- through habitations and land use patterns
- through tools - their technology, curation, and whether any of their variation reflects style

Subsistence

One approach to cognition is reflected in their subsistence activities. The interpretation of these activities from the fauna found associated with human or archaeological remains has been guided by a series of issues raised by L. Binford, whose contributions to understanding the Olduvai sites were already discussed. He rejected the notion that recent or living hunter/gatherers can be used to interpret Middle Paleolithic (and earlier) sites because of the assumptions this requires. In a series of publications he argued that to do so is to deny the possibility of behavioral change, as interpretations in a modern framework will necessarily appear to reflect modern behavior. Avoiding this circularity, Binford challenged the prevailing views

- that Lower and Middle Paleolithic humans were efficient hunters,
- that they practiced significant foresight and advanced planning, and
- that differences in their tools reflected stylistic or symbolic variation.

Much of his focus was placed on how human behavioral capacities are reflected in their subsistence activities. The faunal remains in Middle Paleolithic sites have been compared with living hunter/gatherers with the notion that cognitive differences in the Neandertals will be revealed. But the question is how. Are better adaptations shown through reliance on hunting migratory herds, predominance of one prey species, seasonal exploitation of resources with short stays in any one place, or use of fewer spear points during hunting activities? All have been suggested as "modern attributes", albeit by different scientists. Binford proposes that the most significant change is when organized hunting emerged as a significant adaptive strategy. He characterizes Neandertals as practicing scavenging and limited opportunistic hunting of small or medium sized game. He further suggests that Neandertal men foraged widely, making more elaborate tools than women, and did not share foods with females or young (O. Soffer describes this adaptation as monosexual grouping). Binford concludes that Neandertal adaptations lack in-depth planning as expressed in evidence for seasonally different exploitation patterns and storage. In his interpretation it is only the dramatic changes *within* the Upper Paleolithic that reflect significant developments in cognition and are keyed to the emergence of modern complex language. Several other paleoanthropologists have made similar assertions.

Yet, a an array of behaviors including all of the subsistence patterns is seen in both Middle and Upper Paleolithic contexts. Archaeologists such as M. Stiner, S. Kuhn, B. Hayden and P. Mellars find significant evidence for advanced, in-depth planning at Middle Paleolithic sites such as Champlost and Mauran where there is evidence for sustained intensive hunting of large animals such as bison. P. Chase finds virtually no difference between the prey profiles at Middle and Upper Paleolithic sites. Rejecting Binford's interpretations, he reviews evidence for the persistent hunting of large migratory mammals, the effective use of curated technology, and the pattern of sharing, and, describes the subsistence activities of the Middle and early Upper Paleolithic as "remarkably similar". Of course these strategies were not the same everywhere. As noted above there is evidence for significant change within the Middle Paleolithic. Moreover, in some regions (for instance the Russian Plain, as described by O. Soffer) a more circumcised and opportunistic exploitation develops into a broader, more mobile, and highly seasonal adaptation as the Middle Paleolithic gives way to the Upper Paleolithic. Both strategies are practiced today, and she argues that the difference reflects performance and not cognitive ability.

Habitation and land use

A number of elements surrounding what L. Schepartz describes as intersite diversification have been used in a second approach to describing Neandertal cognitive abilities. Simply put, Upper Paleolithic European sites seem to show a level of complex organization that cannot be found in the middle Paleolithic, according to authors such as Binford and Mellars. Observations leading to the interpretation of complex organization include

- numerous well-defined structures
- hearths
- storage pits
- differential uses of habitation space

However, evidence of structures, including the remnants of huts, stone pavements, and walls are found at European Neandertal sites and even earlier. Hearths are rare but evident at Mousterian sites from Portugal to Israel. At the Riss habitation site of Lazeret there is clear evidence of a man-made structure, including a line of postholes delimiting an area with evidence of artifact debris and charcoal. Stone walls are found within a number of European Würm Mousterian caves and temporary structures are indicated at cave entrances as well as in more open contexts (an open air Mousterian structure at Villerest strongly resembles Upper Paleolithic structures made by the mammoth hunters of the same region somewhat later in time, according to J. Combier [see Chapter 14]). In Châtelperronian Neandertal sites stone hearths are much more common. Levantine Neandertal sites such as Kebara and Hayonim Caves feature numerous hearths in the central area of the cave. In this region of the Kebara Cave the animal bones are heavily marred with cut marks, but only a few gouges from carnivore gnawing, suggesting that this area was differentially used for eating. There is a refuse area with bone and lithic debris on the north wall of the cave. In all, there is clear evidence of differential uses within these (and other) Middle Paleolithic habitation spaces, and of structures ranging from windbreaks to huts.

Moreover, Binford himself describes the structured use of space in the Combe Grenal cave, in his analysis of Mousterian living floors within a sequence yielding only Neandertal remains. In the cave a central area covered with fine ash (perhaps the consequence of periodically burning bedding to kill body parasites inhabiting it) is contrasted with an outer ring of fireplaces associated with the bones of moderate to large mammals.

Yet, the fact is that Upper Paleolithic sites differ from the Middle Paleolithic in some important ways - the technologies and economies they support are not the same. Relevant to the cognition issue is the absence of effective long term storage technologies in the European Middle Paleolithic (apart from seasonal freezing) and its effect on habitation strategies. The development of these technologies was a critical element in the shifting adaptations of some of the Upper Paleolithic Europeans. They were an important element in the development of strategies based on foraging over broad areas with high seasonal mobility. Soffer argues that where this change can be seen, it did not happen overnight, no dramatic behavioral rubicon was crossed, and it is not necessarily associated with different kinds of humans. In other words, by itself the discovery and incorporation of this new technology cannot be taken to reflect dramatic, new cognitive abilities.

Tools

A third approach to understanding cognition derives from certain issues of Middle Paleolithic tool use - their technology, curation, and the question of whether style plays a role in their variation. Tools have become important in the question of Neandertal cognitive abilities in a variety of ways. Fundamentally, several archaeologists have questioned whether Neandertals have the ability to make certain Upper Paleolithic tool types because of their difficulty. On the other hand, anybody with experience in trying to manufacture even the simplest Mousterian flakes can attest to the conceptual and skill-related difficulties involved. J. Simek reports that there are an almost identical number of steps involved in manufacturing Middle and Upper Paleolithic tools. Moreover, tools of the sort said to be beyond Neandertal capabilities (blades struck from prismatic cores, modified bone and antler) are found in the Châtelperronian, an industry uniquely associated with Neandertals. The contention that a limited number of tool types reflect limited mental capacities on the part of their makers is, as Simek says, disturbing, and demonstrably incorrect.

One of Binford's bases for examining Neandertal cognitive abilities is in the issue of whether their tools were curated. He proposes that Neandertals made tools expediently - for an immediate purpose - and therefore that variation in tool types could be explained functionally and not as markers of individual, family, or larger group identity (the common interpretation of much Upper Paleolithic variation). It is from this essential observation that interpretations about the lack of foresight or future tense, comes. However several facts argue against this interpretation, including the use-wear found on many Mousterian tools (for instance spear points with impact fractures and subsequent resharpening) that shows they were kept for long times and used again. Hayden points out that at some Neandertal sites the raw materials for tools came from 30-80 km or even further away, and that tools made from these more exotic sources were resharpened much more often than tools made of local materials. J-M. Geneste argues that some of the artifact sources are well beyond the yearly range of bands lacking sleds or other transport devices, indicating the presence of area-wide trade networks (today, the broadest trade networks are found in areas with the lowest population densities and glacial Europe was lightly inhabited indeed!) As Roebroeks and colleagues put it, we simply do not have convincing technological indications of major differences of fundamental forms of behavior such as in the capacity for anticipation and advance planing of activities.

The resharpening itself raises an interesting contradiction. It can be extensive. At La Cotte in the Channel Island of Jersey, over 2000 resharpening flakes were recovered from a small area but only one could be refit onto the core from which it was struck. The rest were from tools that were discarded elsewhere. H. Dibble has long argued that Middle Paleolithic sites have only a very few tool types, and therefore that the lack of standardization reflects limited cognitive abilities. The *appearance of* many different standardized tool types, he contends, results from mechanical factors and the effects of continually using resharpened tools that become smaller and smaller over their functional lives. However C. Gamble and C. Stringer argue that the extensive resharpening at La Cotte was necessitated because rising sea levels had made flint sources rare in the island. Now these archaeologists cannot have it both ways! If there is an absence of curation, and tools are made and discarded expediently, the resharpening interpretation is wrong and there are many different standardized tool types. If there is a lack of standardization, as a limited number of tool forms are curated and resharpened over long periods, the lack of foresight interpretation is wrong.

The argument that Mousterians lacked ethnicity is based on the idea that variation in Mousterian tools does not reflect differences in style (presumed to be a marker of ethnicity). This is linked to their inability to form alliances because of their lack of future tenses. However, as B. Hayden and several others have pointed out the Middle Paleolithic industries have come to be defined by technology and frequency differences in tool types that are readily interpreted to reflect functional differences (high frequencies of scrapers mean more clothes preparation, etc.). In contrast, Upper Paleolithic industries are defined on the basis of specific "type tools" (Audi Knife, Split Based Bone Point, etc.) that are meant to act as cultural markers. Little wonder there appears to be a contrast in style differences - they are built into the definitions of Upper Paleolithic industries. Moreover, the Mousterian is mischaracterized as an industry whose variation is based only on differences in function and available raw materials. As P. Mellars points out, these two elements could never explain "the virtual restriction of typical handaxe forms to the extreme western fringes of Europe, or the similar restriction of classic leaf-points to particular areas of Central and Eastern Europe." Mellars continuously emphasizes the "Balkanization" of late Mousterian industries, albeit with the intent of showing the Aurignacian (which he believes to be more uniform) could not have evolved locally in many different places from them The astute reader will realize that archaeologically the Neandertals are in a "no-win" situation - either the absence of variation in their cultures show they lacked ethnicity and therefore were not modern, or the presence of variability in their cultures shows they were not the ancestors of the Aurignacians and therefore were not modern. In fact, variation is the reality. O. Bar-Yosef points to the existence of distinct Middle Paleolithic culture zones, based on differences in tools:

- Levantine Mousterian (Western Asia)
- Aterian (North Africa)
- Mousterian with bifacial tools (Central and Eastern Europe)
- Mousterian of Acheulean tradition (Western Europe)

He believes that these "reflect common communication systems and ranges of mobility within large mating systems" in the sense described by M. Wobst. In fact, as far as geographic differences are concerned, it is difficult to describe Mousterian variation in very different terms than variation in the Upper Paleolithic. Bone tool use, for instance, is very common in North and Central-Eastern European Aurignacians but virtually non-existent in Levantine or North African Aurignacians. Bone tools use is virtually non-existent in the West and Central European Mousterians, but has been reported in the Mousterian of the Crimea.

Symbolism

Evidence of symbolic behaviors can be sought in Neandertal burials and their use of art and items of personal adornment.

The burial issue

Perhaps the main issue surrounding Middle Paleolithic symbolism is whether or not Neandertals buried their dead, for as Schepartz argues the burial itself - the intentional positioning of a hominid body as it is interred - is symbolic. There are those like R. Gargett who deny that there were Neandertal burials (perhaps like elephants seeking the legendary elephant graveyard to die in, it is envisioned that Neandertals sought hollows at the back of caves to like down and expire), but generally the evidence for intentional interment is considered overwhelming. The fact that intentional burial first appears in the behaviors of Middle Paleolithic peoples (there are over 50 well-documented burials) belies a taphonomic explanation. Why wouldn't the same taphonomic process be ar work for earlier human populations? The idea, especially promoted by Chase and Dibble, that intentional burial is not necessarily symbolic but may only be a way that people expressed the fact that they liked each other, would suggest that these feelings and emotions about each other were not part of humanity before the Late Pleistocene, the age of the earliest burials. Any reader with experience watching groups of animals will recognize how unlikely this interpretation of human behavior is. The fact is that a sort of double standard is applied to the interpretation of Middle Paleolithic burials. As A. Belfer-Cohen and E. Hovers point out in their comparison of Mousterian and Natufian burials in the Levant (see Chapter 12), many of the Holocene burials from Israel made by the early agriculturists would not be interpreted as human burials if the criteria applied to the Middle Paleolithic were used. They argue that the Neandertals are subject to a more rigorous scrutiny because of their different appearance. How could people who appear so archaic (to the European eye) behave in a modern way? This is not the first time that Europeans have grappled with this question.

The pattern of burials is relevant to the issue of stratification. This has proven difficult to address, given the sparse and often temporary nature of the Neandertal habitations. Many of the Neandertal burials are found with what I believe are grave goods. Like Hayden, Sackett, and several others I do not accept the interpretation that these are generally sweepings of debris off of the cave floor as the grave is filled in. One reason for this is the fact that in most cases it is the males and not the females who have been given these goods, providing, if nothing else, evidence of stratification based on gender. Intentional burials with grave goods are found throughout the Middle Paleolithic world. However, as Hayden points out, it is probably not coincidental that so many Neandertal burials are in the same region of southwestern France where richly adorned Upper Paleolithic burials and the art-covered caves like Lascaux and Rouffignac are found. This is a resource-abundant area where markers of status differences within populations, and boundaries between them, might be expected to have appeared.

Art and personal adornment

Art and personal adornment are a second aspect of symbolic behavior with archaeological visibility. Art is inseparable from esthetics, and many definitions of art emphasize the goal of esthetic appeal or emotional gratification rather than utilitarian function. There certainly was an esthetic sense long before Neandertals first evolved. Chert blanks for Acheulean hand axes were chosen with attractive fossils, and the tools were made to center or otherwise feature the fossils. Non-functional fossils, the teeth of marine animals, and other unusual items were kept and transported for long distances. Workers such as E. Dissanayake consider any evidence of non-functional objects as having potential symbolic significance, as this fits her hypothesis that art expressions began in ritual contexts.

Objects of personal adornment are clearly an example of esthetic expressions. They may also be a potential marker of complex language as they can be a means of communication or information exchange, identify the background or group membership of the owner, and represent or identify individuals who are not present. P. Weissner observes that non-ornamental, but stylistic, artifacts such as arrow heads are used the same way. Their absence in the Middle Paleolithic, as argued by workers such as R. White, would if true bespeak of a lack of complex communication, status differences, group identity (ethnicity), and even non-linguistic displacement behaviors. But are they really absent?

A. Marshack describes evidence for body decoration and personal ornamentation in both Middle and Lower Paleolithic contexts. This includes pierced teeth (presumably for making an amulet or necklace) and other beads and pendants, and worn blocks of pigments such as red ochre and black manganese that can be used to color the skin. Decorating bodies, as suggested by red coloring material at Olduvai Bed II and later at Terra Amata, may have been practiced through the entire Pleistocene. Red and yellow ocher and black manganese remnants are found at many sites, both in powder form and as short sticks that appear to have been rubbed on a soft surface (decorating human skin? softening and coloring animal hides?). Personal adornments, he argues, did not "suddenly emerge" with the appearance of modern populations in Europe, but instead have considerable antiquity.

Table 13.12
Decorated Objects from the European Mousterian[1]

Site	Object
La Quina	drilled fox tooth, pierced reindeer toe bone
La Ferrassie	bone with fine incised parallel lines
Bacho Kiro	bone with engraved zigzags
Tata	modified mammoth molar
Pech de l'Azé	pierced bone fragment
Cueva Morin	bone fragment with incised lines

[1] From Stringer and Gamble (1993, table 63)

The other element of symbolic behavior intricate to the discussion is art. The association of art with some non-Neandertals and post-Neandertals is unquestioned. Yet, the spectacular cave wall art of Western Europe cannot be directly relevant to Neandertal cognition as it first appears considerably later than the first post-Neandertals in the region. Engravings and sculpted figurines are earlier; for instance, one abstract sculpture, of a lion head on a human body, is from the Vogelherd Cave in Germany which is also the site of one of the earliest post-Neandertals. But in fact both parietal art and sculptures are considerably earlier in their first appearance. Cave art, in the form of petroglyphs, are dated to 36 and 43 kyr in Australia, and human figurines are found as far back as the Acheulean of Israel (Chapter 11) - the Berekhat Ram sculpture is older than 230 kyr, according to N. Goren-Inbar. There is an engraving on an ox rib recovered from the Acheulean levels at Pech de l'Azé, France. The basic engraving consists of a series of connected double arcs running from left to right. The various marks were made with different tools, and therefore possibly at different times. Later, other simple figures were added, including a series of angles and sets of double marks. The result is a rather complex set of engravings. Were these notations or representations? Marshack believes that the alterations are clearly "intentional, cumulative, and sequential."

As for the Middle Paleolithic, table 13.12 reviews some of the altered or decorated objects that have been found. A 100 kyr engraving (a plaque carved from a mammoth tooth and covered with red ochre) was found at Tata in Hungary, and other examples of engraving include a capstone covering one of the La Ferrassie Neandertal burials (the La Ferrassie 6 child) and an engraved bone fragment from the adult female burial. Chase and Dibble interpret Middle Paleolithic art as showing an esthetic sense, and J. Simek notes that its frequency is not markedly different than that found in the subsequent earlier Upper Paleolithic. Marshack argues for continuity in European design motifs from the Middle to Upper Paleolithic that he regards as symbolic and not utilitarian, such as zig-zags and randomly placed dots. Some researchers refuse to accept these, and the pendants discussed earlier, as true art forms because they lack the regularity of design found in later examples. Yet, as Schepartz notes if they were used to mark a social persona as opposed to a group identity, regularity may not be necessary, or even desired.

The fact is that Neandertals of the Upper Paleolithic repeatedly made such objects, indicating that the capacity for these behaviors was present in their genome all along. Even skeptical workers such as R. White include the Châtelperronian with other earlier European Upper Paleolithic industries in his description of a florescence of body decoration and art. For instance, at Arcy-sur-Cure the Châtelperronian includes carved and grooved fox and deer teeth that must have been for personal adornment, as well as modified bird bones, shaped and decorated beads, and other manifestations of creativity. Yet the only hominids found with Châtelperronian (at St. Césaire and Arcy-Sur-Cure) *are Neandertals*. It is widely believed that this industry developed out of the earlier Mousterian of the region, but it is clearly Upper Paleolithic in its technology and on the basis of certain "type tools" (these are the defining elements for all European Upper Paleolithic industries - a procedure justified on the assumption that type tools are ethnic markers). Scientists who will not or can not ascribe such abilities to Neandertals (for instance Stringer and Gamble, Chase and Dibble) propose that the body decorations and other symbolic objects appear at Neandertal sites because of trades with their better endowed neighbors (these, however, have never been found as the makers of the early Aurignacian remain unknown) or perhaps because of imitation as the Neandertals stood around the campfires of the more fortunate moderns, wondering what they were doing while dimly perceiving that they should do it themselves.

The implication of the appearance of graphic art is the direct evidence it provides for cross-modal transfer and language capability (this is discussed in depth in several papers by Laughlin and d'Aquili). Marshack argues that decoration results in symbolic artifacts that can only be interpretable in a cultural context. Moreover, he contends that their design and manufacture provide direct evidence of cross-modal transfer, an ability we have previously inferred from the evidence of cerebral asymmetry and the expansion of the relevant brain areas suggested by the endocasts. According to Marshack, the early art objects provide evidence for "motivation, planning, cognitive modeling, symbolic sequencing, and an exceedingly fine acuity in the kinesthetic, somesthetic, and visual inputs." These are the same capabilities that underlie human language behavior and must be associated with the evolution of vocalized language. They are not unlike the requirements of prepared core manufacture, and it may not be accidental that the earliest evidence of graphic art and the appearance of the prepared core technique date to similar times.

There certainly was a creative explosion in Western Europe, as White and others describe, but as Simek notes it came after the Aurignacian, the industry that many of the replacement theorists believe accompanied the populations replacing Neandertals as they swept into Europe. If the creative explosion truly represents a substantial change in cognitive abilities, it happened long after the post-Neandertals appeared. But it is not clear that this explosion was more than a local European phenomenon, and we surely do not conclude that contemporary populations lacked European cognitive abilities! Alternatively, workers such as Hayden suggest the explosion may more accurately reflect the regional consequences of a more complex hunting/gathering lifestyle that developed in response to new technologies in food processing and storage.

A *HUMAN* RACE

The interpretation of Neandertal behavior as lacking significant elements of language and culture fares no better than the anatomical arguments denying them vocalization competence. Hayden characterizes is as a travesty of the available data. Human behavior, without question, has evolved and Binford is quite correct in insisting that we do not impose the present onto the past and thereby undercut out ability to note and explain that evolution. Yet, the fact of behavioral evolution does not inexorably lead to the precept that it happened all at once, in a single integrated package including complex language, cognition, abstract art and symbolism (and in more extreme interpretations the first appearance of male parenting and nuclear families) -- and on the evidence within the last 25 kyr! There can be no single crucial mutation or "modernization gene" that could conceivably account for all or even a significant part of this, and to understand the evolutionary process we need to examine the individual elements that coalesce around the world during the Late Pleistocene.

Most scientists accept the essentially human interpretation of Neandertal cognitive abilities, including language potential. Perhaps this is most succinctly put by P. Mellars (1989, p. 378), one of the replacement theorists:

There is now unmistakable evidence that the final Neanderthal populations in Western Europe were behaving in a way ... which was entirely Upper Paleolithic not only in a basic technological sense but also in at least some spheres of cognitive or symbolic expression. ... There was nothing in the inherent biological makeup ... of the latest Neanderthal populations that prevented them from adopting many of the basic technological features which are conventionally regarded as the hallmarks of fully modern populations

If it looks like a fish, and swims like a fish, it is difficult to deny that it *is* a fish. Perhaps what might best be remembered about this dispute is the failure of culture to reflect biology in the Middle and early Upper Paleolithic (or any subsequent period) - a fact that in and of itself indicates the essential humanity of Neandertals and their relatives. The association of both Neandertals and non-Neandertals such as the Skhul and Qafzeh folk with the Middle Paleolithic of the Levant (Chapter 12), of non-Neandertals with the European and Western Asian Mousterian, or of Neandertals with the early European Upper Paleolithic, belies the validity of associating culture and biology in the past, just as surely as it is invalidated in South Africa and elsewhere today.

Summary

Neandertals evolved in Europe and Western and West-Central Asia from Middle Pleistocene ancestors exhibiting most of the Neandertal features that later coalesced to characterize this race. Continued trends, including the increase in cranial capacity, thinning of the vault bones, reduction of the browridges, retraction of the midface, appearance of chins, and decrease in limb shaft thickness and other strength-related features are European changes that reflect worldwide trends. More unique to Europe are the expansions of the anterior dentition and the corresponding facial changes (for instance expanded maxillary sinus, forward position of the tooth row) that do not change in direction until the onset of the last glaciation. The postcranial skeletons show reduced robustness, but there is no change in average body height. During the last 100,000 years, humans spread into previously unoccupied habitats (especially forests and more northern areas), and developed several different strategies for dealing with the less predictable, seasonal resources.

The Würm populations of Europe were depleted by population movements out of regions at the colder extremes of the continent. Changes in selection are quite evident in those populations that remained in or near glaciated Europe. Many of them are clearly climatic adaptations, while others are probably a direct consequence of the improved efficiency of material culture evolving through the earlier Upper Pleistocene since they involve the further substitution of technology for muscular strength.

The Neandertals in the terminal Mousterian show these trends most clearly. Contemporary with them are Neandertals or Neandertal-like Europeans found in early Upper Paleolithic contexts. This is not the only source of cultural variation. Adaptive differences developed between populations that continued to utilize highland caves and rock shelters (virtually all of the European Neandertal skeletal material is from these groups) and populations that adapted to the open plains. Yet only a few archaeological distinctions separate these adaptive patterns. Instead, we find a wide variety of different traditions. At the sites of plains-adapted groups, a few new artifacts appear. These include some bone points, pick-like axes made of an antler, and bifacially flaked projectile points. The lack of a unique association between Middle Paleolithic industries and Neandertal fossils in Western Asia suggests the question of exactly who is was making the Middle Paleolithic at the flatter European plains and steppe sites.

The Neandertal problem, the place of the Neandertals in human evolution, is a complex and unresolved issue. It is further discussed in the context of modern European origins, in Chapter 14. Many paleoanthropologists have come to view Neandertals as a human race. Their total behavioral pattern was not human, in the sense of being like any recent or living population. Yet, the indirect evidence of language and cognition, organization and technology, land use and habitat utilization all combine to suggest they had fully human behavioral potentials. If Neandertal-modern European behavioral distinctions reflect different habits and histories, it all-the-more supports my contention that modern humans are not an anatomical complex but a state of mind.

ANATOMY OF A CONTROVERSY
Tongues Wag Anew

Reconstructing language ability from the anatomy of human fossils has a long history of controversy. In 1866 the 150th meeting of the Paris Anthropological Society featured an argument about speech in Neandertals, based on the anatomy of the newly discovered toothless mandible from the Belgan site of La Naulette. At that time the debate centered on the area of the chin. Today the debate continues, although progress has pushed its focus down the throat and centered it on the position of the vocal chords, as marked by the free-floating hyoid bone. Recent publications by P. Lieberman, J. Laitman, and their coworkers have suggested that the European Würm Neandertals were incapable of making many of the modern human vowel sounds and thus were incapable of rapid modern speech. The argument initially supporting this is based on a reconstruction of the La Chapelle vocal tract, which (it was claimed) could be reconstituted because it is similar to that of a human infant, and on a computer simulation of the sounds this reconstructed tract could produce. Laitman subsequently modified these ideas, contending that the large nose and flat cranial base of Neandertals is part of their cold adaptation, the part expressed in the respiratory system. However he still believes that they resulted in nasalized, less articulate language sounds (see the discussion reported by J. Fischman).

These are the latest of many attempts to relate speech ability to skeletal features. However, the language issue has come to involve more than anatomy. It has been argued on other grounds that modern complex language abilities appeared recently, and as a complete integrated package (perhaps most coherently by D. Bickerton, although see the review by R. Burling, and also in papers by I Davidson and W. Noble, and R. Milo and D. Quiatt). This appearance is held responsible for everything from the success of Eve and her descendants (the late A. Wilson believed they carried a "language gene" on their mtDNA) to the "behavioral revolution" with its "creative explosion" within the European Upper Paleolithic discussed in Chapter 14. Modern complex language is said to

- reflect complex social relations based on explicit mutual expectations,
- create social systems with enhanced cooperation
- promote self-identification and naming
- allow the development of strategic planning
- stimulate group differences, expressed in linguistic variation isolating groups, that require group identity as might be reflected in symbolism and art

Osteological evidence for language evolution, of course, is limited to those elements that can be used in the reconstruction of speech abilities.

A substantive review by L. Schepartz sheds more light than heat on the issue, thereby playing an unusual role in the ongoing debate. She reviews external and internal aspects of the paleoanthropological evidence that addresses the origin of complex language, testing the hypothesis that it is uniquely associated with modern human populations.

The brain and language can be linked directly through cranial capacity evaluations. These stretch back to Darwin's time. According to L. Van Valen, there is a weak but significant correlation between brain size and some cognitive abilities, and more generally it is difficult to dismiss the notion that brain size expansion in the hominids is connected to behavioral complexities including (if not featuring) language (c.f. Chapter 4). Since modern sized large bodies were attained at the onset of *Homo sapiens* evolution, subsequent brain size expansions can be related to these abilities. The fact that brain size changes have been gradual through the Pleistocene (although certainly not constant) suggests a gradual evolution of cognitive complexities. In particular, there are no jumps or sudden increases at any of the times that the appearance of complex language is said to have created population replacements or dramatic behavioral changes. Another brain-related connection is found in the evidence for neuroanatomical changes reflected in endocast structure. T. Deacon points out that although none of the surface structure of the brain, as preserved on endocasts, can be related to language, the differential development of different parts of the brain reflect circuitry changes. Paleoneurologist R. Holloway, V.

Kochetkova, and M. LeMay agree that there is no basis for distinguishing Neandertal endocasts from those of recent or living people, certainly none in any areas that might be related to language or speech.

A second link is found in the structure of the brain. Workers such as E. d'Aquili and C. Laughlin have presented strong arguments from neuroanatomy to support the notion that culturally defined behaviors such as language, mythology and religion, are ancient additions to the human repertoire. These authors draw on research concerning the structural aspects of brain functions in the two asymmetric cerebral hemispheres. They argue that the simultaneous functioning of both hemispheres may provide a neurological basis for the human ability to deal with the polar opposites that underlie all myth and religious structures. In effect, they suggest that the division of models for conceptualizing external data into polar opposites is a necessary consequence of a functional asymmetry in the brain and thus that generating a myth structure is a basic aspect of human cognition. Given the evidence for neural reorganization found in the australopithecines and the marked asymmetry of virtually all Pleistocene endocasts, these authors believe that language, myth and religion became established in human culture long before the appearance of modern humans.

A third link is in the anatomy preserved for the vocal tract, specifically in the mandible and hyoid. Additional, although more secondary information is found in the soft tissue reconstructions. Below the brain, as the late J. Spuhler liked to point out, there are virtually no unambiguous markers related to speech. The expression of mandibular features such as the genial tubercles are totally irrelevant to this problem. The hyoid is somewhat more interesting, as it is the only bone in the human body lacking direct contact with other bones. Because of the influence of muscle forces on bone shape, hyoid form should directly reflect its position in the throat - an expectation confirmed by the dramatic differences between human and chimpanzee hyoids. The only Pleistocene hyoid known, that of the Mousterian hominid from Kebara (Chapter 12) that is widely believed to be Neandertal, is fully modern in its anatomy. It is pictured by A. Gibbons, who compares it with the hyoid of a pig. This comparison might seem inappropriate, but one of the arguments developed by Laitman and colleagues in defense of their position is that this bone cannot be distinguished from that of a pig (also see the exchange between P. Lieberman and B. Arensburg on this and related issues). As Schepartz points out, it is not clear whether Laitman and colleagues are serious in this assertion, but their intent is irrelevant as they have been widely cited as establishing a pig-like (and therefore non-human) anatomy of the Kebara specimen by workers who believe Neandertals lack human capabilities (for instance Stringer and Gamble, Milo and Quiatt, and others). This is not the high point (or the high ground) of scientific debate.

More indirectly, there have been several vocal tract reconstructions (all before the Kebara hyoid was found). Some of these are anatomical, based indirectly on the preserved anatomy of the region. It could be argued that preserved anatomy does not contain enough information for such reconstructions, but workers such as P. Lieberman and E. Crelin solved this problem through their assumption that ontogeny validly recapitulates phylogeny. In particular, they worked from the assertion that the anatomy of Neandertals resembles newborn humans (humans presumably passing through a Neandertal phase during their growth), so that Neandertal vocal tract anatomy can be modeled after the soft tissue anatomy of newborns even in the absence of critical landmarks. Subsequent analysis of the Neandertal throats revealed that like the newborns they could not utter the full range of human sounds. A number of workers questioned these reconstructions; for instance, D. Falk showed that if the reconstructed Neandertals couldn't talk, they also couldn't swallow. P. Houghton demonstrated that the La Chapelle vocal tract reconstruction was wrong to start with, even if Boule's cranial reconstruction had been correct. When the cranium is properly oriented, it can be seen that the position and orientation of the upper neck vertebrae in the Crelin reconstruction are incorrect. Altering this to the proper position and taking account of mistakes made in sizing and orienting the tongue, shows that the other reconstructed features that *seem* to resemble modern newborns *actually* resemble adults. Neandertal differences, he concluded, mainly affect the midface anterior to the vocal tract. D. Burr shows that a newborn's vocal tract could not be used to model any adult.

Trying to circumvent these problems, J. Laitman and colleagues attempted a more mathematical approach to vocal tract reconstruction, grounded in a series of measurements meant to reflect the flexion of the cranial base. They argued that flexion was linked to the position of the vocal chords in the throat, and therefore to the mobility of the tongue and the resonating capabilities of the vocal chamber. This, too, distinguished Neandertals, but not as clearly and mainly the toothless ones (the lack of teeth influenced the measurements that were taken to detail cranial base flexion). However, a relation between these speech factors and cranial base flatness has never been shown in humans, the only species with significant cranial base shape variation, and Schepartz, Kean and Houghton, and several others, show that their experimental linkage is invalid. In other primates, cranial base flatness is clearly related to relative brain size. For instance, one study by C. Ross and M. Ravosa concludes that in the context of other primates, the highly flexed cranial base of modern humans mainly reflects their large brain and very short cranial base. Laitman and colleagues' approach was further questioned when several specimens of *Australopithecus boisei* were found with very flexed (human-like) cranial bases, and in any event can be dismissed as a means of distinguishing Neandertals with J-L. Heim's new reconstruction of the La Chapelle cranium that reveals a magnitude and pattern of basal flexion that is fully human. Heim wrote:

> Our reconstruction, then, should put an end to the controversies about the existence of articulate language among Neandertals. These humans were anatomically capable of producing the same vowels and the same consonants as us.

Science advances by trying to disprove null hypotheses - the simplest hypotheses that are best supported by the available evidence. At the moment, the simplest hypothesis supported by known observations made on Neandertals is that their ability to speak cannot be distinguished from living humans. The attempts to disprove this hypothesis, as detailed above, have totally failed.

REFERENCES AND FURTHER READINGS

ADLOFF, P. 1937 Über die primitiven und die sogenannten *pithekoiden* Merkmale im Gebiss des rezenten und Fossilen Menschen und ihre Bedeutung. *Zeitschrift für Anatomie und Entwicklungsgeschichte* 107:68-82.

ALCOMBÉ, S. 1958 Die Neandertaler Spaniens. In G.H.R. von Koenigswald (ed): *Hundert Jahre Neanderthaler*. Kemink en Zoon, Utrecht. pp. 9-18.

ALEXEYEV, V.P. 1979 Horizontal profile of the Neandertal crania from Krapina comparatively considered. *Collegium Anthropologicum* 3:7-13.

ARENSBURG, B. 1994 Middle Paleolithic speech capabilities: a response to Dr. Lieberman. *American Journal of Physical Anthropology* 94(2):279-280.

ANTÓN, S.C. 1994 Mechanical and other perspectives on Neandertal craniofacial morphology. In R.S. Corruccini and R.L. Ciochon (eds): *Integrative Paths to the Past. Paleoanthropological Advances in Honor of F. Clark Howell*. Prentice Hall, Englewood Cliffs. pp. 677-695.

ASHTON, N., and J. COOK 1986 Dating and correlating the French Mousterian. *Nature* 324:113.

BALL, G., G. SAINT MARTIN, and E. BERAUD-COLOMB 1987 A systematic study of the amino acid compositions and D/L ratios in fossil bones from two French Neanderthalian sites. *Human Evolution* 2(4):289-296.

BAMFORTH, D. 1986 Technological efficiency and tool curation. *American Antiquity* 51:38-50.

BAR-YOSEF, O. 1988 Evidence for Middle Paleolithic symbolic behavior: a cautionary note. In M. Otte (ed): *L'Homme de Néandertal*. Volume 5:11-16. *Etudes et Recherches Archéologiques de l'Université de Liège, Liège*.

BARRETT, M.J. 1977 Masticatory and non-masticatory uses of teeth. In Wright, R.V.S. (ed): *Stone Tools as Cultural Markers: Change, Evolution, and Complexity*. Humanities Press, Atlantic Highlands. pp. 18-23.

BEALS, K.L., C.L. SMITH, and S.M. DODD 1984 Brain size, cranial morphology, climate, and time machines. *Current Anthropology* 25:301-330.

BERMÚDEZ DE CASTRO, J.M. (editor) 1994 *Human Evolution in Europe and the Atapuerca Evidence*. Museo Nacional de Cienias Naturales, Madrid.

BINFORD, L.R. 1973 Interassemblage variability -- the Mousterian problem and the "functional" argument. In C. Renfrew (ed): *Explanation of Culture Change*. Duckworth, London. pp. 227-254.

___. 1980 Willow smoke and dogs' tails: hunter-gatherer settlement systems and archaeological site formation. *American Antiquity* 45:1-17.

___. 1989 Isolating the transition to cultural adaptations: an organizational approach. In E. Trinkaus (ed): *The Emergence of Modern Humans. Biocultural Adaptations in the Later Pleistocene*. Cambridge University Press, Cambridge. pp. 18-41, and combined references for the volume on pp. 232-276.

BINFORD, L.R., and S.R. BINFORD 1966 A preliminary analysis of functional variability in the Mousterian of Levallois facies. In J.D. Clark and F.C. Howell (eds): *Recent studies in paleoanthropology. American Anthropologist* 68:238-295.

BINFORD, S.R. 1968 A structural comparison of disposal of the dead in the Mousterian and the Upper Paleolithic. *Southwest Journal of Anthropology* 24:139-154.

___. 1972 The significance of variability: a minority report. In F. Bordes (ed): *The Origin of Homo sapiens.* UNESCO, Paris. pp. 199-210.

BLACKWELL, B., and H.P. SCHWARCZ 1986 U-Series analysis of the Lower Travertine at Ehringsdorf, DDR. *Quaternary Research* 25:215-222.

BLACKWELL, B., H.P. SCHWARCZ, and A. DEBÉNATH 1983 Absolute dating of hominids and Paleolithic artifacts of the cave of La Chaise-de-Vouthon (Charente), France. *Journal of Archaeological Science* 10:493-513.

BLANC, A.C. 1961 Some evidence for the ideologies of early man. In S.L. Washburn(ed): *The Social Life of Early Man.* Viking Fund Publication in Anthropology 31:119-136.

BOCHERENS, H., M. FIZET,, A. MARIOTTI, B. LANGE-BADRE, B. VANDERMEERSCH, J.P. BOREL, and G. BELLON 1991 Isotopic biogeochemistry (^{13}C,^{15}N) of fossil vertebrate collagen: application to the study of a past food web including Neandertal man. *Journal of Human Evolution* 20(6):481-492.

BONÉ, E. 1978 Les sépultures néandertaliennes. In: *Les origines humaines et les époques de l'intelligence.* Masson, Paris. pp. 239-250.

BORDES, F. 1959 Le contexte archéologique des hommes de Moustier et de Spy. *L'Anthropologie* 63:154-157.

___. 1961 Mousterian cultures in France. *Science* 134:803-810.

___. 1968 *Le Paléolithique du Monde.* Hachette, Paris.

___. 1969 Os percé Moustérien et os gravé Acheuléen du Pech de L'Azé II. *Quaternaria* 11:1-6.

___. 1972 Du Paléolithique moyen au Paléolithique supérieur, continuité ou discontinuité? In F. Bordes (ed): *The Origin of Homo sapiens.* UNESCO, Paris. pp. 211-218.

BOULE, M., and H.V. VALLOIS 1957 *Fossil Man.* Dryden, New York .

BOWER, B. 1989 Talk of ages. A tiny bone rekindles arguments over the roots of speech and language. *Science News* 136:24-26.

BRACE, C.L. 1964 The fate of the "Classic" Neanderthals: a consideration of hominid catastrophism. *Current Anthropology* 5:3-43 and 7:204-214.

___. 1968 Neandertal. *Natural History* 77(5):38-45.

BRÄUER, G. 1989 The evolution of modern humans: a comparison of the African and non-African evidence. In P. Mellars and C.B. Stringer (eds): *The Human Revolution: Behavioural and Biological Perspectives on the Origins of Modern Humans.* Edinburgh University Press, Edinburgh. pp. . 123-154.

BRESSON, F. 1992 Aptitude au langage chez les néandertaliens: apport d'une approche pluridiscipliniaire. *Bulletins et Mémoires de la Société d'Anthropologie de Paris* (nouvelle serie) 4(1-2):33-51.

BROSE, D.S.., and M.H. WOLPOFF. 1971 Early Upper Paleolithic man and late Middle Paleolithic tools. *American Anthropologist* 73:1156-1194.

BROTHWELL, D. 1975 Adaptive growth changes as a possible explanation for the distinctiveness of the Neanderthalers. *Journal of Archaeological Science* 2:161-163.

BURLING, R. 1992 The crucial mutation for language. *Journal of Linguistic Anthropology* 2(1):81-91,

BUNN, H.T., L.E. BARTHAM, and E.M. KROLL 1988 Variability in bone assemblage formation from Hazda hunting, scavenging, and carcass processing. *Journal of Anthropological Archaeology* 7:412-457.

BURR, D.B. 1976 Neandertal vocal tract reconstructions: a critical appraisal. *Journal of Human Evolution* 5:285-290.

CAMPBELL, T.D. 1939 Food, Food Values and Food Habits of the Australian Aborigines in relation to their dental conditions. *Australians Dental Journal* 34:1-177.

CHASE, P.G. 1990 Tool-making tools and Middle Paleolithic behavior. *Current Anthropology* 31(4):443-447.

CHASE, P.G., and H.L. DIBBLE 1987 Middle Paleolithic symbolism: a review of the evidence and interpretations. *Journal of Anthropological Archaeology* 6(3):263-296.

___. 1992 Scientific archaeology and the origins of symbolism. *Cambridge Archaeological Journal* 2(1):43-51.

CHURCHILL, S.E., and E. TRINKAUS 1990 Neandertal scapular glenoid morphology. *American Journal of Physical Anthropology* 83(2)147-160.

CLARK, G.A., and J.M. LINDLY 1990 Symbolism and modern human origins. *Current Anthropology* 31:233-262.

CONDEMI, S. 1983 Comparison des sphénoïdes des Hommes de Saccopastore I, II et de Gibraltar I. *Comptes Rendus de L'Académie des Sciences*, Séries D, 296:389-392.

___. 1988 Réexamen des hommes fossiles Riss-Würm de Saccopastore (Italie): caractères archaïques et néanderthaliens. Comptes Rendus de L'Academie des Sciences, Séries II, 306:499-504.

___. 1991 Circeo 1 and variability among Classic Neandertals. In M. Piperno and G. Scichilone (eds): *The Circeo 1 Neandertal Skull: Studies and Documentation*. Instituto Poligrafico e Zecca Dello Stato, Dello Stato. pp. 339-355.

CONSTABLE, G. 1973 *The Neanderthals*. Time-Life, New York.

CORNFORD, J. 1986 Specialized resharpening techniques and evidence of handedness. In P. Callow and J. Cornwood (eds): *La Cotte de St. Brelade*. Geo Books, Norwich. pp. 337-352.

CORRUCCINI, R.S. 1975 Metrical analysis of Fontéchevade II. *American Journal of Physical Anthropology* 42:95-98.

COURVILLE, C.B. 1950 Cranial injuries in prehistoric man with particular reference to the Neanderthals. *Yearbook of Physical Anthropology* 6:185-205.

CRELIN, E.S. 1987 *The Human Vocal Tract: Anatomy. Function, Development, and Evolution.* Vantage, New York.

CULOTTA, E. 1991 Pulling Neandertals back onto our family tree. *Science* 252:376.

___. 1993 Old feuds, new finds mark anthropologists' meeting. *Science* 260:892-893.

CZARNETZKI, A. 1977 Artefizielle Veränderungen an den Skelletresten aus dem Neandertal? In P. Schröter (ed): *Festschrift zum 75 jährigen Bestehen der Anthropologischen Staatssammlung München.* Anthropologischen Staatssammlung München, München. pp. 215-220.

D'AQUILI, E.G., and C. LAUGHLIN 1975 The biophychological determinants of religious behavior. *Zygon* 10:32-58.

DAVIDSON, I. 1991 The archaeology of language origins -- a review. *Antiquity* 65:39-48.

DAVIDSON, I., and W. NOBEL 1989 The archaeology of perception. Traces of depiction and language. *Current Anthropology* 30:125-155.

DEACON, T.D. 1992 The neural circuitry underlying primate calls and human language. In J. Wind, B. Chiarelli, B. Bichakjian, and A. Nocentini (eds): *Language Origin: A Multidisciplinary Approach.* Kluwer Academic Publishers, Dordrecht. pp. 121-162.

DEAN, M.C., C.B. STRINGER, and T.G. BROMAGE 1986 Age at death of the Neanderthal child from Devil's Tower, Gibraltar and the implications for studies of general growth and development in Neandertals. *American Journal of Physical Anthropology* 70(3):301-309.

DÉBENATH, A. 1992 On new models for the Neanderthal debate. *Current Anthropology* 33(1):50-51.

DEFLEUR, A., O. DUTOUR, H. VALLADAS, and B. VANDERMEERSCH 1993 Cannibals among the Neanderthals? *Nature* 362:214.

DEMES, B. 1987 Another look at an old face: biomechanics of the Neandertal facial skeleton reconsidered. *Journal of Human Evolution* 16(3):297-303.

DE STEFANO, G.F., and G. HAUSER 1991 Epigenetic traits of the Circeo I skull. In M. Piperno and G. Scichilone (eds): *The Circeo 1 Neandertal Skull: Studies and Documentation.* Instituto Poligrafico e Zecca Dello Stato, Dello Stato. pp. 273-299.

DIAMOND, J.M. 1989 Were Neanderthals the first humans to bury their dead? *Nature* 340:344.

DIBBLE, H.L. 1989 The implications of stone tool types for the presence of language during the Lower and Middle Paleolithic. In P. Mellars and C.B. Stringer (eds): *The Human Revolution: Behavioural and Biological Perspectives on the Origins of Modern Humans.* Edinburgh University Press, Edinburgh. pp. 415-432.

___. 1991 Mousterian assemblage variability on an interregional scale. *Journal of Anthropological Research* 47(2):239-257.

DISSANAYAKE, E. 1992 *Homo aestheticus.* Free Press, New York.

DUFF, I.A., G.A. CLARK, and T.J. CHADDERDON 1992 Symbolism in the early Paleolithic: a conceptual odyssey. *Cambridge Archaeological Journal* 2:211-229.

ENDO, B. 1971 Some characteristics of the deltoid tuberosity of the humerus of the West Asian and European "classic" Neandertals. *Journal of the Anthropological Society of Nippon* 79:249-258.

FALK, D. 1975 Comparative anatomy of the larynx in man and the chimpanzee: Implications for language in Neanderthal. *American Journal of Physical Anthropology* 43:123-132.

FARIZY, C. 1989 The transition from Middle to Upper Paleolithic at Arcy-sur-Cure (Yonne, France): technological, economic, and social aspects. In P. Mellars (ed): *The Emergence of Modern Humans: an Archaeological perspective.* Edinburgh University Press, Edinburgh.

FÉBLOT-AUGUSTINS, J. 1993 Mobility strategies in the late Middle Paleolithic of Central Europe and Western Europe: elements of stability and variability. *Journal of Anthropological Archaeology* 12:211-265.

FEUSTEL, R. 1978 *Abstammungsgeschichte des Menschen.* Fischer, Jena.

FISCHMAN, J. 1992 Hard evidence. *Discover* 13(2):44-51.

FRAYER, D.W. 1984 Biological and cultural change in the European late Pleistocene and early Holocene. In F.H. Smith and F. Spencer (eds): *The Origins of Modern Humans: A World Survey of the Fossil Evidence.* Alan R. Liss, Inc., New York. pp. 211-250.

FRAYER, D.W., and A. MONTET-WHITE 1989 Comment on "Grave shortcomings" by R. Gargett. *Current Anthropology* 30:180-181.

FRAYER, D.W., and M.D. RUSSELL 1987 Artificial grooves on the Krapina Neandertal teeth. *American Journal of Physical Anthropology* 74(3):393-405.

FRAYER, D.W., and M.H. WOLPOFF 1993 Comment on "Glottogenesis and anatomically modern *Homo sapiens*" by R.G. Milo and D. Quiatt. *Current Anthropology* 34(5):582-584.

GARGETT, R.H. 1989 Grave shortcomings: the evidence for Neandertal burial. *Current Anthropology* 30(1): 157-190; 30(3):326-330.

GARN, S.M., and W. BLOCK 1970 The limited nutritional value of cannibalism. *American Anthropologist* 72:106.

GEIST, V. 1981 Neanderthal the hunter. *Natural History* 90(1):26-36.

GENESTE, J-M. 1989 Economie des resources lithiques dans le Moustérien du sud-ouest de la France. In M. Patou and L. Freeman (eds): *L'Homme de Néandertal, La Subsistance.* Volume 6:75-97. *Etudes et Recherches Archéologiques de l'Université Liège, Liège.*

GENOVÉS, S. 1954 The problem of the sex of certain fossil hominids, with special reference to the Neandertal skeletons from Spy. *Journal of the Royal Anthropological Institute* 34:131-144.

GIBBONS, A. 1992 Neandertal language debate: tongues wag anew. *Science* 256:33-34.

___. 1992 Mitochondrial Eve: wounded but not dead yet. *Science* 257:873-875.

GOULD, S.J. 1988 A novel notion of Neanderthal. *Natural History* 6/88:16-21.

GRAVES, P. 1991 New models and metaphors for the Neanderthal debate. *Current Anthropology* 32(5):513-541

GREEN, R.M., and B.W. DARVELL 1988 Tooth wear and position of the mental foramen. *American Journal of Physical Anthropology* 77(1):69-75.

GUANJUN SHEN 1986 U-Series dating of the deposits from the Prince cave, northern Italy. *Archaeometry* 28(2):179-184.

HAMMOND, M. 1980 The expulsion of the Neanderthals from human ancestry: Marcellin Boule and the social context of scientific research. *Social Studies of Science* 12:1-36.

___. 1988 The shadow of man paradigm in paleoanthropology, 1911-1945. In G.W. Stocking Jr. (ed): *Bones, Bodies, Behavior. Essays on Biological Anthropology.* University of Wisconsin Press, Madison. pp. 117-137.

HARROLD, F.B. 1980 A comparative analysis of Eurasian Paleolithic burials. *World Archaeology* 12:195-211.

___. 1989 Mousterian, Châtelperronian, and early Aurignacian in Western Europe: continuity or discontinuity? In P. Mellars and C.B. Stringer (eds): *The Human Revolution: Behavioural and Biological Perspectives on the Origins of Modern Humans.* Edinburgh University Press, Edinburgh. pp. 677-713.

HAYDEN, B. 1993 The cultural capacities of Neandertals: a review and re-evaluation. *Journal of Human Evolution* 24(2):113-146.

HEIM, J-L. 1970 L'Encéphale Néandertalien de l'homme de La Ferrassie. *L'Anthropologie* 74:527-572.

___. 1974 Les Hommes fossiles de La Ferrassie (Dordogne) et le problème de la définition des Néandertaliens classiques. *L'Anthropologie* 78:81-112,321-378.

___. 1976 Les Néandertaliens en Périgord. In H. de Lumley (ed): *La Préhistoire Française.* Centre National de la Recherche Scientifique, Paris. Volume 1:578-583.

___. 1978 Contribution du massif facial à la morphogenèse du crâne Néandertalien. In J. Piveteau (ed): *Les Origines Humaines et les Époques de l'intelligence.* Masson et Cie, Paris. pp. 183-215.

___. 1983 Les variations du squelette post-crânien des hommes de Néandertal suivant le sexe. *L'Anthropologie* 87(1):5-26.

___. 1989 La nouvelle reconstruction de crâne Néandertalien de La Chapelle-aux-Saints: Méthode et résultats. *Bulletin et Mémoires de la Societe d'Anthropologie de Paris*, n.s. 1 (1-2):95-118.

HINTON, R.J. 1981a Changes in articular eminence morphology with dental function. *American Journal of Physical Anthropology* 54:439-455.

___. 1981b Form and patterning of anterior tooth wear among human groups. *American Journal of Physical Anthropology* 54:555-564.

HOLLIDAY, T.W., and E. TRINKAUS 1991 Limb/trunk proportions in Neandertals and early anatomically modern humans (abstract). *American Journal of Physical Anthropology*, Supplement 12:93-94.

HOLLOWAY, R.L. 1981 Volumetric and asymmetry determinations on recent hominid endocasts: Spy I and II, Djebel Irhoud I, and the Salé *Homo erectus* specimens, with some notes on Neandertal brain size. *American Journal of Physical Anthropology* 55(3):385-393.

___. 1985 The poor brain of *Homo sapiens neanderthalensis*: see what you please. In E. Delson (ed): *Ancestors: The Hard Evidence.* Alan R. Liss, New York. pp. 319-324.

___. 1989 On depiction and language. *Current Anthropology* 30(3):331-332.

HOLLOWAY, R.L., and M.C. DE LA COSTE-LAREYMONDIE 1982 Brain endocast asymmetry in pongids and hominids: some preliminary findings on the paleontology of cerebral dominance. *American Journal of Physical Anthropology* 58:101-110.

HOOTON, E. A. 1947 *Up from the Ape*, Revised Edition. MacMillan, New York .

HOUGHTON, P. 1993 Neandertal supralaryngeal vocal tract. *American Journal of Physical Anthropology* 90(2):139-146.

HOWELL, F.C. 1951 The place of Neanderthal man in human evolution. *American Journal of Physical Anthropology* 9:379-416.

___. 1952 Pleistocene glacial ecology and the evolution of "Classic Neandertal" man. *Southwest Journal of Anthropology* 8:377-410.

___. 1957 The evolutionary significance of variation and varieties of "Neanderthal" man. *The Quarterly Review of Biology* 32:330-347.

HOWELLS, W.W. 1975 Neanderthal man: facts and figures. *Yearbook of Physical Anthropology* 18:7-18.

HRDLIČKA, A. 1927 The Neanderthal phase of man. *Journal of the Royal Anthropological Institute of Great Britain and Ireland* 57:249-274.

HUBLIN, J-J. 1978 Quelques caractères apomorphies du crâne néandertalien et leur interpretations phylogénique. *Comptes Rendus de L'Academie des Sciences*, Série D, 287:923-926.

___. 1988 Les presapiens Européens. In E. Trinkaus (ed) *L'Homme Neandertal*, Volume 3, *L'Anatomie. Etudes et Recherches Archéologiques de l'Université de Liège, Liège.* pp. 75-80.

IVANHOE, F. 1970 Was Virchow right about Neandertal? *Nature* 227:577-579.

JELÍNEK, J. 1969 Neanderthal man and *Homo sapiens* in Central and Eastern Europe. *Current Anthropology* 10:475-503.

KEAN, M.R., and P. HOUGHTON 1982 The Polynesian head: growth and form. *Journal of Anatomy* 135:423-435.

KEELEY, L.H. 1977 The functions of Paleolithic flint and tools. *Scientific American* 237(5):108-126.

KEITH, A. 1913 Problems relating to the teeth of earlier forms prehistoric man. *Proceedings of the Royal Society for Experimental Biology and Medicine* 6:103-104.

___. 1949 *A New Theory of Human Evolution.* Philosophical Library, New York.

KENNEDY, K.A.R. 1975 *Neanderthal Man.* Burgess, Minneapolis.

KLAATSCH, H. 1908 Das Gesichtsskelet der Neandertalrasse und die Australier. *Anatomischer Anzeiger* 32:223-271.

KLEIN, R.G. 1990 Human cognitive changes at the Middle to Upper Paleolithic transition: the evidence of Boker Tachtit. In P. Mellars (ed): *The Emergence of Modern Humans: an Archaeological perspective.* Edinburgh University Press, Edinburgh. pp. 499-516.

KLEINSCHMIDT, O. 1931 *Der Urmensch.* Quelle und Meyer, Leipzig.

KOCHETKOVA, V.I. 1972 On brain size and behavior in early man. *Current Anthropology* 11:176.

VON KOENIGSWALD, G.H.R. (editor) 1958 *Hundert Jahre Neanderthaler.* Kemink en Zoon, Utrecht.

KRUKOFF, S. 1970 L'occipital de La Chaise (Suard), caractères métriques, distances de forme et de format. *Comptes Rendus de l'Academie des Sciences,* Série D, 270:42-45.

KUHN, S.L. 1992 On planning and curated technologies in the Middle Paleolithic. *Journal of Anthropological Research* 48: 185-214.

LAITMAN, J.T., R.C. HEIMBUCH, and E.S. CRELIN 1979 The basicranium of fossil hominids as an indicator of their upper respiratory systems. *American Journal of Physical Anthropology* 51:15-34.

LAITMAN, J.T., J.S. REIDENBERG, and P.J. GANNON 1992 Fossil skulls and hominid vocal tracts: new approaches to charting the evolution of human speech. In J. Wind, B. Chiarelli, B. Bichakjian, and A. Nocentini (eds): *Language Origin: A Multidisciplinary Approach.* Kluwer Academic Publishers, Dordrecht. pp. 395-407.

LALUEZA, C., A. PÉREZ-PÉREZ, and D. TURBÓN 1993 Microscopic study of the Banyoles mandible (Girona, Spain): diet, cultural activity, and toothpick use. *Journal of Human Evolution* 24(4):281-300.

LALUEZA FOX, C., and A. PÉREZ-PÉREZ 1993 The diet of the Neanderthal child Gibraltar 2 (Devil's Tower) through the study of the vestibular striation pattern. *Journal of Human Evolution* 24(1):29-41.

LANYON, L.E., and C.T. RUBIN 1984 Static vs. Dynamic loads as an influence on bone remodeling. *Journal of Biomechanics* 17:897-905.

LAUGHLIN, C.D., J. MCMANUS, and C.D. STEPHENS 1981 A model of brain and symbol. *Semiotica* 33(3/4):211-236.

LEE, M.L., and M. GORDON 1982 The origin of the Neanderthal chignon. *Journal of Irreproducible Results* 28(2):25-26.

LE MAY, M. 1975 The language capacity of Neanderthal man. *American Journal of Physical Anthropology* 42:9-14.

LEROI-GOURHAN, A. 1993 *Gesture and Speech.* MIT Press, Cambridge.

LIEBERMAN, P. 1991 *Uniquely Human: The Evolution of Speech, Thought, and Selfless Behavior.* Harvard University Press, Cambridge.

___. 1992 On Neanderthal speech and Neanderthal extinction. *Current Anthropology* 33:409-410.

___. 1993 On the Kebara KMH 2 hyoid and Neandertal speech. *Current Anthropology* 34:172-175.

LIEBERMAN, P., E.. CRELIN, and D.H. KLATT 1972 Phonetic ability and related anatomy of the newborn and adult human, Neanderthal man, and the chimpanzee. *American Anthropologist* 74:287-307.

LIEBERMAN, P., J.T. LAITMAN, J.S. REIDENBERG, and P.J. GANNON 1992 The anatomy, physiology, acoustics, and perception of speech: essential elements in analysis of the evolution of human speech. *Journal of Human Evolution* 23(6):447-467.

LIVINGSTONE, F.B. 1980 Comment on "Sapienization and speech", by G. Krantz. *Current Anthropology* 21:784.

LOVEJOY, C.O., R.S. MEINDL, T.R. PRYZBECK, T.S. BARTON, K.G. HEIPLE, and D. KOTTING 1977 Paleodemography of the Libben site, Ottawa County, Ohio. *Science* 198:291-293.

LOVEJOY, C.O. and TRINKAUS, E. 1980 Strength and robusticity of the Neandertal tibia. *American Journal of Physical Anthropology* 53:465 - 470.

MACCHIARELLI, R., P. PASSARELLO, and L. BONDIOLI 1991 The *fossa mandibularis* in the Neandertal cranium of the Guattari cave: a comparative morphometrical analysis. In M. Piperno and G. Scichilone (eds): *The Circeo 1 Neandertal Skull: Studies and Documentation*. Instituto Poligrafico e Zecca Dello Stato, Dello Stato. pp. 357-389.

MANN, A.E., and E. TRINKAUS 1974 Neandertal and Neandertal-like fossils from the Upper Pleistocene. *Yearbook of Physical Anthropology* 17:169-193.

MANZI, G., and P. PASSARELLO 1989 From Casal de'Pazzi to Grotta Breuil: fossil evidence from Latium (central Italy) before the appearance of modern humans. *Animal and Human Biology* 1:111-143.

___. 1991 Anténeandertaliens et Néandertaliens du Latium (Italie Centrale). *L'Anthropologie* 95(2/3):501-522.

MARSHACK, A. 1988 The Neandertals and the human capacity for symbolic thought: cognitive and problem solving aspects of Mousterian symbol. In O. Bar-Yosef (ed): *L'Homme de Néandertal, la pensée*. Volume 32:57-91. *Etudes et Recherches Archéologiques de l'Université de Liège, Liège*.

___. 1989 On depiction and language. *Current Anthropology* 30(3):332-335.

___. 1990 Early human symbol and evolution of the human capacity. In P. Mellars (ed): *The Emergence of Modern Humans: an Archaeological perspective*. Edinburgh University Press, Edinburgh. pp. 457-498.

MARSHALL, J.C. 1989 The descent of the larynx? *Nature* 338:702-703.

McKEE, J.K., and S.B. HELMAN 1991 Variability of the hominid juxtamastoid eminence and associated basicranial features. *Journal of Human Evolution* 21(4):275-281.

MCKEE, J.K., and R. LUNZ 1990 Correlates of enamel hypoplasia with human dental reduction. *American Journal of Human Biology* 2:459-465.

MELLARS, P. 1986a A new chronology for the French Mousterian period. *Nature* 322:410-411.

___. 1986b Dating and correlating the French Mousterian. *Nature* 324:113-114.

___. 1989 Major issues in the emergence of modern humans. *Current Anthropology* 30(3):349-385.

MINUGH-PURVIS, N. 1992 The inhabitants of Ice Age Europe. In P. Chase (ed): *Ice Age Europeans. Expedition* 34(3):23-36.

MILO, R.G. and D. QUIATT 1993 Glottogenesis and anatomically modern *Homo sapiens.* Evidence for and implications of a late origin of vocal language. *Current Anthropology* 34(5):569-598.

MOLNAR, S., C. HILDEBOLT, I. MOLNAR, J. RADOVČIC´, and M. GRAVIER 1993 Hominid enamel thickness: I. the Krapina Neandertals. *American Journal of Physical Anthropology* 92(2):131-138.

MOLNAR, S., and I.M. MOLNAR 1985 The incidence of enamel hypoplasia among the Krapina Neandertals. *American Anthropologist* 87(3):536-549.

MORRIS, D.H. 1974 Neanderthal speech. *Linguistic Inquiry* 5:144-150.

MORANT, G.M. 1927 Studies of Paleolithic man II. A biometric study of Neanderthal skulls and their relationships to modern racial types. *Annals of Eugenics* 2:318-381.

MUSGRAVE, J.H. 1970 How dexterous was Neandertal man? *Nature* 223:538-541.

NEIBURGER, E.J. 1990 Enamel hypoplasias: poor indicators of dietary stress. *American Journal of Physical Anthropology* 82(2):231-232.

OAKLEY, K. 1971 Fossils collected by the earlier Paleolithic men. In *Mélanges de Préhistoire, d'Archéocivilization et d'Ethnologie Offerts à André Varagnac.* Serpen, Paris. pp. 581-584.

___. 1973 Fossil shell observed by Acheulean man. *Antiquity* 47:59-60.

___. 1981 Emergence of high thought 3.0-0.2 Ma B.P. *Philosophical Transactions of the Royal Society, London* B292:205-211

OGILVIE, M.D., B.K. CURRAN, and E. TRINKAUS 1989 Incidence and patterning of dental enamel hypoplasia among the Neandertals. *American Journal of Physical Anthropology* 79(1):25-41 [and 82(2):232-233].

PESCE DELFINO, V., and E. VACCA 1994 Report of an archaic human skeleton discovered at Altamura (Bari) in the "Lamalunga" district. *Human Evolution* 9(1):1-9.

PRADEL, L. 1966 The transition from Mousterian to Perigordian: skeletal and industrial. *Current Anthropology* 7:33-50.

QUENNELL, M., and C.H.B. QUENNELL 1945 *Everyday Life in the Old Stone Age.* Batsford, London.

RADOVČIC´, J. 1985 Neanderthals and their contemporaries. In E. Delson (ed) *Ancestors: The Hard Evidence.* Alan R. Liss, New York. pp. 310-318.

RAK, Y. 1986 The Neanderthal: a new look at an old face. *Journal of Human Evolution* 15(3):151-164.

___. 1991 Serggio Sergi's method and its bearing on the question of zygomatic bone position in the Neandertal face. In M. Piperno and G. Scichilone (eds) *The Circeo 1 Neandertal Skull: Studies and Documentation.* Instituto Poligrafico e Zecca Dello Stato, Dello Stato. pp. 301-310.

ROEBROEKS, W., J. KOLEN, and E. RENSINK 1988 Planning depth, anticipation, and the organization of Middle Paleolithic technology: the "archaic natives" meet Eve's descendants. *Helenium* 28:17-34.

ROSS, C.F., and M.J. RAVOSA 1994 Basicranial flexion, relative brain size, and facial kyphosis in nonhuman primates. *American Journal of Physical Anthropology* 91(3):305-324.

RUFF, C.B., E. TRINKAUS, A. WALKER, and C.S. LARSEN 1993 Postcranial robusticity in *Homo*. I: Temporal trends and mechanical interpretation. *American Journal of Physical Anthropology* 91(1):21-53.

RUSSELL, M.D. 1987a Bone breakage in the Krapina hominid collection. *American Journal of Physical Anthropology* 72(3):373-379.

___. 1987b Mortuary practices at the Krapina Neandertal site. *American Journal of Physical Anthropology* 72(3):381-397.

SABAN, R. 1993 *Aux Sources du Language Articulé*. Masson, Paris.

SACKETT, J.R. 1982 Approaches to style in lithic archaeology. *Journal of Anthropological Archaeology* 1:59-112.

___. 1988 The Mousterian and its aftermath: a view from the Upper Paleolithic. In H.L. Dibble and A. Montet-White (eds): *Upper Pleistocene Prehistory of Western Asia*. The University Museum Press, Philadelphia. pp. 413-426.

SANTA LUCA, A.P. 1978 A re-examination of presumed Neandertal-like fossils. *Journal of Human Evolution* 7:619-636.

SCHEPARTZ, L.A. 1993 Language and modern human origins. *Yearbook of Physical Anthropology* 36:91-126.

SCHWALBE, G. 1901 Über die specifischen Merkmale des Neanderthalschädels. *Anatomischer Anzeiger* 15:44-61.

___. 1914 Kritische Besprechung von Boule's Werk: "L'homme Fossile de la Chapelle-aux-Saints." *Zeitschrift für Morphologie und Anthropologie* 16:527-610.

SCHWARCZ, H.P., A. BIETTI, W.M. BUHAY, M.C. STINER, R. GRÜN, and A. SERGE 1991 On the reexamination of Grotta Guattari: Uranium-series and Electron-spin-resonance dates. *Current Anthropology* 32(3):313-316.

SCHWARCZ, H.P., and A.G. LATHAM 1984 Uranium-Series age determination of travertines from the site of Vértesszöllös, Hungary. *Journal of Archaeological Science* 11:326-336.

SCHWARCZ, H.P., and I. SKOFLEK 1982 New dates for the Tata, Hungary, archaeological site. *Nature* 295:590-591.

SCOTT, K. 1980 Two hunting episodes of Middle Paleolithic age at La Cotte de Saint-Berlade, Jersey. *World Archaeology* 12(2):137-152.

SENUT, B. 1985 Computerized tomography of a Neanderthal humerus from Le Regourdou (Dordogne, France): Comparisons with modern man. *Journal of Human Evolution* 14:717-723.

SERGI, S. 1962 Morphological Position of the "Prophaneranthropi" (Swanscombe and Fontéchevade). In W.W. Howells (ed): *Ideas on Human Evolution*. Harvard University Press, Cambridge. pp. 507-520.

SHACKLEY, M. 1980 *Neanderthal Man*. Archon (The Shoe String Press), Hamden Connecticut.

___. 1982 The case for Neanderthal survival: fact or fiction? *Antiquity* 56:31-41.

___. 1983 *Wildmen: Yeti, Sasquatch and the Neanderthal enigma*. Thames and Hudson, London.

SIMEK, J. 1992 Neanderthal cognition and the Middle to Upper Paleolithic transition. In G. Bräuer and F.H. Smith (eds): *Continuity or Replacement? Controversies in Homo sapiens Evolution*. Balkema, Rotterdam. pp. 231-245.

SMIRNOV, Y. 1989 Intentional human burial: Middle Paleolithic (last glaciation) beginnings. *Journal of World Prehistory* 3(2):199-233.

SMITH, F.H. 1980 Sexual differences in European Neanderthal crania with special reference to the Krapina crania. *Journal of Human Evolution* 9(5):359-375.

___. 1982 Upper Pleistocene hominid evolution in South-Central Europe: A review of the evidence and analysis of trends. *Current Anthropology* 23:667-703; 24:236-237.

___. 1983 Behavioral interpretations of changes in craniofacial morphology across the archaic/modern *Homo sapiens* transition. In E. Trinkaus (ed): *The Mousterian Legacy: Human Biocultural Change in the Upper Pleistocene. British Archaeological Reports International Series*. pp. 141-163.

___. 1984 Fossil Hominids from the Upper Pleistocene of central Europe and the origin of modern Europeans. In F.H. Smith and F. Spencer (eds): *The Origins of Modern Humans: A World Survey of the Fossil Evidence*. Alan R. Liss, Inc., New York. pp. 137-209.

___. 1991 The Neandertals: evolutionary dead ends or ancestors of modern people? *Journal of Anthropological Research* 47(2):219-238.

SMITH, F.H., and S.P. PAQUETTE 1989 The adaptive basis of Neandertal facial form, with some thoughts on the nature of modern human origins. In E. Trinkaus (ed): *The Emergence of Modern Humans. Biocultural Adaptations in the Later Pleistocene*. Cambridge University Press, Cambridge. pp. 181-210, and combined references for the volume on pp. 232-276.

SMITH, F.H., and G.C. RANYARD 1980 Evolution of the supraorbital region in Upper Pleistocene fossil hominids from South-Central Europe. *American Journal of Physical Anthropology* 53:589-609.

SMITH, F.H., and M.O. SMITH 1986 On the significance of anomalous nasal bones in the Neandertals from Krapina. In V.V. Novotný and A. Mizerová (eds): *Fossil Man. New Facts, New Ideas. Papers in Honor of Jan Jelinek's Life Anniversary. Anthropos* (Brno) 23:217-226.

SMITH, P. 1976 Dental pathology in fossil hominids: What did Neanderthal man do with his teeth? *Current Anthropology* 17:149-151.

SOFFER, O. 1987 Upper Paleolithic Connubia and the archaeological record from eastern Europe. In O. Soffer (ed): *The Pleistocene Old World. Regional Perspectives*. Plenum, New York. pp. 333-348.

___. 1989 The Middle to Upper Paleolithic transition on the Russian plain. In P. Mellars and C.B. Stringer (eds): *The Human Revolution: Behavioural and Biological Perspectives on the Origins of Modern Humans*. Edinburgh University Press, Edinburgh. pp. 714-742.

___. 1992 Social transformations at the Middle to Upper Paleolithic transition: the implications of the European record. In G. Bräuer and F.H. Smith (eds): *Continuity or Replacement? Controversies in Homo sapiens Evolution.* Balkema, Rotterdam. pp. 247-259.

SOLLAS, W.J. 1908 On the cranial and facial characters of the Neanderthal race. *Philosophical Transactions of the Royal Society of London*, Series B, 199:281-339.

SPENCER, F. 1984 The Neandertals and their evolutionary significance: a brief historical survey. In F.H. Smith and F. Spencer (eds): *The Origins of Modern Humans: A World Survey of the Fossil Evidence.* Alan R. Liss, Inc., New York. pp. 1-49.

SPENCER, M.A. and B. DEMES 1993 Biomechanical analysis of masticatoy system configuration in Neandertals and Inuits. *American Journal of Physical Anthropology* 91(1):1-20.

SPENNEMANN, D.H.R 1987 Cannibalism in Fiji: the analysis of butchering marks on human bone, and the historic record. *Domodomo* 5(2):29-46

SPUHLER, J.N. 1977 Biology, speech, and language. *Annual Review of Anthropology* 6:509-561.

STEWART, T.D. 1964 The scapula of the first recognized Neanderthal skeleton. *Bonner Jahrbuch* 164:1-14.

STEÇSLICKA, W. 1968 W. spraeie Stanowiska Systematycznego Dolnplejstocénskiej Kości Potylicznej Z Vértesszöllös. *Przeglad Antropologiczny* 32:267-274.

STINER, M.C. 1990 The use of mortality patterns in archaeological studies of hominid predatory adaptations. *Journal of Anthropological Archaeology* 9:305-351.

___. 1994 *Honor Among Thieves: A Zooarchaeological Study of Neandertal Ecology.* Princeton University Press, Princeton.

STINER, M.C., and S.L. KUHN 1992 Subsistence, technology, and adaptive variation in Middle Paleolithic Italy. *American Anthropologist* 94(2):306-399.

STOLYHWO, K. 1937 Les Prénéanderthaloïdes et leurs rapports avec la race de Néanderthal. *Bulletin Ethnologique de Musée d'Ethnographie de Ljubljana* 10:147-168.

STRAUS, L.G. 1989 On early hominid use of fire. *Current Anthropology* 30(4):488-491.

___. 1992 The early Upper Paleolithic. In L.G. Straus (ed): *Iberia Before the Iberians: The Stone Age Prehistory of Cantabrian Spain.* University of New Mexico Press, Albuquerque. pp. 66-89.

STRAUS, L.G., J.L. BISCHOFF, and E. CARBONELL 1993 A review of the Middle to Upper Paleolithic transition in Iberia. *Préhistoire Européene* 3:11-27.

STRAUS, W.L., and A.J.E. CAVE 1957. Pathology and the Posture of Neanderthal Man. *Quarterly Review of Biology* 32:348-63.

STRINGER, C.B. 1982 Towards a solution to the Neanderthal problem. *Journal of Human Evolution* 11:431-438.

___. 1984 Human evolution and biological adaptation in the Pleistocene. In R. Foley (ed): *Hominid Evolution and Community Ecology.* Academic Press, New York. pp. 55-83.

___. 1992 Reconstructing recent human evolution. *Philosophical Transactions of the Royal Society,* Series B, 337:217-224.

___. 1992 Neanderthal dates debated. *Nature* 356:201.

STRINGER, C.B., and C. GAMBLE 1993 *In Search of the Neanderthals.* Thames and Hudson, London.

STRINGER, C.B., and R. GRÜN 1991 Time for the last Neanderthals. *Nature* 351:701-702.

STRINGER, C.B., J.-J. HUBLIN, and B. VANDERMEERSCH 1984 The origin of anatomically modern humans in western Europe. In F.H. Smith and F. Spencer (eds): *The Origins of Modern Humans: A World Survey of the Fossil Evidence.* Alan R. Liss, Inc., New York. pp. 51-135.

SVOBODA, J., and K. SIMAN 1989 The Middle-Upper Paleolithic transition in southeastern Central Europe. *Journal of World Prehistory* 3:283-322.

TABORIN, Y. 1990 Les prémices de la parure. In C. Farizy (ed): *Paléolithique moyen récent et Paléolithique supérieur ancien en Europe.* Mémoires Musée Préhistorique Ile de France (Nemours) 3:335-344.

TAPPEN, N.C. 1985 The dentition of the "old man" of La Chapelle-aux-Saints and inferences concerning Neandertal behavior. *American Journal of Physical Anthropology* 67(1):43-50.

TARLI, S.B., A. CANCI, P. FRANCALACCI, and E. REPETTO 1991 The hollowed-out skull base of the calvarium Circeo I. Review and discussion of an intriguing finding. In M. Piperno and G. Scichilone (eds): *The Circeo 1 Neandertal Skull: Studies and Documentation.* Instituto Poligrafico e Zecca Dello tato, Dello Stato. pp. 423-455.

TATTERSALL, I. 1992 Species concepts and species identification in human evolution. *Journal of Human Evolution* 22(4/5):341-349.

THOMA, A. 1975 Were the Spy fossils evolutionary intermediates between classic Neanderthal and modern man? *Journal of Human Evolution* 4:387-410.

___. 1981 The position of the Vértesszöllös find in relation to *Homo erectus.* In B.A. Sigmon and J.S. Cybulski (eds): *Homo erectus. Papers in Honor of Davidson Black.* University of Toronto Press, Toronto. pp. 105-114, and combined bibliography at end of volume.

THOMPSON, D.D., and E. TRINKAUS 1981 Age determination for the Shanidar 3 Neandertal. *Science* 212:575-577.

TILLIER, A-M. 1989 The evolution of modern humans: evidence from young Mousterian individuals. In P. Mellars and C.B. Stringer (eds): *The Human Revolution: Behavioural and Biological Perspectives on the Origins of Modern Humans.* Edinburgh University Press, Edinburgh. pp. 286-297.

TILLIER, A-M., L.A. SCHEPARTZ, and B. ARENSBURG 1992 The cervical vertebrae, mandible, and hyoid from the Kebara Mousterian hominid: morphological and behavioural aspects. In M. Toussaint (ed): *5 Millions d'Années, l'Adventure Humaine. Études et Recherches archéologiques de l'Université Liège* 56:191-198.

TOBIAS, P.V. 1970 Brain size, gray matter and race - fact or fiction? *American Journal of Physical Anthropology,* 32(1):3-26.

TRINKAUS, E. 1973 A reconsideration of the Fontéchevade fossils. *American Journal of Physical Anthropology* 39:25-35.

___. 1975 Squatting among the Neandertals: A problem in the behavioral interpretation of skeletal morphology. *Journal of Archaeological Science* 2:327-351.

___. 1977 A functional interpretation of the axillary border of the Neandertal scapulae. *Journal of Human Evolution* 6:231-234.

___. 1978 Hard times among the Neanderthals. *Natural History* 87(10):58-63.

___. 1980 Sexual differences in Neanderthal limb bones. *Journal of Human Evolution* 9:377-397.

___. 1981 Neanderthal limb proportions and cold adaptation. In C.B. Stringer (ed): *Aspects of Human Evolution.* Taylor and Francis, London. pp. 187-224.

___. 1985a Cannibalism and burial at Krapina. *Journal of Human Evolution* 14:203-216.

___. 1985b Pathology and posture of the La Chapelle-aux-Saints Neandertal. *American Journal of Physical Anthropology* 67(1):19-41.

___. 1987 The Neandertal face: evolutionary and functional perspectives on a recent hominid face. *Journal of Human Evolution* 16(5):429-443.

___. 1988 The evolutionary origins of the Neandertals or, why were there Neandertals? In E. Trinkaus (ed) *L'Homme Neandertal*, Volume 3, *L'Anatomie. Etudes et Recherches Archéologiques de l'Université de Liège* 30:11-29.

___. 1992 Paleontological perspectives on Neanderthal behavior. In M. Toussaint (ed): *5 Millions d'Années, l'Adventure Humaine. Études et Recherches archéologiques de l'Université de Liège* 56:151-176.

___. 1994a Variability in the position of the mandibular mental foramen and the identification of Neandertal apomorphies. *Revista di Anthropologia*

___. 1994b Neandertal mortality patterns. *Journal of Archaeological Science* (in press)

TRINKAUS, E., and S.E. CHURCHILL 1988 Neandertal radial tuberosity orientation. *American Journal of Physical Anthropology* 75(1):15-21.

TRINKAUS, E., S.E. CHURCHILL, I VILLEMEUR, K.G. RILEY, J.A. HELLER, and C.B. RUFF 1991 Robusticity *versus* shape: the functional interpretation of Neandertal appendicular morphology. *Journal of the Anthropological Society of Nippon* 99:257-278.

TRINKAUS, E., and W.W. HOWELLS 1979 The Neanderthals. *Scientific American* 241:118,122-133.

TRINKAUS, E., and M. LeMAY 1982 Occipital bunning among later Pleistocene hominids. *American Journal of Physical Anthropology* 57:27-35.

TRINKAUS, E., and C.B. RUFF 1989 Diaphyseal cross-sectional morphology and biomechanics of the Fond-de Forêt femur and the Spy 2 femur and tibia. *Bulletin de la Société Royal Belge d'Anthropologie et de Préhistoire* 100:33-42.

TRINKAUS, E., and P. SHIPMAN 1993 Neandertals: images of ourselves. *Evolutionary Anthropology* 1(6):194-201.

TRINKAUS, E., and F.H. SMITH 1994 Body size of the Vindija Neandertals. *Journal of Human Evolution.*

TRINKAUS, E., and R.L. TOMPKINS 1990 The Neandertal life cycle: probability and perceptibility of contrasts with recent humans. In J. DeRousseau (ed): *Primate Life History and Evolution.* Wiley-Liss, New York. pp. 153-180.

TRINKAUS, E. and I. VILLEMEUR 1991 Mechanical advantages of the Neandertal thumb in flexion: a test of a hypothesis. *American Journal of Physical Anthropology* 84(3):249-260.

TURNBULL, C.M. 1985 Cultural loss can foreshadow human extinctions: the influence of modern civilization. In R.J. Hoage (ed): *Animal Extinctions.* Smithsonian Press, Washington. pp. 175-192.

ULLRICH, H. 1958 Neandertalerfunde aus der Sowjetinion. In G.H.R. von Koenigswald (ed): *Hundert Jahre Neanderthaler.* Kemink en Zoon, Utrecht. pp. 72-106

___. 1982 Artificial injuries on fossil human bones and the problem of cannibalism, skull-cult, and burial rites. *Anthropos* (Brno) 21:253-262.

___. 1989 Neandertal remains from Krapina and Vindija mortuary practices, burials or cannibalism? *Humanbiologie Budapestensis* 19:15-19.

VALLADAS, H., J.M. GENESTE, J.L. JORON, and J.P. CHADELLE 1986 Thermoluminescence dating of Le Moustier (Dordogne, France). *Nature* 322:452-454.

VALLOIS, H. V. 1949. The Fontéchevade Fossil Man. *American Journal of Physical Anthropology* 7:339-360.

___. 1954 Neanderthals and presapiens. *Journal of the Royal Anthropological Institute* 84:111-130.

___. 1961 The social life of early man: the evidence of skeletons. In S.L. Washburn(ed): *The Social Life of Early Man.* Aldine Chicago. pp. 214-235.

VANDERMEERSCH, B. 1965 Position stratigraphique et chronologie relative des restes humains du Paleolithique Moyen du Sud-Ouest de la France. *Annales de Paléontologie des Vertèbrés* 51:69-126.

___. 1978 Les premiers Néandertaliens. *La Recherche* 9:694-696.

___. 1985 Neanderthal man and the origins of modern man. In: *Homo: Journey to the Origins of Man's History.* Marsilio, Venice. pp. 95-102.

___. 1985 The origin of the Neandertals. In E. Delson (ed): *Ancestors: The Hard Evidence.* Alan R. Liss, New York. pp. 306-309.

VANDERMEERSCH, B., A.M. TILLER, and S. KRUKOFF 1976 Position chronologique de restes humains de Fontéchevade. In Thoma A. (ed): *Le Peuplement Anténeandertalien de l'Europe.* IXᵉ Congrès de UISPP (Nice) Prétirage. Centre National de la Recherche Scientifique, Paris. pp. 1-26.

VAN VALEN, L.M. 1974 Brain size and intelligence in man. *American Journal of Physical Anthropology* 40(3):417-424.

VILLA, P. 1992 Cannibalism in prehistoric Europe. *Evolutionary Anthropology* 3(1):93-104.

VLČEK, E. 1967 Die Sinus frontales bei europäischen Neandertalern. *Anthropologischer Anzeiger* 30:166-189.

___. 1970 Étude comparative ontophylogénétique de l'enfant du Pech de l'Azé par rapport à d'autres enfants néandertaliens. In: *L'enfant du Pech de l'Azé. Archives de l'Institut de Paléontologie Humaine*, Mémoire 33: 149-178.

WALLACE, J.A. 1975 Did La Ferrassie 1 use his teeth as a tool? *Current Anthropology* 16:393-401.

WALLS, R.E. 1984 Relict Neanderthals: a folkloristic comment. *Antiquity* 58:52-54.

WECKLER, J.E. 1954 The relationship between Neandertal man and *Homo sapiens*. *American Anthropologist* 56:1003-1025.

___. 1957 Neanderthal man. *Scientific American* 197(6):89-97.

WEIDENREICH, F. 1943. The "Neanderthal Man" and the ancestors of "*Homo sapiens*." *American Anthropologist* 45:39-48.

WENDT, H. 1956 *In Search of Adam*. Houghton Mifflin, Boston.

WHITE, R. 1992 The earliest images: Ice Age "art" in Europe. In P. Chase (ed): *Ice Age Europeans*. *Expedition* 34(3):37-51.

WHITE, T.D., and N. TOTH 1991 The question of ritual cannibalism at Grotta Guattari. *Current Anthropology* 32(2):118-124.

WOBST, M.A, 1976 Locational relationships in Paleolithic society. *Journal of Human Evolution* 5:49-58.

WOLF, E.R. 1994 Perilous ideas: race, culture, people. *Current Anthropology* 35(1):1-12.

WOLPOFF, M.H. 1971 Vértesszöllös and the presapiens theory. *American Journal of Physical Anthropology* 35:209-216.

___. 1977 Some notes on the Vértesszöllös occipital. *American Journal of Physical Anthropology* 47:357-364.

___. 1989 The place of the Neandertals in human evolution. In E. Trinkaus (ed): *The Emergence of Modern Humans. Biocultural Adaptations in the Later Pleistocene*. Cambridge University Press, Cambridge. pp. 97-141, and combined references for the volume on pp. 232-276.

WRESCHNER, E.E. 1980 Red ochre and human evolution: a case for discussion. *Current Anthropology* 21:631-644.

WYNN, T. 1991 Tools, grammar, and the archaeology of cognition. *Cambridge Archaeological Journal* 1:191-206.

Figure 13.3
Stratigraphic Positions for Late Pleistocene *Homo sapiens*
Numerical Dates are given in Brackets

Date (kyr)	Africa ⇑	Asia[a] and Australasia	Western Asia	Europe[1]
30	Témara, Dar es Soltane II Mugharet el Aliya, Zouhra ⇓			Bacho Kiro 6b (32.7) La Quina Bed I teeth (35) St. Césaire (36.3)
40	*Haua Fteah* (46-40)			Le Moustier~ (40) *Bacho Kiro* 11 (>43) *Bañolas* (45), Kůlna (45-38)
50			Amud (55-47)	La Chapelle (56 or 47)
60			Kebara (60)	Mt. Circeo (=Guattari) 1 and 2 (60-50) Combe Grenal (60-56)
70	*Dire Dawa* (77-61)			La Ferrassie D* (75-60) Mt. Circeo 3 (74-60)
80			Tabun B (86/103)	
90	Klasies SAS (94-88)		Qafzeh	
100			Tabun C ⇓	Pech de l'Azé (>103) ⇑
110	Klasies LBS			⇑ Krapina (129-100) ⇓
120	Jebel Irhoud 4 (127-87) Laetoli 18 (129/108)	Xujiayao (125-100)	Tabun D ⇓	⇓ Saccopastore (129-122)[3]
130	Mumba (132-109)			
140		Maba (140-119)		
150				Bourgeois-Delaunay (151)
160		Xindong (169-145)		Prince ilium (160-110) Specimens dated only to Stage 6 (Fontéchevade, Lazeret, Montmaurin, Orgnac III)
170				
180		Jinniushan (187)		

190				Biache (196-159)
⇑	Eyassi Kébibat (=Rabat)	Chaohu (200-167)		Ehringsdorf (205-200)
⇑		Dingcun[a] (210-160) Changyang (216-179)		Vértesszöllös (211-160)
⇑				
Oxygen Isotope Stage 7		Dali[a] (230-180)		
⇓		Narmada Tongzi (240-206)		
⇓	Wadi Dagadlé			Pontnewydd (251-195)

[1] Stringer and Gamble review many numerical dates for European specimens, citing the most recent references
[2] ESR on surface material, including the cranium
[3] Date estimate from fauna
[a] Pope reviews many numerical dates for Chinese specimens, citing the most recent references
~ This assumes that the Neandertal skeleton comes from Bed J, which given the bizarre circumstances of its multiple reburials by the excavators may be far from true
* La Ferrassie D hominid burial date could be younger if specimens were buried *into* the layer

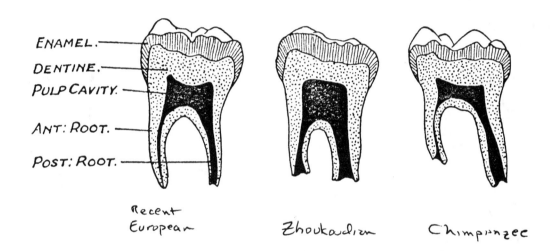

ENAMEL.
DENTINE.
PULP CAVITY.
ANT: ROOT.
POST: ROOT.

Recent European   Zhoukoudian   Chimpanzee

FIGURE 13.1 Taurodont Zhoukoudian molar compared with a recent human and chimpanzee, after Keith (1931).
FROM Keith, A. 1931 New Discoveries Relating to the Antiquity of Man. Williams and Norgate, London, figure 87.

FIGURE 13.2 The Bari Neandertal cranium *in situ*. The drawing, by K. Harvey, shows the heavily encrusted face peering from among its limbs. Bari does not appear to have been a burial but may be the remains of someone who entered the cave and died where he was found.

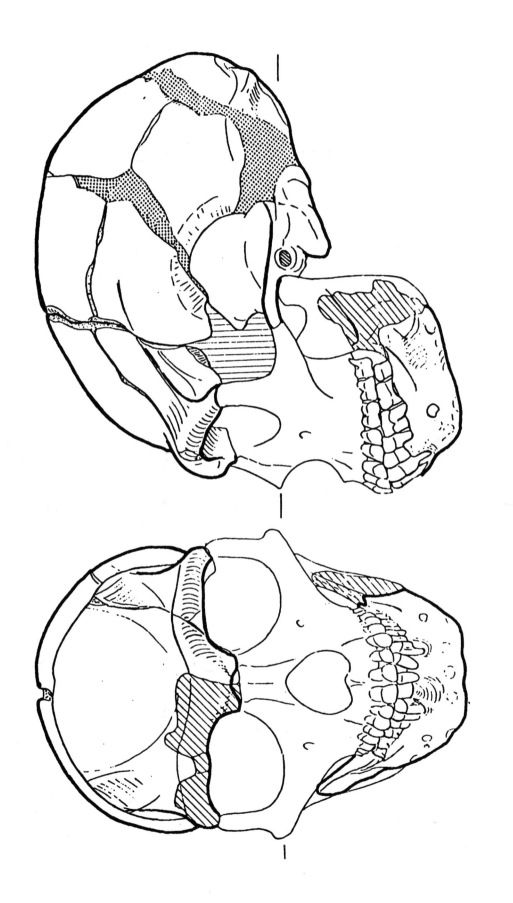

FIGURE 13.3 Vlček's (1992) reconstruction of the Ehringsdorf H cranium.
FROM Vlček, E. 1991 L'Homme fossile en Europe Centrale. *L'Anthropologie 95*(2/3):409-472, figure 10.

FIGURE 13.4 Fontéchevade 2, with various possible reconstructions (dotted) of the missing supraorbital region, according to Vallois (1958).

FROM Vallois, H.V. 1958 La Grotte de Fontéchevade: Anthropologie (deuxième partie). *Archives de l'Institut de Paleontologie Humaine*, Mémoire 29:5-156, figure 29.

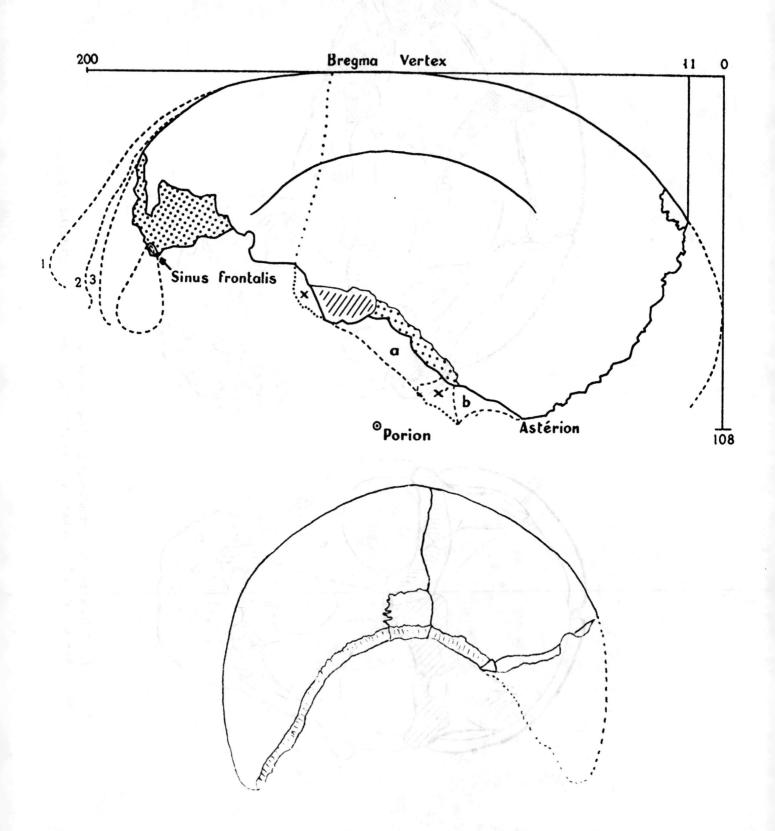

FIGURE 13.5 Age-at-death distribution for Krapina Neandertals.

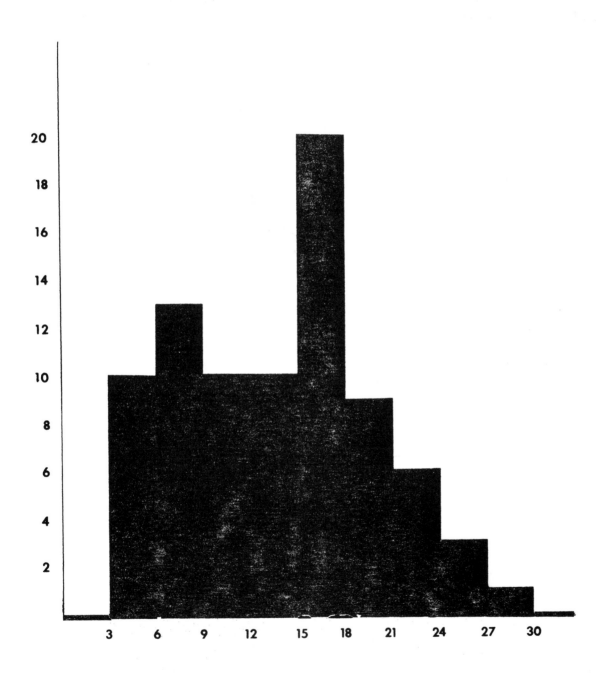

FIGURE 13.6 Transverse breadths of mandibular deciduous teeth, comparing average values for Arago (A), Krapina, and the later European Neandertals (N).

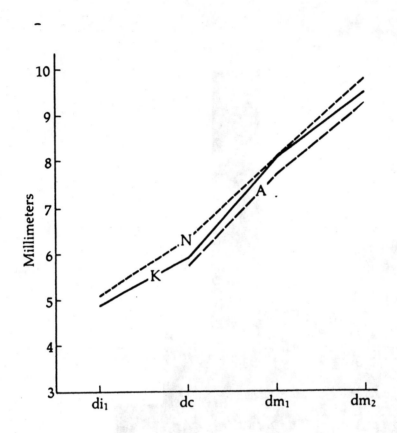

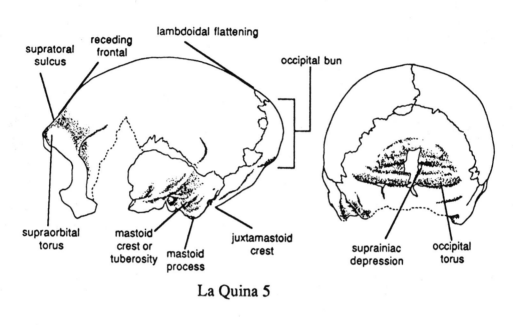

La Quina 5

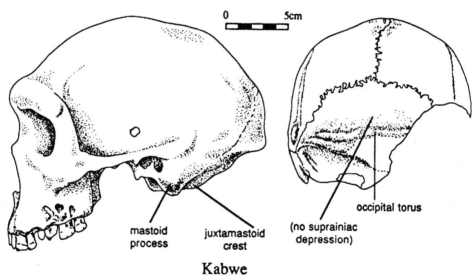

Kabwe

FIGURE 13.7 Neandertal characteristics, shown in the comparison of a European female Neandertal vault (La Quina) and the Kabwe African (see Chapter 12), after Klein (1990).

FROM Klein, R.G. 1990 The Human Career. Human Biological and Cultural origins. University of Chicago Press, Chicago, figure 6.6.

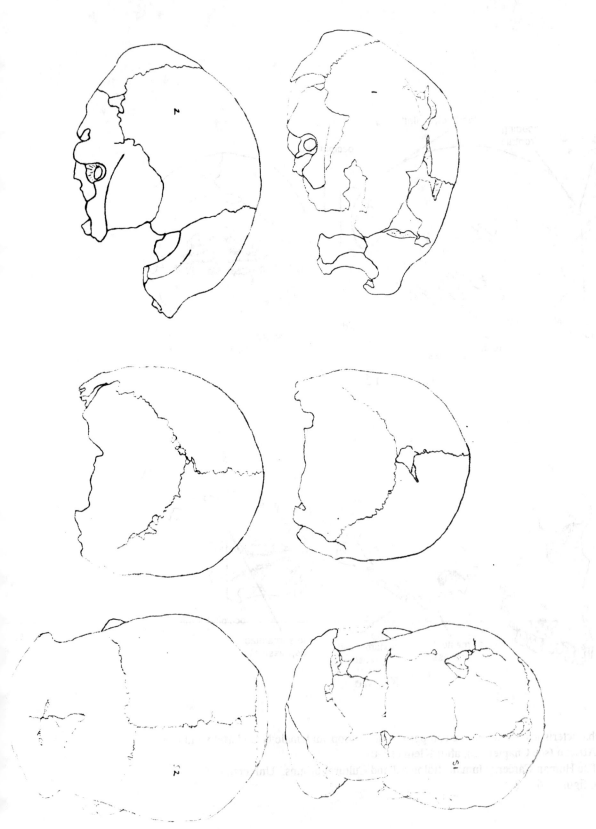

FIGURE 13.8 The two Spy crania, showing variation in virtually every aspect of cranial form from forehead shape to the contour f the crania rear.

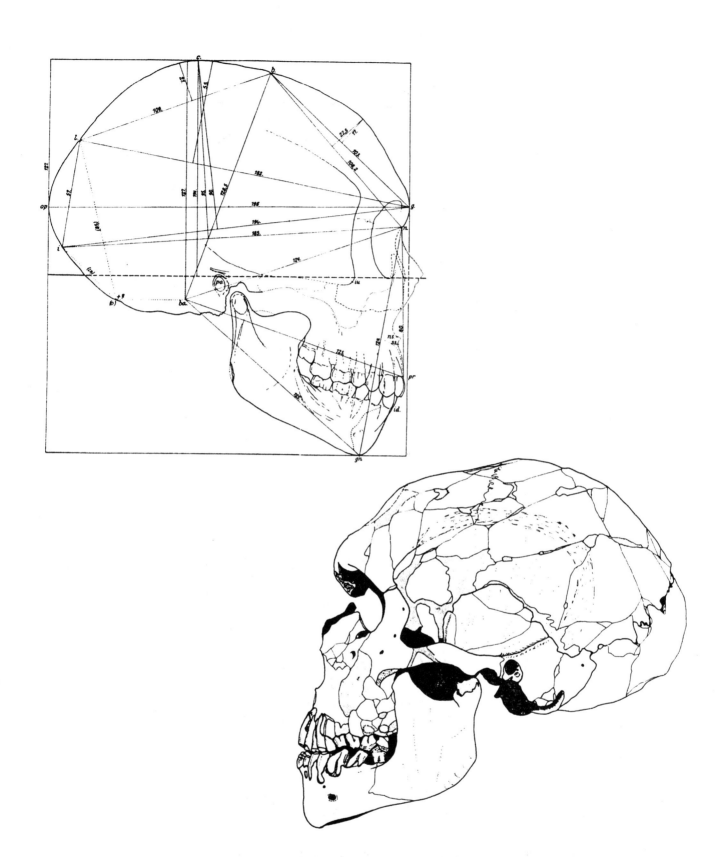

FIGURE 13.9 Comparison of the 13 year old Le Moustier Neandertal (after Weinert 1925) and the La Ferrassie adult male (after Heim 1976). The Le Moustier reconstruction shows the positions and values for measurements commonly taken on complete crania.

FROM Weinert, H. 1925 *Der Schädel des eiszeitlichen Menschen von Le Moustier.* Springer, Berlin, figure 14; Heim, J-L. 1976 Les hommes fossiles de La Ferrassie. Tome I. Le Gisement. Les Squelettes d'adultes: Crâne et squelette du tronc. *Archives de l'Institut de Paléontologie Humaine,* Mémoire 35, figure 51.

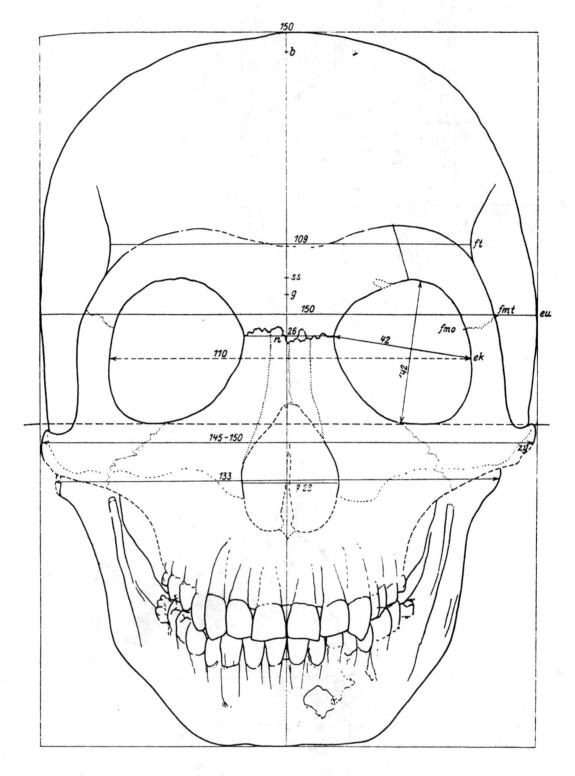

FIGURE 13.10. Le Moustier face, after Weinert (1925), showing the positions and values for measurements commonly taken on complete faces.

FROM Weinert, H. 1925 *Der Schädel des eiszeitlichen Menschen von Le Moustier.* Springer, Berlin, figure 13.

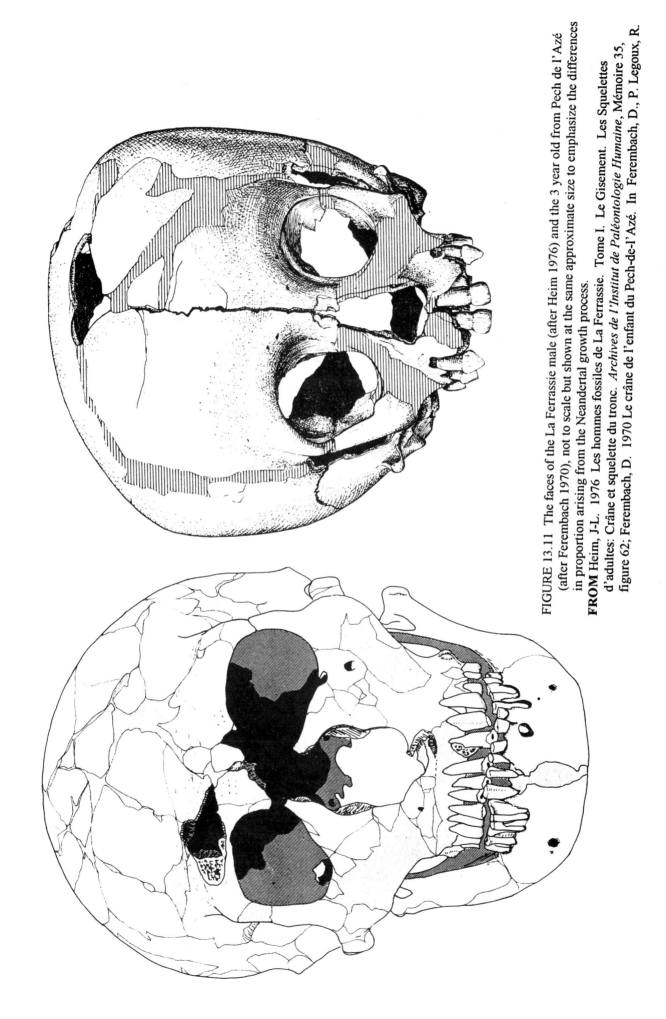

FIGURE 13.11 The faces of the La Ferrassie male (after Heim 1976) and the 3 year old from Pech de l' Azé (after Ferembach 1970), not to scale but shown at the same approximate size to emphasize the differences in proportion arising from the Neandertal growth process.

FROM Heim, J-L. 1976 Les hommes fossiles de La Ferrassie. Tome I. Le Gisement. Les Squelettes d'adultes: Crâne et squelette du tronc. *Archives de l'Institut de Paléontologie Humaine, Mémoire 35,* figure 62; Ferembach, D. 1970 Le crâne de l'enfant du Pech-de-l'Azé. In Ferembach, D., P. Legoux, R.

FIGURE 13.12 Topography of the Mt. Circeo cranium in front and side views, after Belli and Ferri (1992). Topographic figures provide information about depth; for instance, the prominence at glabella and the absence of a canine fossa are visible in the frontal view.

FROM Belli, A., and W. Ferri 1991 Photogammetric survey and computer data processing of the Neandertal cranium Circeo I. In: M. Piperno and G. Scichilone (eds) The Circeo 1 Neandertal Skull: Studies and Documentation. Instituto Poligrafico e Zecca Dello Stato, Dello Stato. pp. 501-512, figure 2-7.

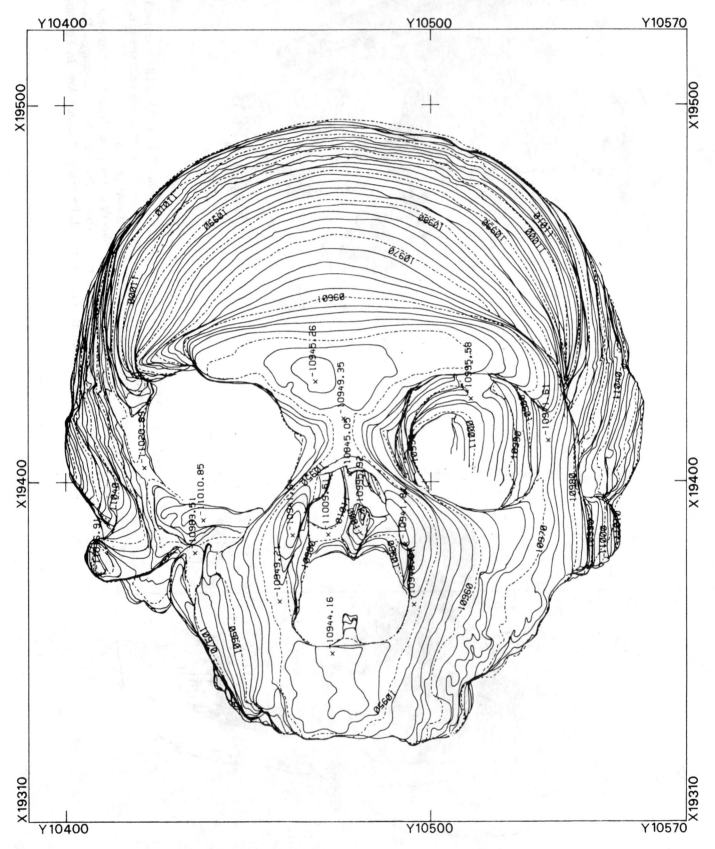

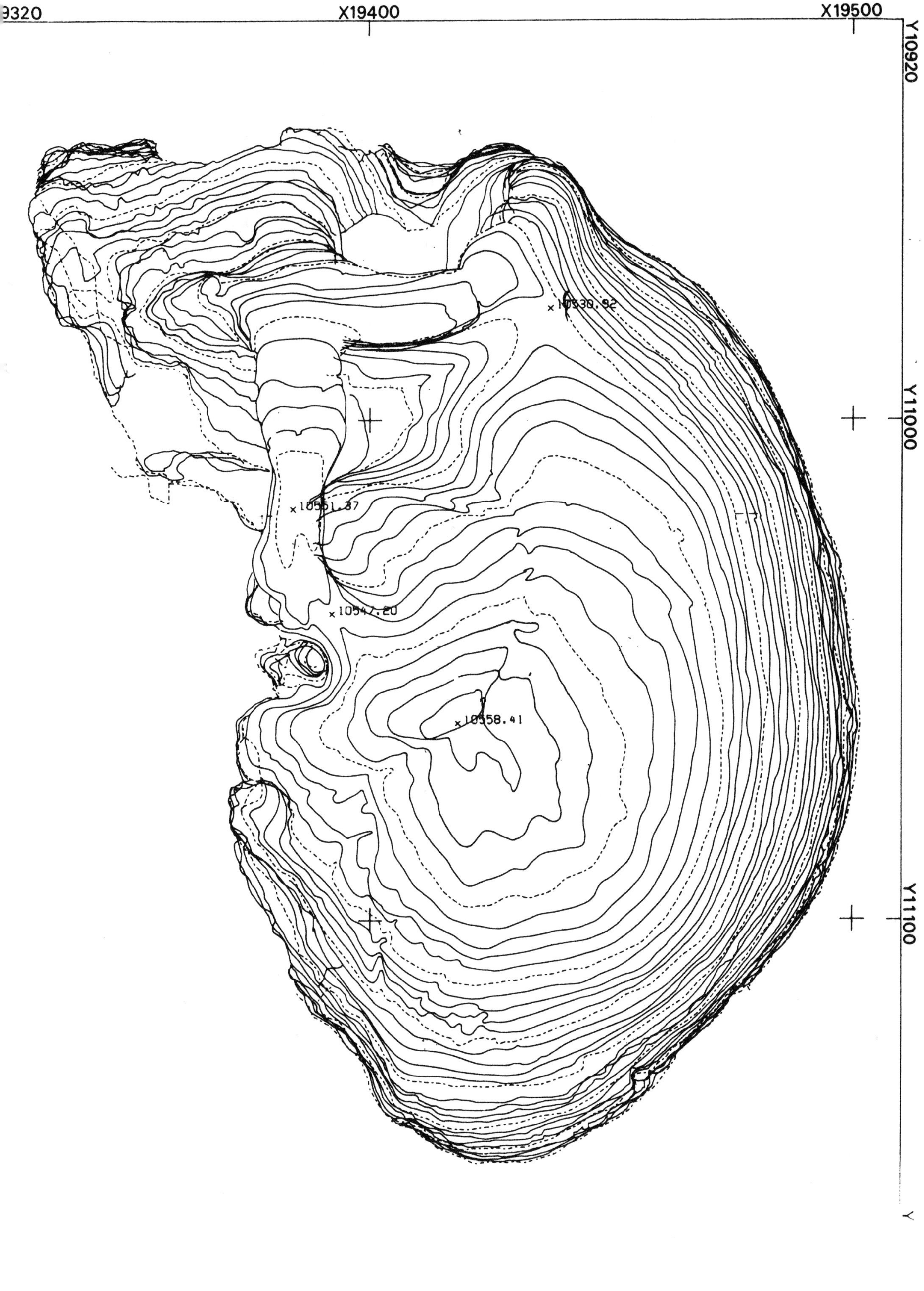

508 —

X19400 X19500

9320

Y10920

Y11000

Y11100

x 10539.92

x 10551.37

x 10547.20

x 10558.41

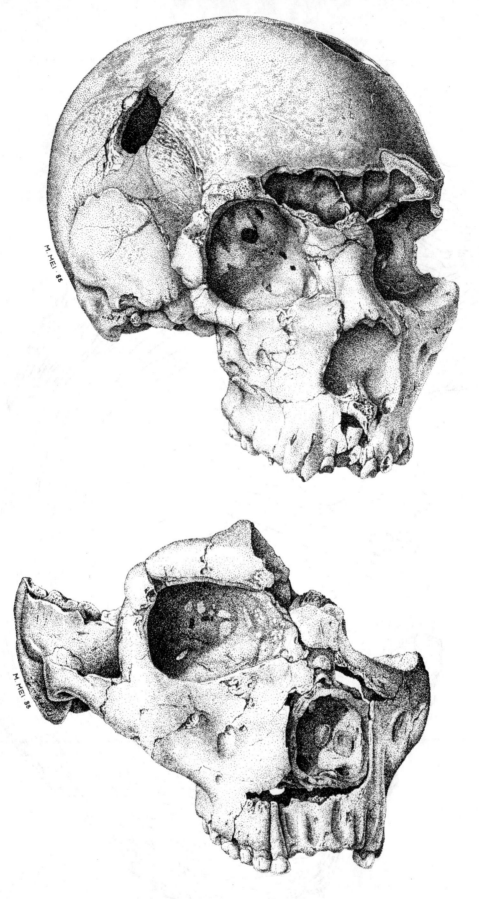

FIGURE 13.13 The three Italian Neandertal crania, from the left Saccopastore 2, Saccopastore 1, and Mt. Circeo, after Manzi and Passarello (1989).

FROM Manzi, G., and P. Passarello 1989 From Casal de'Pazzi to Grotta Breuil: fossil evidence from Latium (central Italy) before the appearance of modern humans. *Animal and Human Biology* 1:111-143, figures 2-4.

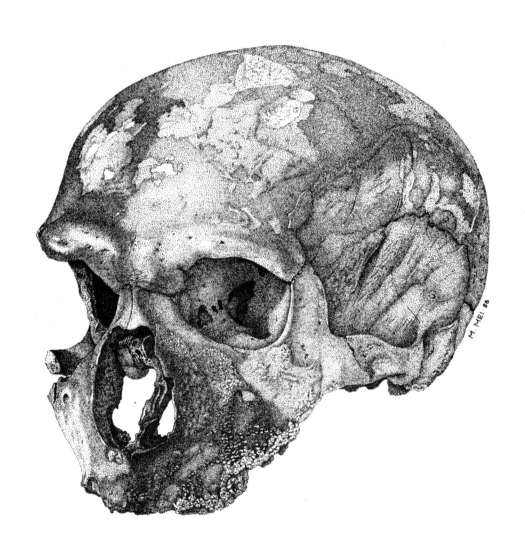

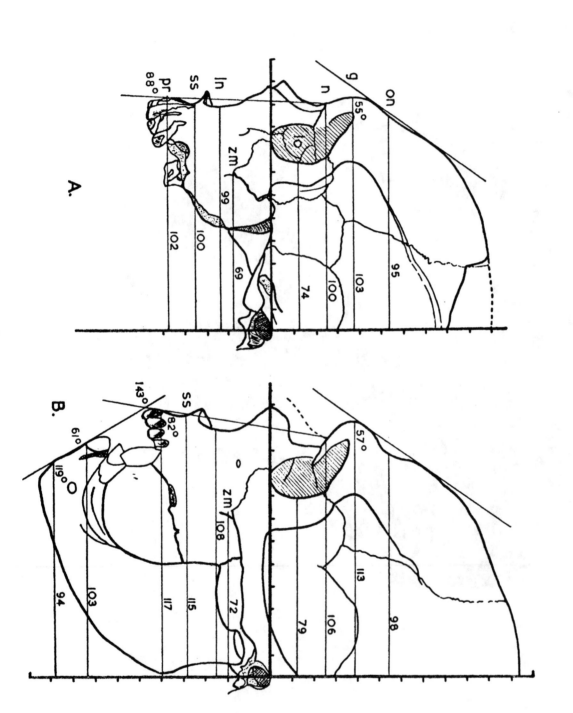

FIGURE 13.14 Comparison of facial profile and projection in a female (Gibraltar, left) and male (La Chapelle) Neandertal, after McCown and Keith (1939).
FROM McCown, T.D. and A. Keith 1939 *The Stone Age of Mount Carmel: The Fossil Human Remains from the Levalloiso-Mousterian.* Vol. II. Oxford at the Clarendon Press, figures 172, 173.

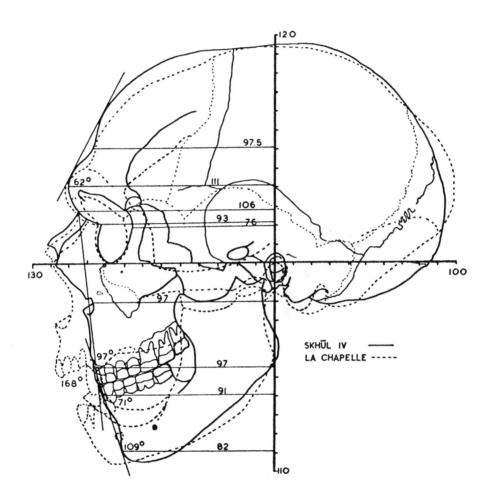

FIGURE 13.15 La Chapelle compared with Skhul 4, in lateral view, after McCown and Keith (1939).
FROM McCown, T.D. and A. Keith 1939 *The Stone Age of Mount Carmel: The Fossil Human Remains from the Levalloiso-Mousterian.* Vol. II. Oxford at the Clarendon Press, figure 195.

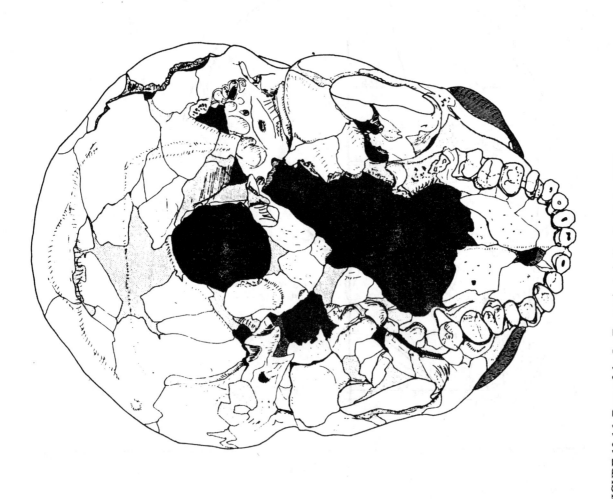

FIGURE 13.16 Base of the La Ferrassie 1 skull, after Heim 1976.
FROM Heim, J-L. 1976 Les hommes fossiles de La Ferrassie. Tome I. Le Gisement. Les Squelettes d'adultes: Crâne et squelette du tronc. *Archives de l'Institut de Paléontologie Humaine, Mémoire 35,* figure 64.

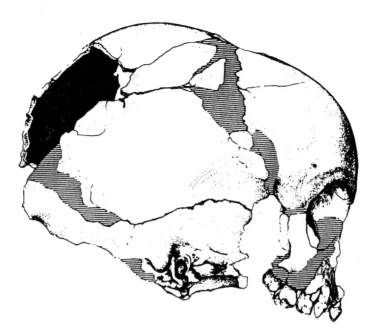

FIGURE 13.17 Pech de l'Azé 3 year old, lateral view, after Ferembach 1970.
FROM Ferembach, D. 1970 Le crâne de l'enfant du Pech-de-l'Azé. In Ferembach, D., P. Legoux, R.
Fenart, R. Empereur-Buisson, and E. Vlček : L'Enfant du Pech-De-L'Azé. *Archives de L'Institut de
Paléontologie, Humaine,* Mémoire 33, figure 6.

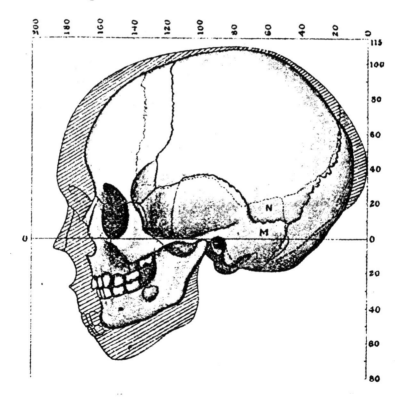

FIGURE 13.18 Devil's Tower superimposed on a modern child of similar dental age, after Keith (1931).
FROM Keith, A. 1931 New Discoveries Relating to the Antiquity of Man. Williams and Norgate, London,
figure 114.

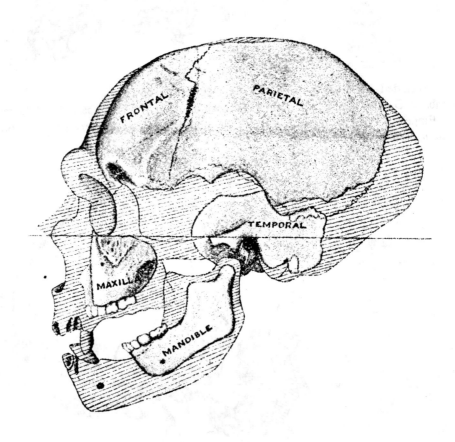

FIGURE 13.19 The 4-5 year old Devil's Tower cranium from Gibraltar superimposed on the La Chapelle
cranium, after Keith (1931).

FROM Keith, A. 1931 New Discoveries Relating to the Antiquity of Man. Williams and Norgate, London,
figure 111.

FIGURE 13.20 Ontogenetic sequence for Neandertal children, after Vlček. Ages are in table 13.8. **PA** is Pech de l'Azé, **Su** is Subalyuk, **Gi** is Devil's Tower, **LQ** is La Quina 18, **E** is Engis, and **TT** is Teshik Tash.

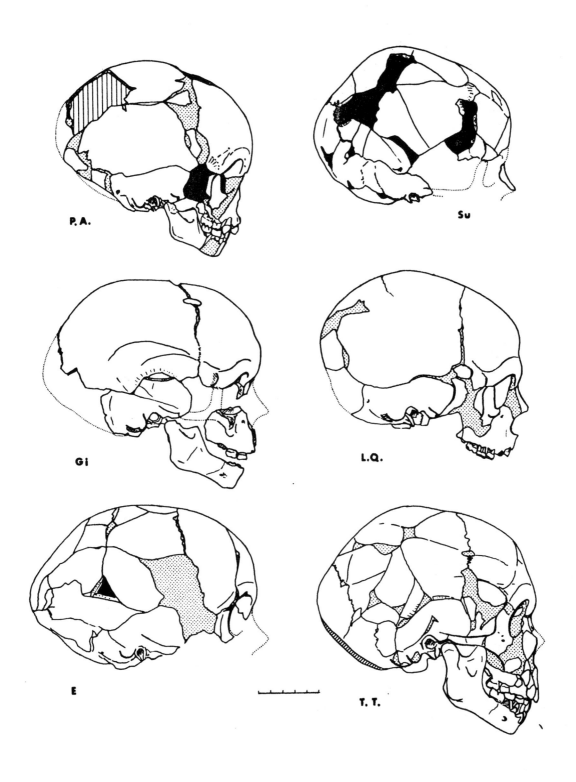

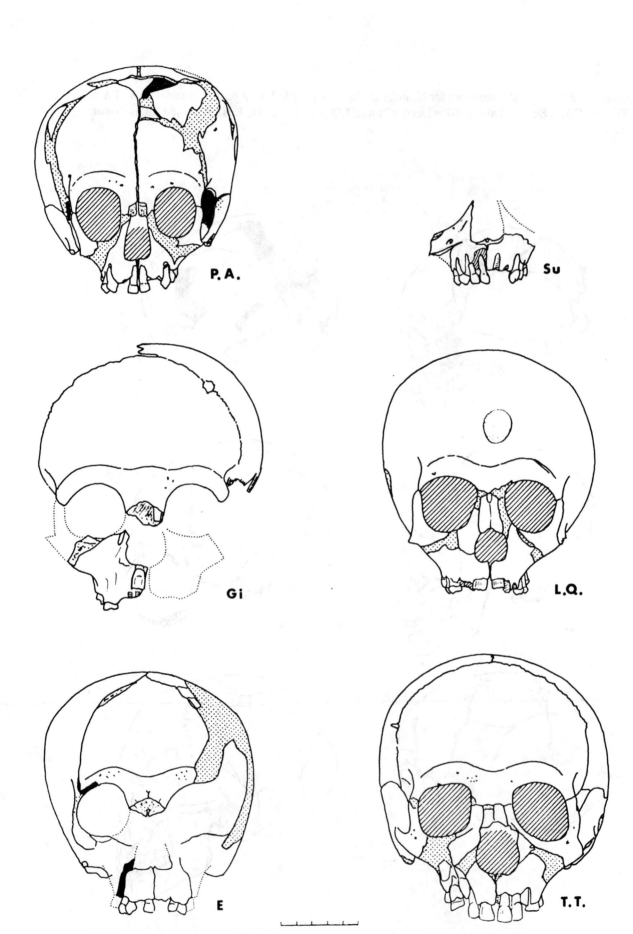

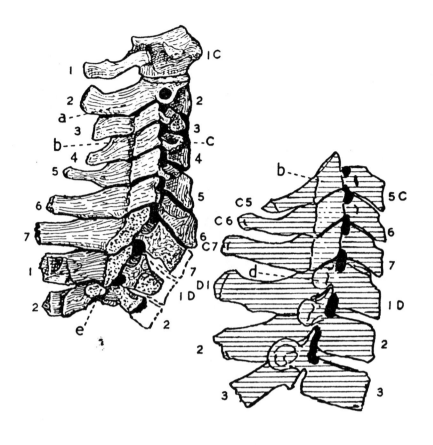

Skhul 5   La Chapelle

FIGURE 13.21 The cervical vertebrae of La Chapelle compared with Skhul 5, in lateral view, after McCown and Keith (1939).

FIGURE 13.22 Comparison of La Ferrassie 1 and 2 radii, after Heim 1982.
FROM Heim, J-L. 1982 Les hommes fossiles de La Ferrassie. Tome II. Les Squelettes d'adultes:
  Squelette des membres. *Archives de l'Institut de Paléontologie Humaine*, Mémoire 38, figure 9.

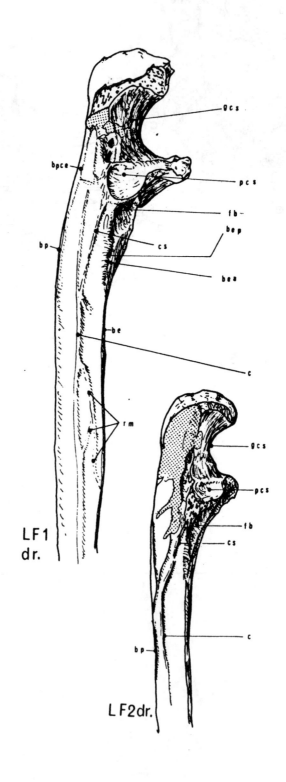

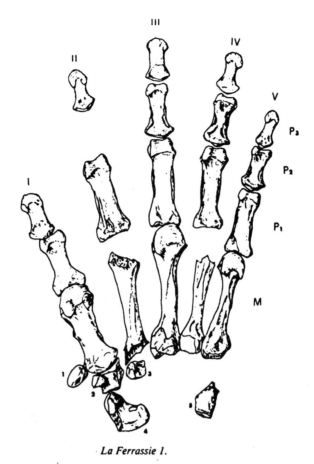

La Ferrassie 1.

FIGURE 13.23 Comparison of La Ferrassie 1 and 2 hands, after Heim 1982.

FROM Heim, J-L. 1982 Les hommes fossiles de La Ferrassie. Tome II. Les Squelettes d'adultes: Squelette des membres. *Archives de l'Institut de Paléontologie Humaine*, Mémoire 38, figures 10, 12.

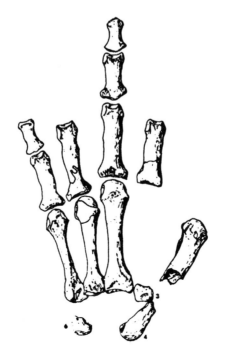

La Ferrassie 2.

FIGURE 13.24 Reconstructed pelvis of La Ferrassie 1, seen from the front, with a superior view of the pubis, after Heim 1982.

FROM Heim, J-L. 1982 Les hommes fossiles de La Ferrassie. Tome II. Les Squelettes d'adultes: Squelette des membres. *Archives de l'Institut de Paléontologie Humaine*, Mémoire 38, figures 20, 21.

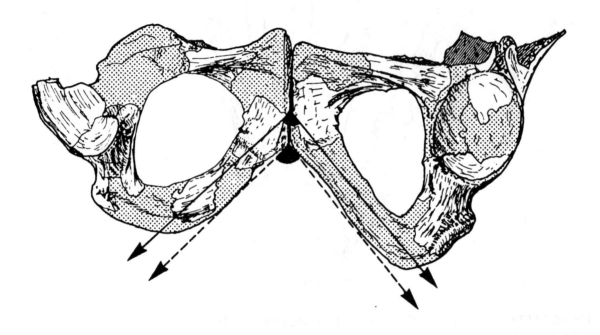

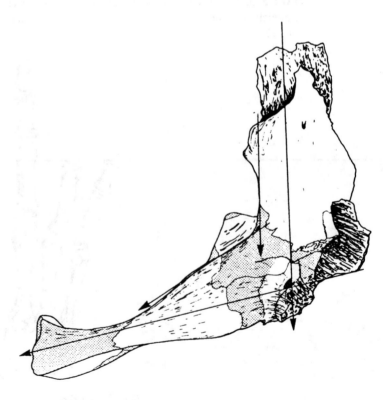

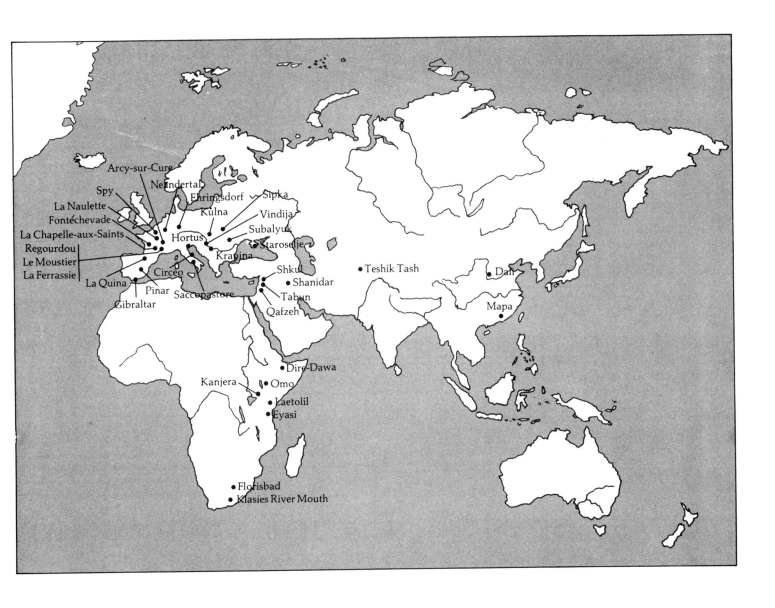

Map 13.1 Distribution of earlier Late Pleistocene humans.
From: First edition, Map 4

CHAPTER FOURTEEN

The Human Revolution

As C. Gamble puts it, "moderns are modern because of the societies they construct and live in". Modern anatomy, as detailed in the past few chapters, is a poor guide to modern behavior - and *vice versa* - whether in the past or today. This chapter focuses on the origins of modern humanity, at least as it was at the beginning of the Pleistocene's end, before the massive post-Pleistocene changes with their enormous sociocultural and biological consequences. The period of origins for the modern complex of behaviors and for the immediate biological predecessors of terminal Pleistocene populations, from roughly 50 to 18 kyr, is the closing scene of the ancient world. In this span there are important behavioral changes, perhaps a behavioral revolution, and by its end humanity was poised on the brink of an explosion of populations and their adaptations that reverberates yet today. It is after the period's end, the time of the maximum extent of the last major glacial advance, that this ancient world gave birth to the modern one.

Probably the most important thing to remember about the earliest modern populations that appeared during this period is that they did not look especially modern. These early modern humans are probably as different from living populations as they are from their predecessors. We recognize them as moderns because they behave in recognizably modern ways and can be linked with recent or living populations, but from the biological perspective, what modern humans are and when they first can be recognized is often based on arbitrary notions and never corresponds to the beginnings of modern behaviors. Like the trip into the city, it seems much easier to tell when we get downtown than when we crossed the city limits. We know who modern humans *are* - that's us - but when and where they began is quite another issue.

There was substantive and important evolutionary change in the later portions of the Late Pleistocene. While biological changes took place all over the world, against the background of rapidly changing cultural systems the changes were not always in the same direction. Regional cultural and morphological variations observed in Middle Paleolithic populations became more distinct and pronounced in their later Pleistocene successors, even as some behavioral and to a lesser extent anatomical changes were universal.

Modern humans were once thought to appear together with the behaviors that revealed their modernity. Clearly this association can no longer be presumed. In Europe and western Asia the contrast between the time of appearance of modern behaviors and modern human anatomy is enough to alert paleoanthropologists to the complexity of the changes. The European archaeological sequence places late Neandertals firmly at the foundation of the behavioral revolution because of their association with the earliest Upper Paleolithic industries, the Châtelperronian and possibly the early Aurignacian. In western Asia the shift to people who look more like us precedes any of the behavioral changes that come with the Upper Paleolithic. While biological capacities and brain structure have clear consequences in the expressions of cultural behavior, and culture has an important influence on biological evolution, it is quite clear that biology and culture cannot be firmly linked at this time, as indeed they could not be throughout the Middle Paleolithic.

Thus, in this Eurasian region modern humans are not invariably linked to Upper Paleolithic industries. When authors refer to the "Mousterian people," whom they are talking about is far from obvious. Similarly, it makes little sense to refer to early modern human samples from Europe or elsewhere as "Upper Paleolithic people," and even less sense to refer to them as "Cro Magnons" as is so often done. This names a worldwide phenomenon after a single site in France, and not even the earliest one (Cro Magnon, once thought to be one of the earliest of the European post-Neandertals, is now recognized to date to the end of this period)! No one has ever proposed calling early modern humans after the remains from Mladeč, although this would be far more appropriate since this important Czech site is much earlier than Cro Magnon and the modern humans there, while recognizably European, are morphologically more archaic. The lack of recognition of the very early modern sapiens sites scattered across Central and East Europe is part of a general eclipse of eastern European physical anthropology, which has had a profound effect on the interpretations of modern human origins.

Modern humans everywhere are distinguished from their archaic predecessors in a number or ways, ranging from greater longevity to biological changes such as the continued reductions in the cranial superstructures, anterior teeth and faces, and postcranial reflections of body strength. Evolutionary changes, remember, are vectors, with magnitudes and directions. These Late Pleistocene changes, while universal, fit different patterns from region to region and are dissimilar in both magnitude and rate; but the other characteristic of vectors, direction, is universal. Frequencies of archaic characteristics can be seen to decrease over time, both their individual occurrence and more dramatically their combined appearance. Thus the characteristics of recent populations combine both their histories and their responses to the problems of adaptation, the common features and differences reflecting the details of both local selection and the morphological complex inherited from their ancestors. Both of these factors have differed from place to place, and the consequence is the continued multiregional evolution of our long lasting polytypic species.

This chapter approaches the complex problems of the later Pleistocene by considering the evolutionary sequences in three broad geographic areas: Asia, Africa, and Europe. The discussion of Asia includes the sequence on the mainland, the peopling of the Americas, and the developments in Island East Asia, to the south in Indonesia, Melanesia, and finally Australia. The discussion of Africa proceeds from south to north: first the South African sequence, then sites in central and east African areas, and last the North African remains. Europe is divided into central/eastern and western portions and evolutionary changes in each, including the fate of the Neandertals, are discussed and compared.

The Last Pleistocene Hunter/Gatherers

As the Middle Paleolithic/Middle Stone Age gave way to the Upper Paleolithic, Late Paleolithic, or Late Stone Age, a series of organized behaviors were seen to emerge that are, by any definition, modern. It is in this emergence and not the origin and spread of a new species, nor some kind of sweeping modernization mutation, that the long sought "origin of modern humans" is to be found. There are two parts to the Eurasian Upper Paleolithic, an earlier and a later. A date of approximately 20-18 kyr divides these and the division is not arbitrary. The later span is clearly associated with the immediate ancestors of recent Eurasian populations while it is unclear which human population or populations are associated with the earlier (some of it is penecontemporary with Mousterian and Châtelperronian-associated Neandertals). Many of the important cultural elements attributed to the Upper Paleolithic (such as cave wall art and specialized hunting) are actually only attributes of its later span, while industries of the earlier are much more Mousterian-like and often contain relatively high proportions of flake tools made on prepared cores. The large, dramatic sites of Central Europe with long-term occupations such as Dolní Věstonice and Předmostí (Czech Republic) and Sungir' (Russia) are from the beginning of the later span and there are other dramatic populational changes - for instance the subsequent depopulating of much of Central Europe, especially after 20 kyr when climate changes that made this region uninhabitable. Ironically, the same changes created moister conditions across Africa where populations reoccupied previously abandoned areas. Even within Europe there were important differences within regions, and in fact regionalization is an aspect of these changes. Thus, as Central Europe depopulated, there was an expansion of populations and their culture in circum-Mediterranean areas. In Cantabrian Spain, for instance, there was a dramatic increase in the number of sites and an explosion of art.

THE ARCHAEOLOGICAL TRANSITION

Where industries described as Upper Paleolithic, Late Paleolithic, or Late Stone Age developed, they persisted long after their Middle Paleolithic predecessors. In many cases these predecessors were the direct ancestors (in so far as one industry can be said to be the ancestor of another). In some places the changes were as early as 43 kyr or even before. These descendant industries are defined by specific technologies and tool types, but most generally reflect social/cultural developments that, through improved organization and increasingly effective seasonal adaptations, allowed human populations to more densely occupy their environment, and expand their ranges as they inhabited the previously uninhabitable and colonized the difficult regions such as mountains, tundra, and deserts. Social networks expanded as well, and communication across broad areas made use of the well developed framework of social contacts. The details of this development, however, are in many cases obscure (or in Gamble's words "fuzzy"), and confused by the fact that the Middle Paleolithic was contemporary with the earlier Upper Paleolithic in Eurasia for as much as 15 kyr. In some regions, for instance Australia, Upper Paleolithic never developed (or spread) at all. In others the details of its origins are simply unknown (according to R. Klein there is a significant shortage of sub-Saharan sites between 60 and 35 kyr, when the Late Stone Age should have been developing). It is unlikely that this is a single worldwide culture that diffused widely from a unique point of origin, although innovations within it may have spread around the inhabited world. While radiocarbon dates for the earliest manifestations once seemed to cluster its appearance within a narrow time span (35-30 kyr), feeding the speculation that there was a single source and a rapid dispersal from it, subsequently developed dating techniques show this narrow span was more the results of radiocarbon's limits than a consequence of true simultaneity. The radiocarbon dates did not provide evidence for a short period in which the Upper Paleolithic began, but as discussed in Chapter 12 they really were minimum dates, meaning >30 kyr.

Looking at one well-studied region, H. Knecht and colleagues identify a number of changes in Western Eurasia that broadly coalesce as the early Upper Paleolithic emerges and begins to develop. In their summary of *Before Lascaux: The Complex Record of the Early Upper Paleolithic*, they conclude the following about the distinctions of the early Upper Paleolithic as it is represented by the Aurignacian, often recognized as the first of the Eurasian Upper Paleolithic industries (especially after the Châtelperronian or Lower Perigordian was exposed as a Neandertal effort):

- The origins of the blade technology of the Upper Paleolithic are in a variant of the Mousterian
- To a considerably greater degree than most Mousterians, there is a complex organic technology (bone, antler, ivory, and shell) in the European Aurignacian (although in some variants such as in the Levantine bone was not used at all)
- Large numbers of personal ornaments exist from the very beginning of the European Aurignacian (as J. Simek points out these may represent only a few multi-part objects)
- There is long distance procurement of novel materials (flint, shells)
- Devices for grinding, polishing, splitting, wedging, drilling, and gouging have their origins in earlier industries but become ubiquitous
- Projectile systems - especially spearthrowers - come into use

The distinction of Middle and Upper Paleolithic is partially a consequence of how they are defined. The whole experience with interpretations of the Châtelperronian (compare L. Pradel, F. Harrold, and P. Mellars) shows how difficult it is to establish when one ends and the other begins. Upper Paleolithic industries are traditionally distinguished by so-called "type tools", such as the split base bone point (figure 14.1) that diagnoses the Aurignacian. Definitions like this make it hard to identify predecessors or examine the process of change. For instance, the Aurignacian is not only diagnosed by the presence of a specialized bone point but is more generally often considered the first industry to incorporate the advantages of bone tool technology, such as easier worked raw materials and freedom from reliance on local raw material sources (this is a real advantage when colonizing unknown areas). Yet, some Mousterian and Middle Stone Age industries incorporate bone working and in certain cases produced quite sophisticated bone tools (such as the African barbed points discussed in Chapter 12). Moreover, Aurignacian is a bone oriented industry only across the northern tier of inhabited Europe - Levantine and Egyptian Aurignacian variants lack almost all bone tools. A. Marks suggests that perhaps bone is only important when wood is hard to get. The implication of all this is that looking at the tools may just be too misleading. As G. Clark puts it:

> if one looks at anything more comprehensive than the retouched stone tools ... there is continuity over the Middle-Upper paleolithic transition on every single archaeological monitor of adaptation. By continuity I mean vectored clinal change in

1. the major technological characteristics of lithic industries
2. raw material procurement and use
3. patterns in faunal exploitation
4. evidence for symbolic behavior and ritual
5. settlement patterns (site numbers, types, settings, and distribution)

in short, all of the criteria archaeologists use to monitor adaptation.

The point is that the Middle to Upper Paleolithic transition, even in Europe and western Asia where replacement scenarios are most often proposed and most widely believed, is local and based on numerous continuities of tradition expressed in many ways.. In one place the earliest Aurignacian may be quite like the Middle Paleolithic organizationally, technologically, artistically, and in terms of subsistence activities, while in another there may be substantial differences in most of these elements (for instance contrast the northern Spain sites and the French site of Isturitz, just to the north across the Pyrenees). It is quite likely that "Aurignacian" means different thing from one place to another, even within Europe, let alone when comparing Aurignacians from Siberia, the Levant, and North Africa. As L. Straus and colleagues put it, "archaeologist-perceived typological similarities do not ethnic nor cultural identities make".

Once the Upper Paleolithic was thought to have been established by new peoples arriving with their new ideas and techniques, but it is now evident that this is an unlikely scenario (although some still grasp onto it through the contention that new peoples bring the Aurignacian into Europe, even though the earliest Aurignacians are unidentified or perhaps, as suggested by J. Lindly and G. Clark, and in Chapter 13, they are Neandertals). Bar-Yosef likens the Middle to Upper Paleolithic transition in the Levant to the Neolithic revolution - the consequence of useful or desirable ideas spreading, not a marker or consequence of biological change. Whether Central Asia, China, North Africa, or the South African Cape are considered (as in the *Regional Perspectives* volume edited by O. Soffer), Upper Paleolithic and related industries are widely interpreted as regional developments, albeit in the Northern Hemisphere influenced by the consequences of the population movements forced by climatic changes.

Moreover, there remains a contradiction over the issue of just how much change occurs. Clearly, by the end of the earlier Aurignacian there are fundamental distinctions that had developed in many places. But what of its beginnings? W. Roeboeks and colleagues write of an absence of dramatic adaptive change in Europe when modern humans appear, particularly with regard to their ability to persist in risky environments, and P. Chase (and others) find no substantial difference between Middle Paleolithic and earlier Upper Paleolithic subsistence, hunting proficiency or seasonal specialization. A number of workers now contend that modern logistical hunting does not appear in Europe until the late Upper Paleolithic (for instance in *Before Lascaux*). J. Simek points out that the evidence for early Aurignacian personal adornment is limited to only a very few sites within a small area where several necklaces or bracelets could account for the hundreds of beads that have been discovered. Later in the Aurignacian jewelry becomes abundant and seemingly ubiquitous. Similarly, there are only three known cases of wall art in the whole Western European Aurignacian (wall art is difficult to date - a radiocarbon determination for the charcoal used in drawing dates the Spanish cave to Altamira to 14 kyr, and the French caves are probably of similar age). The sculptures, including animal and human figurines, from Central European contexts are not from the earliest Aurignacian. The point is that many discussions have confused changes that occur *within* the Aurignacian (or even after it) with changes that mark *when the Aurignacian first appears*. No doubt this is, at least in part, because the Aurignacian does not either originate or change in a uniform way, but differs in pattern from place to place. This makes the biological causation interpretation more difficult to sustain.

Nothing spotlights the independence of biological and behavioral changes, and the havoc this has created, better than the Châtelperronian issues. When it was considered the earliest industry made by moderns in Spain, France, and Italy no discrepancies arose from the discovery of woodworking tools, pierced animal teeth (for necklaces or amulets), central hearths, and huts. These were, after all, found at Upper Paleolithic sites where it was assumed they were made by modern humans. Problems began only when it was discovered that Neandertals and only Neandertals could be associated with this industry. This created a different enigma as it was widely assumed that Neandertals were not capable of these behaviors - the very ones that were thought to be the "superior" attributes that led to their replacement.

Never the less, things are clearly happening as the Upper Paleolithic appears - the absence of a Rubicon that might be implied by a clear distinction does not denote the absence of change. The processes that began within the Middle Paleolithic (this is detailed in Chapters 12 and 13) continue through the earlier Upper Paleolithic as discussed here. But what do these processes involve? Changes in tool types and technologies are easy to document from the archaeological record. Yet, it is most probable that the really critical developments are, as O. Soffer suggests, "in a dramatic change in economic and social relationships" and their consequences.

B. Hayden argues that the most important difference between Middle and Upper Paleolithic traditions in Eurasia is technological and economic. Key elements include

- long term food storage (storage pits are found in the Aurignacian by 32 kyr)
- sophisticated food processing (particularly filleting and preparing for storage)
- spearthrowers
- transport aids

These are important elements of improved adaptation to the highly seasonal environments with scarce fluctuating resources of glacial Europe - they improve both success and predictability. Much higher population densities are indicated by a number of large sites with long occupation periods (especially in Central and Eastern Europe), suggesting that populations did not leave *en masse* as earlier, when climatic conditions deteriorated. However, longer lasting, denser occupations, would suggest fluctuating population sizes in response to the climatic flickers (seasonal environments in temperate-subarctic regions are bound to be most sensitive to these rapid changes). Perhaps the widely distributed Venus sculptures are really fertility figures as originally thought. A. Leroi-Gourhan describes not only the Venuses, but also vulvas, phalluses, and scenes of copulation in the mobile art of this time and it is quite possible that these reflect the desire for high fertility under conditions that can (and presumably did) create rapid population-size crashes.

Yet, there remained the practicality of population movements as a way of escaping the deteriorating climatic conditions. Perhaps the most important innovations of the Upper Paleolithic improved the mobility of populations and their ability to adjust to seasonal changes. This change is reflected in the fact that raw materials for stone knapping are found to come from far away in a much larger proportion of Upper Paleolithic sites than in Middle Paleolithic sites. Food storage was a fundamental invention (even though it was not necessarily a novel one, if the speculation is correct that in the Middle Paleolithic Neandertals learned to store foods by freezing them and thaw the frozen foods in fires - e.g. cooking). With higher population densities and broader exchange systems and other social networks, much better use was made of seasonal environments. Its not just that the adaptations were better, but perhaps most significantly colonization came to involve less and less risk and waves of population expansions and colonizations began that are only now beginning to subside. The four major Old World environments that Gamble describes as "hard habitats" came under continuous occupation. These were the plains, deserts, higher mountains, and forests. But the colonization process did more, as human populations extended into new areas, right up to the Arctic Circle, and all the way down to "down under" with the colonization of Australia beginning at 60 kyr or earlier. There was open water (further than can be seen across) but no Rubicon that was crossed, as the peopling of Australia by people building bamboo rafts, and the specialized hunting adaptation to high mountainous regions were both begun in the Middle Paleolithic.

EFFECTS OF THE MIDDLE-UPPER PALEOLITHIC TRANSITION

The major behavioral changes within the Middle Paleolithic were in organization and technology. At first the Upper Paleolithic/Late Stone age did not differ significantly and changes associated with technological innovations were not always immediate. Organizational changes significantly affected human mobility patterns and their consequences can be seen early on. For instance, long legs are adaptive to tropical climates, but as discussed in Chapter 9 they are also important elements of long distance walking adaptations. Longer limbs create a more rapid walking speed during natural stride (see Chapter 4), according to Alexander, and are more energy efficient in long distance running. With increased mobility, certainly in Europe where the fossil record is particularly good, E. Trinkaus has shown that there is absolute and relative lower limb lengthening; the legs are longer relative to the trunk, and crural indices are higher (meaning the tibia is relatively longer). Anatomical developments include the alteration of femur shaft shape from a rounded structure to one that is elongated in the anterior-posterior direction because of the strongly developed *pilaster* extending down the back of the femur. This reflects the power of muscles that bring the long leg backwards. Other related changes affect the back of the head. R. Caspari's work suggests an emphasis on nuchal muscles important in dragging and hauling. All of these reflect higher levels of individual mobility and an increase in the amount of transported goods, and this fits with indications of wider trade networks and more effective responses (including mobility) to seasonal changes. Even late Neandertals such as Saint Césaire show some of the modifications (probably reflecting the changing adaptations of the Châtelperronian). While most of the cranial rear is missing on this specimen the back of the mastoid fits a neck muscle pattern resembling later Upper Paleolithic people and unlike the other Neandertals, and the shape of the femur shaft is modified because of its stronger pilaster which suggests that the muscle mass distribution was more like later humans.

The impact of continued changes in subsistence activities and specializations in technology on the human skeleton is particularly evident on the face, the robustness of the postcranial skeleton, and the forearm. The continued proliferation and improvement of special-purpose tools was across the inhabited world, whether of wood, bone, or ivory, or made on blades or with microliths. These tools stimulated and accelerated the trend for replacing muscle by technology, which marked the course of much Middle Paleolithic human evolution. Specialized tools were also important for the success of the organizational and mobility related changes discussed above.

One effect of the technological changes was in the use of the anterior teeth, with consequences appearing in the face and cranium. Technological innovations and refinements in the Middle Paleolithic resulted in better-made and more efficient tools such as knives, burins, drills, and scrapers (many of these are tool-making tools), and the invention of composite tools allowed a more effective application of leverage and force. As these changes continued into the Upper Paleolithic (or Late Paleolithic, or Later Stone Age), there were significant decreases in the use of the jaws to hold and pull, the vise-like actions that had gained great importance. When these dental functions changed and crown and root sizes reduced, a series of related biomechanical changes took place and anatomical responses included:

- The lower face reduced significantly, especially the stress-bearing regions supporting anterior loading. Areas that reduced in size include the maxilla below the nose, the maxillary sinus on either side of the nose, and the zygomatics above the masseter attachment (the lower border thinned and became concave in shape).
- Supraorbital reduction occurred everywhere, because of decreased anterior loading and for some populations the ability of the straighter frontofacial angle to resist deformation without additional buttressing.
- In the Neandertal lands, the prominent midfacial prognathism decreased and
  - the foramen magnum shifted rearwards relative to the sides of the cranial base, maintaining the shape and anatomical relations of the throat.
  - mandible length decreased as the face became less prognathic; this positioned the tooth row more posteriorly, closed the gap between the last molar and the ramus, and made the chin appear to be more prominent.
- The nuchal musculature related to anterior tooth loading reduced, resulting in a shorter and lower attachment area and a narrower occiput, as emphasis shifted from broadly distributed muscles used in anterior tooth loading to centrally placed muscles important in carrying and pulling.
- In some regions there was a redistribution of cranial mass into a more spherical shape, as crania became shorter and higher.

The improvements in technological efficiency that were virtually universal, although quite different in detail from place to place, were responsible for the trend of general body strength reduction, marked by many changes in limb form and bone thickness, reduction in muscle attachment areas and robustness, and reduction or loss of the skeletal buttresses. It was probably also responsible for the decrease in the magnitude of skeletal sexual dimorphism in some populations, as improving technology lessened the differences in strength requirements between male and female roles. However all skeletal changes were not reduction, as in the mobility-related leg changes noted above. For example, there was the reduction of the dramatic arm-strength dimorphism in Neandertals, which happened at the same time that the glenoid joint of the scapula became wider (see Chapter 13) and assisted-projectile systems appeared. Together these changes reflect the biological and cultural elements of a weapon-throwing adaptation and are not simply reductions from a previously "robust stage" to a subsequent "gracile" one.

This example illustrates the principle that the specifics of these changes must be considered within the context of ancestry, as populations responded, in many cases to similar causes, with the genome inherited from their past. Because, the organizational and technological changes occurred at different rates in various areas, and since archaic populations varied from place to place, even if the directions *and* rates of change had been the same, there would be differences in modern morphology. For instance, browridges in the East African sample from the earlier Late Pleistocene were already largely reduced, whereas in the penecontemporary West Asian sample, especially in the males, they were large and well developed. Had the rates of change been the same in these areas, one would expect modern East Africans to have smaller browridges, and a lower frequency of individuals with large browridges, than modern Levantines. But not only were the rates of change dissimilar but variation in the pattern of reduction distinguishes these regions as well. The East African supraorbital anatomy highlights evenly developed tori or arches, little separated from the forehead and often only weakly developed across the face, while in West Asia (and Europe) the thinning is all lateral and many individuals are found with strongly developed arches over the nose and extending above the medial sides of the orbits.

A MODEL FOR MODERNIZATION

The model I propose for understanding the appearance of modern humans is a twofold one:

1. modern features appear at different times, in different places, and each spreads through the network created by genic exchanges because of the advantages conferred; as P. Chase and H. Dibble put it, "different biological and behavioral traits [of modern humans], even though they may be linked today, had functionally and temporally separate origins".
2. modern features appear in different populations as they respond to changes in selection that are common because ideas (organizational, technological) have spread through the network of social interactions and exchanges. In some cases these responses are similar, and in others quite different.

Together these account for the modernizations that diffuse widely through humanity during this period, combining changes that are common to all populations with others that reflect different approaches to the same problems. Rates and in many cases the specifics of anatomical changes, may differ from place to place, and parodying W. Howells, different peoples do not all miraculously cross the finish line together, because there is no finish line to cross. What makes humanity modern is not, after all, these anatomical changes but the shared modern behaviors.

The morphological transformations were a consequence of changing activity patterns. Moreover, many of the morphological changes, especially concerning the form and robustness of the postcranial skeleton, may have been a developmental response to reduced stress during growth. A similar explanation may be offered for reductions in facial size and projection. Thus the observed morphological changes may not be an accurate reflection of the magnitude of genetic difference. D. Frayer suggests that male crania and dentitions changed much more than females during the early Upper Paleolithic. This gracilization of the males might be expected to accompany the change in hunting patterns and improved killing technology. Given its nature, it is unlikely to reflect a dramatic genetic change. S. Churchill argues that the similarity in postcranial interrelationships he found in Middle and Upper Paleolithic samples means "the overall integration of morphology remained unchanged across the archaic to modern transition. This finding argues against the idea of major genetic difference (e.g., change in regulator genes)".

Virtually every feature said to characterize modern populations is present, although at lower frequency, in earlier humans. New genetic material (or even more dramatically a "modernizing mutation") spreading from a single source is not required to account for these changes, and there is no compelling evidence that there was such a mutation, if for no other reason that neither modern populations nor features seem to have a single place of origin. Even without new genes, the frequency changes by themselves can lead to the appearance of apparently "new" morphological features as combinations that were once rare become common, and once common combinations become rare. This is a simple fact of probability and a result of independent assortment of the chromosomes. If there are three independent features in a population, each with a frequency of 90%, the expected number of individuals with all three is only 72.9% (.9x 9x.9). If the frequency of each of these features reduces to 50%, they will be found together in only 12.5% of the individuals (5x.5x.5). By changing the frequencies of various characteristics, the evolutionary process affects populations the same way. As the genes responsible for a polygenic structure decrease in frequency, the frequency of the structure does not decrease proportionately but rather much more dramatically. This model resolves a contradiction that exists between the general pattern of change expressed worldwide and its specific nuances in various regions that can be dramatically different. While the general direction of change is the same everywhere, the specific changes in each area, their rate, and their timing differ in a manner which seems dependent on the genetic variation already present in earlier populations.

It would be a mistake to suppose (as some have) that modernizations resulting from shifting frequencies of existing genetic variations are somehow not *major* changes because no new genetic material is involved. Shifting frequencies are the main cause of evolutionary changes and their importance must be judged by the effects on the phenotype, not the magnitude of underlying changes in the genome. And there is no doubt that many consider these changes to be major, although in my own opinion they pale before the rapidity and magnitude of those that accompanied the Neolithic revolution (a topic that will *not* be covered in this text but that, on the biological side involved significant and very rapid changes, so localized that they must have been the result of shifting frequencies of existing genetic material, not spread out from a single source). Modernizations are not just a description of Paleolithic changes - they continued right through to the present. R. Klein, echoing an assertion made by D. Pilbeam some 20 years earlier, contends

> prior to [40 kyr] ... human form and human behavior evolved hand -in-hand, very slowly
> over very long time intervals. Afterward, evolution of the human form all but ceased, while
> ... the evolution of culture accelerated dramatically.

As far as this portrayal of biological non-change is concerned, nothing could be further from the truth.

A HUMAN REVOLUTION?

Anatomically and behaviorally, there were dramatic changes that developed *within* the Upper Paleolithic, after populations with high frequencies of anatomically modern traits had appeared. Archaeological evidence is said to reflect the emergence of fully modern organizational and behavioral patterns, fully expressed by the end of the earlier Upper Paleolithic. These behavioral changes created the populations who colonized the unknown continents of Australia and the Americas, who decorated and enriched their lives with art while perfecting killing at a distance, and extinguished the megafauna of their world and finally so pushed its natural resources that eventually they had to develop their own. They were, in other words, the first true mirror for humankind and the first ancient harbingers of what was to come.

Some have come to view these changes as a true human revolution. C. Stringer and C. Gamble, for instance, describe a saltation with a "behavioral switch" that flicked on, leading to revolutionary changes in human behavior and cognition. These and other authors such as R. White and P. Mellars argue that there was a whole integrated "package" of changes, including:

- populational densities increased,
- more people lived to older ages
- subsistence became more focused and specialized,
- mobility was higher,
- social and communication networks were broader and more elaborate,
- art and personal adornment appeared

They believe that important elements of human society to appear at this time include ethnicity and complex status with social stratification based on much more than sex, age, and alliances formed from friendships. Evidence for these is often drawn from the appearance of body decoration and various forms of art. Hayden suggests that what is unusual about Upper Paleolithic art is found in the cave paintings, not just their skill (complexly rendered, often abstract, rock art is found at the same time and earlier in southern Africa, and considerably earlier in Australia), but is in the deep cave recesses where it is found. It is protected, in a way that earlier art may have not been (Hayden infers that earlier art might have been much more common than we suppose). He further suggests that the use of deep caves might be related to the emergence of rich hunting societies with more status competition. With enhanced abilities to amass resources, where more resources can be procured by a single individual than they can use, such societies develop means of expressing status such as the collecting and control of art and the labor necessary to produce it. Deep caves, he argues, were effective for the preservation of the art work, for their contribution to the psychological impact on spectators, and for creating emotionally binding experiences, for instance as in rites of passage. Upper Paleolithic burials differ as well. F. Harrold believes that while Middle and Upper Paleolithic burials differ in that Upper Paleolithic females were given the same "elaborate funerary treatment" as males (another difference is that Middle Paleolithic females are buried much less often).

But this is all a European phenomenon, with little but lip service to the changes that must have been blossoming across the rest of the world (mainly through the recognition of the importance of the colonization of Australia). The fundamental assumption underlying the "human revolution" interpretation, and tying together the diverse changes in European society and culture, is the precept that they can be bound to the rapid dispersal of modern humans across Europe, as evidenced by the Aurignacian. The earliest Aurignacians must be the earliest modern humans in the region for this explanation to work.

THE MORE THINGS CHANGE ...

Yet, apart from the "human revolutionists" there is broad consensus that the Aurignacian is *not* a single culture. In fact, if it *was* a single culture, one that dispersed from a single source and spread with modern humans, there would be an underlying self-contradiction because (as A. Marks points out) the Aurignacian found in the Levant (where the earliest modern humans are said to have lived) has none of the so-called modernizing features. Further confusing the issue is the fact that populations said to be "modern" are some 60 kyr earlier than the Aurignacian there, necessarily detracting from any contention that the "modernization package" is a functional one. And continuing with the implications of this assumption, to paraphrase Marks, if the behavioral similarities of the European Aurignacians are taken to demonstrate a unity of culture and imply biological kinship, it must be accepted that the cultural identity and biological relations of the even earlier Levantine Skhul/Qafzeh "moderns" are with the "Neandertals" of the region. However, there is no convincing information about who the *earliest* Aurignacians in any particular area were. In Europe they might well have been Neandertals.

Nor is there any compelling basis for the precept that the innovations and changes in this time period came all together or were part of a "modernization package". As M. Stiner points out, the Middle Paleolithic was a period of great diversity and change; so much so, she argues, that in comparison the further changes that come with the Upper Paleolithic in Europe do not seem to be as extreme or unique. And, as O. Bar-Yosef asserts, "the cultural variability of the early Upper Paleolithic may have had its roots in the Middle Paleolithic". The modernizing behaviors, or behaviors that reflect modernization, were there in the European Mousterian all along:

- ethnicity, expressed by non-functional differences between local industries (for instance Mousterian of Acheulean Tradition, plano-convex leaf points, each restricted to limited portions of Europe),
- food storage, at least implied by the speculation that Mousterian hearths were for cooking, and that cooking was invented (or exapted) for defrosting frozen (i.e., stored) foods,
- art and personal adornment found throughout the Neandertal world (albeit much less regularly and elaborately than within the Upper Paleolithic but we must be careful as these kinds of differences distinguish populations today and we do not believe one is more modern than another because of them).

Chase and Dibble assert that "there is no single point in time where we can justifiably draw a line between modern and archaic behavior ... it would be a mistake to attempt to identify the origin of "modern" behavior in the prehistoric record". And, L. Straus maintains

> there was no *one* transition everywhere, even in as small an area as western Europe. There was no necessarily unified 'package' of Cro-Magnon anatomy, Upper Paleolithic stone technology and typology, bone/antler tools, large scale specialized hunting, ornamentation, and art. ... Each region has its own history of changing circumstances and adaptive changes.

Moreover, there is an important sense in which changing activities as a *cause* of modern anatomy just doesn't fit the facts in Europe, just as it doesn't in the Levant where there is no compelling evidence of differing activities (Chapter 12). As Soffer puts it:

> Explanations that involve 'Deus ex machina' - the arrival from somewhere else of [anatomically modern *Homo sapiens*], whether in person or through gene flow, or some combination of the two, are equally unsatisfactory as they neither account for the non-synchrony between morphological forms and cultural behavior nor, more importantly, specify what it is that the [anatomically modern *Homo sapiens*] did that was more adaptive than what the Neandertals did.

This is by no means an attempt to deny the reality of change. As the Middle Paleolithic passed into prehistory the changes were major and fundamental, if perhaps not as sudden, orchestrated, or dramatic as sometimes portrayed. Like the Neolithic, their source cannot be found in human biological evolution.

Moderns in Asia

The appearance of the earliest East Asian populations fully resembling living people is certainly in the Late Pleistocene, but its exact details are blurred by problems in provenience and subsequently in dating. Dates of about 20 kyr are known with certainty from several sites - greater (in some cases much greater) antiquity has been claimed and may well be true, but provenience and other problems provide grounds for doubt.

CONTINENTAL EAST ASIA

The earliest of the diagnostically modern specimens may well be Liujiang in Guangxi Province, South China, but like most early modern remains from the region it's date is not known with certainty (Liujiang Cave has a Uranium series date of 67 kyr but its relation to the specimen is unclear). None of the seemingly early specimens can be aged more accurately than to within a broad time span, later Late

Pleistocene, and even these generalizations are uncertain in some cases. Looking at the best of the dated sites:

- the cranial and limb remains from Salawusu (Ordos, Inner Mongolia) are dated to between 50 and 37 kyr by Uranium series, and some may be older
- Ziyang (Sichuan Province) is radiocarbon dated to either 39-36 or 7 kyr, depending on which level it came from (this can no longer be established),
- the remains from the Upper Cave at Zhoukoudian have accelerator mass spectrometer radiocarbon dates of 29-24 kyr.

At Liujiang a modern-appearing cranium is associated with robust appearing skeletal material (much of a skeleton was found). The cave fauna point to a Late Pleistocene age, although the association of the specimen with the fauna remains to be proved (it is possible that Liujiang fell into a fissure that opened into the cave). The reported date of 67 kyr would not be out of place, but there is no way of associating it with the specimen. Liujiang is a young adult male of diminutive height (about 157 cm, some 6 cm shorter than the mean male height for the much taller people who live in the area today, according to Wu Rukang). The cranium has a short, broad and quite flat face that is vertically oriented and except for the maxilla just below the nose is decidedly *un*prognathic (this contrasts most markedly with the earlier Upper Paleolithic males from Europe who, otherwise, have some Asian features, see below and figure 14.2). The nose is broad and low (both its nasal bones and its guttered nasal opening), and is only moderately angled to the face. Its root is flat and the contour of the suture along the top of the nasal bones fits the Mongoloid pattern. To its sides are moderately developed canine fossae (actually, though, deeper and more prominent than many South Chinese), and the lower cheek border is distinctly notched. Orbits are broad and low, overshadowed by well developed supercillary arches. Above them there is an elongated frontal bone and distinct keeling along the midline. The temporal lines are prominent. Compared with the Dali male, the faces of the two specimens have a similar flatness and broadening but the Dali face is markedly taller and has very prominent supraorbital tori. The Liujiang occipital region is somewhat less modern. In profile it is angled and bun-like (similar to Jinniushan), but the nuchal region is weakly developed, there is no inion prominence, and the mastoids are small.

There are a number of specifically Mongoloid features, including the facial flatness, proportions and orientation of the nose, and rounding of the lower outside borders of the orbits. Other resemblances to living Chinese are in the shoveling of the lateral incisors and the unerupted third molars. Moreover, there are Mongoloid features found in the postcranial skeleton. According to K. Rosenberg these are found in the "feminine" characteristics of the pelvis, especially its broad, open greater sciatic notch (see Chapter 4). Rosenberg found that this sciatic notch form characterizes Chinese, especially in contrast to European and Australian samples where so broad a notch would be in the female range. For the Chinese samples she studied, broad notches characterize males and the corresponding female anatomy is even broader yet.

Other features of the postcranial skeleton are archaic. For instance, the femur is robustly developed; the shaft wall is relatively and absolutely thick and the medullary cavity is small. However, in general the form and dimensions of the lower vertebrae and other skeletal remains are undiagnostic.

There are some more specific similarities to recent populations from South China and further to the south, including facial gracility, dental reduction, weaker shoveling, and facial prognathism, and these are even better expressed in an undated palate (found in a Hong Kong drugstore) which is distinctly similar to Late Pleistocene/Holocene specimens from Indonesia in size, robustness, alveolar prognathism, and guttered (or indistinct) lower nasal margin. A similar set of features is found in the palate of the Quilinshan (= Chilinshan, or Laibin) cranium from Guangxi Zhuang Autonomous Region, also undated. In this specimen, the lower nasal border is quite wide, but alveolar prognathism is only moderate. The zygomatics are rather flattened and are positioned forward, although not as markedly as in many living Chinese. Contrasting with Liujiang, there is no canine fossa, the lower nasal border is sharp, and the nuchal region is well developed and the occiput is robust, with central nuchal torus development and a distinct inion prominence and other features that show it is male.

From the west, the Ziyang cranium also has a dating problem. It is a female specimen from well into the mountainous regions of Sichuan Province. Unfortunately its provenience is uncertain, which is why two different dates are reported for it. Ziyang is smaller and in many respects more gracile than Liujiang, although there is a resemblance in the prominence of the supraorbitals (compared with living Asians). Among the more archaic features are the robust development in the supraorbital area, the frontal keel, the angular torus, the large occipital area, well developed mastoid process, and the positioning of inion high above the internal occipital protuberance position (this is also true of the Shiyu occiput (Shanxi Province) that is dated to 28 kyr). Lijiang (Yunnan Province) is the cranium of an adolescent female of possible Late Pleistocene age (its exact locality is unknown).

To the north, human remains from the Salawusu beds in the Ordos valley were first discovered in 1922 (an incisor, partial humerus, and femur pieces) and 20 additional pieces have been found since. The fragmentary remains have long been considered to represent early modern humans, and Uranium series dates confirm this possibility - as tempered by the fact that none of the pieces thus far reported were excavated, they were all collected by farmers, and only a few details are published of the excavated specimens. Much of the material is undiagnostic, but the three frontal bones have a modern supraorbital anatomy with supercillary arches and large frontal sinuses, an occiput has extrasutural bones, and the incisor has marked marginal ridges and a straight face. Most of the 9 long bones are robust and have thick shaft walls and small medullary cavities. Better dated but as yet unpublished is a 28 kyr specimen from Liashui. Some of its notable features include the "pinched" and elevated nasal bones and the long and vertically thin pubic ramus. Like the Zhoukoudian Upper Cave remains it helps establish the existence of a distinct North Asian morphotype in the Late Pleistocene, and suggests links with western populations because some of the nasal and midfacial features appear there as well, in penecontemporary samples.

The Shandingdong or Upper Cave at Zhoukoudian is the best known of the sites from North China. The remains of approximately eight individuals were found near the bottom of deposits dated to 29-24 kyr. The three crania, an adult male and female and a 13-14 year old boy, are the best known specimens, but there were also mandibles and mandibular fragments, a maxilla, and some postcranial bones, including a femur. Unfortunately, all of these disappeared along with the rest of the Zhoukoudian material. F. Weidenreich, who did a preliminary study of the material before it was lost, described the adult female (number 103) as "Eskimoid", the boy (number 102) as "Melanesoid" and the adult male (number 101) as "proto-Mongoloid." Subsequently Wu Xinzhi downplayed these differences and emphasized the common features in the sample, including

- large crania with elongated head form and a relatively low frontal slope (compared with living North Asians)
- short upper face
- vertical, flat face
- rectangular, widely separated orbits
- wide nasal aperture

He argued that as a group these specimens fit fully within the Mongoloid range, especially in comparison to the Mesolithic and Neolithic materials from China (Weidenreich did not have the opportunity to examine these), and some also would add by comparison with the Ainu of Japan. Wu did not, however, think that they were individually the progenitors of major Mongoloid divisions as Weidenreich seemed to have been suggesting. With other scholars such as N. Cheboksarov, C. Coon, and Wu's his colleague Wu Rukang, Wu Xinzhi posited a continuous line of human evolution in China with these specimens as a centerpiece for his analysis. For Wu all three are especially similar to recent Chinese, Siberians, and Eskimos.

Shandingdong 101 is quite tall, with an estimated height of some 174 cm. The cranium is large (1500 cc), long and rather low, and has very prominent supraorbitals and a marked sulcus (similar to Holocene Siberians reported by C. Laughlin and colleagues). The nose is unusually prominent (a characteristic of other Late Pleistocene North Asians). The zygomatics are large and strongly angled, so that the face is wide and flat. Shandingdong 103 is much shorter, about 159 cm. Her "Eskimoid" female cranium is quite similar to the male, and its zygomatics are even more flaring. However, this cranium is smaller (1290 cc) and more gracile, and there is no browridge or supercillary arch. There is a strong sagittal keel on the frontal. While likened to Eskimos, Wu points out that her features are also common among Northern Chinese and Holocene Siberians. The teenage boy shows evidence of artificial cranial deformation. The frontal is flattened and there are two broad depressions on either side of the frontal squama, connected by a shallow groove. This kind of deformation is not uncommon in some populations, especially when loads are carried on the back supported by a strap across the forehead (the depressions are for the knot). What mainly contributes to the cranium's "Melanesoid" appearance is the forehead flattening and tall forehead, direct consequences of the deformation. This condition did not influence the cranial capacity, estimated at 1380 cc. The four Upper Cave mandibles and postcrania are modern in appearance. Wu reports tori on the 101 mandible and 110 maxilla that strengthen the case for Asian Mongoloid affinities.

The Shandingdong specimens differ from Liujiang and other specimens to the south, and this is not totally surprising as there are formidable water barriers that separate the Shandingdong sample from these others. Besides size, differences from Liujiang are mainly in

- broader frontal,
- relatively and absolutely longer head,
- taller nose,
- greater facial projection,
- stronger development of the zygomatics.

Indeed, midfacial projection seems to be fairly common in northern Asia at the end of the Pleistocene. This is one of the factors that led A. Thoma to conclude that Paleosiberians resembled eastern European Neandertals. He presents evidence for morphological continuity between central and eastern European and Levantine archaics (as represented by Shanidar, Amud, and Teshik Tash) and Paleosiberians. Thus, Thoma argued for genetic continuity between these Neandertals and more recent populations in northern Asia. One aspect of the face that might support the contention of genic exchanges across the northern Eurasian tier is the appearance of prominent, projecting noses in Late Pleistocene North Asians (including North Chinese). The degree of Paleosiberian facial prognathism is low compared with the Neandertals but high by living Asian standards (but similar to the Upper Cave specimens), and of course the supraorbital anatomy and certain other Neandertal features were never present in Siberia, but Thoma's point is that genetic exchanges and not the immigration of Neandertals themselves is the cause of the similarities. However, given the numerous Mongoloid features across East Asia that are penecontemporary or earlier, Thoma's further contention that the Neandertal influence caused the origin of the Mongoloids is unlikely.

Trying to piece all of this evidence together, it seems to me that these Late Pleistocene moderns from East Asia are Mongoloid in their racial anatomy, but do not resemble any specific living group or groups in the area and have a higher frequency of some archaic characteristics. It seems likely that they have sampled the population from which some of the later Mongoloids, including Amerinds and Eskimos, directly evolved. They show a basic division along a north-south axis, and (as discussed below) the southern sample is quite similar to certain penecontemporary and more recent specimens from Okinawa, South Asia, and even Australia. During the later portions of the last glaciation, there is a gradual reduction of the more archaic features and with the Mesolithic and Neolithic, the appearance of recognizably modern populations. The East Asian sample is regionally distinct, showing consistent differences in the combinations of certain features such as the expression of upper incisor shoveling that, according to T. Crummett, combines strong marginal ridges and flat crown shape. P. Habgood suggests several facial features:

- flat (i.e. not depressed) nasal root
- vertically oriented nasal bones
- horizontal course of the suture extending between the eyes, separating the frontal and nasals, and the frontal and maxilla
- strongly angled malar incisure (notch)

And, of course, there are the details of facial flattening and verticality. Yet, when compared with contemporaries in Europe and Africa, it is unlikely that evolution in this area was completely independent. The explanation of local continuity in the presence of worldwide changes requires the presence of gene flow. There always seem to be both characters showing local continuity and characters suggesting the direction of regional relations. In particular, some evidence suggests substantial genic exchanges across the northern Eurasian tier, and when the evidence from Europe is considered, it is evident that these genic exchanges were in both directions.

AMERICAN ABORIGINES

There seems little doubt that the Mongoloid ancestors of Native Americans first reached the New World from Siberia as big-game hunters, perhaps following the game they hunted as the herds migrated. While this would be impossible today, studies show that during the glacial advances, enough ocean water was locked atop the continents in the form of ice to lower the sea level significantly. (Sea level lowering accounts for the much earlier hominids found on what is now the island of Java.) A sea level drop of 50 m or more exposes a land connection between Siberia and Alaska, closing off the Bering straits. This has happened numerous times in the past, including as recently as 14 kyr ago, and game and hunters crossed over this "land bridge" between the two continents, an unglaciated region which along with adjacent unglaciated portions of Siberia and Alaska is called "Beringia". Of course habitation of Beringia is not necessarily the same as habitation of the Americas, as entering the continent from the north during an ice age is easier said than done.

As to when the Americas were first colonized, or perhaps more importantly when *it first happened successfully*, the Beringia connection was in place most recently between about 30 and 10 kyr; the land bridge was submerged for the last time no more recently than 14 kyr, but winter ice would have made it passable on foot for at least several millennia more according to D. Meltzer. Occupation sites in eastern Siberia with actual numerical dates are recent; 14 kyr for the Diuktai Cave and Ushki Lake occupations. If people were already in Beringia, they were in a position to attempt moving into North America. For them it would have been possible to easily reach the interior of the North American continent by land before 20 kyr or after 14 kyr (i.e. people were in eastern Siberia just in time). Moreover, southward migration along the Pacific shore (or hopping along the Pacific coast in short voyages using simple watercraft) was often feasible between these dates, because not all of the coast was icebound. Therefore, these circumstances are not limiting enough to determine the "most probable" time of first colonization based on "windows of opportunity", and the question of "when" must be answered by other means.

Three approaches have been used: archaeological, genetic, and linguistic. They have been used to address two questions, the *time* of earliest occupation and the *pattern* of colonization:

- distinct migrations of different populations - often three are proposed
- a constant (although not necessarily uniform) pattern of two-way genic exchanges.

In spite of a very large number of scientists searching for a very long time, only a handful of New World archaeological sites have claims for great antiquity, and none of these have proven to be widely convincing. The Brazilian rock shelter of Pedra Furada is said to show occupation as early as 50 kyr, but the dates are radiocarbon which is not accurate for this antiquity and more importantly the "tools" showing occupation are made on quartzite pebbles which are very difficult to diagnose. Monte Verde in Chile has two archaeological levels. The upper one, which includes evidence of structures, has radiocarbon dates reported to lie between 12.5 and 13 kyr. It is the lower one with its 33 kyr date that is most problematic - it is not clear that any of the several stone artifacts were modified by humans, and the shallow circular depressions that are interpreted to be hearths may well not be. Other early but problematic findspots include Meadowcroft Rockshelter in Pennsylvania, Pendejo Cave in New Mexico, Taima-Taima in Venezuela, Tagua-Tagua in Chile, and Los Toldos in Argentina. The most recent reviews of the antiquity question continue to find these problematic, but by no means impossible. Perhaps the most damning criticism of early occupation is the absence of archaeologically visible habitation until very much later, 11 kyr or less for slight visibility and no more that 8 kyr for enough sites to suggest a significant level of habitation. These data suggest that even if one or more of the really early dates are valid, they are sampling a population that was so sparsely established that it may represent an unsuccessful colonization attempt.

Genetic approaches are based on nuclear DNA variation and calculations of divergences on mtDNA lineages. E. Szathmary reviews these in some detail and suggests that the most reasonable cause of genetic differentiation in the Americas is not separate population sources (e.g. distinct migrations) but rather the isolation of populations north and south of the last glacial advance, and the subsequent normal causes of increasing variation such as local adaptation and isolation by distance of subdivided populations. This implies an early occupation. However, the different sources of genetic data are often contradictory. While genetic information reflected in dental variation provides equally early dates (if one assumes that dental changes proceed at a constant rate), according to C. Turner the dental information suggests three distinct waves of immigrants. These uses of morphology are not without criticism, and mtDNA has not proved helpful as a provider of dates because of its initial variation within the immigrating populations. MtDNA divergences cannot be linked to population histories because the gene and population divergences were at different times. Its main importance has been to indicate that there were few bottlenecks (periods of extreme population size reductions) during the colonization process, and to support Szathmary's contention that distinctly different populations and/or migrations were not involved.

The linguistic record, as interpreted by J. Greenberg and M. Ruhlen, does seem to support the contention of three separate migrations, but is consistent with a late (12 kyr or slightly earlier) time of initial entry. Others such as J. Nichols attribute the diversity of Native American languages to many multiple entries, but favor a time considerably earlier than that date.

The three approaches do not agree on the question of whether migrations into the New World were in the form of several distinct waves from dissimilar population sources, or a more gradual demic diffusion - as Hrdlička once described it "a dribbling over from Northeast Asia, extending probably over a long stretch of time" (I believe the weight of the evidence, certainly the evidence most likely to be valid, supports the latter). However, the approaches largely concur to suggest that an 18-14 kyr entry into North America below Alaska is the most likely interpretation.

The initial migrants during this period were almost certainly very few in number. Archaeological sites and skeletal remains of Paleoamerinds that represent this time of first habitation are quite rare. R. Kelly and L. Todd suggest that their low population numbers are not unexpected, and reflect some of the unique environmental and social problems they encountered. Beringia was essentially an Arctic desert, a cold and arid treeless plain with woody plants and grasses only in the lowlands or along stream courses. Bison, mammoth, and horse were present, as well as smaller (deer-sized) herbivores, but at densities that could support only relatively small human populations through a full seasonal cycle. These are all herd mammals and their migrations were probably important in defining the pattern of initial colonization. But colonization for these early Native Americans was quite different than many of the other population movements of the Late Pleistocene. It was relatively rapid - the continents were empty of human habitation - but at the same time cautious and adaptively limited and rigid because there were no preëxisting social networks to provide the information necessary to ease local adaptations by minimizing risk taking. After the first immigrants quickly spread to occupy a set of similar environments through both continents, the exploration of new habitats and local specializations developed slowly, and somewhat later.

At this date, really beyond the scope of this chapter, the earliest Native Americans were anatomically and behaviorally modern. A number of scientists have noted that they could easily have been derived from Asians such as those represented at the Zhoukoudian Upper Cave. A. Hrdlička, and subsequently his replacement at the Smithsonian Institution T. Stewart, argued for decades that no Paleoamerind remains fall outside the range of variation found in living Native Americans, and that attempts to show significant evolution came from isolating a few archaeological specimens with seemingly archaic characteristics and assuming that they were early. There was, however, substantial adaptive variation to the wide range of American environments and the increasingly diverse cultural adaptations (including indigenous Neolithic revolutions and several dense, stratified, population centers. The Americas stand as a model for how quickly these changes can occur.

Descriptions of the few early remains are relatively incomplete, with several exceptions. Only three sites with human remains can be dated to older than 10 kyr using techniques not dependent on bone collagen or amino acid dating, which seem especially problematic for the North American material because of treatment (preparation, storage) after their discovery and have been quite misleading (see table 14.1). In order of decreasing age, the best-dated older specimens are from Guitarrero cave in Peru, Tepexpan in Mexico, and Marmes rock shelter in Washington State, all dated to within the 13-11 kyr span.

Table 14.1
Misleading Racemization Dates for Early New World Natives[1]

Skeleton	Racemization age (kyr)	AMS Radiocarbon date (kyr)
Sunnyvale	70	5
Angeles Mesa	>50	8 or 4
Del Mar	48	5
San Jacinto	37	3
Taber (Canada)	28	4
LaJolla Shores	28	2
Otavalo ((Ecuador)	25	3
Yuha	24	4
Truckhaven	24	1
Los Angeles	>23	4
Laguna Beach	17	5

[1] Modified after Aikens (1990)

The Guitarrero female mandible is small but robust and shows a strong differential wear pattern on the teeth, contrasting the heavily worn anterior dentition with the only slightly worn posteriors. T. Lynch and K. Kennedy suggest that this might result from non-masticatory uses of the anterior teeth superimposed on a grit-free diet emphasizing meat. The Tepexpan cranium is robust, especially in the prominent supraorbitals and low forehead, but the great cranial breadth relative to length appears very modern. In spite of the well-developed supramastoid area and the nuchal torus, the occiput should not be regarded as Neandertal-like (as was once claimed). Similar if not more "archaic-appearing" crania can still be found in living Native Americans. The fifty fragments of a subadult from the Marmes rock shelter were described as indicating a robust but modern-appearing individual with some "Mongoloid" features, a description which hardly distinguishes it from other Native Americans.

As a whole, the Paleoamerind sample cannot be distinguished from modern Native Americans by any particular set of features. While successful colonization may have been early (absence of evidence is not evidence of absence), most reasonably cautious assessments make this to have been much more recent and tied to the migrations of big game hunters who had adapted to the Beringia environment and occupied it 18-14 kyr ago, no doubt moving south at their earliest opportunity.

ISLAND EAST ASIA

East

There are a number of Pleistocene hominid sites reported from Japan and the Nansei Islands. These are reviewed and referenced in English by S. Narasaka . Like many of the Chinese specimens, most are plagued by incompleteness and uncertain provenience. The cranial remains from Japan that are most probable Late Pleistocene in age are from the Nekata limestone quarry, Hamakita, Shizoka. The Hamakita site yielded fossilized fragments of a small, thick walled human calvaria and postcranial pieces suggesting diminutive body size. In fact, there are a number of other fragmentary postcranial remains from various Japanese sites which, if correctly identified and actually Late Pleistocene in age, show the ancient inhabitants to be considerably smaller than the Neolithic Japanese. The most complete specimens are from the island of Okinawa: Yamashita-cho is a right femur and tibia of a 7 year old that is radiocarbon dated to 32 kyr, and Pinza-Abu is a fragmentary cranium (with an **Inca bone**) and some postcrania radiocarbon dated to some 26 kyr. The finds at the Minatogawa limestone quarry, about 18 kyr in age, are the most informative.

The Minatogawa remains were described in a detailed monograph edited by H. Suzuki and K. Hanihara. The specimens were found widely scattered around the site, but because of their completeness they surely were burials. There are between 5 and 9 individuals, two of which are male and the others female. Their crania are quite small (1390 cc for the male, 1170 and 1090 for the females 2 and 4), possibly a reflection of their diminutive stature. Minatogawa 1 is estimated at 153 cm, just under the height of the Liujiang male, and the Minatogawa 2 female is some 10 cm less. Like the more fragmentary Japanese specimens these are quite short. The crania are best preserved for 1 (male) and 4 (female). They combine short, low, but relatively broad crania with the rounded contours and weak torus development of living Asians. Tori are better developed posteriorly than anteriorly; the mastoids and supramastoid crests are strong, there are distinct nuchal tori, and above them suprainiac fossae. These are not the only European (and especially Neandertal) similarities as the cranial contours are rounded as seen from the rear. They are anything but Neandertals, however. The faces are as different as possible, short and broad, while the orbits low. The nasal aperture is broad as well, but the nasal bones are "pinched" and elevated (in their upper portion, the lower part is missing in all specimens). The facial contours are vertical, and quite flat with very anterior cheeks.

There are several innominates in this sample and two pelves that can be reconstructed. The male anatomy follows Rosenberg's description of the Asian pattern, in that the male sciatic notch is like that of Liujiang, very wide and in the female range of non-Asians. But these specimens are more complete than Liujiang. The Minatogawa 1 male and 3 female have pubic bones. and in view of the Neandertal discussions these have proven to be quite revealing. Their sizes are similar to the Neandertal relationship; the male bone is considerably longer than the female's (in fact it is the same length as the La Ferrassie male, an individual who was slightly taller and much heavier). Relative to the size of the hip joint the Minatogawa female pubis length is like other moderns but the male length is relatively elevated, as much as or moreso than Neandertal males, who are definitely *not* described as "modern" in this part of the pelvis. Now in this case the problem is with the use of the word "modern" as Minatogawa is modern by any definition, so perhaps to rephrase we can say that the Neandertal males have been mischaracterized when they are called "non-modern", "archaic", "apomorphic", or "specialized" in this region. The Europeans who defined "modern" did not go far enough afield to accurately represent the real human range. These are not the only Neandertal resemblances. For instance, the buttress that extends up the ilium in response to adductor force is prominent and anteriorly located in the male (and also in the females). In spite of these similarities, Minatogawa is no Neandertal, and some of the differences are revealing. In particular, with a cranial capacity of 1390 cc, much less that Neandertal males of similar body size and pubic length, the theory that elongated pubes reflect the need for an enlarged birth canal can be set aside. In fact the pelvic inlets of the Minatogawa 2 and 3 females are quite small (2 is "extraordinarily small", in the words of H. Baba and E. Endo, who described them), as one could expect from the small female sizes and cranial capacities. With the discovery of this pubic anatomy in a modern population, the interpretation that these morphological details reflect a significant locomotor difference can be dismissed as well.

In fact, in their comparisons Baba and Endo isolate a number of archaic characteristics in these skeletons. They systematically compare them to the Neandertal condition and the postcranial anatomy found at Zhoukoudian. In the femur and humerus, bones in which examples of both are known, and differ from each other, the Minatogawa remains resemble the Zhoukoudian folk.

According to Wu Xinzhi an analysis of measurements shows the Minatogawa male to be closest to Liujiang. In fact, they are no more different than the two Minatogawa females. H. Suzuki reaches a similar conclusion in his analysis of metric and nonmetric details. A few characteristics such as the pinched nose, and facial and orbital breadths are closer to the Shandingdong remains, but generally resemblance are with specimens to the south. In Wu's analysis the second closest specimen to the Minatogawa male is the penecontemporary Keilor cranium, from Australia. He suggests a widespread population across South Asia, one perhaps continuing to expand southward as the Pleistocene ended and finally reaching Australia where people with a quite different anatomy were encountered.

Southeast

Further to the south, there is a Late Pleistocene parietal bone from Chocheng, Taiwan, and several specimens from the Tabon cave, on Palawan island of the Philippines. Best known of these are the Tabon frontal and mandibular fragment dated to some 23 kyr - there is additional material from the cave but it may be more recent. The frontal is low, narrow, and rounded, with a compressed ridge between the nasal bones that is similar to that on Dali, Maba, and Shandingdong 101 according to Wu. There is third molar agenesis in the mandible. These details indicate a Mongoloid presence in the region.

A different relationship is suggested by the cranium from the Niah cave in Borneo, whose features are said to resemble Australians. However, there are serious problems with the date (40 kyr) suggested for it; the specimen is probably younger than this date because it was buried from a higher level (there are numerous Holocene burials in the cave), and in any event the actual date comes from what is thought to be an "equivalent" layer in another portion of the cave. Moreover this 1958 radiocarbon date really means >30 kyr, and may indicate no more than that there was insufficient carbon for an accurate age assessment. The Niah specimen is a juvenile (the third molar is unerupted) female in extremely fragmented and distorted condition. Enough of the cranium is present to show that she had no browridge development. The short, broad face, broad nose, and large palate are features that are common in living Australian and Tasmanian females, and workers such as W. Howells assess it as an early Australoid. However, Wu's systematic comparisons with other east Asians show it most similar to the closest specimens to the north, Liujiang and (secondarily) Minatogawa, and only very distantly to specimens further south such as Wadjak (Indonesia) or Keilor and Talgai (Australia).

In Indonesia, two crania and some postcranials that are undated but clearly later than the Solo material come from the site of Wadjak, Java. The Wadjak specimens were discovered in 1888 and 1890, but they were not reported for over thirty years. The crania are large brained with megadont dentitions and well developed cranial superstructures (especially Wadjak 2), and historically played an important role in attempts to understand the evolutionary sequence in Indonesia (replacement *versus in situ* evolutionary change) and the peopling of Australia, because they were thought to be Late Pleistocene in age. While the site is still undated, a combination of Holocene fauna and demonstrated similarities between the crania and Mesolithic cranial remains from Indonesia convincingly indicate that the specimens actually hold little relevance to either problem. It is the Solo sample itself that has the potential to provide a link between the Sangiran folk and Pleistocene Australians.

The problems of interpreting Late Pleistocene evolution in island South and Southeast Asia are exacerbated, perhaps terminally, by problems in dating. With Wadjak most likely positioned in the Holocene, the questions about the dates of Tabon and Niah raised by workers such as D. Bulbeck gain renewed significance. These specimens are also not anatomically distinct from Holocene populations, and the many scenarios woven over the years to explain the Late Pleistocene evolutionary changes and population differentiations in the region collapse for lack of any demonstrably Late Pleistocene specimens.

AUSTRALIA

The initial entry of humans into Australia was raised in Chapter 12, over the issue of links between the Indonesians from Ngandong and Ngawi. The habitation of Australia extends back to at least 60 kyr, according to Australian paleoanthropologists such as R. Jones. This is predates the first appearance of people in the Americas, even by the most liberal interpretation of the evidence. More importantly it provides clear evidence of important behavioral capacities because this colonization requires an early appearance of rather sophisticated maritime technology and, unless one posits that the first settlement was a singular, accidental event, it is a clear marker of foresight and future planning (abilities often denied to penecontemporary Mousterians). I. Davidson and W. Noble describe it as the earliest evidence of truly modern human behavior. Even at the lowest sea level of the Würm, which occurred well after 60 kyr, the straits separating Australia, New Guinea, and Tasmania from the Celebes and Borneo were at least 70 km wide. These separated (what was in low sea levels) the single continent of Australia, New Guinea, and

Tasmania (called Sahul) from the Asian Mainland. Although the Celebes, Borneo, and the rest of Java were connected to the Asian continent during much of the low sea period, as part of a continent called Sunda, even at the lowest sea levels there was never a direct connection to Australia. Therefore, a seafaring technology was needed for humans to disperse into Australia. A. Thorne suggests several reasons why this might not be surprising. These mainly center on the fact that island Southeast Asia was a dynamic area during the Pleistocene, with land surfaces which in aggregate covered as much area as Europe disappearing and reappearing with changing sea levels, and tens of thousands of miles of coasts providing the opportunity to exploit an unstable but potentially rich niche - offshore marine resources. Thorne suggests that bamboo rafts were the key to using this coastal habitat, and ultimately lead to ocean-spanning voyages.

A significant population source for the Aboriginal Australians is found in Indonesia. In spite of the long time span, a surprisingly number of facial features in the Sangiran remains can be linked to Late Pleistocene and more recent Australians (cranial resemblances are more general, and much less often involve unique characteristics). Comparative analysis of my Sangiran 17 reconstruction revealed the following similarities, whose importance lies in their *unique combination* in Pleistocene and more recent Australians:

- marked prognathism, especially at the lower nasal border and below and as reflected in the high facial angle
- a ridge or ridges paralleling the suture between zygomatic and maxillary bones
- eversion of the lower cheek, caused by the fact that the lower outside corner of the cheek, at the corner between the side and front of the face, extends more laterally than any of the face above it and gives the facial profile the outline of a pentagon
- the lower outside rim of the orbit is rounded
- the lower border of the nose lacks a distinct lie marking the change from nasal floor to the face of the maxilla below the nose
- the alveolar plane for the posterior tooth row is convexly curved

The similarities with complete early Holocene faces such as some from the sites of Kow Swamp and Coobool Crossing are quite striking. There are, of course, Australian fossils that are much older than Kow Swamp, but they are not as complete and comparisons with potential source populations are largely limited to upper facial (i.e. supraorbital) and cranial vault characteristics

Actual dated human remains span more than one-half the continent's occupation time, the earliest specimens from the Willandra Lakes system in New South Wales dating to >35 kyr, according to A. Thorne. The Willandra hominids, described by A. Thorne and S. Webb, include three fairly complete specimens that encapsulate the problems of Australian prehistory. WLH 50, mentioned in Chapter 12, is the most robust and archaic of these, sharing numerous similarities to the Solo remains. The fact that most of its characteristics appear later in the Australian fossil record and persist in recent samples, makes it the clearest possible link to an unquestionable Solo element in Aboriginal ancestry. It is a long, low cranium with maximum breadth very low on the vault, at the supramastoid crests. The forehead is flattened, terminating in very strongly developed supracillary arches without any sulcus above them. There is a strongly developed angular torus, and the occiput has a fairly vertical face although the eroded nuchal torus appears much like the Ngandong males, even to the low but very large triangular eminence at the inion. A part of the cheek was recovered, most of a moderately large bone fragment with an unusual anatomy of two ridges paralleling the suture between the zygomatic bone and the maxilla, one above it and the other below. One of its most notable features is the marked cranial wall thickening, so much so that Australian scientists such as S. Webb have suggested pathology as its cause. It is markedly thicker than the next largest Willandra specimen (table 14.2), and as much as four times thicker than the WLH 1 female (see below). In fact, the WLH 50 frontal and anterior parietal are thicker than any specimen at Ngandong. The pattern of thickening, however, is similar to other thick-vaulted Late Pleistocene humans and there is no reason to posit a disease process. Because it is a surface find and no carbon remains in the bone structure, its age is the most poorly established of the Willandra specimens; initial ESR minimally places it in the same span as the other remains (although E. Delson reports a much earlier determination) and the anatomical similarities to the earlier Indonesians suggests that the maximum age could easily be double this. On the other hand, it may be the same age as the others. There are much later specimens such as Coobool Creek 50.76 that are very much like it in general form and numerous details, with a similar cranial shape including low maximum breadth, a prominent nuchal torus covering the entire cranial rear, and in this case an even more Ngandong-like frontal, in that there is a true supraorbital torus. The Coobool specimen is one out of a large sample, at one extreme of a wide range of anatomies, pointing up the fact that morphological dating is rarely valid when only a single specimen is concerned. The problem of the age of WLH 50 is not yet resolved.

Table 14.2
Thickness of Willandra Lakes and Ngandong Crania

	WLH 50	WLH maximum[1]	WLH (Mungo) 1	Ngandong[2] 5	Ngandong[2] 8	Ngandong[2] 9
Thickness at mid-frontal	19	13	5	11		13
bregma	17	10	6	12	8	8
parietal boss	16	14	5	10	13	12
asterion	17	14	4	18	18	15
lambda	15	12	7	13	13	
inion	18	19	10	25		20

[1] without WLH 50
[2] choosing the three thickest Ngandong crania for comparison

The other two of the more complete early specimens are a fragmentary cremated female WLH 1 (Mungo) and a more complete articulated male burial WLH 3 (Mungo). Both are notably more gracile, with well-rounded foreheads, thin vault bone, weak muscle attachments, and weak or moderate supraorbital development. Contrasting with these observations is a marked expansion of the nuchal plane in both crania; for instance, in the WLH 1 female inion is well above the internal occipital protuberance and WLH 3 has a broadly developed nuchal torus. These are functionally associated with very heavy anterior tooth wear - the incisors and canines of WLH 3 are worn much more than the posterior teeth.

What does this gracility mean? Two interpretations have been given and it should be emphasized that they are not the same. In the first the more robust crania are regarded as Australoid and linked to the earlier Indonesians (the case here is very good) while the more gracile ones are linked to East Asians, the more Asian ancestry specifically indicated by the fact that penecontemporary Asians are more gracile than the Ngandong Indonesians, and have rounder foreheads. However this has a way of becoming confused with the second explanation, that robust means an earlier migration from a more archaic ancestral population and gracile means a later migration from a more modernized one. As D. Bulbeck points out, this makes what is interpreted as "modernization" in Asia (and elsewhere) be interpreted as "mongoloidization" in the south, and Mongoloid and Australoid have a way of becoming modern and archaic, which of course they are not meant to be. The most elementary survey of Australian archaeology, beginning with the ocean voyages themselves and including

- petrogpyphs from Wharton Hills with AMS radiocarbon dates of 43 and 36 kyr,
- hafted stone axes 40 kyr old that were seemingly used to ring trees so they could be burnt and open up forest glades where desired plant such as sugar cane, bananas, and yams will grow,
- ground stone axes older than 25 kyr.
- with the boomerang. the invention of the airfoil principle.

belies the judgment that Australoid features can in any way be considered archaic.

Moreover, there is a serious question of whether this Late Pleistocene gracility specifically points to an East Asian ancestry. The evidence here is mixed. A. Thorne argues that these Mungo specimens show particular similarities to Late Pleistocene Chinese such as Ziyang and Liujiang. However the WLH 3 maxilla is extremely projecting below the nose, while it is flat between the prominent canine pillars. In this anatomical region it differs from Liujiang but is quite similar to many early Holocene (for instance Kow Swamp 5) and living Australoids. The forehead rounding in WLH 3 is no greater than in other Australian fossils such as Kow Swamp crania 14 and 15. In fact, it differs from these much later males in its more prominent lateral orbital corner, thicker outer orbital pillar, larger cheeks with more prominent muscle markings, and greater separation of inion and the internal occipital protuberance; that is, greater cranial and upper facial robustness. WLH 3 cannot be specifically linked to "East Asia" on the basis of most features:

- the **temporal process of the zygomatic** is everted, giving the face a pentagon-like profile as seen from the front (like Sangiran 17 and many more recent Australoids),
- the outer orbital border is thick,
- the corner of the torus above the orbit forms a backwards-facing triangle (lateral frontal trigone) as in the Ngandong crania although more weakly expressed,
- there are no extrasutural bones on the lambdoidal suture, or anywhere else,
- the frontal merges into the supraorbital region without a sulcus,
- there are the same two thick ridges extending along the suture between the zygomatic and maxillary bones that WLH 50 has.

Similarly, WLH 1 resembles Kow Swamp 4 and 16, and if its frontal rounding is interpreted to reflect East Asian origins, the same must apply to these later Australoids. But this might be exactly correct! After all, whatever the population origins of the Australians, they did not remain culturally isolated and distinct in Australia and their biology must reflect this as well. The contrasts of the WLH 3 and 50 males strongly suggests different source populations. We may look for "Mongoloid influence" but are unlikely to find Mongoloids. The problem is that features in the Kow Swamp and Coobool specimens vary in magnitudes and patterns that are reasonable to expect in a biological population, while as Thorne argues the differences between the much earlier Willandra specimens are too great for this interpretation.

Generally, the predominant influence in Australian evolutionary morphology is the Indonesian one. But it should be emphasized that the resemblances involve features found in different specimens. No Australian specimen could be mistaken for a member of the Solo sample. Most resemblances are in the frontal (facial similarities are with the earlier Sangiran remains where there are faces for comparison). For instance in Kow Swamp 15 the browridge is continuously developed, dipping only slightly over the nose, and its thickness is close to the Solo average. The frontal of Kow Swamp 1 retains a sagittal keel that runs almost to the browridge and eliminates the groove between the browridge and the forehead. The outer portion of the browridge in Kow Swamp 9 follows the temporal line backward, forming a backward-pointed triangle at the upper corner of the orbit. In Cohuna (a specimen from the Kow Swamp region and almost certainly part of the same sample), the temporal line forms a ridge across much of the frontal, and the minimum breadth of the frontal is well behind the orbits. In Kow Swamp 9, the nuchal torus is thick and backward-projecting, and above it there is a distinct groove. These features argue for continuity with the earlier Indonesians, but of course the Kow Swamp (and other Holocene) folk are considerably different in other features that reflect worldwide evolutionary trends we describe as modernizations, such as larger cranial capacities, marked reduction in bone robustness and thickness, and so on. Kow Swamp, Coobool, and other Holocene populations are hardly archaic relics. They are the immediate predecessors of living Native Australians, with archaeological remains that provide evidence of, what C. Pardoe aptly describes as "the forerunner(s) of a modern, socially complex, dynamic system."

The best cases for East Asian influence in Pleistocene Australian populations are penecontemporary with the earlier of these. Of the several specimens of interest, the most complete is the Keilor cranium, first described by J. Wunderly. An associated femur has a collagen date of some 12 kyr, but collagen dates are not celebrated for their accuracy and parts of the site are much older. Further muddying the assessment of its age is the close similarity Keilor has with Wadjak 1, first noted by F. Weidenreich, a cranium now thought to be quite recent. Nevertheless, it is important to note that Keilor contrasts with much of the morphological variation for subfossil Holocene Australians, from sites such as Kow Swamp and Coobool Crossing, in some interesting ways. The forehead rounding is at the top of the range of variation, while the face is shorter, broader, more vertical, and transversely flatter - a combination which cannot be found at these sites. There is no depression of the nasal root, and the nasal bones are broad and flat. These features do suggest East Asian affinities, although Wu Xinzhi's study shows Keilor to be quite dissimilar from Liujiang and not especially similar to Minatogawa. The differences are not particularly a reflection of gracility. Keilor is a male specimen, with a centrally located nuchal torus and downward pointing inion triangle, large mastoids, a marked buttress extending along the canine roots, eversion of the lower border of the cheeks, a torus along the top of the palate, and a buttress paralleling the suture between the zygomatic and maxilla. These can hardly be characterized as gracile.

Even without WLH 50, A. Thorne and S. Wilson were able to make the case that there was more variation in the past than there is at present. Hybridization of populations from different ancestral sources, and the normal genetic processes of local selection and drift, could account for this. If so, as Th. Dobzhansky pointed out with regard to the Mount Carmel sample (Chapter 12), the usual morphologies in the ancestral samples would be expected to only rarely appear. It is not surprising, as P. Habgood reports, that there is often difficulty in placing individual specimens in morphological extremes - this is because most of the sample is not extreme at all. The Australian situation is somewhat more complex because while immigration was almost certainly persistent for a very long period of time, even if it sprang from the same regions the facts are that the biological sources were multiple (as the early contrasts of gracility and robustness suggest). A further complication is that the population character of at least some of the Southeast Asian source populations were changing over this time span. As Mongoloids became more predominant to the north, their anatomy began to appear more often in Australia. In other words, it is impossible, and possibly irrelevant, to distinguish whether the different biological sources were from different regions as Thorne believes, or from a single region (Indonesia) but sampled different times , as Webb believes. What is clear is that there are not two biologically distinct populations in the Australian Pleistocene, but rather the descendants of immigrants from several distinct populations as the past, once again, presages the present.

By at least 30 kyr, humans were occupying the full range of coastal and inland river- and lake related ecozones on the Australian continent and Tasmania. In spite of the island continent's isolation, local cultural evolution was characterized by innovation, as noted above. Moreover, ground stone axe heads dating to over 20 kyr have been found, making them the oldest in the world. Grinding dishes and millstones are found all over the continent and have great antiquity, at least to 18 kyr. The continent-wide use of seeds and vegetables prepared by grinding might help account for the maintenance of a robust masticatory apparatus.

Indeed, these became more important as time went on. The Late Pleistocene hunting/gathering adaptation could not continue unvarying, as the giant marsupial game animals became extinct towards. Continued hunting innovations such as the boomerang, which allows the possibility of killing from a distance, were widespread by the Holocene (although the boomerang did not reach all portions of Australia and much of the archaic fauna was extinct by then).   Where effective weapons to kill at a distance were developed, there inevitably was accelerated reduction in skeletal robustness and biological change quickened through the Holocene. Kow Swamp and Coobool, source of two populations with a marked degree of robustness, are from an area in southeastern Australia where the boomerang did not spread.

One final point. The isolation of Tasmania from the Australian mainland was for at least 8 kyr and perhaps as long as 13 kyr. The Tasmanians provide us with the only concrete evidence for humans on the effects of long periods of isolation for population differentiation (selection could have played a role in differentiation as well, since the climate of the island was cold and wet, much more European than the Australian mainland, during most of the isolation period. There is a persistent feeling among paleoanthropologists that isolation is the main driving force in accounting for patterns of variation, and that it takes high levels of genic exchanges to slow down or stop the process (this is the genesis of why some have claimed that Multiregional Evolution doesn't work - it is said to require unrealistic levels of genic exchanges). This reasoning underlies the position that the broad spectrum of human variation is quite recent. However C. Pardoe's study of the Tasmanians shows that differentiation is not at all like motion in a Newtonian system - change does not keep on happening unless something stops it. Quite to the contrary, Pardoe shows that Tasmanians are no more different from mainland Australians than they would have been if there was no isolation. Differentiation, in other words, slowed down of its own accord. We cannot assume from this that differentiation is a necessary consequence of isolation. Differences did not automatically accumulate with time, even with isolation, and high levels of genic exchanges are not required to explain the Multiregional pattern of human evolution.

TEETH AND EAST ASIAN PREHISTORY

C. Turner examined dental variation in Late Pleistocene and recent populations. He based his analysis on some 28 key crown and root variables, ranging from the expression of marginal ridges on the incisors and canines to the number of roots on the maxillary molars and premolars. He found these to form combinations whose frequencies systematically differ between regions, although the regions overlap and even in combination the dental characters would often misclassify individuals. Turner's results are heavily influenced by the dramatic population expansions of the past 15-10 kyr. In many respects these have covered up many Late Pleistocene relationships, and have created the impression of more homogeneity than has existed in the past. Nevertheless, he has established some interesting patterns of variation.

Turner reports a basic division between European and Asian (especially North Asian) dental patterns. He characterizes the Europeans as evolving in the general direction of less crown complexity (fewer features such as marginal ridges and wrinkles on the molar crowns, and a smaller number of cusps and maxillary posterior tooth roots. The North Asian teeth are just the opposite, with dental trait intensification and greater complexity. In his reconstructions of population relationships, Central Asians are more like Europeans than North and Northeast Asians (this is a link that specimens such as Teshik Tash show to have persisted since the Middle Paleolithic). Asians from the Northeast differ from this dental anatomy, and show what he considers to be one of the two Asian dental patterns, Sinodonty. Sinodonts are most frequent in China, Japan (except for the Ainu), eastern Siberia, and all of the New World. They have the highest frequencies of strongly expressed marginal ridges, the most highly wrinkled molars, the largest number of molar cusps and roots, and so on. The other Asian group are the Sundadonts, named after the now largely submerged Sunda continent. The highest frequencies of Sundadonty are found in Southeast Asia, Indonesia, and Polynesia, and there is a significant component of Sundadonty in Australia (although not in the Late Pleistocene remains). Sundadonty is a more generalized dental pattern of Mongoloid peoples based on simpler expressions and less frequent appearance of the dental traits, for instance lower frequencies and more moderate expressions of marginal ridges and other complexity-related features. Compared with European and African dentitions, the Sundadont and Sinodont patterns are most similar to each other.

The European and Sinodont patterns, in Turner's view, are quite distinct and neither could have easily evolved out of the other. The prehistory of the Asian division is largely unknown, mainly because of the dearth of well dated specimens with teeth. The basic separation of Sinodonty and Sundadonty, however, extends back to at least the north-south Late Pleistocene gradient discussed above, and unlike some of the multivariate studies on the Shandingdong 101 male, Turner's work clearly links the Upper Cave remains to Mongoloids in general and Native Americans in particular. Turner believes that Sundadonty is the more ancient of the two patterns, and would derive other patterns from it (perhaps *all* other patterns, including the European and African ones, although I believe this is asking too much information from a set of dental characters). Yet Sundadonty is not the most ancient pattern in the region, in Australia it only first appears in the Holocene.

SOUTH ASIA

According to K. Kennedy and colleagues, the earliest modern specimens from South Asia are from Batadomba Lena, a 28 kyr site in Siri Lanka. The specimens are highly fragmented and associated with microlithic tools. In fact, human remains are found through Viet Nam, Cambodia, and Laos. However, even if they have been accurately dated to this time span, they are undiagnostic.

CENTRAL ASIA

Central Asian Upper Paleolithic sites are sparse, even more so than the Middle Paleolithic for which Teshik Tash (Chapter 12) is the earliest specimen known. Somewhat later in Uzbekistan, there are remains of mandibles, teeth, and a humerus from Samarkand that are said to resemble European Upper Paleolithic specimens. The industry, like many of the Siberian and Mongolian occurrences, has large numbers of Middle Paleolithic flake tools - so much so that some scholars such as V. Ranov suggest this Upper Paleolithic is better described as a "post-Mousterian" - a continuation of the Mousterian rather than a development from it. The 22 kyr Mal'ta site, from near Lake Baikal, Siberia, seems to be at the most eastward extension of European anatomy (according to Turner) and Upper Paleolithic culture (or perhaps the Europeans are the westward extension of Central Asians). This is reflected earlier in time, as the nearby Altai Mousterians are the most eastern extension of the Neandertals (or at least of Mousterian-associated Neandertal-like teeth - Turner regards a worn I^1 from the Mousterian of Denisova cave as resembling the Shanidar teeth). East of Lake Baikal both industries and anatomies are generally different. To the west connections seem to be with Europe, but it is clear that people and ideas moved in both directions. For instance, some 1000 km to the west at Kara-Bom, an industry that is described as "Upper Paleolithic" because most of its tools were manufactured on blades is at the limit of AMS radiocarbon dating. Its age, 40 kyr or older, is equivalent to the earliest dates claimed for the European Aurignacian. Yet, at the 21 kyr Afontova Gora site, an open air occupation from north of Kara-Bom, near Krasnoyarsk, the links appear to be in the opposite direction as the human remains include postcranial material and a portion of frontal bone identified as Mongoloid because of its flat upper nasal region.

WESTERN ASIA

Ksar Akil Cave (Lebanon) has a long Paleolithic sequence, perhaps the most complete in the region. Upper Paleolithic in the guise of the Aurignacian is said to first appear there at some 44 kyr (actually this is one of the earlier radiocarbon dates that means "<30 kyr") and within the sequence, below a radiocarbon date of 32 kyr, are two specimens. Ksar Akil 1 is the burial of a 7-9 year old child ("Egbert"), found against the back wall, under a pile of boulders. Its present location is unknown. Ksar Akil 2 is a toothless maxilla from much lower in the cave, said to show affinities with Skhul 5 (like the first specimen, its whereabouts are unknown and it was neither photographed nor described). The "Aurignacian" these are associated with is identified only by some notched flakes and is quite unlike the European industry - there are no bone tools, personal adornments, figurines, engravings, and no evidence of an organized campsite (these do appear in the Levant, but much later in time). A. Marks questions how one could argue the Aurignacian began in the Levant, with "modern" people, and then spread to Europe, when the Levantine Aurignacian lacks all of the distinctive characteristics said to reflect modern behavior? All that can be confirmed of this idea is the association with people of non-Neandertal anatomy (like some of the Middle Paleolithic associations), if we can assume that the burial is not from considerably more recent times. The heavily reconstructed Ksar Akil 1 skull, according to C. Bergman and C. Stringer, shows no evidence of either European or archaic features, except for evidence of a large anterior dentition. Its face is transversely flat, there is no supercillary expansion, and the chin is well-developed. The relation of this specimen to the possibly penecontemporary Darra-i-Kur would be of some interest.

The African Sequence

As recently as 1962, C. Coon was able to describe the appearance and early evolution of modern humans in Africa as an "unsolved mystery." He ultimately argued that the evolutionary process there seemed to "lag behind" that on the other continents. These contentions are a more accurate reflection of unsavory aspects to the history of our discipline (deservedly dissected in S. Gould's *The Mismeasure of Man*) than of the prehistory of Africa. Neither statement could be further from the truth; south of the Sahara modern humanity, whether described by human anatomy or behavior, appeared early. The increasingly excellent record of dated sites and human remains has resulted in a view perhaps best expressed by P. Beaumont and J. Vogel's comments about the rich African savannas: "possession of these preferred regions . . . would have been in the hands of peoples who were culturally advanced, rather than retarded."

The Late Stone Age developed out of the African Middle Stone Age between 40 kyr (or earlier) and 20 kyr ago, depending on where. According to R. Klein its origins are difficult to detail because of the absence of well-dated sites earlier than 40 kyr and the variation between early LSA industries. He characterizes the early LSA as distinguished by the presence of standardized bone artifacts, and art or objects of personal adornment. This would seem to parallel changes claimed for the Middle to Upper Paleolithic transition in other regions but the evidence is not so clear-cut. There are bone tools in the Howiesen's Poort industry, a Middle Stone Age variant from the Southern Cape, and of course the >80 kyr barbed bone points from Zaire, which if correctly dated would indicate an earlier origin for well-made bone artifacts. The later LSA assemblages (postdating 22 kyr) are distinguished by the use of various small stone tools, or **microliths**, that were mounted on bone or wood handles or shafts. Klein characterizes LSA peoples as differing from their MSA predecessors by

- obtaining more dangerous game more often
- using fish and fowl more regularly
- recognizing and responding to seasonality in the availability of key resources

At the moment, the earliest LSA date is uncertain. It may well be close to 40 kyr, as most scientists believe, but some such as S. Ambrose have suggested it may have begun as much as 20 kyr earlier (not quite a conjecture, the estimate is based on the assumption that there are constant rates of sedimentation at certain sites, so that the deposit's thickness is proportional to its age). Even if this more speculative appraisal is correct, it postdates the 80 kyr determination for the earliest population expansion that H. Harpending and colleagues calculate took place in Africa, from their analysis of mtDNA data. The Harpending analysis, if correct, would place this population expansion squarely within the Middle Paleolithic. In sum, no evidence really suggests that the LSA is clearly linked to modern human origins and the interpretation that it represents a significant discontinuity in human behavior is a possible one but continues to be undermined by dates and new discoveries that blur MSA and early LSA distinctions. It does, of course, mark the beginning of the accelerated cultural changes that have continued through the Holocene.

SOUTH AFRICA: THE EARLIEST SPECIMENS

The South African evidence suggests a continuous line of hominid evolution through the Late Pleistocene. F. Thackeray, as noted in Chapter 12, was able to show continuous evolution in mandible form across the past 100 kyr, with early modern sapiens derived from the local archaic sapiens populations, as represented by Broken Hill, Saldanha, and the Cave of Hearths. Unfortunately, few fossil human remains span the later period of evolution. Cranial remains are not as well provenienced or dated as might have been hoped. The most important of these are from Border Cave, Springbok Flats, and Origstad rock shelter. Other specimens once considered Late Pleistocene, such as the Skildergat cave cranium (Fish Hoek), Cape Flats, and Boskop, are of even more dubious antiquity, or in some cases are now known to be historic.

Border Cave

Numerous specimens were discovered at Border Cave, on the KwaZulu side of the border with Swaziland. Specimens discovered 1941 and before, including the BC 1 cranium, the toothless mandible BC 2 and fragments of most of an infant's postcranial skeleton came from a dump were they were left from bat guano mining operations. They have no provenience and all the postcranial remains except for a humerus and ulna fragment and two metatarsals reported by A. Morris, were subsequently lost (and these may have slumped down into the dump from higher - e.g. more recent - sediments). BC 3, a 3 month old infant, and the BC 5 adult mandible are said to come from MSA levels, but their bone preservation is much better than the surrounding MSA animal bones and paleoanthropologists such as R. Klein and F.

Smith believe they may be LSA specimens that became mixed into the MSA deposits. The ESR dates published for these specimens suggest an age of 72 ±10 kyr, but there are many reasons to believe this age is unrelated to the hominids.

In an attempt to resolve this, A. Sillen analyzed the nitrogen in animal bones of known provenience. Their nitrogen content falls to an amount not significantly different from zero by 35-40 kyr Nitrogen in all of the Border Cave specimens except the infant (BC 3) was found to be below 0.05% (not different from zero), which means they are definitely 35 kyr or older and they could be early LSA associated as many have suspected.

It is particularly unfortunate that Border Cave 1, a fairly complete cranial vault, lacks provenience as it could carry important evidence about the origin of African populations. The cranium consists of a frontal portion, side, and part of the base. The back portion is missing. In side view, the forehead is moderately high, although the skull itself does not have extremely great height. The parietals bulge outward in a high position. The frontal region is broad (narrower than the Florisbad cranium but broader than crania of most modern South Africans), and the supraorbitals are tall but not prominent, and certainly not as well developed as in Florisbad. In particular, the form of the torus is different from Florisbad's; it is completely absent over the nasal root, appearing first over the orbital rim, and thinning considerably toward the sides. This morphology, although not the torus thickness, occurs in recent populations of South African Negroes and San, and a general affinity to these groups is certainly suggested.

To be more specific about affinities, a number of different multivariate studies were undertaken. P. Rightmire showed the cranium to be most similar to Khoi, and unlike other Africans. He claimed that it sampled a large San-like population. H. De Villiers and L. Fatti did a multivariate study that showed BC 1 had Negroid affinities. A third study, by A. Ambergen and W. Schaafsma, showed it to be unlike any modern population, although undeniably modern.   G. van Vark and colleagues find it only slightly more distinct from Asian "Pithecanthropines" than it is from recent humans, and R. Corruccini concludes "in no way can it be equated with modern humans - it falls outside of the recent African variation envelope". The problem with these contradictory results is that they are not really comparable. Each used a different set of measurements, different multivariate techniques, and different comparative samples, The last is especially critical, as A. Morris has shown, because most of the San samples were compiled using anatomical criteria - specimens were included because someone thought they looked like San and not because of personal identification or archaeological associations. I remember, when visiting the museum where Florisbad is kept, seeing shelves of different African crania marked "Bushman", "Bantu", and "Mixed". I asked the curator how the materials came to be classified (expecting to hear "different sites" or "different grave goods") and was told that they were from the same site and the Bushman-like skulls went on the "Bushman", shelves, the Bantu-like skulls on the "Bantu" shelves, and the ones they were uncertain of were called mixed.

Morris, who analyzed the several postcranial remains recovered from the dump, finds them to be large and prominently muscular. He speculates that they may represent the BC 1 individual.

When compared with living populations, the Border Cave infant (Number 3) remains show a series of features which, according to H. De Villiers, align the specimen with both South African Negro and San infants. She suggests that it might represent an early undifferentiated population, if the dating and provenience can be confirmed.

Origstad

Discoveries at the Origstad rock shelter support the hypothesis that a widespread late Pleistocene African population with features of, or previewing, living Negroids. The mandible of an infant, dated to about 28,500 years ago and associated with a Late Stone Age industry, was systematically compared with modern South African Bantu and San infant mandibles. The specimen could not be distinguished from the Bantu sample.

Springbok Flats (Tuinplaas)

This cranium, mandible, and portions of a postcranial skeleton from the northern Transvaal has the potential of being in this time range of the Late Pleistocene, but there is no direct date to confirm this. A **calcarious** crust on the bones is dated to 5.5 kyr and the lack of organic remnants in the bones themselves suggest the specimen may be considerably older. The circumstances and provenience are really no worse than Border Cave. The specimen is a large male with an elongated cranium, large prognathic face, and a very large and robust mandible. Where comparable it resembles the Border Cave skull and specimens from eastern Africa. It shows no particular affinities to Boskop (see below).

Origins

If we can assume that some or all of these specimens could be LSA associated, the possibility certainly exists that they reflect the consequences of an early San-Negroid differentiation. The contention of Negroids in the Late Pleistocene of southern Africa raises a difficult set of problems, however, since it is generally assumed that south of the Zambezi River, Africa was inhabited only by San until fairly recently, perhaps Iron Age times. Yet what is lacking to confirm this idea are the remains of diagnosable San with any antiquity worth speaking of. The Klasies fragments, it may be remembered, were related to living San because they are small and gracile, but not because of any unique shared features. It is quite possible that San ancestry can be traced in southern Africa to crania such as Fish Hoek, Boskop, Matjes River Mouth cave, and Otjiseva. These crania combine a small, broad and flat face with a very large cranial vault having a high, domed forehead and a bulging at the rear of the parietal bones. However none appear to be older than the Holocene. In fact, there was virtually no habitation of the Cape for long periods during the Pleistocene, and no skeletal remains are known between these (and other specimens of similar antiquity) and Klasies.

A compromise position has been reached by several different authors, all arguing for various reasons that there were no distinct San and Negroid populations until just before the end of the Late Pleistocene, as modern climatic conditions developed. P. Tobias, for instance, suggests that these modern groups have genetic differences that require no more than 15 kyr of separation to establish. De Villiers stressed the undifferentiated aspects of the Border Cave and Origstad infants. My experience with archaeologically provenienced recent samples from the Cape region that are older than 4 kyr suggests that long before pastoralism the Khoikhoi anatomy was found in this region. Crania are often **dolichocephalic** (longheaded) with angular faces and robust features while San characteristics are uncommon and crania combining many of them are virtually absent. I would argue that the best supported conclusion is that Late Pleistocene populations did not differentiate into the modern groups now living in South Africa until the Holocene, or possibly just before it.

Why would increasing populational differences have evolved toward the end of the Pleistocene? There are probably a number of reasons. LSA culture and technology resulted in a much more efficient use of environmental resources. The earlier adaptations of the MSA were broad but not efficient. For instance, at the Die Keiders cave and Klasies River mouth, evidence for the consumption of edible shellfish in MSA occupations marks the earliest local systematic use of sea resources. However, the mammals hunted seem limited to the more docile of the larger species or, in the case of more formidable prey, females in advanced pregnancy.

In contrast, LSA hunters made much more efficient use of available resources. Grinding and other techniques for plant preparation and technological innovations such as the bow and arrow and poisons greatly expanded the range of edible resources within the same habitats. The extinction of many of the big game animals helped stimulate the trend to make more effective use of the remaining resources, producing what R. Klein calls a "more competent" adaptation. The result was a population increase, with more populations coming into contact with one another but not significantly competing because of the narrowness of their realized niches. Such adjacent populations maintained their separate identities through cultural differentiation and ethnic identities, and local differences subsequently were sustained.

The evolutionary changes resulting from LSA microlithic technology resulted, for some populations, in an extreme "gracilization" of the earlier, more archaic features. The organizational changes and technological innovations of the LSA, especially the use of efficient long-distance hunting weapons, reduced the necessity for large size and skeletal robustness in some hunting populations. Body size reduction as well as many of the other skeletal changes can probably be related to these technological developments in a warm climate.

What seems most likely is that, setting aside some of the more questionable multivariate-based conclusions, the bulk of the evidence suggests that modernization in southern Africa was a local phenomenon. "Suggests", but does not "prove", because there are not enough well provenienced or dated specimens from either the MSA or LSA, and not enough morphological distinctions in the material at hand to contest A. Morris' conclusion that:

> until a larger MSA sample, or a sequence of specimens from the Upper
> Pleistocene through the Holocene is excavated, proof of the continuity of
> southern African peoples over the last 100,000 years cannot be demonstrated.

EAST AND CENTRAL AFRICA

In this portion of the Late Pleistocene in East Africa there are some better dates but unfortunately just as few specimens as in the southern part of the continent. The samples are similar in that specimens show a mixture of Negroid, San-like, and archaic features.

Lukenya Hill

One of the best dated specimens is the 17 kyr cranium from Lukenya Hill (or perhaps slightly earlier - the radiocarbon date is based on bone, not always an accurate procedure, and the associated industry has earlier dates elsewhere). The specimen consists of only the frontal and a single parietal, but this is quite sufficient to show several things. First, while the forehead is low, flattened, and receding by modern African standards, it is not outside the living Negroid range of variation. The top of the nose (nasal root) is flattened, as in many living Negroids and San, and the parietals are markedly bulged outward in a high posterior position. As seen from the top, these bosses create a vault outline that resembles a pentagon—a feature which is characteristic of San. Its archaic features resemble certain earlier African crania. The long and broad frontal, lacking a frontal boss and thick supraorbital torus are similar to Florisbad, although the Lukenya torus is separated into lateral and central elements by a groove. L. Schepartz likens it to Singa (Chapter 12), especially in frontal and parietal contours and nasal shape, even considering the affects of Singa's pathology.

Circumturkana

Several specimens are associated with what was once called the "Guomde Formation" east of Lake Turkana and overlying the Early Pleistocene deposits there. Their stratigraphic position is confused by the subsequent realization that in these strata are mixed deposits of Middle and earliest Late Pleistocene age and of Galana Boi (Holocene) age. Their position is very close to the base of the Galana Boi, and at the moment there is no way to ascertain whether a ±130 kyr date pertains, or if the true age is one-tenth that! My discussion of them in this chapter, rather than Chapter 12, registers a vote for the latter (and later). Morphological dating, however, would suggest neither choice is correct and indicates an intermediate position for the material. The best preserved specimens are the ER 3884 cranium and the ER 999 femur.

In many ways the ER 3884 cranium is intermediate between earlier East African specimens and the LSA populations from the circumturkana region; for instance Kabua, Galana Boi and other Holocene sites such as Lothagam and Lopoy that were described by L. Robbins. It is a large (±1400 cc), thin vaulted specimen with a combination of angled occipital contours, high cranial vault with parallel sides, and very marked breadth. The maximum breadth is very low, just above the mastoids as in Omo 2 and Jebel Irhoud 2 (both of which have similar contours and dimensions, but for less cranial height). Yet, in their comparisons of the specimen G. Bräuer and colleagues show these features (and the index of cranial breadth to height) are within the earlier Holocene East African range. Its most unusual aspect is the supraorbital region. As I reconstructed it, the supraorbitals are moderately thick and fairly evenly developed, and extend in a bar-like manner across the frontal, a pattern that T. Simmons regards as typical of Africans with supraorbitals (for instance Jebel Irhoud). They are closest to Jebel Irhoud in thickness, considerably thinner than Omo 2 (though equally projecting), and better developed in all ways than the Holocene East Africans.

The circumturkana and other early Holocene East Africans form a distinct morphological complex, quite possibly because they were in the process of changing from hunter/gatherers to pastoralists, fisherfolk, and agriculturists. This may not be a biological complex in the sense that it represents the average for any particular population, but together the crania suggest the morphological forms that were common in the immediate past. The skulls are very large and long. They are notable for their marked robustness. Cranial thickness is pronounced, but the browridges vary from moderate to absent (the forehead regions tend to resemble specimens from Omo). The occiput is rounded and high, and there is no nuchal torus. As seen from the top, the outlines of the crania are elongated and oval. The greatest cranial breadth is rather low on the parietals or even below on the temporals, and there is no parietal boss. The best-preserved faces are extraordinarily large and broad. The distance between the orbits is great, and the zygomatics are large and flaring.

The dentitions also tend to be very large. The Lothagam posterior teeth exceed Kabwe's. It is reasonable to speculate that these faces and dentitions would probably not be out of place in the much earlier Omo crania. In many of its details, this complex is similar to that found in many populations of big-game hunters at the end of the Pleistocene, and these are details that reflect similar requirements of their adaptations. The point is that these specimens do not represent a sort of "late-surviving" archaic population in East Africa. And, of course, they vary temporally, individually and populationally, for instance ranging from the thicker browridges of the Lukenya specimen and ER 3884 to the absence of browridges, and sharp orbital margin, in ER-1793 (like Omo 1 or Kanjera (see below)). These folk are clearly the direct ancestry of many living East Africans.

The virtually complete ER-999 femur, once described as an Early Pleistocene specimen, has provenience uncertainties very similar to those of ER 3884. It is a large bone from a tall, powerful individual with a robust shaft having moderately thickened walls, a long femur neck, and prominent muscle attachments. E. Trinkaus identifies three features that, in combination, usually distinguish recent or modern femora from more archaic ones:

1. a prominent *linea aspera* on a strongly developed pilaster along the femur shaft's back (this makes the *pilastric index* which is the anterior-posterior diameter at the middle of the shaft divided by the transverse diameter, higher)
2. the position of the minimum shaft diameter is close to the middle of the shaft (it is well below in archaic femora)
3. the angle between the femur neck and shaft is high

In these details, according to Trinkaus, ER 999 is not archaic, and resembles the Skhul/Qafzeh sample even more than Upper Paleolithic Europeans (Trinkaus did not compare it with other circumturkana specimens). He raises the possibility that the ER 3884 cranium may also show similarities to this sample, and may thereby reflect earlier dates and an extension of their range into East Africa.

Kanjera

The Kanjera remains were discovered by L.S.B. Leakey in an area near the shore of Lake Victoria in Kenya. He claimed that they were Middle Pleistocene in age. There were 42 cranial fragments belonging to four individuals. Of these, 37 were discovered on the surface, and five were excavated from undisturbed deposits. The crania were so badly broken up that accurate reconstructions of their detailed shape can probably never be made, and the exact findspot has never been located again.

Both excavated and surface specimens agree in the virtual lack of any supraorbital development and in the high, rounded form of the occiput. The single facial fragment is lightly built. The only archaic-appearing feature, according to P. Tobias, is the marked occipital curvature of Kanjera 1. When this site was considered Middle Pleistocene in age, it was be used to support hypothesis of modern human contemporaneity with Neandertals. However, K. Oakley found uranium concentrations in the specimens much lower than in the Middle Pleistocene fauna from the site, indicating that the human remains are considerably younger

Ishango

To the west, Ishango is located on the Semiliki River, near the shores of Lake Amin (Edward) in the western rift valley of Zaire. Dated to the Late Pleistocene and earlier Holocene, with determinations extending to over 20 kyr, archaeological debris and human material over a broad time range has been recovered. Fragmentary specimens are associated with barbed bone harpoon points much like the earlier ones from Katanda, which is just up-river. In his discussion of the Holocene human remains, F. Twiesselman emphasized their Negroid features (as did C. Coon in discussing a mandible from Kangatotha, another nearby site).

NEGROID ORIGINS

When C. Coon wrote in 1962, "The origin of the African Negroes, and of the Pygmies, is the greatest unsolved mystery in the field of racial study," was he correct, or was this yet another instance of misunderstanding the fossil evidence? His own conclusion, that "modern Negroes resulted from a backcross between an original proto-Negro stock and Pygmies," is no less bizarre than many of the other explanations that have been debated over the past half-century. It remains a matter of controversy.

What probably can be called the traditional view is that Negro origins were a local west-central African phenomenon. It is argued that during the Late Stone Age, African populations south of the Zambezi were San-like (alternatively called Bushmanoid or Khoisanoid). One variation of this theme is the idea that this area was inhabited by a large Bushman form first called "Boskopoid" (after the large Boskop cranium from the Transvaal, once thought to be MSA but in actuality undated) and later formally named "*Homo capensis*." Because Singa (Chapter 12) was likened to Boskop, Sudanese Mesolithic crania from Wadi Halfa were called "Boskopoid," and with Coon's interpretation of the Jebel Irhoud 1 cranium as "proto-Bushmen," these pre-San populations were thought to have come from the north, where they presumably were the LSA inhabitants of the region.

But further confusing the picture, Leakey also argued that some East African Late Stone Age populations (now recognized as post-Pleistocene Mesolithic populations) were "Caucasoids" of "probable Mediterranean origin", although he also regarded one cranium (number 4) from the Homa Shell Mounds site, on the shores of Lake Victoria, as having "Bushman-like" features while two other individuals from the site appeared to be "Negroids." Subsequently both M. Ostendorf-Smith and L. Schepartz have studied these specimens and find no support for Leakey's suggestions, but as long as they were accepted and the presence of East African San-like populations assumed, it left only West Africa as a place for Negro origins. There, however, the only solid supporting evidence is the 11 kyr Iwo Eleru skullcap from Nigeria and 6.4 kyr skeleton from Asselar, from what was then the border of the Sahara in eastern Mali. It is little wonder that Negro origins, or for that matter any other recent substantive evolutionary problem on the continent, could be regarded as a mystery.

Many of the interpretive problems stem from the identification of a so-called "Boskop" race. Boskop itself is a large, thick-vaulted faceless cranium with a fragment of mandible and postcranial remains indicating large body size. It was found in 1913 and quickly considered a race apart from other Pleistocene remains. R. Dart expanded the definition of this race to include other materials in 1923, and by 1937 A. Galloway defined the "type" as a wide-ranging racial group ancestral to living San. The form of the skull suggested paedomorphosis to him, making the subsequent San descendants into pygmy paedomorphs. During the 1930's, the heyday of racial typologies, they actually were described this way!. The fact that modern San crania with similar form and the same features kept on appearing did not lead these workers to question Boskop's date, or their evolutionary scenario, as these moderns could always be explained as "throwbacks". The cultural associations for Boskop were thought to be MSA. Although these cultural associations are now discredited, and virtually all scientists have come to realize that there never was a definable "Boskop type," as long as the concept was accepted, the search for Negroid ancestry was necessarily pushed into the Middle Stone Age.   It is this framework applied to remains from a more recent time, shifted away from these specimens and used to interpret the significance of Border Cave, that explains why the question of whether it is San-like or Negroid-like has been an issue.

The best evidence, in my view, indicates that the San-Negroid separation in sub-Saharan Africa is a recent one, probably not extending to much before the Holocene. Earlier than this, populations were more archaic in appearance, particularly robust in some regions, and in many areas they combined features of both living groups along a gradient, with the small San-like populations predominating to the south. As Rightmire put it, "there is little or no skeletal evidence to support a Pleistocene occurrence of San populations in East Africa". Certainly by the Holocene there is no evidence of a San contribution to East African LSA associated specimens such as those found around Lake Turkana discussed above with their very robust features (dentitions, for instance, with Middle Pleistocene posterior tooth sizes, robust mandibles, and very large faces), prognathic faces, and elongated crania. Iwo Eleru is similar to Lukenya (and certain earlier specimens), with a low and flattened forehead and an angled occiput. These are anatomies from which modern populations evolved, largely through gracilization and continued adaptive change and population differentiation This contention essentially parallels conclusions drawn by Tobias, Rightmire, de Villiers, and Wells. It is Rightmire, more than any other worker, who has argued for a more generalized model of Negro origins through his demonstration that Leakey's interpretation of "Caucasoid" affinities for the East African post-Pleistocene specimens was incorrect. These specimens associate as Negroids, and not South African San or Mediterranean, in his multifactoral analyses. In sum, there is good reason to believe that during the Late Pleistocene a widespread undifferentiated group occupied sub-Saharan Africa. As in the south, the appearance of marked regional distinctions seems to approximate the Pleistocene's end.

NORTH AFRICA

According to J-J. Hublin the Aterian of North Africa evolves directly from the Mousterian "without any discontinuity". It is, in the words of P. Allsworth-Jones, "definitely Middle Paleolithic in nature, adding tanged pieces and bifacial points to a common Mousterian (often Levallois) stock". In Morocco alone, A. Debénath and colleagues discuss a number of Aterian-associated human remains that a combination of radiocarbon and TL dates bracket between 40 and 20 kyr. These are widely regarded as the earliest modern-appearing humans in northern Africa, and paleoanthropologists such as Hublin suggest that the region is similar to the Levant in that modern-appearing humans first emerge in the Middle Paleolithic.

The older of these would appear to be a mandible and canine from the Zouhra cave (El Harhoura). The younger remains are from the Upper Aterian at Mugharet el Alyia (the 'Tangier maxilla'), Témara and the Dar es Soltane II cave. Only the first, the juvenile Tangier maxilla, has problematic provenience. It was found on the surface, but fluorine analysis suggests association with an "evolved" Aterian.

There are several isolated teeth (including an adult, individual represented a very worn molar) from the Mugharet el Alyia. The canine and P^3 of the 9 year old specimen are extremely large. Although a juvenile, the maxilla is tall, massive and thick. The lower border of the nose is rounded rather than sharply bordered, the midface is flattened and the cheek position is anterior (taking age into account), and there is no canine fossa. In these features it resembles the Rabat maxilla and contrasts with the face of Jebel Irhoud 1 (except for the similar rounded nasal margin). However, N. Minugh-Purvis argues that age must be taken into account in any assessment and her research shows that it is normal for modern children of this age to lack a canine fossa. She argues that while the child is robust and archaic, there are no unique resemblances to Neandertal children and that past assessments suggesting a Neandertal-like anatomy are incorrect.

The Témara specimens include a mandible and cranial pieces (partial occiput, parietals, supraorbital portion) that are not notably different from Mesolithic crania from the region (for instance the Afalou/Taforalt series). The frontal piece lacks a supraorbital torus.

There are at least three individuals from the Dar es Soltane II cave, also Upper Aterian. These include a juvenile calvaria, an adolescent mandible, and the partial adult cranium number 5. This is the most notable of the Aterian material. The cranium bears some resemblance to the Qafzeh males, especially Qafzeh 6, combining a foreshortened broad face (with a canine fossa) with massive browridges which follow the contour of the orbits but project markedly in front of them. The masticatory apparatus (including tooth size) is very well-developed, a characteristic of all the Aterian-associated specimens. Compared with Jebel Irhoud 1, the face is shorter and less prognathic, and the vault is higher and more rounded, but many of the robust features are retained. While Hublin regards it as within the modern human range, the supraorbitals of this specimen would distinguish it from most recent and modern North Africans.

Numerous scientists working with the North African material have interpreted the sequence as an unbroken line of evolution. D. Ferembach believes that Dar-es-Soltane is an evolutionary link between truly archaic North Africans such as Jebel Irhoud (Chapter 12) and the Mesolithic populations of the Holocene. She argues that the most significant evolutionary changes are facial reduction, globularization of the vault, and expansion of the frontal bone. Ferembach suggests that the specific resemblances between the Jebel Irhoud crania and the Mesolithic North African sample indicate that the archaic populations had already developed local geographic differences, corresponding to those which occur today, and that the transformation from archaic to modern humanity occurred in many different areas.

The subsequent sample, descendants of populations represented by Dar-es-Soltane, is very large but, with a few exceptions, not particularly ancient. Egyptian specimens such as Nazlet Khater and Wadi Kubbaniya are burials of robust individuals, in both cases first thought associated with the Upper Paleolithic but more likely intrusive Mesolithic people who were widespread through the region. Sites such as Jebel Sahaba (Nubia), Wadi Halfa (Sudan), Afalou and Mechta El-Abri (Algeria), Taforalt (Morocco), have provided a large skeletal sample from this time, with a marked degree of similarity although the large sample sizes also allow the observation of a great deal of morphological variation at each site. This North African sample tends to be robust, with many males showing prominent supraorbitals, marked temporal lines, and large jaws and teeth. In general, the crania are long and rather broad; the occipitals tend to be angled; and the faces are medium to small, moderately prognathic, and have broad noses. The North African material does not appear particularly similar to the skeletons from East Africa, discussed above. It does show numerous detailed similarities with living populations in North Africa, and it is probably best to consider the sample as representing a considerably more robust ancestral version of these living groups.

D. Carlson and D. van Gerven developed a hypothesis attempting to account for the cranial changes involved in the appearance of modern North Africans from comparisons in this region. Their goal was to provide a more general explanation of Late Pleistocene evolution from this example. They related observed cranial changes to alterations in masticatory function. The idea is that the changes to more intensive utilization of plant products, and eventually the shift to agriculture, resulted in a diet of generally softer, better-cooked foodstuffs with much less grit adhering to them. With the need for powerful chewing reduced, there was reduction in the size of the masticatory muscles and the bony areas supporting them. The main morphological consequences involved marked reduction in robustness, a lower, more posterior positioning of the midface, and reduction of the nuchal plane, which led to cranial shortening (and a commensurate increase in height). There are similarities between Ferembach's explanation for the evolution of North African archaic populations into Mesolithic populations, and this accounting of the changes of Mesolithic populations into modern ones. In fact, they combine to indicate that through the Late Pleistocene to today there has been a continuous single-directional pattern of cranial and dental change, responding mainly to changing diet, new methods of food preparation, and increasing efficiency in hunting and food gathering.

Europeans and their Origins

Skeletal remains of the post-Neandertal Europeans are numerous and diverse. Often called "early modern humans", they are not especially early and in comparison with living Europeans decidedly *not* modern. Nor can they any longer be called "Upper Paleolithic" folk, as Neandertals are clearly associated with some of the Upper Paleolithic variants (see Chapter 13). The fact is that "non-Neandertal" does not necessarily mean "modern". Understanding of the European sequence has been hampered more by problems of dating, reconstruction, and publication than by a lack of sufficient fossil remains. Most of the important specimens were discovered before 1925. Symptomatic of this situation, early attempts by paleoanthropologists such as G. Schwalbe and A. Hrdlička to demonstrate continuity between Neandertals and the more recent inhabitants of the continent were marred by mis-dated specimens and faulty reconstructions, while arguments supporting discontinuity for these populations relied on specimens such as Piltdown and Galley Hill (now recognized to be recent), and the continued representation of La Chapelle as the "typical" Neandertal and Cro Magnon as the "typical" early modern. Even more misleading was the habit of comparing La Chapelle with a modern cranium (usually French) and then claiming that the time available between La Chapelle and the first appearance of "anatomically modern humans" was too short to account for the observed differences. This assumes that the first post-Neandertals looked like the living French, which has been demonstrably false since the turn of the century.

There is no doubt that some of the earlier post-Neandertal crania and postcranial skeletons are Neandertal-like in appearance. The question is by what processes Neandertals gave way to post-Neandertal populations - what combinations of selection and genic exchanges influenced this evolution. The alternative to the evolutionary interpretation that assumes there was such a combination is that Neandertals were largely or completely replaced by populations entering Europe, presumably over the period between approximately 40 and 30 kyr.

To begin answering this question, it is critical to pinpoint the earliest of the European "moderns". If there is significant Neandertal ancestry, it is this sample which would be expected to reflect its consequences through transitional features; specifically, it should be characterized by a higher frequency of Neandertal characteristics than the later, more modern-appearing Europeans who followed. Moreover, one might expect this sample to show a continuation of some of the evolutionary trends visible in the European Neandertal sequence, if continued morphological changes are the result of the action of selection on *in situ* populations.

Central and Eastern Europe is particularly rich in early modern remains. However, no convincingly diagnostic materials are associated with the transitional industries, Szeletian and Ulluzzian, and the earliest tool assemblages to be called Aurignacian may be associated with Neandertals. Europe is quite different from western Asia, where samples often regarded as "Neandertal" and "modern" are neither, and even if they were distinct populations, they never the less lived in the same areas and by in large behaved in the same ways. In Europe the samples are distinguishable, and at the moment the Neandertals seem invariably to have come first - arguments that there are "moderns" overlapping in time rely on the *assumption* that the earliest Aurignacian variations across Europe are the products of "early modern European" activities - an assumption which remains unsupported.

Attempts to link culture and biology seem as invalid for the Upper Paleolithic as they are for the Middle Paleolithic - a point so well established in western Asia. It is not at all clear that all European Mousterians are Neandertals. Two specimens were found in the uppermost strata at Krapina, dated to approximately 100 kyr (see Chapter 13) by ESR analysis of animal teeth. Krapina 11, part of an adult occiput, extends from the temporal articulation to a point not far from the midline. At the equivalent position all other Neandertals have an elliptical suprainiac fossa, and this individual does not. A second specimen from this level is the "A" skull. This is most of the vault of a 10 year old (the age based on assessment of cranium size and anatomical details). Krapina A is quite different from Neandertal children of similar age (8-9 year old Teshik Tash, 13 year old Le Moustier). Many of the differences are found in the forehead

- the supraorbitals are divided into a central supracillary arch and weak lateral area
- the supracillary arches are small and project only weakly in front of the forehead
- the frontal is high and broadly rounded, with an abrupt transition between the front and top of the boss

It is difficult to accurately assess the relationships of children, but the comparison of this specimen with Neandertals of similar age definitely suggests that it, too, may not be a Neandertal. These two are surely not enough to convincingly show some European Mousterians are non-Neandertals. but the possibility is there. The fact that all European Neandertal burials (and for that matter all Neandertal remains of any origin) are from cave or rockshelter sites only steepens interest in the anatomy of those who produced the European Mousterian at open-air sites.

A NEANDERTAL ANCESTRY FOR EUROPEANS?

The fate of the "classic" Neandertals and the question of the extent to which they are ancestral to subsequent Europeans is probably still the most widely debated topic in paleoanthropology. In his essay *Towards a solution to the Neanderthal problem* C. Stringer wrote

> if we cannot resolve the Neanderthal problem and thereby arrive at an understanding of the relationship of Neanderthals to "modern" *Homo sapiens*, there would seem little hope of resolving any of the more complex issues concerning human evolution.

Yet, Stringer himself has offered very different scenarios about the fate of the Neandertals. In one publication, with J-J. Hublin and B. Vandermeersch, he contends that Neandertals persisted into the European Upper Paleolithic "not just in backward or isolated areas either. Saint-Césaire is, in fact, situated in a region densely occupied during the Middle and Upper Paleolithic". However in a subsequent paper with R. Grün, he writes that there was "a gradual replacement to marginal and less favorable environments., where their dwindling numbers would have suffered greater attrition from the vagaries of fluctuating climates and food supplies, as well as disease". In some respects the possibility of resolution seems further away than ever. Reasons for this are well stated by D. Frayer

> Recent publications have produced a set of disjointed interpretations about what European Neanderthals represent morphologically and what they were capable of behaviorally. Trying to piece together all that has been recently written ... results in a picture resembling postmodernist art, where a series of incongruous, completely unrelated images are combined together in the same scene producing a phantasmagoria. For example, while there is still no human fossil evidence which supports the co-existence of Neanderthal and Upper Paleolithic forms in Europe, we now have a series of models and speculations about the details of this co-existence and why one group replaced the other, be it linguistic incompetence, spousal inattention, or inferior hunting practices. ... There are also suggestions that Upper Paleolithic groups are directly derived from African migrants, despite the complete absence of and supportive analysis for the presence of ancient or modern African features in the earliest Upper Paleolithic humans. In short, the study of European Neanderthals has reached a state in paleoanthropology where the [functions of the] fossils themselves [as evidence for human evolution] have been supplanted by speculations about them

NEANDERTALS AS A SEPARATE SPECIES

The parameters of an acceptable solution to problem of European ancestry seem within grasp. This is because of the importance attached to mitochondrial genetics in the "Eve" theory of modern human origins - the theory that all modern races have a unique recent origin in a single population of Africans who lived some 200 kyr ago. This theory *requires* the conclusion that Neandertals are a species apart from ourselves, and this requirement is testable. If there was a separate Neandertal species the Levantine data suggesting mixture over a long period of time, discussed in Chapter 12, would be quite difficult to interpret. But the European situation is quite unlike western Asia as the populations are not contemporary; rather, Neandertals are invariably the earlier. What does overlap are cultures, the Middle and Upper Paleolithic. If there was mixture, it was at this time when changing selection associated with climatic change and emerging (or entering) cultural innovations were also important causes of evolutionary change. It has not proved possible to separate these very different causes of evolution, but perhaps the best evidence for mixture is archaeological. If the Châtelperronian is, as many archaeologists believe, a reflection of "acculturation" as Middle Paleolithic peoples met Upper Paleolithic ones (presumably Neandertals encountering moderns, although by now there is no point in reiterating how little data support this part), as J. Simek points out, in the process of regularly exchanging information these populations would certainly have exchanged genes as well.

There are, it would seem, several ways in which Neandertals may have contributed to the ancestry of the later Europeans:

- through direct ancestry, with differences due to changing selection
- through mixture, as European Neandertals contributed to ancestry of populations evolving outside of Europe
- through mixture in Europe, as populations entering Europe during the interstadials encountered natives

Evidence showing a significant Neandertal contribution to the ancestry of these later Europeans through any of these mechanisms would disprove the assertion that Neandertals are a distinct species.

PERSISTENCE OF NEANDERTAL FEATURES

The place to look for such evidence is in the earliest recognizable post-Neandertal Europeans. The evidence to look for is the persistence of Neandertal features in these subsequent European populations. Ironically, the most useful characteristics for this are the ones most often used to show Neandertals had no descendants - their so-called overspecializations. The concept of overspecialization in the European Neandertals is largely attributable to F.C. Howell. It was his contention (and remains a widely-accepted precept) that their unique features show Neandertals could not have evolved into subsequent populations that lacked them. Evolution could not have reversed itself. But the various cold adaptations and structural consequences of anterior tooth loading do not preclude the possibility of further evolution under changed selection, even if it is in reversed direction. Citing F. Weidenreich, whose pithy comments on this and other issues continue to reverberate across the century, there is

a sport of a certain group of authors to search for the skeletal parts of
Neandertal Man for peculiarities which could be claimed as 'specialization',
thereby proving the deviating course this form has taken in evolution.

But what, we may ask, was the fate of these characteristics as the more modern Europeans emerged?

Neandertals lived only in Europe and Western Asia, and *somebody* who was not Neandertal lived elsewhere. They are often portrayed as more modern than Neandertals, although invariably this actually means they are not Neandertals. In fact, as some of my colleagues have learned to their dismay, there is no anatomical definition that uniquely describes modern humans. Thus, the existence of non-Neandertals does not prove Neandertals couldn't be ancestors for subsequent Europeans *unless* these Europeans can be uniquely traced to one of the other populations. But the fact is that these Neandertal contemporaries do not look European. The Mungo remains resemble Australian Aborigines, Border Cave, whatever its date, is African in appearance, and the Skhul/Qafzeh sample has been regarded as virtually everything but European in their affinities. The same features that make specimens such as the Omo crania (especially Omo l) look "more modern" (that is, a higher forehead, smaller supraorbitals, a larger mastoid, and so on) are exactly those features which best describe average differences between Europeans and Africans today.

The relevance of contemporaries outside of Europe is that one sample of them could be similar to populations that reëntered the continent during periods of milder climate. Ironically, the sample most often called upon to serve in this role, the remains from Skhul and Qafzeh (see Chapter 12) make poor ancestors for the Upper Paleolithic Europeans, because in most features they are not as similar to the later Europeans as the Neandertals are. To begin with, the Skhul/Qafzeh folk virtually or completely *lack* the features listed in table 14.3. Most of these continue into the post-Neandertal European populations at lower frequencies, an observation that would be inexplicable if the Neandertals were completely replaced by these Levantines (or their descendants) who didn't have them. In the anterior dentition (including P3), where the Neandertals are most distinct, the Skhul/Qafzeh teeth would have to increase by considerable amounts to reach the European values while Neandertals would have to change only minimally.

Midfacial prognathism would also have to increase markedly for Skhul/Qafzeh to evolve into the Europeans, while a Neandertal ancestry would involve only a slight decrease. In fact, with the single exception of cranial height, Neandertals are virtually always more similar to the post-Neandertal Europeans than the Skhul/Qafzeh remains are. On anatomical grounds the post-Neandertal Europeans do not particularly resemble any earlier sample, but their *closest* match is with the preceding Neandertals.

Table 14.3
Unique[1] Neandertal Features and their Distribution in Later Europeans[2]

	European Neandertals	Earliest post-Neandertals	Modern Europeans[3]
Projection of nasal root in front of orbits	29 mm	22 mm	20 mm
Puffy maxilla and associated midfacial prognathism	√	absent	absent
Midfacial projection	√√√	√√	absent
Mastoid projection below juxtamastoid process	small (6.8 mm)	small (6.0 mm)	large (>9 mm)
Mastoid tubercle	35%	20%	absent
Suprainiac fossa	96%	39%	2%
Large frontal *and* large maxillary sinuses	√	√	√
Large occipitomastoid crest	normal	rare	absent
Lambdoidal flattening and bun	normal	often present	rare[3]
Circular cranial shape, as seen from the rear	√	absent	absent
Double-arched supraorbital torus	√	absent	absent
Horizontal-oval **mandibular foramen**	53%	18%	1%
Retromolar space	common (<75%)	occasional	rare
Large numbers of perikymata	√	?	√
Relatively large limb joint surfaces	√	√	absent
Dorsal scapular groove	65%	17%	1%
Long pubic ramus	√	?	absent
Proximal femoral flange	√	√	absent

[1] Either autapomorphies or features very common in Neandertals and rare in other Pleistocene populations
[2] After D. Frayer, J. Szilvássy and colleagues, F. Smith, A. Mann, and research by the author.
[3] It has been argued that certain European populations, especially Iron-Age samples from the extreme northwest, especially resemble Neandertals. Resemblances certainly occur, but these comparisons involve only gross lateral profile shape and are insufficient to establish any special relationships.

There are three important elements to the evidence suggesting significant Neandertal contribution to the gene pool of later Europeans:

1. European Neandertals evolved in the direction of later Europeans in their anterior dental reduction, reduced nasal size, combination of increased central and decreased browridge height, more prominent mental eminence, and so on
2. European Neandertals share a number of unique or especially common features with later Europeans, where they are generally expressed at lower frequency
3. No other penecontemporary population shares unique features with the later Europeans.

We must remember what happened in Europe during the last glacial cycle. With the emphasis on the effective Neandertal biocultural adaptations to the cold, it is easy to forget that Europe largely emptied during the last glacial - exodus is also an effective climatic adaptation. Thus, at the beginning of this last glacial cycle, some 75 kyr ago, K. Butzer estimates a European population density *between 1/30 and 1/70* that found at its end. European population dynamics were strongly effected by the glaciations. If many tribes moved to the south and west to escape the deteriorating climate, when they returned to Europe they brought genes of the peoples they intermixed with. But more was in flux than just the gene pool. The

Neandertals, and their more eastern Middle Paleolithic counterparts, inhabited Eurasia from the Atlantic to the middle of the Asian continent, largely between 54° and 45° north and most often in hilly or mountainous regions. Some of the most important changes that spread as the Upper Paleolithic became common across Eurasia are reflected in denser occupation of these areas and effective adaptations to considerably more northern regions and more open environments. They include wider foraging ranges (and broader social networks that provided improved knowledge about distant regions), seasonality, and the advantages of food storage. Along with changing selection created by these much more mobile behaviors developing in the emerging, technologically efficient, Upper Paleolithic cultures, I believe that this combination was the genesis of the post-Neandertal European populations.

Most paleoanthropologists supporting the theory of complete Neandertal replacement and extinctions have relied on "couldn't have" arguments regarding the European Neandertals. Neandertals, it is claimed, couldn't have evolved into modern Europeans because there wasn't enough time, because they were overspecialized, because they couldn't form vowels, because of their cognitive deficiencies, and so on. "Couldn't have" is a phrase this author has come to regret, and there is just enough hard evidence to suggest that it is not appropriate in interpreting the hypothesis of a significant Neandertal ancestry for later Europeans. We can expect that this hypothesis will be met with the by-now familiar Greek Chorus of "its the single species hypothesis again", or more simply "absurd".

EMERGENCE OF THE UPPER PALEOLITHIC

In most regions of the world there is a change from what are broadly regarded as Middle to Upper Paleolithic (or Middle and Late Stone Age) industries. This is not the spread of one culture around the planet, but as discussed above the Eurasian situation is more contentious. Here, there is an unresolved question of whether the Aurignacian, usually considered the first "true" Upper Paleolithic industry, is

1. the manifestation of a single culture (and people) spreading widely and rapidly across the area,
2. the consequence of applying typology to a series of technological and adaptive changes that spread across this area but stimulated the development of many local Aurignacians.

In western Europe, the Châtelperronian, and in Central Europe the Szeletian, are characterized by large numbers of Mousterian tools but many of the unique elements of the Upper Paleolithic. These are alternatively considered transitional industries or areas of culture contact between Middle and Upper Paleolithic peoples. The one thing that is clear is that they do not appear *between* the Middle and Upper Paleolithic as the three (Middle, Upper, and "transition") overlap in a number of places from the extreme east to the extreme west of the region during the period between 41 and 31 kyr. This fact could, however, support either interpretation.

The Upper Paleolithic marks the beginning of an evolving adaptive system that in Eurasia came to encompass virtually all of the specific techniques and equipment known in modern hunting populations. These almost certainly included everything from sophisticated food preparation and cooking technology to missile systems, tailored clothing, and harpoons, and organizationally, widespread networks of contacts between mobile populations that combined to increase their abilities to develop seasonally specific responses. Earlier populations made effective use of the large game animals— mammoths, tundra-adapted oxen, and other large species. As these became rare or extinct, local adaptations shifted to the intensive use of smaller mammals (reindeer, horses, bison) as well as to a more effective use of fish and other water resources.

In my view, the onset of these early Upper Paleolithic industries across the whole of Europe may have been affected by the influx of new peoples and ideas, but there are too many variations from site to site and too many differing elements of local continuity for the emergence of the Upper Paleolithic to be explained this simply. From Spain to the Zagros of Iraq to Siberia, the Aurignacians differ in detail and appear to have developed out of the local Middle Paleolithic. As populations began to move back into Europe with the more moderate and favorable climates of the last interstadial, natives who had remained and adapted to the glacial conditions were encountered. Some of the more classic interpretations of the ensuing events run the gamut from the fate of all native populations - extinction at the hands of the colonialists - to minimal acculturation and marginalization to peripheral areas where the natives succumbed "not with a bang but a whimper". Both of these are unlikely, and are even poor descriptions of the colonial experiences where differences in technology, organization, and behavior were much greater than any ascribed to this period of paleolithic turmoil. What might have happened is much more complex, and perhaps best described by J. Svoboda in his discussion of the Central European area where the anatomical evidence for local continuity between Neandertals and their successors is strongest:

> If dominance of new technologies reflects population influx into Czechoslovakia, then these movements certainly accelerated local Middle/Paleolithic evolution and encouraged the leptolithization trends in lithic technology. We generally observe that the most complex Upper Paleolithic cultures did not appear in the areas where modern humans presumably originated, but in the zones where Neanderthals and modern humans were in contact. Therefore we tend to see the origin of the Upper Paleolithic in Czechoslovakia as a complex developmental process in an area of contact between various populations with generally shared behavioral tendencies

POST-NEANDERTAL EUROPEANS

One missing element in this discussion is the identity of the first European non-Neandertals, the so-called earliest moderns. If the Aurignacian is an intrusive culture across Europe, we don't know who these people were because the earliest diagnostic human remains are not from its earliest stages. If, on the other hand, there are many "Aurignacians" and some of them are indigenous local developments, it may be significant that the few human remains associated with the earliest manifestations of Aurignacian appear similar to Neandertals. In this case we *do* have remains of these earliest moderns in Europe, because any earlier folks were Neandertals. The moderns are from a series of Central European sites associated with earl*ier* (but not earl*iest*) Aurignacian artifacts.

Mladeč

The largest, and in many respects the most informative, of the early Upper Paleolithic sites of eastern and central Europe is Mladeč (Lautsch in German, a relevant point since Moravia was part of the Austro-Hungarian Empire when the remains were discovered). Some of the material from this central Moravian site was described in detail as early as 1925 by J. Szombathy (discoveries began in 1881), certainly the most complete remains, and yet it has been largely ignored, in favor of the much later Cro Magnon specimens from France, in English and French summaries of the Upper Paleolithic hominids and their relation to the earlier Neandertals. Most of the specimens, including several adult crania, were destroyed at the end of World War II by retreating Nazis who took these remains, the whole of the Moravian site of Předmostí (see below) and many art treasures of Moravia and burnt them in the Mikulov Castle. [When one considers the fate of these Central European specimens, the loss of the Zhoukoudian remains, the bombing and subsequent vaporization of Late Pleistocene Europeans such as Combe Capelle, and the unsupervised disposal of virtually the entire Australian Pleistocene fossil record, the reader is asked to forgive the occasional musing that these specimens would have been safer left in the ground as the legacy for future, more rational, civilizations to study].

Mladeč is certainly much younger than Skhul and Qafzeh, allowing one to examine alternative hypotheses of a Skhul/Qafzeh ancestry versus a Neandertal ancestry versus a combined ancestry. The associated Aurignacian industry is from the earlier part of the Central European Aurignacian, but is not the earliest. The human remains are directly associated with numerous bone, antler, and in one case ivory points, numerous items of personal adornment, and other archaeologically diagnostic debris. The date of Mladeč is estimated from the temperate fauna at the site and comparisons with other sites that share some of the unique elements of its industry. It is probably within the warmer period before Würm III (>32 kyr) and stratigraphically earlier than Central European sites with the split-based bone points characteristic of the early Aurignacian in Western Europe. As J. Jelínek points out this would mean it overlapped in time with Central European Neandertals such as the Šipka juvenile mandible, which comes from a nearby area deeper in the mountains (however Šipka's identity is far from clear).

Mladeč is extremely important because of its date and because of the morphological variability present at the site. There were over 100 specimens found in the main cave and a related side cave (that featured a triple burial of two adult men and a child - Mladeč 5, 6, and 46. Of the adult crania, Mladeč 5 and 6 from the sidecave and 4 from the main cave are extraordinarily robust and Neandertal-like (this is not always the same as robust) males, and Mladeč 1 and 2 are quite different females with so many masculine features that in the absence of the males they could well have been considered male specimens. One might say that Mladeč is the Skhul of Europe. In fact, the morphological variability at the site probably exceeds that at Skhul. Unlike the Skhul situation, however, the bulk of the variability results from marked sexual dimorphism.

The three males, crania 4, 5, and 6, are characterized by low braincases, thick cranial bone, posterior cranial flattening forming a Neandertal-like occipital bun, marked spongy bone development, and thick, projecting supraorbitals (although also of the modern form in that they are divided into central and lateral elements). Mladeč 6 is in some respects the most archaic-appearing of the crania, most extreme in the above-mentioned features and with a broad occiput, suprainiac fossa, and other details of Neandertal-form. Mladeč 5 is the only cranium to survive the Mikulov Castle fire - it was inadvertently left in a box in the hallway where it was protected by the collapsing walls. The vault is longer, narrower, and somewhat flatter, with a better developed occipital bun. It is also more complete and thus can readily be compared with Neandertals. The 1650 cc cranial capacity exceeds the 1575 cc male Neandertal average (table 13.5) by about 5%. D. Frayer shows that the cranial contour of this specimen is remarkably similar to La Chapelle's except for the slightly higher forehead and less projecting occiput in the Mladeč male. It shares the upper facial projection and teardrop shape from above of Neandertals, although the vault is higher (at the top of the male Neandertal range) and more vertical-sided. The mastoid process is small and like Neandertals it projects only moderately below a well developed juxtamastoid eminence. Mladeč 4 is the least complete, comprised only of a frontal and parietal that are quite similar to Mladeč 5. It is from the main cave, and therefore directly associated with the females.

While modern European male crania are generally described as smaller, shorter, but broader and higher than Neandertals, none of these comparisons are accurate for their Upper Paleolithic ancestors, who are generally more Neandertal-like. Of the dissimilarities that do discriminate these male samples, there are three ways in which the Mladeč (and the other early European Upper Paleolithic) males differ from their male Neandertal counterparts that suggest functional distinctions. One of these is in the position of the temporal lines. Although the Mladeč crania are no shorter than male Neandertals, their temporal lines rise higher on the vault and extend backwards to a more posterior position. This suggests larger temporal muscles with a better developed posterior component. A second difference is in the occiput. Mladeč occiputs are slightly narrower than their Neandertal counterparts (the narrowing does not effect the nuchal muscles, which are broadly developed and extend right to the backs of the mastoid processes) but are considerably more robust. This is particularly expressed in their heavily developed nuchal lines near inion. The stronger development of the central nuchal muscles reflects neck function and greater upper limb support, according to R. Caspari who relates these changes to pulling (for instance, by using a tumpline) and carrying activities and suggests they may reflect greater individual mobility. A third difference is in the form of the mandibular fossa. The fossa is deeper and has a more vertical front face than its Neandertal counterparts - a difference which according to R. Hinton reflects forces applied when the mandibular condyles are positioned on the horizontal part of the eminence at the front of the mandibular fossa (the fossa can deepen and its front face steepen during life). He relates this to strenuous use of both anterior *and* posterior teeth, and his data show that Mladeč resembles Eskimo mandibular fossa anatomy (there is also similarity in temporal line development). These three differences are better expressed in Mladeč 5 than Mladeč 6, a generally more Neandertal-like cranium.

The adult facial pieces from the side cave must belong to Mladeč 5 or 6, and are therefore male. Mladeč 8, also a male, is quite similar to them, and survives to be studied and compared. It is a very broad and robust piece, but with a narrower nasal aperture than all but the latest Neandertal males, and generally smaller dimensions and not as prognathic. The canine preserved in this maxilla (as well as several other isolated ones) are above the Neandertal average, but the only remaining incisor (a heavily worn lateral one) is small and clearly subequal to the central incisor. The most complete mandible (Mladeč 54, from the side cave) also had very large anterior teeth - the canine above the Neandertal average and lateral incisor just below it.

The adult females, crania 1 and 2, are rather modern in appearance, although quite robust compared with later Upper Paleolithic Europeans (almost equaling the later males). Mladeč 1, a 16-17 year old with a 1540 cc cranial capacity, has a surprisingly well-developed supraorbital torus (given that her last molars are not yet in occlusion), small mastoids, and marked posterior cranial flattening. Mladeč 2, a year or so older, has a smaller capacity, 1390 cc, no supraorbital torus but a very wide innerorbital area and large mastoids, and the back of the cranium (where preserved) is higher and rounder. The vaults are quite large, 14% above the Neandertal female mean and both larger than the biggest of the four Neandertal female vaults.

The completeness of Mladeč 1 allows some comparisons of basic cranial form and facial configuration with the earlier Neandertal women. Apart from her much larger vault size (her vault is the same breadth, longer, and considerably taller than the Neandertal women's mean), she shows a series of similarities and differences. Mladeč has considerably more midfacial prognathism than Late Pleistocene females from other regions, for instance the male from Liujiang or the Jebel Irhoud 1 female, and is like Neandertal women to some extent. Her face is flatter, however, so both its center and its sides extend far forward, and her cheeks are even more anterior than Neandertal women. Their base is somewhat angled, as the cheek merges into the outer wall of the palate, but there is no true maxillary notch. The nose is prominent and the face projects horizontally from the orbit to the nasal border in a puffy, Neandertal-like anatomy. While her face is of equal width it is of markedly shorter height (the difference largely reflects reduced heights of the lower orbits and nose but the height of all portions is less). The nose is also considerably narrower, and to its sides there are distinct canine fossae marking the angle between the flat cheeks and the projecting nasal margins. The differences, according to D. Frayer and colleagues, can be largely attributed to a reduction in the volume of the nasal cavity and a diminution of the amount of force transmitted through the midface by anterior tooth loading (this change also being reflected in the male cranial distinctions in the temporal lines, mandibular fossa, and nuchal plane discussed above).

The supraorbital region of Mladeč 1 is of the modern European form. It is made up of a very well developed central element, directly over the nose and the inner corners of the orbits, divided from the weakly developed portions to the sides by a groove at the approximate position of the middle of each orbit. Its development is great enough for the cranium to have been considered as a male before the Mladeč males were discovered. D. Frayer details a number of systematic differences between these male and female crania. He indicates that while the two best preserved crania of each sex are quite different from each other, generally the males have:

- larger vaults (1650 cc for Mladeč 5 compared with a 1465 cc average for the females, a 13% difference)
- Supercillary arches that are markedly larger and more projecting
- Shallow sulcus at the base of the forehead
- Forehead lower and less vertical
- More angled occipital areas with lambdoidal flattening
- Superior nuchal line thick and broad, extending onto the mastoids
- Nuchal plane larger and inion more prominent and higher
- General cranial form and many details that are considerably more Neandertal-like

Postcranial remains were numerous (over 100 were discovered) but quite fragmentary and many were destroyed. They are mostly modern in their anatomy, but for a few features that reflect strength and muscularity. Size of the acetabulum in the male (22) and female (21) innominates are quite large, in the case of the male larger than any other Upper Paleolithic European and right at the Neandertal male mean. Some of the other articular surfaces are very large, for instance the various bones comprising the Mladeč 25 juvenile (which could also include the male innominate and the large talus in table 14.4), and given the size of the limb shafts it is evident that some of the Mladeč specimens had relatively large joint surfaces - a Neandertal feature. Other features suggesting Neandertal descent include the proximal femoral flange on Mladeč 28. However, some of the causation of the large joint sizes in Mladeč specimens must be due to what appears to be elevated body size. Only a few postcranials are complete (none useful for relative joint size determinations), and these suggest that some of the Mladeč people were quite large compared to Neandertals (and in some cases to penecontemporary Europeans). Moreover, not all joints are relatively large; for instance, the Mladeč 23 humerus has a relatively small head, and Mladeč 24 was even more gracile . Moreover, the humerus head is elongated, not rounded as in most Neandertals. No long bones are complete enough to estimate heights or associated for limb proportions.

Table 14.4
Comparisons of complete Postcranial Remains

	Mladeč	Předmostí maximum	Neandertal mean (*range*)
Talus length	57.5	56.0, out of 4	52.8 (*49-5-55.5*) for 5
3rd metacarpal length	77.8	72.0, out of 6	65.7 (*60.9-70.6*) for 3

Pilastric indices of the femora are high, fitting the model of locomotor changes in these folk.

Mladeč remains are important for three reasons

1. they provide an estimate of the range and pattern of variation in a large, early sample of post-Neandertals
2. they establish unique anatomical links to the preceding Neandertals
3. they show that the rate and sequence of modernization in European males and females were quite different

Other early Central Europeans

Mladeč is probably the earliest of the non-Neandertals sample from Central Europe. Similar remains are known from Zlatý Kůň (Moravia), Cioclovina (Romania), Bacho Kiro levels 6/7 (Bulgaria), Velika Pećina (Croatia), a child's mandible from the Austrian site of Miesslingtal, and the German specimens Stetten (Vogelherd Cave) and Hahnöfersand. Few are well dated but many come from the earlier (never earliest) or middle Aurignacian and precede the Pavolvian specimens (see below), dated by their association with the Pavolvian industry to some 26-25 kyr. The Bacho Kiro 6/7 remains have 33 and 29 kyr radiocarbon dates, but the specimens are most fragmentary and least diagnostic. Among the complete or almost complete remains, Neandertal features are less well marked in the males. Female crania (especially Zlatý Kůň and Stetten) are robust and "masculine" in their anatomy (Zlatý Kůň is older than the Mladeč 1 adolescent, accounting for the differences in robustness), and as Frayer's work has shown the sample as a whole retains more Neandertal features than any of the later Europeans. Several of the crania with more problematic ages seem part of this sample. Individuals such as represented by the Hahnöfersand frontal have been regarded as "hybrids" by authors such as G. Bräuer. Unfortunately Hahnöfersand is not associated with cultural material and its date, a radiocarbon determination from bone collagen, is suspect according to F. Smith.

Apart from some isolated teeth there are no Western Europeans from this time span. Stetten is the furthest west of the Central European sites, and is the latest (at least of those that have archaeological or numerical date estimates) because of its association with a middle Aurignacian industry. The cranial vault of this female is broken, but in the midorbital and outer portions where the supraorbital region is preserved, it is between Mladeč 1 and 5 in thickness. The nuchal region is quite robust, the mastoids very large, and in all Stetten fits the pattern of "masculine" females. An associated mandible has a retromolar space, and one of the few post-Neandertal instances of a horizontal-oval mandibular foramen. An isolated humerus of moderate size, 340 cm, has a relatively thick shaft; compared to its length the diameter of humerus shaft at its middle separates Neandertals from most later specimens, but the Stetten bone falls right at the Neandertal mean. Its muscle attachments are pronounced, especially the deltoid attachment, and in general this individual had as muscular an arm as any male Neandertal.

Later Upper Paleolithic Europeans

EASTERN AND CENTRAL EUROPE

Later in time, while the climate deteriorated and an arctic desert developed across much of Europe, mammoth hunters of the Pavolvian were found all across the northern tier of East-Central Europe. They lived in large, long-lasting villages dotted across this region, seemingly never at large population numbers, and their burial customs have left us with large numbers of remains. The largest samples of these are from 22 kyr deposits at Sungir' in Russia, and slightly older (26-25 kyr) Dolní Věstonice (and nearby Pavlov) specimens described by E. Vlček, and Předmostí , both in Moravia. Předmostí, with 29 individuals (including 18 recovered from a single mass grave formed by a depression lined with mammoth long bones and covered by decorated and colored mammoth shoulder blades), is perhaps the largest Upper Paleolithic sample from anywhere. All were destroyed in the Mikulov Castle fire, but fortunately they had been described in two monographs by J. Matiegka which remains the most detailed portrait of the Pavlovians to date. Sites with individual specimens include the male burial from Francouzská Street, Brno, with its associated grave goods including a necklace and a male puppet with browridges.

Pavlov Hill

Dolní Věstonice and nearby Pavlov are found on the Pavlov Hill in southern Moravia. The skeletal sample is extremely variable. Pavlov is arguably the most robust Upper Paleolithic European known, although not especially Neandertal-like, while Dolní Věstonice 1-3 are very gracile, even petite, females. DV 3 has an unusual facial pathology, which identifies a small sculpture found at the site as her representation. The elderly DV 16 is moderately robust but in his case Neandertal-like traits are preserved, especially in the puffy midface and the shelved lower cheek border. The triple burial of 3 adolescent boys (DV 13-15) must have been an unparalleled disaster for the small tribe living at this long-occupied site. Their almost unworn incisors could be analyzed for the dimensions of shovel shaping, and these were found to be intermediate between the Neandertals and living Central Europeans. As a whole the sample is unquestionably modern, but like the other early Central Europeans the marks of a Neandertal element to their ancestry are unmistakable.

Předmostí

Předmostí is probably the earliest and the sample size is unquestionably the largest of these. At a male mean of 1603 cc and a female mean of 1459 cc (samples of 4 for each), Předmostí cranial size is close enough to Mladeč for the slight difference to be from sampling. The female crania are markedly larger than Neandertals (13%) but the males only slightly larger (2%), reflecting the earlier trend for different patterns of female and male modernization. To some extent the larger cranial capacities must reflect larger body size, as the mean male and female body heights (171 and 162 cm) are about 4% greater than the Neandertals, but the brain size expansion is more and one must conclude this is a significant change. In Chapter 13 it was suggested that in comparison to other cold-adapted populations of similar body size, Neandertals had smaller brain sizes than expected, and these date confirm the idea that Neandertal brain size is anything but "unusually large", or "larger than later Europeans", as it is so often described..
On the average, the crania are shorter and broader, and slightly higher than Neandertals. The greatest single difference in a cranial dimension is the reduction of occipital breadth. Facial projection varies widely and shows considerable sexual dimorphism. The adult crania show distinct sexual dimorphism in morphology. Males are characterized by prominent supraorbitals, fairly low foreheads, and large mastoids, while supraorbital development in the females is reduced, foreheads are higher, and the mastoids are small to moderate. The Předmostí males retain numerous Neandertal-like features, although these are never found together in the same cranium. For instance, the rear of cranium 9 is flattened and

bunned. In cranium 18 the supraorbital is extraordinarily projecting and the forehead is quite low. Cranium 3 is particularly reminiscent of Spy 2 in development of the browridge (continuously developed, horizontal, and thickest in the supercillary region), low position of the cranial breadth, and spongy bone development of the cranial base. Other Předmostí crania differ in that they are more unevenly developed (greater supercillary, less lateral), arch more over the orbits, and are divided into central and lateral portions. Females have many of the masculine features of the earlier Aurignacians, but these are more weakly expressed. The pattern and magnitude of cranial dimorphism in the crania is not different from that found in living populations. There is surprisingly little sex difference in the size and rugosity of the faces. When cranial features that reflect race are examined, the Předmostí crania are unquestionably European in their regional features, an assessment that is founded in the normal forensic criteria for racial determination. The robust aspect of features can be found in many living Europeans, but no living population comes close to matching the Předmostí folk in the extent of their expression or high frequency of the occurrence.

The Předmostí mandibles are characterized by only moderate chin development. In Předmostí 3 the ramus begins behind the third molar, while in Předmostí 4 it begins just at its back border. Specific features showing sexual dimorphism foreshadow living Europeans. For instance, male mandibles are deeper, with vertical rami, while in the females the ramus is lower and angled more posteriorly, and the anterior tooth-bearing portion is more prognathic. The large dental sample also shows moderate variation; generally males have larger teeth than females, although there is some overlap. Only at their largest do the teeth approach the maximums reached in the earlier European 'moderns". The Předmostí sample, with other Pavlovians, shows significant anterior dental reduction when compared to the earlier Aurignacians.

The burials preserved numerous postcrania. Skeletal robustness in the sample is marked. Articular surfaces, for instance, are enlarged relative to limb lengths in a pattern similar to more archaic populations. Although no specimen approaches the Neandertal extreme, characteristics of some fall well within the Neandertal range. However, there is some reduction in shaft thickness and robustness; relative to limb lengths, the shaft diameters are generally smaller. Limb proportions at Předmostí also differ somewhat from the Neandertal condition, which is an important element in considerations of their origin. In spite of the clearly European affinities of the crania, over the years these differences have been used to support a persistent theme in the interpretations of the prehistory of early Upper Paleolithic Europe - that a migration from somewhere to the south or east was largely responsible for the formation of the post-Neandertal populations. The similarity of the longer limb lengths and higher distal to proximal limb indices (e.g. radius to humerus, tibia to femur) of the Skhul and Qafzeh hominids to the post-Neandertal Europeans, as contrasted with the European Neandertals, is regularly used as proof that populations lacking biological adaptations to glacial conditions founded the European Upper Paleolithic populations. In fact, such populations may well have played an important role, but there is a real problem in determining how great a part from the postcranial remains. Moreover, on the basis of the same postcranial features, European Neandertals with their rounded trunks and short distal limb segments have been described as cold-adapted while at the same time eliminated as potential ancestors for succeeding cold-adapted populations for this very reason, which is an unusual interpretation of the role of successful adaptation in the evolutionary process. S. Churchill outlines three reasons why these postcranial features may differ systematically:

1. phylogeny
2. climatic adaptation
3. behaviors such as mobility and weapon use

Climatic adaptation and phylogeny

It is difficult to separate climatic adaptation and phylogeny in this discussion, as it is a discontinuity in climatic adaptation that is used to establish phylogenetic difference between the Neandertals and their successors. In the words of one Paleoanthropologist (C. Stringer, cited in a short editorial by P. Ross) "early modern humans look like they walked straight out of Africa". Three different arguments have been used to support the idea that the Pavlovians (and presumably their ancestors) were adapted to a non-glacial, if not tropical climate:

1. body shape (reflected in relative pelvic breadth)
2. limb lengths relative to the trunk
3. relative lengths of the distal limb segments

C. Ruff's climatic adaptation arguments were developed to examine the basis for markedly different body size and proportions at the origin of *Homo sapiens* (see Chapter 9). They can be applied here. The interpretation is based on a cylindrical model of how the body adapts to climate. Since differences in body width, and not height, are what mainly create variation in relative surface area (the relevant variable - minimized in cold adaptation), Ruff argues that there is no relation between body height and shape (measured by the relation of pelvis width and body height) within broad climatic regimes. Heights may vary for many reasons while body breadths are more constant within similar climates(Ruff measures body breadth as the breadth across the hips). Therefore, comparing populations from different climates, the Ruff model predicts that people of similar heights will be stockier in cold adaptation (broader across the hips), more linear in heat adaptation (narrower across the hips). In fact, the relation of these body shapes to climate differences is an often-repeated observation. What is new about Ruff's explanation is his focus on body breadth as the important variable.

Body shapes have been used to argue for the absence of cold adaptation in the Předmostí folk, because they are both relatively and absolutely narrower in body build than the Neandertals. In fact, the three Předmostí individuals whose hip breadths can be measured are narrower hipped than the modern European mean values that Ruff uses in his analysis, although they not that much different from these averages and are well-within the range of individual Europeans. This is problematic because it shows that while the model was developed from the average shapes of different populations, individuals within them vary so much that they do not fit the expectations of the model. Therefore it is not surprising that even the small fossil sample shows this explanation of the shape-size relation is probably too simplistic to apply to individuals in the past as well. For instance, there are actually no European Neandertals with complete enough pelves to calculate their hip widths (the Bari specimen is an exception but at this writing it is far from being removed from its cave, let alone described). The only value known is for the Levantine specimen from Kebara - and it is "hyper-cold-adapted" according to Ruff's criteria. But what does this mean, since the Levant climate is quite different than Europe (it is a common target for winter vacation-minded Europeans)? Of course it *could* mean that Kebara's ancestors were cold-adapted Europeans *and* that they hadn't been in the Levant for long enough to change their cold-adapted form, but one wonders about an adaptive explanation for important anatomical differences in which the advantages of the adaptation are so minimal that they don't change, even when climate does. Moreover there is an important logical error in this explanation. Kebara appears to be an exception to Ruff's general climatic rule, and it is unreasonable to interpret exceptions with the same explanation that is given for the general rule they are exceptions to. If climate validly explains the general trend, it should not also be used to explain Kebara's deviation from it.

And Kebara is not alone in being a climatically problematic fossil. The 18 kyr Minatogawa women (2 and 3) are among the very few fossils that have known pelvic widths. Inexplicably, these almost-terminal Pleistocene Okinawins are "hyper-heat-adapted" according to Ruff's criteria, at or even below the means for African populations. If we apply the same migratory hypothesis used to explain deviations from climatic explanations in Předmostí and Kebara, we would have to derive these Okinawins from hypothetical ancestors who lived far to the south. In fact, to date virtually all Pleistocene fossils 18 kyr old or older with hip breadths would appear to be exceptions. With individual fossil variation like this for the few specimens with known hip breadths, the best interpretation is *no interpretation* as far as the climatic adaptation of the Předmostí folk's ancestry is concerned.

As noted above, the Pavolvians (as the preceding Aurignacians) from Central Europe are taller than the Neandertals: 171 compared with 165 cm for males; 162 compared with 156 cm for females. Is this greater height a consequence of heat adaptation, at least in the Předmostí folk's immediate ancestry? The Neandertals successors in Europe are often compared to them as basketball players compared to wrestlers. But if the taller populations are the more heat-adapted ones, it is problematic that height continues to increase in Europe until 20-18 kyr, according to D. Frayer, and then decreases, finally to reach Neandertal size in the Holocene. In other words, height reaches its maximum when Europe is the coldest; if tallness is really a cold adaptation (as this would suggest) and not a heat adaptation, then why are the shorter Neandertals considered cold-adapted?

According to T. Holliday, part of this height difference reflects the fact that their limbs are longer relative to trunk length, once again this difference is used to support their heat-adapted ancestry. We expect cold adapted populations to have shorter limbs so that blood does not have as far to travel from the trunk. This expectation seems contradicted by the continued increase in limb lengths described above. Moreover, none of the specimens have complete trunks - their lengths are estimated from the vertebrae. The relation of vertebrae to trunk length is obvious, but for virtually all specimens there are only several vertebrae left and herein lies the problem - the Předmostí folk have longer necks but shorter lower backs than Neandertals. Compared with lower back vertebrae the Předmostí folk do indeed have longer limbs, but compared with the neck vertebrae it is the Neandertals with the longer limbs. The conclusions of Holliday's study are based on lower vertebrae, but even so they are unconvincing. For instance, one of the Pavolvians, Předmostí 14, has relatively shorter legs than any Neandertal and another, Předmostí 10, has arms as short as the shortest-armed Neandertal. Arm and leg proportions to trunk are somewhat different. For instance, the relatively longest armed Neandertal, Regourdou, is well within the range of living Africans. It is difficult to place a consistent explanation based on climatic adaptation on these data of absolute and relative limb lengths. Relative limb length is actually unknown and its estimates provide contradictory conclusions. Absolute limb length has a pattern of change within the Upper Paleolithic Europeans that contradicts a heat-adaptation explanation for its distribution. If these populations were founded by tropical migrants (or even strongly influenced by gene flow from tropical peoples), one would expect over the course of the Upper Paleolithic that limb lengths would gradually reduce as a response to the generally cold conditions of the late Würm in Europe. They do not.

Table 14.5
Brachial Indexes
Replacement and the Cold Adapted Problem

	Colder (European)	Warmer (Near Eastern)
Neandertal	74	78
Non-Neandertal	79[1]	76[2]
Modern	74[3]	79[4]

[1] Předmostí [3] Lapps
[2] Skhul/Qafzeh [4] Egyptians

The final evidence for climatic difference is found in the limb proportion differences, for both upper and lower members, mentioned above. These are expressed in Brachial and Crural Indexes (tables 14.5 and 14.6); the radius is longer relative to the humerus and the tibia is longer relative to the femur, and these resemble Holocene and recent heat-adapted circum-Mediterranean populations such as Afalou, or recent Egyptians. The ancestry issue is more complex, however, unless one assumes the Předmostí folk literally *did* walk right out of Africa, somehow avoiding western Asia. This is because comparisons of arm and leg proportions reveal quite different patterns. Předmostí relative arm length is like the warmer-adapted Levantine "Neandertals" and the European Neandertals are like the Skhul/Qafzeh remains. However for leg proportions just the opposite is the case, as Předmostí resembles the Skhul/Qafzeh remains and the European Neandertals resemble the West Asian ones.

Table 14.6
Crural Indexes
Replacement and the Cold Adapted Problem

	Colder (European)	Warmer (Near Eastern)
Neandertal	77	77
Non-Neandertal	85[1]	83[2]
Modern	79[3]	85[4]

[1] Předmostí [3] Lapps
[2] Skhul/Qafzeh [4] Egyptians

The question of whether these proportions reflect climatic adaptation has proven difficult to answer. On a world-wide basis the proportions do seem to follow a climatic pattern, but there are many exceptions and the problem is that Late Pleistocene Europe may be among them. One reason to suspect this comes from D. Frayer's work. He shows that neither Brachial nor Crural Index changes at all during the European Upper Paleolithic. If people came to Europe with limb proportions that were different than the Neandertals because they were adapted to a warm climate, we would expect their limb proportions to change during the subsequent 20 kyr as the climate became dramatically colder, especially since so many populations have limb proportions that follow the climatic pattern today. And even if we did assume that these Paleolithic proportions reflected past climatic adaptations, the picture is not especially clear. For instance, Skhul 5 has a Brachial Index of only 71 and a Crural Index of 80, both are almost exactly the same as La Chapelle - does this mean that Skhul 5 migrated in from the north? Pavlov has a Brachial Index of 75, did he adapt to the cold much better than its Předmostí neighbors, or perhaps is he more closely related to their cold-adapted predecessors?

Or, are there important non-climatic causes of these limb proportion variations?

Behavioral differences

The arguments above assume that climate is the only cause of the postcranial variation and leave only phylogeny as an explanation of deviations from it. In doing so they deny any importance to or , significant roles for technologies that modify the affects of climate, such as the microclimate created by clothing, or for behaviors of the sort that were argued to be of primary importance in assessments of body shape evolution at the beginning of the Pleistocene. In fact, by necessity these arguments deny any role for locomotor biomechanics and behavioral differences. Yet one of the most influential scientists to argue in support of functional/biomechanical explanations for body form differences, E. Trinkaus, noted in his 1983 essay on the adaptive shift to modern humans that while from these limb proportion data

> one would have to conclude that the Neandertals were cold adapted and early anatomically modern humans were heat adapted. ... the early anatomically modern humans in both the Near East and Europe experienced conditions at least as cold as those to which the Neandertals were subjected. ... It is possible to explain this dilemma by ... postulating that there was a large influx of people into the northwestern Old World from the more tropical regions ... Although such a conclusion is possible, it does not account for this shift in thermal adaptive patterns. ... The limb segment proportions ... suggest that ... early anatomically modern humans were more adept at generating heat, internally through the metabolism of high energy diets and/or externally with carefully controlled fires, and in manipulating that heat around the body with improved insulation.

This makes good sense, and there are two other changing adaptations that must be considered as well, the affects of weapon use on the upper limbs and of changing mobility patterns on the lower ones.

A. Brues first suggested that limb proportions may reflect weapon use, positing that longer arms and increased stature might reflect the use of spears and spearthrowers. Frayer, as mentioned above, subsequently showed that no proportional changes characterized the period when weapon use changed from spearthrowers to bows in Europe, and Bridges has been unable to identify changes in the pattern of degenerative joint disease that follow from weapon use. However the possibility of some kind of link to hunting was re-argued by Churchill and Trinkaus who focused on earlier postcranial evolution, between Neandertals and European "moderns". Their studies show changes in upper limb muscle development and leverage that reflect specific reductions in three Neandertal specializations:

- the ability to resist strong forces with the forearm bent
- the emphasis on upper arm movement in a transverse and downward direction
- the development of a powerful grip

They took these changes to reflect both different behaviors and a lower level of activities. Technological developments affecting hunting and gathering efficiency (and in the case of hunting, also safety) were important in these developments, but Churchill's work indicates that no general gracilization explanation or differing developmental responding to improved technology or reduced activities can account for what happened (in fact, he shows that the only significant reduction in skeletal robustness is between all archaic humans (including Neandertals *and* early European post-Neandertals) and the highly variable recent human groups he studied. For instance, the broader shoulder joints in the Upper Paleolithic are thought to reflect more habitual arm movement from back to front, and suggest that the changed anatomy may reflect much more dramatic movements at the extreme ends of forward and backward motions. One activity that quickly suggests itself is the cocking and release motions of throwing, the dramatic action of baseball or rugby pitching. Churchill and Trinkaus raise the possibility that important increases in projectile weapon use may be reflected in the post-Neandertal changes. Yet, if the different behaviors that are reflected in the anatomical changes also affected upper limb proportions, it must have been at the time that the behavioral changes were taking place and here we encounter a lack of data. There are no remains complete enough to examine limb proportions between Mousterian-associated Neandertals and the Pavlovians. The question of whether these changes occurred within the shift from Middle to Upper Paleolithic or with the appearance of non-Neandertal crania, an important difference for understanding causation, cannot be answered.

Lower limb elongation and proportional change can be directly linked to changing mobility patterns; in particular the markedly increased mobility of the Pavlovians and other Upper Paleolithic peoples. The mobility differences are probably unrelated to hunting strategies. As discussed in the previous chapters and above, these differed considerably within the Middle Paleolithic, and may not have changed dramatically in Europe until the later part of the Upper Paleolithic. They do not correspond in any way to the changes in limb proportions. Archaeologists such as M. Wobst, O. Soffer, and C. Gamble have discussed some of the social changes and variants in use of the landscape that alter mobility related activities at this time, and these are more likely the important elements that orient changes in the lower limb. The behavioral changes also affect limb anatomy, as a stronger pilaster on the back of the femur and a reorientation of the internal bone distribution show that long distance walking was more efficient and more often practiced in these folk. Other evidence, for instance from the analysis of the occipital, are compatible with the interpretation that there were important mobility changes during this period, but once again the evidence is lacking to establish causation.

Churchill, in examining Late Pleistocene upper body evolution, characterizes explanatory models as "integrationist" (meaning single causal, expressed broadly because of the interrelationship of anatomical features) and "particularist" (meaning reductionist, in that particular sources of selection cause specific and often unrelated changes). His research rejects integrationist explanations for the pattern of postcranial evolution, and I would concur. It is clear that the limb changes are more complex than climate (and by implication phylogeny) alone can explain.

WESTERN EUROPE

In contrast to Eastern and Central Europe, in Western Europe "apart from the Saint Césaire skeleton we know nothing of the population of the beginning of the French Upper Paleolithic, particularly those of the early Aurignacian", according to a review article by C. Stringer and colleagues. The only other specimen with pretense to an early date is the robust woman from Combe Capelle in France. She was initially reported to derive from Châtelperronian levels, but from the beginning (the discovery was in 1909) considerable controversy surrounded this claim, and the real age of the specimen can probably never be clearly established. The cranium is clearly a post-Neandertal one, higher and narrower than Neandertals. While the face could be described as robust but modern, it is quite large and retains a considerable degree of total facial prognathism. Combe Capelle has a more prominent browridge and slightly larger face than the Mladeč 1 female but smaller vault dimensions and less cranial capacity. The mandible is short, vertical, and rather deep, with a vertical symphysis featuring a virtual lack of mental eminence projection. The ramus begins just at the back of the third molar. E. Vlček has emphasized it similarities to the Brno skull, but because of the provenience problems Combe Capelle is not widely accepted as a Paleolithic specimen.

There are numerous specimens which date to the later Aurignacian levels or more recent in Western Europe. Few, however, are complete, and no sample approaches the numbers found at Předmostí or Mladeč These western sites are dated to the reëmergence of cold conditions that were even more severe than the earlier Würm stages, and postdate the latest Mousterian occurrences. Later Aurignacian peoples developed effective adaptations to the cold steppe, and hunting technology based on weapons with projectile points. These included spears, possibly catapulted to greater distances by spearthrowers. Bone-working technology proliferated, probably to help replace wood in the prevalent tundra conditions. Isolated cranial fragments, teeth or fragmentary jaws are said to come from the Aurignacian levels at a number of sites across France, Spain, Italy, and a few in Great Britain. Interpretation of these is plagued by uncertain provenience; many were excavated early in this century or in the last, and the possibility of intrusive burial or misidentification of associations is significant. In too many cases the records of the excavations and in some instances the specimens themselves were lost, nothing of value for prehistory remains at the sites, and the original collections only focused on a few type tools, discarding the (then unrecognized) data that would be critical to establish associations. Moreover, a good number of the specimens are highly fragmentary and undiagnostic in nature.

One well known site is the Grotte des Enfants (Grimaldi), once thought to be Mousterian in age. Three specimens (numbers 4-6) from early excavations conducted between 1874 and 1901 are widely believed to be ancient because they were buried into a sterile layer from the Upper Paleolithic above. The source level, however, appears to have been Gravettian and it is likely that they are even younger than the Cro Magnon remains.

The best-known site and the only one with the remains of several specimens is Cro Magnon. It is ironic to end the discussion of fossil remains in this book with Cro Magnon, as it was once considered the earliest modern European (if not the earliest modern human), and "moderns" are often named after the site. Their long-assumed ancient age is another victim of early excavation (the burials were discovered in 1868). The stratigraphy, cultural associations (for what remains, most tools were discarded during the excavation of the skeletons) and the preparation of the bodies and style of the burials suggest that the site dates to just before the last glacial maximum, approximately 20 kyr ago. It is by no means, then, the earliest of the post-Neandertal Europeans as once thought and an inappropriate model for understanding their immediate ancestry and populational interactions.

The crania from Cro Magnon represent two males and a female. The cranial capacity of the males is quite large (1,636 and 1,730 cc for crania 1 and 3 respectively), and the general dimensions of the crania are correspondingly great, except occipital breadth which is reduced (as in the Předmostí sample). Cranium 1, often called "the old man," is high and well rounded, with a rather bulging forehead and little supraorbital development. In contrast, the cranium 3 forehead is lower and the supraorbital better developed, divided into supercillary and lateral elements like most if the Pavolvians described above. The occipital region of cranium 3 is remarkably Neandertal-like, with lambdoidal flattening and a prominent bun. The endocast of this cranium also appears to resemble the Neandertals in size and proportions, according to V. Kochetkova. Cranium 3 is not a Neandertal, but his features confirm the presence of typically Neandertal characteristics in more modern populations.

The best-known male from the site, cranium 1, is the most gracile and modern-appearing of the three. It is also the only male specimen with a face. The face is very broad (in absolute dimension and in proportion to its height). A number of authors had proposed that tall faces should be associated with long crania, and the Cro Magnon face seemed to disprove this contention. It was thus argued that the loss of the front teeth during life led to facial shortening in this male as the result of resorption of the alveolar bone. However, I do not believe this can account for the facial proportions. Not enough bone could have been lost to cause much reduction in facial height. Historically, this question had importance beyond the true dimensions of a single face, since it was used to support the contention that there were different "races" represented in Europe during the Upper Paleolithic. One of the features thought to distinguish these was the facial height relative to cranial length.

The female (cranium 2) is a smaller, more gracile specimen, which was somewhat distorted and has not been well reconstructed. Her facial proportions, extensive midfacial prognathism, and anatomical details such as the large nose and high nasal angle are quite similar to Mladeč 2, but she does not have the massive basal spongy bone development and enlarged mastoids of the earlier Moravian specimen. Broad faces and large noses with high nasal angles are retained in later European specimens such as Chancelade; while his similarity to the morphology of the cold-adapted Eskimos has been used to suggest an ancestral relation, common adaptation is a more likely explanation, as the onset of the later Würm stadials was sudden and intense, and climate was unquestionably a source of selection on European anatomy and behavior.

CONTINUED EVOLUTION IN EUROPE

Frayer argues that there are biological consequences of the fact that Upper Paleolithic Europe is a period of cultural differentiation and regionalization, as widely dispersed, low density populations gave way to denser, more specialized populations. Skeletal changes are driven by changes in technology, organization, and behaviors such as subsistence activities, and all of these reflect the regionalization process.

There is a pattern of continued dental reduction through the post-Neandertal populations of the Upper Paleolithic that is reflected in changes across the entire dentition. These changes are most substantial in the anterior dentition. Frayer demonstrates two aspects of this pattern:

1. there are greater changes *within* the Upper Paleolithic than between the Middle and Upper Paleolithic populations
2. there is a substantial reduction in sexual dimorphism as seen in the dentition

These Upper Paleolithic folk are more often found with very worn dentitions. According to M. Skinner this does not mean that they wore their teeth faster than the Neandertals, but rather that more of them lived to an old age.

The dental changes are matched by corresponding cranial changes. Crania reduce in size over this period, becoming shorter and lower, with less upper and middle facial projection, reduced size and angulation of the nuchal muscle attachment area, and more weakly developed tori. The changes in males are generally greater, and the magnitude of sexual dimorphism is reduced. The sharper dental and cranial reductions in male dentitions contrasts with the earlier pattern of more rapid evolutionary change in the females - the male crania of the earlier Upper Paleolithic are much more Neandertal-like (e.g. like male Neandertals) than are the females (e.g. like female Neandertals). As noted above, Crural and Brachial Indexes do not change through this period. Stature increases through the coldest part of the last stadial, but then reduced through the remainder of the Pleistocene.

These changes reflect what Frayer describes as "a dynamic phase in the evolution of 'anatomically modern *Homo sapiens*'". Their patterns and directions are similar in males and females, reflecting similar selection acting on all members of the population. However, the different rates of change must relate to role differences between the sexes, and the increasingly similar requirements they present to the skeleton and dentition.

50

Summary

clear that localized Eurasian industries such as the Aurignacian reflect the activities of the same peoples
or cultures, from place to place. Regionalization is paramount in human biological variation as well, and
if there is one generalization that applies it is that biological and archaeological modernizations are
disjointed and juxtaposed in different sequences from place to place. Whether it is a single population or
a single mutation that is sought to explain the origin of modern anatomies and behaviors, the search has
been in vain.

Modern populations did appear throughout the Late Pleistocene, and their evolution generally reflects
the sort of complex interaction of local elements of selection and genic exchanges, but at the same time
common elements of selection and increasingly effective mechanisms of population identification and
consequent differentiation by isolation. The backdrop of local ancestry was continually disrupted by the
genic exchanges stimulated by changing climate (and the increased ability of human populations to take
advantage of it), and a dramatically expanding geographic range. In Central, Eastern, and South Asia
the living populations can be traced to their Pleistocene predecessors, and the Native Americans clearly
have a North Asian ancestry. The Australasian situation is biologically more complex because the racial
mixture of the South and Southeast Asians changed during the long colonization process. Native Africans
may have differentiated into Khoisan and Negroid extremes as early as 100 kyr and their archaic
forebearers were largely gone by this time.

The fundamental question about the origins of the post-Neandertal European populations cannot be
clearly answered. It is possible, theoretically reasonable, and perhaps even probable, that the
Multiregional model accounts for the Late Pleistocene changes in Europe as well, and that a combination
of genic exchanges (with population movements) and local selection to a climatically and culturally
changing environment can account for what happened there. What stands in the way of this interpretation
is the sample fact that across the continent the "moderns" are later than the Neandertals, and that the gap
between them is greater in the West than in the East. Industries are juxtaposed and out of sequence, but
culture and biology cannot be linked and the missing element in these ancestry discussions is a clear
picture of the alleged invaders. What is clear is that the establishment of post-Neandertal anatomy in
Europe is anything but the end of the evolutionary process there.

When these modernizations appeared is unclear, but it seems likely that they did not come as a single
package. Changing behaviors, of course, were their ultimate cause (figure 14.4) but within the Late
Pleistocene the rate of behavioral changes, reflected in culture, organization, and technology, came to so
far surpass any possible rate of biological response that even with the dramatic anatomical changes
following the Neolithic revolution, biological evolution is not going to catch up.

ANATOMY OF A CONTROVERSY
Does the Multiregional Evolution Model Work?

The continued Greek Chorus, background for so many contentions about human evolution reveals that
there remains contention in the ranks of the paleoanthropologists, perhaps not surprising in this most
contentious of all disciplines. Perhaps first and foremost, it is an important manifestation of the fact that
while paleoanthropologists are for the main part scientists, as my dear friend and colleague Jakov Radovč
ić first pointed out to me, Paleoanthropology has increasingly become opera. But whether by chorus or by

more scientific forms of contention, the question is raised of whether the Multiregional model is the correct description of the pattern of human evolution - does Multiregionalism work as a valid explanation? Two things have combined to blur, if not actually hinder, attempts to answer this question

1. misunderstandings of the Multiregional model and the data on which it rests
2. substitution of compatability analyses for the refutatory approach

WOULD THE REAL MULTIREGIONAL EVOLUTION PLEASE STAND UP?

Since I developed the Multiregional model with Wu Xinzhi and Alan Thorne, a number of authors have addressed it, in writings ranging from textbook discussions of human evolution, to debates about modern human origins and criticisms of the model. Among these writings there are two persistent patterns of misunderstandings about it:

- the idea that it asserts there is a parallel evolution of different modern races and the simultaneous appearance of modern humans all around the world.
- the confusion about the genic exchanges in the Multiregional model; some authors seem to believe the model minimizes or denies any importance to population movements in Pleistocene human evolution, while others contend that no credible level of genic exchanges could account for the worldwide aspects of human evolution

The origins of the idea that Multiregional evolution means parallel changes are to be found in certain responses to Weidenreich's Polycentric evolution model, and the way in which C. Coon subsequently developed it. Weidenreich had the first world view of a pattern of human evolution. He contended that human evolution was best understood as a network of interconnected populations that retained regional continuity for at least some areas. Each of the four major evolutionary centers he perceived retained regional differences throughout the Pleistocene and could be directly related to races of today, although as biological entities the races themselves were transitory. He envisaged very significant gene flow between the centers. The human species retained its unity because of the tendency for similar evolutionary causes to produce similar biological results, since they were limited and guided by developmental and adaptive constraints shared throughout humanity. The *ancestors* of recent or living people in each region were largely local, but these ancestors contributed genes to populations in other areas as well. The *descendants* of ancient people in each region were largely living there in recent or modern times, but ancient populations in other areas also played a role in their evolution and in some cases the amount of gene flow was substantial. In other words, neither ancestry nor descent are unique. Weidenreich illustrated his evolutionary pattern as something like a trellis, with vertical lines representing the main centers of evolution and diagonal connections between them reflecting the patterns of genetic interchanges.

This interpretation, and its illustration, would seem quite straightforward, but even before his death the model was seriously and most effectively misinterpreted by this century's main antagonist to Weidenreich's ideas, W. Howells. As early as 1944 Howells characterized Weidenreich's interpretations as a "Candelabra" theory in which "human evolution progressed in each corner of the world, *essentially apart* from what was happening in the other corners". Howells illustrated the candelabra by reproducing part of Weidenreich's trellis - he retained the vertical lines of descent but omitted the diagonal lines of genic exchanges. Howells went on to ask of this theory, how one could explain the independent evolution of four major races:

> Weidenreich has at least four different evolving human varieties, living far apart,
> moving ahead by fits and starts, producing their own special peculiarities of form ...
> Yet these four careers at last converged to produce the same kind of man
> everywhere. And all, miraculously enough, breasted the tape at the same time.

He discounted Weidenreich's theory because he could provide no answer as to how this could have happened.

Many misunderstandings of Multiregional Evolution have their basis in Howells' representations of Weidenreich's ideas. The problem, not at all unique to paleoanthropology as D. Paul points out, is that authors go to secondary sources for much of the information they use, and Howells secondary source publications are particularly well written and highly regarded. The reader should appreciate that the purpose in pointing this out is not to discredit the multitudinous works of a quite justifiably highly respected scholar, but is to outline a particular burden placed on the Multiregional model.

This particular misunderstanding is perhaps the most prevalent one, and not just among Howell's students such as C. Brace (who describes Multiregional Evolution as the idea that the human form emerged "gradually and simultaneously throughout the entire occupied world") or antagonists of the model such as C. Stringer and P. Andrews (who describe it as "parallel evolution"). Several of the scientists who continue to contribute to the understanding of modern human origins have exposed some unusual interpretations of the model. For instance P. Habgood asserts that the best explanation for evolution in East Asia would be "regional continuity with some gene flow or gene flow and migration with some regional continuity". C. Stringer contends "if we can turn away from a universal multiregional model for modern human origins, we cannot so easily exclude a dual African and East Asian ancestry model". To the uninitiated reader these authors might sound more like supporters of Multiregional Evolution than the major antagonists they consider themselves to be. The models proposed to replace Multiregional Evolution sound much more like the Multiregional Model discussed here, than the models described as Multiregional Evolution. Similarly, respected paleoanthropology popularizers such as B. Fagan, R. Lewin, and P. Shipman each portray the Multiregional model as involving (with varying emphasis) the independent and simultaneous appearance of modern humans. Shipman bravely asserts "it was during this period of simultaneous evolution that the racial characters of *Homo sapiens* first appeared". This chorus is joined by geneticists such as S. Rouhani, and A. Langaney and colleagues, who find it easy to discredit.

It is always easier to disprove a competing hypothesis if you can fabricate it yourself, and there has been a veritable cottage industry of made-up multiregional models that are subsequently disproved by their authors. A smaller number of attempts have been made to disprove the Multiregional model I have described.

WHAT ARE THE DATA?

A related problem comes when the theory seems to be understood but data are confused. For instance, in the discussions surrounding the single-crystal K-Ar redating for the older Indonesian specimens (see table 10.2), a new chorus of doubts was raised. "The multiregional hypothesis is dead", proclaimed one australopithecine expert. A paleoecologist declared that the new dates "pushes [Multiregionalism] beyond the bounds of possibility". This later assertion suggests that it was *within* the bounds of possibility before the new dates, and there is the rub. R. Lewin argues that with these dates the Multiregional hypothesis "suffered a serious setback" because of "previous claims that certain anatomical characteristics of the Sangiran fossils persist in the Australasian region through to recent times". The confusion come from the fact that *the fossils that are the basis for this claim have **not** been redated.* They are from the time span that, presumably, *is* within the bounds of possibility for the model to work. As discussed in Chapter 10, there is reason to question whether any of the dates can be related to the human fossils. More importantly, none of these dissenters, nor for that matter anybody else, have formally addressed the question of how long partial equilibrium systems might be expected to persist, and what sort of processes would be expected to break them down. The mitochondrial data suggest that the magnitudes of genic exchanges were quite low, and there is no reason to believe (or need to assume) that they were continuous. As noted in the discussion of Tasmania, long periods of isolation are known to have been insufficient.

COMPATIBILITY TESTING VERSUS REFUTATION

There is another problem. The geneticist A. Templeton comments that much of the modern human origins debate has come to focus on *hypothesis compatibility* rather than *hypothesis testing*. Indeed, too many of the mitochondrial and anatomical discussions of the "Eve" theory and other Single Origins hypotheses describe their analyses as being "compatible with" or "supportive of" these theories, where it is the refutation of the alternative that finally counts. Only a few studies propose to refute the multiregional interpretation of modern human origins that envisages modernity as the coalescence of adaptive features that appear in different regions at different times. (Refutation of the entire Multiregional Evolution model, another matter, is discussed in Chapter 11).

Several of these, for instance G. Bräuer's and R. Lewin's, simply assert that the data do not support Multiregional Evolution. Strictly speaking they are not tests as they do not analyze actual data. Others do depend on a test procedure to provide results. D. Waddle's work is based on matrices of relationships she developed. These were used to graphically pattern genealogical configurations and genic exchanges. The "expectations" of the two models tested were in the form of numbers that were assigned to denote the strength of the various relationships said to characterize Multiregional Evolution and some Single Origin theories. The analysis part correlates these matrices with matrices of anatomical distances between sets of fossil and recent crania from Europe, Western Asia, and Africa and seeks to find the highest correlation. A fair test in this comparison would hold the relationships between modern races constant and let the origins models that underlie these relationships vary. This would allow one to examine the influence of these variations on the correlations between expected and observed matrices. Well conceived experiments hold all but one independent variable constant. Waddle's test is flawed, however, because it *does not hold modern racial relationships constant* between the models, but instead assumes that both the origins of modern populations *and* the relationships between them vary between the two models "tested". Her Single Origins models posit races to be closely linked by genic exchanges while Multiregional Evolution is represented to consider races more distantly related. (In fact, there is no difference between the varying hypotheses as far as variation within modern humans and the relationships between different human groups are concerned.) Waddle concluded that multiple origins was the correct model because multiple origins matrices had higher correlations with the anatomical data. Yet, the results also show that Multiregional Evolution cannot be disproved when specimens with dubious provenience such as Border Cave are removed from the sample.

In another attempt to examine the fossil record for evidence of regional continuity (the observation that the Multiregional Evolution model explains), M. Lahr defines a set of 30 skeletal traits and proposes to test the criterion that Multiregional Evolution predicts higher frequencies of regional features linking fossil and living populations in each area examined. She shows that 37% of her features fit this regional patterning, but rejects Multiregional Evolution in favor of a single African origin for all modern populations. Lahr's study of regionality is flawed by its lack of focus on a clear refutatory procedure and her choice of a test criterion - she disregards the critical observation that past and present regionality is marked by *differing combinations* of features, and not particularly by differences between their individual frequencies. Additional difficulties come from the samples chosen to compare for evidence of regionality. For instance, in the "Africa" sample of 25 crania, 2 are identified as mulattos. This sample consists of individuals ranging from Bantu to Egyptians to San, and even without the mulattos it would hardly exemplify the variation of any recognizable biological or ethnic group. Other samples are equally heterogeneous. In another example 25 "Australians" include Mongoloid Polynesians. With these problems it is surprising there is any evidence of regional continuity at, let alone 37%.

While multiregional evolution as an explanation for modern human origins would appear to be very robust to hold up under tests like these, they are actually not tests at all, but little more than additional compatibility analyses. Both show that the data they analyze are consistent with Multiregional and Single Origins models. Both approaches had the potential to refute Multiregional Evolution, but neither was able to do so.

So does it work? At the moment the answer would seem to be yes. Genetic and anatomical evidence are without a doubt compatible with the Multiregional Evolution explanations. But compatibility is the bare requirement of a hypothesis - its pretensions of validity must rest on the continued consequences of attempts to disprove it. There have been such attempts, beginning with the "Eve" theory but after this was discredited, for various reasons attempts at disproof have been mostly invalid, poorly designed tests. The demonstration of punctuational explanations for changes during Pleistocene human evolution would be a valid refutation, and there are others. Focus on the real Multiregional Model and the search for valid tests that could potentially refute it will no doubt be the basis for some interesting years of research and publications.

REFERENCES AND FURTHER READINGS

ADOVASIO, J.M., and R.C. CARLISLE 1984 An Indian hunter's camp for 20,000 years. *Scientific American* 250(5):130-136.

AIELLO, L.C. 1992 Allometry and the analysis of size and shape in human evolution. *Journal of Human Evolution* 22(2):127-147.

AIKENS, M.C. 1990 From Asia to America: the first peopling of the New World. *Prehistoric Mongoloid Dispersals* Number 7:1-34.

ALEXANDER, R. McNEILL 1984 Walking and running. *American Scientist* 72:348-354.

ALEXSEEV, V.P., and I.I. GOKHMAN 1983 Physical anthropology of Soviet Asia. In I. Schwidetzky (ed) *Rassengeschichite der Menschenheit II: Asien.* Oldenbourg, Vienna.

ALLEN, J. 1989 When did humans first colonize Australia? *Search* 20:149-154.

ALLEY, R.B., D.A. MEESE, C.A. SHUMAN, A.J. GOW, K.C. TAYLOR, P.M. GROOTES, J.W.C. WHITE, M. RAM, E.D. WADDINGTON, P.A. MAYEWSKI, and G.A. ZIELINSKI 1993 Abrupt increase in Greenland snow accumulation at the end of the Younger Dryas event. *Nature* 362:527-529.

ALLSWORTH-JONES, P. 1990 The Szeletian and the stratigraphic succession in Central Europe and adjacent areas: main trends, recent results, and problems for resolution. In P. Mellars (ed): *The Emergence of Modern Humans: an Archaeological perspective.* Edinburgh University Press, Edinburgh. pp. 160-242.

AMBERGEN, A.W., and W. SCHAAFSMA 1984 Interval estimates for posterior probabilities, applications to Border Cave. In G.N. van Vark and W.W. Howells (eds): *Multivariate Statistical Methods in Physical Anthropology.* Reidel, Dordrecht. pp. 115-134.

ANTON, S.C. 1989 Intentional cranial vault deformation and induced changes of the cranial base and face. *American Journal of Physical Anthropology* 79(2):253-267.

BAHN, P.G. 1986 No sex please, we're Aurignacians. *Rock Art Research* 3:99-120.

___. 1992 50,000 year old Americans of Pedra Furada. *Nature* 362:114-115.

___. 1994 New advances in the field of Ice Age art. In M.H. Nitecki and D.V. Nitecki (eds): *Origins of Anatomically Modern Humans.* Plenum Press, New York. pp. 121-132.

BAKER, J.R. 1968 Cro-Magnon Man, 1868-1968. *Endeavour* 27:87-90.

BARTSTRA, G-J., S.G. KEATES, BASOEKI, and B. KALLUPA 1991 On the dispersion of *Homo sapiens* in eastern Indonesia: the Paleolithic of south Sulawesi. *Current Anthropology* 32(3):317-321

BAR-YOSEF, O. 1987 Late Pleistocene adaptations in the Levant. In O. Soffer (ed): *The Pleistocene Old World. Regional Perspectives.* Plenum, New York. pp. 219-236.

___. 1992 Middle Paleolithic chronology and the transition to the Upper Paleolithic in southwest Asia. In G. Bräuer and F.H. Smith (eds): *Continuity or Replacement? Controversies in Homo sapiens Evolution.* Balkema, Rotterdam. pp. 261-272.

___. 1994 Beyond stone tools. *Cambridge Archaeological Journal* 4(1):107-109, 117-119.

BELLWOOD, P. 1987 The prehistory of island southeast Asia: a multidisciplinary review of recent research. *Journal of World Prehistory* 1:171-224.

BINFORD, L.R. 1983 *In Pursuit of the Past: Decoding the Archaeological Record.* Thames and Hudson, London.

BIRDSELL, J.B. 1963 The origin of human races. *Quarterly Review of Biology* 38:178-185.

___. 1967 Preliminary data on the trihybrid origin of the Australian Aborigines. *Archaeology and Physical Anthropology in Oceania* 2:100-155.

___. 1977 The recalibration of a paradigm for the peopling of Greater Australia. In J. Allen, J. Golson and R. Jones (eds): *Sunda and Sahul: Prehistoric studies in Southeast Asia, Melanesia and Australia.* Academic Press, London.

BISCHOFF, J.L., N. SOLER, J. MAROTO, and R. JULIA 1989 Abrupt Mousterian/Aurignacian boundary at c. 40 ka BP: accelerator ^{14}C dates from L'Arbreda Cave (Cataunya, Spain). *Journal of Archaeological Science* 16(6):553-576.

BLACKWOOD, B., and P.M. DANBY 1955 A study of artificial cranial deformation in New Britain. *Journal of the Royal Anthropological Institute* 85:173-191.

VON BONIN, G. 1935 European races of the Upper Paleolithic. *Human Biology* 7:196-Z21.

BORDES, F. 1972 Physical evolution and technological evolution in man: a parallelism. *World Archaeology* 3:1-5.

___. 1973 On the chronology and contemporaneity of different Paleolithic cultures in France. In C. Renfew (ed): *The Explanation of Cultural Change.* Duckworth, London. pp. 217-226.

BORDES, F., and C. THIBAULT 1977 Thought on the initial adaptation of hominids to European glacial climates. *Quaternary Research* 8:115-127.

BOWDLER, S. 1977 The coastal colonization of Australia. In J. Allen, J. Golson, and R. Jones (eds): *Sunda and Sahul: Prehistoric Studies in Southeastern Asia, Melanesia, and Australia.* Academic Press, London. pp. 205-246.

___. 1993 *Homo sapiens* in Southeast Asia and the antipodes: archaeological versus biological interpretations. In T. Akazawa, K. Aoki, and T. Kimura (eds): *The Evolution and Dispersal of Modern Humans in Asia.* Hokusen-sha, Tokyo. pp. 559-589.

BOWLER, J.M., A.G. THORNE, and H.A. POLACH 1972 Pleistocene man in Australia: age and significance of the Mungo skeleton. *Nature* 240:48-50.

BOWLER, P.J. 1992 From "savage" to "primitive": Victorian evolutionism and the interpretation of marginalized peoples. *Antiquity* 66:721-729.

BRACE, C.L. 1978 Tooth reduction in the Orient. *Asian Perspectives* 19(2):203-219.

BRACE, C.L., and D.P. TRACER 1992 Craniofacial continuity and change: a comparison of Late Pleistocene and Recent Europe and Asia. In T. Akazawa, K. Aoki, and T. Kimura (eds): *The Evolution and Dispersal of Modern Humans in Asia.* Hokusen-sha, Tokyo. pp. 439-471.

BRÄUER, G. 1981 New evidence on the transitional period between Neanderthal and modern man. *Journal of Human Evolution* 10:467-474.

BRIGGS, L.C. 1949 Les Hommes préhistoriques du Maghreb au Paléolithque Supérieur et au Mésolithique: Étude comparative. *Bulletin de la Société d'Histoire Naturelle de l'Afrique du Nord* 40:27-80.

___. 1968 Hominid evolution in Northwest Africa and the question of the North African "Neanderthaloids". *American Journal of Physical Anthropology* 29:377-386.

BRIDGES, P.S. 1990 Osteological correlates of weapon use. In J.E. Buikstra (ed): *A Life in Science: Papers in Honor of J. Lawrence Angel.* Center for American Archaeology Scientific Paper 6: 87-98.

BROOM, R.A. 1918 The evidence afforded by the Boskop skull of a new species of primitive man (*Homo capensis*). *Anthropological Papers of the American Museum of Natural History* 23:33-79.

BROWN, J.A. 1987 The case for the regional perspective: a new world view. In O. Soffer (ed): *The Pleistocene Old World. Regional Perspectives.* Plenum, New York. pp. 365-376.

BROWN, P. 1981 Artificial cranial deformation: a component in the variation in Pleistocene Australian Aboriginal crania. *Archaeology in Oceania* 16:156-167.

___. 1987 Pleistocene homogeneity and Holocene size reduction: the Australian human skeletal evidence. *Archaeology and Physical Anthropology in Oceania* 22:41-67.

___. 1991 Diachronic variation and sexual dimorphism in Australian Aboriginal vault thickness. Archaeology in Oceania (in press).

___. 1992 Post-Pleistocene change in Australian Aboriginal tooth size: dental reduction or relative expansion? In T. Brown and S. Molnar (eds) *Craniofacial Variation in Pacific Populations.* Anthropology and Genetics Laboratory, University of Adelaide, Adelaide. pp. 33-51.

BROWN, T., S.K. PINKERTON, and W. LAMBERT 1979 Thickness of the cranial vault in Australian Aboriginals. *Archaeology and Physical Anthropologie in Oceania* 14:54-71.

BRUES, A. 1959 The spearman and the archer: an essay on selection in body build. *American Anthropologist* 61:457-469.

BULBECK, D. 1982 A re-evaluation of possible evolutionary processes in Southeast Asia since the Late Pleistocene. *Bulletin of the Indo-Pacific Prehistory Association* 3:1-20.

BURNEY, D.A. 1993 Recent animal extinctions: recipes for disaster. *American Scientist* 81(6):530-541.

BUTZER, K. W. 1977 Environment, culture, and human evolution. *American Scientist* 65:572-584.

___ K. 1990 A human ecosystem framework for archaeology. In E. Moran (ed): *The Ecosystem Approach in Anthropology.* University of Michigan Press, Ann Arbor,

BRYAN, A.L. (editor) 1986 *New Evidence for the Pleistocene Peopling of the Americas.* Center for the Study of Early Man, Orono.

CABRERA VALDES, V., and J.L. BISCHOFF 1989 Accelerator ^{14}C dates for early Upper Paleolithic (basal Aurignacian) at El Castillo Cave (Spain). *Journal of Archaeological Science* 16(6):577-584.

CALCAGNO, J.M. 1986 Dental reduction in Post-Pleistocene Nubia. *American Journal of Physical Anthropology* 70(3):349-363.

CANN, R.L. 1993 Human dispersal and divergence. *Tree* 8(1):27-31.

CARLSON, D.S., and D. P. VAN GERVEN 1977 Masticatory function and post-Pleistocene evolution in Nubia. *American Journal of Physical Anthropology* 46:495-506.

CAVALLI-SFORZA, L.L. 1989 The last 100,000 years of human evolution: the vantage points of genetics and archaeology. In G. Giacobini (ed): *Hominidae: Proceedings of the 2nd International Congress of Human Paleontology.* Jaca, Milan. pp. 401-413.

CHASE, P.G. 1989 How different was Middle Paleolithic subsistence? A zooarchaeological perspective on the Middle to Upper Paleolithic transition. In P. Mellars and C.B. Stringer (eds): *The Human Revolution: Behavioural and Biological Perspectives on the Origins of Modern Humans.* Edinburgh University Press, Edinburgh. pp. 321-337.

___. 1991 Symbols and Paleolithic artifacts: style, standardization, and the imposition of arbitrary form. *Journal of Anthropological Archaeology* 10:193-214.

___. 1994 Paleolithic archaeology and the human mind. *Cambridge Archaeological Journal* 4(1):110-112.

CHASE, P.G., and H. DIBBLE 1990 On the emergence of modern humans. *Current Anthropology* 31(1):58-59.

___. 1992 Scientific archaeology and the origins of symbolism. *Cambridge Archaeological Journal* 2:43-51.

CHEBOKSAROV, N.N. 1959 On the continuous development of physical type, economic activities, and Paleolithic culture of the people in the territory of China. *Soviet Ethnography* 4:1-25.

___. 1966 *The Ethnic Anthropology of Eastern Asia.* Nauka, Moscow.

CHEN TIEMEI, R.E.M. HEDGES, and YUAN ZHENXIN 1989 Accelerator radiocarbon dating for Upper Cave of Zhoukoudian. *Acta Anthropologica Sinica* 8(3):216-221.

___ 1992 The second batch of accelerator radiocarbon dates for the Upper Cave site of Zhoukoudian. *Acta Anthropologica Sinica* 11(2):112-116.

CLARK, G.A., M.A. KELLEY, T.M. GRANGE, and M.C. HILL 1987 The evolution of Mycobacterial disease in human populations: a reevaluation. *Current Anthropology* 28(1):45-62

CLARK, G.A., and J.M. LINDLY 1989 The case for continuity: observations on the biocultural transition in Europe and Western Asia. In P. Mellars and C.B. Stringer (eds): *The Human Revolution: Behavioural and Biological Perspectives on the Origins of Modern Humans.* Edinburgh University Press, Edinburgh. pp. 626-676.

CLOTTES, R. and J. COURTIN 1993 Neptune's Ice-Age gallery. *Natural History* 102(4):64-71.

COLLIER, S. 1989 The influence of economic behaviour and environment upon robusticity of the post-cranial skeleton: a comparison of Australian Aborigines and other populations. *Archaeology in Oceania* 24(1):178-30.

___. 1993 Sexual dimorphism in relation to big-game hunting and economy in modern human populations. *American Journal of Physical Anthropology* 91(4):485-504.

COMBIER, J. 1994 Les habitats de Villerest. In J. Combier (ed): *Les Habitats du Paléolithique*. Centre de Recherches de Solutré, Solutré.

CONKEY, M.W. 1987a Interpretive problems in hunter-gatherer studies: some thoughts on the European Upper Paleolithic. In O. Soffer (ed): *The Pleistocene Old World: Regional Perspectives*. Plenum, New York. pp. 63-77.

___. 1987b Style and information in cultural evolution: toward a predictive model for the Paleolithic. In C.L. Redman, M.J. Berman, E.V. Curtin, W.T. Langhorne Jr., N.M. Versaggi, and J.C. Wanser (eds): *Social Archaeology: Beyond Subsistence and Dating*. Academic Press, New York. pp. 61-85.

___. 1993 Humans as materialists and symbolists: image making in the Upper Paleolithic. In D.T. Rasmussen (ed): *The Origin and Evolution of Humans and Humanness*. Jones and Bartless, Boston. pp. 95-118.

CORRUCCINI, R.S. 1994 Reaganomics and the fate of the progressive Neandertals. In R.S. Corruccini and R.L. Ciochon (eds): *Integrative Paths to the Past. Paleoanthropological Advances in Honor of F. Clark Howell*. Prentice Hall, Englewood Cliffs. pp. 697-708.

DART, R.A. 1923 Boskop remains from the south-east African coast. *Nature* 112:623-625.

DAVIDSON, I. 1990 Prehistoric Australian demography. In B. Meehan and N. White (eds): *Hunter-Gatherer Demography. Past and Present*. University of Sydney, Sydney. pp. 41-58.

DAVIDSON. I. and W. NOBLE 1992 Why the first colonization of the Australian region is the earliest evidence of modern human behavior. *Archaeology in Oceania* 27(3):113-119.

DAVIS, R.S. 1987 Regional perspectives on the Soviet Central Asian Paleolithic. In O. Soffer (ed): *The Pleistocene Old World. Regional Perspectives*. Plenum, New York. pp. 121-133.

DEACON, H.J. 1989 Late Pleistocene paleoecology and archaeology in the southern Cape, South Africa. In P. Mellars and C.B. Stringer (eds): *The Human Revolution: Behavioural and Biological Perspectives on the Origins of Modern Humans*. Edinburgh University Press, Edinburgh. pp. 547-564.

DEBÉNATH, A., J.P. RAYNAL, J. ROCHE, J.P. TEXIER and D. FEREMBACH 1986 Position, habitat, typologie, et devenir de l'Atérien marocain: données récentes. *L'Anthropologie* 90:233-246.

DELSON, E. 1985 Late Pleistocene human fossils and evolutionary relationships. In E. Delson (ed): *Ancestors: The Hard Evidence*. Alan R. Liss, New York. pp. 296-300.

DEREVIANKO, A.P. 1989 New archaeological discoveries in North and Central Asia and the problem of early man's migrations. *Quaternary Research* 28:219-236.

DE SONNEVILLE-BORDES, D. 1959 Position stratigraphique et chronologie relative des restes humains du Paléolithique supérieur entre Loire et Pyrénées. *Annales de Paléontologie des Vertébrés* 45:2-51.

___. 1963 Upper Paleolithic cultures in Western Europe. *Science* 142:347-355.

___. 1972 Environnement et culture de l'homme de Périgordien ancien dans le sud-ouest de la France: données récentes. In F. Bordes (ed): *The Origin of Homo sapiens*. UNESCO, Paris. pp. 141-146.

DE VILLIERS, H., and L.P. FATTI 1982 The antiquity of the Negro. *South African Journal of Science*. 78:321-332.

DIAMOND, J.M. 1987 Who were the first Americans? *Nature* 329:580-581.

___. 1989 The great leap forward. *Discover* (May):50-60.

DIBBLE, H. 1992 Paleolithic archaeology. In P. Chase (ed): *Ice Age Europeans. Expedition* 34(3):14-22.

DILLEHAY, T.D., and D.J. MELTZER (editors) 1991 *The First Americans: Search and Research.* CRC Press, Boca Raton.

DODO, Y. 1986 A study of the facial flatness in several cranial series from East Asia and North America. *Journal of the Anthropological Society of Nippon* 94:81-93.

DUFF, A.I., G.A. CLARK, and T.J. CHADDERON 1992 Symbolism in the early Paleolithic: a conceptual odyssey. *Cambridge Archaeological Journal* 2:211-229.

ECKHARDT, R.B. 1985 Rapid morphometric change in human skeletal traits: an example from the Andean Highlands. In P.V. Tobias (ed): *Hominid Evolution: Past, Present, and Future. Proceedings of the Taung Diamond Jubilee International Symposium.* Alan R. Liss Inc., New York. Pp. 381-386.

___. 1989 Evolutionary morphology of human skeletal characteristics. *Anthropologischer Anzeiger* 47(3):193-228.

FAGAN, B. 1990 *The Journey from Eden: The Peopling of Our World.* Thames and Hudson, London.

FAIRBANKS, R.G. 1993 Flip-flop end to last ice age. *Nature* 362:495.

FARIZY, C. 1994 Behavioral and cultural changes at the Middle to Upper Paleolithic transition in Western Europe. In M.H. Nitecki and D.V. Nitecki (eds): *Origins of Anatomically Modern Humans.* Plenum Press, New York. pp. 93-100.

FATTI, L.P. 1986 Discriminant analysis in prehistoric physical anthropology. In R. Singer and J.K. Lundy (eds): *Variation, Culture, and Evolution in African Populations: Papers in Honour of Dr. Hertha de Villiers.* University of the Witwatersrand Press, Johannesburg. pp. 27-34.

FEREMBACH, D. 1973 L'évolution humaine au Proche-Orient. *Paléorient* 1:213-221.

___. 1976 Les Cromagnoïdes Circum-Méditerranéens (particulièrement en Orient) et les origines des types Méditerranéens. In G. Camps (ed): *Chronologie et Synchronisme dans la Préhistoire Circum-Méditerranéene.* Centre National de la Recherche Scientifique, Paris. pp. 128-143.

___. 1986 Les Hommes de Paléolithique Supérieur autour du Basin Méditerranéens. *L'Anthropologie* 90(3):579-587.

___. 1989 L'émergence d'*Homo sapiens.* In J. Bons and M. Delson (eds): *Evolution Biologique.* Boubée, Paris. pp. 265-291.

FORMICOLA, V. 1989 The Upper Paleolithic burials of Barma Grande, Grimaldi, Italy. In G. Giacobini (ed): *Hominidae: Proceedings of the 2nd International Congress of Human Paleontology.* Editoriale Jaca, Milan. pp. 483-486.

FOSTER, M.L. 1990 Symbolic origins and transitions in the Paleolithic. In P. Mellars (ed): *The Emergence of Modern Humans: an Archaeological perspective.* Edinburgh University Press, Edinburgh. pp. 517-539.

FRAYER, D.W. 1977. Metric dental change in the European Upper Paleolithic and Mesolithic. *American Journal of Physical Anthropology* 46:109-120.

___. 1980 Sexual dimorphism and cultural evolution in the Late Pleistocene and Holocene of Europe. *Journal of Human Evolution* 9(5):399-415.

___. 1981 Body size, weapon use, and natural selection in the European Upper Paleolithic and Mesolithic. *American Anthropologist* 83:57-73.

___. 1986 Cranial variation at Mladeč and the relationship between Mousterian and Upper Paleolithic hominids. In V.V. Novotný and A. Mizerová (eds): *Fossil Man. New Facts, New Ideas. Papers in Honor of Jan Jelínek's Life Anniversary. Anthropos* (Brno) 23:243-256.

___. 1988 Biological evidence for differences in social patterning in the European Upper Paleolithic and Mesolithic. *Rivista di Antropologia* 66:127-140.

___. 1992 The persistence of Neandertal features in post-Neandertal Europeans. In G. Bräuer and F.H. Smith (eds): *Continuity or Replacement? Controversies in <u>Homo</u> <u>sapiens</u> Evolution.* Balkema, Rotterdam. pp. 179-188.

___. 1993 Evolution at the European edge: Neanderthal and Upper Paleolithic relationships. *Préhistoire Européenne* 2:9-69.

FRAYER, D.W., J. JELÍNEK, F.H. SMITH, and M.H. WOLPOFF 1995 *Upper Pleistocene Human Remains from Mladeč Cave, Moravia.* In *preparation.*

FRAYER, D.W., M.H. WOLPOFF, A.G. THORNE, F.H. SMITH, and G.G. POPE 1994 Getting it straight. *American Anthropologist* 96(2):424-438.

FREEMAN, L.G., and J. GONZÁLEZ-ECHEGARAY 1970 Aurignacian structural features and burials at Cueva Morín (Santander, Spain). *Nature* 226:722-726.

GALLOWAY, A. 1937a The characteristics of the skull of the Boskop physical type. *American Journal of Physical Anthropology* 23(1):31-47.

___. 1937b Man in Africa in the light of recent discoveries. *South African Journal of Science* 34:89-120.

GAMBIER, D. 1989 Fossil hominids from the early Upper Paleolithic (Aurignacian) of France. In P. Mellars and C.B. Stringer (eds*): The Human Revolution: Behavioural and Biological Perspectives on the Origins of Modern Humans.* Edinburgh University Press, Edinburgh. pp. 194-211.

GAMBLE, C.S. 1986 *The Paleolithic Settlement of Europe.* Cambridge University Press, Cambridge.

___. 1991a Raising the curtain on modern human origins. *Antiquity* 65:412-417.

___. 1991b The social context for European Paleolithic art. *Proceedings of the Prehistoric Society* 57(1):3-15.

___. 1993 Exchange, foraging, and local hominid networks. *Proceedings of the Prehistoric Society*

GIBBONS, A. 1993 Pleistocene population explosions. *Science* 262:27-28.

GILL, G.W., and S. RHINE (editors) 1990 *Skeletal Attribution of Race: Methods for Forensic Anthropology.* Anthropological papers of the Maxwell Museum of Anthropology, Number 4.

GILMAN, A. 1984 Explaining the Upper Paleolithic revolution. In M. Spriggs (ed): *Marxist Perspectives in Archaeology.* Cambridge University Press, Cambridge. pp. 115-126.

GOEBEL, T., A.P. DEREVIANKO, and V.T. PETRIN 1993 Dating the Middle-to-Upper Paleolithic transition at Kara-Bom. *Current Anthropology* 34(4):452-458.

GOULD, R.A. 1970 Spears and spear-throwers of the Western Desert Aborigines of Australia. *American Museum Novitates* 2403:1-42.

GOULD, S.J. 1988 Honorable men and women. *Natural History* 3/88:16-20.

GOWLETT, J.A.J. 1987 The coming of modern man. *Antiquity* 61:210-219.

GREENBERG, J.H., and M. RUHLEN 1992 Linguistic origins of native Americans. *Scientific American* 267(5):94-99.

GREENBERG, J.H., C.G. TURNER, and S.L. ZEGURA 1986 The settlement of the Americas: a comparison of the linguistic, dental, and genetic evidence. *Current Anthropology* 27(5):477-497.

GRIBBIN, J., and M. GRIBBIN 1990 *Children of the Ice.* Basil Blackwell, Cambridge.

LES GROUBE, L., J. CHAPELL, J. MUKE, and D. PRICE 1986 A 40 000 year old occupation site at Huon Peninsula, Papua New Guinea. *Nature* 324:453-455.

GROVES, C.P. 1989 A regional approach to the problem of the origin of modern humans in Australasia. In P. Mellars and C.B. Stringer (eds): *The Human Revolution: Behavioural and Biological Perspectives on the Origins of Modern Humans.* Edinburgh University Press, Edinburgh. pp. 274-285.

GRÜN, R. 1987 On the settlement of the Americas: South American evidence for an expanded time frame. *Current Anthropology* 28(3):363-365.

GRÜN, R., P.B. BEAUMONT, and C.B. STRINGER 1990 ESR dating for early modern humans at Border Cave in South Africa. *Nature* 344:537-539.

HABGOOD, P.J. 1991 Aboriginal fossil hominids: evolution and migrations. In R. Foley (ed): *The Origins of Human Behavior.* Unwin Hyman, London. pp. 97-113.

HAHN, J. 1972 Aurignacian signs, pendants and art objects in Central and Eastern Europe. *World Archaeology* 3:252-266.

___. 1987 Aurignacian and Gravettian settlement patterns in central Europe. In O. Soffer (ed): *The Pleistocene Old World. Regional Perspectives.* Plenum, New York. pp. 251-262.

HARPENDING, H.C., S.T. SHERRY, A.R. ROGERS, and M. STONEKING 1993 The genetic structure of ancient human populations. *Current Anthropology* 34(4):483-496.

HARROLD, F.B. 1992 Paleolithic archaeology, ancient behavior, and the transition to modern *Homo.* In G. Bräuer and F.H. Smith (eds): *Continuity or Replacement? Controversies in Homo sapiens Evolution.* Balkema, Rotterdam. pp. 219-230.

HAUSMAN, A.J. 1982 The biocultural evolution of Khoisan populations of southern Africa. *American Journal of Physical Anthropology* 58(3):315-330.

HAYDEN, B. 981 Subsistence and ecological adaptations of modern hunter/gatherers. In R.S.O. Harding and G. Teleki (eds): *Omnivorous Primates. Gathering and Hunting in Human Evolution.* Columbia University, New York. pp. 344-421.

___. 1987 Alliances and ritual ecstasy: human responses to resource stress. *Journal of the Scientific Study of Religion* 26:81-91.

___. 1992 Ecology and complex hunter/gatherers. In. B. Hayden (ed):*A Complex Culture of the British Columbia Plateau.* University of British Columbia, Vancouver. pp. 525-563.

HENKE, W. 1987 The application of multivariate statistics to the problems of Upper Paleolithic and Mesolithic samples. *Human Evolution* 2(2):149-167.

___. 1992 A comparative approach to the relationships of European and non-European late Pleistocene and early Holocene populations. In M. Toussaint (ed): *Five Million Years, the Human Adventure. Etudes et Recherches Archéologiques de l'Université de Liège, Liège.* pp. 229-268.

HINTON, R.J. 1981a Changes in articular eminence morphology with dental function. *American Journal of Physical Anthropology* 54:439-455.

___. 1981b Form and patterning of anterior tooth wear among human groups. *American Journal of Physical Anthropology* 54:555-564.

HOFFECKER, J.F., W.R. POWERS, and T. GOEBEL 1993 The colonization of Beringia and the peopling of the New World. *Science* 259-46-53.

HOWELLS, W.W. 1976a Metrical analysis in the problem of Australian origins. In R.L. Kirk and A.G. Thorne (eds): *The Origin of the Australians.* Australian Institute of Aboriginal Studies, Canberra. pp. 141-160.

___. 1976b Physical variation and prehistory in Melanesia and Australia. *American Journal of Physical Anthropology* 45:641-650.

___. 1983 Origins of the Chinese people: interpretations of the recent evidence. In D.N. Keightley (ed): *The Origins of Chinese Civilization.* University of California Press, Berkeley. pp. 297-319.

___. 1986 The physical anthropology of the prehistoric Japanese. In R.J. Pearson (ed): *Windows on the Japanese Past.* Michigan Center for Japanese Studies, Ann Arbor. pp. 85-99.

HRDLIČKA, A. 1907 Skeletal remains suggesting or attributed to early man in North America. *Bureau of American Ethnology Bulletin* 33:21-28.

___. 1937 Early man in America: what have the bones to say? In G.G. MacCurdy (ed): *Early Man.* Lippincott, Philadelphia. pp. 93-104.

HUBLIN, J-J. 1983 Les origines de l'homme de type moderne en Europe. *Pour la Science* 64:62-71.

IRVING, W.N. 1985 Context and chronology of early man in the Americas. *Annual Review of Anthropology*, B.J. Siegel, A.R. Beals, and S.A. Tyler eds. Annual Reviews, Palo Alto. Volume 14:529-555.

JACOBS, K.H. 1985 Climate and the hominid postcranial skeleton in Würm and early Holocene Europe. *Current Anthropology* 26(4):512-514.

JELINEK, A.J. 1994 Hominids, energy, environment, and behavior in the Late Pleistocene. In M.H. Nitecki and D.V. Nitecki (eds): *Origins of Anatomically Modern Humans*. Plenum Press, New York. pp. 67-92

JELÍNEK, J. 1976a A contribution to the origin of *Homo sapiens sapiens*. *Journal of Human Evolution* 5:497-500.

___. 1976b The *Homo sapiens neanderthalensis* and *Homo sapiens sapiens* relationship in Central Europe. *Anthropologie* (Brno) 14:79-81.

___. 1983 The Mladeč finds and their evolutionary importance. *Anthropologie* (Brno) 21:57-64.

JIOCHIM, M.A. 1976 *Hunter-Gatherer Subsistence and Settlement: A Predictive Model*. Academic Press, New York.

___. 1987 Late Pleistocene refugia in Europe. In O. Soffer (ed): *The Pleistocene Old World. Regional Perspectives*. Plenum, New York. pp. 317-332.

___. 1991 Archeology as long-term ethnography. *American Anthropologist* 93(2):308-321.

JONES, R. 1992 The human colonization of the Australian continent. In G. Bräuer and F.H. Smith (eds): *Continuity or Replacement? Controversies in Homo sapiens Evolution*. Balkema, Rotterdam. pp. 289-301.

KAMMINGA, J. 1992 New interpretations of the Upper Cave, Zhoukoudian. In T. Akazawa, K. Aoki, and T. Kimura (eds): *The Evolution and Dispersal of Modern Humans in Asia*. Hokusen-sha, Tokyo. pp. 379-400.

KELLY, R.L., and L.C. TODD 1988 Coming into the country: early Paleoindian hunting and mobility. *American Antiquity* 53(2):231-244.

KENNEDY, K.A.R., and S.U. DERANIYAGALA 1989 Fossil remains of 28,000-year-old hominids from Siri Lanka. *Current Anthropology* 30(3):394-399.

KIMURA, T., and H. TAKAHASHI 1992 Cross sectional geometry of the Minatogawa limb bones. In T. Akazawa, K. Aoki, and T. Kimura (eds): *The Evolution and Dispersal of Modern Humans in Asia*. Hokusen-sha, Tokyo. pp. 305-320.

KINGDON, J. 1993 *Self-Made Man: Human Evolution from Eden to Extinction*. John Wiley, New York.

KLAATSCH, H. 1910 Die Aurignac-Rasse und ihre Stellung im Stammbaum der Menschheit. *Zeitschrift für Ethnologie* 42:513-577.

KLEIN, R.G. 1975 The relevance of Old World archaeology to the first entry of man into the New World. *Quaternary Research* 5:391-394.

___. 1991 The invention of computationally plausible knowledge systems in the Upper Paleolithic. In R.A. Foley (ed): *The Origins of Human Behavior*. One World Archaeology 19. Unwin Hyman, London. pp. 67-81.

___. 1992 The impact of early people on the environment: the case of large mammal extinctions. In J.E. Jacobsen and J. Firor (eds): *Human Impact on the Environment: Ancient Roots, Current Challenges.* Westview, Boulder. pp. 13-34.

___. 1994 The problem of modern human origins. In M.H. Nitecki and D.V. Nitecki (eds): *Origins of Anatomically Modern Humans.* Plenum Press, New York. pp. 3-17

KLÍMA, B. 1987 A triple burial from the Upper Paleolithic of Dolní Věstonice, Czechoslovakia. *Journal of Human Evolution* 16(8/8):831-835.

___. 1991 Das paläolithische Massengrab von Předmostí, Versuch einer Rekonstruction. *Quatär* 41/42:187-194.

KNECHT, H., A. PIKE-TAY, and R. WHITE (editors) 1993 *Before Lascaux: The Complex Record of the Early Upper Paleolithic.* CRC Press, Boca Raton.

KOCHETKOVA, V.I. 1964 Juliaj Mozgovoi Polosti Iskipaemovo Cheloveka Kro-Magnon. *Trudi Moscovskogo Obshschestva Ispitateli Prirodi* 14:111-135.

KOZLOWSKI, J.K. 1986 The Gravettian of central and eastern Europe. *Advances in World Archaeology* 5:131-200.

KURTÉN, B. 1986 *How to Deep-Freeze a Mammoth.* Columbia University Press, New York.

LAHR, M.M. 1994 The Multiregional model of modern human origins: a reassessment of its morphological basis. *Journal of Human Evolution* 26(1):23-56.

LANGANEY, A., D. ROESSLI, H. HUBERT VAN BLYENBURGH, and P. DARD 1992 Do most human populations descend from phylogenetic trees? *Human Evolution* 7(2):47-61.

LARNACH, S.L. 1974 Frontal recession and artificial deformation. *Archaeology and Physical Anthropology in Oceania* 3:214-216.

LARNACH, S.L., and N.W.G. MACINTOSH 1974 A comparative study of Solo and Australian Aboriginal crania. In A.P. Elkin and N.W.G. Macintosh (eds): *Grafton Elliot Smith: The Man and his Work.* Sydney University, Sydney. pp. 95-102.

LARSEN, C.S. 1987 Bioarchaeological interpretations of subsistence economy and behavior from human skeletal remains. *Advances in Archaeological Method and Theory* 10:339-445.

LAUGHLIN, W.S., A.P. OKLADNIKOV, A.P. DEREVYANKO, A.B. HARPER, and I.V. ATSEEV 1976 Early Siberians from Lake Baikal and Alaskan population affinities. *American Journal of Physical Anthropology* 45:651-660.

LAVILLE, H., J.P. RIGAUD, and J. SACKETT 1980 *Rock shelters of the Peragord.* Academic Press. New York.

LAYTON, R., R. FOLEY, and E. WILLIAMS 1991 The transition between hunting and gathering and the specialized husbandry of resources: a socio-ecological approach. *Current Anthropology* 32(3):255-274.

LEAKEY, L.S.B. 1935 *The Stone Age Races of Kenya.* Oxford University Press, Oxford.

LEHMAN, S. 1993 Flickers within cycles. *Nature* 361:404-405

LEROI-GOURHAN, A. 1968 The evolution of Paleolithic art. *Scientific American* 218(2):58-70.

LEWIN, R. 1987 The Origin of the Modern Mind. *Science* 236:668-670.

___. 1993 *The Origin of Modern Humans.* Scientific American Library, New York.

___. 1994 Human origins: the challenge of Java's skulls. *New Scientist* (7 May):36-40.

LINDLY, J., and G. CLARK 1990 On the emergence of modern humans. *Current Anthropology* 31(1):59-63.

LOURANDOS, H. 1993 Hunter-Gatherer cultural dynamics: long- and short-term trends in Australian prehistory. *Journal of Archaeological Research* 1(1):67-88.

LYNCH, T.F. 1990 Glacial age man in South America? A critical review. *American Antiquity* 55:12-36.

MACINTOSH, N.W.G. 1963 Origin and physical differentiation of the Australian aborigines. *Australian Natural History* 14:248-252.

___. 1965 The physical aspect of man in Australia. In R.M. and C.H. Berndt (eds): *Aboriginal Man in Australia.* Angus and Robertson, Sydney. pp. 29-70.

___. 1967 Fossil man in Australia. *Australian Journal of Science* 30:86-98.

MARKS, A.E. 1993 The early Upper Paleolithic: the view from the Levant. In H. Knecht, A. Pike-Tay, and E. White (eds): *Before Lascaux: The Complex Record of the Early Upper Paleolithic.* CRC Press, Boca Raton. pp. 5-21.

MARSHACK, A. 1989 Evolution of the human capacity: the symbolic evidence. *Yearbook of Physical Anthropology* 32:1-34.

___. 1991 The Taï plaque and calendrical notation in the Upper Paleolithic. *Cambridge Archaeological Journal* 1:25-61.

MELLARS, P.A. 1992 Archaeology and the population-dispersal hypothesis of modern human origins in Europe. *Philosophical Transactions of the Royal Society,* Series B, 337:225-234.

___. 1991 Cognitive changes and the emergence of modern humans. *Cambridge Archaeological Journal* 1(1):63-76.

___. 1994 The European evidence. *Cambridge Archaeological Journal* 4(1):103-104.

MELLARS, P., H.M. BRICKER, J.A.J. GOWLETT, and R.E.M. HEDGES 1987 Radiocarbon accelerator dating of the French Upper Paleolithic sites. *Current Anthropology* 28(1):129-133.

MELTZER, D.J. 1993 Pleistocene peopling of the Americas. *Evolutionary Anthropology* 1(5):157-169.

MERCIER, N., H. VALLADAS, J-L. JORON, J-L. REYSS, F. LÉVÊQUE, and B. VANDERMEERSCH 1991 Thermoluminescence dating of the late Neanderthal remains from Saint-Césaire. *Nature* 351:737-739.

MICHAEL, H.N. 1984 Absolute chronologies of Late Pleistocene and Holocene cultures of northeastern Asia. *Arctic Anthropology* 21:1-68.

MINUGH-PURVIS, N. 1993 Reexamination of the immature hominid maxilla from Tangier, Morocco. *American Journal of Physical Anthropology* 92(4):449-461.

MORANT, G.M. 1925 Studies of Paleolithic man I. The Chancelade skull and its relation to the modern Eskimo skull. *Annals of Eugenics* 1:257-276.

___. 1930 Studies of Paleolithic man IV. A biometric study of the Upper Paleolithic skulls of Europe and their relationships to earlier and later forms. *Annals of Eugenics* 4:109-214.

MORRIS, A.G. 1986 Khoi and San craniology: a re-evaluation of the osteological reference samples. In R. Singer and J.K. Lundy (eds): *Variation, Culture, and Evolution in African Populations: Papers in Honour of Dr. Hertha de Villiers*. Witwatersrand University Press, Johannesburg. pp. 1-12.

___. 1992 Biological relationships between Upper Pleistocene and Holocene populations in southern Africa. In G. Bräuer and F.H. Smith (eds): *Continuity or Replacement? Controversies in Homo sapiens Evolution*. Balkema, Rotterdam. pp. 131-143.

MUSGRAVE, J.H. 1973 The phalanges of Neanderthal and Upper Paleolithic hands. In M.H. Day (ed): *Human Evolution*. Taylor and Francis, London. pp. 59-85.

MÜLLER-BECK, H. 1966 Paleohunters in America: origins and diffusion. *Science* 152:1191-1210.

___. 1982 Late Pleistocene man in Northern Alaska and the mammoth-steppe biome. In D.M. Hopkins, J.V. Matthews, C.E. Schweger, and S.B. Young (eds): *Paleoecology of Beringia*. Academic, New York.

NEUMANN, G.K. 1952 Archaeology and race in the American Indian. In J.B. Griffin (ed): *Archaeology of the Eastern United States*. University of Chicago, Chicago. pp. 13-34.

___ 1956 The Upper cave skulls from Chou-Kou-Tien in the light of Paleo-Amerindian material (abstract). *American Journal of Physical Anthropology* 14:380.

NEWMAN, M.T. 1953 The application of ecological rules to the racial anthropology of the aboriginal new world. *American Anthropologist* 55:311-327.

___. 1966 Evolutionary changes in body size and head form in American Indians. *American Anthropologist* 64:237-257.

NICHOLS, J. 1990 Linguistic diversity and the first settlement of the New World. *Language* 66:475-521.

NOBLE, W., and I. DAVIDSON 1991 The evolutionary emergence of modern human behaviour: language and its archaeology. *Man* 26:223-253.

OLSEN, J.W. 1987 Recent developments in the Upper Pleistocene prehistory of China. In O. Soffer (ed): *The Pleistocene Old World. Regional Perspectives*. Plenum, New York. pp. 135-146.

OLSZEWSKI, D.I., and H.L. DIBBLE 1994 The Zagros Aurignacian. *Current Anthropology* 35(1):68-75.

ORQUERA, L.A. 1984 Specialization and the Middle/Upper Paleolithic transition. *Current Anthropology* 25(1):73-98.

OSSENBERG, N.S. 1992 Native people of the American Northwest: population history from the perspective of skull morphology. In T. Akazawa, K. Aoki, and T. Kimura (eds): *The Evolution and Dispersal of Modern Humans in Asia*. Hokusen-sha, Tokyo. pp. 493-530.

OTTE, M. 1993 *Préhistoire des Religions.* Masson, Paris.

___. 1994 Origine de l'homme moderne: approache comportementale. *Comptes Rendus de l'Académie des Sciences,* Série II, 318:267-273.

OWEN, R.C. 1984 The Americas: The case against an Ice-Age human population. In F.H. Smith and F. Spencer (eds): *The Origins of Modern Humans: A World Survey of the Fossil Evidence.* Alan R. Liss, Inc., New York. pp. 517-563.

PARDOE, C. 1988 The cemetery as symbol. *Archaeology in Oceania.* 23:1-16.

___. 1990 The demographic basis of human evolution in southeastern Australia. In B. Meehan and N. White (eds): *Hunter-Gatherer Demography. Past and Present.* University of Sydney, Sydney. pp. 59-70.

___. 1991 Isolation and evolution in Tasmania. *Current Anthropology* 32(1):1-21.

PARKINGTON, J. 1990 A critique of the consensus view on the age of Howiesons Poort assemblages in South Africa. In P. Mellars (ed): *The Emergence of Modern Humans: an Archaeological perspective.* Edinburgh University Press, Edinburgh. pp. 34-55.

PAUL, D.B. 1987 The nine lives of discredited data. *The Sciences* (May)

PAVELKA, M.S.M. and L.M. FEDIGAN 1991 Menopause: a comparative life history perspective. *Yearbook of Physical Anthropology* 34:13-38.

PFEIFFER, J.E. 1982 *The Creative Explosion.* Cornell University Press, Ithica.

___. 1990 The emergence of modern humans. *Mosaic* 21(1):15-23.

PICQ, P.G. 1987 Les relations bioméchaniques entre la boîte crânienne de la face au cours de l'évolution humaine. *Annales de la Foundation Fyssen* 3:37-46.

PRADEL, L. 1966 The transition from Mousterian to Perigordian: skeletal and industrial. *Current Anthropology* 7:33-50.

PRIDEAUX, T. 1973 *Cro-Magnon Man.* Life-Time Books, New York

PUTMAN, J.J. 1988 The search for modern humans. *National Geographic* 174(4): 438-477.

RANOV, V.A., and R.S. DAVIS 1979 Toward a new outline of the Soviet Central Asian Paleolithic. *Current Anthropology* 20:249-270.

RIGAUD, J-P. 1988 Lascaux Cave: art treasures from the Ice Age. *National Geographic* 174(4):482-499.

___. 1989 From the Middle to the Upper Paleolithic: transition or convergence? In E. Trinkaus (ed): *The Emergence of Modern Humans. Biocultural Adaptations in the Later Pleistocene.* Cambridge University Press, Cambridge. pp. 142-153, and 232-276.

RIGAUD, J-P., and J.F. SIMEK 1987 "Arms too short to box with God": problems and prospects for paleolithic prehistory in Dordogne, France. In O. Soffer (ed): *The Pleistocene Old World. Regional Perspectives.* Plenum, New York. pp. 47-62.

RIGHTMIRE, G. P. 1970 Bushman, Hottentot, and South African Negro crania studied by distance and discrimination. *American Journal of Physical Anthropology* 33(2):169-196.

___. 1975. Problems in the study of later Pleistocene man in Africa. *American Anthropologist* 77(1):28-52.

___. 1978 Human skeletal remains from the southern Cape Province and their bearing on the Stone Age prehistory of South Africa. *Quaternary Research* 9:219-230.

___. 1979 Implications of Border Cave skeletal remains for later Pleistocene human evolution. *Current Anthropology* 20:23-35; 22:199-200.

___. 1984 *Homo sapiens* in sub-Saharan Africa. In F.H. Smith and F. Spencer (eds): *The Origins of Modern Humans: A World Survey of the Fossil Evidence*. Alan R. Liss, Inc., New York. pp. 295-325.

RIQUET, R. 1970. La race Cro-Magnon, abus de langage ou realite objective? In G. Camps and G. Oliver (eds): *L'Homme de Cro-Magnon*. Arts et Metiers Graphiques, Paris. pp. 37-58.

ROBERTS, D.F. 1983 Paradoxes of evolution in recent man. Raymond Dart Lectures 20. Institute for the Study of Man, University of the Witwatersrand Press, Johannesburg.

ROBERTS, R.G., R. JONES, and M.A. SMITH 1990 Thermoluminescence dating of a 50,000 year old human occupation site in northern Australia. *Nature* 345:153-156.

ROGINSKIJ, Y. 1972 Sur l'ancêtre le plus proche de l'*Homo sapiens* et le lieu de sa transformation en homme moderne. In F. Bordes. (ed): *The Origin of Homo sapiens*. Proceedings of the Paris INQUA Symposium. UNESCO, Paris. pp. 59-64.

ROSS, P,E. 1991 Mutt and Jeff. Did Cro-Magnons and Neanderthals coexist? *Scientific American* 265(3):40-48.

ROUHANI, S. 1989 Molecular genetics and the pattern of human evolution: plausible and implausible models. In P. Mellars and C.B. Stringer (eds): *The Human Revolution: Behavioural and Biological Perspectives on the Origins of Modern Humans*. Edinburgh University Press, Edinburgh. pp. 47-61.

RUFF, C.B. 1987 Sexual dimorphism in the human lower limb bone structure: relationship to subsistence strategy and sexual division of labor. *Journal of Human Evolution* 16(5):391-416.

RUFF, C.B., C.S. LARSEN, and W.C. HAYES 1984 Structural changes in the femur with the transition to agriculture on the Georgia coast. *American Journal of Physical Anthropology* 64(2):125-136.

SACKETT, 1. R. 1973. Style, function, and artifact variability in Paleolithic assemblages. In C. Renfrew (ed): *The Explanation of Cultural Change*. University of Pittsburgh Press, Pittsburgh. pp. 317-328.

SCHWALBE, G. 1906 *Studien zur Vorgeschichte des Menschen*. Schweizerbartsche Verlagsbuchhandlung, Stuttgart.

SIMEK, J.F. 1987 Spatial order and behavioural change in the French Paleolithic. *Antiquity* 61:25-40.

SKINNER, M.F. 1986 An enigmatic hypoplastic defect of the deciduous canine. *American Journal of Physical Anthropology* 69(1):59-69.

SMITH, F. H. 1976. The skeletal remains of the earliest Americans: a survey. *Tennessee Anthropologist* 1:116-147.

___. 1992 The role of continuity in modern human origins. In G. Bräuer and F.H. Smith (eds): *Continuity or Replacement? Controversies in Homo sapiens Evolution*. Balkema, Rotterdam. pp. 145-156.

SMITH, F.H., J.F. SIMEK, and M.S. HARRILL 1989 Geographic variation in supraorbital torus reduction during the later Pleistocene (c. 80,000-15,000 BP). In P. Mellars and C.B. Stringer (eds): *The Human Revolution: Behavioural and Biological Perspectives on the Origins of Modern Humans.* Edinburgh University Press, Edinburgh. pp. 172-193.

SMITH, P., O. BAR-YOSEF, and A. SILLEN 1984 Archaeological and skeletal evidence for dietary change during the Late Pleistocene/Early Holocene in the Levant. In M.N. Cohen and G.J. Armelagos (eds): *Paleopathology at the Origins of Agriculture.* Academic Press, Orlando. pp. 101-136.

SMITH, P., Y. WAX, F. ADLER, Y. SILBERMAN, and G. HEINIC 1986 Post-Pleistocene changes in tooth root and jaw relationships. *American Journal of Physical Anthropology* 70(3):339-348.

SMITH, P., Y. WAX, A, BECHER, and S. EINY 1985 Diachronic variation in cranial thickness. *American Journal of Physical Anthropology* 67:127-133.

SINGER, R. 1958 The Boskop "race" problem. *Man* 58:173-178.

SOFFER, O. 1989 Storage, sedentism, and the Eurasian Paleolithic record. *Antiquity* 63(241):719-732.

___. 1991 Lithics and lifeways -- the diversity in raw material procurement and settlement systems in the Upper Paleolithic East European plain. In A. Monet-White and S. Holen (eds): *Raw Material Economics among Prehistoric Hunter-Gatherers.* University of Kansas Publications in Anthropology 19:221-234.

___. 1994 Ancestral lifeways in Eurasia - the Middle and Upper Paleolithic records. In M.H. Nitecki and D.V. Nitecki (eds): *Origins of Anatomically Modern Humans.* Plenum Press, New York. pp. 101-119.

SOFFER, O., and C. GAMBLE (editors) 1990 *The World at 18,000 BP.* Unwin Hyman, London.

STEELE, D.G., and J.F. POWELL 1992 Peopling of the Americas: paleobiological evidence. *Human Biology* 64:303-336.

___. 1993 Paleobiology of the first Americans *Evolutionary Anthropology* 2(4):138-146.

STEWART, T.D. 1957 American neanderthaloids. *Quarterly Review of Biology* 32:364-369.

___. 1974 Perspectives on some problems of early man common to America and Australia. In A.P. Elkin and N.W.G. Macintosh (eds): *Grafton Elliot Smith: The Man and his Work.* Sydney University Press, Sydney. pp. 114-135.

STEWART, T.D. and M.T. NEWMAN 1951 An historical resume of the concept of differences in Indian types. *American Anthropologist* 53:19-36.

STINER, M.C. (editor) 1991 *Human Predators and Prey Mortality.* Westview Press, Boulder.

STONEKING, M. 1993 DNA and recent human evolution. *Evolutionary Anthropology* 2(2):60-73.

STORM, P. 1991 Microevolution of the human skull: implications of the Javanese Wadjak study for East Africa. In R.E. Leakey and L.J. Slikkerveer (eds): *Origins and Development of Agriculture in East Africa: The Ethnosystems Approach to the Study of Early Food Production in Kenya.* Studies in Technology and Social Change 19. Iowa State University Research Foundation, Ames. pp. 25-37.

STORM, P., and A.J. NELSON 1992 The many faces of Wadjak man. *Archaeology in Oceania* 27(1):37-46.

STRAUS, L.G. 1983 From Mousterian to Magdalenian: cultural evolution viewed from Vasco-Cantabrian Spain and Pyrenean France. In E. Trinkaus (ed): *The Mousterian Legacy. Human Biocultural Change in the Upper Pleistocene.* BAR International Series 164, Oxford. pp. 73-111.

____. 1990 On the emergence of modern humans. *Current Anthropology* 31(1):63-64.

____. 1991 Human geography of the late Upper Paleolithic in Western Europe: present state of the question. *Journal of Anthropological Research* 47(2):259-278.

STRAUS, L.G., G.A. CLARK, J. ALTUNA, and J.A. ORTEA 1980 Ice-Age subsistence in Northern Spain. *Scientific American* 242(6):142-152.

STRINGER, C. B. 1986 Direct dates for the hominid fossil record. In J. Gowlett and R. Hedges (eds): *Archaeological Results from Accelerator Dating.* Oxford University Press, London. pp. 45-50.

____. 1989 The origin of early modern humans: a comparison of the European and non-European evidence. In P. Mellars and C.B. Stringer (eds): *The Human Revolution: Behavioural and Biological Perspectives on the Origins of Modern Humans.* Edinburgh University Press, Edinburgh. pp. 232-244.

STRINGER, C.B., and G. BRÄUER 1994 Methods, misreading, and bias. *American Anthropologist* 96(2):416-424.

STRINGER, C.B., and C. GAMBLE 1994 Confronting the Neanderthals. *Cambridge Archaeological Journal* 4(1):112-117.

SUZUKI, H. 1982 Pleistocene man in Japan. *Journal of the Anthropological Society of Nippon* 9:11-26.

SUZUKI, H., and K. HANIHARA (editors) 1982 *The Minatogawa Man: Upper Pleistocene Man from the Island of Okinawa.* University Museum, University of Tokyo, Bulletin 19.

SVOBODA, J. 1986 The *Homo sapiens neanderthalensis* to *Homo sapiens sapiens* transition in Moravia: chronological and archaeological background. In V.V. Novotný and A. Mizerová (eds): *Fossil Man. New Facts, New Ideas. Papers in Honor of Jan Jelínek's Life Anniversary. Anthropos* (Brno) 23:237-242.

____. 1993 The complex origin of the Upper Paleolithic in the Czech and Slovak Republics. In H. Knecht, A. Pike-Tay, and R. White (eds): *Before Lascaux: The Complex Record of the Early Upper Paleolithic.* CRC Press, Boca Raton. pp. 23-36.

SZATHMARY, E.J.E 1993 Genetics of aboriginal North Americans. *Evolutionary Anthropology* 1(6):202-220.

SZILVÁSSY, J., H. KRITSCHER and E. VLČEK 1987 Die Bedeutung röntgenologischer Methoden für anthropologische Untersuchung ur- und frühgeschichtlicher Gräberfelder. *Annals of the Vienna Natural History Museum* 89:313-352.

SZOMBATHY, J. 1926 Die Menschenrassen im obern Paläolithikum, inbesondere die Brüx-Rasse. *Mitteilungen der Anthropologischen Gesellschaft in Wein* 56:202-219.

TATTERSALL, I. 1991 What was the human revolution? *Journal of Human Evolution* 20(1):77-83.

THOMA, A. 1964 Die Entstehung de Mongoliden. *Homo* 15:1-22.

___. 1973 New evidence for the polycentric evolution of *Homo sapiens*. *Journal of Human Evolution* 2:529-536.

___. 1978 L'origine des Cromagnoïdes. In J. Piveteau (ed): *Les Origines Humaines et les Époques de l'Intelligence*. Masson, Paris. pp. 261-282.

___. 1982 *Homo sapiens sapiens*? *Bulletins et Mémoires de la Société d'Anthropologie de Paris* 13(9):293-298.

THORNE, A.G. 1971 The racial affinities and origins of the Australian Aborigines. In D. J. Mulvaney and J. Golson (eds): *Aboriginal Man and Environment in Australia*. Australian National University, Canberra. pp. 316-325.

___. 1976 Morphological contrasts in Pleistocene Australians. In R.L. Kirk and A.G. Thorne (eds): *The origin of the Australians*. Australian Institute of Aboriginal Studies, Canberra. pp. 95-112.

___. 1977 Separation or reconciliation? Biological clues to the development of Australian society. In J. Allen, J. Golson and R. Jones (eds): *Sunda and Sahul: Prehistoric Studies in Southeast Asia, Melanesia, and Australia*. Academic Press, London. pp. 187-204.

___ 1980 The longest link: human evolution in Southeast Asia and the settlement of Australia. In J.J. Fox, R.G. Garnaut, P.T. McCawley, and J.A.C. Maukie (eds): *Indonesia: Australian Perspectives*. Research School of Pacific Studies, Canberra. pp. 35-43.

___. 1989 The emergence of the Pacific peoples. In L.H. Schmitt, L. Freedman, and N.W. Bruce (eds): *The Growing Scope of Human Biology*. University of Western Australia, Nedlands. pp. 103-111.

THORNE, A.G., and R. RAYMOND 1989 *Man on the Rim. The Peopling of the Pacific*. Angus and Robertson, Sydney.

THORNE, A.G., and S.R. WILSON 1977 Pleistocene and recent Australians: A multivariate comparison. *Journal of Human Evolution* 6:393-402.

TOBIAS, P.V. 1985 History of physical anthropology in southern Africa. *Yearbook of Physical Anthropology* 28:1-52.

TORRENCE, R. 1989 Retooling: towards a behavioural theory of stone tools. In R. Torrence (ed): *Time, Energy, and Stone Tools*. Cambridge University Press, Cambridge. pp. 57-66.

TRINKAUS, E. 1976 The evolution of the hominid femoral diaphysis during the Upper Pleistocene in Europe and the Near East. *Zeitschrift für Morphologie und Anthropologie* 67:291-319.

___. 1983 Neandertal postcrania and the adaptive shift to modern humans. In E. Trinkaus (ed.) *The Mousterian Legacy: Human Biocultural Change in the Upper Pleistocene*. British Archaeological Report International Series 164: 165-200.

___. 1986 The Neandertals and modern human origins. *Annual Review of Anthropology*, B.J. Siegel, A.R. Beals, and S.A. Tyler eds. Annual Reviews, Palo Alto. Volume 15:193-218.

___. 1989a Issues concerning human emergence in the later Pleistocene. In E. Trinkaus (ed): *The Emergence of Modern Humans. Biocultural Adaptations in the Later Pleistocene*. Cambridge University Press, Cambridge. pp. 1-17, 232-276.

___. 1989b The Upper Pleistocene transition. In E. Trinkaus (ed): *The Emergence of Modern Humans. Biocultural Adaptations in the Later Pleistocene*. Cambridge University Press, Cambridge. pp. 42-66, 232-276.

___. 1992 Cladistics and later Pleistocene human evolution. In G. Bräuer and F.H. Smith (eds): *Continuity or Replacement? Controversies in Homo sapiens Evolution*. Balkema, Rotterdam. pp. 1-7.

TRINKAUS, E., and F.H. SMITH 1985 The fate of the Neandertals. In E. Delson (ed): *Ancestors: The Hard Evidence*. Alan R. Liss, New York. pp. 325-333.

TURNER, C.G. 1985 The dental search for Native American origins. In R. Kirk and E. Szathmary (eds): *Out of Asia. Peopling of the Americas and the Pacific*. Australian National University, Canberra. pp. 31-78.

___. 1989 Teeth and prehistory in Asia. *Scientific American* 260(2):88-96.

___. 1990 Major features of Sundadonty and Sinodonty, including suggestions about east Asian microevolution, population history, and late Pleistocene relationships with Australian Aboriginals. *American Journal of Physical Anthropology* 82(3):295-317.

___. 1992 Microevolution of East Asian and European populations: a dental perspective. In T. Akazawa, K. Aoki, and T. Kimura (eds): *The Evolution and Dispersal of Modern Humans in Asia*. Hokusen-sha, Tokyo. pp. 415-438.

VALDES, V.C., and J.L. BISCHOFF 1989 Accelerator ^{14}C dates for early Upper Paleolithic (basal Aurignacian) at el Castillo cave (Spain). *Journal of Archaeological Science* 16(6):577-584.

VALLADAS, H., H. CACHIER, P. MAURICE, F. BERNALDO DE QUIROS, J. CLOTTES, V. CABRERA VALDÉS, P. UZQUANO, and M. ARNOLD 1992 Direct radiocarbon dates for prehistoric paintings at the Altamira, El Castillo, and Niaux caves. *Nature* 357:68-70

VALOCH, K. 1968 Evolution of the Paleolithic in Central and Eastern Europe. *Current Anthropology* 9:351-390.

VAN VARK, G.N., A. BILSBOROUGH, and J. DIJKEMA 1989 A further study of the morphological affinities of the Border Cave 1 cranium, with special reference to the origin of modern man. *Anthropologie et Préhistoire* 100:43-56.

VASILI'EV, S. 1993 The Upper Paleolithic of Northern Asia. *Current Anthropology* 34(1):82-92.

VERNEAU, R. 1924. La Race Neanderthal et la Race de Grimaldi; leur Rôle dans l'Humanitée. *Journal of the Royal Anthropological Institute* 54:211-230.

VLČEK, E. 1967 Morphological relations of the fossil human types Brno and Cro Magnon in the European Late Pleistocene. *Folia Morphologica* 15:214-221.

___. 1991 L'Homme fossile en Europe Centrale. *L'Anthropologie* 95(2/3):409-472

WADDLE, D.M. 1994 Matrix correlation tests support a single origin for modern humans. *Nature* 368:452-454.

WEAVER, K.F. 1985 The search for our ancestors. *National Geographic* 168:560-623.

WEBB, S.G. 1990 Cranial thickening in an Australian hominid as a possible palaeoepidemological indicator. *American Journal of Physical Anthropology* 82(4):403-411.

WEIDENREICH, F. 1939 On the earliest representatives of modern mankind recovered on the soil of East Asia. *Peking Natural History Bulletin* 13:161-174.

___.1947a Facts and speculations concerning the origin of *Homo sapiens. American Anthropologist* 49:187-203.

___. 1947b The trend of human evolution. *Evolution* 1:221-236.

WELLS, L.H. 1972 Late Stone Age and Middle Stone Age tool-makers. *South African Archaeological Bulletin* 27:509.

WHALLON, R. 1989 Elements of cultural change in the later Paleolithic. In P. Mellars and C.B. Stringer (eds*): The Human Revolution: Behavioural and Biological Perspectives on the Origins of Modern Humans.* Edinburgh University Press, Edinburgh. pp. 433-454.

WHITE, R. 1982 Rethinking the Middle/Upper Paleolithic transition. *Current Anthropology* 23:169-192.

___. 1989 Toward a contextual understanding of the earliest body ornaments. In E. Trinkaus (ed): *The Emergence of Modern Humans. Biocultural Adaptations in the Later Pleistocene.* Cambridge University Press, Cambridge. pp. 211-231, 232-276.

___. 1992 Beyond art: toward an understanding of the origins of material representation in Europe. In B.J. Siegel, A.R. Beals, and S.A. Tyler (eds): *Annual Review of Anthropology.* Annual Reviews, Palo Alto. Volume 21:537-564.

___. 1993 The dawn of adornment. *Natural History* 102(5):60-67.

WOBST, M. 1990 Minitime and megaspace in the Paleolithic at 18K and otherwise. In O. Soffer and C. Gamble (eds): *The World at 18,000 BP.* Unwin Hyman, London. pp. 331-343.

WOLPOFF, M.H. 1989 Multiregional evolution: the fossil alternative to Eden. In P. Mellars and C.B. Stringer (eds*): The Human Revolution: Behavioural and Biological Perspectives on the Origins of Modern Humans.* Edinburgh University Press, Edinburgh. pp. 62-108.

___. 1994 The calm before the storm. *Cambridge Archaeological Journal* 4(1):97-103.

WOLPOFF, M.H., and D.W. FRAYER 1992 Neanderthal dates debated. *Nature* 356:200-201.

WOOD-JONES, F. 1934 Contrasting types of Australian skulls. *Journal of Anatomy* 68:323-330.

WU XINZHI 1987a Relation between Upper Paleolithic men in China and their southern neighbors in Niah and Tabon. *Acta Anthropologica Sinica* 6(3):180-183.

___. 1987b The influence in the human evolution in Australia from China. Collected Papers of the China-Australia Symposium on Quaternary Studies, Science Press, Beijing. pp. 246-250.

___ 1988 The relationship between Upper Paleolithic human fossils of China and Japan. *Acta Anthropologica Sinica* 7(3):235-238.

___ 1992 The origin and dispersal of anatomically modern humans in East and Southeast Asia. In T. Akazawa, K. Aoki, and T. Kimura (eds): *The Evolution and Dispersal of Modern Humans in Asia.* Hokusen-sha, Tokyo. pp. 373-378.

WU XINZHI and ZHANG ZHENBIAO 1985 *Homo sapiens* remains from late Paleolithic and Neolithic China. In Wu Rukang and J.W. Olsen (eds): *Palaeoanthropology and Paleolithic Archaeology in the People's Republic of China.* Academic Press, New York. pp. 107-133.

YI, S., and G.A. CLARK 1985 The "Dyuktai" culture and New World origins. *Current Anthropology* 26(1):1-20.

ZUBROW, E. 1989 The demographic modeling of Neanderthal extinction. In P. Mellars and C.B. Stringer (eds): *The Human Revolution: Behavioural and Biological Perspectives on the Origins of Modern Humans.* Edinburgh University Press, Edinburgh. pp. 212-231.

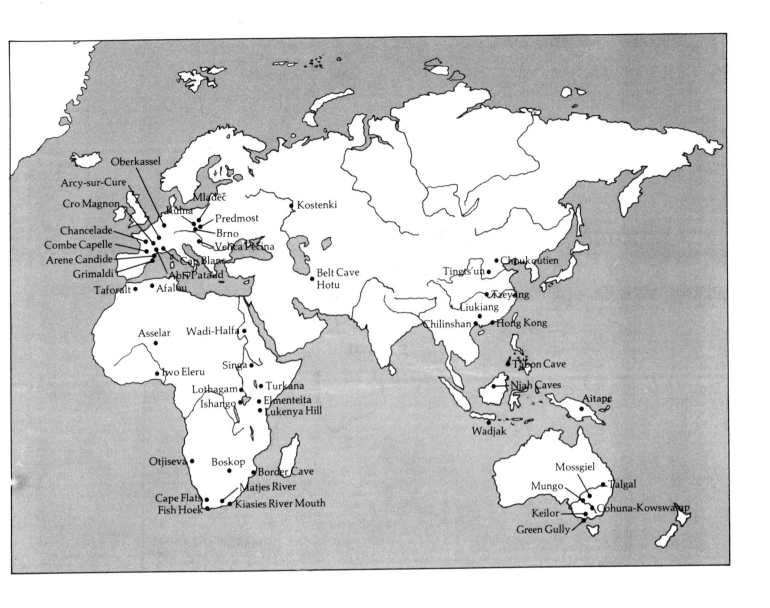

Map 14.1 Distribution of Late Pleistocene humans.

Map 14.2 Hominid and archaeological sites in Greater Australia, as exposed at low sea level, after Habgood (1991).

FROM HABGOOD, P.J. 1991 Aboriginal fossil hominids: evolution and migrations. In R. Foley (ed): *The Origins of Human Behavior*. Unwin Hyman, London. pp. 97-113, figure 7.1.

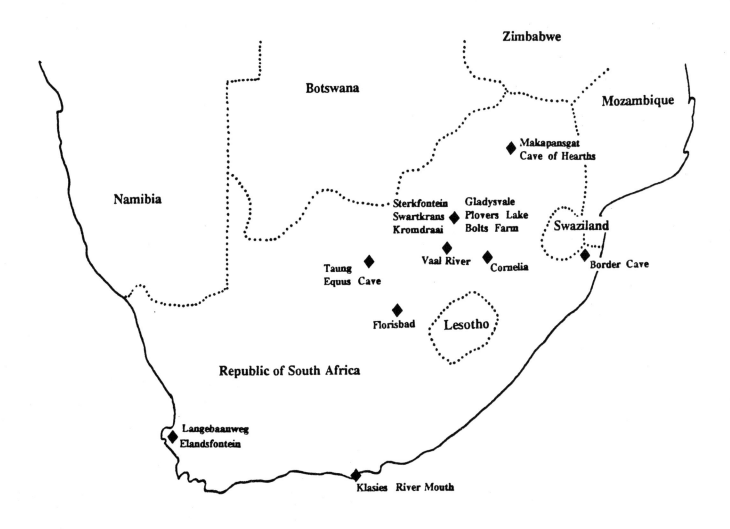

Map 14.3 South African sites, courtesy of J. McKee.

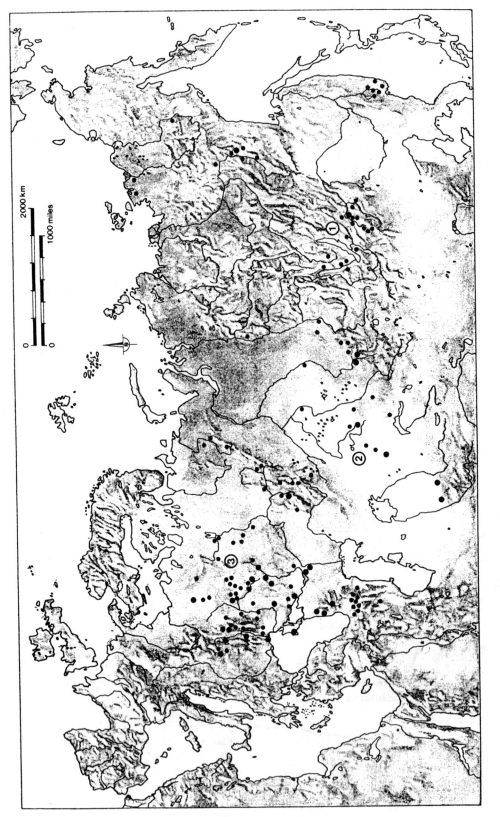

Map 14.4 Distribution of the Paleolithic across the Eurasian plain, after Otte (1994). Otte argues that the Eurasian plain forms one large occupation area, the Paleolithic sites (dots) reflect occupations of similar environments. He contends that the origin of modern Central and Western Eurasians can be traced to the westward extension of Upper Paleolithic industries.

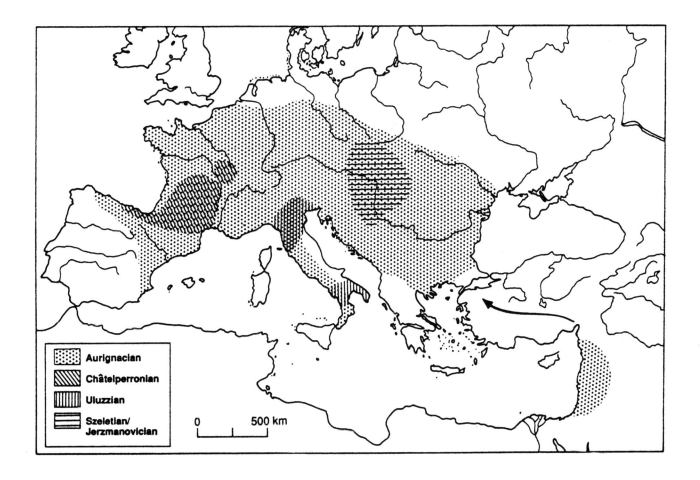

Map 14.5 Distribution of the Aurignacian and other early Upper Paleolithic industries in Eurasia, after Mellars (1992). Châtelperronian, Szeletian, and Uluzzian were regarded as transitional industries, linking Middle and Upper Paleolithic cultures, before Neandertals were found at Châtelperronian sites. These Upper Paleolithic facies are now recognized as the results of Neandertal behavior, and the makers of the *earliest* Aurignacian remain unknown.

FROM Mellars, P.A. 1992 Archaeology and the population-dispersal hypothesis of modern human origins in Europe. Philosophical Transactions of the Royal Society, Series B, 337:225-234, figure 1.

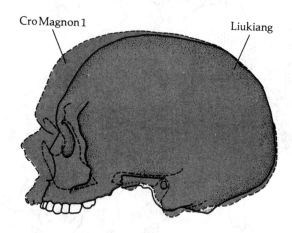

Figure 14.2 Liujiang and Cro Magnon males superimposed, contrasting the marked facial projection in the European and its absence in Asia.
FROM First edition, figure 13.1

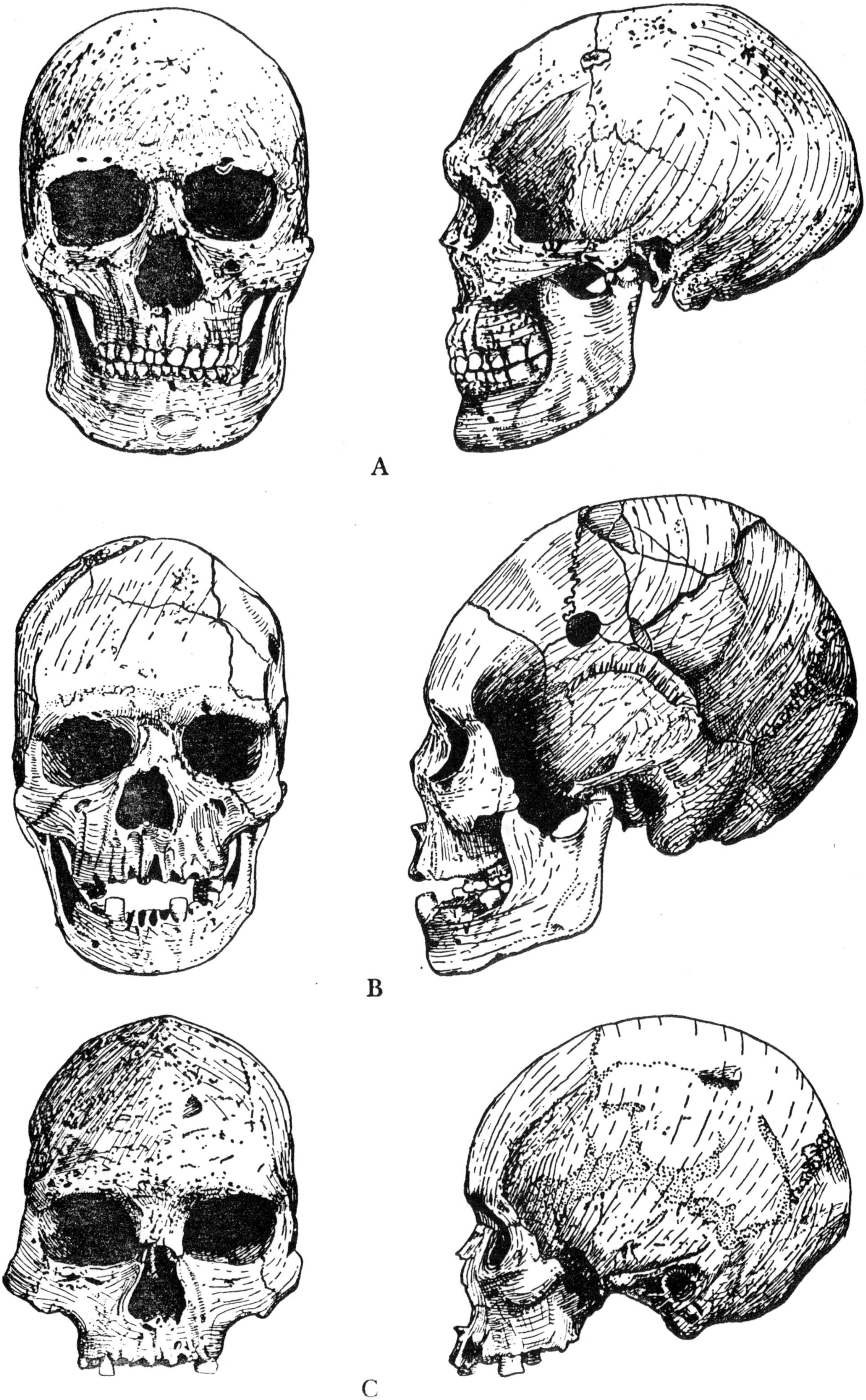

FIGURE 14.3 The three crania from the upper Cave at Zhoukoudian, after Hooton, 1947. A is the male 101, B the "Melanesoid" female 102 with artificial deformation (actually a 12-13 year old boy), and C is the "Eskimoid" female 103.

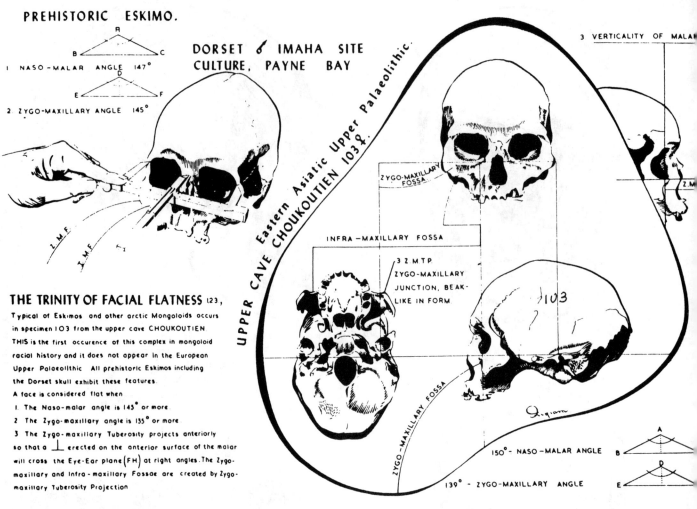

PREHISTORIC ESKIMO.

DORSET ♂ IMAHA SITE CULTURE, PAYNE BAY

1. NASO-MALAR ANGLE 147°
2. ZYGO-MAXILLARY ANGLE 145°

UPPER CAVE CHOUKOUTIEN 103 ♀ — Eastern Asiatic Upper Palaeolithic

3 VERTICALITY OF MALAR

ZYGO-MAXILLARY FOSSA

INFRA-MAXILLARY FOSSA

3 Z.M.T.P. ZYGO-MAXILLARY JUNCTION, BEAK-LIKE IN FORM.

ZYGO-MAXILLARY FOSSA

THE TRINITY OF FACIAL FLATNESS [23]

Typical of Eskimos and other arctic Mongoloids occurs in specimen 103 from the upper cave CHOUKOUTIEN. THIS is the first occurence of this complex in mongoloid racial history and it does not appear in the European Upper Palaeolithic. All prehistoric Eskimos including the Dorset skull exhibit these features.

A face is considered flat when

1. The Naso-malar angle is 145° or more.
2. The Zygo-maxillary angle is 135° or more.
3. The Zygo-maxillary Tuberosity projects anteriorly so that a ⊥ erected on the anterior surface of the malar will cross the Eye-Ear plane (FH) at right angles. The Zygomaxillary and Infra-maxillary Fossae are created by Zygomaxillary Tuberosity Projection

150° - NASO-MALAR ANGLE

139° - ZYGO-MAXILLARY ANGLE

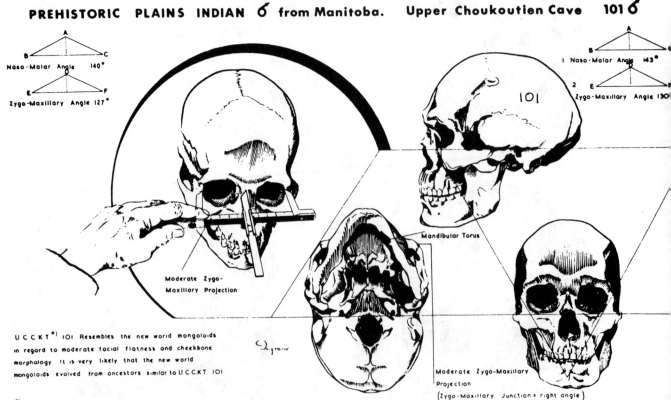

PREHISTORIC PLAINS INDIAN ♂ from Manitoba.

Naso-Malar Angle 140°

Zygo-Maxillary Angle 127°

EASTERN ASIATIC Upper Palaeolithic
Upper Choukoutien Cave 101 ♂

1. Naso-Malar Angle 143°
2. Zygo-Maxillary Angle 130°

Moderate Zygo-Maxillary Projection

Mandibular Torus

Moderate Zygo-Maxillary Projection
(Zygo-Maxillary Junction = right angle)

U.C.C.K.T.*) 101 Resembles the new world mongoloids in regard to moderate facial flatness and cheekbone morphology. It is very likely that the new world mongoloids evolved from ancestors similar to U.C.C.K.T. 101

FIGURE 14.4 Mongoloid features of the Upper Cave adults, as reviewed by Oschinsky (1964). From Weidenreich in the late 1930's to Brown today, numerous scientists have recognized Mongoloid features in these crania

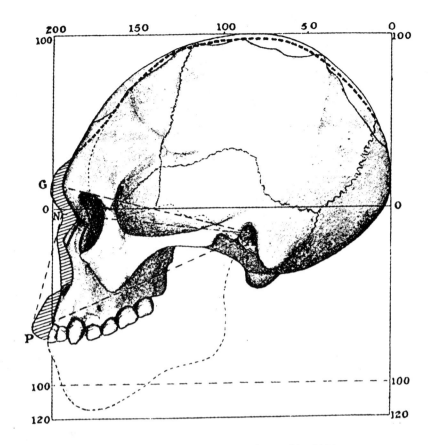

FIGURE 14.5 Cohuna and a reconstructed Talgai superimposed, after Keith (1931).
FROM Keith, A. 1931 New Discoveries Relating to the Antiquity of Man. Williams and Norgate, London, figure 100.

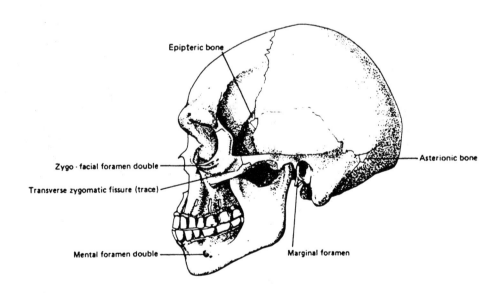

FIGURE 14.6 An Australian Aborigine cranium showing some of the nonmetric features used in Pardoe's (1991) analysis.
FROM Pardoe, C. 1991 Isolation and evolution in Tasmania. *Current Anthropology* 32(1):1-21.

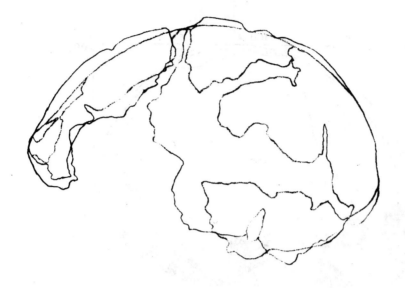

FIGURE 14.7 Eyassi and Kabua vaults superimposed.

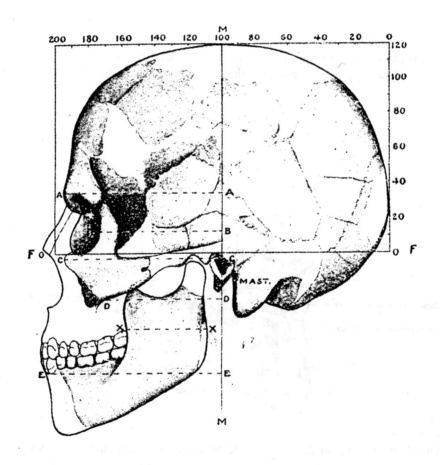

FIGURE 14.8   Springbok Flats, after Keith (1931).
FROM Keith, A. 1931 New Discoveries Relating to the Antiquity of Man. Williams and Norgate, London,
figure 45.

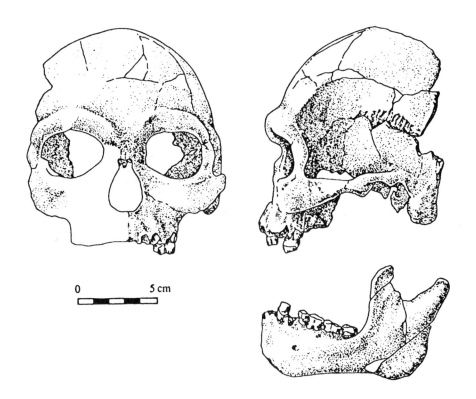

FIGURE 14.9 Dar es Soltane II, after Klein (1990).
FROM Klein, R.G. 1990 The Human Career. Human Biological and Cultural origins. University of Chicago Press, Chicago, figure 6.17.

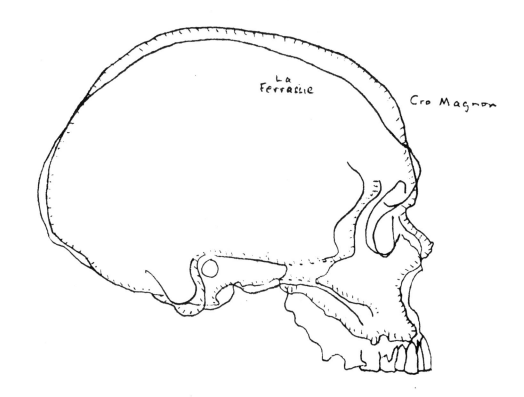

FIGURE 14.10 Cro Magnon and La Ferrassie males superimposed.

FIGURE 14.11 A comparison of Shanidar 1 and a Pavolvian cranium from Předmostí, after Klein (1990).
The crania are quite similar in many respects, although some details clearly differentiate them.
FROM Klein, R.G. 1990 The Human Career. Human Biological and Cultural origins. University of
Chicago Press, Chicago, figure 6.7.

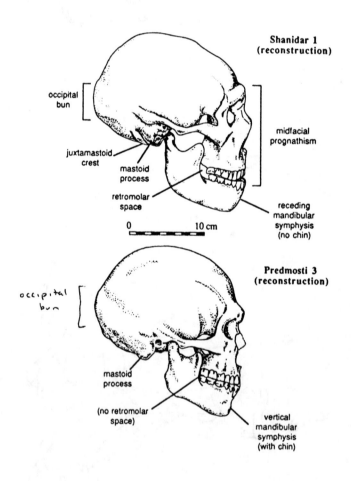

FIGURE 14.12 Mladeč 1 female, after Szombathy (1925)
FROM Szombathy, J. 1925 Die diluvialen Menschenreste aus der Fürst-Johanns-Höhle bei Lausch
in Mähren. *Die Eiszeit* 2:1-34, 73-95, figures 13-17.

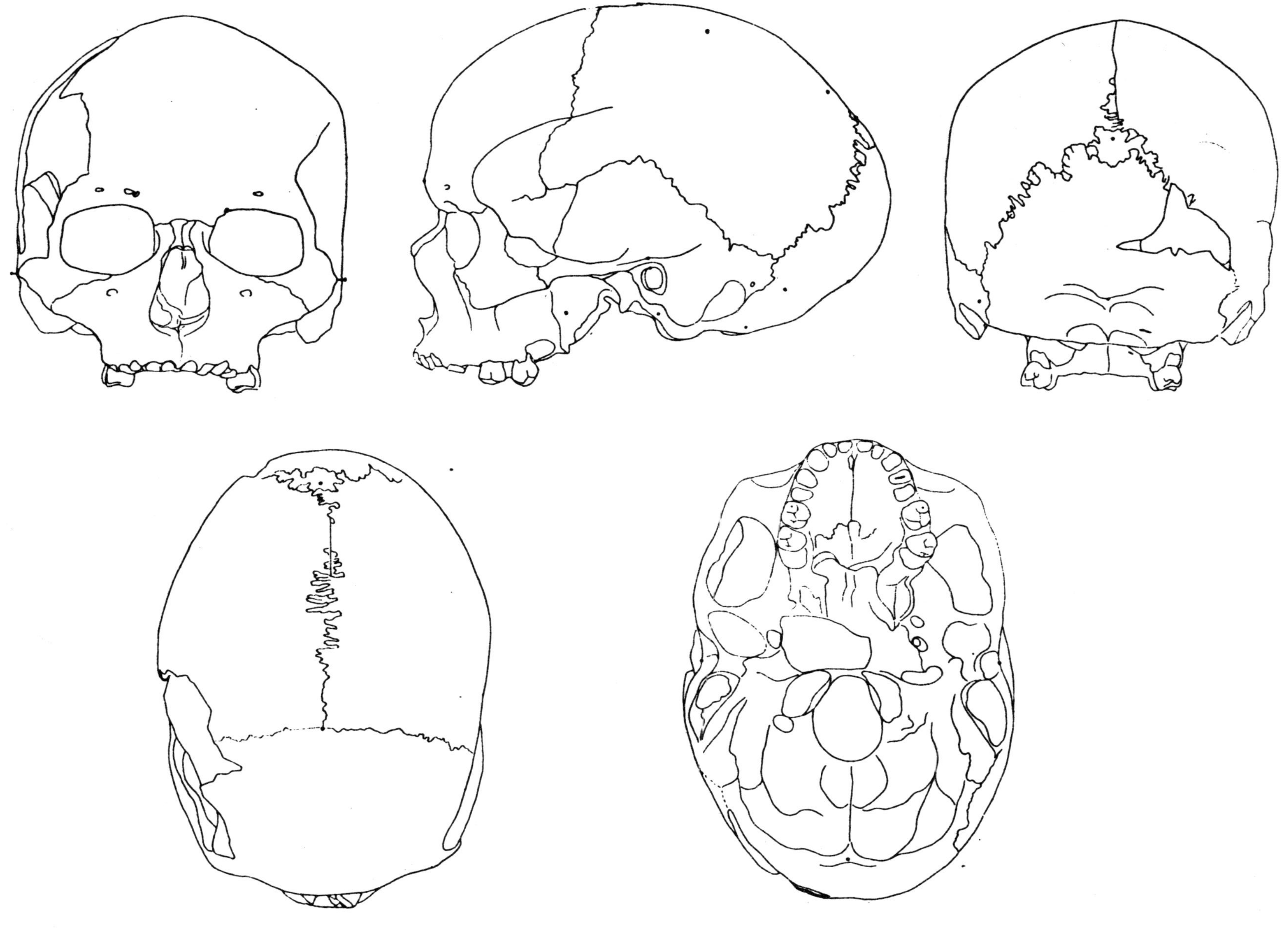

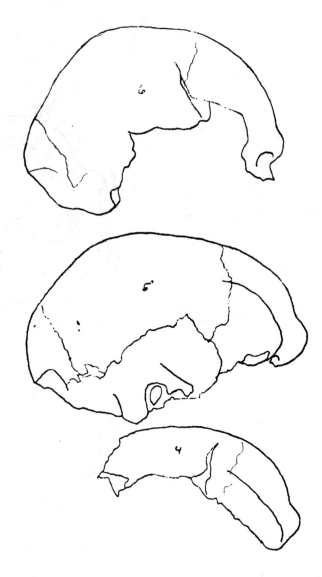

FIGURE 14.13 Mladeč males.

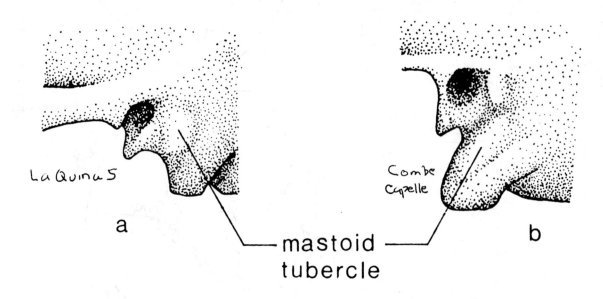

FIGURE 14.14 Mastoid tubercle in La Quina 5 and Combe Capelle, courtesy of D. Frayer.

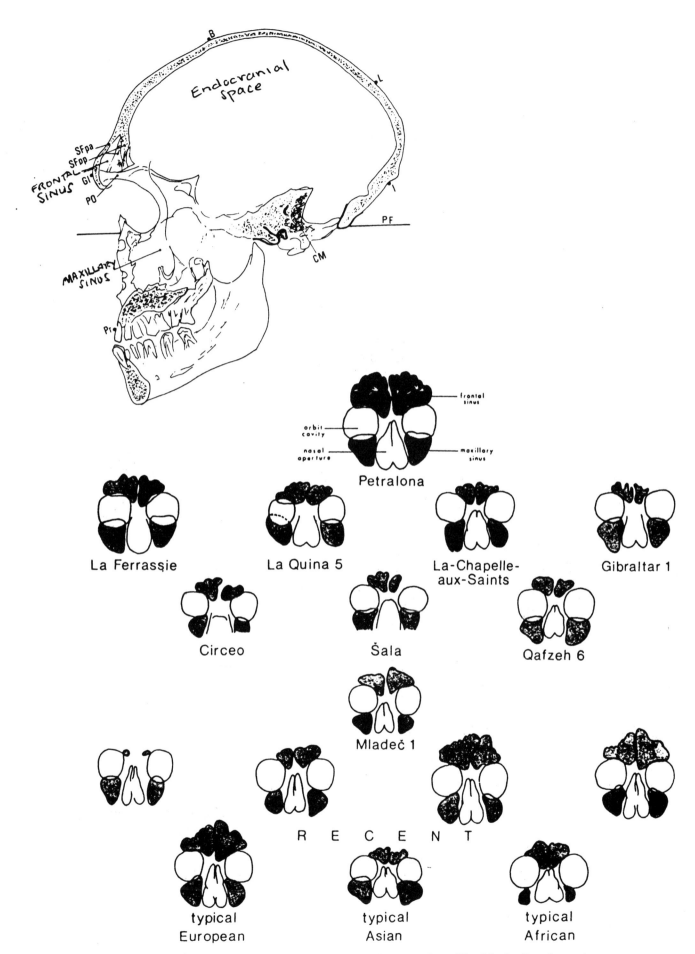

FIGURE 14.15 Geographic distribution of paranasal sinuses (frontal and maxillary) in fossil and recent crania, after Szilvássy and colleagues, with a cross-section of La Ferrassie (after Heim 1976) showing the sinus positions. In the European pattern these sinuses are about equal in size; frontal sinuses predominate in Africans and Maxillary sinuses in Asians according to these authors.

FIGURE 14.16 Suprainiac fossa in La Quina 5 and Předmostí 3, courtesy of D. Frayer. While several early Upper Paleolithic Europeans have a suprainiac fossa, only that of Mladeč 6 closely resembles the Neandertal anatomy.

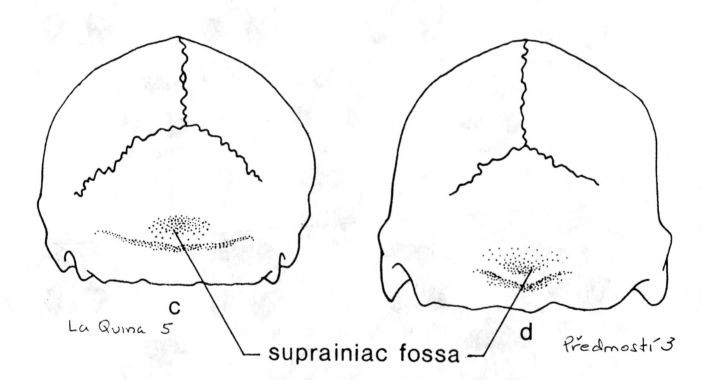

La Quina 5

c

d

Předmostí 3

— suprainiac fossa —

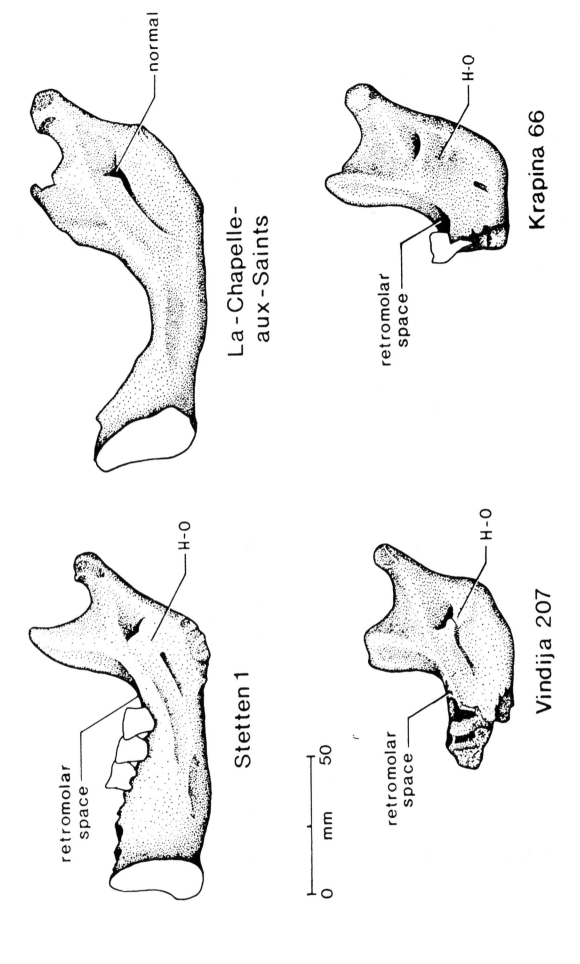

FIGURE 14.17 Retromolar space and mandibular foramen types, courtesy of D. Frayer. The features are shown in both Neandertal and earlier Upper Paleolithic mandibles.

FIGURE 14.18   Proximal femoral flange (arrow), a feature common for European femurs (and absent in Skhul 4 and other Levant specimens), courtesy of D. Frayer.

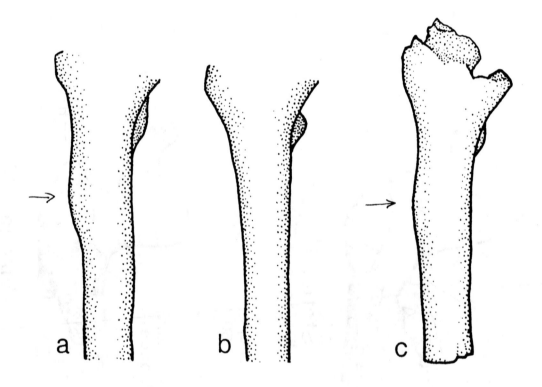

Proximal femoral flange in Spy 2 (a), Skhul 4 (b), and Mladec 28 (c), from casts.

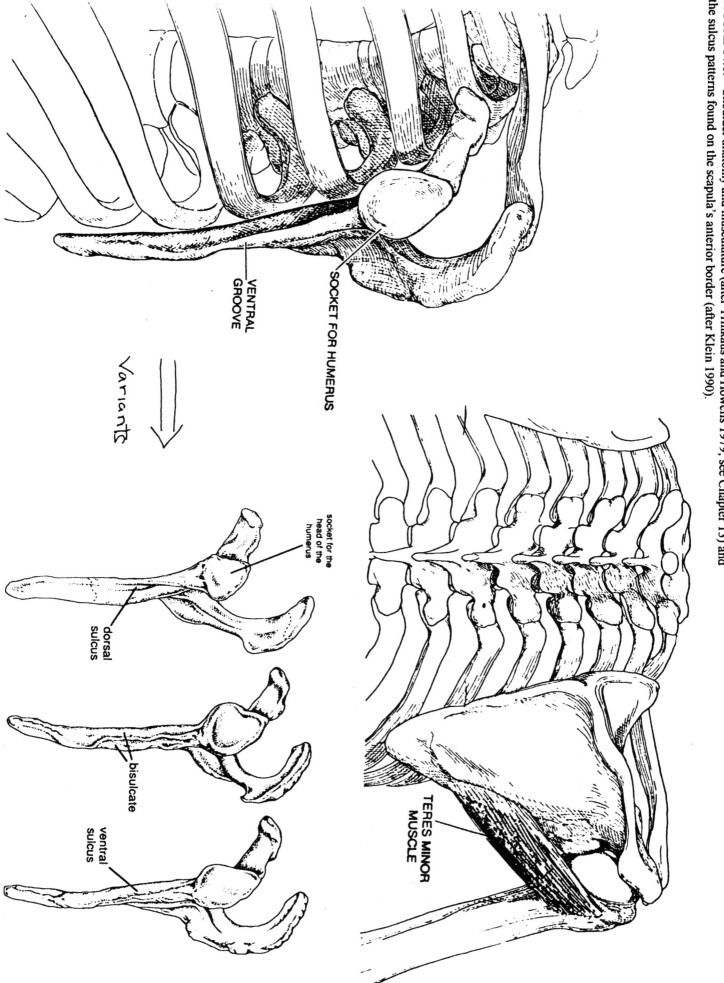

FIGURE 14.19 Shoulder anatomy and musculature (after Trinkaus and Howells 1979, see Chapter 13) and the sulcus patterns found on the scapula's anterior border (after Klein 1990).

VENTRAL GROOVE

SOCKET FOR HUMERUS

Variants

socket for the head of the humerus

dorsal sulcus

bisulcate

ventral sulcus

TERES MINOR MUSCLE

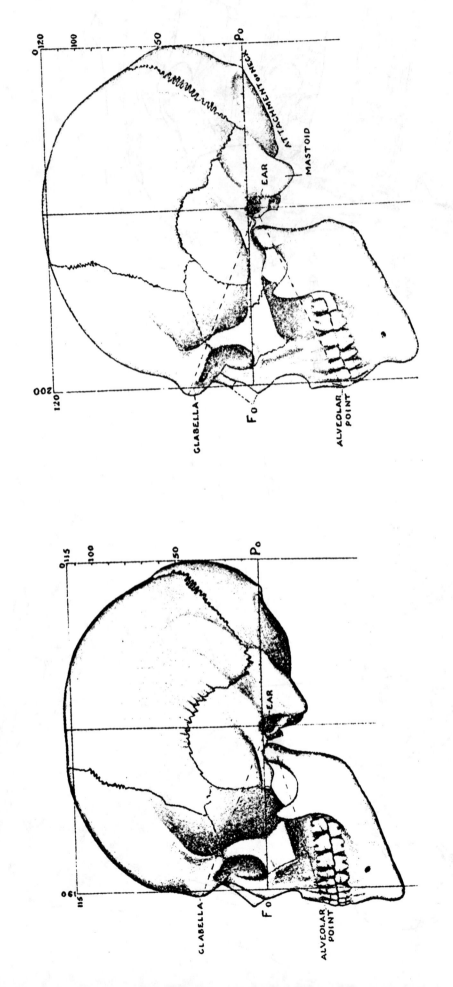

FIGURE 14.20 Předmostí female (4, left) and male (3) crania, after Keith (1931).
FROM Keith, A. 1931 *New Discoveries Relating to the Antiquity of Man.* Williams and Norgate, London, figures 122, 123.

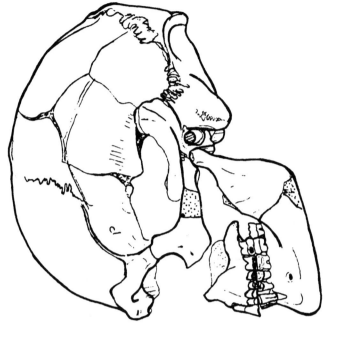

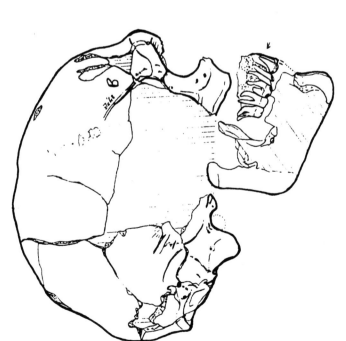

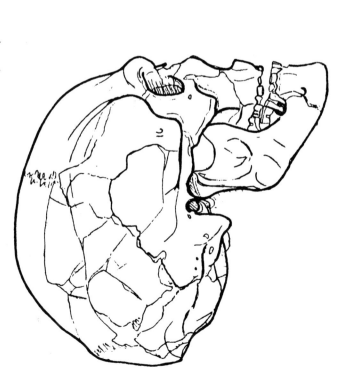

FIGURE 14.21 Pavolvian male crania Brno 2 (above, left), Pavlov (right), Dolní Věstonice 16 (below, left) and Předmostí 3, after Vlček (1991).

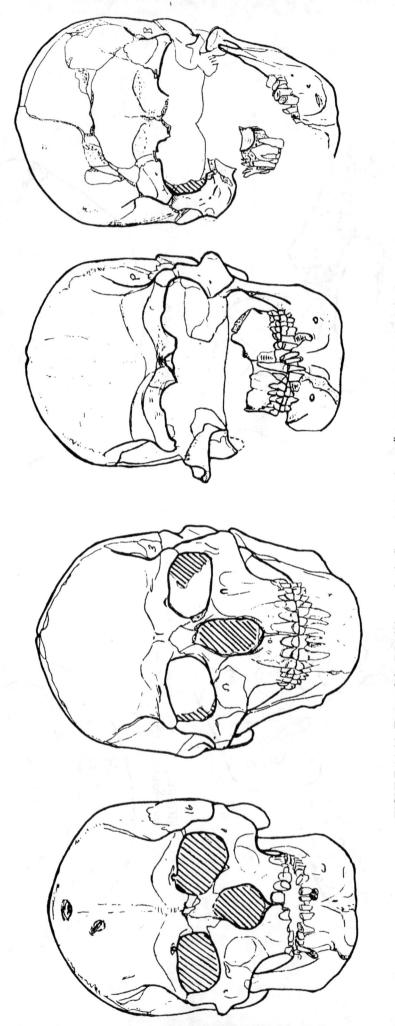

FIGURE 14.22 Faces of the Pavolvian males in figure 14.21, after Vlček (1991). From the left, the specimens are Dolní Věstonice 16, Předmostí 3, Pavlov, and Brno 2.

FROM Vlček, E. 1991 *Die Mammutjäger von Dolní Věstonice.* Anthropologische Bearbeitung der Skelette aus Dolní Věstonice und Pavlov. Archäologie und Museum Heft 22. Arbeit des Amtes für Museen und Archäologie des Kantons, Baselland. Liestal, Switzerland, figures 35, 37-9.

FIGURE 14.23 Dolní Věstonice 3 and Brno 3, two of the best preserved Pavlovian females, after Vlček
(1991).
FROM Vlček, E. 1991 *Die Mammutjäjer von Dolní Věstonice.* Anthropologische Bearbeitung der Skelette
aus Dolní Véstonice und Pavlov. Archäologie und Museum Heft 22. Arbeit des Amtes für Museen und
Archäologie des Kantons, Baselland. Liestal, Switzerland, figures 42, 44.

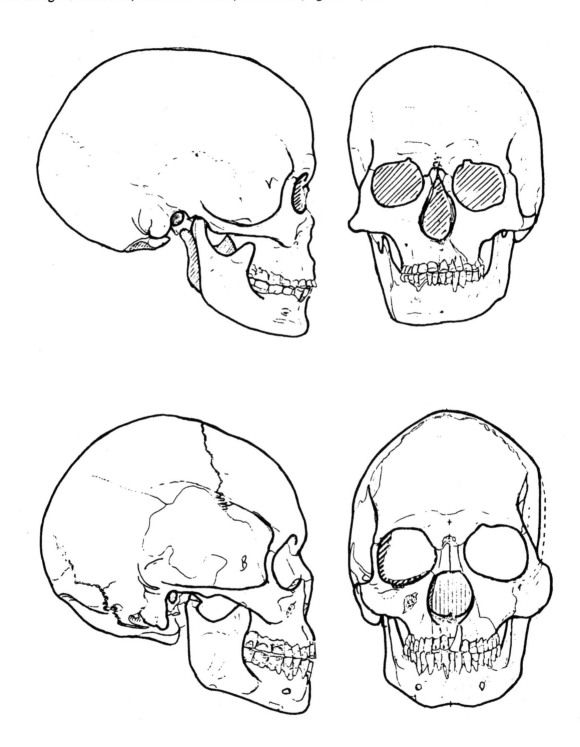

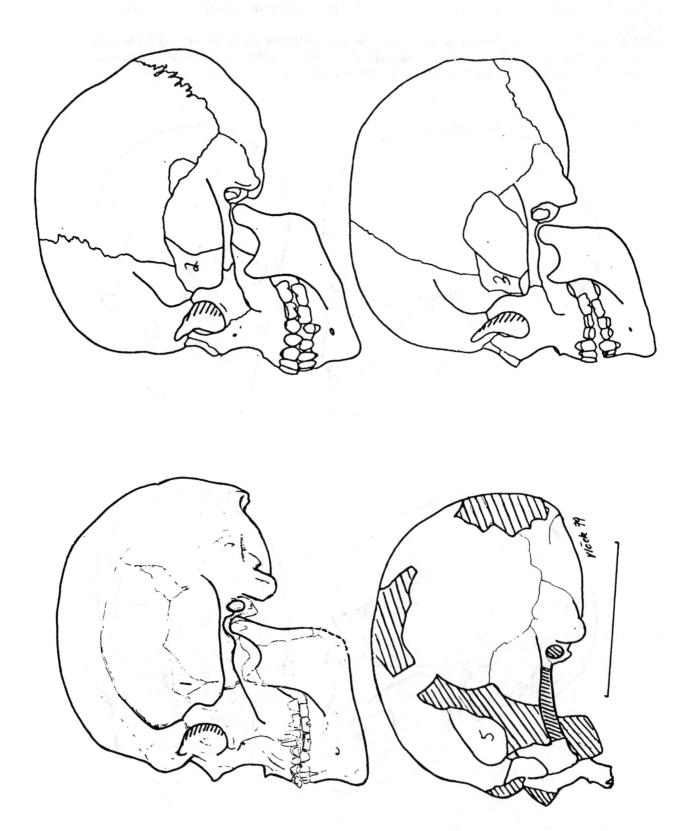

FIGURE 14.24 Sungir crania, after Vlček (1991).
FROM Vlček, E. 1991 *Die Mammutjäjer von Dolní Věstonice*. Anthropologische Bearbeitung der Skelette aus Dolní Véstonice und Pavlov. Archäologie und Museum Heft 22. Arbeit des Amtes für Museen und Archäologie des Kantons, Baselland. Liestal, Switzerland, figures 40, 41, 49.

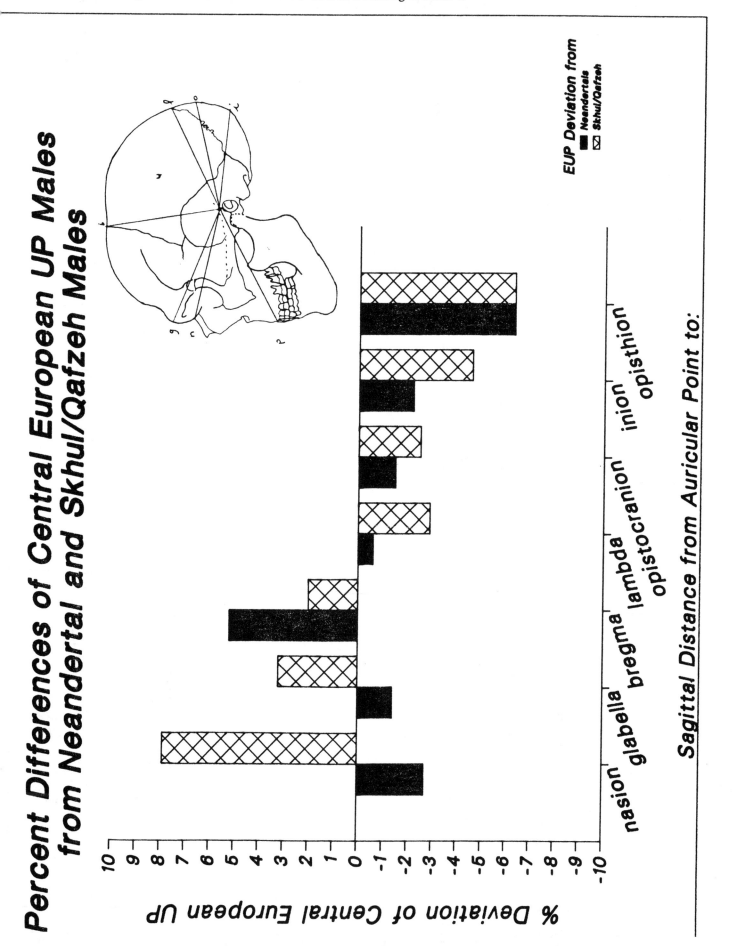

FIGURE 14.25 Cranial shape, as expressed in measurements from the auricular point. The mean male values for the early Central European Upper Paleolithic are expressed as deviations from the Neandertal and Skhul/Qafzeh male means. Excepting the distance to bregma (cranial height), the deviation from Neandertals is invariably less. The measurements are shown on a drawing of Skhul 4.

Mandibular Tooth Breadth Deviations of European EUP

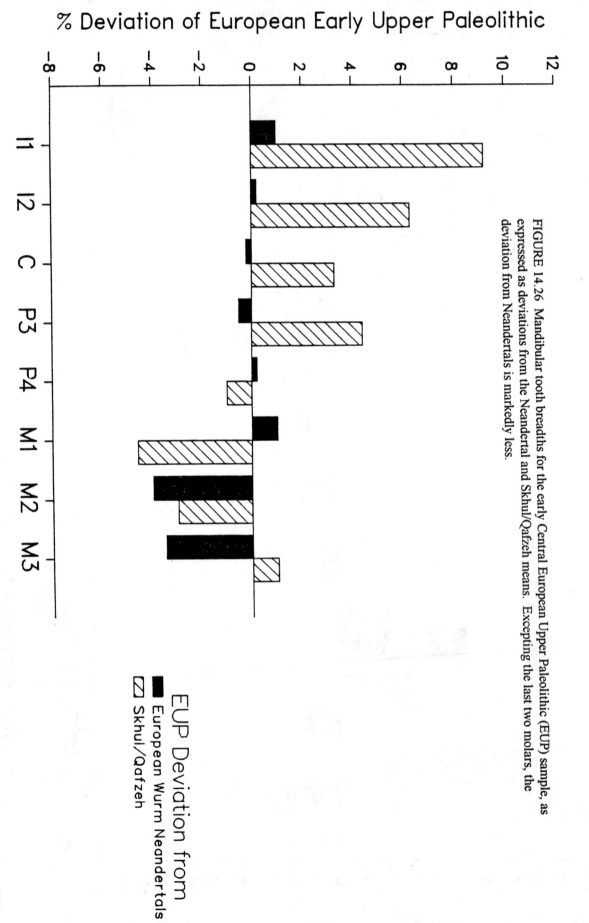

FIGURE 14.26 Mandibular tooth breadths for the early Central European Upper Paleolithic (EUP) sample, as expressed as deviations from the Neandertal and Skhul/Qafzeh means. Excepting the last two molars, the deviation from Neandertals is markedly less.

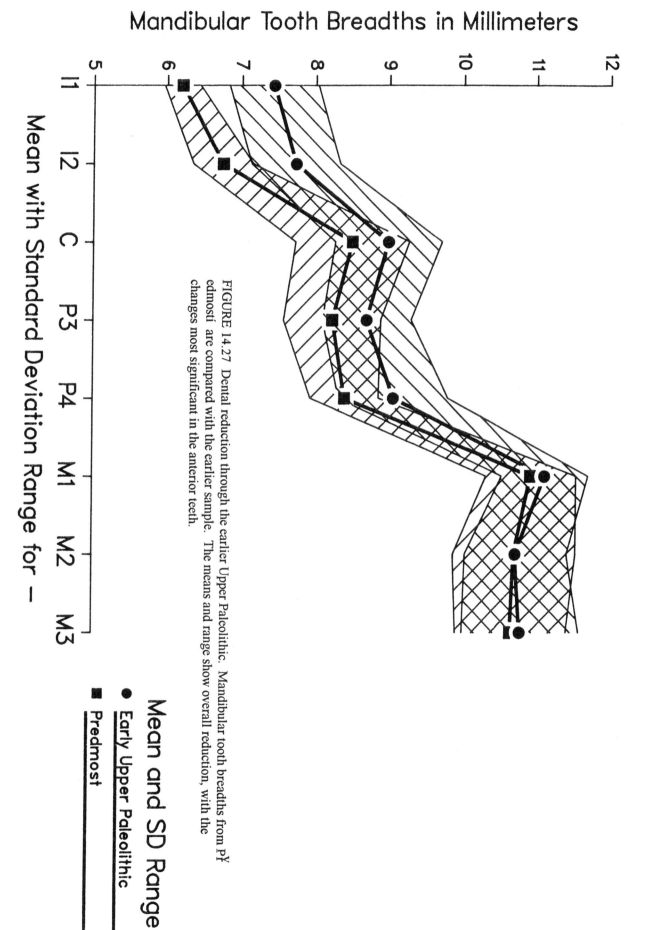

Mandibular Tooth Breadths in Millimeters

European Early Upper Paleolithic and Predmost Mandibular Tooth Breadths

Mean with Standard Deviation Range for —

FIGURE 14.27 Dental reduction through the earlier Upper Paleolithic. Mandibular tooth breadths from Předmostí are compared with the earlier sample. The means and range show overall reduction, with the changes most significant in the anterior teeth.

Mean and SD Range

● Early Upper Paleolithic
■ Predmost

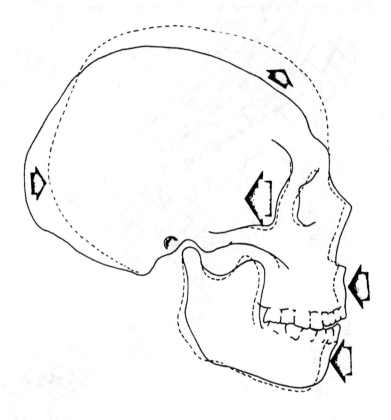

FIGURE 14.28 A model of facial reduction as a consequence of diminished masticatory function, based on a comparison of Shanidar and a Nubian Mesolithic specimen, courtesy of D. Carlson.

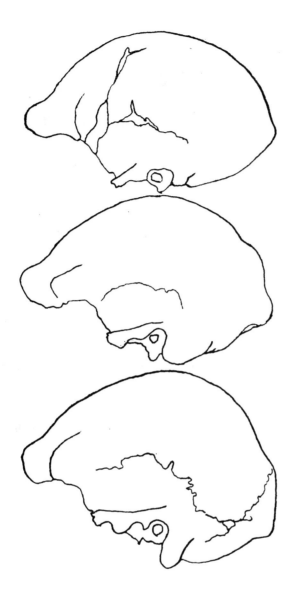

FIGURE 14.29 Weidenreich found evidence of regional continuity in Australasia even before faces were known from the Indonesian fossil record. This figure shows his comparison of Sangiran (above), Ngandong (middle), and a modern cranium (with the face removed to make the comparison easier).

Glossary

These are definitions that may be helpful in reading the book. Definitions are provided for terms not fully defined in the text, or used often throughout. They are not meant to be descriptions or summaries of the topics substantively discussed in it. Other recommended sources that provide more detailed technical descriptions of skeletal anatomy and function are Aiello and Dean (1990), Kraus, Jordan, and Abrams (1969), and White (1991). See References for details.

abduction. Movement of a limb away from the sagittal plane of the body, or of a digit away from the long axis of a limb.

absolute dating. See numerical dating.

acetabulo-cristal buttress. See iliac pillar.

acetabulum. Joint depression in the innominate into which the head of the femur fits - the socket in the ball-and-socket hip joint. The three bones of the innominate (ilium, ischium, pubis) meet in the acetabulum.

adaptation. Changing to fit, or respond to, the requirements of the environment.

adaptive radiation. Multiplication of species from a single phyletic line into a series of closely related taxa occupying different niches or adaptive zones.

adaptive valleys (c.f. adaptive peaks). Stable morphological configurations based on effective genetic compromises that maximize overall fitness in specific adaptive niches, envisioned as a series of dips across a fitness plateau.

adduction. Movement of a limb toward the sagittal plane of the body, or of a digit toward the long axis of a limb.

airorhynchy An upward rotation of the front of the palate (the alveolar portion of the face under the nose).

allele. Any of the alternative forms of a gene at a specific locus (position) on a chromosome.

Allen's rule. To retain heat, warm-blooded animals tend to have shorter and bulkier limbs in colder climates than their relatives in warmer regions. Also see Bergman's rule.

allometry (allometric scaling). Generally, the effect of size on shape. Specifically, any relationship of anatomical variables that fits the equation $Y = AX^k$ (A is a constant, k the coefficient of allometry).

alloparenting(aunting). assistance in care of infants and juveniles by individuals other than parents.

allopatric speciation. Species formation when there is geographical isolation (cf. sympatric speciation).

allopatry. Nonoverlapping geographic ranges.

altricial. Having the young born in an immature and helpless condition.

altruism. Behavior that benefits another individual at a cost to the actor, where cost and benefit are defined in terms of reproductive success.

alveolar height. The vertical dimension of the lower part of the skeletal face, from the lower nasal border to the bone between the upper incisors.

alveolar margin. The rim of the alveolar process.

alveolar process. The tooth-bearing portion of the jaw.

alveolar prognathism. Forward projection of the portions of the jaws that hold the teeth and their roots.

alveoli (s. alveolus) Tooth sockets in the mandible or maxilla.

anagenesis. Anatomical change in a single lineage over time that is sufficient to name a new species.

angular trigone. See lateral frontal trigone.

angular torus. A raised and thickened ridge at the back of the posterior temporalis muscle attachment, where the line marking the furthest backward extent of its fan-shaped fibers angles downward and forward.

anterior. Front.

anterior iliac spines. in hominids, two bony projections (superior and inferior) for muscles to attach that extend the leg, protruding from the front edge of the ilium. *Sartorius* attaches on the anterior superior spine and *rectus femoris* (one of the quadriceps) on the anterior inferior spine.

anterior pillars (of the maxilla). Two vertical columns of bone, on either side of the nasal aperture, extending above and lengthening the pilaster of bone surrounding the canine roots.

anterior tooth loading. Forces placed on the front teeth when an object is held between them. The source of the force on the teeth of each jaw is the opposite jaw and the force applied to the object.

anthropithecine. A member of the subfamily Anthropithecinae, the group including the African apes and the hominids.

antimeres. Equivalent teeth from opposite sides of the jaw; i.e., as in left and right M_1.

apomorphy. A derived character, a feature whose state is unlike the ancestral condition. If it is a unique variation it is an autapomorphy, if shared by more than one taxon, it is a synapomorphy.

appendicular skeleton. The bones of the limbs and the shoulder girdle.

arboreal. Living mainly in trees; for instance, arboreal quadrupeds are animals that use all four limbs in walking and running on tree limbs.

Arboreal theory. A theory that many of the cranial and postcranial adaptations found in primates are actually exaptations for life in the trees.

articular surface. Portion of a bone that is linked to another bone through an intervening joint of cartilage.

articular eminence. The articular surface in front of the mandibular fossa, where the mandibular condyle is located when it transmits force during mastication. The eminence may be expressed as anything from a straight, angled, plane to vertical and horizontal surfaces that meet along an edge.

articulation. Joint between two or more bones.

artifacts. Humanly modified objects.

ascending ramus (rami). Vertical portion of the mandible, extending from the corpus to the condyle.

assemblage. All the artifacts, fauna, and other debris found in a single layer or excavation unit at a site.

association area (of the brain). One of the many regions of the cerebral cortex not devoted exclusively to either primary sensory perception such as vision and audition, or to motor movement, but rather to more complex associations between these modalities. There are frontal, parietal, and temporal association areas.

asterion. A point on the back of the skull at which the lambdoidal, parietomastoid and occipital sutures meet.

asterionic notch. See mastoid notch.

astragalus (talus). Ankle bone.

atlas. Most superior of the cervical vertebrae, supporting the cranial articulation.

atrical. Late in development.

auditory meatus. External opening of the ear canal.

auditory tube. The tube of bone holding the tympanic part of the temporal, the passage leading to the tympanic membrane.

auricular point. A point often used for measurements, particularly projected into the sagittal plant, located vertically above the center of the auditory meatus and porion, on the root or base of the zygomatic arches. This point is located a few millimeters above, and lateral to, the porion.

australopithecine. Referring to members of the genus *Australopithecus*.

autapomorphy. An apomorphy unique to a single species.

axial skeleton. The part of the skeleton along the central axis of the body: vertebral column, pelvis, and thorax.

axillary. Of or pertaining to the arm-pit.

B.P. Before present.

balanced polymorphism. A multiplicity of forms in which the frequencies of the different forms do not differ significantly over time because of selection against the more heterozygotic variants.

band. A simple form of human social organization, consisting of one or more families.

basicranium. Base of the skull, formed mainly by the occipital, petrosal (of the temporal) and sphenoid bones.

basi-occiput. The most anterior portion of the occipital bone on the cranial base, the process that is in front of the foramen magnum and meets the sphenoid.

basion. The point there the anterior border of the foramen magnum crosses the midline.

bauplan. The basic inter-related structural characteristics of a species.

bed. In geology, a small, distinct rock unit.

Bergmann's rule. Warm-blooded animals of similar shape tend to be larger in cold climates because larger animals loose heat less rapidly than the smaller ones. Also see Allen's Rule.

Beringia. The continent, or wide land bridge, spanning the Bering Strait between Alaska and Siberia at times of low sea level, including contiguous parts of both.

biceps brachialis **muscle.** Muscle extending from below the humerus midshaft, across the front of the elbow, and attaching on the top of the ulna. It flexes the elbow.

biceps brachii **muscle.** A two-joint muscle extending from the scapula (two attachments), across the shoulder and elbow joints, to the radial tuberosity. It can flex the humerus and rotate the forearm, most effectively supinating it.

bicondylar angle (of the femur). The angle from vertical that the shaft of the femur makes when the bone is stood upright on its condyles.

bicuspid. A premolar tooth.

biface. Stone artifact with flakes removed from two intersecting surfaces, creating a sharp edge.

bilateral symmetry. Anatomical features for which the right and left sides are close to being mirror images of one another.

bilophodont. Teeth with two crests, a type of molar construction in which there are two parallel enamel ridges on the occlusal surface, running from side to side connecting the cusps.

binocular vision. Vision in which both eyes can focus on a distant object to produce a stereoscopic (three-dimensional) image.

biological species. Defines a species as a reproductively isolated aggregate of populations which can actually or potentially interbreed and produce fertile offspring. The concept focuses on the importance of reproductive isolation and the anatomical and behavioral mechanisms that create it.

biomass. The total weights of all the organisms in a particular area.

biomechanics. Pertaining to the physics of the skeletal system, especially its static and dynamic analyses.

biostratigraphy. Sequential or temporal ordering of strata based on the fossils they contain.

bipedal. Two-legged.

bipolar technique. Removal of flakes from a core resting on a hard surface, giving the flakes different thickness characteristics and the core a unique form because there is a shock-wave from percussion at both ends.

blade tool. An artifact formed on a parallel-sided stone flake, usually removed from a carefully prepared core but defined as any flake whose length is more than double its breadth.

bonobo. A supposed species of chimpanzee, *Pan paniscus,* that live in forested habitats of central Africa south of the Zaire River; the closest living relative of the common chimpanzee, *Pan troglodytes.*

boss. A round, broad, bulging eminence on cranial bones.

bottleneck. A period of intense selection or very small population size through which only certain genes survive, and come to characterize the population.

bovid. A member of the family Bovidae, cloven-hoofed ungulates (bison, antelopes, deer, goats, sheep, etc.). Most bones found at African sites are bovid.

Brachial index. Ratio of the length of the forearm divided by the length of the upper arm (radius/humerus x 100).

brachiation. Arm-over-arm arboreal locomotion in which the animal progresses below branches by swinging its body between forelimb supports.

brachycephalic broad-headed, having a Cephalic Index (cranial breadth/cranial length) above 80.

breccia sedimentary rock composed of angular fragments of derived material cemented together, often the main component of cave or fissure fillings..

bregma. The point at the top of the head where the coronal and sagittal sutures of the skull meet, or where the two parietals meet with the frontal.

bregmatic (prebregmatic) eminence. Small prominence on the cranial midline at or near bregma.

Broca's area. A cortical region of the human brain located on the side of the frontal lobe, just above the temporal lobe (directly beneath a finger placed at the temple). This area is important in speech production and injury to it will result in aphasia (language dysfunction).

brow ridge See supraorbital torus.

buccal. The cheek-facing side of a postcanine tooth.

bun. See occipital bun.

bunodont. Teeth with low, rounded cusps.

burin. A chisel-like stone tool for engraving bone, wood, horn or soft stone.

calcaneus. Heel bone.

calotte. The bones of the cranial vault, the calvaria without the cranial base.

calvaria (calvarium). The bones of the cranium without the face or mandible.

cancellous (spongy, trabecular) bone. Internal bone tissue that is porous and lightweight.

canine. A conical or spade-like tooth (depending on species) located between the incisors and premolars.

canine cutting complex. The slashing effect as the outer front (mesiobuccal) edge of the most anterior lower premolar slides along the back of the upper canine when the jaws close.

canine fossa. A vertical furrow on the maxilla under the infraorbital foramen, extending toward the base of the zygomatic process of the maxilla and to the side of the nose.

canine jugum (juga). Vertical ridge in the maxilla caused by an enlarged canine root.

caniniform. Shaped like a canine of conical form.

carnivore. (1) an animal that eats primarily the flesh of other animals; (2) members of the mammalian order Carnivora (which include cats, dogs, skunks, raccoons, and bears).

carpals. Small bones of the wrist; in humans the scaphoid, lunate, triquetrum, pisiform, hamate, capitate, trapezoid and trapezium.

carrying capacity. The number of individuals that can be optimally supported, given a particular subsistence adaptation.

cartilage. A flexible connective tissue that is an important part of most of the skeleton and that calcifies at various stages of growth.

caudal vertebrae. The vertebrae of the tail, below the sacrum.

cementum. A soft, bone-like tissue covering tooth roots, that anchors them to the ligament covering the alveolar bone.

Cephalic index. The ratio of the breadth to the length of the skull.

cercopithecine. Referring to members of the monkey subfamily Cercopithecinae.

cerebellar fossae. Two broad depressions on the internal surface of the occiput, holding the cerebellar lobes of the brain.

cerebellar lobe. One of the lobes of the cerebellum.

cerebellum. Area of the brain lying below and behind the cerebrum, functioning in proprioception - replaying feedback from muscle activity and motions back to the cortex for finer adjustments and coordination of movement.

cerebral cortex. Pertaining to the cerebrum, the front and upper portion of the brain, including the frontal, parietal, temporal, and occipital lobes.

cerebral fossae. Two broad depressions on the internal surface of the occiput, holding the posterior part of the occipital lobes of the cerebral cortex.

cerebral lobe. A division of the cerebral cortex at the rear of the brain.

cerebrum. The major part of the brain, occupying the upper part of the cranium, comprised of the two cerebral hemispheres connected by the corpus callosum.

cervical. Pertaining to the neck, as in the seven neck vertebrae.

character. A feature.

character displacement. A divergence of characters in competing sympatric species resulting from selection to reduce competition over limiting resources.

character state. The particular expression of a feature; for instance, the Cephalic index might be low, or hair color might be red.

cheek teeth. See postcanine teeth.

chignon. See occipital bun.

chopper. A stone made by taking a few flakes off of a pebble or rock fragment, to produce a sharp cutting edge.

chron (polarity chron or epoch). A main subdivision of time having predominately one magnetic polarity.

cingulum (pl. cingula) A shelf of enamel running partially or completely around the base of a tooth crown.

clade. A group composed of all the species descended from a single common ancestor; a monophyletic group.

cladistic homology. Homologies based on comparing features in different clades or lineages.

cladistics (cladism) Classification reflecting genealogy (recency of common descent) by means of shared derived characters; also call phylogenetic systematics.

cladogenesis. Species formation - the branching of a single lineage to form two lineages.

cladogram. A branching diagram, or dendogram, based on genealogy and used to represent phyletic relationships (*rates* of evolutionary divergence are ignored).

clavicle. Collarbone; the bone connecting the sternum (breastbone) to the scapula (shoulder blade).

clinal variation. Continuous, gradual variation of a trait. In the context of geographic patterns of a trait's variation, **gradients** are lines in space that follow its unchanging expression, and **clines** are the lines that are perpendicular to the gradients.

co-adapted genes. Sets of genes whose frequencies in a population reflect a compromise from different magnitudes and directions of selection acting on their various effects.

coccyx. Tailbone; made up of the caudal vertebrae, it is most often fused into a single unit.

codon. The three bases read in a row on DNA that code for a specific amino acid.

coefficient of variation (CV). A dimensionless measure of relative variability, designed to allow comparison of variation samples with different average sizes, calculated as the ratio of the **standard deviation** (σ) to the mean (M): $CV = 100 \times (\sigma/M)$.

cognitive map. Our mental construct of the physical and social world and our position in them.

collagen. A fibrous protein that is the chief constituent part of connective tissue in bone.

colobine. Referring to members of the monkey subfamily Colobinae.

colonizing species. A species with a high rate or reproduction, readily able to take advantage of new habitats because of its genetic variation and internal subdivisions.

compact (cortical) bone. The dense bone tissue found on the outside of bones or the walls of long bone shafts.

competitive exclusion. The principle that no two species can coexist a the same locality if they reply on the same limiting resources.

condyle. A smooth rounded articular surface that is found in pairs.

conspecific. Belonging to the same species.

convergence. The independent evolution of the same, or very similar, features in two or more species from different features in their last common ancestor.

Cope's rule. The generalization that there is a steady increase in size in phyletic series.

core. A piece of stone from which flakes have been removed.

coronal plane. A vertical plane extending from side to side that divides the body into front and back portions.

coronal suture. The suture between the frontal bone and the parietals behind it.

coronoid process. A hooked or curved projection. (1) The front part of the ascending ramus of the mandible, forming a pointed projection at its top, where part of the *temporalis* muscle attaches. (2) The lower projecting part of the ulna's trochlear notch, below the olecranon process.

corpus. Body, the principal part of a bone. See mandibular corpus.

corpus callosum. The bundle of neurons that connects the left and right cerebral hemispheres.

cortex (cortical layer). Outer surface or layer, the dense outer layer of most bones.

cranial base angle. The angle between the basi-occiput and the body of the sphenoid, incorrectly thought to be related to speech capacity.

cranium (crania). The skull without the mandible.

crenulation. Wrinkled surface of the tooth enamel.

crepuscular. Active primarily in dim light, around the hours of dawn and dusk.

crest. A ridge with a sharp edge caused by muscle pull. A **simple crest** is created by the unidirectional pull of a single muscle, a **compound crest** by the opposing pulls of two muscles.

cross-modal transfer. The integration of sensory, motor, and cognitive actions in the parietal association area.

cross-sectional studies. Examination of changes by studying many individuals of different ages at a single time.

Crural index. Ratio of the length of the lower leg (tibia) divided by the length of the upper leg (femur) $\times$ 100.

culturgen (meme). A basic unit of culture.

curated behavior Behaviors or strategies reflected in the archaeological record showing foresight and planning through repairs, recycling, and reuse (c.f. expedient behavior).

cursorial. Fast running.

cusp. An elevation on the occlusal surface of an unworn tooth.

decay. In physics, the breaking apart of nuclei into smaller constituent nuclei, releasing energetic particles in the process as there is less total energy.

deltoid muscle. A complex shoulder muscle with humerus, clavicle, and scapula attachments that brings the arm up, flexing or extending the humerus depending on which part of the muscle is used.

deciduous (milk) teeth. The first set of teeth in a mammalian jaw, replaced by the permanent dentition.

deme. A local population of a species; the community of potentially interbreeding individuals at a given locality; a population or race sampled over time.

demography. The study of a population's main life-history parameters - its growth, size, composition, and the age-specific rates of births and deaths.

dendogram. A branching diagram beginning with a single source.

dental arcade. The toothrow.

dental caries. A pathological process, with destruction of tooth enamel and dentine, leading to infection and loss of the tooth.

dental comb. A primate feature in which the incisors and canines of the lower jaw are of similar size and form, short peg-like teeth that are set horizontally across the front of the mouth.

dental eruption. A continuous process in which teeth emerge out of their crypts (alveolar eruption), through the gums (gingival eruption), and into occlusion with the opposing teeth of the opposite jaw (occlusal eruption), finally ending when the tooth is lost because it erupts out of the mouth.

dental formula. A shorthand notation of the number of incisors, canines, premolars, and molars on one side of the upper and lower dentition of a species (given as a single formula when upper and lower quadrants are the same). For example, the normal adult human dental formula is 2.1.2.3 or 2.1.2.2.

dental hypoplasia. Defects in the enamel of teeth created by interruptions in enamel development, usually because of stresses such as poor nutrition or infection.

dental microwear. Scratches, pits, and gouges on the occlusal surface of teeth that are so small they must be studies by an optical or **scanning electron microscope**.

dentin. Internal tissue in a tooth, surrounding the pulp cavity and surrounded by the enamel. This bone-like substance is softer than the enamel.

dentocranial. Pertaining to the teeth and cranium.

dentofacial. Pertaining to the teeth and face.

dentognathic. Pertaining to the teeth and jaws.

derived feature. (See apomorphic).

diagnosis. In taxonomy, a statement of the characters which uniquely distinguish a taxon from other taxa.

diagnostic. Distinguishing or uniquely characteristic.

diagonal grip. A hand hold in which the object or support (in climbing) is held diagonally across the fingers, without use of the palm.

diaphysis. The shaft portion of long bones.

diastema (pl. diastemata) space or gap between adjacent teeth in the tooth row, often present to accommodate a projecting canine from the opposing jaw; in the mandible the diastema is between the canine and anterior premolar, in the maxilla between the lateral incisor and canine..

Dietary Hypothesis. A theory developed by J.T. Robinson to explain the South African australopithecine variations. The hypothesis relates the differences in the gracile and robust South African australopithecines to ecological differences that were reflected in dietary adaptations. The gracile australopithecines are regarded as omnivores and the robust australopithecines as vegetarians.

differential reproduction. Differences in successful reproduction - some individuals have more surviving offspring than others.

differential tooth wear. Differences in the amount of wear between adjacent teeth.

digastric sulcus. A long furrow following the medial surface of the mastoid process, where the digastric muscles attach (muscles important in opening the mandible and moving the hyoid bone).

digital flexors. Muscles that cause bending in the fingers or toes.

digitigrade. A type of quadrupedal locomotion in which animals support their body weight on their phalanges.

dimorphism. Occurrence of two distinct forms, or sizes in a single population (cf. sexual dimorphism).

diploë. Spongy bone that is sandwiched between inner and outer cortical bone tables.

distal. further from the midline of the body, when applied to the appendicular skeleton, or further from the center of the jaw as directed along the tooth row, when applied to teeth.

diurnal. Usually active during daylight hours.

divergent digits. A finger or toe that is offset in its direction from the remaining digits, allowing some grasping ability.

division of labor. Different cooperative strategies, usually for males and females.

DNA (deoxyribonucleic acid). The molecule that carries the genetic information (genes) in all organisms except the RNA viruses. It consists of two long polysugar-phosphate strands connected by base pairs connecting congruent bases out of a set of 4, and twisted in a double helix.

dolichocephalic. Longheaded, having a Cephalic Index of less than 75.

dorsal. Toward the rearward side of the body; the opposite of ventral. The back of the hand and the "top" of the foot in humans are also considered the dorsal side.

dorsiflexion. Bending the dorsal surface of the hand (or foot) toward the arm (or leg).

dorsoventral. (Usually motion in) a front to back direction.

drift (genetic drift). Changes in gene frequencies due to random or stochastic variation and not the result of selection, mutation, or genic exchanges. Drift changes are most prominent in small populations.

dryopithecine . Member of the subfamily Dryopithecinae.

ear ossicles. The three small bones of the inner that transmit and transform sound, changing it from an auditory to a nervous signal. The three bones are **malleus** (hammer), **incus** (anvil), and **stapes** (stirrup).

eclectic. coming from many sources, as an eclectic diet.

ecotones. A boundary region between ecological zones.

edentuous. Toothless - jaws without any teeth remaining or preserved.

embryo. An organism during the first eight weeks of in-utero development.

eminence. A bony projection.

enamel. The hard, prismatically structured outer surface of a tooth crown.

enamel wrinkling. Secondary folding of the enamel at the occlusal surface of a tooth.

encephalization. The relative increase of brain size with respect to body weight.

endinion. The internal occipital protuberance, or internal inion, where the transverse sulcus dividing the internal surface of the occiput into the cerebral fossa superiorly and the cerebellar fossae inferiorly, meets the internal occipital crest separating the left and right cerebellar fossae.

endocast. A cast made of the mold formed of the impression the brain makes on the inside of the neurocranium, providing a replica of the brain with the grosser details of its outer surface. Also called endocranial cast.

endocranium. The inside of the neurocranium.

endogamy. Mating or marriage within a social or cultural unit (c.f. exogamy).

epigenetic rule. A regularity occurring during the interaction of genes and environment that channels anatomical, behavioral, or cognitive development in a particular direction.

epimerization. Racemization of the protein amino acid that occurs in egg shells.

epiphysis (plural epiphyses). A secondary center of ossification (bone formation) usually located at the ends of long bones, separated from the primary center (diaphysis, the shaft) by a cartilage growth plates that fuse when bone elongation is completed.

eruption priorities. Which tooth erupts first of a pair that emerge close together in time.

eruption standards The pattern of average eruptions in a population.

estrus. A time of increased female sexual activity, often accompanied by enhancement of visual or olfactory sexual signals, that occurs at and around the time of ovulation.

ethmoid bone. A small bone in the skull that contributes to the inner orbital wall and also forms a small portion of the floor of the braincase under the frontal lobes.

ethmoidal sinuses. Air spaces within the ethmoid bone.

eutherian. Placental mammal.

eversion. turning outward; for example, of the bottom of the foot.

evolution. Genetic change, change in a population's gene pool from generation to generation (Darwin's descent with modification).

evolutionary species. A single monophyletic lineage of ancestral-descendant populations which maintains its identity from other such lineages and which has its own evolutionary tendencies and historical fate. Reproductive isolation is implied by this definition, but not explicit in it.

exaptation. The name given for a character that evolved to fulfill a different function than the one it currently serves.

exogamy. Mating or marriage outside a social or cultural unit (c.f. endogamy).

expedient behavior. Behaviors and strategies reflected ion the archaeological record that serve to solve an immediate problem (c.f. curated behavior).

extant. Living, as opposed to extinct.

extension. Straightening out, a movement in which the angle of a limb joint increases. Opposite of flexion.

extensor. Any muscle that acts to increase the angle between two bones at their joint.

external occipital protuberance. See inion.

extramolar sulcus (mandibular). The gutter between the molar teeth and the interior surface of the ascending ramus, for attachment of the *buccinator* muscle of the cheek.

extrasomatic. Outside the body.

extrasutural bone. See Wormian bone.

facet. Small articulation face, a smooth limited area on a bone.

facial dishing. A condition in some hominid faces where the nasal bones and the borders of the piriform aperture are recessed relative to the cheeks, making the midface area concave.

facies. Varieties.

family. A monophyletic group of genera separated from similar groups by distance of common ancestry.

fauna. Animals.

faunal assemblage. A group of living or fossil animals found in a particular geographic or geological context, thought to sample part of a naturally occurring community.

faunal correlation. determination of the relative ages of different geological strata by comparing the fossils within the strata and assigning similar ages to strata with similar fossils; a method of relative dating.

faunivore. an animal that primarily eats other animals (includes insectivores and carnivores).

fecundity. Number of offspring a female can or does give birth to over her lifetime.

femur (femora). Long bone of the thigh or upper leg.

fertility. Number of offspring produced over a given interval or lifetime.

fetus. human organism from eight weeks of development until birth.

fibula. One of two long bones of the lower leg, this is the more slender, lateral one.

fitness. A measure of fertility and survivorship reflecting genetic variation.

flake (flake tools). An usually sharp-edged stone fragment struck or pressured off of a core (a larger rock or nodule).

flexion. Bending, a movement in which the angle of a limb joint decreases; the opposite of extension.

flexor. A muscle whose action decreases the angle between the bones in a joint.

flora. Plants.

fluvial. Pertaining to streams or rivers.

folivorous (folivory, folivore). Leaf eating: folivores are animals whose primary source of food is foliage.

fontanelle. A region between skull bones that is unossified at birth.

forage. Gather, collect, hunt, or scavenge foods.

foraging strategy. Behaviors that lead to the acquisition of food.

foramen (pl. foramina). A hole or tube-like passageway into or through a bone.

foramen magnum. The large opening in the occipital bone on the base of the skull though which the spinal cord passes to join the base of the brain.

formation. A defined unit of rock within a stratigraphic section at a given locality.

fossa (pl. fossae). Literally a "ditch", a shallow depression, concavity, or trough.

fossil. Preserved remains of one-living plants or animals in which the replacement of organic or inorganic materials by soil minerals has begun. Naturally occurring casts are also considered fossils.

founder effect. A special case of genetic drift in which descendants of a very small colonizing group are not genetically representative of the population from which the colonists came.

fovea. A shallow depression or pit.

Frankfurt plane. A widely agreed upon plane for orienting crania to allow valid comparisons, and to approximate the position of the head during life. In this plane a line between the top of the external auditory meatus and the lowest point on the orbit is made horizontal.

frontal boss (metopic eminence). A bulge or eminence on the frontal, at the middle of the squama. It may be centrally located, or exist as paired frontal tubers that mark the location of the original ossification centers.

frontal breadth. The maximum transverse breadth of the frontal, taken on the coronal suture.

frontal keel or torus. A thickening of bone passing sagittally down the frontal squama from its top (posterior), for part, most, or all of the squama's length.

frontal sinus. An open space found in the frontal bone where the squama meets the top of the orbits.

frontal trigone. A concave smooth triangular area on the frontal bone just behind the orbits. Its base is formed by the supraorbital torus and its apex by converging temporal lines. To be distinguished from **lateral frontal trigone.**

frontoethmoidal sinus. See ethmoidal sinus.

frontofacial. Pertaining to the frontal bone and facial bones.

frugivore. An animal that feeds primarily on fruit.

gallery forest a forest along a river or stream.

gathering. Food acquisition with postponed consumption.

gene flow. Exchange of genetic material between populations because of interbreeding or mate exchanges between them.

gene frequency. The percentage of a given allele in a sample.

gene pool. All of the genes found in the members of a population.

gene. A hereditary determiner; a unit of inheritance carried on a chromosome, transmitted from generation to generation by the gametes and controlling some aspect the development of an individual.

genealogical species. Species that are defined by common ancestry and are treated as distinct individuals with definite beginnings and ends.

generalized. (1) primitive or plesiomorphic, similar to the ancestral condition; (2) adapted to a broad range of resources.

genetic correlation (pleiotropy). Covariation of features in a populations because they share some genes.

genetic drift. A mechanism for evolutionary change caused by the random fluctuations of gene frequencies from one generation to the next, or from any form of random sampling from a gene pool.

genetic reorganization. The dislinking of coadapted alleles (alleles with interdependent frequencies) due to random fluctuations because of small population effects during peripatric speciation, followed by the establishment of new coadapted allele systems.

genic exchange. The sharing of genetic material because of gene flow or migration.

genioglossal pit. The notch on the inside border of the mandibular symphysis marking the origin of the *genioglossus* (tongue) muscle.

genome. The entire DNA component of a cell, a structured array consisting of genes and their parts, units of DNA replication, and non-functioning regions.

genotype. The genetic make-up of an organism, its total genetic material.

genus (genera). A monophyletic category for the taxon above the species level, including one or more species of common phylogenetic origin.

glabella. A place on the midline of the frontal bone between the brow ridges, supercillary arches, or upper orbital borders.

glenoid fossa. See mandibular fossa.

glenoid joint. (1) the temporo-mandibular articulation; (2) the socket part of the shoulder ball-and-socket joint on the scapula.

gluteus maximus. Large muscle extending from the lateral and rear surface of the ilium to the gluteal tuberosity of the femur, causing extension and rotation at the hip.

gluteus medius. Muscle extending from the lateral surface of the ilium to the greater trochanter of the femur, causing abduction at the hip.

gluteus minimus. Large muscle extending from the lateral surface of the ilium to the greater trochanter of the femur, causing abduction and rotation at the hip.

gonial angle(mandible). The smoothly curved area where the back of the ramus meets the bottom of the corpus.

gracile. Slender, delicately built, weak muscle attachments or bony buttresses.

grade. A grouping characterized by a general level of organization (or sharing a suite of features). Grades are composed of independent lineages that may or may not be monophyletic.

gradualism. A theory that evolution progresses by the extension of microevolutionary processes over long periods of time - the gradual modification of populations. The concept does not imply continuous evolution, or evolution at a constant rate.

graminivore. An animal that eats primarily grains; often used to describe seed-eating.

greater sciatic notch. U shaped notch at the back of the innominate characteristic of bipedal hominid pelves caused by the rearward and inferior displacement of the sacrum relative to the ape anatomy.

greater trochanter of the femur. Very large process on the lateral and proximal end of the femur shaft, for the attachment of muscles that stabilize the hip during one-legged balance (whether in standing or in bipedal locomotion).

gregarious. Social orientation to behavior, living in regular social groups.

grooming. Cleaning the body surface by licking, biting, picking with fingers or claws, or other kinds of manipulation.

group selection. Evolutionary process involving differential survival and reproduction of competing groups.

gummivore. An animal specializing in gums, saps, and other tree exudates.

gyrus (gyri). One of the convolutions on the surface of the brain caused by the folding of the cortex.

habiline. Referring to the australopithecine-like species of *Homo*. If more than one species is represented, the group may not be monophyletic.

hafting. Attaching, for instance when a bone or stone point is attached to a wood shaft.

half-life. the length of time in which one-half of the nuclei in an unstable isotope of an element decay into smaller nuclei (releasing energy).

hallux. First digit on the foot (big toe).

hammerstone. A hard rock used to strike flakes from cores, usually identifiable by a battered region on its surface.

hamstrings. A group of muscles including *biceps femoris, semimembranosus* and *semitendinosus,* extending from the ischial tuberosity to the back of the femur and top of the tibia, mainly acting to flex the hip joint.

handaxe. A teardrop or pear shaped, bifacially flaked stone implement.

haploid. Having only a single set of chromosomes, half the number in a normal somatic cell. Gametes are normally haploid.

hearth. A circle of stones enclosing a camp fire that focuses, contains, and sustains its heat.

hemisphere. One of the two sides of the cerebrum.

heritability. A measure of the extent to which a feature is inherited: that proportion of variation of a trait in a population that is due to the variation of genotypes.

herniate. Protrude through an abnormal opening.

hetero-. Different.

heterochrony. Evolutionary changes caused by variation in the relative time of appearance and rate of development of features.

heterodontic. Teeth of the same type that differ in size or form.

heteromorphic. Different size and shape.

heterozygosity. The occurrence of two different alleles at a locus.

heterozygote. A form of a polymorphism controlled by different alleles at a locus.

higher primate. Anthropoid.

home base. A particular place where individuals can expect to meet each other and engage in social and other activities.

home range. The area within which a group of primates usually moves over the course of their yearly cycle.

hominid. Extant humans and their unique ancestors and collateral relatives, extending back in time until the split with the line leading to chimpanzees (the closest human relative).

hominoid. Member of the Hominoidea, the superfamily including humans and apes and their unique ancestors.

homo-. Same.

homodontic. Teeth of the same type with similar anatomy.

homology. A feature in two or more species that is the same because of descent - it evolved from the same feature in the last common ancestor of the species.

homoplasy (parallelism). The independent appearance of a feature with the same character state in two or more species that developed independently from a different character state of the feature in the last common ancestor.

homozygosity. The occurrence of two identical alleles at a locus.

homozygote. A feature controlled by a locus at which the two alleles are the same.

honing facet. A worn surface with a sharp edge on the front or back of a tooth that slides against a similar facet on the opposing tooth in the opposite jaw, producing a scissors-like cutting action.

horizon. A particular stratigraphic level or time interval, definable geologically or by the fauna or artifacts in it..

Humerofemoral index. Ratio of the length of the humerus divided by the length of the femur × 100.

humerus. Long bone of the upper arm.

hyoid. Small bone of the throat supporting the vocal chords, and the site of muscle attachments functioning in the control of fine movements of the lower jaw.

hypervitaminosis. A condition resulting from a dietary excess of the vitamin concerned.

hypoplasia. Interrupted enamel formation, leaving transverse lines, pits, or grooves on the enamel surface.

hypsodont. Having teeth with tall crowns, as in horses or *Gigantopithecus*.

iliac pillar. A bony buttress extending vertically down the iliac blade, supporting it against the powerful muscular forces generated by the hip abductor muscles.

ilium (iliac blades). The side, or broad and flat blade of the innominate, forming its upper portion.

Inca bone. A triangular shaped Wormian bone found where the lambdoidal suture meets the sagittal suture.

incisiform. Shaped like an incisor.

incisive canal. Tubular passageway between the anterior portion of the hard palate and the floor of the nose, to carry the nerves and vessels running between the nasal and oral cavities.

incisive foramen (foramina). Opening of the incisive canal onto the roof of the hard palate, located just behind (and above) the roots for the central incisors.

incisor. Broad tooth at the front-most part of the jaw.

inclusive fitness. A characterization of how well a feature's genetic material is represented in the next generation because of the survival of the group of those relatives who share it.

industry. A group of archaeological assemblages found over a specific region or time whose artifacts are similar.

infanticide. the killing of infants.

inferior. Below.

infraorbital foramen. A opening under the lower orbital rim for the infraorbital nerve and vessels.

inion. The center of the *tuberculum linearum*, a protuberance of varying expression that develops where the superior nuchal lines meet at the sagittal plane. It is not necessarily what is called the external occipital protuberance (although this describes what it *is*) which occurs above it, at or below where the supreme nuchal lines meet at the midline.

innerorbital. Encompassing the orbits.

innervated. Served by the branches of one of the nerves.

innominate. *Os coxae*. Large bone forming the sides of the pelvis.

insertion. The attachment of a muscle or ligament farthest from the trunk or center of the body.

intercostal muscles. Muscles situated between the ribs.

interglacial. A warm period between two major periods of multiple glaciations.

internal buttress (of the mandible). Transverse torus or tori on the inside surface of the symphysis. When the most inferior one is the most posterior point on the internal surface, it is a **simian shelf.**

internasal angle. The angle formed by the lengthwise join of the two nasal bones, where they meet at the internasal suture.

internasal suture. The suture between the two nasal bones where they meet at the midline.

interorbital. Between the orbits.

interpluvial. A dry phase between two rainy periods.

interproximal facet. Wear surface between the vertical crown walls of two adjacent teeth, created by anterior forces and transverse motions during mastication.

interproximal wear. Tooth wear between adjacent teeth.

interspecific allometry. The relationship between size and shape among a range across a range of different species.

interstadial. A warmer interval between stadials within a major glaciation.

interstitial wear. See interproximal wear.

intraspecies clade. A group of ancestral-descendant populations that share common descent (although not *unique* common descent) within a species.

inversion. Turning inward, for example, of the sole of the foot.

ischial Tuberosity. The roughened area at the base of the ischium for the hamstrings attachment.

ischium. The lower rear bone of the innominate.

isolating Mechanisms. Biological or behavioral characteristics of individuals which prevent sympatric groups from interbreeding.

isometry. Change in overall size that maintains the same shape.

isotope. Chemically identical but atomically different forms of an element (the number of neurons are different so the atomic weight differs).

jugular foramen. The opening formed by the temporal notches on the petrous temporal and occipital bones.

juxtamastoid process. A name given to the process or processes just medial to the mastoid process, individually referred to as the paramastoid process and occipitomastoid crest.

karstic caves. Caves formed in limestone by the action of water.

kin selection. Differential aid or favoritism toward relatives that promotes the inclusive fitness of shared genes.

kinship. Relationships between people that are based on real or imagined descent and (sometimes) marriage.

knuckle-walking. A type of quadrupedal walking used by chimpanzees and gorillas, in which the forearms rest on the dorsal surface of the middle phalanges of the hands.

kyphosis. (1) Dorsally convex curvature of the spine. (2) Flexion of the cranial base, closing the angle between the basi-occiput and the body of the sphenoid.

labial. Toward the lips, a direction on the anterior teeth toward the outside.

labial convexity. The degree of curvature in the mesial-distal direction of the labial surface of an incisor.

labiolingual. The breadth dimension of an incisor or canine, from the lip side to tongue side.

lacrimal bone. In the skull, a small bone forming part of the medial orbital wall, between the maxilla and the ethmoid behind it.

lacrimal duct. Tear duct, connecting the orbit with the nasal cavity.

lacrimal foramen. Opening of the tear duct.

lacrimal fossa. Depression in which the lacrimal foramen sits.

lacustrine. Lacustrine deposits are laid down in relatively still water lakes.

lambda. A point on the back of the skull at the juncture of the occiput and the parietals, where the sagittal and lambdoidal sutures meet.

lambdoidal flattening. A flattened surface at lambda, always extending anteriorly onto the parietals and in some cases extending posteriorly onto the occiput when a true occipital bun is formed.

lambdoidal suture. The transverse suture at the back of the cranium where the parietal and occipital bones join.

land use pattern. The pattern found in the way the traces of hominid activities are distributed across the landscape.

larynx. The uppermost part of the windpipe, the sphincter guarding the entrance to the trachea and functioning as the sound-producing organ of the throat.

lateral. Away from the midline of the body.

lateral frontal trigone. A backward-facing triangular form to the lateral-most part of the supraorbital torus. The apex is created by a prominent temporal ridge, and the torus is thicker at the trigone than it is more medially. To be distinguished from **frontal trigone**.

lesser trochanter of the femur. Large blunt process on the posterior face of the femur shaft, just below the neck, for attachment of muscles that flex the thigh.

Levallois. A technique for flake production in which a stone core is shaped like a tortoise shell and a single flake with performed shape is struck from it.

Levallois flakes. A flake struck from a Levallois core.

Levallois points. A point made of a Levallois flake.

lexicon. The collection of words in a language.

limbic system. A complex part of the brain comprised of deep nuclei and fiber tracts related to the control and expression of the emotions.

limiting resources. Environmental factors whose abundance in a given habitat limits population size.

linea (line). A raised surface in the form of a narrow crest or ridge.

linea aspera. The elevated line that extends down the posterior surface of the femur shaft.

lineage. A group of ancestral-descendent species that are reproductively isolated from other lineages.

lingual. Toward the tongue, the tongue-facing side of a tooth.

lithic. Of or pertaining to stone.

living floor. A preserved campsite.

load. The application of a force.

locus. A specific location (1) on a chromosome, matched to the corresponding position on the other chromosome of a pair, the site of the maternal and paternal alleles that are often considered together as a gene; (2) defined within a paleontological or archaeological site.

loess. A fine-grained deposit of wind-blown material.

London oblique. An unusual, non-standard orientation for crania which, when used to align an illustration, makes it particularly difficult to compare specimens with each other or with other published illustrations. See Frankfurt plane.

longitudinal study. Examination of changes in individuals over a given time span.

loph. A crest or ridge of enamel on the occlusal surface of a tooth.

LSA. Late Stone Age.

lordosis. Ventrally convex curvature of the spine, contrasting with the normally concave condition.

lumbar. Pertaining to the lower back, the vertebrae that lie between thoracic vertebrae and the sacrum.

lumper. One who emphasizes similarities and formalizes variation at higher taxonomic levels (c.f. splitter).

macroevolution. Evolution above the species level; the evolution of higher taxa, and the processes that result from differences in species survivorship or rates of speciation.

malar. See zygomatic.

malar incisure (notch). See maxillary notch.

malleolus, a hammer-headed or rounded protuberance.

mamelon. Small elevations found along the occlusal margin of newly erupted incisor.

mandible. Lower jaw.

mandibular corpus (body). Horizontal or tooth-bearing portion of the mandible.

mandibular foramen. Opening on the internal surface of the ramus for the mandibular vessels and nerve to pass. There are two distinct anatomies to its rim. In the common form the rim is "V" shaped, with a groove separating the anterior and posterior parts. In the **horizontal-oval** form there is no groove and the rim is horizontally oriented and oval in shape, the anterior and posterior parts connected.

mandibular (glenoid) fossa. Joint for the mandibular articulation with the skull, a depression on the base of the temporal bone, just in front of the ear opening, into which the mandibular condyles fit.

mandibular ramus. See ascending ramus.

mandibular symphysis. The midline join connecting the two sides of the mandible, fused in adult Anthropoidea.

mandibular (transverse) torus. Shelf-like thickening of bone on the inside of the mandibular symphysis; **superior** and **inferior** transverse tori can be present but there can also only be one. The inferior transverse torus is a simian shelf if it is thin and projects so far to the rear that its lowest point is also its most posterior.

mandibular (symphyseal) trigone. An upward facing triangular form at the base of the symphysis.

manuport. An unmodified piece of rock known to be carried to a locality by a hominid because it could not have gotten there naturally.

marginal ridges. Elevated ledge on the edges of the inner surface of the incisors.

masseter muscle. A short, quadrangular muscle between the zygomatic arch and the lower edge of the jaw, along its outside, supplying bite power.

mastication. Chewing.

mastoid notch. The notch at the bottom-rear of the parietal bone, located over the mastoid process.

mastoid process. A pyramid-shaped prominence of cancellous bone on the temporal bone behind the external auditory meatus. Muscles that extend and turn the head attach on it..

mastoid tubercle. A distinct bump on the lateral face of the mastoid process, just behind the external auditory meatus. It is usually treated as a nonmetric trait.

mate recognition system. the system of signals (chemical, olfactory, vocal, visual) that bring together potential breeding partners.

matrifocal. Family or other group headed by a female.

matrilineal. Descent reckoned through the female line.

maxilla. Paired bone of the upper jaw, enclosing the nose and the inner and lower rims of the eye and holding the teeth.

maxillary notch (also called *incisura malaris,* malar incisure, malar notch). A distinct angle between the lower border of the cheek at the zygomatic process of the maxilla and the external palate wall, which establishes a notched lower cheek contour.

maxillary pillar eversion. Expansion and outward projection of the frontal process of the maxillary bones - the part of the maxilla that joins the frontal and supports the nasal bones along the insides of the orbits.

maxillary shelving. A straight lower cheek border that merges smoothly into the lateral wall of the palate and creates a continuous bone mass between the masseter attachment and toothrow.

maxillary sinus. Air space within the maxillary bone, under the lower surface of the orbits and above the tooth roots.

maximum frontal breadth. See frontal breadth.

meatus. A tube-like passageway.

medial. Toward the midline of the body.

medullary cavity. The hollow or marrow-filled center of long bones.

megadont. Having large teeth (usually large postcanine teeth).

menarche. Onset of menstruation, marked by the first menstrual period.

mental eminence. Projecting mandibular trigone, or chin.

mental foramen. A large, sometimes multiple, foramen on the lateral anterior surface of the mandibular corpus, for the mental nerve and vessels.

mesial. The side of a tooth nearest the midline of the jaw, as directed along the toothrow.

mesial drift. Movement of the teeth slowly move toward the front of the mouth as the distance between adjacent decreases with interproximal wear.

mesiodistal. Front to back direction along the toothrow, or length of a tooth.

mesocephalic. Describes an intermediate Cephalic index, between brachycephalic and dolichocephalic.

metabolism. The internal processes that make energy available.

metacarpals. Five bones of the hand connecting the phalanges (finger bones) with the carpals (bones of the wrist).

metatarsals. Five bones of the foot connecting the phalanges (toe bones) with the tarsal bones (bones of the arch).

metopic suture. Midline suture joint between the two sides of the frontal bone, an uncommon variation.

microevolution. Evolution of populations over short periods of time, responding to observable causes.

microhabitat. The immediate environment surrounding an organism.

microliths. Very small flake tools, often hafted.

midden. A deposit of occupation debris, rubbish, or other by-products of human activities.

midface. The central portion of the face, comprised mainly of the cheeks and nose.

midsex average. The mean for a sample estimated by taking the average of mean of the male average and the female mean.

migration (as a cause of genic exchange). The movements of genes caused by individuals moving, including new individuals entering (**immigration**) or leaving (**emigration**) a population, introducing or removing genetic material and thereby changing allele frequencies..

milk teeth. See deciduous teeth.

minimum frontal breadth. See postorbital breadth.

mitochondria. The small extra-nuclear bodies within a cells cytoplasm that control the cell's production of energy from food through the production of ATP (adenosine triphosphate).

mitochondrial DNA (mtDNA). The single (double stranded) DNA molecule that controls the development and functioning of the mitochondrion containing it. Because reproduction is by cloning, mtDNA is usually passed along female lines, as part of the egg's cytoplasm.

molar. The flat posterior-most teeth.

molariform or molarized. Molar-like in form and function; for instance, a premolar adding cusps and becoming more closely rectangular in outline.

molecular clock. A means of determining dates of evolutionary divergences using genetic similarities between extant species and assuming that molecular evolution proceeds at a constant rate.

moment (of inertia). The effect of the distribution of the mass of an object on its resistance to changes in motion. A moment is calculated by multiplying the magnitude of a force by the length of its lever arm, the perpendicular distance between the line of action of the force and the point where it is applied.

monogamy. A social system based on mated pairs and their offspring.

monophyletic group. a number of related entities (individuals, species, etc.) who are all the descendants of their last common ancestor.

monotypic. A taxon containing limited variatrion or internal subdivision, with one immediately subordinate taxon,. For instance, a species with only one subspecies or race.

morph. Any of the genetic forms (individual variants) that account for polymorphism.

morphemes. Meaningful combinations of sound units in a language.

morphocline. A continuous gradation of anatomical change over space or time.

morphology. The form, shape and/or structure of organisms.

morphospecies. A typological species recognized on the basis of morphological differences or discontinuities.

mosaic evolution. Evolution which proceeds at different rates for different features.

motor area (of the brain). The posterior regional of the frontal cortex which controls motor movements.

MSA. Middle Stone Age.

Multiregional Evolution. The evolutionary model that posits humans evolved as a polytypic species from a single origin in Africa. The small population effects during initial colonizations helped establish regional differences, which were subsequently maintained through isolation-by-distance and adaptive variation. Advantageous changes spread widely because of genic exchanges and the common background of the evolving cultural system whose elements also could spread. Most modernizing features arose at different times and places and diffused independently according to this model.

multivariate statistics. statistical procedures that are designed to treat simultaneously (and to assess relationships among) several variables per object.

Murphy's Law. "Anything that *can* go wrong, will". Often amended by Sod's correlate - "at the worst possible time".

mutagens. Physical or chemical causes of mutations.

mutation. An error in replication or other alteration of the nucleotide base sequence creating a change in the sequence of base pairs on a DNA molecule. If the change occurs in the DNA of a somatic cell, the mutation may cause a change in the organism's phenotype (leading, for example, to cancer) but will not affect the organism's offspring; only mutations in the germ cells can cause heritable changes in the offspring.

nasal root. The top of the nose, above the nasal aperture.

nasal spine(anterior). The thin projection of bone at the midline on the lower nasal margin, holding the cartilaginous center of the nose.

nasion. The point on the midline where the two nasal bones and the frontal come together.

nasoalveolar clivus. portion of the premaxilla extending from the nasal cavity to the incisor root sockets.

nasofrontal suture. The suture along the upper border of the nasal bones with the frontal. Its shape can help determine geographic origin.

nasolacrimal duct. See lacrimal duct.

natural selection. Differences in reproductive success and/or survivorship of individuals that result in the unequal contribution of genotypes to the gene pool of the next generation.

neck. A constricted portion of a bone immediately below the "head".

neocortex. The cortex, or outer surface of the cerebral hemispheres of the brain.

neonate. A newborn infant.

neoteny. Retention of the features of a juvenile of an ancestral species in the adult form of a descendant species, by slowing down the rate of development.

neural canal. The large opening through the vertebrae that encloses the spinal cord, also called the vertebral canal.

neurocranium. The portion of the skull enclosing the brain, as distinct from the facial bones and the basicranium.

neuron. Nerve cell.

neutral evolution. Genetic changes which do not affect the fitness of the individual or its offspring.

New World primate. A primate from North or South America.

niche. The limited portions of the environment, in terms of space, resources, etc., that a species fits and/or which it requires for its survival and reproductive success.

nocturnal. Primarily active during the night.

nonmetric trait. Feature whose expression is better or more accurately described in discrete character states than as measurements.

normal polarity epoch. Period of geological time in which the earth's magnetic field is directed as it is at present.

nuchal. Pertaining to the nape of the neck.

nuchal crest. A raised bony ridge at the back of the skull caused by the attachment of neck muscles.

nuchal line. Three lines transversely cross the cranial rear. From lowest to highest they are:
1. **inferior nuchal line** extends across the middle of the nuchal plane, separating the nuchal muscles *semispinalis capitis* above from *rectus capitis* below
2. **superior nuchal line**, the most prominent, develops along the top of the *semispinalis capitis* muscle and some of the muscles lying over it attach directly to the line - *trapezius* more centrally and *sternocleidomastoid* more laterally. It separates the nuchal from the occipital planes of the occiput
3. **supreme nuchal line** lies above the superior line, on the occipital plane. It may be totally absent, a distinct line dipping downwards at the midline, or the superior border of the nuchal torus (if there is one).

nuchal plane (lower scale). The area at the nape of the neck where the neck muscles attach, the lower portion of the occipital bone below the superior nuchal line.

nuchal torus. A thickened bony prominence transversely across some or all of the back of the head, on the occipital bone, reflecting the pattern of muscle use as it separates the nuchal plane below from the occipital plane above.

numerical dating. Age estimation in calendar years before the present; also known as absolute dating, chronometric dating.

obstetrical. Of or relating to childbirth.

obturator foramen (pl. foramina). A space at the front of the pelvis enclosed by the pubis and ischium.

occipital bone. The bone forming the vault posterior and much of the basicranium.

occipital bun. A backward extension of the cranial rear in the form of a protuberance bounded by the nuchal plane below, a short vertical face for the occiput behind, and a flat surface above (lambdoidal flattening).

occipital plane (upper scale). The portion of the occiput above the superior nuchal line, and for the most part above the nuchal muscles.

occipitomastoid. A process, usually in the form of a crest, paralleling or straddling the occipitomastoid suture and separated from the more lateral paramastoid process, if there is one, by an occipital groove. See juxtamastoid eminence.

occlusal. The surfaces of the opposing teeth that meet for chewing; in an occlusal view the crowns of the teeth are shown.

occlusal force. The force produced between the teeth during chewing.

Old World primate. Any primate from Africa or Eurasia.

olecranon fossa (pl. fossae). A depression at the posterior side of the distal humerus, at the elbow, for accommodating the olecranon process of the ulna when the elbow is extended.

olecranon process. A beak-like projection on the proximal end of the ulna, at the elbow, for articulation with the humerus and attachment of the triceps muscles.

olfaction . The sense of smell.

oligopithecine. Member of the subfamily Oligopithecinae.

omnivore. An organism that eats diversity of food types.

ontogeny. The developmental history of an individual from egg to adult.

opisthion. The midline point of the posterior margin of the foramen magnum.

opistocranion The back of the skull, located as far from the center of the brows that it is possible to get on the midline.

opportunistic evolution. Species adapt to fill all available niches.

opposability. The ability to touch the thumb tip to the finger tips of the same hand.

orbit. bony socket for the eye.

orbital pillar. The outer bony rim found on orbits that face anteriorly, made up of the zygomatic process of the frontal and the frontal process of the zygomatic bone.

order. A monophyletic higher-level taxon (made up of suborders, superfamilies, etc.) whose members generally share a basic structural pattern.

orthognathous. Having a relatively vertical, non-protruding face (c.f. prognathic).

ossicle. Very small bone, such as the ear ossicles or the finger joint seasmoids.

ossification. The process of forming new bone.

osteo. Pertaining to bone.

osteodontokeratic. Artifacts made of bone, tooth and horn, as in the Osteodontokeratic "culture" of the Makapansgat australopithecines.

osteology. The study of bones and their variations.

overspecialized. Adapted to a particular niche so specifically that the genetic variation necessary to meet changing conditions has been lost.

ovulation. Release of an unfertilized gamete (egg) from the ovary.

paedomorphy. Heterochronic changes which result in the adult descendent resembling the juvenile ancestor.

palaeosol. Rock or sediment formed from an ancient or fossil soil.

paleolithic. Literally the old stone age, the period when humans relied on a lithic technology to sustain a scavenging/hunting/gathering adaptation.

paleomagnetic reversal. An orientation of the earth's magnetic field in the opposite direction of today's orientation.

paleomagnetic stratigraphy. The arrangement of geological strata based upon the alternating direction residual magnetism, compared with the world geomagnetic polarity column by other aspects of the sequence such as preserved fauna.

paleomagnetism. Residual magnetism from the earth's magnetic field detectable in rock.

palimpsest. Writing material that is used more than one time after the earlier writing has been erased.

palmar. Pertaining to the palm side of the hand.

palmigrade. refers to a type of quadrupedal locomotion characterized by weight bearing on the palms of the hands rather than on the digits or knuckles.

palynology. Study of plant pollens and spores.

panmictic population. one in which genotypes associate at random, i.e., with equal probabilities of mating between any two individuals of opposite sex.

parallelism. (see homoplasy).

paramastoid process. A raised eminence paralleling the long axis of the mastoid process, medial to it and separated by the digastric groove. It is separated from the more medial occipitomastoid crest by the occipital groove. See juxtamastoid process.

parapatric. Having geographic ranges that border extensively on one another.

parapatric speciation. The progressive divergence of two neighboring populations, while meeting in a contact zone, until they have become two different species.

parasagittal. Refers to a plane through the body parallel to the sagittal plane.

parietal. A flat paired bone forming part of the lateral wall of the skull.

parietal association area. Part of the parietal association cortex that is posterior to the sensory region of the parietal lobe. The integration of sensory, motor, and cognitive actions, or cross-modal transfer, takes place in this area.

parsimony. The use of as few assumptions as possible in an explanation or theory. "Occam's razor" is an example .

patella. Kneecap, a large sesmoid bone at the knee.

patellar groove. Depression on the distal femur in which the kneecap patella moves.

pathology. A feature related to disease or its consequences.

patristic homology. Homologies based on comparing features in the same clade or lineage.

pebble tools. Simple artifacts made on cores of stone, sometimes also applied to the cores themselves even when they are not used as tools *per se*.

pelvis. The bony structure comprised of the sacrum and three paired bones: the ilium, ischium, and pubis which fuse together in adults as paired innominates.

penecontemporary. Living at or almost at the same time.

petrosal crest. A crest that follows along the base of the auditory tube.

petrous pyramid. The petrous portion of the temporal bone is the pyramid-shaped process that extends across the cranial base, housing the internal ear.

peramorphy. Heterochronic changes which cause the juvenile descendant to resemble the adult ancestor.

precision grip. Fine manipulation with the finger and thumb tips, as in turning a screwdriver.

periglacial. A region near or surrounding a glacial area.

perikymata. Elevations between the grooves encircling tooth crowns that are caused by growth-related segmentation of enamel crystals.

peripatric speciation. Speciation at the periphery - through the modification of a peripherally isolated founder population.

permafrost. Permanently frozen subsoil.

phalanx (phalanges). Bone of the finger or toe digits.

phenetics. A method of systematics in which relationships are determined by degrees of similarity.

phenogram. A diagram indicating degree of similarity among taxa..

phenon. A sample of anatomically similar specimens.

phenotype. Appearance of an individual; the observed set of characteristics, the result of the interaction between genotype and environment.

phonemes. The individual sound units in a language.

phyletic. Pertaining to a descent (cf. phylogeny).

phylogenetic species. A monophyletic group of individuals whose identity can be diagnosed by at least one shared unique feature.

phylogenetics. The study of how genealogical relationships can be determined from morphological similarities that are homologous.

phylogeny. A hypothesis about how fossil and living species are related in a genealogical framework.

pilaster (femur). A stout ridge of bone extending down the distal surface of the central part of the demur shaft, supporting the *linea aspera*.

Pilastric index. A measure of shape at the midshaft of the femur, determined by dividing the anterior-posterior length by the transverse breadth.

plantar. Pertaining to the sole of the foot.

plantarflexion. Bending action at the ankle or internal foot joints so that the toes point downward.

plantigrady. A stance or locomotion in which the body is positioned so that the palms and soles point down.

platymeria. Anteroposterior flattening of the upper shaft of the femur.

Platymeric index. A measure of shape at the upper part of the shaft of the femur, determined by dividing the anterior-posterior length by the transverse breadth just below the lesser trochanter.

platyrrhine. New World monkey infraorder.

pleiotropic. Genes that influence the expression of more than one trait.

plesiomorphic. A characteristic whose form is like the ancestral condition.

Plio-Pleistocene. Shorthand term literally referring to the Pliocene and Pleistocene together, but usually meaning the Pliocene and Early Pleistocene.

pluvial. A continent-wide unusually wet period.

pneumatization. Air spaces in cranial bones such as mastoid area, or nasal sinuses.

pollex. Thumb.

polygenic. A character, controlled by several or numerous genes.

polygyny. Any type of social organization in which one male mates with more than one female.

polymorphic. Showing a variety of forms, a feature with alternative character states.

polytypic. A variable taxon that contains more than one taxon of the next lower category, such as a species with several subspecies or races.

pongid. A member of the family Pongidae, humans and the great apes (chimpanzees, gorillas, and orangutans) and their unique ancestors and collateral's.

pongine. Member of the subfamily Ponginae (the large bodied Asian apes).

population. A community of potentially interbreeding individuals, usually at a given locality or within a limited geographic region.

porion. The uppermost point in the margin of the auditory meatus; the points which, with the lowest point on the orbit, defines the Frankfort Horizontal.

positional behavior. How, when and why an animal postures and moves itself within a particular environment.

positive feedback. A system's response to external stimuli that leads to further change and reinforces it.

postcanine teeth. The premolars and molars, also called cheek teeth.

postcranium (postcranial skeleton). All elements of the skeleton below the skull and mandible.

posterior. Back.

posterior tooth loading. Force placed on the postcanine teeth, usually during mastication.

postorbital bar. bony ring surrounding the lateral side of the orbit in some primates and many other mammals.

postorbital breadth. The minimum transverse breadth of the frontal bone, the distance across the postorbital constriction.

postorbital constriction. Narrowing of the (frontal and sphenoidal walls of the) skull behind the orbits, where they form the inner wall of the temporal fossa.

power grip. Hand hold in which there is grasping with the fingers positioned perpendicular to the object but with the palm diagonal, and using the thumb for applying significant force.

preadaptation. The concept that species, or their features, can be predesigned to meet the requirements of future environments.

prebregmatic eminence. See bregmatic eminence.

precocial. Early in development.

prehensile. Capable of grasping.

premastication. Preparing foods by softening or pounding before they are chewed, or chewing foods before they are presented to infants and young children.

premaxilla. Front part of the palate and subnasal maxilla, anterior to the middle of the canine roots and housing the incisors.

premolar. Teeth lying between the canine and molars, usually smaller than the molars and generally flat except for the most anterior lower tooth in species with a canine cutting complex.

Preneandertal Hypothesis. The theory, mainly applied to Europe, that proposes two separate human lineages can be found in the terminal Middle or Late Pleistocene. It posits that Neandertals diverged from a line leading to modern Europeans just before they became specialized.

Presapiens Hypothesis. The theory, mainly applied to Europe, that proposes two separate human lineages can be found in the Middle Pleistocene. One lineage (presapiens) evolved directly into modern *H. sapiens* populations and closely resembled these modern forms at an early date. The second lineage (preneandertal) evolved into the European Neandertal populations of the earlier Würm glaciation and subsequently became extinct.

prestructuring. The inherent tendency for certain neural connections to form, with the consequence that particular behavioral association are easier or more likely to be learned.

primitive feature. (see plesiomorphic).

process. A long, tapering bony projection.

procumbent. Inclined forward or protruding.

prognathous. Forward protrusion of the facial region, as a whole or in part (see alveolar prognathism), c.f. orthognathous.

pronation. Rotation of the forearm so that the palm faces downward, the reverse movement from supination.

propliopithecine. Member of the subfamily Propliopithecinae.

provenience. The exact circumstances of how a specimen is related to the deposit in which it is found.

proximal. Closer to the midline of the body - applies to the appendicular skeleton.

pterion. Temple region of the skull, where the frontal, parietal, temporal, and sphenoid bones meet.

pterygoid muscle. A two-part muscle extending from the lateral pterygoid plate to the medial ramus and gonial angle (medial part, closing the jaw and generating occlusal force) and the top of the ramus (lateral part, opening the jaw and moving it from side to side).

pterygoid plates. Paired bony plates on the inferior surface of the sphenoid bone, the lateral ones for attachment of two muscles of mastication, the lateral and medial pterygoid muscles.

pubis. The front of the pelvis, formed by the parts of the innominate that meet at the midline.

pulp (cavity). The vascularized and innervated tissue enclosed in the center of a tooth.

Pulse hypothesis. A theory that begins with the assumption that all evolutionary changes are related to speciations and extinctions. If so, during a period of climate change the rates of speciation and extinction would be expected to accelerate, and therefore major climatic changes create a turnover pulse of rapid evolutionary change as whole new species groups replace older ones.

Punctuated Equilibrium theory. A model of evolution in which changes occur when new species are formed and only rarely are slowly and gradually accumulated during the stable periods between speciations.

pyriform aperture. The pear-shaped nasal opening of the skull; anterior nasal aperture.

quadriceps femoris. A package of four muscles that join in a large tendon surrounding the patella and attaching to the anterior tuberosity of the tibia. The largest of these, *rectus femoris*, has an ilium attachment on the anterior inferior spine and brim of the acetabulum. The bundle flexes the hip and extends the knee.

quadrumanous. Four-handed; as in quadrumanous climbing.

quadrupedalism. Four-footed posture and locomotion.

race. A group of individuals geographically (and for humans also culturally) determined who share a common gene pool and varying combinations of distinguishing characteristics.

racemization. The conversion of some amino acids from their original ":left handed' form to "right handed" form, after death, so that the two forms occur in about equal numbers.

radial notch of the ulna. Smooth facet on the ulna's proximal shaft where the head of the radius articulates during radius rotation.

radius. One of two long bones of the forearm, or lower arm, which rotates against the ulna so that its lower end the hand can be turned.

ramus. The portion of bone at an angle to the body, as in ascending ramus (mandible), pubic ramus (innominate).

range. Territory normally occupied.

recapitulation. The theory that "ontogeny recapitulates phylogeny".

reciprocal altruism. Exchange of favors by two individuals I which one individual temporarily sacrifices potential fitness in expectation of a return.

recombination. The bringing together of novel combinations of genes by the process of meiosis and crossover during sexual reproduction.

regional continuity. The observation that there is a sequence of anatomical features, often found together, spanning the time from earlier to later populations in a geographic region, that seems to reflect some degree of ancestral-descendant relationship.

relative dating. Determination of the ordered sequence of sites, artifacts, or fossils.

resorb. To destruct and remove bone or parts of bone by osteoclasts (bone cells with digestive enzymes).

retouch. Trimming of the edges of a stone tool to sharpen it.

retract. Pull backwards.

retromolar space (gap). A space or gap at the rear of a mandible between the back of the last molar and the anterior edge of the ascending ramus where it crosses the alveolar margin.

reversed polarity epoch. Period of geological time in which the earth's magnetic field is directed the opposite to what it is at present (the north end of a compass would point north, rather than south).

rhinarium. A hairless patch of skin between the nose and upper lip that is kept moist to enhance the sense of smell.

ridge. A narrow roughened elevation on a bone's surface.

robust. A large, or heavily built body or body part.

robusticity index. An index obtained by expressing a diameter (or circumference) of a bone in terms of its length.

Romer's rule. The generalization that new adaptations are often allowed by evolutionary changes that initially better adapt a species to its old way of life.

sacculated. Subdivided.

sacral vertebrae. The fused vertebrae that make up the sacrum, at the back of the pelvis.

sacroiliac joint. The joint at the back of the pelvis between the sacrum and the ilium.

sacrum. Triangular block of fused vertebrae forming the back part of the pelvis, articulating with the lumbar vertebrae.

sagittal crest. A compound crest of bone running along the midline of the skull for attachment of enlarged temporalis muscles that meet along the midline.

sagittal keel (torus). A thickening of bone on part or all of the midline of the frontal, or parietals where they meet sagittally, or both bones.

sagittal plane. A vertical plane on the midline that divides the body into a right and left half.

saltation. Discontinuous variation produced all at once by major mutation.

sampling error. A change in gene frequencies between parents and offspring in a population that is due to the small sample size of each generation when populations themselves are small. Small samples usually do not exactly duplicate the characteristics of the larger population they are drawn from.

sartorius. A muscle extending from the anterior superior spine of the ilium to the medial side of the proximal tibia, flexing the hip and knee joints.

savanna. A plain characterized by coarse grasses and scattered trees, often with seasonal rainfall.

scanning electron microscope (SEM). An instrument for analyzing the surfaces of tiny structures by using a focused beam of electrons to produce an enlarged image.

scapula (pl. scapulae). The flat, triangular bone at the back of the shoulder.

scapular spine. The projecting structure extending transversely across the back of the scapula, holding the attachments for muscles such as the deltoid and trapezius, and terminating in the **acromion process** that meets the clavicle.

seasonality. Aspects of the environment, or of adaptations to it, that differ from season to season.

secondary sexual characteristics. Gender-related features that develop at or after puberty.

sectorial (tooth crown). Tooth with an elliptical or circular cross-section and a single cusp, in anthropoids generally overlapping with a tooth in the opposing jaw and wearing to a honing facet for cutting in a scissors-like action during occlusion.

selection. (see natural selection).

semispinalis capitis. A muscle of the nuchal region traveling down the back where it attaches to cervical and thoracic vertebrae, important in extending and stabilizing the head (for instance in conjunction with anterior tooth loading).

semitendinosus. one of the hamstring muscles, which extend the thigh and flex the leg.

sensory area (of the brain). One of the three areas of the cerebral cortex devoted to reception of information from the body's senses.

seriation. Placement in an order (chronological, developmental, etc.).

sesamoid. A bone formed within a tendon.

settlement pattern: Distribution of semi-permanent or permanent human habitations on the landscape and within archaeological communities.

sex-linked character. A feature whose expression is controlled by genes located on the sex chromosome.

sexual dimorphism. A polymorphic character in which males and females of a species differ in some aspect of their anatomy not directly related to reproduction or birth.

sexual selection. The increased reproductive success of males or females because of characters which enhances either their ability to compete with members of the same sex or their attractiveness to members of the opposite sex.

shaft. The long part of a long bone, formed from the diaphysis.

shovel-shaped incisors. Incisors that have a scooped out lingual surface because of lingual marginal ridges, crown curvature, or a basal tubercle alone or in combination.

sigmoid notch (ulna). See trochlear notch.

simian shelf. See mandibular torus.

Single Species Hypothesis. The theory that only one hominid species at a time could be expected because culture should so broaden hominid niches that competition for limiting resources between species would be inevitable and lead to enhanced cultural abilities and further niche broadening. Only one of the competing species would be expected to persist. The hypothesis rests on the assumption that all manifestations of culture result in effective niche expansion.

sinus. A pocket or cavity within a cranial bone, also applied to describe the grooved pathways for blood vessels on the endocranial surface.

sister groups. two groups that result from a single split in a cladogram; they, and only they, share the same parent taxon.

skull. The bony skeleton of the head, including the lower jaw.

sociobiology. The study of the biological basis of all social behavior.

soft percussion (soft hammer). An Acheulean technology that used wood, bone, or antler instead of rock to chip flakes from a core.

spatulate. Spade-like, referring to upper incisors that are broad, often with marginal ridges along the edges of their internal surface.

specialized. (1) derived or apomorphic, differing from the ancestral condition; (2) adapted to a limited range of resources.

speciation. The process whereby species multiply; the acquisition of reproductive isolation between populations, splitting one species into two.

species. In living animals a group of populations (**Biological** species) that can actually or potentially interbreed and have fertile offspring, and are reproductively isolated from other species, Also see **Evolutionary, Genealogical, Morpho-,** and **Phylogenetic** species.

sphenoid bone. Irregularly shaped bone forming part of the base and sides of the skull and the back of the orbit.

spine. A sharp projection or short ridge.

splitter. One who emphasizes differences and formalizes variation at lower taxonomic levels (c.f. lumper).

spongy bone. See **cancellous bone.**

squama. The flat portion of a cranial bone.

squamosal suture. Suture between the parietal and temporal bones, in he form of a beveled edge with the temporal overlapping on the outside.

stadial. A cold period during a glaciation.

standard deviation (σ). Approximately, the mean difference between all of the data points in a sample and their average. Formally the square root of the variance (V), where $V = \sum (X_i - X_{av})/n^2$: X_i is each data point, X_{av} is the mean of the points, and n is the number of points.

stasis. Little or no evolutionary change occurring over a long period of time; see also punctuated equilibrium.

sternocleidomastoid **muscle.** Extends from the mastoid process and superior nuchal line to the sternum and clavicle, rotating and stabilizing the head.

sternum. Breastbone.

stochastic. Random.

stratigraphy. The location or position of fossil or other deposits relative to other buried layers or features.

styloid process. A pencil shaped, pointed process of bone that rests in the vaginal foramen of the temporal petrous, fusing with it in older individuals. It is the seat of attachment for the stylohyoid ligament .

stylohyoid ligament. A ligament extending from the styloid process on the cranial base to the hyoid bone.

sub-. Below.

subadults. An age category - young individuals including infants, children, and juveniles.

subchron (polarity subchron or event). A short period (10 - 100 kyr) of polarity reversal within a chron.

subfossil. Recent, often only partially fossilized, remains often from the Holocene or historical time periods.

subnasal alveolar process. part of the anterior maxilla below the nose, housing the roots of the upper incisors.

subspecies. A geographically defined aggregate of local populations which differs with various degrees of significance (depending on the author) from other such subdivisions of the species.

sulcus (sulci). A broad groove.

supercillary arches. Smoothly rounded bulges of bone found on the frontal bone of the skull at its center and extending over the inner portion of the upper orbital border.

superior. Above.

supination. Rotation of the forearm so that the palm faces upward; the reverse movement from pronation.

supra-. above.

suprainiac fossa. An elliptic depression on the occiput above the superior nuchal line, or inion.

supramastoid. The pneumatized region on the temporal bone just above the mastoid process base. It marks the backward extension of the root of the zygomatic process of the temporal.

supraorbital torus (tori). Browridge: a thickened ridge or shelf of bone above the orbits at the base of the forehead, continuously although not necessarily evenly developed from the middle of the cranium to each side.

supraspecific. Above the species level.

supratoral sulcus. A broad depression or groove between the brow ridges and the frontal bone, creating an angle between the top of the brow ridge and the front of the frontal squama.

suspensory. Hanging, locomotor and postural habits with the body below or among branches.

suture. A joint where two bone interdigitate and are separated by fibrous tissue. The joints between most of the bones of the skull are sutures. Most sutures join and the bones eventually fuse together as individuals grow older.

Sutural bone. See Wormian bone.

sympatric speciation. Speciation without geographic isolation, with isolating mechanisms developing within populations.

sympatry. The occurrence of two or more populations (species, etc.) in the same area.

symphysis (pl. symphyses). A flexible fibrocartilaginous joint found on the midline of the body, such as the mandibular symphysis and the pubic symphysis.

symphyseal angle. The angle made by the mandibular symphysis face and the lower-border of the body of the mandible.

symplesiomorphy. The sharing of ancestral characters by several species.

synapomorphy. The sharing of apomorphies, or derived characters, by two or more species.

syntax. Grammar.

systematics. The science of the diversity of organisms and their relationships and classification.

talonid. A distal shelf on a tooth.

talus (astragalus). Ankle bone.

taphonomy. Study of the processes that affect the remains of organisms from the death of the organism through its fossilization.

tarsals. Small bones of the ankle and foot, In humans these are the talus, calcaneus, navicular, cuboid, and three cuneiforms.

taurodont. Teeth having enlarged pulp cavities in their roots.

taxon (pl. taxa). A monophyletic group of organisms recognized as a formal unit, at any level of a hierarchic classification.

taxonomy. The theory and practice of classifying organisms.

technology. The techniques used to produce artifacts.

tektites. Streamlined glassy objects found in some soils that result from meteoric impacts that throw silicon-rich material into the upper atmosphere that fuses into a glass as it heats up during its return.

temporal bone. Complex bone on the side and base of the cranium that includes the ear, mandibular joint, and a portion of the side of the brain case.

temporal fossa. The space enclosed by the side of the skull and the zygomatic arch, which is occupied by the *temporalis* muscle as it passes from its mandibular attachment to its attachment on the cranium.

temporal line. The line caused by the edge of the temporalis muscle where it attaches along the cranial vault. There are two lines, an inferior line from the deep part of the muscle and a superior line from the superficial part.

***temporalis* muscle.** A fan-shaped muscle that moves the jaw in mastication and creates force between the teeth, joining the inside of the mandibular ramus and the side and rear of the skull.

temporonuchal crest. A compound crest on the back of the skull formed by convergence of the temporal lines and the nuchal crest.

terminations. In glacial studies, the midpoints in deglaciations leading to interglacial periods.

terrestrial. On the ground.

terrestrial quadruped Ground-living animal that moves about primarily on all four limbs.

territory. Part of a home range that is exclusive to a group of animals and is actively defended from other groups of the same species.

thoracic. Pertaining to the thorax, especially the rib-bearing vertebrae below the cervical and above the lumbar vertebrae.

tibia. Long bone of the lower leg, between the knee and the foot.

tomography (computed assisted) A CAT scan is a radiographic technique that can display 'slices' taken through bones or skulls that will show the shape and extent of internal cavities..

tool. An artifact with a functional use. **Curated tools** are kept for use in the future, while **expedient tools** are made in response to an immediate need.

toothpick grooves. Elongate grooves between adjacent teeth, usually on the roots just below the crown level and marked on their facing sides.

torsion. Twisting.

torus. A smooth rounded ridge or protuberance.

trabecular bone. See **cancellous bone.**

transverse torus (tori). See superior or inferior mandibular torus.

trapezius muscle. A muscle extending from the nuchal plane to the clavicle and scapula that stabilizes the shoulder and brings the scapula upwards.

travertine. A calcium carbonate rock deposited around lime-rich springs and lakes.

trochanter. A large process, for muscle attachment.

trochlea. Any smooth, saddle-shaped bony surface that forms part of a joint.

trochlear (sigmoid) notch. The notch within the hook-like proximal end of the ulna that slides in and out of the olecranon fossa of the humerus.

tubercle. A small eminence.

tuff. A consolidated deposit of volcanic ash, transported to the site by air or more often water.

tympanic bone. The portion of the temporal bone that encloses the inner ear.

tympanic crest. See petrosal crest.

tympanic membrane. Eardrum.

type. (1) a complete or incomplete specimen which serves as the base for the name of a taxon; (2) a single individual used to epitomize a sample..

typology. The classification of forms.

ulna. The bone of the lower arm that hinges at the elbow with the humerus.

uniformitarianism. Originally a concept in geology, the precept that the processes observable in the present can be used to explain the past.

vaginal process of the temporal bone. A small downward projecting open cylinder on the petrous pyramid of the temporal, to the inside and in front of the mastoid process, that holds the styloid process.

valgus. an angulation of the femur in which the knees are closer together than the hip joints; "knock-kneed."

variance. See standard deviation.

vascularized. Having blood vessels.

ventral. The belly side of an animal; the opposite of dorsal.

vertebra (plural, vertebrae) One of the bony segments of the vertebral column.

vertebral canal. See neural canal.

vertebral column, or spine. A structure made up of the vertebrae, from the cervical to the thoracic and lumbar.

vertebral spine. A blade of bone projecting dorsally from a vertebra, serving as attachment site for several ligaments and muscles, also called a spinous process.

vibrissae. Facial hairs surrounding the mouth in many mammals especially sensitive to the touch.

visual cortex. The outer portion of the brain at the rear of the cerebrum responsible for visual input and association.

visual overlap. The ability to see objects simultaneously with both eyes, a requirement of three-dimensional vision.

Wahlund effect. Internally subdivided species have more homozygosity than an equivalent fused population would, creating more phenotypically expressed variation.

woodland. a vegetation type characterized by discontinuous stands of relatively short trees separated by grassland.

Wormian bones. Small bones formed within sutures from isolated centers of ossification between major components of the skull vault. Commonly found between the occipital and parietal bones.

woven bone. Bone of a coarse, fibrous texture that results from rapid, relatively disorganized growth; normally replaced later in development by more geometrically organized bone.

Y-5. A cusp pattern found in lower molars in which there are 5 main cusps separated by grooves, and the mesiolingual and distobuccal cusps touch.

zygomatic (also malar) bone (pl. zygoma).. The facial bone that makes up the cheek corner and outer orbital pillar, and encloses the front part of the temporal fossa.

zygomatic arch. Bony arch on the lateral part of the cheek formed by projections of the zygomatic bone and the temporal bone, enclosing the fibers of the temporalis muscle and for attachment of the masseter muscle.

zygomatic base. Place where the lower border of the cheek merges with the outer wall of the palate.

zygomatic process. Part of a bone extending toward and meeting the zygomatic bone; there is a zygomatic process of the frontal, temporal, and maxilla.

zygomatic root (suprameatal crest). The rearward base of the zygomatic process of the temporal, as it extends over the outer ear opening.

zygomaxillary region. The cheek, comprised of the anterior faces of the maxilla and zygomatic.

zygomaxillary ridge. A low ridge that extends along the suture between the zygomatic and the maxillary bones.

zygote. The fertilized egg that results from the union of two gametes.

PALEOANTHROPOLOGY
BIBLIOGRAPHY

The references presented here are basic to paleoanthropology. While not exhaustive, this bibliography is designed to allow further research and readings on both an introductory and a more advanced level. It is arranged in three categories.

1. **Catalogues, Atlases and Evolutionary Anatomies, and Paleoanthropology Textbooks**: catalogues relate the basic information on human fossils—discoverer, associations, date of discovery, age of the site, parts represented, references to descriptive and analytical publications, location of the remains, and availability of casts. Atlases refer the reader to references that define and describe anatomical features of the musculature and skeleton (particularly in an evolutionary context), measuring points, and the fundamentals of skeletal analysis. Textbooks present introductory to advanced perspectives on human evolution (but mind the publication date for currency of the most recent information).
2. **Descriptive Monographs** and **Papers**: basic descriptions of the most important fossil hominid remains.
3. **Edited Collections**: recent volumes of readings mainly concerning human paleontology.

Catalogues, Atlases, and Paleoanthropology Textbooks

Aiello, L., and C. Dean 1990 *An Introduction to Human Evolutionary Anatomy.* Academic Press, New York.

Alexeev, V.P. 1986 *The Origin of the Human Race.* Progress Publishers, Moscow.

Angela, P., and A. Angela 1993 *The Extraordinary Story of Human Origins.* Prometheus, Buffalo.

Bass, W. M. 1971 *Human Osteology: A Laboratory and Field Manual to the Human Skeleton.* Special Publications of the Missouri Archaeological Society, Columbia.

Bennett, K.A. 1981 *A field Guide for Human Skeletal Identification.* C.C. Thomas, Springfield.

Bilsborough, A. 1992 *Human Evolution.* Blackie Academic and Professional, London.

Birdsell, J.B. 1972 *Human Evolution.* Rand McNally, Chicago.

Bordes, F. 1968 *The Old Stone Age.* McGraw-Hill, New York.

Brace, C.L., H. Nelson, and N Korn 1971 *Atlas of Fossil Man.* Holt, Rinehart, and Winston, New York.

Brothwell, D. R. 1981 *Digging Up Bones.* Third Edition. British Museum (Natural History) and Cornell University Press, Ithaca, New York.

Boule, M., and H.V. Vallois 1957 *Fossil Men.* Dryden, New York.

Butzer, K.W. 1971 *Environment and Archaeology.* Revised Edition. Aldine, Chicago.

Cartmill, M., W.L. Hylander, and J. Shafland 1987 *Human Structure.* Harvard University Press, Cambridge.

Clark, W.E. LeGros 1963 *The Antecedents of Man.* Harper and Row, New York:

Clark, W.E. LeGros 1964 *The Fossil Evidence for Human Evolution.* Second Edition. University of Chicago Press, Chicago.

Coon, C.S. 1962 *The Origin of Races.* Knopf, New York.

Coon, C.S. 1965 *The Living Races of Man.* Knopf, New York.

Coon, C.S. 1982 *Racial Adaptations. A Study of the Origins, Nature, and Significance of Racial Variations in Humans.* Nelson-Hall, Chicago.

Day, M.H. 1986 *Guide to Fossil Man*, Fourth Edition. University of Chicago Press, Chicago.

Feder, K.L., and M.A. Park 1989 *Human Antiquity.* Mayfield, Mountain View CA.

Gamble, C. 1994 *Timewalkers. The Prehistory of Global Colonization.* Harvard University Press, Cambridge.

Genet-Varcin, E. 1979 *Les Hommes Fossiles.* Boubée, Paris.

Goldberg, K.E. 1982 *The Skeleton.* U.S. News Books, Washington D.C.

Groves, C.P. 1989 *A Theory of Human and Primate Evolution.* Oxford University Press, New York.

Howell, F.C. 1965 *Early Man.* Time Life, New York.

Howell, F.C. 1978 Hominidae. In V.J. Maglio and H.B.S. Cooke (eds): *Evolution of African Mammals.* Harvard University Press, Cambridge. pp. 154-248.

Howells, W.W. 1973 *Evolution of the Genus Homo.* Addison-Wesley, Reading.

Howells, W.W. 1993 *Getting There. The Story of Human Evolution.* Compass Press, Washington DC.

Hrdlička, A. 1930 *The Skeletal Remains of Early Man.* Smithsonian Miscellaneous Collections, Volume 83.

Keith, A. 1925 *The Antiquity of Man,* Revised Edition. 2 volumes. Lippincott, Philadelphia.

Keith, A. 1931 *New Discoveries Relating to the Antiquity of Man.* Williams and Norgate, London.

Kraus, B.S., R.E. Jordan, and L. Abrams 1969 *Dental Anatomy and Occlusion.* Williams and Wilkins, Baltimore.

Krogman, W.M. 1962 *The Human Skeleton in Forensic Medicine.* C.C. Thomas, Springfield.

Kurtén, B. 1972 *Not from the Apes.* Pantheon, New York.

Kurtén, B. 1992 *Our Earliest Ancestors.* Columbia University Press, New York.

Lambert, D. 1987 *The Cambridge Guide to Prehistoric Man.* Cambridge University Press, Cambridge.

Lambert, D., and the Diagram Group 1987 *The Field Guide to Early Man.* Facts on File Publications, New York.

Larsen, C.S., and R.M. Matter 1985 *Human Origins. The Fossil Record.* Waveland Press, Prospect Heights.

Leakey, L.S.B. 1961 *Adam's Ancestors.* Harper and Roe, New York.

Leakey, L.S.B., and V.M. Goodall 1969 *Unveiling Man's Origins.* Schenkman, Cambridge.

Leakey, R.E. 1981 *The Making of Mankind.* Dutton, New York.

Leakey, R.E. and R. Lewin 1977 *Origins.* Dutton, New York.

Lewin, R. 1993 *Human Evolution,* Third Edition. Blackwell, London.

Martin, R., and K. Saller 1956 *Lehrbuch der Anthropologie.* Fischer, Stuttgart.

Nesturkh, M. 1967 *The Origin of Man.* Progress Publishers, Moscow.

Oakley, K. P., and B. G. Campbell. 1977 *Catalogue of Fossil Hominids, Part 1: Africa,* Revised edition. British Museum (Natural History), London.

Oakley, K.P., B.G. Campbell, and T.I. Molleson 1971 *Catalogue of Fossil Hominids, Part II: Europe.* British Museum (Natural History), London.

___. 1975 *Catalogue of Fossil Hominids, Part III: Americas, Asia, Australia.* British Museum (Natural History), London.

Olivier, G. 1969 *Practical Anthropology.* C.C. Thomas, Springfield.

Oxnard, C.E. 1984 *The Order of Man.* Yale University Press, New Haven.

Oxnard, C.E. 1987 *Fossils, Teeth, and Sex. New Perspectives on Human Evolution.* University of Washington Press, Seattle.

Pfeiffer, J.E. 1985 *The Emergence of Humankind,* Fourth Edition. Harper and Row, New York.

Piveteau, J. 1957 *Traité de Paléontologie.* Volume 7, *Les Primates et l'Homme.* Masson, Paris.

Protsch, R. 1978 *Catalog of Fossil Hominids of North America.* Fischer, Stuttgart.

Reichs, K.J. (ed) 1986 *Forensic Osteology. Advances in the Identification of Human Remains.* C.C. Thomas, Springfield.

Radovčić, J., F.H. Smith, E. Trinkaus, and M.H. Wolpoff 1988 *The Krapina Hominids: An Illustrated Catalog of the Skeletal Collection.* Mladost and the Croatian Natural History Museum, Zagreb.

Rogers, S.L. 1984 *The Human Skull: , Its Mechanics, Measurements, and Variations.* C.C. Thomas, Springfield.

Rogers, S.L. 1988 *The Testimony of Teeth. Forensic Aspects of Human Dentition.* C.C. Thomas, Springfield.

Sattler, H.R. 1988 *Hominids: A Look Back at our Ancestors.* Lothrop, Lee, and Shepard, New York.

Schwalbe, G. 1904 *Die Vorgeschichte des Menschen.* Friedrich Viewug, Braunschweig

Shipman, P., A.C Walker, and D. Bichell 1986 *The Human Skeleton.* Harvard University Press, Cambridge.

Skinner, M.F., Sperber, G.H. 1982 *Atlas of the Radiographs of Early Man.* Alan R. Liss, New York.

Steele, D.G., and C.A. Bramblett 1988 *The Anatomy and Biology of the Human Skeleton.* Texas A&M University Press, College Station.

Swindler, D.R., and C.D. Wood 1973 *An Atlas of Primate Gross Anatomy. Baboon, Chimpanzee, and Man.* University of Washington, Seattle.

Tattersall, I. 1993 *The Human Odyssey: Four Million Years of Evolution.* Prentice-Hall, New York.

Tattersall, I., and E. Delson 1984 *Ancestors. Four Million Years of Humanity.* American Museum of Natural History, New York.

Thoma, A. 1985 *Éléments de Paléoanthropologie.* Institut Supérieur d'Archéologie et d'Histoire de d'Art, Louvain-la-Neuve (Belgium).

Ubelaker, D.H. 1989 *Human Skeletal Remains. Excavation, Analysis, Interpretation,* 2nd Edition. Taraxacum, Washington D.C.

White, T.D. 1990 *Human Osteology.* Academic Press, New York.

Wolpoff, M.H. 1980 *Paleoanthropology,* First Edition. Knopf, New York.

Descriptive

Aguirre, E., and M.A. Lumley 1977 Fossil men from Atapuerca in Spain; Their bearing on human evolution in the Middle Pleistocene. *Journal of Human Evolution* 6(8):681-688.

Alexeyev, V.P. 1981 Fossil man on the territory of the USSR and related problems. In D. Ferembach (ed): *Les Processus de l'Hominisation.* Centre National de la Recherche Scientifique, Paris. pp. 183-188.

Allen, A.L. 1926 A report on the Australoid calvaria found at Mistkraal, Cape Province. *South African Journal of Science* 23:943-950.

Anderson, J.E. 1968 Later paleolithic skeletal remains from Nubia. In F Wendorf (ed): *The Prehistory of Nubia,* Volume 2. Southern Methodist University, Dallas. pp. 996-1040.

Angel, J.L. 1952 The human skeletal remains from Hotu, Iran. *Proceedings of the American Philosophical Society* 96(3):258-269.

___. 1972 A Middle Paleolithic temporal bone from Darra-i-Kur, Afghanistan. In L. Dupree (ed): *Prehistoric Research in Afghanistan (1959-1966). Transactions of the American Philosophical Society* 62:54-56.

Angel, J.L., and C.S. Coon 1954 La Cotte de St. Brelade II: present status. *Man* 54:53-55.

Arambourg, C. 1963 *Le Gisement de Ternifine. Archives de l'Institut de Paléontologie Humaine,* Mémoire 32.

___. 1969 Résultats de la Nouvelle Mission de l'Omo (2e campagne 1969). *Comptes Rendus de l'Académie des Sciences,* Série D, 268:759-762.

Arambourg, C., and P. Biberson 1956 Fossil Human Remains from the Paleolithic Site of Sidi Abderrahman (Morocco). *American Journal of Physical Anthropology* 14:267-290.

___. 1967 Sur la Découverte Pléistocène Inférieur de la Vallée de l'Omo, d'une Mandibule d'Australopithecien. *Comptes Rendus de l'Académie des Sciences,* Série D, 265:689-690.

Arambourg, C., M. Boule, H. Vallois, and R. Verneau. 1934 *Les grottes paléolithiques des Beni-Ségoual, Algérie. Archives de L'Institut de Paléontologie Humaine.* Mémoire 13.

Arambourg, C., J. Chavaillon, and Y. Coppens 1967 Premiers Resultats de la Nouvelle Mission de l'Omo 1967. *Comptes Rendus de l'Académie des Sciences,* Série D, 265:1891-1896.

Arambourg, C., and Y. Coppens 1968 Découverte d'un Australopithecien Nouveau dans les Gisements de l'Omo (Ethiopie). *South African Journal of Science* 64:58-59.

Arambourg, C., and J. Fromaget 1938 Le gisement Quaternaire de Tam-Nang (Chain, Annamitique septenrionale): sa stratigraphie et ses faunes. *Comptes Rendus de l'Académie des Sciences,* Série D, 207:793-795.

Arensburg, B. 1991 The vertebral column, thoracic cage, and hyoid bone. In O. Bar-Yosef and B. Vandermeersch (eds): *Le squelette Moustérien de Kébara 2.* Cahiers de Paléoanthropologie, Centre National de la Recherche Scientifique, Paris.

Arsuaga, J-L., A. Gracia, I. Martínez, J.M. Bermúdez de Castro, A. Rosas, V. Villaverde, and M.P. Fumanal 1989 The human remains from Cova Negra (Valencia, Spain) and their place in European Pleistocene human evolution. *Journal of Human Evolution* 18(1):55-92.

Arsuaga, J-L., I. Martínez, A. Gracia, J-M. Carretero, and E. Carbonell 1993 Three hew human skulls from the Sima de los Huesos Middle Pleisatocene siye in Sierra de Atapuerca, Spain. *Nature* 362:534-537.

Arsuaga, J.L., J.M. Carretero, I. Martinez, and A. Garcia 1991 Cranial remains and long bones from Atapuerca/Iberas (Spain). *Journal of Human Evolution* 20(3):191-230.

Ascenzi, A., and A.G. Segre 1971 A New Neanderthal child mandible from an Upper Pleistocene site in Southern Italy. *Nature* 233, 280-283.

Asfaw, B. 1983 A new hominid parietal from Bodo, Middle Awash Valley, Ethiopia. *American Journal of Physical Anthropology* 61(3):367-371.

Asfaw, B. 1987 The Belohdelie frontal: new evidence of early hominid cranial morphology from the Afar of Ethiopia. *Journal of Human Evolution* 16(7/8):611-624.

Baba, H., and F. Aziz 1992 Human tibial fragment from Sambungmachan, Java. In T. Akazawa, K. Aoki, and T. Kimura (eds): *The Evolution and Dispersal of Modern Humans in Asia*. Hokusen-sha, Tokyo. pp. 349-361.

Baba, H., and B. Endo 1982 Postcranial skeleton of the Minatogawa Man. In H. Suzuki and K. Hanihara (eds): *The Minatogawa Man. The Upper Pleistocene Man from the Island of Okinawa*. The University Museum of the University of Tokyo Bulletin Number 19:61-195.

Bailly, R. 1933 Asselar skeleton. *Revue Anthropologique* 43:172-181.

Barral, L., and R.-P. Charles 1963 Nouvelles données anthropométriques et précisions sur les affinités systématiques des "Négroides de Grimaldi". *Bulletin du Musée d'Anthropologie Préhistorique de Monaco* 10:123-139.

Bartucz. L., and J. Szabo 1938 Der Urmensch der Mussolinihöhle (Subalyuk) bei Czeréphalu. *Geologia Hungarica* 14:49-112.

Battaglia, R. 1948 L'uomo fossile di Quinzano. *Memoires Del Museo Civcio di Storia Naturale di Verona* 8:245-281.

Begun, D., and A.C. Walker 1993 The endocast. In A.C. Walker and R.E. Leakey (eds): *The Nariokotome Homo erectus Skeleton*. Harvard University Press, Cambridge. pp. 326-358, 443-445.

Berger, L.R., A.W. Keyser, and P.V. Tobias 1993 Gladysvale: first early hominid site discovered in South Africa since 1948. *American Journal of Physical Anthropology* 92(1):107-111.

Bergman, C.A. and C.B. Stringer 1989 Fifty years after: Egbert, an early Upper Paleolithic juvenile from Ksar Akil, Lebanon. *Paléorient* 15(2):99-111.

Bermúdez de Castro, J.M. 1986 Dental remains from Atapuerca (Spain) I. Metrics. *Journal of Human Evolution* 15(4):265-287.

___. 1988 Dental remains from Atapuerca/Ibeas (Spain) II. Morphology. *Journal of Human Evolution* 17(3):279-304.

___. 1992 A human mandibular fragment from the Atapuerca trench (Burgos, Spain). *Journal of Human Evolution* 22(1):41-46.

Bermúdez De Castro, J-M. 1993 Atapuerca dental remains. New evidence (1987-1991 excavations) and interpretations. *Journal of Human Evolution* 24(5):339-371.

Billy, G. 1969 Le squelette postcrânien de l'homme de Chancelade. *L'Anthropologie* 73:207-246.

Billy, G. 1985 Les restes humains de la grotte du Coupe-Gorge à Montmaurin (Haute-Garonne). *Zeitschrift für Morphologie und Anthropologie* 75:223-237.

Billy, G. and H.V. Vallois 1977 La Mandibule pré-Rissienne de Montmaurin. *L'Anthropologie* 81:273-312, 411-458.

Black, D. 1930 On an Adolescent skull of *Sinanthropus pekinensis* in comparison with an adult skull of the same species and with other hominid skulls, recent and fossil. *Palaeontologia Sinica*, Series D, Volume 7, Fascicle 2.

___. 1933 On Six Specimens of *Sinanthropus* Mandibulae. *Palaeontologia Sinica*, Series D, Volume 7.

Boaz, N.T., and F.C. Howell 1977 A gracile hominid cranium from upper member G of the Shungura formation, Ethiopia. *American Journal of Physical Anthropology* 46:93-108.

Bonfiglio, I., P.F. Cassoli, F. Mallegni, M. Piperno, and A. Solano 1986 Neanderthal parietal, vertebrate fauna, and stone artifacts freom the Upper Pleistocene deposits of Contrada Ianni di San Calogero (Catanzaro, Calabria, Italy). *American Journal of Physical Anthropology* 70:241-250.

Bonnet, R. 1919 Der Diluvaile Menschenfund von Obercassel bei Bonn. In M. Verworn, R. Bonnet, and G. Steinmann (eds): *Die Skelet*. Bergmann, Weisbaden.

Borgognini Tarli, S.M. 1983 A Neanderthal lower molar from Fondo Cattíe (Maglie, Lecce). *Journal of Human Evolution* 12:383-401.

Bouchud, J. 1966 Remarques sur les fouilles de L. Lartet à l'abri Cro-Magnon (Dordogne). *Bulletin de la Société d'Études et de Recherche Préhistorique Les Eyzies* 15:1-9.

Boule, M. 1911-1913 L'homme fossile de la Chapelle-aux-Saints. *Annales de Paléontologie* 6:111-172, (7):21-56, 85-192, (8):1-70; and in 1913 published by Masson, Paris.

Boule, M., and H.V. Vallois 1932 L'homme fossile d'Asselar, Sahara. *Archives de l'Institut de Paleóntologie Humaine*, Mémorie 9.

Bouvier, M. and J.M. Rousseau 1972 Fragment crânien humain d'âge Rissien des dilluvions de la Dordogne. *L'Anthropologie* 76:325-330.

Bouzat, J-L.. 1982 Le malaire de l'homme de Tautavel. In H. de Lumley (ed): *L'Homo erectus et la Place de l'Homme de Tautavel parmi les Hominidés Fossiles*. 1ᵉʳ Congrès International de Paléontologie Humaine, Nice, Prétirage. Volume 1:137-153. Louis-Jean, Nice.

Bowler, J.M. and A.G. Thorne 1976 Human remains from Lake Mungo: discovery and excavation of Lake Mungo III. In The Origin of the Australians, R.L. Kirk and A.G. Thorne, eds. Australian Institute of Aboriginal Studies, Canberra, pp. 127-138.

Bowler, J.M., D.J. Mulvaney, D.A. Casey, and T.A. Darragh 1967 Green Gully Burial. *Nature* 213:152-154.

Bowler, J.M., R. Jones, H. Allen, and A.G. Thorne 1970 Pleistocene human remains from Australia: a living site and human cremation from Lake Mungo, western New South Wales. World Archaeology 2:39-60.

Bräuer, G. 1980 Die morphologischen Affinitäten des jungpleistozänen Stirnbeines aus dem Elbmündungsgebiet bei Hahnöfersand. *Zeitschrift für Morphologie und Anthropologie* 71:1-42.

Bräuer, G., and R.E. Leakey 1986 The ES-11693 cranium from Eliye Springs, West Turkana, Kenya. *Journal of Human Evolution* 15(4):289-312.

Bräuer, G., R.E. Leakey, and E. Mbua 1992 A first report on the ER-3884 cranial remains from Ileret/East Turkana, Kenya. In G. Bräuer and F.H. Smith (eds): *Continuity or Replacement? Controversies in Homo sapiens Evolution*. Balkema, Rotterdam. pp. 111-119.

Bräuer, G., and M.J. Mehlman 1988 Hominid molars from a Middle Stone Age level at the Mumba Rock Shelter, Tanzania. *American Journal of Physical Anthropology* 75(1):69-76.

Brabant, H., A. Sahly 1964 Étude des dents néanderthaliennes découvertes dans la Grotte du Portel en Ariège. *Bulletin du Groupement International pour la Recherche Scientifique en Stomatologie* 7:237-254.

Breitinger, E. 1964 Reconstruction of the Swanscombe skull. In Ovey, C,D, (ed.) *The Swanscombe skull: A survey of research in a Pleistocene site*. Royal Anthropological Institute, London. pp. 161-172.

Briggs, L.C. 1950 On three skulls from Mechta-el-Arbi, Algeria. *American Journal of Physical Anthropology* 8:305-314.

Broom, R.A. and J.T. Robinson 1952 Swartkrans Ape-Man. Transvaal Museum Memoir 6, Pretoria.

Broom, R.A., and G.W.H. Schepers 1946 The South African Fossil Ape-Men, the Australopithecinae. Transvaal Museum Memoir 2, Pretoria.

Broom, R.A., J.T. Robinson, and G.W.H. Schepers 1950 Sterkfontein Ape-Man *Plesianthropus*. Transvaal Museum Memoir 4, Pretoria.

Brothwell, D.R. 1960 Upper Pleistocene human skull from Niah caves, Sarawak. Sarawak Museum Journal 9:323-349.

Brothwell, D.R., and T. Shaw 1971 A late Upper Pleistocene proto-West African Negro from Nigeria. Man 6:221-227.

Brown, B., and A.C. Walker 1993 The dentition. In A.C. Walker and R.E. Leakey (eds): *The Nariokotome Homo erectus Skeleton*. Harvard University Press, Cambridge. pp. 161-192, 438.

Brown, P. 1989 Coobool Creek. Terra Australis 13. Department of Prehistory, Research School of Pacific Studies, Australian National University, Canberra.

Bush, M.E., Lovejoy, C.O., Johanson, D.C., and Coppens, Y. 1982 Hominid carpal, metacarpal, and phalangeal bones recovered from the Hadar formation:1974-1977 collections. *American Journal of Physical Anthropology* 57(4):651-678.

Buxton, L.H.D. 1928 Excavation of a Mousterian rock shelter at Devil's Tower, Gibraltar: human remains. *Journal of the Royal Anthropological Institute* 58:57-85.

Campy, M., J. Chaline, C. Guérin, and B. Vandermeersch 1974 Une canine humaine associée à une faune Mindel récent dans le réplissage de l'Aven de Vergranne (Doubs). *Comptes Rendus de l'Académie des Sciences*, Série D, 278:3187-3190.

Carney, J., A. Hill, J.A. Miller, and A. Walker 1971 Late australopithecine from Baringo disrict, Kenya. *Nature* 230:509-514.

Cecchi, J.M., and B. Chiarelli 1991 Evaluation of the asymmetry of the internal cranial vault of Circeo I at the level of the Broca's area. In M. Piperno and G. Scichilone (eds): The Circeo 1 Neandertal Skull: *Studies and Documentation*. Instituto Poligrafico e Zecca Dello Stato, Dello Stato. pp. 415-421.

Cesnola, A.P. di, P. Messeri 1967 Quatre dents humaines paléolithiques trouvées dans les cavernes d'Italie méridionales. *L'Anthropologie* 71:249-262.

Chavaillon, J., C. Brahimi, and Y. Coppens 1974 Première découverte d'Hominidé dans l'un des sites acheuléens de Melka Kunturé (Ethiopie). *Comptes Rendus de l'Académie des Sciences*, Série D, 278:3299-3302.

Chia Lanpo 1957 Notes on human and some other mammalian remains from Changyang, Hupei. *Vertebrata PalAsiatica* 1:247-258.

Chia Lanpo and Woo Jukang 1959 Fossil human skull base of Late Paleolithic stage from Ch'ilinshan, Leipin District, Kwangsi, China. *Vertebrata PalAsiatica* 3:37-39.

Chia Lanpo, Wei Qi, and Li Chaorong 1979 Report on the excavation of Xujiayao (Hsuchiayao) man site in 1976. *Vertebrata PalAsiatica* 17:277-293.

Chiu Chunglang, Gu Yümin, Zhang Yinyun, and Chang Shenshui 1973 Newly discovered *Sinanthropus* remains and stone artifacts at Choukoutien. *Vertebrata PalAsiatica* 11:109-131.

Clark, J.D., D.R. Brothwell, R. Powers, and K.P. Oakley 1968 Rhodesian man: notes on a new femur fragment. *Man* 3:105-111.

Clark, J.D., K.P. Oakley, L.H. Wells, and J.A.C. McClelland 1950 New Studies on Rhodesian Man. *Journal of the Royal Anthropological Institiute* 77(Pt. 1):1-32.

Clark, W.E. LeGros 1938a General features of the Swanscombe skull bones. *Journal of the Royal Anthropological Insititute* 68:58-60.

Clark, W.E. LeGros 1938b The endocranial cast of the Swanscombe skull bones. *Journal of the Royal Anthropological Insititute* 68:61-67.

Clarke, G.A., and J.M. Lindly 1991 On paradigmatic biases and Paleolithic research traditions. *Current Anthropology* 32(5):577-587.

Coffing, E., C. Feibel, M. Leakey, and A. Walker 1994 Four-million-year-old hominids from east Lake Turkana, Kenya. *American Journal of Physical Anthropology* 93:55-65.

Condemi, S. 1991 *Les Hommes Fossiles de Saccopastore, et leurs relations phylogénétiques.* Cahiers de Paléoanthropologie, Centre National de la Recherche Scientifique, Paris.

Conroy, G.C., C.J. Jolly, D. Cramer, and J.E. Kalb 1978 Newly discovered fossil hominid skull from the Afar depression, Ethiopia. *Nature* 276:67-70.

Conroy, C.G., M.H.L. Pickford, B. Senut, J. Van Couvering, and P. Mein 1992 *Otavipithecus namibiensis*, first Miocene hominoid from southern Africa. *Nature* 356:144-147.

Coon, C.S. 1971 A fossilized human mandibular fragment from Kangatotha, Kenya, East Africa. *American Journal of Physical Anthropology* 34:157-164.

Coppens, Y. 1966 Le Tchadanthropus. *L'Anthropologie* 70:5-16.

Coppens, Y. 1970 Les restes d'Hominidés des séries inférieures et moyennes des formations plio-villafranchiennes de l'Omo en Ethiopie. *Comptes Rendus de l'Académie des Sciences*, Séries D, 271:2286-2289.

Coppens, Y. 1973a Les restes d'Hominidés des séries inférieures et moyennes des formations Plio-villafranchiennes de l'Omo en Ethiopie (récoltes 1970,1971, et 1972). *Comptes Rendus de l'Académie des Sciences*, Séries D, 276:1823-1826.

Coppens, Y. 1973b Les restes d'Hominidés des Séries supérieures des formations plio-villafranchiennes de l'Omo en Ethiopie (récoltes 1970, 1971, et 1972). *Comptes Rendus de l'Académie des Sciences*, Séries D, 276:1981-1984.

Coppens, Y., and M. Sakka 1983 Un nouveau crâne d'australopithèque. In Sakka (ed): *Morphologie, évolutive, morphologenèse du crâne et anthropogenèse*. Actes du VIIᵉ Congrès de la Société Primatologique Internationale. Centre National de la Recherche Scientifique, Paris. pp. 185-194.

Cotrozza, S., F. Mallegni, and A.M. Radnielli 1985 Fémur d'un enfant Néanderthalien dans la Buca del Tasso à Melato, Alpia Apuana (Italie). *L'Anthropologie* 89(1):111-116.

Czarnetzki, A. 1989 Ein archaischer Hominiden calvariarest aus einer Kiesgrube in Reilingen, Rhein-Neckar-Kreis. *Quartär* 39/40:191-208.

Dart, R.A. 1934 The dentition of *Australopithecus africanus*. *Folia Anatomica Japonica* 12:207-222.

Dart, R.A. 1948 The First Human Mandible from the Cave of Hearths, Makapansgat. *South African Archaeological Bulletin* 3(12):96-98.

Dart, R.A. 1948a The Makapansgat proto-human *Australopithecus prometheus*. *American Journal of Physical Anthropology* 6:259-284.

Dart, R.A. 1948b The adolescent mandible of *Australopithecus prometheus.American Journal of Physical Anthropology* 6:391-409.

Dart, R.A. 1949a Innominate fragments of *Australopithecus prometheus*. *American Journal of Physical Anthropology* 7:301-333.

Dart, R.A. 1949b The first pelvic bones of *Australopithecus prometheus*: a preliminary note. *American Journal of Physical Anthropology* 7:255-258.

Dart, R.A. 1949c The cranio-facial fragment of *Australopithecus prometheus*. *American Journal of Physical Anthropology* 7:187-214.

Dart, R.A. 1949d The second adult palate of *Australopithecus prometheus*. *American Journal of Physical Anthropology* 7:335-338.

Dart, R.A. 1954 The second or adult female mandible of *Australopithecus prometheus*. *American Journal of Physical Anthropology* 12:313-343.

Dart, R.A. 1958 A further adolescent ilium from Makapansgat. *American Journal of Physical Anthropology* 16:473-479.

Dart, R.A. 1962a A cleft adult madible and nine other lower jaw fragments from Makapansgat. *American Journal of Physical Anthropology*, 20:267-286.

Dart, R.A. 1962b The Makapansgat pink breccia australopithecine skull. *American Journal of Physical Anthropology* 20:199-126.

David, P. 1960 Étude de deux dents néanderthaliennes découvertes à la Chaise. *Bulletin de la Société Préhistorique Française* 57:424-427.

David, P. and F. Bordes 1950 Découverte d'une Calotte cranienne fragmentaire et de dents humaines dans un Niveau moustérien ancien de la Chaise (Charente). *Comptes Rendus de l'Académie des Sciences*, Série D, 230(8):779-780.

Day, M.H. 1969 Omo human skeletal remains. *Nature* 222:1135-1138.

Day, M.H. 1969 Femoral fragment of a robust australopithecine from Olduvai Gorge, Tanzania. *Nature* 221:230-233.

Day, M.H. 1971 Postcranial remains of *Homo erectus* from Bed IV, Olduvai Gorge, Tanzania. *Nature* 232:383-387.

Day, M.H., and R.E. Leakey 1973 New evidence of the genus *Homo* from East Rudolf, Kenya. I. *American Journal of Physical Anthropology*. 39:341-354.

Day, M.H., and R.E. Leakey 1974 New evedence for the genus *Homo* from East Rudolf, Kenya, III. *American Journal of Physical Anthropology*. 41:367-380.

Day, M.H., M.D. Leakey, and, C. Magori 1980 A new hominid fossil skull (L.H.18) from the Ngaloba Beds, Laetoli, northern Tanzania. *Nature* 284:55-56.

Day, M.H., R.E. Leakey, A.C. Walker, and B.A. Wood 1975 New hominids from East Rudolf, Kenya, I. *American Journal of Physical Anthropology*. 42:461-476.

Day, M.H., R.E. Leakey, A.C. Walker, and B.A. Wood 1976 New hominids from East Turkana, Kenya. *American Journal of Physical Anthropology*. 45:369-436.

Day, M.H., and T. Molleson 1976 The puzzle from JK2 - A femur and a tibial fragment (O.H. 34) from Olduvai Gorge, Tanzania. *Journal of Human Evolution* 5:455-466.

Day, M.H., and J.R. Napier 1964 Hominid fossils from Bed I, Olduvai Gorge: fossil foot bones. *Nature* 201: 967-971.

Day, M.H., and J.R. Napier 1966 A hominid fossils toe bone from from Bed I, Olduvai Gorge, Tanzania. *Nature* 211: 929-930.

Day, M.H., and J.L. Scheuer 1973 SKW 14147: A new hominid metacarpal from Swartkrans. *Journal of Human Evolution* 2:429-438.

Day, M.H., and C.M.B. Thornton 1986 The extremity bones of *Paranthropus robustus* from Kromdraai B, east Formation Member 3, Republic of South Africa - a reappraisal. In V.V. Novotný and A. Mizerová (eds): *Fossil Man. New Facts, New Ideas. Papers in Honor of Jan Jelínek's Life Anniversary. Anthropos* (Brno) 23:91-99.

Day, M.H., M.H.C. Twist, and S. Ward 1991 Les vestiges post-crâniens d'Omo 1 (Kibish). *L'Anthropologie* 95(2/3):595-610.

De Bonis, L., G. Bouvrain, D. Geraads, G. Koufos 1990 New hominid skull material from the late Miocene of Macedonia in Northern Greece. *Nature* 345:712-714.

De Bonis, L., D. Geraads, G. Guérin, A. Haga, J-J. Jaeger, and S. Sen 1984 Découverte un hominidé fossile dans le Pléistocène de la République de Djibouti. *Comptes Rendus de l'Académie des Sciences*, Série D, 299:1097-1100.

De Lumley, H., M-A. De Lumley and A. Fournier. 1982 La mandibule de l'homme de Tautavel. In H. de Lumley (ed): L'*Homo erectus* et la Place de l'Homme de Tautavel parmi les Hominidés Fossiles. 1ᵉʳ Congrès International de Paléontologie Humaine, Nice, Prétirage. Volume 1:178-221. Louis-Jean, Nice.

De Lumley, M-A. 1970 Le pariétal humain anténéndertalien de Cova Negra (Jative, Espagne). *Comptes Rendus de l'Académie des Sciences*, Série D, 270:39-41.

De Lumley, M-A. 1972a L'Os iliaque anténéandertalien de la Grotte du Prince. *Bulletin du Musée d'Anthropologie Préhistorique de Monaco* 18:89-112.

De Lumley, M-A. 1972b La Mandubula de Bañolas. *Ampurias* 33-34:1-91.

De Lumley, M-A. 1972c Les Néandertaliens de la grotte de l'Hortus. *Études Quaternaires* (Université de Province), Mémoire 1:375-385.

De Lumley, M-A. 1973 Anténéandertaliens et Néandertaliens du bassin Méditerranéen Occidental Européen. *Études Quaternaires* (Université de Province), Memoire 2.

De Lumley, M-A. 1976a Les Anténéandertaliens du Sud. In H. de Lumley (ed): *La Préhistoire Française*. Centre Nationale de la Recherche Sciéntifique, Paris. 1:547-560.

De Lumley, M-A. 1976b Les Néandertaliens dans le Nord et le Centre. In H. de Lumley (ed): *La Préhistoire Française*. Centre Nationale de la Recherche Sciéntifique, Paris. 1:588-594.

De Lumley, M-A. 1976c Les Néandertaliens dans le Midi Méditerranéen. In H. de Lumley (ed): *La Préhistoire Française*. Centre Nationale de la Recherche Sciéntifique, Paris. 1:595-603.

De Lumley, M.A. 1987 Les restes humains Néandertaliens de la Brèche de Genay, Côte-D'or, France. *L'Anthropologie* 91:119-162.

De Lumley, M-A., and M. Garcia-Sanchez 1971 L'Enfant Néandertalien de Cariegüela a Piñar (Andalousie). *L'Anthropologie* 75:29-56.

De Lumley, M-A., and P. Lamy 1982 Le membre inférieur de l'homme de Tautavel: fémurs et fibulae. In H. de Lumley (ed): L'*Homo erectus* et la Place de l'Homme de Tautavel parmi les Hominidés Fossiles. 1ᵉʳ Congrès International de Paléontologie Humaine, Nice, Prétirage. Volume 1:276-318. Louis-Jean, Nice.

De Lumley, M-A., and J. Piveteau 1969 Les restes humains de la grotte du Lazaret (Nice, Alpes-Maritimes). *Mémoires de la Société Préhistorique Française* 7:223-232.

De Lumley, M-A., and A. Sonakia 1985 Première découverte d'un *Homo erectus* sur le Continent indien, à Hathnora, dans la Moyenne Vallée de la Narmada. *L'Anthropologie* 89(1):13-61.

De Lumley, M-A., and J. Spitery 1982 Le maxillaire de l'homme de Tautavel. In H. de Lumley (ed): L'*Homo erectus* et la Place de l'Homme de Tautavel parmi les Hominidés Fossiles. 1ᵉʳ Congrès International de Paléontologie Humaine, Nice, Prétirage. Volume 1:154-177. Louis-Jean, Nice.

De Terra, H., J. Romero, and T.D. Stewart 1949 *Tepexpan Man*. Viking Fund Publication in Anthropology 11, New York.

De Villiers, H. 1972 The first fossil human skeleton from South West Africa. *Transactions of the Royal Society of South Africa* 40:187-196.

De Villiers, H. 1973 Human skeletal remains from Border Cave, Ingwavuma District, Kwazulu, South Africa. *Annals of the Transvaal Museum* 28(13):229-256.

De Villiers, H. 1976 A second adult human mandible from Border Cave, Ingwavuma District, Kwa Zulu, South Africa. *South African Journal of Science* 72:212-215.

Debénath, A. 1967 Découverte d'un mandibule humaine à la Chaise de Vouthon (Charente). *Comptes Rendus de l'Académie des Sciences*, Série D, 281:875-876..

Debénath, A. 1975 Découverte de restes humains probablement atériens à Dar Es Soltane (Moroc). *Comptes Rendus de l'Académie des Sciences*, Série D, 265:1170-1171.

Debénath, A. 1991 Les Atériens du Maghreb. *Les dossiers d'Archéologie* 161:52-57.

Debénath, A., and J. Piveteau 1969 Nouvelles découvertes de restes humains fossiles à la Chaise-de-Vouthon (Charente). *Comptes Rendus de l'Académie des Sciences*, Série D, 269:24-28.

Debénath, A., J.P. Raynal, J.P. Roche, J.P. Texier, and D. Ferembach 1986 Position, habitat, typologie, et devenir de l'atérien marocain: données récentes. *L'Anthropologie* 90:233-246.

Debénath, A., J.P. Raynal, and J.P. Texier 1982 Position stratigraphique des restes humains paléolithiques Marocains sur la base des travaux récents. *Comptes Rendus de l'Académie des Sciences*, Série D, 294:1247-1250.

Delfino, V.P., E. Vacca, F. Potente, T. Lettini, and P. Ragone 1991 Analytical morphometry of the Neanderthal cranium from Monte Circeo (Circeo 1). In M. Piperno and G. Scichilone (eds): *The Circeo 1 Neandertal Skull: Studies and Documentation.* Instituto Poligrafico e Zecca Dello Stato, Dello Stato. pp. 197-251.

Deloison, Y. 1986 Description d'un calcanéum fossile avec des calcanéums de Pongidés, d'Australopithèques, et d'Homo. *Comptes Rendus de l'Académie des Sciences*, Série D, 302:257-262.

Delson, E. 1977 Reconstruction of hominid phylogeny: a testable framework based on cladistic analysis. *Journal of Human Evolution* 6, 263-278.

Delson, E. 1981 Paleoanthropology: Pliocene and Pleistocene human evolution. *Paleobiology* 7:298-305.

Dong, G., S. Gao, and B. Li 1982 New discoveries of the fossil Ordos man. *Kexue Tongbao* 27:754-758.

Drennan, M.R. 1929 An Australoid Skull from the Cape Flats. *Journal of the Royal Anthropological Institute* 59:417-427

Drennan, M.R. 1937 The Florisbad skull and brain cast. *Transactions of the Royal Society of South Africa* 25(1).

Drennan, M.R. 1955 The special features and status of the Saldanha skull. *American Journal of Physical Anthropology* 13:625-634.

Drennan, M.R., and R. Singer 1955 A mandibular fragment, probably of the Saldanha skull. *Nature* 175-364.

Dubois, E. 1894 *Pithecanthropus erectus: eine Menschenähnliche Übergangsform von Java.* Landes Drucherei, Batavia.

Dubois, E. 1922 The proto-Australian fossil man of Wadjak, Java. *Koninklijke Akademie Wetenschappen te Amsterdam*, Series B, 23:1013-1051.

Dubois, E. 1924a On the principle characters of the cranium and the brain, the mandible and the teeth of ^(Pithecanthropus erectus). *Koninklijke Akademie Wetenschappen te Amsterdam*, Series B, 27:265-278.

Dubois, E. 1924b Figures of the calvarium and endocranial cast, a fragment of the mandible and three teeth of ^(Pithecanthropus erectus). *Koninklijke Akademie Wetenschappen te Amsterdam*, Series B, 27:459-464.

Dubois, E. 1926 Figures of the femur of *Pithecanthropus erectus*. *Koninklijke Akademie Wetenschappen te Amsterdam*, Series B, 29:1275-1277.

Dubois, E. 1926 On the principle characters of the femur of *Pithecanthropus erectus*. *Koninklijke Akademie Wetenschappen te Amsterdam*, Series B, 29:730-743.

Dubois, E. 1935 The sixth (fifth new) femur of *Pithecanthropus erectus*. *Koninklijke Akademie Wetenschappen te Amsterdam*, Series B, 38:850-852.

Duckworth, W.L.H. 1915 *Studies in Anthropology*, Revised Edition, Volume 1. Cambridge University Press, Cambridge.

Duday, H., and B. Arensburg 1991 La Pathologie. In O.Bar-Yosef and B. Vandermeersch (eds): *Le squelette Moustérien de Kébara 2.* Cahiers de Paléoanthropologie, Centre National de la Recherche Scientifique, Paris. pp. 179-194.

Duport, L., and C. Vandermeersch 1976 La mandibule moustérienne de Mountgaudier. *Comptes Rendus de l'Académie des Sciences*, Série D, 238:1161-1164.

Dutour, O. 1989 *Les Hommes Fossiles du Sahara.* Centre National de la Recherche Scientifique, Paris.

Elsner, F.W. 1914 Die Zähne von La Rochette. *Archiv für Anthropologie* 41:127-129.

Endo, B., and T. Kimura 1970 Postcranial skeleton of the Amud man. In H. Suzuki and F. Takai (eds): *The Amud Man and his Cave Site.* University of Tokyo, Tokyo. pp. 231-406.

Ennouchi, E. 1953 Découverte d'un Homme de Mechta, à Rabat *L'Anthropologie* 57:272-283.

Ennouchi, E. 1969 Présence d'un Enfant Néanderthalien au Jebel Irhoud (Maroc). *Annales de Paléontologie des Vertébrés* 55:251-265.

Ennouchi, E. 1970 Un nouvel archanthropien au Maroc. *Annales de Paléontologie des Vertébrés* 56:95-107.

Ennouchi, E. 1972 Nouvelle découverte d'un archanthropien au Maroc. *Comptes Rendus de l'Académie des Sciences*, Série D, 274:3088-3090.

Ennouchi, E. 1976 Un deuxième archanthropien à la carrière Thomas III (Maroc): étude préliminaire. *Bulletin de Muséum national d'histoire naturelle*, Série 2, Sciences de la Terre 56:273-296.

Facchini, F., and G. Giusberti 1992 *Homo sapiens sapiens* remains from the island of Crete. In G. Bräuer and F.H. Smith (eds): *Continuity or Replacement? Controversies in Homo sapiens Evolution*. Balkema, Rotterdam. pp. 189-208.

Fenner, F.J. 1941 Fossil Human Skull Fragments of Probable Pleistocene Age from Aitape, New Guinea. *Records of the South Australia Museum* 6(4):335-356.

Ferembach, D. 1962 La Deuxième molaire déciduale inférieure de la grotte de Salemas (Portugal). Com. Servs. Geol. Port., 46:177-187.

Ferembach, D. 1962 *La Nécropole Épipaléolithique de Taforalt: Etude des Squelettes humain*. Centre National de la Recherche Sciéntifique, Mission Universitaire et Culturelle Francaise au Maroc, Rabat.

Ferembach, D. 1974 Les hommes de l'Epipaléolithique et du Mésolithique de la France et du Nord-Ouest du Bassin Méditerranéen. *Bulletins et Mémoires de la Société d'Anthropologie de Paris*, Série 13, 2:201-236.

Ferembach, D. 1976a Les Restes humains atériens de Témara (Campagne 1975). *Bulletins et Mémoires de la Société d'Anthropologie de Paris*, Série 13, 3:175-180.

Ferembach, D. 1976b Les restes humains de la Grotte de Dar-es-Soltane 2 (Maroc) Campagne 1975. *Bulletins et Mémoires de la Société d'Anthropologie de Paris*, Série 13, 3:183-193.

Ferembach, D. 1978a Les Natoufiens et l'homme de Combe-Capelle. *Bulletins et Mémoires de la Société d'Anthropologie de Paris*, Série 13, 5:131-136.

Ferembach, D. 1978b A propos des Magdaléniens et des Mésolithique influence possible de modifications du milieu sur l'évolution morphologique. *Bulletins et Mémoires de la Société d'Anthropologie de Paris*, Série 13, 5:239-247.

Ferembach, D., P. Legoux, R. Fenart, R. Empereur-Buisson, and E. Vlček 1970 L'Enfant du Pech-De-L'Azé. *Archives de L'Institut de Paléontologie Humaine*, Mémoire 33.

Fleagle, J.G., D.T. Rasmussen, S. Yirga, T.M. Brown, and F.E. Grine 1991 New hominid fossils from Fejej, Southern Ethiopia. *Journal of Human Evolution* 21(2):145-152.

Formicola, V. 1988 The male and the female in the Upper Paleolithic burials from Grimaldi caves (Liguria, Italy). *Bulletin de Musée d'Anthropologie Préhistorique de Monaco*, Number 31:41-48.

Formicola, V. 1989 Early Aurignacian deciduous incisor from Riparo Bombrini at Balzi Rossi (Grimaldi, Italy). *Rivista di Antropologia* (Roma) 67:287-292.

Formicola, V. 1989 The dentition of the "Cro-Magnon type" Grotte des Enfants 4 (Grimaldi, Italy). *Bulletin de Musée d'Anthropologie Préhistorique de Monaco* 32:51-62.

Fox, R. 1970 *The Tabon Caves - archaeological explorations and excavations on Palawan Island, Philippines*. Monograph of the National Museum 1

Fraipont, C. 1914 Sur l'importance des caractères de l'astragale chez l'homme fossile. *Bulletins et Mémoires de la Société d'Anthropologie Brüssel* 32.

Fraipont, C. 1927 Su l'omoplate et le sacrum de l'homme de Spy. Ses affinités. *Revue Anthropologique* 37:189-195.

Fraipont, C. 1936 Les hommes fossiles d'Engis. *Archives de l'Institut de Paleontologie Humaine*. Mémorie 16:1-52.

Fraipont, J. and M. Lohest 1887 La race humaine de Néanderthal ou de Canstadt en Belgique: recherche ethnographiques sur des ossements humains, découverts dans dépôts quaternaires d'une grotte á Spy. *Archives de Biologie* 7:587-757.

Freedman, L., and M. Lofgren 1979 Human skeletal remains from Cossack, Western Australia. *Journal of Human Evolution* 8:283-300.

Gabunia, L., A. Justus, and A. Vekua 1989 Der Menschliche Unterkiefer von Dmanisi. In Der altpaläolithische Fundplatz Dmanisi in GGeorgien (Kaukasus). *Jahrbuch des Römisch-Germanischen Zentralmuseums Mainz* 36.

Galloway, A. 1959 *The Skeletal Remains of Bambandyanolo* (edited by P.V. Tobias, forward by R.A. Dart). Johannesburg: Witwatersrand University Press.

Gambier, D. 1982 Etude ostéométrique des astraghales néanderthaliens du Régourdou (Montignac, Dordogne). *Comptes Rendus de l'Académie des Sciences*, Série D, 295:517-520.

García Sanchez, M. 1985 Estudio preliminar de los restos Neandertalenses del Boquete Zafarraya (Alcaucin, Malaga). In *Homenaje a Luis Siret (1934-1984)*. General de Bellas Artes, Granada.

Genet-Varcin, E. 1966 Etude des Dents Permanentes Prouvenant du Gisement Mousterien de la Croze del Dua. *Annales de Paléontologie des Vertébrés* 52:89-114.

Genet-Varcin, E. 1974 Etude de dents humaines Isolées provenant des Grottes de La Chaise de Vouthon. I. *Bulletins et Mémoires de la Sociéte d'Anthropologie de Paris*, Série 13, 1:373-384.

Genet-Varcin, E. 1975 Etude de dents humaines Isolées provenant des Grottes de La Chaise de Vouthon. II. *Bulletins et Mémoires de la Société d'Anthropologie Paris*, Série 13, 2:129-141.

Geraads, D., and E. Tchernov 1983 Fémurs humains du Pléistocène moyen de Gesher Benot Ya'acov (Israël). *L'Anthropologie* 87(1):138-141.

Giacobini, G., and M-A. de Lumley 1984 Restes humains Néandertaliens de la Caverna delle Fate (Finale, Ligurie Italienne). *L'Anthropologie* 87(1):142-144.

Giacobini, G., M-A. DeLumley, Y. Yokoyama, and Huu-Van Nguyen 1984 Neanderthal child and adult remains from a Mousterian deposit in northern Italy (Caverna Delle Fate, Finale Ligure). *Journal of Human Evolution* 13:687-707.

Gieseler, W. 1941 Die urgeschichtlichen Menschenfunde aus dem Lontal und ihre Bedeutung für die deutsche Urgeschichte. *Jahrbuch Akademie der Wissenschaften Tübingen* 1:102-127.

Gieseler, W. 1977 Das jungpaläolithische Skelett von Neuessing. In P. Schröter (ed): *Festschrift zum 75 jährigen Bestehen der Anthropologischen Staatssammlung München*. Anthropologischen Staatssammlung München, München. pp. 39-52.

Gleń, E., and K. Kaczanowski 1982 Human remains. In K. Kozlwoski (ed): *Excavation in the Bacho Kiro Cave (Bulgaria): Final report*. Paôn'stwowe Wydawnictwo Naukowe, Warsaw. pp. 75-79.

Godinot, M., and M. Mahboubi 1992 Earliest known simian primate found in Algeria. *Nature* 357:324-326.

Gorjanović-Kramberger, D. 1906 *Der diluviale Mensch von Krapina in Kroatia. Ein Bertrag zur Paläoanthropologie*. Kreidel, Wiesbaden.

Gorjanović-Kramberger, D. 1908a Die Zähne des *Homo primigenisus* von Krapina. *Anatomischer Anzeiger*, 32:145-156.

Gorjanović-Kramberger, D. 1908b Anomalien und pathologische Erschienungen am Skelett des Urmenschen von Krapina. *Korrespondenzblatt des Deutschen Gesellschaft für Anthropologie, Ethnologie, und Urgeschichte* 38:108-112.

Gorjanović-Kramberger, D. 1908c Uber prismatische Molarwurzeln rezenter und diluvialer Menschen. *Anatomischer Anzeiger* 32:401-413.

Gorjanović-Kramberger, D. 1908d Anomalien und Krankhafte Erscheinungen am Skelett des Urmenschen von Krapina. *Die Umschau* 12:623-662.

Gorjanović-Kramberger, D. 1909 Der vordere Unterkieferabschnitt des Altdiluvialen Menschen in seinem genetischen Beziehungen zum Unterkiefer des rezenten Menschen und jenem der Anthropoiden. *Zeitschrift für Inductive Abstammungs und Vererbungslehre* 1:403-439.

Gorjanović-Kramberger, D. 1914 Der Axillarand des Schutterblattes des Menschen von Krapina. *Glasnik Hrvatskog prirodoslovnog društva* 26:231-257.

Gould, S.J. 1992 The most unkindest cut of all. *Natural History* 5/92:2-11.

Gramly, R.M. and G.P. Rightmire 1973 A fragmentary cranium and dated Later Stone Age assemblage from Lukenya Hill, Kenya. *Man* (N.S.) 8:571-579.

Gremiatsky, M.A. 1922 The Podkumok cranium and its morphological peculiarities. *Russian Anthropological Journal* 12:92-110.

Gremiatsky, M.A. 1925 Remains of the lower jaw and teeth of Podhumok man. *Russian Anthropological Journal* 14:91-99.

Gremiatsky, M.A. 1949 Cranium of the Neanderthal child from the Cave of Teshik-Tash, Southern Uzbekistan. In M.A. Gremiatsky and M.F. Nesturkh (eds): *Teshik-Tash: Palaeolithic Man*. Papers of the Institute for Scientific Research in Anthropology. State University Press, Moscow. pp. 137-182.

Grimaud, D. 1982 Le pariétal de l'homme de Tautavel. In H. de Lumley (ed): *L'Homo erectus et la Place de l'Homme de Tautavel parmi les Hominidés Fossiles*. 1er Congrès International de Paléontologie Humaine, Nice, Prétirage. Volume 1:62-88. Louis-Jean, Nice.

Grimaud-Hervé, D., and T. Jacob 1983 Les pariétaux de Pithécanthrope Sangiran 10. *L'Anthropologie* 87:469-474.

Grine, F.E. 1981a A new complete juvenile specimen of *Australopithecus africanus* (mammalia: primates) from member 4, Sterkfontein formation, Transvaal. *Annals of the South African Museum* 84(4):169-201.

Grine, F.E. 1981b Description of some juvenile hominid specimens from Swartkrans, Transvaal. *Annals of the Transvaal Museum* 86(2):43-71.

Grine, F.E. 1982 A new juvenile hominid (mammalia: primates) from member 3, Kromdraai formation, Transvaal. *Annals of the Transvaal Museum* 33:165-239.

Grine, F.E. 1982 Note on a new hominid specimen from Member 3, Kromdraai Formation, Transvaal. *Annals of the Transvaal Museum* 33:287-290.

Grine, F.E. 1989 New hominid fossils from the Swartkrans formation (1979-1986 excavations): craniodental specimens. *American Journal of Physical Anthropology* 79(4):409-449.

Grine, F.E. 1993 Description and preliminary analysis of new hominid craniodental fossils from the Swartkrans Formation. In C.K. Brain (ed): *Swartkrans. A Cave's Chronicle of Early Man.* Transvaal Museum Monograph 8:75-116.

Grine, F.E., and R.G. Klein 1993 Late Pleistocene human remains from the Sea Harvest site, Saldanha Bay, South Africa. *South African Journal of Science* 89:145-142.

Grine, F.E., and D.J. Daegling 1993 New mandible of *Paranthropus robustus* from Member 1, Swartkrans Formation, South Africa. *Journal of Human Evolution* 24(4):319-333.

Grine, F.E., R.G. Klein, and T.P. Volman Dating, archaeology, and human fossils from the Middle Stone Age levels of Die Kelders, South Africa. *Journal of Human Evolution* 21(5):363-396.

Grine, F.E., and D.S. Straight 1994 New hominid fossils from Member 1 "Hanging Remnant", Swartkrans Formation, South Africa. *Journal of Human Evolution* 26(1):57-75.

Grine, F.E., and R.L. Susman 1991 Radius of *Paranthropus robustus* from Member 1, Swartkrans formation, South Africa. *American Journal of Physical Anthropology* 84(3)229-248.

Hanihara, K., and B. Ueda 1982 Dentition of the Minatogawa Man. In H. Suzuki and K. Hanihara (eds): *The Minatogawa Man. The Upper Pleistocene Man from the Island of Okinawa.* The University Museum of the University of Tokyo Bulletin Number 19:51-60.

Heim, J-L. 1976 Les hommes fossiles de La Ferrassie. Tome I. Le Gisement. Les Squelettes d'adultes: Crâne et squelette du tronc. *Archives de L'Institut de Paléontologie Humaine*, Mémoire 35.

Heim, J-L. 1982a Les Enfants Néandertaliens de La Ferrassie. Paris: Masson.

Heim, J-L. 1982b Les hommes fossiles de La Ferrassie. Tome II. Les Squelettes d'adultes: Squelette des membres. *Archives de L'Institut de Paléontologie Humaine*, Mémoire 38.

Heinrich, R.E, M.D. Rose, R.E. Leakey, and A.C. Walker 1993 Hominid radius from the Middle Pliocene of Lake Turkana, Kenya. *American Journal of Physical Anthropology* 92(2):139-148.

Henke, W., and N. Xirotiris 1982 New human Upper Paleolithic fossils of Middle Europe. In J. Jelínek (ed): *Man and His Origins.* Moravian Museum, Brno. pp. 263-280.

Henri-Martin, G. 1923 L'homme fossile de La Quina. *Archives de Morphologie Générale et Expérimentale* 15:1-253.

Herrmann, B. 1977 Über die Reste des postcranialen Skelettes des Neanderthalers von Le Moustier. *Zeitschrift für Morphologie und Anthropologie* 68:129-149.

Hill, A.H. 1985 Early hominid from Baringo, Kenya. *Nature* 315:222-224.

Howell, F.C. 1969 Remains of hominidae from Pliocene/Pleistocene formations in the lower Omo basin, Ethopia. *Nature* 223:1234-1239.

Howell, F.C., and B.A. Wood 1974 Early hominid ulna from the Omo basin, Ethiopia. *Nature* 249:174-176.

Howell, F.C., and Y. Coppens 1973 Deciduous teeth of hominidae from the Pliocene/Pleistocene of the Lower Omo basin, Ethiopia. *Journal of Human Evolution* 2:461-472.

Hu Chengzhi 1973 Ape-man teeth from Yuanmou, Yunnan. *Acta Geologica Sinica* 1:65-71.

Huang Wanpo, and C. Fang 1991 *Wushan Hominid Site.* Ocean Press, Beijing.

Huang Wanpo, Fang Dushen, and Ye Yongxiang 1982 Preliminary study of the fossil hominid skull and fauna from Hexian, Anhui. *Vertebrata PalAsiatica* 20(3):248-256.

Hublin, J-J. 1980b La Chaise Suard, Engis 2 et La Quina H. 18: développement de la morphologie occipitale externe chez l'enfant preneanderthalien et néanderthaliens. *Comptes Rendus de l'Académie des Sciences*, Série D, 291:669-672.

Hublin, J-J., and A.M. Tillier 1981 The Mousterian juvenile mandible from Irhoud (Morocco): a phylogenetic interpretation. In C.B. Stringer (ed): *Aspects of Human Evolution*. Taylor and Francis, London. pp. 167-185.

Hublin, J-J., A.M. Tillier, and J. Tixier 1987 L'humérus d'enfant mousterién (Homo 4) du Jebel Irhoud (Maroc) dans son contexte archéologique. *Bulletins et Mémoires de la Société d'Anthropologie de Paris*, Series 25, 4:115-142.

Hughes, A.R., and P.V. Tobias 1977 A fossil skull probably of the genus *Homo* from Sterkfontein, Transvaal. *Nature* 265:310-312.

Ishida, H., M. Pickford, H. Nakaya, and Y. Nakaya 1986 Fossil anthropoids from Nachola and Samburu Hills, Samburu District, Kenya. *African Study Monographs* (Kyoto University, Kyoto) 2:73-85.

Jacob, T. 1966 The sixth skull cap of *Pithecanthropus erectus*. *American Journal of Physical Anthropology* 25:243-260.

Jacob, T. 1967 *Some Problems Pertaining to the Racial History of the Indonesian Region*. Drukkerij Neerlandia, Utrecht.

Jacob, T. 1968 A human Wadjakoid maxillary fragment from China. *Koninklijke Akademie Wetenschappen te Amsterdam*, Series B, 71:232-235.

Jaeger, J.J. 1975a The mammalian faunas and hominid fossils of the Middle Pleistocene of the Maghreb. In After the Australopithecines, K. Butzer and G. Isaac, eds., Mouton, The Hague, pp. 399-418.

Jaeger, J.J. 1975b Découverte d'un crâne d'hominidé dans le Pléistocene moyen du Maroc. In *Problèmes actuels de Paléontologie (Evolution des Vertébrés)*. Centre National de la Recherche Scientifique, Colloques Internationaux 218:897-902.

Jelínek, J. 1966 Jaw of an intermediate type of Neandertal man from Czechoslovakia. *Nature* 212:701-702.

Jelínek, J. 1981 Neanderthal parietal bone from Kůlna Cave, Czechoslovakia. *Anthropologie* (Brno) 19:195-196.

Jelínek, J, J. Pališek, and K. Valoch 1959 Der fossile Mensch Brno II. *Anthropos* 9:17-22.

Jellema, L., B. Latimer, and A.C. Walker 1993 The rib cage. In A.C. Walker and R.E. Leakey (eds): *The Nariokotome Homo erectus Skeleton*. Harvard University Press, Cambridge. pp. 294-325, 443.

Jerison, H.J. 1973 Evolution of the Brain and Intelligence. New York: Academic Press.

Johanson, D.C., F.T. Masao, G.G. Eck, T.D. White, R.C. Walter, W.H. Kimbel, B. Asfaw, P. Manega, P. Ndessokia, and G. Suwa 1987 New partial skeleton of *Homo habilis* from Olduvai gorge, Tanzania. *Nature* 327:205-209.

Johanson, D.C., Lovejoy, C.O., Kimbel, W.H., White, T.D., Ward, S.C., Bush, M.E., Latimer, B.M., and Coppens, Y. 1982 Morphology of the Pliocene partial hominid skeleton (A.L. 288-1) from the Hadar formation, Ethiopia. *American Journal of Physical Anthropology* 57(4):403-452.

Johanson, D.C., T.D. White, and Y. Coppens 1982 Dental remains from the Hadar Formation Ethiopia:1974-1977 Collections. *American Journal of Physical Anthropology* 57(4):545-604.

Jones, J.S. 1981 How different are human races? *Nature* 293:188-190.

Jones, J.S. 1985 The point of a toucan's bill. *Nature* 315:182-183.

Jordaan, H.V.F. 1976a Newborn:adult brain ratios in hominid evolution. *American Journal of Physical Anthropology* 44:271-278.

Keith, A. 1912 Description of the teeth of the Paleolithic man from Jersey. *Journal of Anatomy and Physiology* 46:12-27.

Keith, A. 1927 A report on the Galilee skull. In F. Turville-Petre (ed.): *Researches in Prehisotric Galilee, 1925-26*. Council of the British School of Archaeology in Jerusalem, London. pp. 53-106

Keith, A. 1932 A descriptive account of the Human Skulls from Matjes River Cave, Cape Province. *Transactions of the Royal Society of South Africa* 21:151-185.

Kennedy, K.A.R., S.U. Deraniyagala, W.J. Roertgen, J. Chiment, and T. Disotell 1987 Upper Pleistocene fossil hominids from Sri Lanka. *American Journal of Physical Anthropology* 72(4):441-461.

Kimbel, W.H. 1988 Identification of a partial cranium of *Australopithecus afarensis* from the Koobi Fora Formation, Kenya. *Journal of Human Evolution* 17(7):647-656.

Kimbel, W.H., D.C. Johanson, and Y. Coppens 1982 Pliocene cranial remains from the Hadar Formation, Ethiopia. *American Journal of Physical Anthropology* 57(4):453-500.

Kimbel, W.H., D.C. Johanson, and Y. Rak 1994 The first skull and other new discoveries of *Australopithecus afarensis* at Hadar, Ethiopia. *Nature* 368:449-451.

Klaatsch, H. 1901 Das Gliedmassenskelet des Neanderthalmenschen. *Anatomischer Anzeiger* 19:121-154.

Klaatsch, H. 1902 Occipitalia und Temporalia der Schädel von Spy vergleichen mit denen von Krapina. *Zeitschrift für Ethnologie.* 34:392-409.

Klaatsch, H., and O. Hauser 1909 *Homo mousteriensis* Hauseri. Ein Altdiluvialer Skelettfund im Departement Dordogne und seine Zugehörigkeit zum Neandertaltypus. *Archiv für Anthropologie* 7:287-297.

Klaatsch, H., and O. Hauser 1910 *Homo aurignacensis* Hauseri. Ein paläolithischer Skelefund aus dem untern Aurignacien der Station Combe-Capelle bei Montferrand (Périogord). *Praehistorische Zeitschrift* 1:273-338.

Klaatsch, H., and W. Lustig 1914 Morphologie der paläolithischer Skeletreste des mittleren Aurignacian der Grotte von La Rochette. *Archiv für Anthropologie* 41:81-126.

Koby, F. 1956 Une incisive néandertalienne trouvée en Suisse. *Verhandlungen der Naturforschers Gesellschaft in Basel* 67:1-15.

Kolossov, Yu.G., V.M. Kharitonov, and Y.P. Yakimov 1974 Discovery of the skeletal remains of a paleoanthrope at the Zaskal'naia VI site in the Crimea. *Voprosy Anthropologii* 46:79-88.

Kordos, L. 1987 Description and reconstruction of the skull of *Rudapithecus humgaricus* Kretzoi (Mammalia). *Annales Historico-Naturales Musei Nationalis Hungarici* 79:77-88.

Kyauka, P.S., and P. Ndessokia 1990 A new hominid tooth from Laetoli, Tanzania. *Journal of Human Evolution* 19(6-7)747-750.

Lamy, P. 1982 Le métatarsien Arago XLIII. In H. de Lumley (ed): L'*Homo erectus* et la Place de l'Homme de Tautavel parmi les Hominidés Fossiles. 1er Congrès International de Paléontologie Humaine, Nice, Prétirage. Volume 1:319-336. Louis-Jean, Nice.

Latimer, B.M., Lovejoy, C.O., Johanson, D.C., and Coppens, Y. 1982 Hominid tarsal, metatarsal, and phalangeal bones recovered from the Hadar formation:1974-1977 collections. *American Journal of Physical Anthropology* 7(4):701-719.

Lévêque, F., and B. Vandermeersch 1981 Le néandertalien de Saint-Césaire. *La Recherche* 12:242-244.

Leakey, L.S.B. 1935 *Stone Age Races of Kenya.* Oxford University Press, Oxford.

Leakey, M.D.M., P.V. Tobias, J.E. Martyn, and R.E. Leakey 1969 An Acheulean industry and hominid mandible, Lake Baringo, Kenya. *Proceedings of the Prehistoric Society* 35:48-76.

Leakey, M.G., and R.E. Leakey (eds) 1978 *Koobi Fora Research Project, Volume 1. The Fossil Hominids and an Introduction to their Context: 1968-1974.* Clarendon, Oxford.

Leakey, R.E., K.W. Butzer, and M.H. Day 1969 Early *Homo sapiens* remains from the Omo River region of South-west Ethiopia. *Nature* 222:1132-1138.

Leakey, R.E., J.M. Mungai, and A.C. Walker 1971 New australopithecines from East Rudolf, Kenya (I). *American Journal of Physical Anthropology* 35:175-186.

Leakey, R.E., J.M. Mungai, and A.C. Walker 1972 New Australopithecines from East Rudolf, Kenya (II). *American Journal of Physical Anthropology* 36:235-252.

Leakey, R.E., and A.C. Walker 1973 Further hominids from the Plio-Pleistocene of Koobi Fora, Kenya *American Journal of Physical Anthropology* 67(2):135-163.

Leakey, R.E., and A.C. Walker 1973 New australopithecines from East Rudolf, Kenya (III). *American Journal of Physical Anthropology* 39:205-222.

Leakey, R.E. and A.C. Walker 1985 Further hominids from the Plio-Pleistocene of Koobi Fora, Kenya. *American Journal of Physical Anthropology* 67(2):135-163.

Leakey, R.E.F., and A. Walker 1988 New *Australopithecus boisei* specimens from east and west lake Turkana, Kenya. *American Journal of Physical Anthropology* 76(1):1-24.

Leakey, R.E., and B.A. Wood 1973 New Evidence of the genus *Homo* from East Rudolf, Kenya. II. American Journal fo Physical Anthropology 39:355-368.

Leakey, R.E., and B.A. Wood 1974 New evidence of *Homo* from East Rudolf, Kenya (IV). *American Journal of Physical Anthropology* 41:237-244.

Leakey, R.E., and B.A. Wood 1974b A hominid mandible from East Rudolf, Kenya. *American Journal of Physical Anthropology* 41:245-250.

Lee, P.C. 1988 Comparative ethological approaches in modelling hominid behaviour. *OSSA (International Journal of Skeletal Research)* 14:113-126.

Legoux, P. 1966 *Détermination de L'Âge dentaire des Fossiles de la Lignée Humaine.* Librairie Maloine. Societé Anonyme d'Editions *Medicales* et Scientifiques, Paris.

Lele, S., and J.T. Richtsmeier 1992 On comparing biological shapes: detection of influential landmarks. *American Journal of Physical Anthropology* 87(1):67-82.

Leroi-Gourhan, A. 1958 Étude des restes humains fossiles provenant des Grottes d'Arcy-sur-Cure. *Annales de Paléontologie* 44:87-148.

Leroi-Gourhan, A. 1961 Les Fouilles d'Arcy-Sur-Cure (Yonne). *Gallia* 4:1-16.

Leroi-Gourhan, A. 1964 Chronologie des Grotte d'Arcy-sur-Cure (Yonne) *Gallia Préhistoire* 8:1-64.

Lovejoy, C.O., and K.G. Heiple 1981 The analysis of fractures in skeletal populations with an example from the Libben site, Ottowa County, Ohio. *American Journal of Physical Anthropology* 55:529-541.

Lovejoy, C.O., D.C. Johanson, and Y. Coppens 1982a Elements of the axial skeleton recovered from the Hadar formation:1974-1977 collections. *American Journal of Physical Anthropology* 57(4):631-636.

___. 1982b Hominid upper limb bones recovered from the Hadar formation:1974-1977 collections. *American Journal of Physical Anthropology* 57(4):637-650.

___. 1982c Hominid lower limb bones recovered from the Hadar formation:1974-1977 collections. *American Journal of Physical Anthropology* 57(4):679-700.

Lü Zun'e 1990 La Découverte de l'homme fossile de Jing-niu-shan. Première étude. *L'Anthropologie* 94(4):899-902.

___. 1992 The human fossils of Gezi cave, Liaoning Provence. *Acta Anthropologica Sinica* 11(1):10-12.

Lü Zun'e, Huang Yunping, Li Pingsheng, and Meng Zhenya 1989 Yiyuan fossil man. *Acta Anthropologica Sinica* 8(4):301-313.

Lynch, T. 1966 The "Lower Perigordian" in French archaeology. *Proceedings of the Prehistoric Society* 32:156-198.

Macintosh, N.W.G. 1952 The Cohuna cranium, history and commentary from November 1925 to November 1951. *Mankind* 4:307-329.

Macintosh, N.W.G. 1970 The Green Gully remains. *Memoirs of the National Museum of Victoria* 10:93-100.

Macintosh, N.W.G. 1971 Analysis of an aboriginal skeleton and a pierced tooth neckless from Lake Nitchie, Australia. *Anthropologie* (Brno) 9:49-62.

Macintosh, N.W.G., and S.L. Larnach 1976 Aboriginal affinities looked at in world context. In R.L. Kirk and A.G. Thorne (eds): *The Origin of the Australians.* Australian Institute of Aboriginal Studies, Canberra, pp. 113-126.

MacLarnon, A. 1993 The vertebral canal. In A.C. Walker and R.E. Leakey (eds): *The Nariokotome Homo erectus Skeleton.* Harvard University Press, Cambridge. pp. 359-390, 445-446.

Madre-Dupouy, M. 1992 *L'Enfant du Roc de Marsal: Étude analytique et comparative.* Cahiers de Paléoanthropologie. Centre National de la Recherche Scientifique, Paris.

Magori, C.C., and M.H. Day 1983 Laetoli hominid 18: an early *Homo sapiens* skull. *Journal of Human Evolution* 12:747-753.

Makowsky, A. 1882 Der Diluviale Mensch im Löss von Brünn. Mitteilungen der Anthropologischen *Mitteilungen der Anthropologischer Gesellschaft im Wein* 20:60-65, 22:73-82.

Malez, M., F. Smith, D. Rukavina, and J. Radovčić 1980 Upper Pleistocene fossil hominids from Vindija, Croatia, Yugoslavia. *Current Anthropology* 21:365-367.

Mallegni, F 1986 Les restes humains du gisement de Sedia del Daivolo (Rome) remontant au Riss final. *L'Anthropologie* 90:539-553.

Mallegni in AJPA 62

Mallegni, F., and A.M. Radmilli 1988 Human temporal bone from the lower Paleolithic site of Castel di Guido, near Rome, Italy. *American Journal of Physical Anthropology* 76(2):175-182.

Mallegni, F., and A.T. Ronshitelli 1989 Deciduous teeth of the Neandertal mandible from Molare Shelter, near Scario (Salerno, Italy). *American Journal of Physical Anthropology* 79(4):475-482.

Mallegni, F., M. Piperno, and A. Segre 1987 Human remains of *Homo sapiens neanderthalensis* from the Pleistocene deposit of Sants Croce Cave, Bisceglie (Apulia), Italy. *American Journal of Physical Anthropology* 72(4):421-429.

Mania, D. 1975 Bilzingsleben (Thüringen): eine neue Altpaläolithische Fundstelle mit Knochenresten des *Homo erectus. Archäologisches Korrespondenzblatt* 5:263-272.

Mania, D., and E. Vlček 1977 Altpaläolithische funde mit *Homo erectus* von Bilzinglseben (DDR). Archeologicke rozhledy 29:603-616.

Manzi, G. 1991 Platycephaly and encephalization in the Grotta Guattari cranium (Monte Circeo): parieto-occipital morphology of a typical Neandertal. In M. Piperno and G. Scichilone (eds): *The Circeo 1 Neandertal Skull: Studies and Documentation*. Instituto Poligrafico e Zecca Dello Stato, Dello Stato. pp. 253-272.

Marshall, E. 1990 Paleoanthropology gets physical. *Science* 247:798-801.

Marston, A.T. 1937 The Swanscombe skull. *Journal of the Royal Anthropological Institute* 67:339-406.

Martyn, J., and P.V. Tobias 1967 Pleistocene deposits and new fossil localities in Kenya. *Nature* 215:476-480.

Matiegka, J. 1924 Crâne de Podhaba (Böhmen). *Anthropologie* (Prague) 2:1-14.

Matiegka, J. 1929 The skull of the fossil man "Brno III" and the cast of its interior. *Anthropologie* (Prague) 7:90-107.

Matiegka, J. 1934 *Homo Předmostensis: Fosiliní Člověk z Předmostí na Moravě*. 1. Lebky. Prague: Česká Akademie Věd i Umění.

Matiegka, J. 1938 *Homo Předmostensis: Fosiliní Člověk z Předmostí na Moravě*. 2. Ostatní Cásti Kostrové. Prague: Česká Akademie Věd i Umění.

McCown, T.D. and A. Keith 1939 *The Stone Age of Mount Carmel:The Fossil Human Remains from the Levalloiso-Mousterian*. Vol. II. Oxford at the Clarendon Press.

McCrossin, M.L. 1993 Human molars from later Pleistocene deposits of Witkrrans cave, Gaap escarpment, Kalahari margin. *Human Evolution* 7(3):1-10.

McHenry, H.M. 1994 Early hominid postcrania: phylogeny and function. In R.S. Corruccini and R.L. Ciochon (eds): *Integrative Paths to the Past. Paleoanthropological Advances in Honor of F. Clark Howell*. Prentice Hall, Englewood Cliffs. pp. 251-268.

Morant, G.M. 1938 The form of the Swanscombe skull. *Journal of the Royal Anthropological Insititute* 68:67-97.

Mu Xinan, Xu Hankui, Mu Daocheng, Zhong Shilan, Xu Qinqi, Zhang Hong, and Zhang Yinyun 1993 Discovery of *Homo erectus* remains from Tangshan, Nanjing, and its significance. *Acta Anthropologia Sinica* 32(4):396-399.

Napier, J.R. 1959 Fossil metacarpals from Swartkrans. *Fossil Mammals of Africa* 17. British Museum of Natural History, London.

Nehring, A. 1895 Über einen menschlichen Molar aus dem Diluvium von Taubach bei Weimar. *Zeitschrift für Ethnologie* 27:573-577.

Obermaier, H. 1907 Quaternary human remains in Central Europe. *Annual Report of the Smithsonian Institution* (1906): 373-397.

Ogawa, T., T. Kamiya, S. Sakai, and H. Hosokawa 1970 Some observations on the endocranial cast of the Amud man. In H. Suzuki and F. Takai (eds): *The Amud Man and his Cave Site*. University of Tokyo, Tokyo. pp. 407-420.

Oppenoorth, W.F.F. 1932 Ein neuer diluvialer Urmensch von Java. *Natur und Museum* 62:269-279.

Palma de Cesnola, A., et P. Messeri 1967 Quatre dents humaines Paleolithiques trouvées dans des Cavernes de L'Italie Meridionale. *L'Anthropologie*, 71:249-261.

Passarello, P., and R. Diotallevi 1982 Paranasal sinuses of Saccopastore I and II. In J. Jelínek (ed): *Man and His Origins*. Moravian Museum, Brno. pp. 229-235.

Patte, E. 1954 Le Crâne aurignacien des Cottés. *L'Anthropologie* 58:450-472.

Patte, E. 1955 *Les Néanderthaliens. Anatomie, Physiologie, Comparaisons*. Masson et Cie, Paris.

Patte, E. 1960 Découverte d'un Néandertalien dans la Vienne. *L'Anthropologie* 64:512-517.

Patte, E. 1962 *La Dentition des Néanderthaliens*. Masson et Cie, Paris.

Patterson, B., and W.W. Howells 1967 Hominid humeral fragment from early Pleistocene of Northwerstern Kenya. Science 156:64-66.

Puech, P-F.. 1982 L'usure dentaire de l'homme de Tautavel. In H. de Lumley (ed): *L'Homo erectus et la Place de l'Homme de Tautavel parmi les Hominidés Fossiles*. 1er Congrès International de Paléontologie Humaine, Nice, Prétirage. Volume 1:249-275. Louis-Jean, Nice.

Pickford, M., D.C. Johanson, C.O. Lovejoy, T.D. White, and J.L. Aronson 1983 A hominoid humeral fragment from the Pliocene of Kenya. *American Journal of Physical Anthropology* 60(3):337-346.

Piveteau, J. 1951 Restes Humains de la Grotte de la Verrerie à Macassargues (Gard). *Annales de Paléontologie* 37:175-183.

Piveteau, J. 1963 La Grotte de Regourdou I. *Annales de Paléontologie des Vertébrés* 49:285-304.

Piveteau, J. 1964 La Grotte de Regourdou II. *Annales de Paléontologie des Vertébrés* 50:155-194.

Piveteau, J. 1966 La Grotte de Regourdou III. *Annales de Paléontologie des Vertébrés* 52:63-94.

Piveteau, J. 1967 Un pariétal humain de la grotte du Lazaret. *Annales de Paléontologie des Vertébrés* 53:167-199.

Piveteau, J. 1970 Les Grottes de La Chaise (Charente). Paléontologie Humaine 1. L'Homme de L'Abri Suard. *Annales de Paléontologie des Vertébrés* 56:175-225.

Piveteau, J. 1976 Les Anté-Néandertaliens du Sud-Ouest. In H. de Lumley (ed): *La Préhistoire Française*. Centre National de la Recherche Sciéntifique Paris. 1:561-567.

Piveteau, J., M-A. de Lumley, and A. Debenath 1982 Les hominidés de La Chaise . In H. de Lumley (ed): *L'Homo erectus et la Place de l'Homme de Tautavel parmi les Hominidés Fossiles*. 1er Congrès International de Paléontologie Humaine, Nice, Prétirage. Volume 2:901-917. Louis-Jean: Nice.

Potts, R., P. Shipman, and E. Ingall 1988 Taphonomy, paleoecology, and hominids of Lainyamok, Kenya. *Journal of Human Evolution* 17(6):597-614.

Protsch, R. 1981 *The palaeoanthropological finds of the Pliocene and Pleistocene*. Volume 3 of H. Müller-Beck (ed): *Die Archäologischen und Anthropologischen Ergebnisse der Kohl-Larsen-Expeditionen in Nord-Tanzania 1933-1939*. Verlag Archaeologica Venatoria, Tübingen

Pycraft, W.P. 1925 On the calvaria found at Boskop, Transvaal, in 1913, and its relationship to Cromagnoid and negroid skulls. *Journal of the Royal Anthropological Institute* London 55:179-198.

Pycraft, W.P. 1928 Rhodesian man: description of the skull and other human remains from Broken Hill. In F.A. Bather (ed): *Rhodesian Man and Associated Remains*. British Museum (Natural History), London. pp. 1-51.

Qiu Zhonglang, Gu Yumin, Zhang Yinyun, and Zhang Senshui 1973 Newly discovered *Sinanthropus* remains and stone artifacts at Choukoutien. *Vertebrata PalAsiatica* 11(2):109-131.

Qiu Zhonglang, Xu Chunhua, Zhang Weihua, Wang Rulin, Wang Jianzhong, and Zhao Chengfu 1982 A human fossil tooth and fossil mammals from Nanzhao, Henan. *Acta Anthropologica Sinica* 1(2):109-117.

Qiu Zhonglang, Zhang Yinyun, and Hu Shaojin 1985 Human tooth and paleoliths found at locality 2 of Longtanshan, Chenggong, Kunming. *Acta Anthropologica Sinica* 4(3):233-241.

Rak, Y. 1991 The pelvis. In O.Bar-Yosef and B. Vandermeersch (eds): *Le squelette Moustérien de Kébara 2*. Cahiers de Paléoanthropologie, Centre National de la Recherche Scientifique, Paris. pp.147-156.

Rak, Y., and B. Arensburg 1987 Kebara 2 Neandertal pelvis: first look at a complete inlet. *American Journal of Physical Anthropology* 73(2):227-231.

Rak, Y. and F.C. Howell 1978 Cranium of a juvenile Australopithecus boisei from the lower Omo Basin, Ethiopia. *American Journal of Physical Anthropology* 48:345-366.

Rak, Y., W.H. Kimbel, and E. Hovers 1994 A Neandertal infant from Amud Cave, Israel. *Journal of Human Evolution* 26(4):313-324.

Reed, K.E., J.W. Kitching, F.E. Grine, W.J. Jungers, and L. Sokoloff 1993 Proximal femur of *Australopithecus africanus* from Member 4, Makapansgat, South Africa. *American Journal of Physical Anthropology* 92(1):1-15.

Rightmire, G.P. 1983 The Lake Ndutu cranium and early *Homo sapiens* in Africa. *American Journal of Physical Anthropology* 61(2):245-254.

Rightmire, G.P. 1990 *The Evolution of Homo erectus. Comparative Anatomical Studies of an Extinct Human Species*. Cambridge University Press, Cambridge.

Rightmire, G.P. and H.J. Deacon 1991 Comparative studies of late Pleistocene human remains from Klasies River Mouth, South Africa. *Journal of Human Evolution* 20(2):131-156.

Robbins, L.H. 1974 *The Lothagam Site*. Michigan State University Anthropological Series 1(2).

Robbins, L.H. 1980 *Lopoy: A Late Stone Age fishing and pastoral settlement in the Lake Turkana basin, Kenya*. East Lansing: Michigan State University Museum Anthropological Series 3(1):1-139.

Roberts, M.B., C.B. Stringer, and S.A. Parfitt 1994 A hominid tibia from Middle Pleistocene sediments at Boxgrove, UK. *Nature* 369:311-313.

Robinson, J.T. 1956 *The Dentition of the Australopithecinae*. Transvaal Museum Memoir 9, Pretoria.

Robinson, J.T. 1972 *Early Hominid Posture and Locomotion.* University of Chicago, Chicago.

Roche, J., and P. Texier 1976 Découverte de restes humains dans un niveau atérien supérieur de la grotte des Contrebandiers, à Témara (Maroc). *Comptes Rendus de l'Académie des Sciences,* Série D, 282:45-47.

Rosas, A. 1987 Two new mandibular fragments from Atapuerca/Ibeas (SH site). A reassessment of the affinities of the Ibeas mandibles sample. *Journal of Human Evolution* 16(5):417-427.

Roth, H.. 1982 Les arcades alvéolaires et dentaire de l'homme de Tautavel. In H. de Lumley (ed): *L'Homo erectus et la Place de l'Homme de Tautavel parmi les Hominidés Fossiles.* 1ᵉʳ Congrès International de Paléontologie Humaine, Nice, Prétirage. Volume 1:222-248. Louis-Jean, Nice.

Saban, R. 1975 Les restes humains de Rabat (Kébibat). *Annales de Paléontologie des Vertébrés* 61(2):153-207.

Saban, R. 1982 Les emprientes du réscau vasculaire duremérien du frontal de l'homme d'Hahnöfersand, d'après le moulage endocrânien. *Bulletins et Mémoires de la Société d'Anthropologie de Paris,* Série 13(9):309-320.

Sakura, H. 1970 State of the skeletons of the Amud man *in situ.* In H. Suzuki and F. Takai (eds): *The Amud Man and his Cave Site.* University of Tokyo, Tokyo. pp. 117-122.

Sakura, H. 1970 Dentition of the Amud man. In H. Suzuki and F. Takai (eds): *The Amud Man and his Cave Site.* University of Tokyo, Tokyo. pp. 207-230.

Salvadei, L., D. Massani, and P. Passarello 1991 Tomographic analysis of the paranasal sinuses of the Neandertal cranium of the Guattari cave. In M. Piperno and G. Scichilone (eds): *The Circeo 1 Neandertal Skull: Studies and Documentation.* Instituto Poligrafico e Zecca Dello Stato, Dello Stato. pp. 311-320.

Santa Luca, A.P. 1980 *The Ngandong Fossil Hominids.* Yale University Publications in Anthropology, No. 78. Yale University Press, New Haven.

Sartono, S. 1961 Notes on a new find of a *Pithecanthropus* mandible. *Publikasi Teknik Seri Paleontologi* 2:1-51.

Sartono, S. 1968 Early man in Java: *Pithecanthropus* skull VII, a male specimen of *Pithecanthropus erectus.* *Koninklijke Akademie Wetenschappen te Amsterdam,* Series B, 71:396-442.

Sartono, S. 1971 Observations on a new skull of *Pithecanthropus erectus* (*Pithecanthropus* VIII) from Sangiran, Central Java. *Koninklijke Akademie Wetenschappen te Amsterdam,* Series B, 74:185-194.

Sartono, S. 1982 Characteristics and chronology of early men in Java. In H. de Lumley (ed): *L'Homo erectus et la Place de l'Homme de Tautavel parmi les Hominidés Fossiles.* 1ᵉʳ Congrès International de Paléontologie Humaine, Nice, Prétirage. Volume 2:491-541. Louis-Jean, Nice.

Sartono, S., and D. Grimaud-Hervé 1983 Les pariétaux de l'hominidé Sangiran 31. *L'Anthropologie* 87:465-468.

Sausse, F. 1975 La Mandibule Atlanthropienne de la Carrière Thomas I (Casablanca). *L'Anthropologie* 79:81-112.

Schoetensack, O. 1908 *Unter Kiefer des Homo heidelbergensis, aus den Sanden von Maur bei Heidelberg.* W. Englemann, Leipzig.

Schrenk, F., T.G. Bromage, C.G. Betzler, U. Ring, and Y.M. Juwayeyl 1993 Oldest *Homo* and Pliocene biogeography of the Malawi Rift. *Nature* 365:833-836.

Schwalbe, G. 1899 Studien über *Pithecanthropus erectus* Dubois. *Zeitschrift für Morphologie und Anthropologie* 1:16-240.

Schwalbe, G. 1901 Der Neanderthalschädel. *Bonner Jahrbücher* 106:1-72.

Schwalbe, G. 1921 Studien über das Femur von *Pithecanthropus erectus* Dubois. *Zeitschrift für Morphologie und Anthropologie* 21:289-350.

Senyürek, M.S. 1940 Fossil man in Tangier. *Papers of the Peabody Museum of American Archaeology and Ethnology* 16:1-27.

Senut, B. 1983 Quelques remarques à propos d'un humérus d'hominoïde pliocène provenant de Chemeron (bassin du lac Baringo, Kenya). *Folia Primatologia* 41:267-276.

Senut, B., and P.V. Tobias 1989 A preliminary examination of some new hominid upper limb remains from Sterkfontein (1974-1984). *Comptes Rendus de l'Académie des Sciences,* Série D, 308:565-571.

Sergi, S. 1944 Craniometria e craniograf del primo paleanthropo di Saccopastore. *Richerche de Morfologia* 21:733-791.

Sergi, S. 1948a Craniometria e craniografia del primo paleantropo di Saccopastore. *Atti della Accademia Nazionale dei Lincei* 5:1-59.

Sergi, S. 1948b Il crania del secondo paleanthropo de Saccopastore. *Paleontolographia Italica* 42:25-164.

Sergi, S. 1951 Circeo III. Il rinvenimento della mandibola di un terzo paleantropo al Monte Circeo. *Rivista di Anthropologia* 38:271-276.

Sergi, S. 1954 La mandibola neandertaliana Circeo II. *Rivista di Anthropologia* 41:305-344.

Sergi, S. 1958 Die neandertalischen palaeanthropen in Italien. In Hundert Jahre Neanderthaler, ed. G.H.R. von Koenigswald. Böhlau, Köln. pp. 38-51.

Sergi, S. 1974 Il Cranio Neandertaliano del Monte Circeo (Circeo I). Accademia Nazionale dei Lincei, Roma. Republished in M. Piperno and G. Scichilone (eds): *The Circeo 1 Neandertal Skull: Studies and Documentation.* Instituto Poligrafico e Zecca Dello Stato, Dello Stato. pp. 23-173.

Shipman, P., R. Potts, and M. Pickford 1983 Lainyamok: a new Middle Pleistocene hominid site. *Nature* 306:365-368.

Siffre, A. 1908 Etude de dents humaines du Petit-Puymoyen. *Revue de l'École d'Anthropologie* 18:66-72.

Silipo, P., M. Dazzi, M. Feliciani, G. Guglielmi, G. Guidetti, S. Martini, D. Massani, S. Mori, and G. Tanfani 1991 Computrized tomographic analysis of the Neandertal cranium of the Guattari cave. In M. Piperno and G. Scichilone (eds): *The Circeo 1 Neandertal Skull: Studies and Documentation.* Instituto Poligrafico e Zecca Dello Stato, Dello Stato. pp. 513-538.

Sim, R., and A.G. Thorne 1990 Pleistocene human remains from King Island, southeastern Australia. *Australian Archaeology* 31:44-50.

Simons, E.L. 1987 New faces of *Aegyptopithecus* from the Oligocene of Egypt. *Journal of Human Evolution* 16(3):273-289.

Simons, E.L. 1990 Discovery of the oldest known Anthropoidean skull from the Paleogene of Egypt. *Science* 247:1567-1569.

Singer, R. 1954 The Saldanha skull from Hopefield, South Africa. *American Journal of Physical Anthropology* 12:345-362.

Singer, R., and J. Wymer 1982 *The Middle Stone Age at Klasies River Mouth in South Africa.* University of Chicago Press, Chicago.

Smith, B.H. 1993 Physiological age of KNM-WT 15000. In A.C. Walker and R.E. Leakey (eds): *The Nariokotome Homo erectus Skeleton.* Harvard University Press, Cambridge. pp. 195-220.

Smith, F.H. 1976a A fossil hominid frontal from Velika Pećina (Croatia) and a consideration of Upper Pleistocene hominids from Yugoslavia. *American Journal of Physical Anthropology* 44:127-134.

Smith, F.H. 1976 *The Neandertal Remains from Krapina: A Descriptive and Comparative Study.* University of Tennessee Department of Anthropology Reports of Investigations 15:1-359.

Smith, F.H., and J.C. Ahern 1994 Additional cranial remains from Vindija Cave, Croatia. *American Journal of Physical Anthropology* 93(2):275-280.

Smith, F.H., D.C. Boyd, and M. Malez 1985 Additional Upper Pleistocene human remains from Vindija cave, Croatia, Yugoslavia. *American Journal of Physical Anthropology* 68(3):375-383.

Smith, P., and A-M. Tillier 1989 Additional human remains from the Mousterian strata, Kebara Cave (Israel). In O. Bar-Yosef and B. Vandermeersch (eds): *Investigations in South Levantine Prehistory.* Bar International Series 508:375-384.

Smith, P., and B. Arensburg 1977 A Mousterian skeleton from Kebara Cave. *Eretz Israel* 13:164-176.

Smith, S.A. 1918 The fossil human skull found at Talgai, Queensland. *Transactions of the Royal Society of London,* Series B, 208:351-387.

Solan, M., and M.H. Day 1992 The Baringo (Kapthurin) ulna. *Journal of Human Evolution* 22(4/5):307-314.

Sollas, W.J. 1913 Paviland Cave: an Aurignacian station in Wales. *Journal of the Anthropological Institute* 43:337-364.

Sonakia, A. 1985 Skull cap of an early man from the Narmada Valley alluvium (Pleistocene) of Central India. American Anthropologist 87(3):612-616.

Spitery, J. 1982 Le frontal de l'homme de Tautavel. In H. de Lumley (ed): *L'Homo erectus et la Place de l'Homme de Tautavel parmi les Hominidés Fossiles.* 1er Congrès International de Paléontologie Humaine, Nice, Prétirage. Volume 1: 21-61. Louis-Jean, Nice.

Spitery, J. 1982 La face de l'homme de Tautavel. In H. de Lumley (ed): *L'Homo erectus et la Place de l'Homme de Tautavel parmi les Hominidés Fossiles*. 1er Congrès International de Paléontologie Humaine, Nice, Prétirage. Volume 1: 110-135. Louis-Jean, Nice.

Spoor, C.F., and P.Y. Sondaar 1986 Human fossils from the Endemic Island fauna of Sardinia. *Journal of Human Evolution* 15(5):399-408.

Stewart, T.D. 1977 The Neanderthal skeletal remains from Shanidar cave, Iraq: a summary of findings to date. *Proceedings of the American Philosophical Society* 121:121-165.

Stewart, T.D. 1985 Preliminary report on an early human burial in the Wadi Kubbaniya, Egypt. In P.V. Tobias (ed): *Hominid Evolution: Past, Present, and Future. Proceedings of the Taung Diamond Jubilee International Symposium*. Alan R. Liss Inc., New York. pp. 335-340.

Stringer, C.B., and A.P. Currant 1986 Hominid specimens from La Cotte de St. Brelade. In P. Callow and J. Cornford (eds). *La Cotte de St. Brelade: 1961-1978*. Geo Books, Norwich. pp. 155-157.

Sullivan, L.R., and M. Hellman 1925 The Punin calvarium. *Anthropological Papers of the American Museum of Natural History* 23(7):309-337.

Susman, R.L. 1989 New hominid fossils from the Swartkrans formation (1979-1986 excavations): postcranial specimens. *American Journal of Physical Anthropology* 79(4):451-474.

Susman, R.L. 1993 Hominid postcranial remains from Swartrkans. In C.K. Brain (ed): *Swartkrans. A Cave's Chronicle of Early Man*. Transvaal Museum Monograph 8:117-136.

Susman, R.L., and T.M. Brain 1988 First new metatarsal (SKX 5017) from Swartkrans and the gait of *Paranthropus robustus. American Journal of Physical Anthropology* 77(1):7-15.

Suzuki, H. 1970 The skull of the Amud man. In H. Suzuki and F. Takai (eds): *The Amud Man and his Cave Site*. University of Tokyo, Tokyo. pp. 123-206.

Suzuki, H. 1982 Skulls of the Minatogawa Man. In H. Suzuki and K. Hanihara (eds): *The Minatogawa Man. The Upper Pleistocene Man from the Island of Okinawa*. The University Museum of the University of Tokyo Bulletin Number 19:7-50.

Svoboda, J. 1987 A new male burial from Dolní Věstonice. *Journal of Human Evolution* 16(7/8):827-830.

Svoboda, J., and E. Vlček 1991 La Nouvelle Sépulture de Dolní Věstonice (DV XVI), Tchécoslovaquie. *L'Anthropologie* 95(1):323-328.

Szombathy, J. 1925 Die diluvialen Menschenreste aus der Fürst-Johanns-Höhle bei Lautsch in Mähren. *Die Eiszeit* 2:1-34, 73-95.

Szombathy, J. 1950 Der menschliche Unterkeifer aus dem Miesslingtal bei Spitz, N-Ö. *Archeologia Austriaca* 5:1-5.

Thoma, A. 1963 The dentition of the Subalyuk Neandertal child. *Zeitschrift für Morphology und Anthropology* 54:127-150.

Thoma, A. 1966 L'Occipital de l'Homme *Mindélien* de Vértessöllös. *L'Anthropologie* 70:495-534.

Thoma, A. 1967 Human Teeth from the Lower Paleolithic of Hungary. *Zeitschrift für Morphologie und Anthropologie* 58:152-180.

Thoma, A. 1969 Biometrische Studie über das Occipitale von Vértesszöllös. *Zeitschrift für Morphologie und Anthropologie* 60:229-241.

Thoma, A. 1975 L'occipital de la grotte Bourgeois-Delaunay (La Chaise, Charente). Etude biométrique. *Comptes Rendus de l'Académie des Sciences*, Série D, 281:1821-1824.

Thoma, A. 1984 Morphology and affinities of the Nazlet Khater Man. *Journal of Human Evolution* 13:287-296.

Thoma, A. 1990 Human tooth and bone remains from Vértesszöllös. In M. Kretzoi and V.T. Dobosi (eds): *Vértesszöllös: Site, Man, and Culture*. Akadémiai Kiadó, Budapest. pp. 253-256.

Thorne, A.G. 1971 Mungo and Kow Swamp: morphological variation in Pleistocene Australians. *Mankind* 8(2):85-89.

Thorne, A.G., and P.G. Macumber. 1972. Discoveries of Late Pleistocene man at Kow Swamp, Australia. *Nature* 238:316-319.

Tillier, A-M. 1977 La pneumatisation du massif cranio-facial chez les Hommes actuels et fossiles. *Bulletins et Mémoires de la Société d'Anthropologie de Paris*, Série 13, 4:177-189, 287-316.

Tillier, A-M. 1979 La dentition de l'enfant mousterian Chateauneuf 2 découvert à l'Abri de Hauteroche (Charente). *L'Anthropologie* 83, 417-438.

Tillier, A-M. 1982 Les enfants neanderthaliens de Devil's Tower (Gibraltar). *Zeitschrift für Morphologie und Anthropologie* 73:125-148.

Tillier, A-M. 1983a L'enfant néandertalien du Roc de Marsal (Campagne du Bugue, Dordogne). Le squelette facial. *Annales de Paléontologie des Vertébrés* 69.

Tillier, A-M. 1983b Le crâne d'enfant d'Engis 2: Un exemple de distribution des caractères juvéniles, primitifs et néandertaliens. *Bulletin de la Société Royal Belge d'Anthropologie et de Préhistoire* 94:51-75.

Tillier, A-M. 1984 L'enfant *Homo* 11 de Qafzeh (Israël) et son apport à la compréhension des modalités de la croissance des squelettes moustériens. *Paléorient* 10:7-48.

Tillier, A-M. 1991 La mandibule et les dents. In O.Bar-Yosef and B. Vandermeersch (eds): *Le squelette Moustérien de Kébara 2*. Cahiers de Paléoanthropologie, Centre National de la Recherche Scientifique, Paris. pp. 97-112.

Tillier, A-M. and Genet-Varcin E. 1980 La plus ancienne mandibule d'enfant découverte en France dans le gisement de La Chaise - Vouthon (Abri Suard) en Charente. *Zeitschrift für Morphologie und Anthropologie* 71:196-214.

Tobias, P.V. 1966 Fossil hominid remains from Ubediya, Israel. *Nature* 211:130-133.

Tobias, P.V. 1967a *Olduvai Gorge, Volume II. The Cranium and Maxillary Dentition of Zinjanthropus (Australopithecus) boisei.* Cambridge University Press, London.

Tobias, P.V. 1967b The fossil hominid remains of Haua Fteah. In C.B.M. McBurney (ed): *The Haua Fteah (Cyrenaica) and the Stone Age of the South-East Mediterranian.* Cambridge University Press, London. pp. 336-352.

Tobias, P.V. 1971 Human skeletal remains from the Cave of Hearths, Makapansgat, Northern Transvaal. *American Journal of Physical Anthropology* 34:335-368.

Tobias, P.V. 1991 *Olduvai Gorge Volume IV. Homo habilis: Skulls, Endocasts, and Teeth.* Cambridge University Press, New York.

Toussaint, M., and A. Leguebe 1984 Morphologie et morphométrie des restes humains de La Naulette (Belgique). *Comptes Rendus de l'Académie des Sciences*, Série D, 299:1363-1368.

Turner, C.G. 1990 Paleolithic teeth of the central Siberian Altai Mountains. In *Chronostratigraphy of Paleolithic North, Central, and East Asia and America.* Siberian Branch of the USSR Academy of Sciences, Novosibirsk. pp. 239-243.

Trinkaus, E. 1983 *The Shanidar Neandertals.* Academic Press, New York.

Trinkaus, E. 1987 The Upper Pleistocene human molar from Me'art Shovakh (Mugharet esh-Shubbabiq), Israel. *Paléorient* 13(1):95-100.

Trinkaus, E. 1993 A note on the KNM-ER 999 hominid femur. *Journal of Human Evolution* 24(6):493-504.

Twiesselmann, F. 1958 Les ossements humains du site Mésolithique d'Ishango. *Exploration du Parc National Albert* 5:1-125.

Twiesselmann, F. 1961 Le Fémur Néanderthalien de Fond-de-Forêt. *Institut Royal des Sciences Naturelles de Belgique Mémoire* 148:1-164.

Vallois, H.V. 1941 Nouvelles Recherches sur le Squelette de Chancelade. *L'Anthropologie* 50:165-202.

Vallois, H.V. 1949 The Fontéchevade fossil man. *American Journal of Physical Anthropology* 7:339-360.

Vallois, H.V. 1951 La mandibule humaine fossile de la Grotte du Porc-Epic près Diré-Daoua (Abyssinie). *L'Anthropologie* 55:231-238.

Vallois, H.V. 1952 Les Restes Humains du Gisement *Moustérien* de Monsempron. *Annales de Paléontologie* 38:100-120.

Vallois, H.V. 1956 The pre-Mousterien mandible from Montmaurin. *American Journal of Physical Anthropology* 14:319-323.

Vallois, H.V. 1958 La Grotte de Fontéchevade: Anthropologie (deuxième partie). *Archives de l'Institut de Paleontologie Humaine*, Mémoire 29:5-156.

Vallois, H.V. 1959 L'Homme de Rabat. *Bulletin d'Archeologie Marocaine* 3:87-91.

Vallois, H.V. 1965 Le Sternum neanderthalien du Regourdou. *Anthropologischer Anzeiger* 29:273-289.

Vallois, H.V. 1969 Le Temporal *Néandertalien* H 27 de La Quina. *L'Anthropologie* 73:365-400, 525-544.

Vallois, H.V. and G. Billy 1965 Nouvelles recherches sur les Hommes Fossiles de l'Abri de Cro-Magnon. *L'Anthropologie* 69:47-74, 249-272.

Vallois, H.V., and J. Roche 1958 La Mandible Acheuléenne de Témara, Maroc. *Comptes Rendus de l'Académie des Sciences*, Série D, 246:3113-3116.

Vandermeersch, B. 1976a Les Néandertaliens en Charente. In H. de Lumley (ed): *La Préhistoire Française.* Centre National de la Recherche Sciéntifique, Paris. Vol I:584-587.

Vandermeersch, B. 1976b La mandibule moustérienne de Montgaudier (Montbront, Charente). *Comptes Rendus de l'Académie des Sciences,* Série D, 283:1161-1164.

Vandermeersch, B. 1978 Le Crâne Pré-Wurmien de Biache-Saint Vaast (Pas-de-Calais). In F. Bordes (ed): *Les Origines Humaines et les Époques de l'Intelligence.* Masson, Paris. pp. 153-157.

Vandermeersch, B. 1981 *Les hommes fossiles de Qafzeh (Israël).* Cahiers de Paléoanthropologie, Centre National de la Recherche Sciéntifique, Paris.

Vandermeersch, B. 1982 L'homme de Biache-Saint-Vaast. Comparaison avec l'homme de Tautavel. In H. de Lumley (ed): *L'Homo erectus et la Place de l'Homme de Tautavel parmi les Hominidés Fossiles.* 1er Congrès International de Paléontologie Humaine, Nice, Prétirage. Volume 2:894-900. Louis-Jean: Nice.

Vandermeersch, B. 1984 À propos de la découverte du squelette Néandertalien de Saint-Cesaire. *Bulletins et Mémoires de la Société d'Anthropologie de Paris,* Série 14, 1:191-196.

Vandermeersch, B. 1991 La cienture scapulaire et les membres supéieurs. In O.Bar-Yosef and B. Vandermeersch (eds): *Le squelette Moustérien de Kébara 2.* Cahiers de Paléoanthropologie, Centre National de la Recherche Scientifique, Paris. pp. 157-178.

Vandermeersch, B., and A-M. Tillier 1977 Étude préliminaire d'une mandibule d'adolescent provenant des niveaux Moustériens de Qafzeh, Israël. *Eretz Israel* 13:177-183.

Verneau, R. 1906 Les Grottes de Grimaldi (Baousse-Rousse) III. *Imprimerie de Monaco* 2:1-212.

Verneau, R. 1924 La race Néanderthal et la race de Grimaldi; leur rôle dans l'Humanité. *Journal of the Royal Anthropological Institute* 54:211-230.

Virchow, H. 1917 Der Taubacher Zahn des Praehistorischen Museums der Universität Jena. *Praehistorische Zeitschrift* 9:1-18.

Virchow, H. 1920 *Die menschlichen Skeletrreste aus dem Kämpfeschen Bruch in Travertine von Ehringsdorf bei Weimar.* Fischer, Jena.

Virchow, H. 1924 Der Unterkiefer von Ochos. *Zeitschrift für Ethnologie* 56:197-205.

Virchow, H. 1939 Skelett von Le Moustier. *Anatomischer Anzeiger* 88:261-274.

Virchow, R. 1882 Der Kiefer aus der Schipka-Höhle und der Kiefer von La Naulette. *Zeitschrift für Ethnologie* 14:277-310.

Vlček, E. 1955 The fossil man of Gánovce, Czechoslovakia. *Journal of the Royal Anthropological Institute* 85:163-171.

Vlček, E. 1957 Pleistocenní člověk z jeskyně na Zlatém Koni u Koněprus. *Anthropozoikum* 6:283-311.

Vlček, E. 1968 Der jungpleistozäne Menschenfund aus Svitáka in Mähren. *Anthropos* 19:262-270.

Vlček, E. 1969 *Neandertaler der Tschechoslowakei.* Tschechoslowakeschen Akademie die Wissenschaften, Prague.

Vlček, E. 1973 Postcranial skeleton of a Neandertal child from Kiik-Koba, U.S.S.R. *Journal of Human Evolution* 2:537-544.

Vlček, E. 1975 Morphology of the first metacarpal of Neandertal individuals from the Crimea. *Bulletins et Mémoires de la Société d'Anthropologie de Paris,* Série 13, 2:257-276.

Vlček, E. 1978 A new discovery of *Homo erectus* in Central Europe. *Journal of Human Evolution* 7:239-251.

Vlček, E. 1991 *Die Mammutjäjer von Dolní Véstonice.* Anthropologische Bearbeitung der Skelette aus Dolní Véstonice und Pavlov. Archäologie und Museum Heft 22. Arbeit des Amtes für Museen und Archäologie des Kantons, Baselland. Liestal, Switzerland.

Vlček, E., and D. Mania 1989 Die Hominidenreste von Bilzingsleben. Funde von 1972 bis 1987. *Zeitschrift für Archäologie* 23:219-235.

Von Koenigswald, G.H.R. 1940 Neue Pithecanthropus-Funde 1936-1938. *Weterschappelijke Mededeelungen, Dienst von den Mijnbouw in Nederlandisch-Indië* 28.

Von Koenigswald, G.H.R. 1968 Observations on Pithecanthropus mandibles from Sangiran, Central Java. *Koninklijke Akademie van Wetenschappen, Amsterdam,* Series B, 71:1-9.

Walker, A.C. 1971 Late australopithecine form Baringo district, Kenya: Partial australopithecine cranium. *Nature* 230:513-514.

Walker, A.C. 1973 New *Australopithecus* femora from East Rudolf, Kenya. *Journal of Human Evolution* 2:545-555.

Walker, A.C. and R.E. Leakey 1993a The skull. In A.C. Walker and R.E. Leakey (eds): *The Nariokotome Homo erectus Skeleton.* Harvard University Press, Cambridge. pp. 63-94, 437.

Walker, A.C. and R.E. Leakey 1993b The postcranial bones. In A.C. Walker and R.E. Leakey (eds): *The Nariokotome Homo erectus Skeleton.* Harvard University Press, Cambridge. pp. 95-160, 437-438.

Walker, A.C., R.E. Leakey, J.M. Harris, and F.H. Brown 1986 2.5-Myr *Australopithecus boisei* from west of Lake Turkana, Kenya. *Nature* 322:517-522.

Walker, A.C., and C.B. Ruff 1993 The reconsruction of the pelvis. In A.C. Walker and R.E. Leakey (eds): *The Nariokotome Homo erectus Skeleton.* Harvard University Press, Cambridge. pp. 221-233, 441.

Ward, S.C., and A. Hill 1987 Pliocene hominid partial mandible from Tabarin, Baringo, Kenya. *American Journal of Physical Anthropology* 72(1):21-33.

Ward, S.C., D.C. Johanson, and Y. Coppens 1982 Subocclusal morphology and alveolar process relationships of hominid gnathic elements from the Hadar Formation:1974-1977 collections. *American Journal of Physical Anthropology* 57(4):605-630.

Webb, S.G. 1989 *The Willandra Lakes Hominids.* Department of Prehistory, Research School of Pacific Studies ANU, Canberra.

Weidenreich, F. 1928 Der Schädel fund von Weimar-Ehringsdorf. Fischer, Jena.

Weidenreich, F. 1936a The mandibles of *Sinanthropus pekinensis*: a comparative study. *Palaeontologia Sinica*, Series D., Volume 7, Fascicle 3.

Weidenreich, F. 1936b Observations on the form and the proportions of the endocranial casts of Sinanthropus pekinensis, other hominids and the great apes: a comparative study of brain size. *Palaeontologia Sinca*, Series D, Volume 7, Fascicle 4.

Weidenreich, F. 1937 The dentition of *Sinanthropus pekinensis*: a comparative odontography of the hominids. Palaeontologica Sinica, New Series D, 1 (Whole Series 101):1-180.

Weidenreich, F. 1941 The extremity bones of *Sinanthropus pekinensis*. *Palaeontologia Sinica*, New Series D, 5 (Whole Series 116).

Weidenreich, F. 1943 The skull of *Sinanthropus pekinensis*: A comparative study of a primitive hominid skull. *Palaeontologia Sinica*, n.s. D, No. 10 (whole series No. 127).

Weidenreich, F. 1945a The Keilor skull. A Wadjak skull from southeast Australia. *American Journal of Physical Anthropology* 3:21-33.

Weidenreich, F. 1945b The paleolithic child from the Teshik-Tash Cave in Southern Uzbekistan. *American Journal of Physical Anthropology* 3:151-164.

Weidenreich, F. 1945c Giant early man from Java and south China. *Anthropological Papers of the American Museum of Natural History* 40:1-134.

Weidenreich, F. 1951 Morphology of Solo man. *Anthropological Papers of the American Museum of Natural History* 43(3):205-290.

Weinert, H. 1925 *Der Schädel des eiszeitlichen Menschen von Le Moustier.* Springer, Berlin.

Weinert, H. 1928 *Pithecanthropus erectus. Zeitschrift für Anatomie und Entwicklungs Geschichte* 87:429-547.

Weinert, H. 1936 Der Urmenschenschädel von Steinheim. *Zeitschrift für Morphologie und Anthropologie* 35:413-518.

Weinert, H., W. Bauermeister, and A. Remane 1940 *Africanthropus njarasensis.* Beschreibung und phylogenetische einordnung des ersten affenmenschen aus Ostafrika. *Zeitschrift für Morphologie und Anthropologie* 38:252-308.

Wells, L.H. 1929 Fossil Bushmen from the Zuurberg. *South African Journal of Science* 26:806-834.

Wells, L.H. 1947 A note on the broken maxillary fragment from the Broken Hill cave. *Journal of the Royal Anthropological Institute* 77:11-12.

Wells, L.H. 1951 The fossil human skull from Singa. In *The Pleistocene Fauna of two Blue Nile Sites. Fossil Mammals of Africa* 2: 29-42. British Museum of Natural History, London.

White, T.D. 1976 On a newly associated composite mandible from Swartkrans (Mammalia: Hominidae). *Annals of the Transvaal Museum* 30(8):97-98.

White, T.D. 1977 New fossil hominids from Laetolil, Tanzania. *American Journal of Physical Anthropology* 46:197-230.

White, T.D. 1980 Additional fossil hominids from Laetoli, Tanzania:1976-1979 specimens. *American Journal of Physical Anthropology* 53:487-504.

White, T.D. 1981 Primitive hominid canine from Tanzania. *Science* 213:348-349.

White, T.D. 1984 Pliocene hominids from the middle Awash, Ethiopia. In P. Andrews and J.L. Franzen (eds): *The Early Evolution of Man, with Special Emphasis on Southeast Asia and Africa. Courier Forschungsinstitut Senckenberg* 69:57-68.

White, T.D. and D.C. Johanson 1982 Pliocene hominid mandibles from the Hadar Formation, Ethiopia:1974-1977 collections. *American Journal of Physical Anthropology* 57(4):501-544.

Whitworth, T. 1966 A fossil hominid from Rudolf. *South African Archaelogical Bulletin* 21:138-150.

Widianto, H., A-M. Sémah, T. Djubiantono, and F. Sémah 1994 A tenative reconstruction of the cranial human remains of Hanoman 1 from Bukuran, Sangiran (Central Java). In J.L. Franzen (ed): *100 years of Pithecanthropus: The Homo erectus problem. CourierForschungsinstitut Senckenberg* 171:47-59.

Wolpoff, M.H. 1979 The Krapina dental remains. *American Journal of Physical Anthropology* 50:67-114.

Wolpoff, M.H., F.H. Smith, M. Malez, J. Radovčić, and D. Rukavina 1981 Upper Pleistocene human remains from Vindija Cave, Croatia, Yugoslavia. *American Journal of Physical Anthropology* 54:499-545.

Wood, B.A. 1991 *Koobi Fora Research Project*, Volume 4: *Hominid Cranial Remains*. Oxford University Press, New York.

Wood, B.A., and F.L. Van Noten 1986 Preliminary observations on the BK 8518 mandible from Baringo, Kenya. *American Journal of Physical Anthropology* 69(1):117-127.

Wu Maolin 1980 Human fossils discovered at Xujiayao site in 1977. *Vertebrata PalAsiatica* 18:229-238.

Wu Maolin 1983 *Homo erectus* from Hexian, Anhui, found in 1981. *Acta Anthropologica Sinica* 2(2):109-115.

Wu Maolin 1984 New discoveries of human fossil in Tongzi, Guizhou. *Acta Anthropologica Sinica* 3(3):195-201

Wu Maolin 1986 Study of the temporal bone of Xujiayao man. *Acta Anthropologica Sinica* 5(3):220-226.

Wu Maolin, Wang Linghong, Zhang Yinyun, and Chang Senshui 1975 Fossil human teeth and associated cultural remains from Tonzi County, Guizhou Provence. *Vertebrata PalAsiatica* 13:14-23.

Wu Rukang 1958a Fossil human parietal bone and femur from Ordos, Inner Mongolia. *Vertebrata PalAsiatica* 2:208-212.

Wu Rukang 1958b Tzeyang Paleolithic man -- earliest representative of modern man in China. *American Journal of Physical Anthropology* 16:459-471.

Wu Rukang 1959 Human fossils found in Liujiang, Kwangsi, China. *Vertebrata PalAsiatica* 3:109-118.

Wu Rukang 1961 Fossil human humerus from Chienping, Liaonng Province. *Vertebrata PalAsiatica* 4:287-290.

Wu Rukang 1964 Mandible of the *Sinanthropus*-type discovered at Lantian, Shensi. *Vertebrata PalAsiatica* 8:1-12.

Wu Rukang 1966 The hominid skull of Lantian, Shensi. *Vertebrata PalAsiatica* 10:1-22.

Wu Rukang and Chao Tzekuei 1959 New discovery of *Sinanthropus* mandible from Choukoutien. *Vertebrata PalAsiatica* 3:169-172.

Wu Rukang and Chia Lanpo 1954 New discoveries about *Sinanthropus pekinensis* in Choukoudian. *Acta Anthropologica Sinica* 2:267-288.

Wu Rukang and Dong Xingren 1980 The fossil human teeth from Yunxian, Hubei. *Vertebrata PalAsiatica* 18:142-149.

Wu Rukang and Dong Xingren 1982 Preliminary study of *Homo erectus* remains from Hexian, Anhui. *Acta Anthropologica Sinica* 1(1):2-13.

Wu Rukang and Peng Ruce 1959 Fossil human skull of early Paleolithic stage found at Mapa, Shaoquan, Kwangtung Provence. *Vertebrata PalAsiatica* 3:176-182.

Wu Rukang and Wu Xinzhi 1982a Human fossil teeth from Xichuan, Henan. *Vertebrata PalAsiatica* 20:1-9.

Wu Xinzhi 1961 Study on the Upper Cave man of Choukoutien. *Vertebrata PalAsiatica* 3:202-211.

Wu Xinzhi 1981 A well-preserved cranium of an archaic type of early *Homo sapiens* from Dali, China. *Scientia Sinica* 24(4):530-41.

Wüst, K. 1950 Uber der Unterkiefer von Mauer im Vergleich zu andern Fossilen und Rezenten Unterkieferen von Anthropoiden und Hominiden. *Zeitschrift für Morphologie und Anthropologie* 42:1-112.

Wunderly, J. 1943 The Keilor fossil skull: anatomical description. *Memoirs of the National Museum of Melbourne* 13:57-70.

Xu Chunhua, Zhang Yinyun, Chen Caidi, and Fang Dusheng 1984 Human occipital bone and mammalian fossils from Chaoxian, Anhui. *Acta Anthropologica Sinica* 3(3):202-209.

Xu Qinqi and You Yuzhu 1982 Four post-Nihowananian Pleistocene mammalian faunas of North China: correlation with deep-sea sediments. *Acta Anthropologica Sinica* 1:180-190.

Xue Xiangxu 1987 Human fossil tooth from Luonan, Shaanxi, and its geological age. *Acta Anthropologica Sinica* 6(4):284-288.

Yakimov, V.P. 1980 New materials of skeletal remains of ancient peoples in the territory of the Soviet Union. In L-K. Könnigson (ed): *Current Argument on Early Man*. Pergamon Press, Oxford. pp. 152-169.

You Yuzhu, Dong Xingren, Chen Cunxi, and Fan Xuechun 1989 A fossil human tooth from Qingliu, Fujian. *Acta Anthropologica Sinica* 8(3):197-202.

Zhang Yinyun 1984 Human fossil newly discovered at Chaoxian, Anhui. *Acta Anthropologica Sinica* 4:305-310

Zheng Liang 1985 A human fossil from Zhaotong, Yunnan. *Acta Anthropologica Sinica* 4(2):105-108.

Edited Volumes
Primarily Paleoanthropology

Andrews, P.J., and J.L. Franzen 1984 *The Early Evolution of Man, with Special Emphasis on Southeast Asia and Africa. Courier Forschungsinstitut Senckenberg* 69.

Bar-Yosef, O. and B. Vandermeersch 1991 *Les squelette Moustérien de Kébara 2.* Cahiers de Paléoanthropologie. Centre National de la Recherche Scientifique, Paris.

Bräuer, G., and F.H. Smith 1992 *Continuity or Replacement? Controversies in Homo sapiens Evolution.* Balkema, Rotterdam.

Brace, C.L., and J. Metress 1973 *Man in Evolutionary Perspective.* John Wiley & Sons, New York.

Bordes, F. 1972 *The Origin of Homo sapiens.* Unesco, Paris.

Ciochon, R.L. and R.S. Corruccini 1983 *New Interpretations of Ape and Human Ancestry.* Plenum, New York.

Ciochon, R.L., and J.G. Fleagle 1985 *Primate Evolution and Human Origins.* Benjamin/Cummings, Menlo Park.

___. 1992 *The Human Evolution Source Book.* Prentice Hall, Englewood Cliffs.

Coppens, Y. 1984 Les Australopithèques. Actes de Deux Séances de la Société d'Anthropologie de Paris sur le Thème Australopithèques. *Bulletins et Mémoires de la Société d'Anthropologie de Paris* 10 (Série 13).

Coppens, Y., and B. Senut 1991 Origine(s) de la Bipédie chez les Hominidés. Centre National de la Recherche Scientifique, Paris.

Coppens, Y., F.C. Howell, G.Ll. Isaac, and R.E. Leakey 1976 *Earliest Man and Environments in the Lake Rudolf Basin: Stratigraphy. Paleoecology, and Evolution.* University of Chicago Press, Chicago.

Corruccini, R.S., and R.L. Ciochon 1994 *Integrative Paths to the Past: Paleoanthropological Advances in Honor of F.C. Howell.* Prentice-Hall, New York.

Day, M.H. 1973 *Human Evolution. Symposia of the Society for the Study of Human Biology*, Volume XI. Taylor and Francis, London.

Delson, E., I Tattersall, and J. Van Couvering 1991 (and following) *Paleoanthropology Annuals.* Garland, New York.

DeVore, P.L. 1965 *The Origin of Man.* Wenner-Gren Foundation, New York.

Delson, E. 1985 *Ancestors: The Hard Evidence.* Alan R. Liss, New York.

Durant. J.R. 1989 *Human Origins.* Clarendon Press, Oxford.

Ferembach, D. 1981 *Les Processus de l'Hominisation.* Centre National de la Recherche Scientifique, Paris

Grine, F.E. 1988 *Evolutionary History of the "Robust" Australopithecines.* Aldine de Gruyter, New York.

Grine, F.E., J.G. Fleagle, and L.B. Martin 1988 *Primate Phylogeny.* Academic Press (Harcourt Brace, and Jovanovich Publishers), New York.

Hamburg, D.A., and E.R. McCown 1979 *Perspectives on Human Evolution, Volume 5. The Great Apes.* Benjamin/Cummings, Menlo Park.

Howell, F.C. and F. Bourliere 1963 *African Ecology and Human Evolution.* Viking Fund Publication in Anthropology, Chicago.

Howells, W.W. 1957 *Ideas on Human Evolution.* Harvard University Press, Cambridge.

Isaac, B. 1989 *The Archaeology of Human Origins: Papers by Glynn Isaac.* Cambridge University Press, New York.

Isaac, G.Ll. and E.R. McCown 1976 *Human Origins: Louis Leakey and the East African Evidence.* Benjamin, Menlo Park.

Jelínek, J. 1980 *Homo erectus and his Time: Contributions to the Origin of Man and his Cultural Development.* Volume 1. *Anthropologie* (Brno) 18(2-3).

___. 1981 *Homo erectus and his Time: Contributions to the Origin of Man and his Cultural Development.* Volume 2. *Anthropologie* (Brno) 19(1).

Jolly, C.J. 1978 *Early Hominids of Africa.* St. Martin's Press, New York.

Jones, S., R. Martin, and D. Pilbeam 1992 *The Cambridge Encyclopaedia of Human Evolution.* Cambridge University Press, New York.

Kimbel, W.H. and L.B. Martin 1993 *Species Concepts and Primate Evolution.* Plenum, New York.

von Koenigswald, G.H.R. 1958 *Hundert Jahre Neanderthaler.* Kemink en Zoon, Utrecht.

Königsson, L-K. 1980 *Current Argument on Early Man*. Report from a Nobel Symposium. Pergamon, Oxford.

de Lumley, H. 1982 *L'Homo erectus et la Place de l'Homme de Tautavel parmi les Hominidés Fossiles*. 1er Congrès International de Paléontologie Humaine, Nice, Prétirage. Louis-Jean, Nice.

McCown, T.D., and K.A.R. Kennedy 1972 *Climbing Man's Family Tree*. A Collection of Major Writing on Human Phylogeny. Prentice-Hall, Englewood Cliffs.

MacCurdy, G.G. 1937 *Early Man*. Lippincott, Philadelphia.

Meikle, W.E., and S.T.Parker 1994 *Naming our Ancestors: An Anthology of Hominid Taxonomy*. Waveland, Prospect Heights.

Mellars, P. and C.B. Stringer 1989 T*he Human Revolution: Behavioural and Biological Perspectives on the Origins of Modern Humans*. Edinburgh University Press, Edinburgh.

Nishida, T., W.C. McGrew, P. Marler, M. Pickford, and F.B.M. DeWaal 1992 *Human Origins*. Volume 1. Proceedings of the XIII Congress of the International Primatological Society. Columbia University Press, New York.

Novotný, V.V. and A. Mizerová. 1986 *Fossil Man. New Facts, New Ideas*. Papers in Honor of Jan Jelínek's Life Anniversary. *Anthropos* (Brno) 23.

Otte, M. 1988 *L'Homme de Néandertal* (8 volumes). Etudes et Recherches Archéologiques de l'Université de Liège (Numbers 28-35), Liège.

Peretto, C. 1985 *Homo. Journey to the Origins of Man's History: Four Million Years of Evidence*. Cataloghi Marsilio, Venezia.

Piperno, M. and G. Scichilone 1991 *The Circeo 1 Neandertal Skull: Studies and Documentation*. Instituto Poligrafico e Zecca Dello Stato, Dello Stato.

Rasmussen, D.T. 1993 *The Origin and Evolution of Humans and Humanness*. Jones and Bartless, Boston.

Sigmon, B.A., and J.S. Cybulski 1981 *Homo erectus. Papers in Honor of Davidson Black*. University of Toronto Press, Toronto.

Smith, F.H. and F. Spencer 1984 *The Origins of Modern Humans: A World Survey of the Fossil Evidence*. Alan R. Liss Inc., New York.

Straus, L.G. 1991 A quarter century of paleoanthropology: views from the USA. *Journal of Anthropological Research* 47(2):125-283.

Stringer, C.B. 1981 *Aspects of Human Evolution*. Symposium of the Society for the Study of Human Biology XXI. Taylor and Francis, London.

Suzuki, H., and F. Takai 1970 *The Amud Man and his Cave Site*. University of Tokyo Press, Tokyo.

Suzuki, H., and K. Hanihara 1982 *The Minatogawa Man. The Upper Pleistocene Man from the Island of Okinawa*. The University Museum of the University of Tokyo Bulletin Number 19.

Tattersall, I., E. Delson, and J. Van Couvering 1988 *Encyclopedia of Human Evolution and Prehistory*. Garland, New York.

Tobias, P.V. 1985 *Hominid Evolution: Past, Present, and Future*. Proceedings of the Taung Diamond Jubilee International Symposium. Alan R. Liss Inc., New York.

Trinkaus, E. 1983 *The Mousterian Legacy: Human Biocultural Change in the Upper Pleistocene*. British Archaeological Reports International Series, Cambridge University Press, Cambridge.

___. 1989 *The Emergence of Modern Humans. Biocultural Adaptations in the Later Pleistocene*. Cambridge University Press, Cambridge.

Tuttle, R.H. 1975 *Paleoanthropology, Morphology and Paleoecology*. Mouton, The Hague.

Von Koenigswald, G.H.R. 1958 *Hundert Jahre Neanderthaler*. Böhlau, Köhn.

Walker, A.C., and R.E. Leakey 1993 *The Nariokotome Homo erectus Skeleon*. Harvard University Press, Cambridge.

Washburn, S.L. 1963 *Classification and Human Evolution*. Aldine, Chicago.

Wood, B.A., L. Martin, and P. Andrews 1986 *Major Trends in Primate and Human Evolution*. Cambridge University Press, Cambridge.

Wu Rukang and J.W. Olsen 1985 *Palaeoanthropology and Paleolithic Archaeology in the People's Republic of China*. Academic Press, New York.